AF513079

About Pearson

Pearson is the world's learning company, with presence across 70 countries worldwide. Our unique insights and world-class expertise comes from a long history of working closely with renowned teachers, authors and thought leaders, as a result of which, we have emerged as the preferred choice for millions of teachers and learners across the world.

We believe learning opens up opportunities, creates fulfilling careers and hence better lives. We hence collaborate with the best of minds to deliver you class-leading products, spread across the Higher Education and Test Preparation spectrum.

Superior learning experience and improved outcomes are at the heart of everything we do. This product is the result of one such effort.

Your feedback plays a critical role in the evolution of our products and you can contact us - reachus@pearson.com. *We look forward to it.*

NVision

FOUNDATION MATHEMATICS

CLASS 9

Second Edition

Pearson

Photo Credits

Chapter Opening Background: Vilmos Varga / Shutterstock

ISBN 978-93-6713-468-9

First Impression

Published by Pearson India Education Services Pvt. Ltd, CIN: U72200TN2005PTC057128.

Head Office: 1st Floor, Berger Tower, Plot No. C-001A/2, Sector 16B, Noida - 201 301, Uttar Pradesh, India.
Registered Office: Featherlite, 'The Address' 5th Floor, Survey No 203/10B, 200 Ft MMRD Road,
Zamin Pallavaram, Chennai - 600044
Website: in.pearson.com, Email: companysecretary.india@pearson.com

Compositor: D Book Media, Delhi
Printed in India by: Rahul Print O Pack

Contents

Preface

When you envision something, you are looking ahead. With this series, you are looking ahead anew; with a whole 'N'ew perspective backed by immense knowledge. This book is designed to help the students perform well in the class, as well as prepare for various competitive examinations like JEE, NEET, and Olympiads like NSO, IOM, IMO, NSTSE, IOS, etc. Let's see how to use the different components of the book.

- **Theory:** The theoretical portion of the book has been written to perfectly integrate text and important notes with solved examples. Theory-based exercises have been inserted at relevant checkpoints to enhance the reading experience of the students. Use of testing room, tables, and figures highly enrich the overall learning experience.
- **Assessment Level 1:** This exercise is a **Concept-Building Exercise (CBE)**. The questions in this exercise are clear and simple, and include match the following, true and false, fill in the blanks, assertion-reason based, comprehension-type, case-based, very short answer, short answer, and long answer questions. They focus on the application of freshly learnt theory discussed in the chapter. This aids the students assimilate the concepts included in the chapter (which justifies the name). The question patterns covered are in accordance with the patterns followed in school examinations. This gives the students an edge while preparing for school examinations. Case-based problems and comprehension-type problems follow the current structure of CBSE examinations. The important point to remember is that the homework for this exercise needs to be neatly maintained in a separate exercise book.
- **Assessment Level 2:** This exercise is a **Competitive Level Exercise (CLE)**. After completing the Concept-Building Exercise and absorbing the important concepts, students are prepared to apply their learning at a slightly higher level. These questions include MCQs and ones that focus on improving higher order thinking skills (HOTS) and are in line with the level being asked in the National Level Competitive Examinations as mentioned in the opening paragraph. These questions are imperative for all students looking to strengthen their concepts.
- **Archive Corner:** This exercise comprises questions from previous year papers of competitive examinations like NSO, IOM, IOS, NTSE, IMO, etc. It has been added for students to assess their current level of chapter proficiency in relation to the competitive examinations.

After reading the theory and completing the exercises, a student should have a solid conceptual understanding and problem-solving aptitude of that particular chapter. For best results, **all exercises should be solved in a fair notebook and all the solutions should be kept so that this notebook proves handy while revising**.

Parents are requested to regularly check their children's homework. It is not necessary to check everything, just make sure that the answers to all the questions are being meticulously maintained. This simple observation serves a dual purpose. First, the child believes that his or her education is important to the parent. Second, he or she regularly completes the assigned homework. I am hoping that by combining the efforts of the student, the parents, and the teacher, we can get the most and the best out of this book.

Prashant Jain
B. Tech (CSE), IIT Bombay
Lead Author, NVision Series

About the Authors

Prashant Jain (*Series Lead Author*)
Popularly known as PJ Sir, Mr. Jain is the team lead and main author of the NVision book series. He is an IIT-Bombay graduate (AIR 42-2008), an Indian National Chemistry Olympiad (INChO) Gold Medalist, has qualified Indian National Physics Olympiad (INPhO), and ranked #1 in Rajasthan PTET (2019). He has authored various books like *IOQM Mathematics and CUET* with Pearson. In addition to being a top educator, he is the National Outcomes Head and National Foundation Head in Unacademy, with a strong social media (YouTube, etc.) presence with more than 10+ million views on most of his videos and is behind the success of *1000+ learners* in IOQM in last 2 years.

Ajay Singh (*Lead Author – Mathematics*)
With many years of rich teaching experience in Kota, Mr. Singh is an expert in Mathematics. He has previously been associated with institutes like Resonance, Unacademy, Let's Crack Foundation, and NTSE, and has also taught on Unacademy, with more than 2.5 lakh subscribers.

Chapter Insights

Learning Outcomes
These outline the targets the chapter aims to achieve. It gives the learner a to-do list to adhere to while going through the chapter.

Learning Outcomes

After reading this chapter, you would be able to:

- classification of numbers.
- rational number in decimal form.
- representation of rational number on a real number line.
- conversion of recurring decimal into fraction.
- find a rational number between two integers.

Geekspeak

- Real number
- Rational number
- Irrational number
- Natural number
- Whole number
- Integers
- Positive integers
- Negative integers
- Prime number
- Co-prime number
- Twin prime number
- Decimal

Geekspeak
This introduces the learner to the keywords they shall learn from the chapter.

Theory Followed by Solved Examples
Assimilate the concepts with the help of practical examples, solved for your benefit.

Inter Conversion and Mixed Problems

In this section, we shall discuss problems pertaining to the conversion of a solid (discussed in the previous classes) into another solid of different shape. For example, a metallic sphere is melted and recast into a cylindrical wire, the earth taken out by digging a well and spreading it uniformly around the well to form an embankment in the form of a cylindrical shell from its original shape of right circular cylinder, etc.

Illustration 13.21

A well of diameter 2 m is dug 14 m deep. The earth taken out of it is spread evenly all around it to a width of 5 m to form an embankment. Find the height of the embankment.

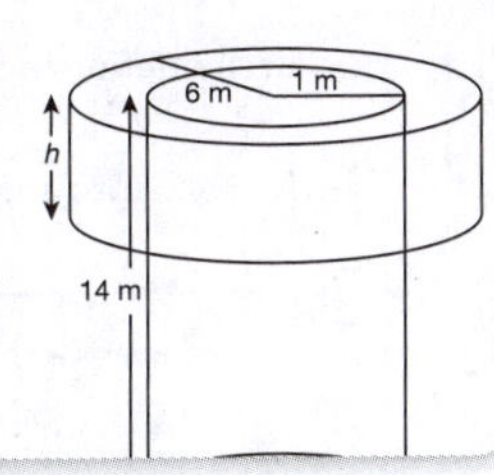

Solution: Let h be the required height of the embankment.

The shape of the embankment will be like the shape of a cylinder of internal radius 1 m and external radius $(5 + 1)$ m = 6 m.

The volume of the embankment will be equal to the volume of the earth dug out from the well. Now, the volume of the earth dug out = volume of the cylindrical well $= \pi \times 1^2 \times 14\ m^3 = 14\ pm^3$

Also, the volume of the embankment $= \pi (6^2 - 1^2)\ h\ m^3 = 35\pi h\ m^3$

Hence, we have

Check Point 1

1. Represent the number $\frac{3}{5}$ on the number line.
2. Find a fraction between $\frac{3}{8}$ and $\frac{2}{5}$.
3. Insert 5 rational numbers between 3 and 4.
4. Which of the following fractions yield a recurring decimal?

$$\frac{5}{3}; \frac{7}{16}; \frac{9}{14}; \frac{5}{7}; \frac{12}{5}; \frac{6}{11}$$

5. Represent 1. 129129129.. as a fraction.

Check Points
Self-analyse your learning by answering some questions based on recently learnt concepts.

Keystone
Enhance the knowledge of trivia with fun little tidbits about surrounding things.

Keystone

- 1 is neither a prime more a composite number.
- Every prime number more than 3 leaves the remainder 1 or 5 when divided by 6.
- Pairs of prime numbers are always co-prime numbers. (3, 7)
- Pairs of consecutive natural numbers are always co-prime. E.g. (4, 5)

Competition Corner

- Internal angle sum of an n-sided polygon $= (n-2)\times 180°$
- External angle sum of an n-sided polygon $= 360°$.
- Each interior angle of a regular polygon of n-side $= \dfrac{(n-2)\times 180°}{n}$.
- Each exterior angle of a regular polygon of n-side $= \dfrac{360°}{n}$.

Competition Corner
Attain competitive edge by learning some additional definitions to help with basic concept-learning.

Structural Outline
Quickly revise the concepts learnt by going through this simple flowchart that summarises the key ideas.

STRUCTURAL OUTLINE

Fundamental properties of triangles

1. Sum or any two sides is always greater than the third side.
2. The difference of any two sides is always less than the third side.
3. Greater angle has a greater side opposite to it.
4. Let a, band c be the three sides of a AABC and cis the largest side, then
   (i) if $c^2 < a^2 + b^2$, the triangle is acute angle triangle
   (ii) if $c^2 = a^2 + b^2$, the triangle is right angled triangle
   (iii) if $c^2 > a^2 + b^2$, the triangle is obtuse angle triangle
5. The sum of all the three interior angles is alwayss 180°.
6. The sum of three (ordered) exterior angles of a triangle is 360°.
7. A triangle must have at least two acute angles.
8. In a triangle, the measure of an exterior angle equals the sum of the measure of the interior angle equals the sum of the measures of the interior opposite angle.

Sufficient conditions for congruence of two triangle

(i) SAS Congruence criterion
(ii) ASA Congruence criterion
(iii) AAS Congruence criterion
(iv) SSS Congruence criterion
(v) RHS Congruence criterion

Triangle

EXEMPLIFICATION

1. In figure, two sides *AB* and *BC* and the median *AM* of a ΔABC are respectively equ median *DN* of ΔDEF. Prove that $\Delta ABC \cong \Delta DEF$.

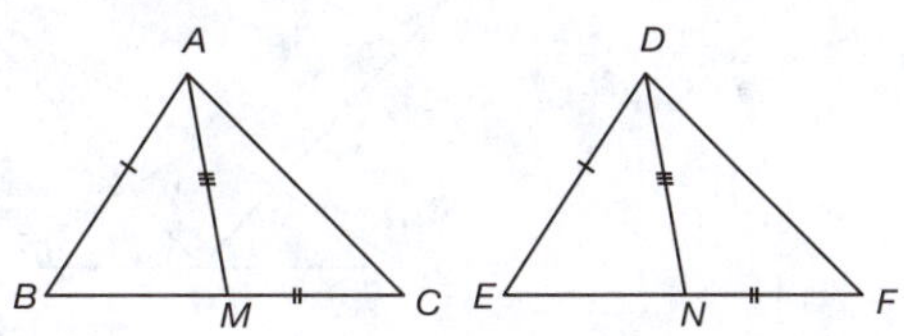

Solution: $\because$ *AM* and *DN* are medians of ΔABC and ΔDEF respectively

$\therefore$ $BM = MC$ and $EN = NF$

$\Rightarrow$ $BM = \frac{1}{2} BC$ and $EN = \frac{1}{2} EF$

But, $BC = EF$

$\therefore$ $BM = EN$

Exemplification
Enhance concept learning with examples that have been solved for your benefit.

NCERT Compendium
Solutions of all intext NCERT exercises have also been provided in NCERT Compendium.

("*This section is available in the elibrary app provided with this book*".)

NCERT COMPENDIUM

Exercise 7.1

1. In quadrilateral *ACBD*, $AC = AD$ and *AB* bisect $\angle A$ (see Fig. 7.16). Show that $\Delta ABC \cong \Delta ABD$. What can you say about *BC* and *BD*?

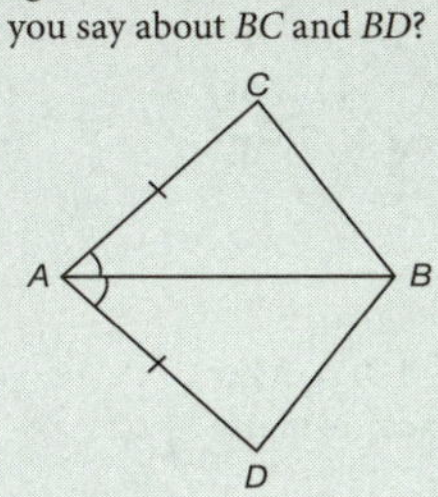

(It is the common arm)
$\angle DAB = \angle CBA$ and $AD = BC$
(These are given i
So, triangles *ABD* and *BAC* a
i.e., $\Delta ABD \cong \Delta BAC$.
Hence proved.

(ii) It is now known that $\Delta ABD \cong$
so, $BD = AC$ (by the

(iii) Since $\Delta ABD \cong \Delta BAC$
so, Angles $\angle ABD = \angle BAC$
(by the

3. *AD* and *BC* are equal perpen line segment *AB* (see Fig. 7.18).

Fixed Response Type

Fill in the Blanks

1. In the figure, it is given that $AB = CF$, $EF = BD$ and $\angle AFE = \angle CBD$. then $\Delta AFE \cong \Delta$ _______

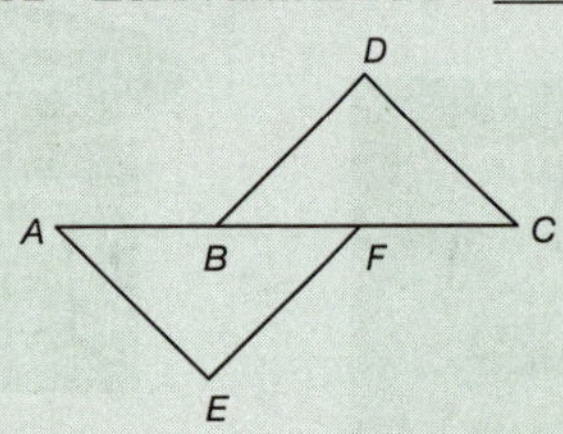

2. In the figure, it is given that $\angle A = \angle C$ and $AB = BC$. Then $\Delta ABD \cong \Delta$ _______

Fill in the Blanks
Fill in the gaps in your learning by finding answers to the blanks in the sentences.

True/False
Double-check your concepts by fact-checking your answers.

True/False

1. In the figure $AC = BC$, $\angle DCA = \angle ECB$ and $\angle DBC = \angle EAC$. Then triangles DBC and EAC are congruent, and hence $DC = EC$ and $BD = AE$.

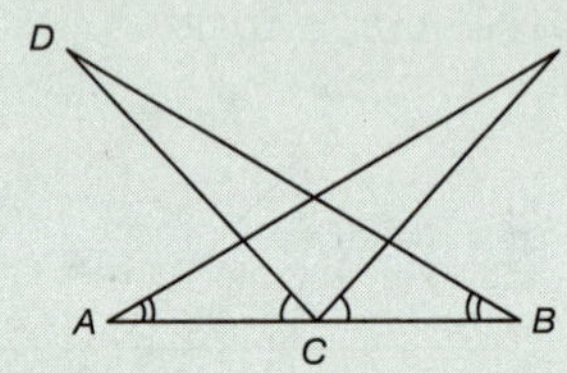

2. In the figure, BD and CE are altitudes. If $BE = CD$, then $BD = DE$.

Single Correct Type Questions

Level 1

1. $ABCD$ is a square and P, Q, R are points on AB, BC and CD respectively such that $AP = BQ = CR$ and $\angle PQR = 90°$, then $\angle QPR$:
   (A) 45° (B) 50°
   (C) 60° (D) 70°

2. In a ΔXYZ, $LM \parallel YZ$ and bisectors YN and ZN of $\angle Y$ and $\angle Z$ respectively meet at N on LM. Then $YL + ZM =$
   (A) YZ (B) XY
   (C) XZ (D) LM

3. In ΔAOC and ΔXYZ, $\angle A = \angle X$, $AO = XZ$, $AC = XY$, then by which congruence rule is

Single Correct Type Questions (Level 1 and Level 2)
Learn to avoid confusions by confidently answering the questions asked in this exercise.

Match Type Questions

This exercise is like solving a puzzle. Find the best match so two halves of a sentence can fit together.

Match Type Questions

Column-I and Column-II contain four entries each. Entries of Column-I are to be matched with some entries of Column-II. One or more than one entries of Column-I may have the matching with the same entries of Column-II and one entry of Column-II may have one or more than one matching with entries of Column-I

1.

Column-I	Column-II
(i) $\sqrt{7+4\sqrt{3}}$	(P) $\sqrt{6}$
(ii) $\sqrt[6]{216}$	(Q) $\sqrt[6]{72}$
(iii) $\left(\frac{2ab^3}{5c^3b}\right)^0$	(R) $2+\sqrt{3}$
(iv) $\sqrt[3]{3}\times\sqrt[2]{2}$	(S) 1

2. It is given that $x=-2, y=-3$ match the following

Column-I	Column-II
(i) x^{1-y}	(P) 1

Comprehension Type Questions

If $x=7-4\sqrt{3}$

1. Find the value of $x+\frac{1}{x}$
   (A) 28 (B) 14
   (C) $8\sqrt{3}$ (D) 1/14
2. Find the value of $x^3+\frac{1}{x^3}$
   (A) 2744 (B) 2740
   (C) 2072 (D) 2702
3. Find the value of $x^2-\frac{1}{x^2}$
   (A) $-112\sqrt{3}$ (B) $8\sqrt{3}$
   (C) 112 (D) $-64\sqrt{3}$
4. Find the value of $\frac{x^2-1}{x^2+1}$

Comprehension Type Questions

This exercise tests concept learning by checking for a learner's level of understanding.

Numerical Type Questions

Play with numbers in this fun activity that checks for your understanding of mathematical concepts.

Numerical Type Questions

1. The digit at the 100th place in the decimal representation of $\frac{6}{7}$, is:
2. xy is a number that is divided by ab where $xy < ab$ and gives a result 0. $xyxyxy...$ then ab equals:
3. When the repeating decimal 0.45454545... is written in simplest fractional form, the sum of the numerator and denominator is:
4. If $\sqrt{9-(n-2)^2}$ is a real number, then the number of integral values of n is:

Very Short Answer Type Questions
Summarise your learning in a few words by answering these questions.

Free Response Type

Very Short Answer Type Questions

1. Find the product of any two irrational numbers.
2. Find a rational number between $\sqrt{2}$ and $\sqrt{3}$.
3. Find the value of 1.999... in the form $\frac{p}{q}$, where p and q are integers and $q \neq 0$.
4. Find the number obtained on rationalising the denominator of $\frac{1}{\sqrt{7}-2}$.
5. After rationalising the denominator of $\frac{7}{3\sqrt{3}-2\sqrt{2}}$, what will be the denominator

Short Answer Type Questions

1. Find the product $\sqrt[3]{2}.\sqrt[4]{2}.\sqrt[12]{32}$.
2. Rationalise the denominator of the following:

(i) $\frac{2}{3\sqrt{3}}$ (ii) $\frac{\sqrt{40}}{\sqrt{3}}$ (iii) $\frac{3+\sqrt{2}}{4\sqrt{2}}$

(iv) $\frac{16}{\sqrt{41}-5}$ (v) $\frac{2+\sqrt{3}}{2-\sqrt{3}}$ (vi) $\frac{\sqrt{6}}{2+\sqrt{3}}$

(vii) $\frac{\sqrt{3}+\sqrt{2}}{\sqrt{3}-\sqrt{2}}$ (viii) $\frac{3\sqrt{5}+\sqrt{3}}{\sqrt{5}-\sqrt{3}}$

(ix) $\frac{4\sqrt{3}+5\sqrt{2}}{\sqrt{48}+\sqrt{18}}$

Short Answer Type Questions
Summarise your learning in a short sentence by answering these questions.

Long Answer Type Questions
Elaborate on concepts learnt by knowing exactly what to include in these long-answer type questions.

Long Answer Type Questions

1. Find the values of a and b in each of the following:

(i) $\frac{5+2\sqrt{3}}{7+4\sqrt{3}} = a - 6\sqrt{3}$

(ii) $\frac{3-\sqrt{5}}{3+2\sqrt{5}} = a\sqrt{5} - \frac{19}{11}$

2. Find the values of a and b in each of the following:

(i) $\frac{\sqrt{2}+\sqrt{3}}{3\sqrt{2}-2\sqrt{3}} = 2 - b\sqrt{6}$

(ii) $\frac{7+\sqrt{5}}{7-\sqrt{5}} - \frac{7-\sqrt{5}}{7+\sqrt{5}} = a + \frac{7}{11}\sqrt{5}b$

3. If $a = 2 + \sqrt{3}$, then find the value of $a - \frac{1}{}$

ARCHIVE CORNER

1. What is the square root of $9 + 2\sqrt{14}$?

(A) $1+2\sqrt{2}$ (B) $\sqrt{3}+\sqrt{6}$

(C) $\sqrt{2}+\sqrt{7}$ (D) $\sqrt{2}+\sqrt{5}$

2. $\sqrt[3]{1-\frac{127}{343}}$ is equal to:

(A) $\frac{5}{9}$ (B) $1-\frac{1}{7}$

(C) $\frac{4}{7}$ (D) $1-\frac{2}{7}$

3. What is the value of $2.\overline{6} - 1.\overline{9}$?

9. Which of the followi number?

(A) $2+\sqrt{5}$

(C) $\frac{7}{\sqrt{5}}$

10. The multiplication of al 1 and 10 is:

(A) 105

(C) 210

11. Statement P: x and y negative statements wil

(A) P: x and y both are

(B) P: x is not integer c

Archive Corner
Reassess your learning by understanding and remembering questions you have already answered and concepts you have already learnt.

Answer Key
Cross-check your answers by referring to this comprehensive list provided.

ANSWER KEY

CHECK POINTS

Check Point 1

2. $\frac{31}{80}$ 3. $\frac{19}{6}, \frac{20}{6}, \frac{21}{6}, \frac{22}{6}, \frac{23}{6}$ 4. $\frac{5}{3}, \frac{9}{14}, \frac{5}{7}, \frac{6}{11}$ 5. $x = \frac{1128}{999}$

Check Point 2

6. 0.05005000500005; 5.51551555151; 7. $\sqrt{5.1}, \sqrt{5.2}$

CHAPTER 1 NUMBER SYSTEM

CHECK POINT 1

1. Represent $\frac{3}{5}$ on the number line

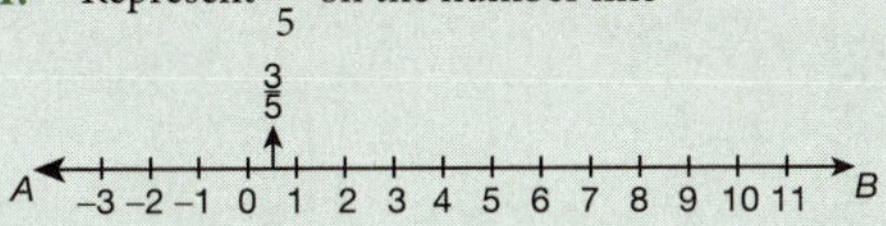

2. $\frac{3}{8}$ and $\frac{2}{5}$ then $\frac{30}{80}$ and $\frac{32}{80}$ then fraction between them will be $\frac{31}{80}$.

3. $\frac{18}{6}$ and $\frac{24}{6}$ then $\frac{19}{6}, \frac{20}{6}, \frac{21}{6}, \frac{22}{6}, \frac{23}{6}$

4. $\frac{5}{3}, \frac{9}{14}, \frac{5}{7}, \frac{6}{11}$

- We determine 343 × **3** = from 1100 and get the rei down the next pair of zerc new dividend.
- Repeat the same division the quotient approximatec Thus, we have evaluated √
- This is a never-ending p terminating and non-repe decimal point. $\sqrt{3}$ = 1.73 it goes on.

```
          1. 7
     1 | 3. 0 0
    +1 |-1
    ---|------
    27 | 2 0 0
    +7 |-1 8 9
```

Hints and Explanations
Address any and all gaps in learning by referring to hints and explanations provided for better understanding of concepts and questions.

CHAPTER 1

Number System

Learning Outcomes

After reading this chapter, you would be able to:

- classification of numbers.
- rational number in decimal form.
- representation of rational number on a real number line.
- conversion of recurring decimal into fraction.
- find a rational number between two integers.
- proof of irrationality of numbers.
- insertion of irrational numbers between two real numbers.
- irrational number on a number line.
- geometrical representation of real numbers.
- surds.
- law of surds.
- operation on surds.
- comparison of surds.
- rationalization of surds.
- exponents of real numbers.
- law of rational exponents.

Geekspeak

- Real number
- Rational number
- Irrational number
- Natural number
- Whole number
- Integers
- Positive integers
- Negative integers
- Prime number
- Co-prime number
- Twin prime number
- Decimal
- Terminating decimal
- Non-terminating
- Repeating
- Non-repeating
- Rationalization
- Surds
- Exponents

Introduction

A number system defines a set of values used to represent quantities. We talk about the number of people attending class and the number of modules taken per student and also use numbers to represent grades achieved by students in tests. The study of number systems is not just limited to computers. We use numbers every day, and knowing how numbers work gives us insight into how computers manipulate and store numbers.

Number System

The Number System is a way to classify and organize numbers based on their properties. Numbers are categorized into different types such as natural numbers, whole numbers, integers, rational numbers, irrational numbers, and real numbers.

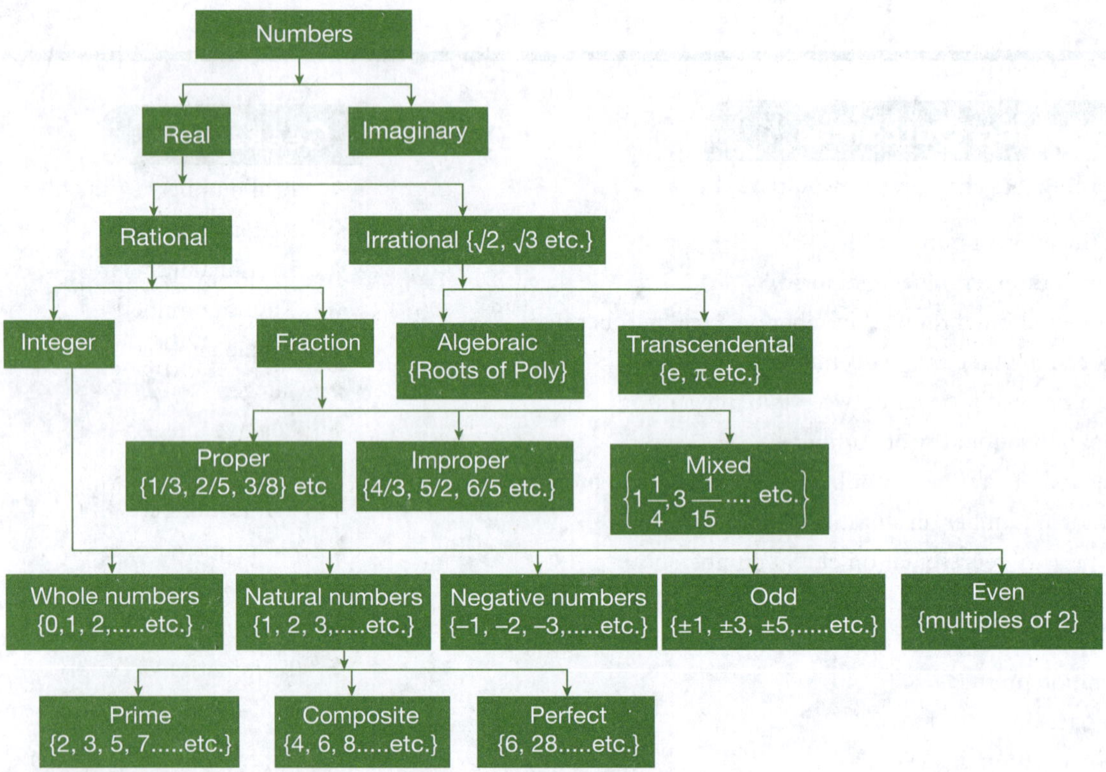

Classification of Numbers

(i) Natural numbers: Counting numbers are known as **natural numbers**.
$N = \{1, 2, 3, 4, ...\}$.

(ii) Whole numbers: All natural numbers and 0 form the collection of all integers are called **whole numbers**.
$W = \{0, 1, 2, 3, 4, ...\}$.

(iii) Integers: All whole numbers and negative of natural numbers form the collection of all **integers**.
I or $Z = \{..., -3, -2, -1, 0, 1, 2, 3, ...\}$.

(iv) Rational numbers: The numbers which can be expressed in the form of $\frac{p}{q}$, where p and q are integers and $q \neq 0$.

For example: $\frac{2}{3}, -\frac{37}{15}$.

All natural numbers, whole numbers and integers are rational.

(v) **Real numbers:** Numerical values that can meaningfully represent actual physical quantities are called **real numbers**. They can be represented on the number line.
Real numbers include all rational and irrational numbers.

(vi) **Prime numbers:** Prime numbers are natural numbers greater than 1 and each of which is divisible by 1 and itself only. For example: 2, 3, 5, 7, 11, 13, 17, 19, 23, ... etc.

(vii) **Composite numbers:** All natural numbers greater than 1 which are not prime numbers.
1 is neither a prime nor composite number.

(viii) **Co-prime Numbers:** If the H.C.F. of the given numbers (not necessarily prime) is 1 then they are known as **co-prime numbers**. For example: 8, 15 are co-prime as H.C.F. of (8, 15) = 1.
Any two consecutive numbers will always be co-prime.

(ix) **Even Numbers:** Integers divisible by 2.
$E = \{..., -2, 0, 2, ...\}$.

(x) **Odd Numbers:** Integers not divisible by 2.
$E = \{..., -3, -1, 1, 3, ...\}$.

Keystone

- 1 is neither a prime more a composite number.
- Every prime number more than 3 leaves the remainder 1 or 5 when divided by 6.
- Pairs of prime numbers are always co-prime numbers. (3, 7)
- Pairs of consecutive natural numbers are always co-prime. E.g. (4, 5)

Rational Number in Decimal Form

(i) **Terminating Decimal:** Let x be a rational number whose decimal expansion terminates. Then, x can be expressed in the form $\frac{p}{q}$ where p and q are co-prime, In such finite decimal number of digit occurs after the decimal.

For example: $\frac{1}{2} = 0.5, \frac{11}{16} = 0.6875, \frac{3}{20} = 0.15$, etc.

(ii) **Non-Terminating and Repeating (Recurring Decimal):**

Let $x = \frac{p}{q}$ be a rational number, such that the prime factorization of q is not of the form $2^m \times 5^n$, where m *and* n are non-negative integers. Then, x has a decimal expansion which is non-terminating repeating. In this, a set of digits or a digit is repeated continuously.

For example: $\frac{2}{3} = 0.6666... = 0.\overline{6}$ and $\frac{5}{11}$ = and $0.454545 \ldots 0.\overline{45}$

Competition Corner

In terminating decimal, prime factorization of the denominator is of the form $2^m \times 5^n$, where m, n are non-negative integers.

Rational Numbers on the Real Number Line

Rational numbers can be represented on the number line just like integers and other real numbers. A number line extends infinitely in both directions, with negative numbers on the left, positive numbers on the right, and zero at the center.

Terminating Decimals on the Number Line

The process of visualization of the number on the number line through a magnifying glass is known as **successive magnification.**

Sometimes, we are unable to check the numbers like 3.765 and $4.\overline{26}$ on the number line. Divide the parts into subparts and divide the subparts into equal subparts again to ensure the accuracy of the given numbers with the help of a magnifier.

Numbers on the Number Line

1. Choose the two consecutive integral numbers in which the given number lies.
2. Choose the two consecutive decimal points in which the given decimal part lies by dividing the two given decimal parts into required equal parts.
3. Visualize the required number through a magnifying glass.

Conversion of Decimal into Fraction

(i) **Long Method:**

Step 1: Makes the mixed repeating decimal equal to x.
Step 2: Count the number of nonrecurring digits after the decimal point. Let it be $\boldsymbol{n}$.
Step 3: Multiply both sides of the equation by $\mathbf{10}^n$ so that only the repeating decimal is on the right-hand side of the decimal point.
Step 4: Multiply both sides of the equation obtained in step 3 by 10^m, where m is the repeating number of digits in the fractional part.
Step 5: Subtract the equation in **step 3** from the equation obtained in **step 4**.
Step 6: Divide both sides of the resulting equation by the coefficient of $\boldsymbol{x}$.
Step 7: Write the rational number thus obtained in the simplest $\frac{p}{q}$ form.

(ii) **Direct Method:**

Step 1: To obtain the numerator subtract the number formed by non-repeating digits from the complete number without decimal. (Consider repeated digits only once.)
Step 2: To obtain the denominator take number of nines = Number of repeating digits and after that put number of zeros = number of non-repeating digits.

Rational Numbers Between Two Integral Numbers

Method - I

Let a and b are two given rational numbers such that $a < b$.
If n rational numbers are inserted between a and b.

Then, multiply numerator and denominator of a and b by $\frac{n+1}{n+1}$.

$$a = a \times \frac{n+1}{n+1} \text{ and } b = b \times \frac{n+1}{n+1}.$$

Then, as we increase the value of the numerator we get rational numbers between a and b.

Method - II

Let a and b be two given rational numbers such that $a < b$ then, $a < b$.

$$\Rightarrow a + a < b + a \qquad \text{[adding } a \text{ both sides]}$$

$$\Rightarrow 2a < a + b \Rightarrow a < \frac{a+b}{2}$$

Again, $a < b$

$$\Rightarrow a + b < b + b \qquad \text{[adding } b \text{ both sides]}$$

$$\Rightarrow a + b < 2b \Rightarrow \frac{a+b}{2} < b.$$

$$\therefore \quad a < \frac{a+b}{2} < b. \text{ i.e. } \frac{a+b}{2} \text{ lies between } a \text{ and } b.$$

Hence, 1st rational number between a and b is $\frac{a+b}{2}$.

For the next rational number

$$\frac{a+\frac{a+b}{2}}{2}=\frac{\frac{2a+a+b}{2}}{2}=\frac{3a+b}{4}$$

$\therefore$ $$a<\frac{3a+b}{4}<\frac{a+b}{2}<b$$

Next $$\frac{\frac{a+b}{2}+b}{2}=\frac{a+b+2b}{2\times 2}=\frac{a+3b}{4}$$

$\therefore$ $$a<\frac{3a+b}{4}<\frac{a+b}{2}<\frac{a+3b}{4}<b \text{ and continues like this.}$$

Illustration 1.1

Is (39, 93) a co-prime?

Solution: HCF of (39, 93) is 3.

$\therefore$ (39, 93) is not co-prime.

Illustration 1.2

Represent $\frac{7}{5}$ on a real number line.

Solution: $\frac{7}{5}=1\frac{2}{5}$

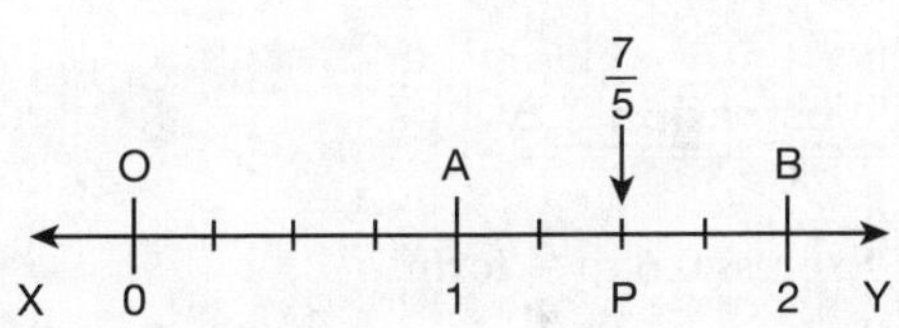

(i) Draw a line *XY* which extends endlessly in both directions.

(ii) Take a point *O* on it and let it represent 0 (zero).

(iii) Taking the fixed length, called unit length, mark off $OA = 1$ unit and $OB = 2$ units.

(iv) Divide *OA* and *AB* into 5 equal parts. *OP* represents the rational number $\frac{7}{5}$.

Illustration 1.3

Represent $-\frac{13}{4}$ on a real number line.

Solution: $-\frac{13}{4}=-3\frac{1}{4}$

(i) Draw a line *XY* which extends endlessly in both directions.

(ii) Take a point *O* on it and let it represent 0 (zero).

(iii) Taking the fixed length, called unit length, mark off $OA = 1$ unit and $OB = 2$ unit and $OC = 3$ unit on the left side of *O*.

(iv) Divide *OA*, *AB*, *BC* and *CD* into 4 equal parts. *OP* represents the rational number $-\frac{13}{4}$ of a unit.

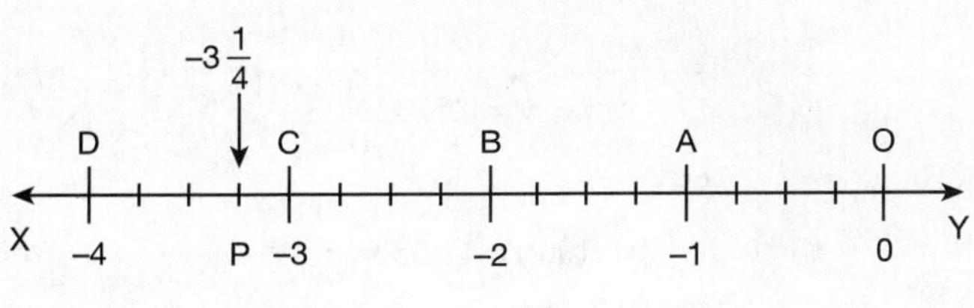

Illustration 1.4

Represent 2.5 on a real number line.

Solution:

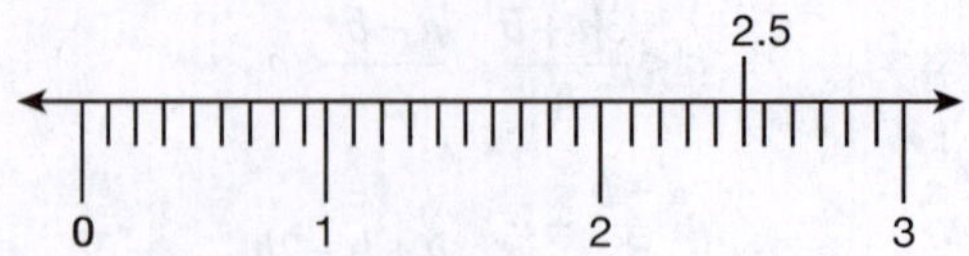

Illustration 1.5

Represent 2.65 on a real number line by process of magnification.

Solution:

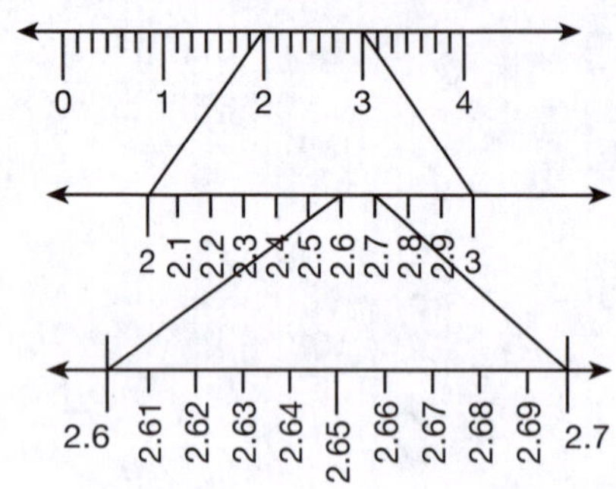

Illustration 1.6

Express $0.\overline{6}$ to $\frac{p}{q}$ form.

Solution: Let $x = 0.\overline{6}$

$$\text{i.e., } x = 0.6666\ldots \qquad \ldots\text{(i)}$$

Multiply both sides of eq.(i) by 10.

$$10x = 6.666\ldots \qquad \ldots\text{(ii)}$$

Subtract eq.(i) from eq.(ii)

$$10x = 6.666\ldots$$
$$-x = -0.666\ldots$$
$$9x = 6$$
$$\Rightarrow x = \frac{6}{9} \Rightarrow x = \frac{2}{3}$$

Illustration 1.7

Express $0.12\overline{3}$ to $\frac{p}{q}$ form.

Solution: Let $x = 0.12\overline{3}$

$$\text{i.e. } x = 0.12333 \qquad \ldots\text{(i)}$$

Multiply both sides of eq.(i) by 100.

$$100x = 12.333 \qquad \ldots\text{(ii)}$$

Multiply both sides of eq.(ii) by 10

$$1000x = 123.333 \qquad \ldots\text{(iii)}$$

Subtract eq.(ii) from eq.(iii)

$$\begin{aligned} 1000x &= 123.333\ldots \\ -\,100x &= -\,12.333\ldots \\ \hline 900x &= 111.000 \end{aligned}$$

$$\Rightarrow x = \frac{111}{900} \Rightarrow x = \frac{3\times 37}{900} = \frac{37}{300}$$

Illustration 1.8

Express the following to $\frac{p}{q}$ form using the direct method:

(i) $0.\overline{45}$ **(ii)** $0.7\overline{37}$ **(iii)** $0.46\overline{573}$

Solution:

(i) $0.\overline{45} = \frac{45-0}{99} = \frac{45}{99} = \frac{5}{11}$

(ii) $0.7\overline{37} = \frac{737-7}{990} = \frac{730}{990} = \frac{73}{99}$

(iii) $0.46\overline{573} = \frac{46573-46}{99900} = \frac{46527}{99900}$

Illustration 1.9

Find 4 rational numbers between 2 and 3.

Solution:

Steps:

(i) Multiplying 2 and 3 in N^r and D^r with (4 + 1).

(ii) $2 = \frac{2\times(4+1)}{(4+1)} = \frac{10}{5}$ and $\frac{3\times(4+1)}{(4+1)} = \frac{15}{5}$

(iii) So, the four required numbers are $\frac{11}{5}, \frac{12}{5}, \frac{13}{5}, \frac{14}{5}$

Check Point 1

1. Represent the number $\frac{3}{5}$ on the number line.
2. Find a fraction between $\frac{3}{8}$ and $\frac{2}{5}$.
3. Insert 5 rational numbers between 3 and 4.
4. Which of the following fractions yield a recurring decimal?

$$\frac{5}{3}; \frac{7}{16}; \frac{9}{14}; \frac{5}{7}; \frac{12}{5}; \frac{6}{11}$$

5. Represent 1. 129129129.. as a fraction.

Irrational Numbers

All real numbers which are not rational are called irrational numbers. These are non-recurring as well as the non terminating type of decimal numbers.

$$\text{i.e., } \sqrt{2}, \sqrt[3]{4}, 2+\sqrt{3}, \sqrt{2+\sqrt{3}}, \sqrt[4]{\sqrt[7]{3}}, \pi, \text{ etc..}$$

Proof of Irrationality of Numbers

To prove the irrationality of a given number, the process is done by the contradiction method. In logic, proof by contradiction is a form of proof and more specifically a form of indirect proof, that establishes the truth or validity of a proposition. It starts by assuming that the opposite proposition is true and then shows that such an assumption leads to a contradiction.

Irrational Numbers Between Two Real Numbers

Let a and b be two given real numbers, then the irrational number between a and b is $\sqrt{a \times b}$. Providing $a \times b$ is not a perfect square.

Irrational Number in Decimal Form

$\sqrt{2} = 1.414213\ldots$ i.e., it is non-recurring as well as non-terminating.

$\sqrt{3} = 1.732050807\ldots$ i.e., it is non-recurring as well as non-terminating.

Properties of Irrational Number

(i) Negative of an irrational number is an irrational number, for example, $-\sqrt{3}, -\sqrt[4]{5}$ are irrational.

(ii) Sum and difference between a rational and an irrational number is always an irrational number.

(iii) Sum, product and difference of two irrational numbers is either rational or irrational number.

(iv) Product of a rational number with an irrational number is either rational or irrational.

Real Numbers

To represent any real number $\sqrt{x}$ on the number line we follow the following steps:

STEP I: Obtain the positive real number x (say).

STEP II: Draw a line and mark a point A on it.

STEP III: Mark a point B on the line such that $AB = x$ units.

STEP IV: From point B mark a distance of 1 unit and mark the new point as C. Such that ABC is a straight line.

STEP V: Find the mid-point of AC by drawing the perpendicular bisector of line segment AC and mark the point as O.

STEP VI: Draw a semi-circle with centre O and radius OC.

STEP VII: Draw a line perpendicular to AC passing through B and intersecting the semi-circle at D. Length BD is equal to $\sqrt{x}$.

STEP VIII: Taking B as centre and BD as radius, draw an arc cutting OC produced at E. Distance BE represents $\sqrt{x}$.

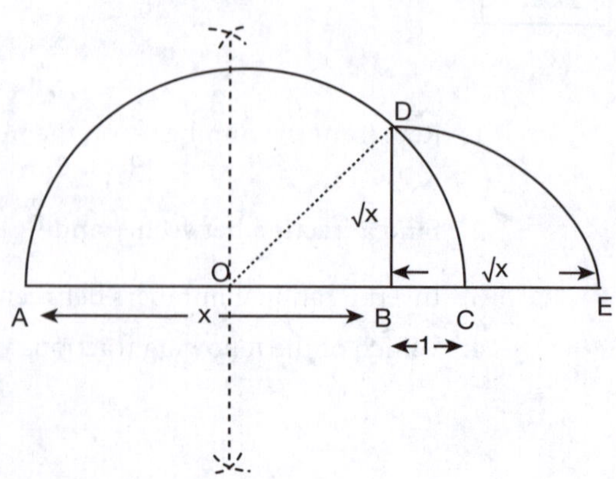

Figure 1.1

Explanation:

We have,

$$AB = x \text{ units and } BC = 1 \text{ unit.}$$

$$\therefore AC = (x + A) \text{ units}$$

$$\Rightarrow OA = OC = \frac{x+1}{2} \text{ units}$$

$$\Rightarrow OD = \frac{x+1}{2} \text{units} \qquad [\because OA = OC = OD]$$

Now, $OB = AB - OA$

$$= x - \frac{x+1}{2} = \frac{x-1}{2}$$

Using Pythagoras Theorem in $DOBD$, we have

$$OD^2 = OB^2 + BD^2 \Rightarrow BD^2 = OD^2 - OB^2$$

$$\Rightarrow BD^2 = \left(\frac{x+1}{2}\right)^2 - \left(\frac{x-1}{2}\right)^2$$

$$\Rightarrow BD = \sqrt{\frac{(x^2+2x+1)-(x^2-2x+1)}{4}}$$

$$\Rightarrow BD = \sqrt{\frac{4x}{4}} \Rightarrow BD = \sqrt{x}$$

This shows that $\sqrt{x}$ exists for all real numbers $x > 0$.

Illustration 1.10

Prove that $\sqrt{2}$ is an irrational number.

Solution: Let's assume on the contrary that $\sqrt{2}$ is a rational number.

Then, there exist positive integers a and b such that $\sqrt{2} = \frac{a}{b}$ where, a and b are coprime i.e., their HCF is 1.

$$\Rightarrow (\sqrt{2})^2 \left(\frac{a}{b}\right)^2 \Rightarrow 2 = \frac{a^2}{b^2}$$

$$\Rightarrow a^2 = 2b^2 \Rightarrow a^2 \text{ is a multiple of 2}$$

$$\Rightarrow a \text{ is a multiple of 2} \qquad \text{...(i)}$$

$a = 2c$ for some integer c.

$$\Rightarrow a^2 = 4c^2 \Rightarrow 2b^2 = 4c^2$$

$$\Rightarrow b^2 = 2c^2 \Rightarrow b^2 \text{ is a multiple of 2}$$

$$b \text{ is a multiple of 2} \qquad \text{...(ii)}$$

From (i) and (ii), a and b have at least 2 as common factors. But this contradicts the fact that a and b are co-prime. This means that $\sqrt{2}$ is an irrational number.

Illustration 1.11

Insert an irrational number between 2 and 3.

Solution: $\sqrt{2 \times 3} = \sqrt{6}$

Illustration 1.12

Find two irrational numbers between 2 and 2.5.

Solution:
1st Method: $\sqrt{2 \times 2.5} = \sqrt{5}$.
Since, there is no rational number whose square is 5. So, $\sqrt{5}$ is an irrational number.

Also, $\sqrt{2 \times \sqrt{5}}$ is an irrational number.

2nd Method: 2.101001000100001… is between 2 and 5 and it is non-recurring as well as nonterminating.
Also, 2.201001000100001 … and so on.

Illustration 1.13

Plot $\sqrt{2}, \sqrt{3}, \sqrt{5}$ on a number line.

Solution: Let $X'OX$ be a horizontal line, taken as the x-axis and let O be the origin. Let O represents 0 (zero).
Take $OA = 1$ unit and draw $AB \perp OA$ such that $AB = 1$ unit.
Join OB. Then,

$$OB = \sqrt{OA^2 + AB^2} = \sqrt{1^2 + 1^2} = \sqrt{2} \text{ units.}$$

With O as centre and OB as radius, draw an arc, meeting OY at P.
Then, $OP = OB = \sqrt{2}$ units.

Thus the point P represents $\sqrt{2}$ on the real line.
Now draw $BC \perp OB$ such that $BC = 1$ unit.
Join OC. Then,

$$OC = \sqrt{OB^2 + BC^2} = \sqrt{(\sqrt{2})^2 + 1^2} = \sqrt{3} \text{ units.}$$

$$2 + 1 = 3 \text{ units.}$$

With O as the centre and OC as the radius, draw an arc, meeting OY at Q.
Then, $OQ = OC = \sqrt{3}$ units.
Thus, point Q represents $\sqrt{3}$ on the real line.
Now draw $CD \perp OC$ such that $CD = 1$ unit.
Join OD. Then,

$$OD = \sqrt{OC^2 + CD^2} = \sqrt{(\sqrt{3})^2 + 1^2} = \sqrt{4} = 2 \text{ units}$$

Now draw $DE \perp OD$ such that $DE = 1$ unit.
Join OE. Then,

$$OE = \sqrt{OD^2 + DE^2} = \sqrt{(2)^2 + 1^2} = \sqrt{5} \text{ units.}$$

With O as the centre and OE as the radius, draw an arc, meeting OY at R.

Then, $OR = OE = \sqrt{5}$ units.

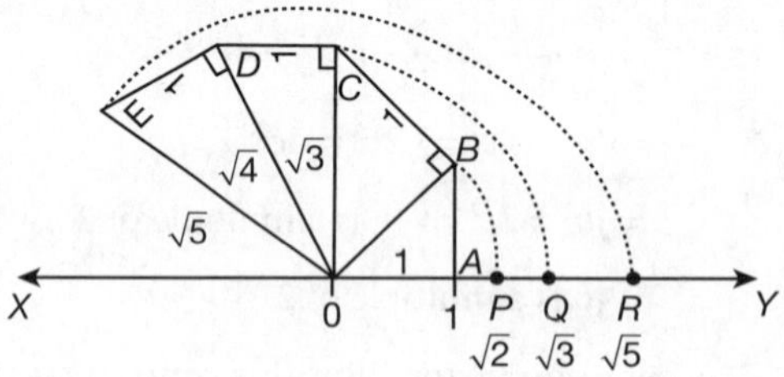

Another Method for:

(i) Plot $\sqrt{2}, \sqrt{3}$

Draw a number line and mark a point O, representing zero, on it. Suppose point A represents 1. Then $OA = 1$. Now draw a right triangle OAB such that $AB = OA = 1$.
By Pythagoras theorem,

$$OB = \sqrt{OA^2 + AB^2} = \sqrt{1^2 + 1^2} = \sqrt{2} \text{ units.}$$

Now, draw an arc with centre O and radius OB. It cuts the number line at C.

Then, $OC = OB = \sqrt{2}$ units.

Thus, point C represents $\sqrt{2}$ on the real line.
Now, draw a right triangle OEC such that $CE = AB = 1$ unit.
Again by Pythagoras theorem,

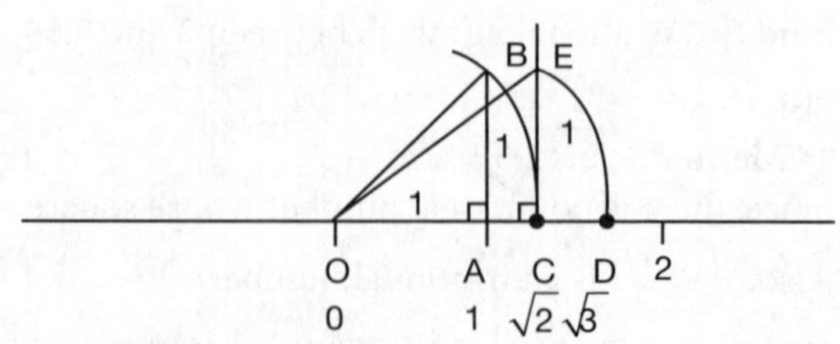

$$OE = \sqrt{OC^2 + CE^2} = \sqrt{\left(\sqrt{2}\right)^2 + 1^2} = \sqrt{3} \text{ units.}$$

Now, draw an arc with centre O and radius OE. It cuts the number line at D.

Then, $OD = OE = \sqrt{3}$ units.

Check Point 2

6. Which of the following numbers are not rational?
1.256; 0.45454545; 0.05005000500005; 5.51551555151; 2.012340123401234.;

7. Find two irrational numbers between $\sqrt{5}$ and $\sqrt{6}$.

8. Prove that $\sqrt{3}$ is irrational number.

9. Represent $\sqrt{6}$ on the number line.

10. Represent $\sqrt{7.3}$ on the number line.

Surds

An irrational number of the form $\sqrt[n]{a}$ is given a special name **Surd**, where '*a*' is called **radicand** and it should always be a rational number. Also, the symbol $\sqrt[n]{a}$ is called the **radical sign** and the index ***n*** is called **order** of the surd. $\sqrt[n]{a}$ is read as '***n*^th^ root of *a***' and can also be written as $a^{\frac{1}{n}}$.

Law of Surds

(i) $(\sqrt[n]{a})^n = \sqrt[n]{a^n} = a$ **(ii)** $\sqrt[n]{a} \times \sqrt[n]{b} = \sqrt[n]{ab}$ **(iii)** $\sqrt[n]{a} \div \sqrt[n]{b} = \sqrt[n]{\frac{a}{b}}$ **(iv)** $\sqrt[n]{a} \times \sqrt[n]{b} = \sqrt[n]{ab}$

(v) $\sqrt[n]{a} = \sqrt[n\times p]{a^p}$ or $\sqrt[n]{a^m} = \sqrt[n\times p]{a^{m\times p}}$

Operation on Surds

(i) Addition and Subtraction of Surds: Addition and subtraction of surds are possible only when order and radicand are the same i.e., only for like surds. The addition of surds follows the following rules. Summation of same degree surds is distributive.

$$a\sqrt[n]{p} + b\sqrt[n]{p} = (a+b)\sqrt[n]{p}$$

The subtraction of surds follows the following rules. Subtraction of the same degree surds is distributive.

$$a\sqrt[n]{p} - b\sqrt[n]{p} = (a-b)\sqrt[n]{p}$$

(ii) Multiplication and Division of Surds: For multiplication and division we have to check the order if it is not the same then first we make the order of surd the same by using laws of indices. Then we follow the following rule

$$a\sqrt[n]{p} \times b\sqrt[n]{q} = (a\times b)\sqrt[n]{p\times q}$$

$$\frac{a\sqrt[n]{p}}{b\sqrt[n]{q}} = \left(\frac{a}{b}\right)\sqrt[n]{\left(\frac{p}{q}\right)}$$

(iii) Comparison of Surds: It is clear that if $x > y > 0$ and $n > 1$ is a positive integer then $\sqrt[n]{x} > \sqrt[n]{y}$.

Rationalization of Surds

Product of two surds is a rational number then each of them is called the **rationalizing factor (R.F.)** of the other. The process of converting a surd to a rational number by using an appropriate multiplier is known as **rationalization.**

When the denominator of an expression contains a term with a square root (or a number with radical sign), the process of converting it to an equivalent expression whose denominator is a rational number is called **rationalizing** the **denominator.**

Competition Corner

Rationalizing factor of $a^{\frac{1}{n}}$ is $a^{1-\frac{1}{n}}$ where a is real no.

Illustration 1.14

$\sqrt{75}-\sqrt{45}+\sqrt{50}-\sqrt{32}$

Solution:

$$\begin{aligned}&\sqrt{75}-\sqrt{45}+\sqrt{50}-\sqrt{32}\\&=5\sqrt{3}-3\sqrt{5}+5\sqrt{2}-4\sqrt{2}\\&=5\sqrt{3}-3\sqrt{5}+\sqrt{2}.\end{aligned}$$

Illustration 1.15

Simplify: $5\sqrt[3]{250}+7\sqrt[3]{16}-14\sqrt[3]{54}$

Solution: $5\sqrt[3]{250}+7\sqrt[3]{16}-14\sqrt[3]{54}=5\sqrt[3]{125\times 2}+7\sqrt[3]{8\times 2}-14\sqrt[3]{27\times 2}$

$$=5\times 5\sqrt[3]{2}+7\times 2\sqrt[3]{2}-14\times 3\times\sqrt[3]{2}=(25+14-42)\sqrt[3]{2}=-3\sqrt[3]{2}.$$

Illustration 1.16

Simplify: $\sqrt[3]{2}\times\sqrt[4]{3}$.

Solution: $\sqrt[3]{2}\times\sqrt[4]{3}$.

$$\begin{aligned}&=\sqrt[12]{2^4}\times\sqrt[12]{3^3}\text{ [order should be made same]}\\&=\sqrt[12]{2^4\times 3^3}=\sqrt[12]{16\times 27}=\sqrt[12]{432}.\end{aligned}$$

Illustration 1.17

Divide: $\sqrt{24}\div\sqrt[3]{200}$.

Solution: $\sqrt{24}\div\sqrt[3]{200}=\dfrac{\sqrt{24}}{\sqrt[3]{200}}=\dfrac{\sqrt[6]{(24)^3}}{\sqrt[6]{(200)^2}}=\sqrt[6]{\dfrac{216}{625}}$.

Illustration 1.18

Which is greater:

(i) $\sqrt[3]{6}$ and $\sqrt[5]{8}$ **(ii)** $\sqrt{\dfrac{1}{2}}$ and $\sqrt[3]{\dfrac{1}{3}}$

Solution:

(i) $\sqrt[3]{6}$ and $\sqrt[5]{8}$

L.C.M. of 3 and 5 is 15.

$$\sqrt[3]{6} = \sqrt[3\times5]{6^5} = \sqrt[15]{7776}$$

$$\sqrt[5]{8} = \sqrt[3\times5]{8^3} = \sqrt[15]{512}$$

$$\therefore \sqrt[15]{7776} > \sqrt[15]{512} \Rightarrow \sqrt[3]{6} > \sqrt[5]{8}$$

(ii) $\sqrt{\frac{1}{2}}$ and $\sqrt[6]{\frac{1}{3}}$

L.C.M. of 2 and 3 is 6.

$$\sqrt[6]{\left(\frac{1}{2}\right)^3} \text{ and } \sqrt[6]{\left(\frac{1}{3}\right)^2}$$

$$\sqrt[6]{\frac{1}{8}} \text{ and } \sqrt[6]{\frac{1}{9}} \left[\text{As } 8 < 9 \therefore \frac{1}{8} > \frac{1}{9}\right]$$

So,

$$\sqrt[6]{\frac{1}{8}} > \sqrt[6]{\frac{1}{9}} \Rightarrow \sqrt{\frac{1}{2}} > \sqrt[3]{\frac{1}{3}}.$$

Illustration 1.19

Arrange $\sqrt{2}, \sqrt[3]{3}$ and $\sqrt[4]{5}$ in ascending order.

Solution: $\sqrt{2}, \sqrt[3]{3}$ and $\sqrt[4]{5}$

L.C.M. of 2, 3, 4 is 12.

$$\therefore \sqrt{2} = \sqrt[2\times6]{2^6} = \sqrt[12]{64}$$

$$\sqrt[3]{3} = \sqrt[3\times4]{3^4} = \sqrt[12]{81}$$

$$\sqrt[4]{5} = \sqrt[4\times3]{3^4} = \sqrt[12]{125}$$

As, $64 < 81 < 125$.

$$\therefore \sqrt[12]{64} < \sqrt[12]{81} < \sqrt[12]{125} \Rightarrow \sqrt{2} < \sqrt[3]{3} < \sqrt[4]{5}.$$

Illustration 1.20

Rationalize the denominator $\frac{1}{\sqrt{162}}$.

Solution:

$$\frac{1}{\sqrt{162}} = \frac{1}{\sqrt{81\times2}}$$

$$= \frac{1}{9\sqrt{2}} \times \frac{\sqrt{2}}{\sqrt{2}} = \frac{\sqrt{2}}{18}.$$

Rationalising factor of $a + b\sqrt{c}$ is $a - b\sqrt{c}$ where a, b, c are rational numbers.

Illustration 1.21

Rationalize the denominator of $\frac{a^2}{\sqrt{a^2+b^2}+b}$.

Solution: $$\frac{a^2}{\sqrt{a^2+b^2}+b}\times\frac{\sqrt{a^2+b^2}-b}{a^2+b^2-b}=\frac{a^2\left(\sqrt{a^2+b^2}-b\right)}{\left(\sqrt{a^2+b^2}\right)^2-(b)^2}$$

$$=\frac{a^2\left(\sqrt{a^2+b^2}-b\right)}{a^2+b^2-b^2}=\left(\sqrt{a^2+b^2}-b\right).$$

Illustration 1.22

If $\frac{3+2\sqrt{2}}{3-\sqrt{2}}=a+b\sqrt{2}$, where a and b are rationales in a reduced form then, find the values of a and b.

Solution: LHS $$\frac{3+2\sqrt{2}}{3-\sqrt{2}}=\frac{(3+2\sqrt{2})(3+\sqrt{2})}{(3-\sqrt{2})(3+\sqrt{2})}$$

$$=\frac{9+3\sqrt{2}+6\sqrt{2}+4}{9-2}$$

$$=\frac{13+9\sqrt{2}}{7}=\frac{13}{7}+\frac{9}{7}\sqrt{2}$$

$$\because =\frac{13+9\sqrt{2}}{7}=a+b\sqrt{2}$$

Equating the rational and irrational parts

We get $a=\frac{13}{7}$, $b=\frac{9}{7}$.

Illustration 1.23

If $x=\frac{1}{2+\sqrt{3}}$, find the value of $x^3-x^2-11x+3$.

Solution: As, $x=\frac{1}{2+\sqrt{3}}=2-\sqrt{3}\Rightarrow x-2=-\sqrt{3}$

$$\Rightarrow (x-2)^2=(-\sqrt{3})^2 \text{ [by squaring both sides]}$$

$$\Rightarrow x^2+4-4x=3\Rightarrow x^2-4x+1=0$$

Now, $$x^3-x^2-11x+3=x(x^2-4x+1)+3(x^2-4x+1)$$

$$=x(0)+3(0)=0+0=0.$$

Illustration 1.24

If $\sqrt{5}=2.236$ and $\sqrt{2}=1.414$, then evaluate: $\frac{3}{\sqrt{5}+\sqrt{2}}+\frac{4}{\sqrt{5}-\sqrt{2}}$

Solution: $$\frac{3}{\sqrt{5}+\sqrt{2}}+\frac{4}{\sqrt{5}-\sqrt{2}}$$

$$=\frac{3\left(\sqrt{5}-\sqrt{2}\right)+4\left(\sqrt{5}+\sqrt{2}\right)}{\left(\sqrt{5}-\sqrt{2}\right)\left(\sqrt{5}+\sqrt{2}\right)}$$

$$=\frac{3\sqrt{5}-3\sqrt{2}+4\sqrt{5}+4\sqrt{2}}{5-2}$$

$$= \frac{7\sqrt{5}+\sqrt{2}}{5-2}$$

$$= \frac{7\sqrt{5}+\sqrt{2}}{3}$$

$$= \frac{7\times 2.236+1.414}{3}$$

$$= \frac{15.652+1.414}{3} = \frac{17.066}{3} = 5.689 \text{ (approximately)}$$

Check Point 3

11. What is the simplest form of $\sqrt{200}-\sqrt{50}$?

12. Rationalise the denominator of $\frac{5}{\sqrt{10}+\sqrt{5}}$.

13. If $x = \sqrt{2} - 1$ what is the value of $x - 1/x$?

14. Simplify $(\sqrt{5}+1)^2 + (\sqrt{5}-1)^2$.

15. If $x = \frac{\sqrt{5}-2}{\sqrt{5}+2}$, find the value of $x + \frac{1}{x}$.

Exponents

(i) Positive Integral Power: For any real number a and a natural number **'*n*'** we define ***an*** as:
$a^n = a \times a \times a \times \ldots \times a$ (n times)
an is called the $\boldsymbol{n^{th}}$ power of ***a***. The real number **'*a*'** is called the **base** and **'*n*'** is called the **exponent** of the $\boldsymbol{n^{th}}$ power of ***a***.
e.g. $2^3 = 2 \times 2 \times 2 = 8$

(ii) Negative Integral Power: For any non-zero real number **'*a*'** and positive integer **'*n*'** we define $\boldsymbol{a^{-n}} = \frac{1}{a^n}$.
Thus we have defined $\boldsymbol{a^n}$ for all integral values of ***n***, positive, zero or negative. $\boldsymbol{a^n}$ is called the $\boldsymbol{n^{th}}$ power of ***a***.

(iii) Rational Exponents of a Real number: Principal of $\boldsymbol{n^{th}}$ Root of Positive Real Numbers:
If **'*a*'** is a positive real number and **'*n*'** is a **positive integer**, then the principal $\boldsymbol{n^{th}}$ **root** of ***a*** is the unique positive real number ***x*** such that $\boldsymbol{x^n = a}$.
The principal nth root of a positive real number a is denoted by $\boldsymbol{a^{1/n}}$ or $\sqrt[n]{a}$.

Keystones

For any non-zero real number '*a*' we define $a^0 = 1$.
e.g.: Thus, $3^0 = 1$, 5^0, $\left(\frac{3}{4}\right)^0 = 1$ and so on.

Keystones

If **'*a*'** is a negative real number and **'*n*'** is an **even positive** integer, then the principal $\boldsymbol{n^{th}}$ root of ***a*** is not defined, because an even power of a real number is always positive. Therefore $(-9)^{1/2}$ is a meaningless quantity, if we confine ourselves to the set of real numbers, only.

Law of Rational Exponents

The following laws hold the rational exponents:

(i) $a^m \times a^n = a^{m+n}$

(ii) $a^m \div a^n = a^{m-n}$

(iii) $(a^m)^n = a^{mn}$

(iv) $a^{-n} = \dfrac{1}{a^n}$

(v) $a^{m/n} = (a^m)^{1/n} = (a^{1/n})^m$ i.e. $a^{m/n} = \sqrt[n]{a^m} = \sqrt[n]{a^m} = (\sqrt[n]{a})^m$

(vi) $(ab)^m = a^m b^m$

(vii) $\left(\dfrac{a}{b}\right)^m = \dfrac{a^m}{b^m}$

(viii) $a^{bn} = a^{b+b+b\ldots n \text{ times}}$

where a, b are positive real numbers and m *and* n are rational numbers.

Illustration 1.25

Evaluate each of the following:

(i) $5^8 \div 5^3$ (ii) $\left(\dfrac{3}{4}\right)^{-3}$

Solution: Using the laws of indices, we have:

$$\text{(i) } 5^8 \div 5^3 = \frac{5^8}{5^3} = 5^{8-3} = 5^5 = 3125. \ [\because a^m \div a^n = a^{m-n}]$$

$$\text{(ii) } \left(\frac{3}{4}\right)^{-3} = \frac{1}{\left(\frac{3}{4}\right)^3} = \frac{1}{\frac{3^3}{4^3}} = \frac{1}{\frac{27}{64}} [\because a^{-n} = \frac{1}{a^n}]$$

Illustration 1.26

Evaluate each of the following:

(i) $\left(\dfrac{1}{2}\right)^5 \times \left(\dfrac{-2}{3}\right)^4 \times \left(\dfrac{3}{5}\right)^{-1}$ (ii) $\left(\dfrac{2}{3}\right)^3 \times \left(\dfrac{2}{5}\right)^{-3} \times \left(\dfrac{3}{5}\right)^2$

Solution:

(i) We have,

$$\left(\frac{1}{2}\right)^5 \times \left(\frac{-2}{3}\right)^4 \times \left(\frac{3}{5}\right)^{-1} = \left(\frac{1}{2}\right)^5 \times \left(\frac{-2}{3}\right)^4 \times \left(\frac{1}{\frac{3}{5}}\right) = \frac{1^5}{2^5} \times \frac{(-2)^4}{3^4} \times \frac{5}{3}$$

$$= \frac{1 \times 16 \times 5}{32 \times 81 \times 3} = \frac{5}{2 \times 81 \times 3} = \frac{5}{486}.$$

(ii) We have,

$$\left(\frac{2}{3}\right)^3 \times \left(\frac{2}{5}\right)^{-3} \times \left(\frac{3}{5}\right)^2 = \frac{2^3}{3^3} \times \frac{1}{(2/5)^3} \times \frac{3^2}{5^2}$$

$$= \frac{2^3 \times 5^3 \times 3^2}{3^3 \times 2^3 \times 5^2} = \frac{5}{3}.$$

Illustration 1.27

Simplify:

(i) $\dfrac{(25)^{3/2}\times(243)^{3/5}}{(16)^{5/4}\times(8)^{4/3}}$ (ii) $\dfrac{16\times2^{n+1}-4\times2^{n}}{16\times2^{n+2}-2\times2^{n+2}}$

Solution: We have,

(i) $$\frac{(25)^{3/2}\times(243)^{3/5}}{(16)^{5/4}\times(8)^{4/3}}=\frac{(5^2)^{3/2}\times(3^5)^{3/5}}{(2^4)^{5/4}\times(2^3)^{4/3}}=\frac{5^{2\times3/2}\times3^{5\times3/5}}{2^{4\times5/4}\times2^{3\times4/3}}=\frac{5^3\times3^3}{2^5\times2^4}=\frac{125\times27}{32\times16}=\frac{3375}{512}.$$

(ii) $$\frac{16\times2^{n+1}-4\times2^{n}}{16\times2^{n+2}-2\times2^{n+2}}=\frac{32\times2^n-4\times2^n}{64\times2^n-8\times2^n}=\frac{2^n(32-4)}{2^n(64-8)}=\frac{1}{2}$$

Illustration 1.28

Prove that: $\dfrac{x^{-1}}{x^{-1}+y^{-1}}+\dfrac{x^{-1}}{x^{-1}-y^{-1}}=\dfrac{2y^2}{y^2-x^2}$

Solution:

$$\frac{x^{-1}}{x^{-1}+y^{-1}}+\frac{x^{-1}}{x^{-1}-y^{-1}}=\frac{\frac{1}{x}}{\frac{1}{x}+\frac{1}{y}}+\frac{\frac{1}{x}}{\frac{1}{x}-\frac{1}{y}}=\frac{\frac{1}{x}}{\frac{y+x}{xy}}+\frac{\frac{1}{x}}{\frac{y-x}{xy}}=\frac{xy}{x(y+x)}+\frac{xy}{x(y-x)}$$

$$=\frac{xy(y-x)+xy(y+x)}{x(y^2-x^2)}=\frac{y(y-x)+y(y+x)}{y^2-x^2}=\frac{y^2-xy+y^2+xy}{y^2-x^2}=\frac{2y^2}{y^2-x^2}.$$

Illustration 1.29

Find the value of x: $\left(\frac{3}{5}\right)^x\left(\frac{5}{3}\right)^{2x}=\frac{125}{27}$.

Solution:

$$\left(\frac{3}{5}\right)^x\left(\frac{5}{3}\right)^{2x}=\frac{125}{27}$$

$$\left(\frac{5}{3}\right)^{-x}\left(\frac{5}{3}\right)^{2x}=\frac{125}{27}$$

$$\left(\frac{5}{3}\right)^{2x-x}=\frac{125}{27}$$

$$\left(\frac{5}{3}\right)^{x}=\left(\frac{5}{3}\right)^{3}$$

Because the base is the same, so comparing the powers $x = 3$.

Illustration 1.30

If $25^{x-1} = 5^{2x-1} - 100$, find the value of x.

Solution: We have,

$$\Rightarrow 25^{x-1} = 5^{2x-1} - 100$$

$$\Rightarrow (5^2)^{x-1} = 5^{2x-1} - 100$$

$$\Rightarrow 5^{2x-2} - 5^{2x-1} = -100$$
$$\Rightarrow 5^{2x-2} - 5^{2x-2}.5^1 = -100$$
$$\Rightarrow 5^{2x-2}(1-5) = -100$$
$$\Rightarrow 5^{2x-2}(-4) = -100$$
$$\Rightarrow 5^{2x-2} = 25$$
$$\Rightarrow 5^{2x-2} = 5^2$$
$$\Rightarrow 2x - 2 = 2$$
$$\Rightarrow 2x = 4$$
$$\Rightarrow x = 2.$$

Check Point 4

16. Find the value of the following:
(i) $81^{1/4}$ (ii) $64^{1/3}$ (iii) $32^{3/5}$ (iv) $27^{2/3}$

17. Simplify the following:
(i) $3^{1/3}.3^{2/5}$ (ii) $\left(\frac{4}{9}\right)^{1/2}$ (iii) $2^{2/3}.3^{2/3}$ (iv) $\left(2^{1/3}\right)^3$

18. Simplified value of $2^n \times 4^n \times 8^{1-n}$

19. Find x, if $8^x = 16$

20. Find x, y, z if $15^3 \times 12^2 \times 16^4 = 2^x \times 3^y \times 5^z$

STRUCTURAL OUTLINE

Number System

Classification of Numbers

(i) **Natural numbers :** **N** = {1, 2, 3, 4, ...}.
(ii) **Whole numbers :** **W** = {0, 1, 2, 3, 4, ...}.
(iii) **Integers : I** or **Z** = {..., − 3, − 2, − 1, 0, 1, 2, 3, ...}.
(iv) **Rational numbers :** $\frac{2}{3}, -\frac{37}{15}$.
(v) **Real numbers**
(vi) **Prime numbers :** 2, 3, 5, 7, 11, 13, 17, 19, 23, ... etc.
(vii) **Composite numbers**
(viii) **Co-prime Numbers**
(ix) **Even Numbers :** Integers divisible by 2
(x) **Odd Numbers :** Integers not divisible by 2

Irrational Number

All real number which are not rational are called irrational numbers. These are non-recurring as well as nonterminating type of decimal numbers.

Proof of Irrationality

By Long Division Method

Special Points

- 1 is neither prime nor composite number.
- Every prime number more than 3 leaves remainder 1 or 5 when divided by 6.
- Pairs of prime numbers are always co-prime number. (3,7)
- Pairs of consecutive natural Number are always coprime. Eg. (4,5)

Law of Rational Exponents

(i) $a^m \times a^n = a^{m+n}$
(ii) $a^m \div a^n = a^{m-n}$
(iii) $(a^m)^n = a^{mn}$
(iv) $a^{-n} = \frac{1}{a^n}$
(v) $a^{m/n} = (a^m)^{1/n} = (a^{1/n})^m$ i.e. $a^{m/n} = \sqrt[n]{a^m} = \sqrt[n]{a^m} = (\sqrt[n]{a})^m$
(vi) $(ab)^m = a^m b^m$
(vii) $\left(\frac{a}{b}\right)^m = \frac{a^m}{b^m}$
(viii) $a^{bn} = a^{b+b+b.....n \text{ times}}$

where a, b are positive real numbers and m, n are rational numbers.

Surds and their Application

(i) $(\sqrt[n]{a})^n = a$
(ii) $\sqrt[n]{a} \times \sqrt[n]{b} = \sqrt[n]{ab}$
(iii) $\sqrt[n]{a} \div \sqrt[n]{b} = \sqrt[n]{\frac{a}{b}}$
(iv) $\sqrt[n]{a} = \sqrt[n \times p]{a^p}$

EXEMPLIFICATION

1. Represent $\frac{3}{7}$ on a real number line.

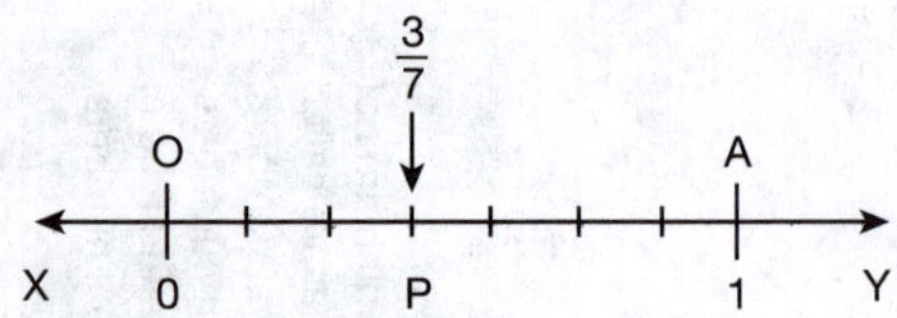

Solution:

(i) Draw a line *XY* which extends endlessly in both directions.

(ii) Take a point *O* on it and let it represent *O* (zero).

(iii) Taking the fixed length, called unit length, mark off $OA = 1$ unit, as shown in the figure below

(iv) Divide *OA* into 7 equal parts. *OP* represents $\frac{3}{7}$ of a unit.

2. Visualize the representation of 5.37 on the number line up to 5 decimal places.

Solution:

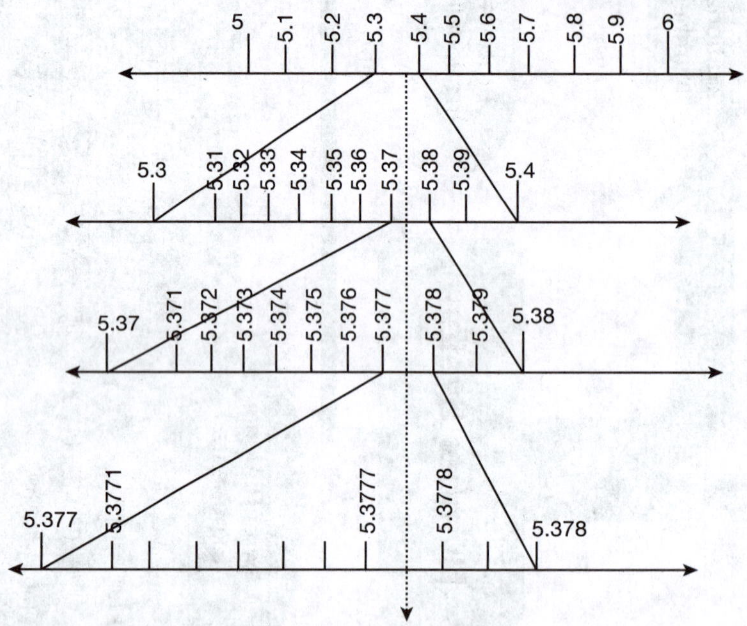

3. Express $0.\overline{47}$ to $\frac{p}{q}$ form.

Solution: Let $x = 0.47$

$$\text{i.e. } x = 0.474747\ldots \quad \ldots\text{(i)}$$

Multiply both sides of eq.(i) by 100.

$$100x = 47.474747 \quad \ldots\text{(ii)}$$

Subtract eq.(i) from eq.(ii)

$$\begin{aligned} 100x &= 47.474747\ldots \\ -x &= -0.474747\ldots. \\ \hline 99x &= 47 \end{aligned}$$

$$\Rightarrow x = \frac{47}{99}.$$

4. Find 3 rational numbers between $\frac{1}{3}$ and $\frac{1}{2}$.

Solution:

$$\frac{\frac{1}{3}+\frac{1}{2}}{2}=\frac{\frac{2+3}{6}}{2}=\frac{5}{12}$$

$$\therefore\ \frac{1}{3},\frac{5}{12},\frac{1}{2}$$

$$\frac{\frac{1}{3}+\frac{5}{12}}{2}=\frac{\frac{4+5}{12}}{2}=\frac{9}{24}$$

$$\therefore\ \frac{1}{3},\frac{9}{24},\frac{5}{12},\frac{1}{2}$$

$$\frac{\frac{5}{12}+\frac{1}{2}}{2}=\frac{\frac{5}{12}+\frac{6}{12}}{2}=\frac{11}{24}$$

$$\therefore\ \frac{1}{3},\frac{9}{24},\frac{5}{12},\frac{11}{24},\frac{1}{2}.$$

5. Prove that $3-\sqrt{5}$ is an irrational number.

Solution: Let's assume that on the contrary that $3-\sqrt{5}$ is rational.
Then, there exist co-prime positive integers a and b such that,

$$3-\sqrt{5}=\frac{a}{b}\Rightarrow 3-\frac{a}{b}=\sqrt{5}$$

$$\Rightarrow \frac{3b-a}{b}=\sqrt{5}\Rightarrow \sqrt{5}\text{ is rational }\left[\because a, b\text{ are integer }\therefore \frac{3b-a}{b}\text{ is a rational number}\right]$$

This contradicts the fact that $\sqrt{5}$ is an irrational number.
Hence, $3-\sqrt{5}$ is an irrational number.

6. Simplify: $\sqrt{8a^5b}\times\sqrt[3]{4a^2b^2}$.

Solution:

$$\sqrt{8a^5b}\times\sqrt[3]{4a^2b^2}=\sqrt[6]{8^3a^{15}b^3}\times\sqrt[6]{4^2a^4b^4}$$

$$=\sqrt[6]{2^{13}a^{19}b^7}=2^2a^3b\sqrt[6]{2ab}=4a^3b\sqrt[3]{2ab}.$$

7. Rationalize the denominator $\frac{1}{7+5\sqrt{3}}$.

Solution:

$$\frac{1}{7+5\sqrt{3}}=\frac{1}{7+5\sqrt{3}}\times\frac{7-5\sqrt{3}}{7-5\sqrt{3}}$$

$$=\frac{7-5\sqrt{3}}{49-75}=\frac{7-5\sqrt{3}}{-26}=\frac{5\sqrt{3}-7}{26}.$$

8. If $x=3-\sqrt{8}$, find the value of $x^3+\frac{1}{x^3}$.

Solution:

$$x=3-\sqrt{8}$$

$$\therefore\quad \frac{1}{x}=\frac{1}{3-\sqrt{8}}\Rightarrow\frac{1}{x}=3+\sqrt{8}$$

Now, $$x+\frac{1}{x}=3-\sqrt{8}+3+\sqrt{8}=6$$

$$\Rightarrow \quad x^3+\frac{1}{x^3}=\left(x+\frac{1}{x}\right)^3-3x\frac{1}{x}\left(x+\frac{1}{x}\right)\Rightarrow \quad x^3+\frac{1}{x^3}=(6)^3-3(6)$$

$$\Rightarrow x^3+\frac{1}{x^3}=216-18 \Rightarrow x^3+\frac{1}{x^3}=198.$$

9. Simplify $\left(\frac{81}{16}\right)^{-3/4}\times\left[\left(\frac{25}{9}\right)^{-3/2}\div\left(\frac{5}{2}\right)^{-3}\right]$.

Solution: We have,

$$\left(\frac{81}{16}\right)^{-3/4}\times\left[\left(\frac{25}{9}\right)^{-3/2}\div\left(\frac{5}{2}\right)^{-3}\right]=\left(\frac{3^4}{2^4}\right)^{-3/4}\times\left[\left(\frac{5^2}{3^2}\right)^{-3/2}\div\left(\frac{5}{2}\right)^{-3}\right]$$

$$=\left[\left(\frac{3}{4}\right)^4\right]^{-3/4}\times\left[\left(\frac{5}{2}\right)^2\right]^{-3/2}\div\left[\left(\frac{5}{2}\right)^{-3}\right]=\left(\frac{3}{2}\right)^{4x-3/4}\times\left[\left(\frac{5}{3}\right)^{2x-3/2}\div\left(\frac{5}{2}\right)^{-3}\right]$$

$$=\left(\frac{3}{2}\right)^{-3}\times\left[\left(\frac{5}{3}\right)^{-3}\div\left(\frac{5}{2}\right)^{-3}\right]=\left(\frac{2}{3}\right)^3\times\left[\left(\frac{3}{5}\right)^3\div\left(\frac{2}{5}\right)^3\right]$$

$$=\frac{2^3}{3^3}\times\left[\frac{3^3}{5^3}\div\frac{2^3}{5^3}\right]=\frac{2^3}{3^3}\times\left[\frac{3^3}{5^3}\times\frac{5^3}{2^3}\right]=1.$$

10. Assuming that x is a positive real number and a, b and c are rational numbers, show that:

$$\left(\frac{x^b}{x^c}\right)^a\left(\frac{x^c}{x^a}\right)^b\left(\frac{x^a}{x^b}\right)^c=1$$

Solution: $$\left(\frac{x^b}{x^c}\right)^a\cdot\left(\frac{x^c}{x^a}\right)^b\cdot\left(\frac{x^a}{x^b}\right)^c=1=(x^{b-c})^a\cdot(x^{c-a})^b\cdot(x^{a-b})^c=x^{ab-ac}.x^{bc-ba}.x^{ac-bc}$$

$$=x^{ab-ac+bc-ba+ac-bc}=x^0=1.$$

ASSESSMENT CORNER

Fixed Response Type

Fill in the Blanks

1. If $x = 2 + \sqrt{3}$, then the value of $x^3 + \dfrac{1}{x^3}$ ______.

2. The value of x if $5^{x-2} \times 3^{2x-3} = 135$ ______.

3. Evaluate: $\dfrac{3^{-3} \times 6^2 \times \sqrt{98}}{5^2 \times \sqrt{1/25} \times (15)^{-4/3} \times 3^{1/3}}$. = ______.

4. Simplify:
$$\frac{1}{1+x^{b-a}+x^{c-a}}+\frac{1}{1+x^{a-b}+x^{c-b}}+\frac{1}{1+x^{a-c}+x^{b-c}}.$$
= ______.

5. If $\dfrac{9^n \times 3^2 \left[3^{-n/2}\right]^{-2} - (27)^n}{3^{3m} \times 2^3} = \dfrac{1}{27}$, then $m - n =$ ______.

6. $\dfrac{3^{5x} \times (81)^2 \times 6561}{3^{2x}} = 3^7$, then the value of x is ______.

True/False

1. $\dfrac{\sqrt{2}}{3}$ is a rational number.

2. There are infinitely many integers between any two integers.

3. Number of rational numbers between 15 and 18 is finite.

4. There are numbers which cannot be written in the form $\dfrac{p}{q}$, $q \neq 0$, p and q both are integers.

5. The square of an irrational number is always rational.

Single Correct Type Questions

1. If $x = 2 + \sqrt{3}$, then $\left(x + \dfrac{1}{x}\right)$ equals to:
   (A) $-2\sqrt{3}$ (B) 2
   (C) 4 (D) $4 - 2\sqrt{3}$

2. The exponential form of $\sqrt{\sqrt{2}\sqrt{3}}$ is:
   (A) $6^{1/2}$ (B) $6^{1/3}$
   (C) $6^{1/4}$ (D) 6

3. The simplest rationalisation factor of $\sqrt{50}$ is:
   (A) $5\sqrt{2}$ (B) $\sqrt{2}$
   (C) 50 (D) $\sqrt{50}$

4. If $x = 3 + \sqrt{8}$ and $y = 3 - \sqrt{8}$ then $\dfrac{1}{x^2} + \dfrac{1}{y^2} =$
   (A) -34 (B) 34
   (C) $12\sqrt{8}$ (D) $-12\sqrt{8}$

5. If $\dfrac{3+\sqrt{7}}{2-\sqrt{7}} = a + b\sqrt{7}$ then $(a, b) =$
   (A) $(8, -5)$ (B) $(-8, -5)$
   (C) $(-8, 5)$ (D) $(-13/3, -5/3)$

6. Which one is greatest in the following?
   (A) $\sqrt{2}$ (B) $\sqrt[3]{3}$
   (C) $\sqrt[3]{4}$ (D) $\sqrt[3]{2}$

7. The value of $\sqrt[5]{(32)^{-3}}$ is:
   (A) 1/8 (B) 1/16
   (C) 1/32 (D) None of these

8. If $x = \dfrac{\sqrt{3}-\sqrt{2}}{\sqrt{3}+\sqrt{2}}$ and $y = \dfrac{\sqrt{3}+\sqrt{2}}{\sqrt{3}-\sqrt{2}}$ the value of $x^2 + xy + y^2$ is:
   (A) 99 (B) 100
   (C) 1 (D) 0

9. Simplify: $\dfrac{2}{\sqrt{5}+\sqrt{3}} + \dfrac{1}{\sqrt{3}+\sqrt{2}} - \dfrac{3}{\sqrt{5}+\sqrt{2}}$.
   (A) 1 (B) 0
   (C) 10 (D) 100

10. Which of the following is smallest?
    (A) $\sqrt[4]{5}$ (B) $\sqrt[5]{4}$
    (C) $\sqrt{4}$ (D) $\sqrt{3}$

11. The product of $\sqrt{3}$ and $\sqrt[3]{5}$ is:
    (A) $\sqrt[6]{375}$ (B) $\sqrt[6]{675}$
    (C) $\sqrt[6]{575}$ (D) $\sqrt[6]{475}$

12. Number of prime numbers less than 10 is
    (A) 2 (B) 3
    (C) 4 (D) 5

13. $\sqrt[3]{\frac{54}{250}}$ equals:

(A) $\frac{9}{25}$ (B) $\frac{3}{5}$

(C) $\frac{27}{125}$ (D) $\frac{\sqrt[3]{2}}{5}$

14. The value of x, if $5^{x-3} \cdot 3^{2x-8} = 225$, is:

(A) 1 (B) 2

(C) 3 (D) 5

15. The decimal representation of $\frac{27}{400}$ is:

(A) Terminating

(B) Non-terminating recurring

(C) Non terminating non-recurring

(D) None of these

16. $2.2\overline{34}$ is:

(A) Non-terminating only

(B) Non-repeating only

(C) Non-terminating and repeating

(D) Non-terminating and non-repeating

17. Number of composite numbers less than 15 is

(A) 10 (B) 8

(C) 9 (D) 7

18. Let p and q be the number of natural numbers which are less than or equal 20 and are prime & composite respectively, then $20 - p - q$ is equal to

(A) 1 (B) 0

(C) 2 (D) 3

19. Which of the following number is irrational?

(A) $\sqrt{16} - 4$ (B) $(3 - \sqrt{3})(3 + \sqrt{3})$

(C) $\sqrt{5} + 3$ (D) $-\sqrt{25}$

20. Which of the following number is irrational?

(A) $\sqrt{\frac{4}{9}}$ (B) $\sqrt[3]{\frac{8}{27}}$

(C) $\frac{7\pi}{22}$ (D) $\pi + \sqrt{16 - 8\pi + \pi^2}$

21. If $p, q \in N$ and $0.1\bar{2} = \frac{p}{q}$ where p and q are relatively prime then identify which of the following is incorrect

(A) p is a prime number

(B) $q - p$ is a prime number

(C) $q + p$ is a prime number

(D) q is a prime number

22. Consider the following statements

(i) The sum of a rational number with an irrational number is always irrational.

(ii) The product of two rational numbers is always rational.

(iii) The product of two irrationals is always irrationals.

(iv) The sum of two rational is always rational.

(v) The sum of two irrationals is always irrational.

The correct order of True/False of above statements is :

(A) T F T F F (B) F F T T T

(C) T T F T F (D) T T F F T

23. Every point on a number line represents:

(A) A natural number

(B) A real number

(C) A rational number

(D) A irrational number

24. A rational number lying between $\sqrt{2}$ and $\sqrt{3}$ is:

(A) $\frac{\sqrt{2}+\sqrt{3}}{2}$ (B) $\sqrt{6}$

(C) 1.6 (D) 1.9

25. If $\sqrt{3} = 1.732$ and $\sqrt{2} = 1.414$, the value of $\frac{1}{\sqrt{3}-\sqrt{2}}$ is:

(A) 0.318 (B) 3.146

(C) $\frac{1}{3.146}$ (D) $\sqrt{1.732} - \sqrt{1.414}$

Multiple Correct Type Questions

1. Which of the following statements is/are true?

(A) The sum or difference of a rational and an irrational number is always an irrational number.

(B) The sum or difference of two irrational numbers is always an irrational number.

(C) The product of two irrational numbers can be rational or irrational

(D) The product of two rational numbers is always a rational number

2. The simplified form of $\left[\sqrt{7+4\sqrt{3}} - \sqrt{3}\right]$ is

(A) 2 (B) 1

(C) $4^{1/2} \times 3^{3/2} \times 9^{-3/4}$ (D) $\sqrt{4 \times 3^3 \times 9^{-3/2}}$

3. Identify the correct statement

(A) If a, b, c are odd integers $a + b + c$ cannot be zero

(B) If a, b, c are odd integers $a^2 + b^2 - c^2 \neq 0$

(C) If $a^2 + b^2 = c^2$, then at least one of a, b, c is even, given that a, b, c are integers

(D) If $a^2 + b^2 = c^2$ where a, b, c are integers then $c > a + b$

4. $\left(\frac{a^x}{a^y}\right)^{x+y} \cdot \left(\frac{a^y}{a^z}\right)^{y+z} \cdot \left(\frac{a^z}{a^x}\right)^{z+x}$

(A) 0 (B) 1
(C) natural (D) whole number

5. Let $a, b \in Q$ such that $\frac{39\sqrt{2}-5}{3-\sqrt{2}} = a + b\sqrt{2}$, then

(A) $\sqrt{\frac{b}{a}}$ is a rational number
(B) b and a are coprime rational numbers
(C) $b - a$ is a composite number
(D) $\sqrt{a+b}$ is a rational number

6. Simplify: $1+\cfrac{6}{5+\cfrac{4}{3-\cfrac{1}{2}}}$

(A) $\frac{14}{45}$ (B) $\frac{63}{33}$
(C) $\frac{13}{19}$ (D) $\frac{21}{11}$

7. π is
(A) Rational (B) Irrational
(C) Imaginary (D) Real Number

8. Identify the correct statement
(A) If $\sqrt{x} \in Q \Rightarrow x \in Q$
(B) If $x^2 \in Q$ and $x^7 \in Q \Rightarrow x \in Q$
(C) If $x^3 \in Q$ and $x^7 \in Q \Rightarrow x \in Q$
(D) If $x^4 \in Q$ and $x^{11} \in Q \Rightarrow x \in Q$

9. Which of the following statements is false?
(A) Every point on the number line represents a rational number
(B) Irrational numbers cannot be represented by points on the number line
(C) $\frac{22}{7}$ is a rational number
(D) None of these

10. The sum of rational and irrational number is always:
(A) Rational (B) Irrational
(C) Both (A) and (B) (D) Can't say

11. The product of rational and irrational number is always:
(A) Rational (B) Irrational
(C) Both (A) and (B) (D) Can't say

12. Which of the following pair is co-prime?
(A) (7, 8) (B) (13, 7)
(C) (8, 15) (D) (3, 6)

13. Decimal form of $\frac{37}{300}$ is:

(A) $0.\overline{123}$ (B) $0.1\overline{23}$
(C) $0.12\overline{3}$ (D) None of these

14. Solve: $4.\overline{26} + 4.2\overline{6} =$

(A) $8.\overline{529}$ (B) $8.52\overline{9}$
(C) $8.5\overline{29}$ (D) 8.529

15. The value of $\frac{\left(a^{x+y}\right)^3 \left(a^{y+z}\right)^3 \left(a^{z+x}\right)^3}{\left(a^x a^y a^z\right)^6}$ is:

(A) 1 (B) Prime Number
(C) Real Number (D) Integer

16. The value of $\left(\frac{\sqrt{6}+\sqrt{3}}{\sqrt{8}-\sqrt{3}}\right)\left(\frac{\sqrt{6}-\sqrt{3}}{\sqrt{8}+\sqrt{3}}\right)$ is:

(A) $\frac{3}{5}$ (B) Rational Number
(C) Irrational Number (D) $\frac{11}{9}$

17. The fraction $\frac{2\left(\sqrt{2}+\sqrt{6}\right)}{3\sqrt{\left(2+\sqrt{3}\right)}}$ is equal to:

(A) $\frac{\left(2\sqrt{2}\right)}{3}$ (B) 1.3
(C) $\frac{\left(2\sqrt{3}\right)}{3}$ (D) $\left(\frac{4}{3}\right)$

18. Among the numbers 2^{250}, 3^{200}, 4^{150} and 5^{100}, the greatest is:
(A) 2^{250} (B) 3^{200}
(C) 4^{150} (D) 5^{100}

19. Which real number lies between 2 and 2.5?
(A) $\sqrt{11}$ (B) $\sqrt{8}$
(C) $\sqrt[3]{7}$ (D) $\sqrt[3]{9}$

20. If $x = \sqrt[4]{16} + \sqrt[4]{625}$, then what is x=?
(A) 7 (B) 29
(C) 12 (D) Prime Number

21. The simplest rationalising factor of $\sqrt[4]{48}$ is:
(A) $\sqrt[4]{9}$ (B) $\sqrt[4]{27}$
(C) $\sqrt[3]{9}$ (D) None of these

ASSESSMENT CORNER

22. Multiply: $\sqrt[3]{2} \times \sqrt[4]{3}$

(A) $\sqrt[12]{6}$ (B) $\sqrt[12]{72}$

(C) $\sqrt[12]{648}$ (D) $\sqrt[12]{432}$

23. If $3^{(x+y)} = 81$ and $81^{(x-y)} = 3$, then the values of x and y are:

(A) $\frac{17}{8}, \frac{9}{8}$ (B) $\frac{17}{8}, \frac{15}{8}$

(C) $\frac{17}{8}, \frac{11}{8}$ (D) $\frac{5}{8}, \frac{11}{8}$

24. A rational number between 3 and 4 is:

(A) 3.5 (B) $\frac{5}{2}$

(C) $\frac{7}{2}$ (D) $\frac{9}{2}$

25. Which of the following number is rational?

(A) $\sqrt{16} - 4$ (B) $(3 - \sqrt{3})(3 + \sqrt{3})$

(C) $\sqrt{5} + 3$ (D) $-\sqrt{25}$

Match Type Questions

Directions: Column-I and Column-II contain four entries each. Entries of Column-I are to be matched with some entries of Column-II. One or more than one entries of Column-I may have the matching with the same entries of Column-II and one entry of Column-II may have one or more than one matching with entries of Column-I

1.

Column-I	Column-II
(i) $\sqrt{7+4\sqrt{3}}$	(P) $\sqrt{6}$
(ii) $\sqrt[6]{216}$	(Q) $\sqrt[6]{72}$
(iii) $\left(\frac{2ab^3}{5c^3b}\right)^0$	(R) $2+\sqrt{3}$
(iv) $\sqrt[3]{3}\times\sqrt[2]{2}$	(S) 1

2. It is given that $x = -2$, $y = -3$ match the following

Column-I	Column-II
(i) x^{1-y}	(P) 1
(ii) $(x-y)^{x-y}$	(Q) 9
(iii) $(x+y)^{y-x}$	(R) $\frac{-1}{5}$
(iv) y^{-x}	(S) 16

3.

Column-I	Column-II
(i) $\frac{4+\sqrt{5}}{4-\sqrt{5}}+\frac{4-\sqrt{5}}{4+\sqrt{5}}$	(P) 42/11
(ii) $\left(\sqrt{8}-\sqrt{2}\right)\left(\sqrt{8}+\sqrt{2}\right)$	(Q) Rational
(iii) $\frac{\sqrt[4]{243\times16}}{\sqrt[4]{3}}$	(R) 6
(iv) 6^{-2}	(S) Irrational

4.

Column-I	Column-II
(i) $\left(\sqrt{3}+\sqrt{5}\right)^2$	(P) $8+2\sqrt{15}$
(ii) $0.\overline{54}$	(Q) Non-terminating and recurring
(iii) $\sqrt[3]{\frac{216}{1331}}$	(R) Irrational
(iv) $\sqrt[3]{\frac{216}{1331}}$	(S) $\frac{6}{11}$

Assertion and Reason Type Questions

1. If R: Every fraction is a rational number and T: Every rational number is a fraction, then which of the following is correct?
(A) R is True and T is False.
(B) R is False and Tis True.
(C) Both R and T are True.
(D) Both R and T are False.

2. If x : Every whole number is a natural number and y : 0 is not a natural number, then which of the following statement is true?
(A) x is false and y is the correct explanation of x.
(B) x is true and y is the correct explanation of x.
(C) x is true and y is false.
(D) Both x and y are true.

Comprehension Type Questions

Comprehension 1: If $x = 7 - 4\sqrt{3}$

1. Find the value of $x + \frac{1}{x}$

(A) 28 (B) 14

(C) $8\sqrt{3}$ (D) 1/14

2. Find the value of $x^3 + \frac{1}{x^3}$

(A) 2744 (B) 2740

(C) 2072 (D) 2702

3. Find the value of $x^2 - \frac{1}{x^2}$

(A) $-112\sqrt{3}$ (B) $8\sqrt{3}$

(C) 112 (D) $-64\sqrt{3}$

4. Find the value of $\frac{x^2-1}{x^2+1}$

(A) $\frac{-8\sqrt{3}}{7}$ (B) $\frac{-2\sqrt{3}}{7}$

(C) $\frac{-4\sqrt{3}}{7}$ (D) None

Numerical Type Questions

1. The digit at the 100th place in the decimal representation of $\frac{6}{7}$, is:

2. There are four prime numbers written in ascending order. The product of the first three is 385 and that of the last three is 1001. The last number is :

(A) 11 (B) 13

(C) 17 (D) 19

3. When the repeating decimal 0.45454545... is written in simplest fractional form, the sum of the numerator and denominator is:

4. If $\sqrt{9-(n-2)^2}$ is a real number, then the number of integral values of n is:

5. If x is a positive integer less than 100, then the number of x which make $\sqrt{1+2+3+4+x}$ an integer is:

6. If $\frac{\sqrt{954+\sqrt{\sqrt{484}+\sqrt{704+\sqrt{625}}}}}{0.00155} = \frac{\sqrt{0.0004}}{(0.009)^2 \cdot x}$.

Then the approximate value of x is:

7. The four-digit number 2652 is such that any two consecutive digits from it make a multiple of 13. Another number N has this same property, is 100 digits long and begins with a 9. The last digit of N, is:

8. The expression

$$\left(\frac{1}{2}+\frac{1}{3}\ldots+\frac{1}{2008}\right)\left(1+\frac{1}{2}+\frac{1}{3}\ldots+\frac{1}{2007}\right)-$$

$$\left(1+\frac{1}{2}+\frac{1}{3}\ldots+\frac{1}{2008}\right)\left(\frac{1}{2}+\frac{1}{3}\ldots+\frac{1}{2007}\right)$$

simplifies to:

9. How many positive integer x are there such that $3x$ has 3 digits and $4x$ has four digits ?

10. Let $N = (2+1)(2^2+1)(2^4+1) \ldots\ldots (2^{32}+1)+1$ and $N = 2^{\lambda}$ then the value of λ is

(A) 63 (B) 64

(C) 65 (D) 66

11. If $x = \frac{\sqrt{3}-\sqrt{2}}{\sqrt{3}+\sqrt{2}}$ and $y = \frac{\sqrt{3}+\sqrt{2}}{\sqrt{3}-\sqrt{2}}$ the value of $x^2 + xy + y^2$ is:

12. The value of the expression

$$\sqrt{\frac{1}{\sqrt{2}+1}+\frac{1}{\sqrt{3}+\sqrt{2}}+\frac{1}{\sqrt{4}+\sqrt{3}+}\ldots \text{ up to 99 terms}}$$

is equal to:

13. If $2^{2008} - 2^{2007} - 2^{2006} + 2^{2005} = k.\,2^{2005}$ then the value of k is equal to:

14. If $2^x = 3^y = 6^{-z}$, then $\left(\frac{1}{x}+\frac{1}{y}+\frac{1}{z}\right)$ is equal to:

15. If $a = \frac{1}{3-2\sqrt{2}}, b = \frac{1}{3+2\sqrt{2}}$ than the value of $a^2 + b^2$ is:

Higher Order Thinking Skills (HOTS)

1. If $m^2 - n^2 = 7$, where $m, n \in Z$, then number of ordered pairs (m, n) is

(A) 1 (B) 2

(C) 3 (D) 4

2. The sum of a number and its reciprocal is thrice the difference between the number and its reciprocal. The number is:

(A) $\pm\sqrt{2}$ (B) $\pm\frac{1}{\sqrt{2}}$

(C) $\pm\sqrt{3}$ (D) Both (A) and (B)

3. Solve for x: $\frac{2^{x-3}}{8^{-x}} = \frac{32}{4^{(1/2)x}}$

(A) $2\frac{1}{5}$ (B) $1\frac{1}{5}$

(C) $3\frac{1}{5}$ (D) $1\frac{3}{5}$

4. $2.\overline{6} - 0.\overline{82} =$

(A) $\frac{182}{99}$ (B) $\frac{1820}{999}$

(C) $\frac{175}{99}$ (D) $\frac{184}{999}$

ASSESSMENT CORNER

5. Let r and s be integer. Then $\frac{6^{r+s} \times 12^{r-s}}{8^r \times 9^{r+2s}}$ is an integer if:
(A) $r + s \le 0$ (B) $s \le 0$
(C) $r \le 0$ (D) $r \ge s$

6. If $4^x - 4^{x-1} = 24$, then the value of $(2x)^x$ equals:
(A) $5\sqrt{5}$ (B) $\sqrt{5}$
(C) $25\sqrt{5}$ (D) 25

7. $2^{73} - 2^{72} - 2^{71}$ is the same as:
(A) 2^{69} (B) 2^{70}
(C) 2^{71} (D) 2^{72}

8. If $m, n \in$ N and $m^2 - n^2 = 13$, then $(m + 1)(n + 1)$ is equal to
(A) 42 (B) 56
(C) 50 (D) None of these

9. Number of ordered pairs of integers (n, m) for which $n^2 - m^2 = 14$ is
(A) 0 (B) 1
(C) 2 (D) 4

10. If $x = 7 + 4\sqrt{3}$, then the value of $\sqrt{x} + \frac{1}{\sqrt{x}}$ is:
(A) 8 (B) 6
(C) 5 (D) 4

11. If $\frac{\sqrt{3}-1}{\sqrt{3}+1} = a + b\sqrt{3}$, then the value of '$a$' and '$b$' is:
(A) $a = 2, b = -1$ (B) $a = 2, b = 1$
(C) $a = -2, b = 1$ (D) $a = -2, b = -1$

12. The value of $\frac{1}{\sqrt{3}+\sqrt{2}-1}$ on simplifying up to 3 decimal places, given that $\sqrt{2} = 1.4142$ and $\sqrt{6} = 2.4495$ is:
(A) 0.1666 (B) 0.3666
(C) 0.466 (D) 0.566

13. If $a = \frac{1}{3-2\sqrt{2}}, b = \frac{1}{3+2\sqrt{2}}$ then the value of $a^3 + b^3$ is:
(A) 194 (B) 196
(C) 198 (D) 200

14. If $x = (7 + 4\sqrt{3})$, then the value of $x^2 + \frac{1}{x^2}$ is:
(A) 193 (B) 194
(C) 195 (D) 196

15. When simplified, the product
$\left(1-\frac{1}{3}\right)\left(1-\frac{1}{4}\right)\left(1-\frac{1}{5}\right)\ldots\left(1-\frac{1}{n}\right)$ equals:
(A) $\frac{1}{n}$ (B) $\frac{2}{n}$
(C) $\frac{2(n-1)}{n}$ (D) $\frac{2}{n(n+1)}$

16. $\frac{\left(x^{a+b}\right)^2 (x^{b+c})^2 (x^{c+a})^2}{(x^a \cdot x^b \cdot x^c)^4} =$
(A) -1 (B) 0
(C) 1 (D) None

17. If $x > 0$, $y > 0$ and $z > 0$ and $x^3 + y^3 + z^3 - 3xyz = \frac{1}{2}(x + y + z)\,[(x - y)^2 + (y - z)^2 + (z - x)^2]$, then
(A) $x^3 + y^3 + z^3 \ge 3xyz$ (B) $x^3 + y^3 + z^3 \ge 6xyz$
(C) $x^3 + y^3 + z^3 > 3xyz$ (D) $x^3 + y^3 + z^3 < 3xyz$

18. The value of $\sqrt[\ell+m]{\frac{x^{\ell^2}}{x^{m^2}}} \cdot \sqrt[m+n]{\frac{x^{m^2}}{x^{n^2}}} \cdot \sqrt[n+\ell]{\frac{x^{n^2}}{x^{\ell^2}}} =$
(A) x (B) -1
(C) 1 (D) 0

19. If $2^x = 4^y = 8^z$ and $\frac{1}{2x} + \frac{1}{4y} + \frac{1}{6z} = \frac{24}{7}$, then the value of z is:
(A) $\frac{7}{16}$ (B) $\frac{7}{32}$
(C) $\frac{7}{48}$ (D) $\frac{7}{64}$

20. If $a^x = b$, $b^y = c$ and $c^z = a$, then the value of $x^2y^2z^2$ is ________
(A) $a^2b^2c^2$
(B) 1
(C) 4
(D) $\frac{1}{a^2b^2c^2}$

Free Response Type

Very Short Answer Type Questions

1. The smallest natural number of the form 123X43Y, which is exactly divisible by 6 is ________.

2. Find a rational number between $\sqrt{2}$ and $\sqrt{3}$.

3. Find the value of 1.999... in the form $\frac{p}{q}$, where p and q are integers and $q \ne 0$.

4. Find the number obtained on rationalising the denominator of $\frac{1}{\sqrt{7}-2}$.

5. The number $3.1\overline{45}$ when expressed as a rational number in lowest form, is equal to ______.

6. Find the value of $\frac{\sqrt{32}+\sqrt{48}}{\sqrt{8}+\sqrt{12}}$.

7. Simplify $\sqrt[4]{\sqrt[3]{2^2}}$.

8. Can two numbers has 16 as H.C.F. and 380 as L.C.M.

9. If $\sqrt{2} = 1.4142$, then find the value of $\sqrt{\frac{\sqrt{2}-1}{\sqrt{2}+1}}$.

10. Find the value of $(256)^{0.16} \times (256)^{0.09}$.

Short Answer Type Questions

1. Find the product $\sqrt[3]{2}.\sqrt[4]{2}.\sqrt[12]{32}$.

2. If x, y are rational numbers such that $(x + y) + (x - 2y)\sqrt{2} = 2x - y + (x - y - 1)\sqrt{5}$ then value of x and y are

3. Locate $\sqrt{13}$ on the number line.

4. Express $0.12\overline{3}$ in the form $\frac{p}{q}$, where p and q are integers and $q \neq 0$.

5. Find the value of a in the following:

$$\frac{6}{3\sqrt{2}-2\sqrt{3}} = 3\sqrt{2} - a\sqrt{3}$$

6. If $B = \frac{12}{3+\sqrt{5}+\sqrt{8}}$ and $A = \sqrt{1}+\sqrt{2}+\sqrt{5}-\sqrt{10}$, then value of A/B is

7. Represent the following numbers on the number line: 7, 7.2, $\frac{-3}{2}, \frac{-12}{5}$

8. The positive integers p, q and r are all primes if $p^2 - q^2 = r$, then find all possible values of r.

9. Insert a rational number and an irrational number between the following:

   (i) 2 and 3 (ii) $\frac{1}{3}$ and $\frac{1}{2}$

   (iii) $\frac{-2}{5}$ and $\frac{1}{2}$ (iv) $\sqrt{2}$ and $\sqrt{3}$

   (v) 0.0001 and 0.001

10. Locate $\sqrt{5}$, $\sqrt{10}$ and $\sqrt{17}$ on the number line.

11. Represent geometrically the following numbers on the number line:

    (i) $\sqrt{4.5}$ (ii) $\sqrt{2.3}$

12. Simplify the following:

    (i) $\sqrt{45} - 3\sqrt{20} + 4\sqrt{5}$ (ii) $\frac{\sqrt{24}}{8} + \frac{\sqrt{54}}{9}$

    (iii) $\sqrt[4]{12} \times \sqrt[7]{6}$ (iv) $4\sqrt{28} \div 3\sqrt{7} \div \sqrt[3]{7}$

    (v) $3\sqrt{3} + 2\sqrt{27} + \frac{7}{\sqrt{3}}$ (vi) $(\sqrt{3}-\sqrt{2})^2$

    (vii) $\sqrt[4]{81} - 8\sqrt[3]{216} + 15\sqrt[5]{32} + \sqrt{225}$

    (viii) $\frac{3}{\sqrt{8}} + \frac{1}{\sqrt{2}}$ (ix) $\frac{2\sqrt{3}}{3} - \frac{\sqrt{3}}{6}$

Long Answer Type Questions

1. Find the values of a and b in each of the following:

   (i) $\frac{5+2\sqrt{3}}{7+4\sqrt{3}} = a - 6\sqrt{3}$

   (ii) $\frac{3-\sqrt{5}}{3+2\sqrt{5}} = a\sqrt{5} - \frac{19}{11}$

2. Find the sum $\frac{1}{1+\sqrt{2}} + \frac{1}{\sqrt{2}+\sqrt{3}} + \frac{1}{\sqrt{3}+\sqrt{4}} +$ .... upto 99 terms.

3. If $a = 2 + \sqrt{3}$, then find the value of $a - \frac{1}{a}$.

4. Represent the following in fractional form (p/q, where $p, q \in$ I and $q \neq 0$)

   (i) 2.35 (ii) $1.1\overline{4}$

   (iii) $3.3\overline{79}$ (iv) $\sqrt{12}$

5. Which is greater ?

   (i) $\sqrt[3]{3}$ or $\sqrt[4]{5}$

   (ii) $\sqrt[8]{12}$ or $\sqrt[4]{6}$

   (iii) $\sqrt{2}$ or $\sqrt[3]{3}$

6. If $x = \frac{\sqrt{3}+\sqrt{2}}{\sqrt{3}-\sqrt{2}}$ and $y = \frac{\sqrt{3}-\sqrt{2}}{\sqrt{3}+\sqrt{2}}$, then find the value of $x^2 + y^2$.

7. Express $0.6 + 0.\overline{7} + 0.4\overline{7}$ in the form $\frac{p}{q}$, where p and q are integers and $q \neq 0$.

8. Simplify: $\frac{7\sqrt{3}}{\sqrt{10}+\sqrt{3}} - \frac{2\sqrt{5}}{\sqrt{6}+\sqrt{5}} - \frac{3\sqrt{2}}{\sqrt{15}+3\sqrt{2}}$.

ARCHIVE CORNER

1. What is the square root of $9 + 2\sqrt{14}$?
(A) $1+2\sqrt{2}$ (B) $\sqrt{3}+\sqrt{6}$
(C) $\sqrt{2}+\sqrt{7}$ (D) $\sqrt{2}+\sqrt{5}$

2. $\sqrt[3]{1-\frac{127}{343}}$ is equal to:
(A) $\frac{5}{9}$ (B) $1-\frac{1}{7}$
(C) $\frac{4}{7}$ (D) $1-\frac{2}{7}$

3. What is the value of $2.\overline{6} - 1.\overline{9}$?
(A) $0.\overline{6}$ (B) $0.\overline{9}$
(C) $0.\overline{7}$ (D) 0.7

4. An equivalent expression of $\frac{5}{7+4\sqrt{5}}$ after rationalizing the denominator is:
(A) $\frac{20\sqrt{5}-35}{31}$ (B) $\frac{20\sqrt{5}-35}{129}$
(C) $\frac{35-20\sqrt{5}}{31}$ (D) $\frac{35-20\sqrt{5}}{121}$

5. Four positive integers sum to 125. If the first of these numbers is increased by 4, the second is decreased by 4. The third is multiplied by 4 and the fourth is divided by 4 we find four equal numbers then four original integers are:
(A) 16, 24, 5, 80 (B) 8, 22, 38, 57
(C) 7, 19, 46, 53 (D) 12, 28, 40, 45

6. If $a=\sqrt{6}+\sqrt{5}; b=\sqrt{6}-\sqrt{5}$, then find the value of $2a^2 - 5ab + 2b^2$
(A) 36 (B) 37
(C) 39 (D) 41

7. $\sqrt{m^4n^4} \times \sqrt[6]{m^2n^2} \times \sqrt[3]{m^2n^2} = (mk)^k$, then find the value of k.
(A) 6 (B) 3
(C) 2 (D) 1

8. Which one of the following decimal expansions is not terminating?
(A) $\frac{3}{8}$ (B) $\frac{6}{15}$
(C) $\frac{17}{512}$ (D) $\frac{29}{343}$

9. Which of the following is not an irrational number?
(A) $2+\sqrt{5}$ (B) $\sqrt{2}$
(C) $\frac{7}{\sqrt{5}}$ (D) $\frac{2\sqrt{11}}{7\sqrt{11}}$

10. The multiplication of all prime numbers between 1 and 10 is:
(A) 105 (B) 945
(C) 210 (D) 1890

11. Statement P: x and y both are integers, then negative statements will be ______
(A) P: x and y both are integers
(B) P: x is not integer or y is not integer.
(C) P: x and y both are not integers
(D) P: x and y both are not integers.

12. If G.C.D. of two numbers is 8 and their product is 384, then their L.C.M. is ______.
(A) 24 (B) 16
(C) 32 (D) 48

13. $\frac{317}{3125}$ represents ______
(A) A terminating decimal
(B) A non-recurring decimal
(C) A recurring decimal
(D) An Integer

14. The sum of the five consecutive numbers is equal to 170. What is the product of the largest and the smallest numbers?
(A) 1512 (B) 1102
(C) 1152 (D) 1210

15. The HCF of two numbers is 15 and their LCM is 225. If one of the numbers is 75, find another number.
(A) 105 (B) 90
(C) 60 (D) 45

16. If $2^{x-1} + 2^{x+1} = 2560$, find the value of x.
(A) 10 (B) 12
(C) 9 (D) 8

17. Simplify 6 –{9 –{18 –(15 –12 –9)}}
(A) 21 (B) 4
(C) 5 (D) 3

18. The product of two numbers is 12960 and their HCF is 36. The number of pairs of such numbers that can be formed is:
(A) 2 (B) 3
(C) 4 (D) 5

19. Five ninth of 60% of a number is equal to 2790. What is the number?
(A) 8100 (B) 7200
(C) 6300 (D) None of these

20. Number r is termed as rational number if it can be expressed as p/q, where p and q are integers and:
(A) $p = 0$ (B) $p \neq 0$
(C) $q = 0$ (D) $q \neq 0$

21. Product of any three consecutive even numbers is divisible by:
(A) 12 (B) 4
(C) 16 (D) All of these

22. If $x = \frac{1}{3-2\sqrt{2}}$ and $y = \frac{1}{3+2\sqrt{2}}$ then find the value of $x + y$.
(A) 3 (B) 0
(C) 6 (D) 1

23. If a and b are odd integers, then which of the following is an even integer?
(A) ab (B) $2a + b$
(C) $ab + 1$ (D) $a + 2b$

24. The sum of $0.\overline{6}$ and $0.\overline{7}$ is:
(A) $1.\overline{3}$
(B) 1.3
(C) $1.\overline{4}$
(D) an irrational number

25. If $5^{x+1} + 5^{2-x} = 126$, then x is equal to:
(A) −2, −1 (B) 1, 2
(C) −1, 3 (D) 2, −1

ARCHIVE CORNER

ANSWER KEY

Check Points

Check Point 1

2. $\frac{31}{80}$ **3.** $\frac{19}{6}, \frac{20}{6}, \frac{21}{6}, \frac{22}{6}, \frac{23}{6}$ **4.** $\frac{5}{3}, \frac{9}{14}, \frac{5}{7}, \frac{6}{11}$ **5.** $x = \frac{1128}{999}$

Check Point 2

6. 0.05005000500005; 5.51551555151; **7.** $\sqrt{5.1}, \sqrt{5.2}$

Check Point 3

11. $5\sqrt{2}$ **12.** $\sqrt{10} - \sqrt{5}$ **13.** –2 **14.** 12 **15.** 18

Check Point 4

16. (i) 3 (ii) 4 (iii) 8 (iv) 9 **17.** (i) $3^{11/15}$ (ii) 2/3 (iii) $6^{2/3}$ (iv) 2
18. 8 **19.** 4/3 **20.** $x = 20, y = 5, z = 3$

Assessment Corner

Fixed Response Type

Fill in the Blanks

1. 52 **2.** 3 **3.** $2^{\frac{5}{2}} \times 7 \times 5^{\frac{1}{3}}$ **4.** 1 **5.** –1 **6.** –3

True/False

1. False **2.** False **3.** False **4.** True **5.** False

Single Correct Type Questions

1. C **2.** C **3.** B **4.** B **5.** D **6.** C **7.** A **8.** A **9.** B
10. B **11.** B **12.** C **13.** B **14.** D **15.** A **16.** C **17.** D **18.** A
19. C **20.** C **21.** D **22.** C **23.** B **24.** C **25.** B

Multiple Correct Type Questions

1. ACD **2.** ACD **3.** ABC **4.** BCD **5.** ABD **6.** BD **7.** BD **8.** ABCD **9.** A
10. B **11.** D **12.** ABC **13.** C **14.** C **15.** ACD **16.** AB **17.** BD **18.** B
19. D **20.** AD **21.** B **22.** D **23.** B **24.** AC **25.** ABD

Match Type Questions

1. (i)-R; (ii)-P; (iii)-S; (iv)-Q
2. (i)-S; (ii)-P; (iii)-R; (iv)-Q
3. (i)-P, Q; (ii)-Q, R; (iii)-Q, R; (iv)-Q
4. (i)-R; (ii)-P, Q; (iii)-P, Q, S; (iv)-P, Q, S

Assertion and Reason Type Questions

1. A 2. A

Comprehension Type Questions

1. B 2. D 3. A 4. D

Numerical Type Questions

1. 1 2. B 3. 16 4. 7 5. 7 6. 20/81 7. 9 8. 1/2008 9. 84
10. B 11. 99 12. 3 13. 3 14. 0 15. 34

Higher Order Thinking Skills (HOTS)

1. D 2. A 3. D 4. A 5. B 6. C 7. C 8. B 9. A
10. D 11. A 12. C 13. C 14. B 15. B 16. C 17. A 18. C
19. C 20. B

Free Response Type

Very Short Answer Type Questions

1. 1230432 2. 1.6 3. 2 4. $\frac{\sqrt{7}+2}{3}$ 5. $\frac{173}{55}$ 6. 2 7. $2^{\frac{1}{6}}$
8. No 9. 0.4142 10. 4

Short Answer Type Questions

1. 2 2. (i) $\frac{2\sqrt{3}}{9}$ (ii) $\frac{\sqrt{120}}{3}$ (iii) $\frac{3\sqrt{2}+2}{8}$ (iv) $\sqrt{41}+5$ (v) $7+4\sqrt{3}$
(vi) $2\sqrt{6}-3\sqrt{2}$ (vii) $5+2\sqrt{6}$ (viii) $9+2\sqrt{15}$ (ix) $\frac{9+16\sqrt{6}}{15}$
4. $\frac{37}{300}$ 5. $a=-2$ 6. **5** 8. **5**
12. (i) $\sqrt{5}$ (ii) $\frac{7\sqrt{6}}{12}$ (iii) $\sqrt[28]{2^{18}.3^{11}}$ (iv) $\frac{8}{3}$ (v) $\frac{34}{\sqrt{3}}$
(vi) $5-2\sqrt{6}$ (vii) 0 (viii) $\frac{5\sqrt{2}}{4}$ (ix) $\frac{\sqrt{3}}{2}$

Long Answer Type Questions

2. 9 3. $2\sqrt{3}$ 4. (i) $\frac{47}{20}$ (ii) $\frac{103}{90}$ (iii) $\frac{1673}{495}$ (iv) not possible 5. (i) $\sqrt[4]{5}$ (ii) $\sqrt[4]{6}$ (iii) $\sqrt[3]{3}$ 6. 98
7. $\frac{167}{90}$ 8. 1

Archive Corner

1. C 2. B 3. A 4. A 5. A 6. C 7. B 8. D 9. D
10. C 11. B 12. D 13. A 14. C 15. D 16. A 17. A 18. A
19. D 20. D 21. D 22. C 23. C 24. C 25. D

CHAPTER 2

Polynomials

Learning Outcomes

After reading this chapter, you would be able to understand:

- definition of polynomials.
- classification of polynomials on basis of basic terms.
- classification of polynomials on basis of basic degree.
- value of polynomials.
- roots of polynomials.
- remainder theorem.
- factor theorem.
- division algorithm of polynomials.
- algebraic identities.
- factorization.

Geekspeak

- Algebraic expression
- Polynomials
- Coefficient
- Degree
- Monomial
- Binomial
- Trinomial
- Value of polynomial
- Roots/zeroes
- Remainder
- Factor
- Identities

Introduction

An algebraic expression $f(x)$ of the form $f(x) = a_0 + a_1x + a_2x^2 + \ldots + a_nx^n$, where $a_0, a_1, a_2, \ldots, a_n$ are real numbers and all the index of 'x' are non-negative integers is called a **polynomial** in x. In this chapter, we are going to discuss the classification of polynomials and various terminology of polynomials. Later on the value of polynomials and zeroes of polynomials will be discussed. In the last remainder theorem, the factor theorem division algorithm of polynomials and algebraic identities will be discussed.

Polynomials

Polynomials are fundamental in algebra and are used in various fields of mathematics, science, and engineering.

Basic Term and Definition

(i) **Constant:** A symbol having a fixed numerical value is called a 'constant', for example, '2' has a definite value. So, it is a constant.

(ii) **Variable:** A symbol which takes on various numerical values is called a 'variable'.
e.g. $x, y \ldots$

(iii) **Coefficient:** In the product of a constant and a variable, each is called the coefficient of the other.
For example, in $6x$, 6 is the coefficient of x.

(iv) **Algebraic expression:** A combination of constants and variables with (+), (–), (×), (÷) is called an 'Algebraic expression', e.g., $17 - x$, $3x^2 - 4x + 12$, etc.

(v) **Equation:** Two expressions combined with the equality symbol (=) are called an equation, e.g., $17 - x = 0$, $3x^2 - 4x + 12 = 2x^2 - 3x$, etc.

(vi) **Degree of an expression:** The highest number of times the variable is present in the terms of an expression is the degree of an expression.

Identification of Polynomial

For this, we have the following examples:

(i) $\sqrt{3}x^2 + x - 5$ is a polynomial in variable x as all the exponents of x are non-negative integers.

(ii) $\sqrt{3}x^2 + \sqrt{x} - 5x$ is not a polynomial as the exponent of the second term ($\sqrt{x} = x^{1/2}$) is not a non-negative integer.

(iii) $5x^3 + 2x^2 + 3x - \frac{5}{x} + 6$ is not a polynomial as the exponent of the fourth term $\left[-\frac{5}{x} = -5x^{-1}\right]$ is not a non-negative integer.

Degree of the Polynomial

Highest index of x in algebraic expression is called the **degree of the polynomial**, here $a_0, a_1x, a_2x^2, \ldots, a_nx^n$, are called the terms of the polynomial and $a_0, a_1, a_2, \ldots, a_n$ are called various coefficients of the polynomial $f(x)$.

For example:

(i) $p(x) = 3x^4 - 5x^2 + 2$ is a polynomial of degree 4

(ii) $q(x) = 5x^4 + 2x^5 - 6x^6 - 5$ is a polynomial of degree 6

(iii) $f(x) = 2x^3 + 7x - 5$ is a polynomial of degree 3.

Types of Polynomials

Generally, we divide the polynomials in the following categories.

Based on Degrees

There are types of polynomials based on degrees. These are listed below:

- **Zero degree polynomial:** Any non-zero number (constant) is regarded as a polynomial of degree zero or **zero degree polynomial**. i.e. $f(x) = a$, where $a \neq 0$ is a zero degree polynomial, since we can write $f(x) = a$ as $f(x) = ax^{o}$.
- **Linear Polynomial:** A polynomial of degree one is called a **linear polynomial**. The general form of linear polynomial is $\boldsymbol{ax + b}$, where $\boldsymbol{a}$ and $\boldsymbol{b}$ are any real constant and $\boldsymbol{a \neq 0}$.
- **Quadratic Polynomial:** A polynomial of degree two is called a **quadratic polynomial**. The general form of a quadratic polynomial is $\boldsymbol{ax^2 + bx + c}$, where $\boldsymbol{a \neq 0}$.
- **Cubic Polynomial:** A polynomial of degree three is called a **cubic polynomial**. The general form of a cubic polynomial is $\boldsymbol{ax^3 + bx^2 + cx + d}$, where $\boldsymbol{a \neq 0}$.
- **Biquadratic (or quartic) Polynomials:** A polynomial of degree four is called a **biquadratic (quartic) polynomial**. The general form of a biquadratic polynomial is $\boldsymbol{ax^4 + bx^3 + cx^2 + dx + e}$, where $\boldsymbol{a \neq 0}$.

Keystone

A polynomial of degree five or more than five does not have any particular name. Such a polynomial is usually called a polynomial of degree five or six or … etc.

Based on Number of Terms

There are types of polynomials based on the number of terms. These are as follows:

- **Monomial:** A polynomial is said to be a **monomial** if it has only one term.
  e.g. x, $9x^2$, $5x^3$ all are monomials.
- **Binomial:** A polynomial is said to be a **binomial** if it contains two terms.
  e.g. $2x^2 + 3x$, $\frac{x}{2} + 5x^3$, $-8x^3 + 3$, all are binomials.
- **Trinomials:** A polynomial is said to be a **trinomial** if it contains three terms.
  e.g. $3x^3 - 8x + \frac{5}{2}$, $5 - 7x + 8x^9$, $\sqrt{7}x^{10} + 8x^4 - 3x^2$ are all trinomials.

Keystone

A polynomial having four or more than four terms does not have a particular name. These are simply called **polynomials**.

Operation on Polynomials

- **Addition:** The addition of all like terms in given polynomials gives the sum of polynomials.
- **Subtraction:** The difference between the like term in given polynomials is known as the subtraction of the given polynomials.
- **Multiplication:** multiply each term of the multiplicand by each term of the multiplier and take the algebraic sum of the products. This gives the product of the given polynomials.
- Division Algorithm for Polynomial

If $p(x)$ and $g(x)$ are any two polynomials with $g(x) \neq 0$, then we can find polynomials $r(x)$ and $q(x)$ such that $p(x) = g(x) \times q(x) + r(x)$

i.e., Dividend = (Divisor *x* Quotient) + Remainder

where $r(x) = 0$ or degree of $r(x) <$ degree of $g(x)$.

- If $r(x) = 0$, $g(x)$ is a factor of $p(x)$
- If $\deg(p(x)) > \deg(g(x))$, then $\deg(q(x)) = \deg(p(x)) - \deg(g(x))$
- If $\deg(p(x)) = \deg(g(x))$, then $\deg(q(x)) = 0$ and $\deg(r(x)) < \deg(g(x))$

Value of a Polynomial

The value of a polynomial $f(x)$ at $x = \alpha$ is obtained by substituting $x = \alpha$ in the given polynomial and is denoted by $f(\alpha)$.

Consider the polynomial $f(x) = x^3 - 6x^2 + 11x - 6$,

If we replace x by -2 everywhere in $f(x)$, we get

$$\because \quad f(-2) = (-2)^3 - 6(-2)^2 + 11(-2) - 6$$

$$f(-2) = -8 - 24 - 22 - 6$$

$$f(-2) = -60 \neq 0.$$

So, we can say that value of $f(x)$ at $x = -2$ is -60.

Zero or Root of a Polynomial

The real number α is a root or zero of a polynomial $f(x)$, if $f(\alpha) = 0$.

Consider the polynomial $f(x) = 2x^3 + x^2 - 7x - 6$,

If we replace x by 2 everywhere in $f(x)$, we get

$$\because \quad f(2) = 2(2)^3 + (2)^2 - 7(2) - 6$$

$$= 16 + 4 - 14 - 6 = 0$$

Hence, $x = 2$ is a root of $f(x)$.

Remainder Theorem

Let '$p(x)$' be any polynomial of degree greater than or equal to one and **a** be any real number and If $p(x)$ is divided by $(x - a)$, then the remainder is equal to $p(a)$.

Factor Theorem

Let $p(x)$ be a polynomial of degree greater than or equal to 1 and 'a' be a real number such that $p(a) = 0$, then $(x - a)$ is a factor of $p(x)$. Conversely, if $(x - a)$ is a factor of $p(x)$, then $p(a) = 0$.

Illustration 2.1

Find the sum of the following: $P(x) = 4t^3 - 3t^2 + 2$, $Q(x) = t^4 - 2t^3 + 6$ and $R(x) = t^3 + 4t^2 - 4$

Solution:

$$P(x) = 4t^3 - 3t^2 + 2$$

$$Q(x) = t^4 - 2t^3 + 6$$

$$R(x) = t^3 + 4t^2 - 4$$

$$P(x) + Q(x) + R(x) = t^4 + 3t^3 + t^2 + 4$$

Illustration 2.2

Subtract $g(x)$ from $f(x)$ where $f(x) = 2 + x^2 + 4x^3$, $g(x) = x^4 + x^2 + 3x + 5$.

Solution: $f(x) = 4x^3 + x^2 + 0{\cdot}x + 2 = 0{\cdot}x^4 + 4x^3 + x^2 + 0{\cdot}x + 2$

$$g(x) = x^4 + 0.x^3 + x^2 + 3x + 5$$

$$f(x) - g(x) = (0.x^4 + 4x^3 + x^2 + 0.x + 2) - (x^4 + 0x^3 + x^2 + 3x + 5)$$

$$f(x) - g(x) = (0 - 1)x^4 + (4 - 0)\,x^3 + (1 - 1)x^2 + (0 - 3)x + (2 - 5)$$

$$= -x^4 + 4x^3 + 0.\,x^2 - 3x - 3$$

$$= -x^4 + 4x^3 - 3x - 3.$$

Illustration 2.3

Multiply: $(x^2 - 5x + 2)$ by $(3x^2 + 2x - 5)$

Solution: We have

$$\begin{array}{rr} & x^2 - 5x + 2 \\ \times & 3x^2 + 2x - 5 \\ \hline & 3x^4 - 15x^3 + 6x^2 \\ & + 2x^3 - 10x^2 + 4x \\ & - 5x^2 - 25x + 10 \\ \hline & 3x^4 - 13x^3 - 9x^2 + 29x - 10 \\ \hline \end{array}$$

Illustration 2.4

If $p(x) = x^2 - 2x + 1$ and $q(x) = x^3 - 3x^2 + 2x - 1$. Find $p(x) \times q(x)$ and check the degree of $p(x) \times q(x)$

Solution: $p(x) \times q(x) = (x^2 - 2x + 1) \times (x^3 - 3x^2 + 2x - 1)$

$$= x^2(x^3 - 3x^2 + 2x - 1) - 2x(x^3 - 3x^2 + 2x - 1) + 1\,(x^3 - 3x^2 + 2x - 1)$$

$$= (x^5 - 3x^4 + 2x^4 + 2x^3 + 6x^3 + x^3 - x^2 - 4x^2 - 3x^2 + 2x + 2x - 1$$

$$= x^5 - 5x^4 + 9x^3 - 8x^2 + 4x - 1$$

The degree of $p(x) \times q(x)$ is '5'

Illustration 2.5

What must be subtracted from $x^3 - 6x^2 - 15x + 80$ so that the result is exactly divisible by $x^2 + x - 12$.

Solution: Let $p(x) = x^3 - 6x^2 - 15x + 80$ so that it is exactly divisible by $q(x) = x^2 + x - 12$. We know if $p(x)$ is divided by $q(x)$ which is a quadratic polynomial then the remainder is $r(x)$ and the degree of $r(x)$ is less than $q(x)$ or divisor.

∴ By long division method

$$\begin{array}{r|l} & x-7 \\ \hline x^2+x-12 & x^3 - 6x^2 - 15x + 80 \\ & -x^3 + x^2 - 12x \\ \hline & -7x^2 - 3x + 80 \\ & -7x^2 - 7x + 84 \\ \hline & 4x - 4 \end{array}$$

Hence, if in $p(x)$ we subtract $4x - 4$ then it is exactly divisible by $x^2 + x - 12$.

Illustration 2.6

If $x = \frac{4}{3}$ is a root of the polynomial $f(x) = 6x^3 - 11x^2 + kx - 20$ then find the value of k.

Solution: $f(x) = 6x^3 - 11x^2 + kx - 20$

$$\Rightarrow \quad f\left(\frac{4}{3}\right) = 6\left(\frac{4}{3}\right)^3 - 11\left(\frac{4}{3}\right)^2 + k\left(\frac{4}{3}\right) - 20 = 0$$

$$\Rightarrow \quad 6 \times \frac{64}{9 \times 3} - 11 \times \frac{16}{9} + \frac{4k}{3} - 20 = 0$$

$$\Rightarrow \quad 128 - 176 + 12k - 180 = 0$$

$$\Rightarrow \quad 12k = 228$$

$$\Rightarrow \quad k = 19.$$

Illustration 2.7

Find the remainder, when $f(x) = x^3 - 6x^2 + 2x - 4$ is divided by $g(x) = 1 - 2x$.

Solution: $f(x) = x^3 - 6x^2 + 2x - 4$

Let, $1 - 2x = 0$

$$\Rightarrow \quad 2x = 1$$

$$\Rightarrow \quad x = \frac{1}{2}$$

$$\text{Remainder} = f\left(\frac{1}{2}\right)$$

$$f\left(\frac{1}{2}\right) = \left(\frac{1}{2}\right)^3 - 6\left(\frac{1}{2}\right)^2 + 2\left(\frac{1}{2}\right) - 4$$

$$= \frac{1}{8} - \frac{3}{2} + 1 - 4$$

$$= \frac{1 - 12 + 8 - 32}{8} = -\frac{35}{8}.$$

Illustration 2.8

The polynomials $ax^3 + 3x^2 - 13$ and $2x^3 - 5x + a$ are divided by $x + 2$ and if the remainder in each case is the same, find the value of a.

Solution: $p(x) = ax^3 + 3x^2 - 13$ and $q(x) = 2x^3 - 5x + a$

When $p(x)$ and $q(x)$ are divided by $x + 2$

Let $x + 2 = 0 \Rightarrow x = -2$.

∴ Remainder are the same.

So, $p(-2) = q(-2)$

$$\Rightarrow \quad a(-2)^3 + 3(-2)^2 - 13 = 2(-2)^3 - 5(-2) + a$$

$$\Rightarrow \quad -8a + 12 - 13 = -16 + 10 + a$$

$$\Rightarrow \quad -9a = -5 \Rightarrow a = \frac{5}{9}.$$

Illustration 2.9

The polynomials $ax^3 + 3x^2 - 3$ and $2x^3 - 5x + a$ when divided by $(x - 4)$ leaves remainder R_1 and R_2 respectively then find the value of 'a' if $2R_1 - R_2 = 0$.

Solution: Let $f(x) = ax^3 + 3x^2 - 3$ and $g(x) = 2x^3 - 5x + a$

$$R_1 = f(4) = a(4)^3 + 3(4)^2 - 3$$

$$R_1 = 64a + 45.$$

$$R_2 = g(4) = 2(4)^3 - 5(4) + a$$

$$= 128 - 20 + a$$

$$= 108 + a.$$

Given: $2R_1 - R_2 = 0$

$$2(64a + 45) - (108 + a) = 0$$

$$128a + 90 - 108 - a = 0$$

$$127a = 18$$

$$a = \frac{18}{127}.$$

Illustration 2.10

Show that $x + 1$ and $2x - 3$ are factors of $2x^3 - 9x^2 + x + 12$.

Solution: To prove that $(x + 1)$ and $(2x - 3)$ are factors of $2x^3 - 9x^2 + x + 12$ it is sufficient to show that $p(-1)$ and $p\left(\frac{3}{2}\right)$ both are equal to zero.

$$p(-1) = 2(-1)^3 - 9(-1)^2 + (-1) + 12 = -2 - 9 - 1 + 12 = -12 + 12 = 0.$$

And,
$$p\left(\frac{3}{2}\right) = 2\left(\frac{3}{2}\right)^3 - 9\left(\frac{3}{2}\right)^2 + \left(\frac{3}{2}\right) + 12 = \frac{27}{4} - \frac{81}{4} + \frac{3}{2} + 12$$

$$= \frac{27 - 81 + 6 + 48}{4} = \frac{-81 + 81}{4} = 0.$$

Hence, $(x + 1)$ and $(2x - 3)$ are the factors $2x^3 - 9x^2 + x + 12$.

Example 2.11

Find the values of a and b so that the polynomials $x^3 - ax^2 - 13x + b$ have $(x - 1)$ and $(x + 3)$ as factors.

Solution: Let $f(x) = x^3 - ax^2 - 13x + b$

Because $(x - 1)$ and $(x + 3)$ are the factors of $f(x)$,

$\therefore$ $f(1) = 0$ and $f(-3) = 0$

$f(1) = 0$

$\Rightarrow$ $(1)^3 - a(1)^2 - 13(1) + b = 0$

$\Rightarrow$ $1 - a - 13 + b = 0$

$\Rightarrow$ $-a + b = 12$ ...(i)

$f(-3) = 0$

$\Rightarrow$ $(-3)^3 - a(-3)^2 - 13(-3) + b = 0$

$\Rightarrow$ $-27 - 9a + 39 + b = 0$

$\Rightarrow$ $-9a + b = -12$ ...(ii)

Subtracting equation (ii) from equation (i)

$(-a + b) - (-9a + b) = 12 + 12$

$\Rightarrow$ $-a + 9a = 24$

$\Rightarrow$ $8a = 24$

$\Rightarrow$ $a = 3.$

Put $a = 3$ in equation (i)

$-3 + b = 12$

$\Rightarrow$ $b = 15.$

Hence, $a = 3$ and $b = 15$.

Illustration 2.12

If $ax^3 + bx^2 + x - 6$ has $x + 2$ as a factor and leaves a remainder 4 when divided by $(x - 2)$, find the values of a and b.

Solution: Let $p(x) = ax^3 + bx^2 + x - 6$ be the given polynomial.

Now, $(x + 2)$ is a factor of $p(x)$.

$\Rightarrow$ $p(-2) = 0 \Rightarrow a(-2)^3 + b(-2)^2 + (-2) - 6 = 0$

$\Rightarrow$ $-8a + 4b - 2 - 6 = 0$

$\Rightarrow$ $-8a + 4b = 8$ ...(i)

It is given that $p(x)$ leaves remainder 4 when it is divided by $(x - 2)$.

$\Rightarrow$ $p(2) = 4 \Rightarrow a(2)^3 + b(2)^2 + (2) - 6 = 4$

$\Rightarrow$ $8a + 4b + 2 - 6 = 4$

$\Rightarrow$ $8a + 4b = 8$ ...(ii)

Add equation (i) and (ii)

$$-8a + 4b + 8a + 4b = 8 + 8 \Rightarrow 8b = 16 \Rightarrow b = 2.$$

Put $b = 2$ in equation (i)

$$-8a + 4(2) = 8 \Rightarrow -8a + 8 = 8$$

$$\Rightarrow \quad -8a = 0 \Rightarrow a = 0.$$

Hence, $a = 0$ and $b = 2$.

Check Point 1

1. Classify the following polynomials based on the number of terms.

(a) $x + 3$ (b) $x^2 + x + 2$ (c) $x^3 + 1$ (d) $8x^3$

(e) $7x^2 + 8x + 3$ (f) $\frac{x^3}{12}$ (g) $x^4 + \frac{x^2}{2}$ (h) $x^2 + x + 3$

2. Classify the following polynomials based on their degree.

(a) $3x^2 + 4x$ (b) $2x^3 + \frac{x}{2} + 3$ (c) $7x + 2$ (d) $5x^2$

(e) $x^3 + \sqrt{2}x^2 + 1$ (f) $x^3 - 1$ (g) $8x + 3$

3. Find zeroes of the following polynomials

(a) $7x - 14$ (b) $8x + 1$ (c) $x^2 - 5x - 6$ (d) $2x^2 + 3x + 1$

4. Divide $6x^2 + 13x + 16$ by $2x + 3$ and find the quotient and remainder.
5. The polynomial $5x^2 + 7x + 3$ is divided by $x - 2$. Find the remainder by using the remainder theorem.

Algebraic Identities

Some important identities are:

(i) $(a + b)^2 = a^2 + 2ab + b^2$

(ii) $(a - b)^2 = a^2 - 2ab + b^2$

(iii) $a^2 - b^2 = (a + b)(a - b)$

(iv) $(a + b + c)^2 = a^2 + b^2 + c^2 + 2ab + 2bc + 2ca$

(v) $a^3 + b^3 = (a + b)(a^2 - ab + b^2)$

(vi) $a^3 - b^3 = (a - b)(a^2 + ab + b^2)$

(vii) $(a + b)^3 = a^3 + b^3 + 3ab(a + b)$

(viii) $(a - b)^3 = a^3 - b^3 - 3ab(a - b)$

(ix) $a^3 + b^3 + c^3 - 3abc = (a + b + c)(a^2 + b^2 + c^2 - ab - bc - ac)$

Special case: if $a + b + c = 0$ then $a^3 + b^3 + c^3 = 3abc$.

Value Form:

(i) $a^2 + b^2 = (a + b)^2 - 2ab$, if $\boldsymbol{a + b}$ and $\boldsymbol{ab}$ are given.

(ii) $a^2 + b^2 = (a - b)^2 + 2ab$, if $\boldsymbol{a - b}$ and $\boldsymbol{ab}$ are given.

(iii) $a + b = \sqrt{(a-b)^2 + 4ab}$, if $\boldsymbol{a - b}$ and $\boldsymbol{ab}$ are given.

(iv) $a - b = \sqrt{(a+b)^2 - 4ab}$, if $\boldsymbol{a + b}$ and $\boldsymbol{ab}$ are given.

(v) $a^2 + \frac{1}{a^2} = \left(a + \frac{1}{a}\right)^2 - 2$, if $a - \frac{1}{a}$ is given.

(vi) $a^2 + \frac{1}{a^2} = \left(a - \frac{1}{a}\right)^2 + 2$, if $a - \frac{1}{a}$ is given.

(vii) $a^3 + b^3 = (a + b)^3 - 3ab(a + b)$, if $\boldsymbol{(a + b)}$ and $\boldsymbol{ab}$ are given.

(viii) $a^3 - b^3 = (a - b)^3 + 3ab(a - b)$, if $\boldsymbol{(a - b)}$ and $\boldsymbol{ab}$ are given.

(ix) $a^3+\frac{1}{a^3}=\left(a+\frac{1}{a}\right)^3-3\left(a+\frac{1}{a}\right)$, if $a+\frac{1}{a}$ is given.

(x) $a^3-\frac{1}{a^3}=\left(a-\frac{1}{a}\right)^3+3\left(a-\frac{1}{a}\right)$ if $a-\frac{1}{a}$ is given.

(xi) $a^4-b^4=(a^2+b^2)(a^2-b^2)=[(a+b)^2-2ab](a+b)(a-b)$.

Keystone

(i) (x^n-a^n) is divisible by $(x-a)$ for all the values of n.

(ii) (x^n-a^n) is divisible by $(x+a)$ and $(x-a)$ for all the even values of n.

(iii) (x^n+a^n) is divisible by $(x+a)$ for all the odd values of n.

Illustration 2.13

$$\left(\frac{x^a}{x^b}\right)^{a^2+ab+b^2}\left(\frac{x^b}{x^c}\right)^{b^2+bc+c^2}\left(\frac{x^c}{x^a}\right)^{c^2+ca+a^2}=1$$

Solution: $\left(\frac{x^a}{x^b}\right)^{a^2+ab+b^2}\left(\frac{x^b}{x^c}\right)^{b^2+bc+c^2}\left(\frac{x^c}{x^a}\right)^{c^2+ca+a^2}$

$$=(x^{a-b})^{a^2+ab+b^2}(x^{b-c})^{b^2+bc+c^2}(x^{c-a})^{c^2+ca+a^2}=\left(x^{a^3-b^3}\right)\left(x^{b^3-c^3}\right)\left(x^{c^3-a^3}\right)$$

$$x^{a^3-b^3+b^3-c^3+c^3-a^3}=x^0=1$$

Illustration 2.14

Expand:

(i) $\left(2x-\frac{1}{3x}\right)^2$ **(ii)** $(3x^2+5y)^2$ **(iii)** $(\sqrt{2}x-3y)(\sqrt{2}x+3y)$ **(iv)** $\left(\frac{1}{4}a-\frac{1}{2}b+1\right)^2$

Solution:

(i) $\left(2x-\frac{1}{3x}\right)^2=(2x)^2-2(2x)\left(\frac{1}{3x}\right)+\frac{1}{(3x)^2}=4x^2-\frac{4}{3}+\frac{1}{9x^2}$.

(ii) $(3x^2+5y)^2=(3x^2)^2+2(3x^2)(5y)+(5y)^2=9x^4+30x^2y+25y^2$

(iii) $(\sqrt{2}x-3y)(\sqrt{2}x+3y)=(\sqrt{2}x)^2-(3y)^2=2x^2-9y^2$

(iv) $\left(\frac{1}{4}a-\frac{1}{2}b+1\right)^2=\left(\frac{1}{4}a\right)^2+\left(-\frac{1}{2}b\right)^2+(1)^2+2\left(\frac{1}{4}a\right)\left(-\frac{1}{2}b\right)+2\left(-\frac{1}{2}b\right)(1)+2(2)\left(\frac{1}{4}a\right)$

$$=\frac{1}{16}a^2+\frac{1}{4}b^2+1-\frac{ab}{4}-b+\frac{a}{2}.$$

Illustration 2.15

Simplify:

(i) $(2x+y)(2x-y)(4x^2+y^2)$ **(ii)** $(x+y-2z)^2-x^2-y^2-3z^2+4xy$

Solution:

(i) $(2x+y)(2x-y)(4x^2+y^2)=[(2x)^2-(y)^2](4x^2+y^2)$

$$=(4x^2-y^2)(4x^2+y^2)=(4x^2)^2-(y^2)^2=16x^4-y^4.$$

(ii) $(x+y-2z)^2-x^2-y^2-3z^2+4xy$

$$=x^2+y^2+(-2z)^2+2(x)(y)+2(y)(-2z)+2(-2z)(x)-x^2-y^2-3z^2+4xy$$

$$=x^2+y^2+4z^2+2xy-4yz-4zx-x^2-y^2-3z^2+4xy$$

$$=z^2+6xy-4yz-4zx.$$

Illustration 2.16

Evaluate:

(i) $(107)^2$ **(ii)** $(94)^2$ **(iii)** $(0.99)^2$

Solution:

(i) $(107)^2=(100+7)^2$

$=(100)^2+(7)^2+2\times 100\times 7$

$=10000+49+1400$

$=11449$

(ii) $(94)^2=(100-6)^2$

$=(100)^2+(6)^2-2\times 100\times 6$

$=10000+36-1200$

$=8836$

(iii) $(0.99)^2=(1-0.01)^2$

$=(1)^2+(0.01)^2-2\times 1\times 0.01$

$=1+0.0001-0.02$

$=0.9801$

Illustration 2.17

If $x^2+\frac{1}{x^2}=23$, find the values of $\left(x+\frac{1}{x}\right)$, $\left(x-\frac{1}{x}\right)$ and $\left(x^4+\frac{1}{x^4}\right)$

Solution: $x^2+\frac{1}{x^2}=23$ ...(i)

$\Rightarrow$ $x^2+\frac{1}{x^2}+2=25$ [Adding 2 on both sides of (i)]

$\Rightarrow$ $(x^2)+\left(\frac{1}{x}\right)^2+2\cdot x\cdot\frac{1}{x}=25$

$\Rightarrow$ $\left(x+\frac{1}{x}\right)^2=(5)^2$

$\Rightarrow$ $x+\frac{1}{x}=\pm 5$

$$\left(x-\frac{1}{x}\right)^2=x^2+\frac{1}{x^2}-2\Rightarrow\left(x-\frac{1}{x}\right)^2=23-2=21$$

$\Rightarrow$ $\left(x-\frac{1}{x}\right)=\pm\sqrt{21}.$

$$\left(x^2+\frac{1}{x^2}\right)^2=\left(x^4+\frac{1}{x^4}\right)+2$$

$$\Rightarrow \quad \left(x^4 + \frac{1}{x^4}\right) = (23)^2 - 2 = 529 - 2$$

$$\Rightarrow \quad \left(x^4 + \frac{1}{x^4}\right) = 527.$$

Example 2.18

Prove that: $a^2 + b^2 + c^2 - ab - bc - ca$

$$= \frac{1}{2}\left[(a-b)^2 + (b-c)^2 + (c-a)^2\right]$$

Solution: Here, L.H.S. $a^2 + b^2 + c^2 - ab - bc - ca$

$$= \frac{1}{2}\left[2a^2 + 2b^2 + 2c^2 - 2ab - 2bc - 2ca\right]$$

$$= \frac{1}{2}\left[\left(a^2 - 2ab + b^2\right) + \left(b^2 - 2bc + c^2\right) + (c^2 - 2ca + a^2)\right]$$

$$= \frac{1}{2}\left[(a-b)^2 + (b-c)^2 + (c-a)^2\right]$$

$= \text{RHS}$

Hence Proved.

Illustration 2.19

If $a + b + c = 9$ and $ab + bc + ca = 23$, then find the value of $a^2 + b^2 + c^2$.

Solution: $(a + b + c)^2 = a^2 + b^2 + c^2 + 2(ab + bc + ca)$

$(9)^2 = a^2 + b^2 + c^2 + 2(23)$

$a^2 + b^2 + c^2 = 81 - 46$

$a^2 + b^2 + c^2 = 35.$

Illustration 2.20

Expand:

(i) $\left(\frac{1}{3x} - \frac{2}{5y}\right)^3$ **(ii)** $(4 + 3x)^3$

Solution:

(i) $\left(\frac{1}{3x} - \frac{2}{5y}\right)^3$

$$= \left(\frac{1}{3x}\right)^3 - \left(\frac{2}{5y}\right)^3 - 3\left(\frac{1}{3x}\right)\left(\frac{2}{5y}\right)\left(\frac{1}{3x} - \frac{2}{5y}\right)$$

$$= \frac{1}{27x^3} - \frac{8}{125y^3} - \frac{1}{5xy}\left(\frac{1}{3x} - \frac{2}{5y}\right)$$

$$= \frac{1}{27x^3} - \frac{8}{125y^3} - \frac{2}{15x^2y} + \frac{4}{25xy^2}$$

(ii) $(4 + 3x)^3 = (4)^3 + (3x)^3 + 3(4)(3x)(4 + 3x)$

$= 64 + 27x^3 + 36x\,(4 + 3x)$

$= 64 + 27x^3 + 144x + 108x^2$

Illustration 2.21

Simplify:

(i) $(3x+4)^3 - (3x-4)^3$ **(ii)** $\left(x+\frac{2}{x}\right)^3 + \left(x-\frac{2}{x}\right)^3$

Solution:

(i) $(3x+4)^3 - (3x-4)^3$

$$= [(3x)^3 + (4)^3 + 3(3x)(4)(3x+4)] - [(3x)^3 - (4)^3 - 3(3x)(4)(3x-4)]$$
$$= [27x^3 + 64 + 36x(3x+4)] - [27x^3 - 64 - 36x(3x-4)]$$
$$= [27x^3 + 64 + 108x^2 + 144x] - [27x^3 - 64 - 108x^2 + 144x]$$
$$= 27x^3 + 64 + 108x^2 + 144x - 27x^3 + 64 + 108x^2 - 144x$$
$$= 128 + 216x^2.$$

(ii) $\left(x+\frac{2}{x}\right)^3 + \left(x-\frac{2}{x}\right)^3$

$$= x^3 + \left(\frac{2}{x}\right)^3 + 3(x)\left(\frac{2}{x}\right)\left(x+\frac{2}{x}\right) + x^3 - \left(\frac{2}{x}\right)^3 - 3(x)\left(\frac{2}{x}\right)\left(x-\frac{2}{x}\right)$$
$$= x^3 + \frac{8}{x^3} + 6x + \frac{12}{x} + x^3 - \frac{8}{x^3} - 6x + \frac{12}{x} = 2x^3 + \frac{24}{x}.$$

Illustration 2.22

If $x - \frac{1}{x} = 5$, find the value of $x^3 - \frac{1}{x^3}$

Solution: We have, $x - \frac{1}{x} = 5$ ...(i)

$\Rightarrow$ $\left(x-\frac{1}{x}\right)^3 = (5)^3$ [Cubing both sides of (i)]

$\Rightarrow$ $x^3 - \frac{1}{x^3} - 3x\cdot\frac{1}{x}\cdot\left(x-\frac{1}{x}\right) = 125$

$\Rightarrow$ $x^3 - \frac{1}{x^3} - 3\left(x-\frac{1}{x}\right) = 125$

$x^3 - \frac{1}{x^3} - 3\times 5 = 125$ [Substituting $\left(x-\frac{1}{x}\right) = 5$]

$\Rightarrow$ $x^3 - \frac{1}{x^3} - 15 = 125$

$\Rightarrow$ $x^3 - \frac{1}{x^3} = (125+15) = 140$

Illustration 2.23

Find the products of the following expression:

(i) $(4x+3y)(16x^2 - 12xy + 9y^2)$ **(ii)** $(5x-2y)(25x^2 + 10xy + 4y^2)$

Solution:

(i) $(4x+3y)(16x^2 - 12\,xy + 9y^2)$

$= (4x+3y)[(4x)^2 - (4x)\times(3y) + (3y)^2]$

$= (a+b)(a^2 - ab + b^2)$ [Where $a = 4x$, $b = 3y$]

$= a^3 + b^3$

$= (4x)^3 + (3y)^3 = 64x^3 + 27y^3.$

(ii) $(5x-2y)(25x^2 + 10xy + 4y^2)$

$= (5x-2y)[(5x)^2 + (5x)\times(2y) + (2y)^2]$

$= (a-b)(a^2 + ab + b^2)$ [Where $a = 5x$, $b = 2y$]

$= a^3 - b^3$

$= (5x)^3 - 2y^3 = 125x^3 - 8y^3.$

Illustration 2.24

Find the product of the following expression:

(i) $(3x - 4y + 5z)\ (9x^2 + 16y^2 + 25z^2 + 12xy - 15zx + 20yz)$ **(ii)** $(2a - 3b - 2c)\ (4a^2 + 9b^2 + 4c^2 + 6ab - 6bc + 4ca)$

Solution:

(i) $(3x - 4y + 5z)(9x^2 + 16y^2 + 25z^2 + 12xy\ .15zx + 20yz)$

Let, $a = 3x$, $b = -4y$, $c = 5z$

$= (a + b + c)(a^2 + b^2 + c^2 - ab - bc - ca)$

$= (a^3 + b^3 + c^3 - 3abc)$

$= (3x)^3 + (-4y)^3 + (5z)^3 - 3(3x)(-4y)(5z)$

$= 27x^3 - 64y^3 + 125z^3 + 180\ xyz$

(ii) $(2a - 3b - 2c)(4a^2 + 9b^2 + 4c^2 + 6ab - 6bc + 4ca)$

Let $x = 2a$, $y = -3b$, $z = -2c$

$= (x + y + z)(x^2 + y^2 + z^2 - xy - yz - zx)$

$= (x^3 + y^3 + z^3 - 3xyz)$

$= (2a)^3 + (-3b)^3 + (-2c)^3 - 3(2a)(-3b)(-2c)$

$= 8a^3 - 27b^3 - 8c^3 - 36abc$

Illustration 2.25

If $a + b + c = 9$ and $ab + bc + ac = 26$, find the value of $a^3 + b^3 + c^3 - 3abc$.

Solution: We have $a + b + c = 9$ ...(i)

$\Rightarrow \quad (a + b + c)^2 = 81$ [On squaring both sides of (i)]

$\Rightarrow \quad a^2 + b^2 + c^2 + 2(ab + bc + ac) = 81$

$\Rightarrow \quad a^2 + b^2 + c^2 + 2 \times 26 = 81$ $[\because ab + bc + ac = 26]$

$\Rightarrow \quad a^2 + b^2 + c^2 = (81 - 52)$

$\Rightarrow \quad a^2 + b^2 + c^2 = 29.$

Now, we have

$$a^3 + b^3 + c^3 - 3abc$$

$$= (a + b + c)\ (a^2 + b^2 + c^2 - ab - bc - ac)$$

$$= (a + b + c)\ [(a^2 + b^2 + c^2) - (ab + bc + ac)]$$

$$= 9 \times [(29 - 26)]$$

$$= (9 \times 3) = 27.$$

Illustration 2.26

Prove that: $(x - y)^3 + (y - z)^3 + (z - x)^3 = 3(x - y)(y - z)(z - x)$.

Solution: Let $(x - y) = a$, $(y - z) = b$ and $(z - x) = c$.

Then, $a + b + c = (x - y) + (y - z) + (z - x) = 0$

$\therefore \quad a^3 + b^3 + c^3 = 3abc$

or $\quad (x - y)^3 + (y - z)^3 + (z - x)^3 = 3(x - y)\ (y - z)\ (z - x).$

Check Point 2

6. Expand $(2x + 3y - 2z)^2$.
7. If $a + b = 7$ and $ab = 12$, find the value of $a^3 + b^3$.
8. If $a + \frac{1}{a} = 5$ then $a^2 + \frac{1}{a^2}$ is:
9. If $a + \frac{1}{a} = 4$ then $a^3 + \frac{1}{a^3}$ is equal to:
10. If $p - q = 9$, prove that $p^3 - q^3 - 27pq = 729$.

Factorization

To express a given polynomial as the product of polynomials, each of degree less than that of the given polynomial such that no such factor has a factor of lower degree, is called **factorization**.

Taking Out the Common Factor

Working Rule: When each term of an expression has a common factor, divide each term by this factor and take it out as a multiple.

Grouping

Working Rule: Sometimes in a given expression it is not possible to take out a common factor directly. However, the terms of the given expression are grouped in such a manner that we may have a common factor. This can be factorized as discussed above.

Making a Perfect Square

Working Rule: $a^2 + 2ab + b^2 = (a + b)^2$

Factorization of the Difference of Two Squares

Working Rule: $a^2 - b^2 = (a + b)(a - b)$

Factorization of a Quadratic Polynomial

Working Rule:

Case-1: Polynomials of the form $x^2 + bx + c$

we find integers p and q such that $p + q = b$ and $pq = c$.

Then,

$$x^2 + bx + c = x^2 + (p + q)x + pq$$
$$= x^2 + px + qx + pq$$
$$= x(x + p) + q(x + p)$$
$$= (x + p)(x + q)$$

Case-2: Polynomials of the form $ax^2 + bx + c$

we find integers p and q such that $p + q = b$ and $pq = ac$.

Then,

$$ax^2 + bx + c = ax^2 + (p + q)x + \frac{pq}{a}$$
$$= ax^2 + apx + aqx + pq$$
$$= ax(ax + p) + q(ax + p)$$
$$= (ax + p)(ax + q)$$

Factorization of an Algebraic Expression

Factorization of an algebraic expression is the process of breaking it down into simpler components, or factors, that, when multiplied together, yield the original expression.

Sum or Difference of Two Cubes

Working Rule:

(i) $a^3 + b^3 = (a + b)(a^2 - ab + b^2)$

(ii) $a^3 - b^3 = (a - b)(a^2 + ab + b^2)$

Form $a^3 + b^3 + c^3 - 3abc$

Working Rule: $a^3 + b^3 + c^3 - 3abc = (a + b + c)(a^2 + b^2 + c^2 - ab - bc - ac)$

Special case: if $a + b + c = 0$ then $a^3 + b^3 + c^3 = 3abc$.

Illustration 2.27

Factorize:

(i) $2a(x + y) - 3b(x + y)$ **(ii)** $x(x + y)^3 - 3x^2y(x + y)$ **(iii)** $8(3a - 2b)^2 - 10(3a - 2b)$

Solution:

(i) $2a(x+y) - 3b(x+y) = (x+y)(2a-3b)$.

(ii) $x(x+y)^3 - 3x^2y(x+y)$

$= x(x+y)[(x+y)^2 - 3xy]$

$= x(x+y)[x^2+y^2+2xy-3xy]$

$= x(x+y)[x^2+y^2-xy] = x(x^3+y^3)$.

(iii) $8(3a-2b)^2 - 10(3a-2b)$

$= 2(3a-2b)[4(3a-2b)-5]$

$= 2(3a-2b)[12a-8b-5]$.

Illustration 2.28

Factorize:

(i) $x^2+\frac{1}{x^2}+2-2x-\frac{2}{x}$ **(ii)** $(x^2+3x)^2 - 5(x^2+3x) - y(x^2+3x) + 5y$

Solution:

(i) $x^2+\frac{1}{x^2}+2-2x-\frac{2}{x} = \left(x+\frac{1}{x}\right)^2 - 2\left(x+\frac{1}{x}\right) = \left(x+\frac{1}{x}\right)\left(x+\frac{1}{x}-2\right)$.

(ii) $(x^2+3x)^2 - 5(x^2+3x) - y(x^2+3x) + 5y$

$= (x^2+3x)(x^2+3x-5) - y(x^2+3x-5)$

$= (x^2+3x-5)(x^2+3x-y)$.

Illustration 2.29

Factorize:

(i) $4(x-y)^2 - 12(x-y)(x+y) + 9(x+y)^2$ **(ii)** $2a^2+2\sqrt{6}ab+3b^2$ **(iii)** $25x^2+4y^2+9z^2-20xy-12yz+30xz$

Solution:

(i) $4(x-y)^2 - 12(x-y)(x+y) + 9(x+y)^2$

Let, $x-y=a$ and $x+y=b$

$= 4a^2 - 12ab + 9b^2$

$= (2a)^2 - 2(2a)(3b) + (3b)^2$

$= (2a-3b)^2$

$= [2(x-y) - 3(x+y)]^2$

$= [2x-2y-3x-3y]^2$

$= [-x-5y]^2$.

(ii) $2a^2+2\sqrt{6}ab+3b^2$

$= \left(\sqrt{2}a\right)^2 + 2\left(\sqrt{2}a\right)\left(\sqrt{3}b\right) + \left(\sqrt{3}b\right)^2 = \left(\sqrt{2}a+\sqrt{3}b\right)^2$.

(iii) $25x^2+4y^2+9z^2-20xy-12yz+30xz$

$= (5x)^2 + (-2y)^2 + (3z)^2 + 2(5x)(-2y) + 2(-2y)(3z) + 2(3z)(5x)$

$= (5x-2y+3z)^2$.

Illustration 2.30

Factorize:

(i) x^4+5x^2+9 **(ii)** x^4+4x^2+3 **(iii)** $x^4+x^2y^2+y^4$

Solution:

(i) x^4+5x^2+9

$= (x^2)^2 + 5x^2 + (3)^2$

$= (x^2)^2 + 6x^2 + (3)^2 - x^2$

$= (x^2+3)^2 - (x)^2$

$= (x^2+3+x)(x^2+3-x)$.

(ii) x^4+4x^2+3

$= (x^2)^2 + 2(2)x^2 + (2)^2 - 1$

$= (x^2+2)^2 - (1)^2$

$= (x^2+2+1)(x^2+2-1)$

$= (x^2+3)(x^2+1)$.

(iii) $x^4+x^2y^2+y^4$

$= (x^2)^2 + 2.x^2.y^2 + (y^2)^2 - x^2y^2$

$= (x^2+y^2)^2 - (xy)^2$

$= (x^2+y^2+xy)(x^2+y^2-xy)$.

Illustration 2.31

Factorize:

(i) $x^2 + 6\sqrt{2}x + 10$ **(ii)** $5\sqrt{5}x^2 + 20x + 3\sqrt{5}$ **(iii)** $2x^2 - \frac{5}{6}x + \frac{1}{12}$ **(iv)** $7(x - 2y)^2 - 25(x - 2y) + 12$

Solution:

(i) $x^2 + 6\sqrt{2}x + 10 = x^2 + 5\sqrt{2}x + \sqrt{2}x + 10$

$= x(x + 5\sqrt{2}) + \sqrt{2}(x + 5\sqrt{2}) = (x + 5\sqrt{2})(x + \sqrt{2})$

(ii) $5\sqrt{5}x^2 + 20x + 3\sqrt{5} = 5\sqrt{5}x^2 + 15x + 5x + 3\sqrt{5}$

$= 5x(\sqrt{5}x + 3) + \sqrt{5}(\sqrt{5}x + 3) = (5x + \sqrt{5})(\sqrt{5}x + 3)$

$= \sqrt{5}(\sqrt{5}x + 1)(\sqrt{5}x + 3)$

(iii) $2x^2 - \frac{5}{6}x + \frac{1}{12} = \frac{24x^2 - 10x + 1}{12}$

$= \frac{1}{12}(24x^2 - 4x - 6x + 1) = \frac{1}{12}[4x(6x - 1) - 1(6x - 1)]$

$= \frac{1}{12}(6x - 1)(4x - 1)$

(iv) $7(x - 2y)^2 - 25(x - 2y) + 12$

Let, $x - 2y = a = 7a^2 - 25a + 12$

$= 7a^2 - 21a - 4a + 12 = 7a(a - 3) - 4(a - 3)$

$= (a - 3)(7a - 4) = (x - 2y - 3)(7x - 14y - 4)$

Illustration 2.32

What are the possible expressions for the dimensions of the cuboid whose volume is $3x^2 - 12x$.

Solution: Volume of cuboid $= 3x^2 - 12x = 3x(x - 4)$

Possible dimensions are:

Length = 3 unit, Breadth = x unit and Height = $(x - 4)$ unit.

Illustration 2.33

Factorize:

(i) $27a^3 + 125b^3$ **(ii)** $(a - 2b)^3 - 512b^3$ **(iii)** $x^9 - y^9$ **(iv)** $a^3 - \frac{1}{a^3} - 2a + \frac{2}{a}$

Solution:

(i) $27a^3 + 125b^3$

$= (3a)^3 + (5b)^3$

$= (3a + 5b)[(3a)^2 + (5b)^2 - (3a)(5b)]$

$= (3a + 5b)[9a^2 + 25b^2 - 15ab]$.

(ii) $(a - 2b)^3 - 512b^3$

$= (a - 2b)^3 - (8b)^3$

$= (a - 2b - 8b)[(a - 2b)^2 + (8b)^2 + (a - 2b)(8b)]$

$= (a - 10b)[a^2 + 4b^2 - 4ab + 64b^2 + 8ab - 16b^2]$

$= (a - 10b)[a^2 + 52b^2 + 4ab]$

(iii) $x^9 - y^9$

$= (x^3)^3 - (y^3)^3$

$= (x^3 - y^3)[(x^3)^2 + x^3y^3 + (y^3)^2]$

$= (x - y)(x^2 + xy + y^2)(x^6 + x^3y^3 + y^6)$

(iv) $a^3 - \frac{1}{a^3} - 2a + \frac{2}{a}$

$= a^3 - \frac{1}{a^3} - 2\left(a - \frac{1}{a}\right)$

$= \left(a - \frac{1}{a}\right)\left(a^2 + 1 + \frac{1}{a^2}\right) - 2\left(a - \frac{1}{a}\right)$

$= \left(a - \frac{1}{a}\right)\left(a^2 + 1 + \frac{1}{a^2} - 2\right)$

$= \left(a - \frac{1}{a}\right)\left(a^2 + \frac{1}{a^2} - 1\right)$

Illustration 2.34

Factorize:

(i) $2\sqrt{2}a^3 + 8b^3 - 27c^3 + 18\sqrt{2}abc$ **(ii)** $(2x - 3y)^3 + (4z - 2x)^3 + (3y - 4z)^3$

(iii) $p^3(q - r)^3 + q^3(r - p)^3 + r^3(p - q)^3$

Solution:

(i) $2\sqrt{2}a^3 + 8b^3 - 27c^3 + 18\sqrt{2}\,abc = (\sqrt{2}a)^3 + (2b)^3 + (-3c)^3 - 3(\sqrt{2}\,a)(2b)(-3c)$

$$= (\sqrt{2}a + 2b - 3c)\left[(\sqrt{2}a)^2 + (2a)^2 + (-3c)^2 - (\sqrt{2}a)(2b) - (-3c) - (-3c)(\sqrt{2}a)\right]$$

$$= (\sqrt{2}\,a + 2b - 3c)\left[2a^2 + 4b^2 + 9c^2 - 2\sqrt{2}ab + 6bc + 3\sqrt{2}ac\right]$$

(ii) $(2x - 3y)^3 + (4z - 2x)^3 + (3y - 4z)^3$

Let $a = 2x - 3y$, $b = 4z - 2x$ and $c = 3y - 4z$

So, $(2x - 3y)^3 + (4z - 2x)^3 + (3y - 4z)^3 = a^3 + b^3 + c^3$

Now, $a + b + c = 2x - 3y + 4z - 2x + 3y - 4z = 0$

So, $a^3 + b^3 + c^3 = 3abc$

$= 3(2x - 3y)(4z - 2x)(3y - 4z)$.

(iii) $p^3(q - r)^3 + q^3(r - p)^3 + r^3(p - q)^3$

Let $x = p(q - r)$, $y = q(r - p)$, $z = r(p - q)$

So, $p^3(q - r)^3 + q^3(r - p)^3 + r^3(p - q)^3 = x^3 + y^3 + z^3$

Now, $x + y + z = p(q - r) + q(r - p) + r(p - q)$

$= pq - pr + qr - qp + rp - rq = 0$

So, $x^3 + y^3 + z^3 = 3xyz = 3p(q - r)\,q(r - p)\,r(p - q)$

$= 3pqr(q - r)(r - p)(p - q)$.

Check Point 3

11. Factorize: $x^2(xy + 5) - 2y^2(xy + 5)$

12. Factorize: $3x^2 + 8x + 4$

13. Factorize: $2a + 4b - ac - 2bc$

14. Factorize: $27a^3 - b^3 + c^3 + 9abc$.

15. Factorize: $32x^3 - 4d^3$

STRUCTURAL OUTLINE

Polynomials

Types of Polynomials

Based on Number of terms

(I) **Monomial :** A polynomial is said to be a **monomial** if it has only one term. e.g. x, $9x^2$, $5x^3$ all are monomials.

(II) **Binomial :** A polynomial is said to be a **binomial** if it contains two terms. e.g. $2x^2 + 3x$.

(III) **Trinomials :** A polynomial is said to bea **trinomial** if it contains three terms. e.g. $3x3 - 8x + \frac{5}{2}$

Based On Degree

(I) **Zero degree polynomial:** If degree of polynomials is 0.
$f(x) = ax^o$.

(II) **Linear Polynomial:** If degree of polynomial is 1.
$f(x) = ax + b$, **and** $a \neq 0$.

(III) **Quadratic Polynomial:** If degree of Polynomial is 2.
$F(x) = ax^2 + bx + c$, **where** $a \neq 0$.

(IV) **Cubic Polynomial:** If degree of polynomial is 3.
$f(x) = ax^3 + bx^2 + cx + d$, **where** $a \neq 0$.

(V) **Biquadratic Polynomial:** If degree of polynomial is 4.
$f(x) = ax^4 + bx^3 + cx^2 + dx + e$, **where** $a \neq 0$.

Algebraic Identities and Factorization

(i) $(a + b)^2 = a^2 + 2ab + b^2$
(ii) $(a - b)^2 = a^2 - 2ab + b^2$
(iii) $a2 - b^2 = (a + b)(a - b)$
(iv) $(a + b + c)^2 = a^2 + b^2 + c^2 + 2ab + 2bc + 2ca$
(v) $a^3 + b^3 = (a + b)(a^2 - ab + b^2)$
(vi) $a^3 - b^3 = (a - b)(a^2 + ab + b^2)$
(vii) $(a + b)^3 = a^3 + b^3 + 3ab(a + b)$
(viii) $(a - b)^3 = a^3 - b^3 - 3ab(a - b)$
(ix) $a^3 + b^3 + c^3 - 3abc =$
$(a + b + c)(a^2 + b^2 + c^2 - ab - bc - ac)$

Special case : if $a + b + c = 0$ then $a^3 + b^3 + c^3 = 3abc$.

(a) Factorization by taking out the common factor
Working Rule: When each term of an expression has a common factor, divide each term by this factor and take out as a multiple.

(b) Factorization by grouping :
Working Rule: Sometimes in a given expression it is not possible to take out a common factor directly. However, the terms of the given expression are grouped in such a manner that we may have a common factor. This can be factorized as discussed above.

(c) Factorization by using identities.

Remainder Theorem

Let **p(x)** be any polynomial of degree greater than or equal to one and **'a'** be any real number. If **p(x)** is divided by **(x –a),** then the remainder is equal to **p(a)**.

Factor Theorem

Let **p(x)** be a polynomial of degree greater than or equal to 1 and **'a'** be a real number such that **p(a) = 0**, then **(x –a)** is a factor of **p(x)**. Conversely, if **(x –a)** is a factor of **p(x)**, then **p(a) = 0**.

Division Algorithm for Polynomial

If p(x) and g(x) are any two polynomials with $g(x) \neq 0$, then we can find polynomials r(x) and q(x) such that
$p(x) = g(x) \times q(x) + r(x)$

i.e. Dividend = (Divisor x Quotient) + Remainder where $r(x) = 0$ or degree of r(x) < degree of g(x).

(i) If $r(x) = 0$, g(x) is a factor of p(x)

(ii) If $\deg(p(x)) > \deg(g(x))$,
then $\deg(q(x)) = \deg(p(x)) - \deg(g(x))$

(iii) If $\deg(p(x)) = \deg(g(x))$,
then $\deg(q(x)) = 0$ and $\deg(r(x)) < \deg(g(x))$

EXEMPLIFICATION

1. What must be added to $3x^3 + x^2 - 22x + 9$ so that the result is exactly divisible by $3x^2 + 7x - 6$?

Solution: Let $p(x) = 3x^3 + x^2 - 22x + 9$ and $q(x) = 3x^2 + 7x - 6$

We know if $p(x)$ is divided by $q(x)$ which is a quadratic polynomial then the remainder is $r(x)$ and the degree of $r(x)$ is less than $q(x)$ or divisor.

$\therefore$ By long division method,

$$\begin{array}{r|l} & x-2 \\ \hline 3x^2+7x-6 & 3x^3 + x^2 - 22x + 9 \\ & -3x^3 \pm 7x^2 \mp 6x \\ \hline & -6x^2 + 16x + 9 \\ & \mp 6x^2 \mp 14x \pm 12 \\ \hline & -2x - 3 \end{array}$$

Hence if in $p(x)$ we added $2x + 3$ then it is exactly divisible by $3x^2 + 7x - 6$.

2. If $x = 2$ and $x = 0$ are two roots of the polynomial $f(x) = 2x^3 - 5x^2 + ax + b$. Find the values of a and b.

Solution: $f(2) = 2(2)^3 - 5(2)^2 + a(2) + b = 0$

$\Rightarrow$ $16 - 20 + 2a + b = 0$

$\Rightarrow$ $2a + b = 4$ ...(i)

$f(0) = 2(0)^3 - 5(0)^2 + a(0) + b = 0$

$\Rightarrow$ $b = 0$

Put $b = 0$ in eq. (i)

$\Rightarrow$ $2a + 0 = 4$

So, $2a = 4$

$\Rightarrow$ $a = 2.$

Hence, $a = 2$, $b = 0$.

3. If $f(x) = x^4 - 2x^3 + 3x^2 - ax + b$ is a polynomial such that when it is divided by $x - 1$ and $x + 1$, the Remainders are respectively 5 and 19. Determine the remainder when $f(x)$ is divided by $(x - 2)$.

Solution: When $f(x)$ is divided by $(x - 1)$ and $(x + 1)$ the remainders are 5 and 19 respectively.

$\therefore$ $f(1) = 5$

$\Rightarrow$ $1^4 - 2(1)^3 + 3(1)^2 - a(1) + b = 5$

$\Rightarrow$ $1 - 2 + 3 - a + b = 5$

$\Rightarrow$ $-a + b = 3$ ...(i)

and $f(-1) = 19$

$\Rightarrow$ $(-1)^4 - 2(-1)^3 + 3(-1)^2 - a(-1) + b = 19$

$\Rightarrow$ $1 + 2 + 3 + a + b = 19$

$\Rightarrow$ $a + b = 13$ ...(ii)

From equation (i) and (ii)

We have $a = 5$ and $b = 8$

So, $f(x) = x^4 - 2x^3 + 3x^2 - 5x + 8$

The remainder when $f(x)$ is divided by $(x - 2)$ is equal to $f(2)$.

$$f(2) = 2^4 - 2(2^3) + 3(2)^2 - 5(2) + 8$$

$$= 16 - 16 + 12 - 10 + 8 = 10.$$

4. Find the value of $(28)^3 - (78)^3 + (50)^3$.

Solution: Let $a = 28, b = -78, c = 50$

Then, $a + b + c = 28 - 78 + 50 = 0$

$$\therefore \quad a^3 + b^3 + c^3 = 3abc.$$

So, $(28)^3 + (-78)^3 + (50)^3 = 3 \times 28 \times (-78) \times 50 = -327600$.

5. Simplify: $\dfrac{(a^2-b^2)^3+(b^2-c^2)^3+(c^2-a^2)^3}{(a-b)^3+(b-c)^3+(c-a)^3}$

Solution: Here, $(a^2 - b^2) + (b^2 - c^2) + (c^2 - a^2) = 0$

$$\therefore \quad (a^2 - b^2)^3 + (b^2 - c^2)^3 + (c^2 - a^2)^3 = 3(a^2 - b^2)(b^2 - c^2)(c^2 - a^2)$$

Also, $(a - b) + (b - c) + (c - a) = 0$

$$\therefore \quad (a - b)^3 + (b - c)^3 + (c - a)^3 = 3(a - b)(b - c)(c - a)$$

$$= \frac{3(a^2-b^2)(b^2-c^2)(c^2-a^2)}{3(a-b)(b-c)(c-a)}$$

$$= \frac{3(a-b)(a+b)(b-c)(b+c)(c-a)(c+a)}{3(a-b)(b-c)(c+a)}$$

$$= (a + b)(b + c)(c + a)$$

6. Evaluate:

(i) $(1005)^3$ **(ii)** $(997)^3$

Solution:

(i) $(1005)^3 = (1000 + 5)^3$

$= (1000)^3 + (5)^3 + 3\,(1000)\,(5)\,(1000 + 5)$

$= 1000000000 + 125 + 15000\,(1000 + 5)$

$= 1000000000 + 125 + 15000000 + 75000$

$= 1015075125.$

(ii) $(997)^3 = (1000 - 3)^3$

$= (1000)^3 - (3)^3 - 3 \times 1000 \times 3 \times (1000 - 3)$

$= 1000000000 - 27 - 9000 \times (1000 - 3)$

$= 1000000000 - 27 - 9000000 + 27000$

$= 991026973.$

7. Simplify: $\left(x-\dfrac{1}{x}\right)\left(x+\dfrac{1}{x}\right)\left(x^2+\dfrac{1}{x^2}\right)\left(x^4+\dfrac{1}{x^4}\right)$

Solution:

$$\left(x-\frac{1}{x}\right)\left(x+\frac{1}{x}\right)\left(x^2+\frac{1}{x^2}\right)\left(x^4+\frac{1}{x^4}\right)=\left(x^2-\frac{1}{x^2}\right)\left(x^2+\frac{1}{x^2}\right)\left(x^4+\frac{1}{x^4}\right)$$

$$=\left[(x^2)^2-\left(\frac{1}{x^2}\right)^2\right]\left(x^4+\frac{1}{x^4}\right)=\left(x^4-\frac{1}{x^4}\right)\left(x^4+\frac{1}{x^4}\right)$$

$$=(x^4)^2-\left(\frac{1}{x^4}\right)^2$$

$$=x^8-\frac{1}{x^8}.$$

8. Factorize $x^8 - y^8$

Solution: $x^8 - y^8$

$$= (x^4)^2 - (y^4)^2$$

$$= (x^4 + y^4)(x^4 - y^4)$$

$$= (x^4 + y^4)\,[(x^2)^2 - (y^2)^2]$$

$$= (x^4 + y^4)(x^2 + y^2)(x^2 - y^2)$$
$$= (x^4 + y^4)(x^2 + y^2)(x - y)(x + y).$$

9. Prove that: $\dfrac{0.87 \times 0.87 \times 0.87 + 0.13 \times 0.13 \times 0.13}{0.87 \times 0.87 \times -0.87 \times 0.13 \times +0.13 \times 0.13} = 1$

Solution: $\dfrac{0.87 \times 0.87 \times 0.87 \times 0.13 \times 0.13 \times 0.13}{0.87 \times 0.87 \times -0.87 \times 0.13 \times +0.13 \times 0.13}$

Let $0.87 = a$ and $0.13 = b$

$$= \frac{a^3 + b^3}{a^2 - ab + b^2} = \frac{(a+b)(a^2 - ab + b^2)}{a^2 - ab + b^2}$$
$$= a + b = 0.87 + 0.13 = 1.0$$

10. If $p = 2 - a$, then find the value of $a^3 + 6ap + p^3 - 8$.

Solution: $p = 2 - a$

$$a + p - 2 = 0$$

Now, $a^3 + 6ap + p^3 - 8 = a^3 + p^3 + (-2)^3 - 3(a)(p)(-2)$

$$= (a + p - 2)(a^2 + p^2 + 4 - ap + 2p + 2a)$$
$$= (0)(a^2 + p^2 + 4 - ap + 2p + 2a) = 0.$$

ASSESSMENT CORNER

FIXED RESPONSE TYPE

Fill in the Blanks

1. $\sqrt{2}$ is a polynomial of degree ______.
2. The remainder obtained when the polynomial $p(x)$ is divided by $(b - ax)$ is ______.
3. The coefficient of x^2 in $(3x^2 - 5)(4 + 4x^2)$ is ______.
4. If $ax^2 + 2a^2x + b^3$ is divisible by $x + a$, then relationship between a and b is ______.
5. If $a^3 - 3a^2b + 3ab^2 - b^3$ is divided by $(a - b)$, then the remainder is ______.
6. The remainder when $1 + x + x^2 + x^3 + \ldots + x^{2006}$ is divided by $x - 1$ is ______.

True/False

1. If $\frac{p}{q} + \frac{q}{p} = 2$, the value of $\left(\frac{p}{q}\right)^{23} + \left(\frac{q}{p}\right)^{7}$ is 2
2. If $p(x) = 2x^3 - 3x^2 + 5x - 4$ is divided by $(x - 2)$, then the remainder is -10 ?
3. The co-efficient of x^2y^2 in the expansion of $(x + y)^4$ is 12
4. If $x^2 - 3x + 1 = 0$, then the value of $x^5 + \frac{1}{x^5}$ is 123
5. If $(x + 2)$, is a factor of $2x^3 - 5x + k$, then the value of k is 26

Single Correct Type Questions

Level 1

1. If $x^{51} + 51$ is divided by $(x + 1)$ the remainder is:
   (A) 0 (B) 1
   (C) 49 (D) 50
2. One of the factors of the expression $(2x - 3y)^2 - 7(2x - 3y) - 30$ is:
   (A) $2x - 3y - 10$ (B) $2x - 3y + 10$
   (C) $3x - 2y + 5$ (D) $6x - 4y - 15$
3. If $x + \frac{1}{x} = 3$, then the value of $x^6 + \frac{1}{x^6}$ is:
   (A) 927 (B) 114
   (C) 364 (D) 322
4. If $(a - 5)^2 + (b - c)^2 + (c - d)^2 + (b + c + d - 9)^2 = 0$, then the value of $(a + b + c)(b + c + d)$ is:
   (A) 0 (B) 11
   (C) 33 (D) 99
5. If $x + y + z = 1$, then $1 - 3x^2 - 3y^2 - 3z^2 + 2x^3 + 2y^3 + 2z^3$ is equal to:
   (A) $6xyz$ (B) $3xyz$
   (C) $2xyz$ (D) xyz
6. If $x + \frac{1}{x} = 4$, then the value of $x^6 + \frac{1}{x^6}$ is:
   (A) 927 (B) 114
   (C) 364 (D) 2702
7. If $(x + a)$ is a factor of $x^2 + px + q$ and $x^2 + mx + n$ then the value of a is:
   (A) $\frac{m-p}{n-q}$ (B) $\frac{n-q}{m-p}$
   (C) $\frac{n+q}{m+p}$ (D) $\frac{m+p}{n+q}$
8. If a, b, c are real and distinct numbers, then the value of $\frac{(a-b)^3 + (b-c)^3 + (c-a)^3}{(a-b).(b-c).(c-a)}$ is :
   (A) 1 (B) 2
   (C) 3 (D) 4
9. The value of p for which $x + p$ is a factor of $x^2 + px + 3 - p$ is:
   (A) 1 (B) -1
   (C) 3 (D) -3
10. Which of the following is a cubic polynomial.
    (A) $x^3 + 3x^2 - 4x + 3$ (B) $x^2 + 4x - 7$
    (C) $3x^2 + 4$ (D) $3(x^2 + x + 1)$
11. The product of $(x + a)(x + b)$ is:
    (A) $x^2 + (a + b)x + ab$
    (B) $x^2 - (a - b)x + ab$
    (C) $x^2 + (a - b)x + ab$
    (D) $x^2 + (a - b)x - ab$
12. The value of 150×98 is:
    (A) 10047 (B) 14800
    (C) 14700 (D) 10470
13. The expansion of $(x + y - z)^2$ is:
    (A) $x^2 + y^2 + z^2 + 2xy + 2yz + 2zx$
    (B) $x^2 + y^2 - z^2 - 2xy + yz + 2zx$
    (C) $x^2 + y^2 + z^2 + 2xy - 2yz - 2zx$
    (D) $x^2 + y^2 - z^2 + 2xy - 2yz - 2zx$

14. The value of $(x+2y+2z)^2+(x-2y-2z)^2$ is:
(A) $2x^2+8y^2+8z^2$
(B) $2x^2+8y^2+8z^2+8xyz$
(C) $2x^2+8y^2+8z^2-8yz$
(D) $2x^2+8y^2+8z^2+16yz$

15. The value of $25x^2 + 16y^2 + 40\ xy$ at $x = 1$ and $y=-1$ is:
(A) 81 (B) −49
(C) 1 (D) None of these

Level 2

16. On simplifying $(a+b)^3+(a-b)^3+6a(a^2-b^2)$ we get:
(A) $8a^2$ (B) $8a^2b$
(C) $8a^3b$ (D) $8a^3$

17. The factor of the polynomial $x^3+3x^2+4x+12$ is
(A) $x+3$ (B) $x-3$
(C) $x+2$ (D) $x-2$

18. If $(x+y+z)=1$, $xy+yz+zx=-1$, $xyz=-1$, then value of $x^3+y^3+z^3$ is:
(A) −1 (B) 1
(C) 2 (D) −2

19. The remainder when the polynomial $P(x) = x^4 - 3x^2 + 2x + 1$ is divided by $x - 1$ is
(A) 0 (B) 1
(C) 2 (D) 3

20. If $x^3 + y^3 + 1 = 3xy$, where $x \neq y$ determine the value of $x + y + 1$.

21. Factors of $(42-x-x^2)$ are:
(A) $(x-7)(x-6)$ (B) $(x+7)(x-6)$
(C) $(x+7)(6-x)$ (D) $(x+7)(x+6)$

22. Factors of $\left(x^2+\frac{x}{6}-\frac{1}{6}\right)$ are:
(A) $\frac{1}{6}(2x+1)(3x+1)$ (B) $\frac{1}{6}(2x+1)(3x-1)$
(C) $\frac{1}{6}(2x-1)(3x-1)$ (D) $(2x-1)(3x+1)$

23. The number of real roots of the equation, $(x-1)^2 + (x-2)^2 + (x-3)^2 = 0$ is :
(A) 0 (B) 1
(C) 2 (D) 3

24. One of the factors of the expression $(2a+5b)^3 + (2a-5b)^3$ would be:
(A) $4a$ (B) $10b$
(C) $2a+5b$ (D) $2a-5b$

25. If $(x-a)$ is a factor of $x^3 - a^2x + x + 2$, then 'a' is equal to
(A) 0 (B) 2
(C) −2 (D) 1

Multiple Correct Type Questions

1. The value of $\left(2x-\frac{y}{3}\right)^3$ is:
(A) $4x^2(2x+y)-y^3\left(\frac{1}{27}+\frac{2x}{3}\right)$
(B) $\left(2x-\frac{y}{3}\right)\left(4x^2+\frac{y^2}{9}-\frac{4xy}{3}\right)$
(C) $\left(2x-\frac{y}{3}\right)\left(4x^2+\frac{y^2}{9}+\frac{4x^2y^2}{9}\right)$
(D) $8x^3-\frac{y^3}{27}-2xy\left(2x-\frac{y}{3}\right)$

2. If $p=x^{1/3}+x^{-1/3}$, then p^3-3p is equal to:
(A) $\frac{1}{2}(x+x^{-1})$ (B) $(x+x^{-1})$
(C) $x^{-1}(x^2+1)$ (D) $2(x+x^{-1})$

3. If $x+y+z=0$, then $\frac{x^2}{yz}+\frac{y^2}{xz}+\frac{z^2}{xy}$ is:
(A) $3x^2y^2z^2$ (B) 3
(C) $3x^3y^3z^3$ (D) $x^o+y^o+z^o$

4. If (x^2-1) is a factor of $ax^4+bx^3+cx^2+dx+e$, then which of the following is: correct?
(A) $a+c+e=b+d$ (B) $a+b+e=c+d$
(C) $a+b+c+d+e=0$ (D) $a+c+e=0$

5. If $a+b+c=3x$ then the value of $(x-a)^3+(x-b)^3+(x-c)^3-3(x-a)(x-b)(x-c) =$
(A) abc (B) $3abc$
(C) 0 (D) $2abc$

6. Which two of the following can be factorised with integral coefficients?
(A) x^4+x^2+1 (B) x^4+2x+2
(C) x^4-2x^2+1 (D) $x^4=x+1$

7. P(x) is a polynomial with integral cofficient such that for four distinct integers a, b, c, d; P(a) = P(b) = P(c) = P(d) = 3. If P(e) = 5 (e is an integer), then e can't be
(A) 1 (B) 3
(C) 4 (D) 5

8. Evaluate:

$$\frac{(a-b)^2}{(b-c)(c-a)}+\frac{(b-c)^2}{(a-b)(c-a)}+\frac{(c-a)^2}{(a-b)(b-c)}.$$

(A) 0 (B) 1
(C) 2 (D) 3

9. If the remainder $R(x) = ax + b$ is obtained by dividing the polynomial x^{100} by the polynomial $x^2 - 3x + 2$ then
(A) $a = 2^{100} - 1$ (B) $b = 2(2^{99} - 1)$
(C) $b = -2(2^{99} - 1)$ (D) $a = 2^{100}$

10. If $x^2 + \frac{1}{x^2} = 38$, then the value of $x - \frac{1}{x}$ is:
(A) 6 (B) −6
(C) 0 (D) None of these

11. The simplest form of $(2x + 3)^3 - (2x - 3)^3$ is:
(A) $54 + 72x^2$ (B) $72 + 54x^2$
(C) $54 + 54x^2$ (D) None of these

12. $p(x) = \sqrt{3}x^2 + 11x + 6\sqrt{3}$ is same as:
(A) $(x+3\sqrt{3})(\sqrt{3}x+2)$ (B) $(x-3\sqrt{3})(\sqrt{3}x+2)$
(C) $(x-3\sqrt{3})(\sqrt{3}x-2)$ (D) $(x-3\sqrt{3})(\sqrt{3}x+2)$

13. Find the L.C.M. of the given polynomials $8(x^3 - x^2 + x)$ and $28(x^3 + 1)$.
(A) $8x(x^3 + 1)$ (B) $28x(x^3 + 1)$
(C) $56x(x^3 + 1)$ (D) $28(x^3 + 1)$

14. In the method of factorisation of an algebraic expression, which of the following statements is false?
(A) Taking out a common factor from two or more terms
(B) Taking out a common factor from a group of terms
(C) By using remainder theorem
(D) By using standard identities

15. Factors of $(a + b)^3 - (a - b)^3$ are
(A) $2ab(3a^2 + b^2)$ (B) $ab(3a^2 + b^2)$
(C) $2b(3a^2 + b^2)$ (D) $3a^2 + b^{20}$

16. If $x + y = -4$, then the value of $x^3 + y^3 - 12xy + 64$ will be:
(A) 0 (B) 128
(C) 64 (D) − 64

17. The value of $\left[\frac{a^2-5ab}{a^2-6ab+5b^2}\times\frac{a^2-b^2}{a^2+ab}\right]$ is:
(A) −1 (B) $\frac{a}{b}$
(C) $\frac{1}{a}$ (D) 1

18. If $x = \frac{1}{1+\sqrt{2}}$, then value of $x^2 + 2x + 3$ is:
(A) 3 (B) 0
(C) 4 (D) 1

19. If $x + \frac{1}{x} = 5$, then $x^3 - 5x^2 + x + \frac{1}{x^3} - \frac{5}{x^2} + \frac{1}{x} = \ldots$:
(A) − 5 (B) 0
(C) 5 (D) 10

20. If $x + y = 1$ then $x^3 + y^3 + 3xy = \ldots..$
(A) 0 (B) 1
(C) 2 (D) None of these

21. If $x - y = 5$, $xy = 24$ then the value of $x^3 + y^3$ will be:
(A) 23 (B) 539
(C) 65 (D) 74

22. If $x + \frac{1}{x} = 2$ then $\sqrt{x} + \frac{1}{\sqrt{x}}$ will be:
(A) 2 (B) 2
(C) $\sqrt{2} + 1$ (D) 1

23. If $x + y = 8$, $xy = 15$, the value of $x^2 + y^2$ will be:
(A) 32 (B) 34
(C) 36 (D) 38

24. If $p - q = -8$ and p.q. $= -12$ then the value of $p^3 - q^3$ is:
(A) 224 (B) −224
(C) 242 (D) −242

25. $(a + b + c)(ab + bc + ca) - abc$ is equal to the:
(A) $(a + b)(c + b)(c + a)$
(B) $(a - b)(b + c)(c + a)$
(C) $(a + b)(b - c)(c + a)$
(D) $(a + b)(b + c)(c - a)$

Match Type Questions

1. In Column-I polynomial is given and in Column-II root of the polynomial is given. Then match Column-I with Column-II accordingly

Column-I	Column-II
(i) $x^2 - x - 2$	(A) $x = 1$
(ii) $5x - 4x^2 + 6$	(B) $x = -1$
(iii) $3x^4 - 4x^3 - 3x + 4$	(C) $x = 2$
(iv) $x^3 + 1$	(D) $x = -2$

2. In Column-I polynomial is given and in Column-II factor of the polynomial is given. Then match Column-I with Column-II accordingly.

ASSESSMENT CORNER

Column-I	Column-II
(i) $x^3+6x^2+11x+6$	(A) $(x+1)$
(ii) $x^3+13x^2+32x+20$	(B) $(x+2)$
(iii) $2x^3-x^2-2x+1$	(C) $(x+3)$
(iv) $x^3-10x^2-53x-42$	(D) $(x-1)$

3. In Column-I polynomial is given and in Column-II name of the polynomial on the basis of degree and terms is given. Then match Column-I with Column-II accordingly

Column-I	Column-II
(i) $(x+1)^2-(x-1)^2$	(A) Quadratic
(ii) $x(x+5)=-x(3-x)+7$	(B) Linear
(iii) $x(x+y-z)-xy$	(C) Binomial
(iv) $\left(\sqrt{2x^2}-1\right)^2-3\sqrt{2x^2}$	(D) Monomial

4. In Column-I an algebraic expression is given and in Column-II factorization is given. Then match Column-I with Column-II accordingly.

Column-I	Column-II
(i) $a^3-\frac{1}{a^3}+4$	(A) $\left(a+\frac{1}{a}+1\right)\left(a^2+\frac{1}{a^2}-a-\frac{1}{a}\right)$
(ii) $a^3+\frac{1}{a^3}-2$	(B) $(a^2-a+3)(a^2+a+3)$
(iii) a^4+a^2+1	(C) $(a^2+a+1)(a^2-a+1)$
(iv) a^4+5a^2+9	(D) $\left(a-\frac{1}{a}+1\right)\left(a^2+\frac{1}{a^2}+\frac{1}{a}-a+2\right)$

5. Column-I [($p(x)$ = dividend, $g(x)$ = divisor)] Column-II (Remainder)

Column-I	Column-II
(i) $p(x)=2x^4-6x^3+2x^2-x+2, g(x)=x+2$	(A) 8
(ii) $p(x)=x^4-3x^2+4, g(x)=x-2$	(B) -3
(iii) $f(x)=9x^3-3x^2+x-5, g(x)=x-2/3$	(C) 92
(iv) $f(x)=x^3+4x^2-3x+10, g(x)=x+4$	(D) 22

Assertion and Reason Type Questions

Directions: In the following questions an Assertion (A) is given followed by a Reason (R). Mark your responses from the following options.

(A) Both Assertion and Reason are true and Reason is the correct explanation of 'Assertion'.
(B) Both Assertion and Reason are true and Reason is not the correct explanation of 'Assertion'.
(C) Assertion is true but Reason is false.
(D) Assertion is false but Reason is true.

1. $(x+1)$ is a factor of $f(-1)=0$
Assertion: $f(-1)$ is 0
Reason: $(x-a)$ is a factor of $f(x)$ if $f(a)=0$

2. $3y-5xy+7xy^2$ is a trinomial
Assertion: The number of terms in the given polynomial is 3.
Reason: A polynomial having two nonzero terms is called a binomial.

3. $3\sqrt{y}+4$ is not a polynomial.
Assertion: Given term does not contain the integral power of y.
Reason: An algebraic expression having only the non-negative integral power of y is called a polynomial.

Comprehension Type Questions

Comprehension 1: It is given that when polynomials $p(x) = x^3+ax^2+3x+2$ and $q(x)=2x^3+3x^2-4x-7$ are divided by $x-1$, the remainders obtained in each case are equal.

1. What is the value of 'a' for polynomial $p(x)$
(A) $a=12$ (B) $a=-12$
(C) $a=0$ (D) $a=6$

2. What should be subtracted from polynomial $p(x)$ so as to make the remainder zero.
(A) 8 (B) −8
(C) 6 (D) −6

3. If polynomial $p(x)+q(x)$ is divided by $x-1$, the remainder obtained is:
(A) 6 (B) 7
(C) −12 (D) 4

Numerical Type Questions

1. The remainder of $x^4+x^3-x^2+2x+3$ when divided by $x-3$ is:

2. If $x-3$ is a factor of x^3+3x^2+3x+p, then the value of p is:

3. The value of ax^2+bx+c when $x=0$ is 6. The remainder when divided by $x+1$ is 6. The remainder when divided by $x+2$ is 8. Then the sum of a, b and c is:

ASSESSMENT CORNER

ASSESSMENT CORNER

4. Find the number of positive integers x for which $f(x) = x^3 - 8x^2 + 20x - 13$, is a prime number.

5. If $ax^3 + 9x^2 + 4x - 1$ is divided by $(x + 2)$, the remainder is -6; then the value of 'a' is:

6. If $x + y + z = 10$, $x^2 + y^2 + z^2 = 60$, find $xy + yz + zx$

7. If $x^2 + \frac{1}{x^2} = 62$, then the value of $x^4 + \frac{1}{x^4}$ is:

8. The polynomials $P(x) = kx^3 + 3x^2 - 3$ and $Q(x) = 2x^3 - 5x + k$, when divided by $(x - 4)$ leave the same remainder. The value of k is

9. If $(x + y)^2 = 2(x^2 + y^2)$ and $(x - y + \lambda)^2 = 4$, $\lambda > 0$, then λ is equal to :

10. If $x^3 - (x + 1)^2 = 2001$ then the value of x is:

11. If the expressions $ax^3 + 3x^2 - 3$ and $2x^3 - 5x + a$, on dividing by $x - 4$ leave the same remainder, then the value of a is:

12. If the polynomial $x^6 + px^5 + qx^4 - x^2 - x - 3$ is divisible by $x^4 - 1$, then the value of $p^2 + q^2$ is:

13. What is the degree of the polynomial $\sqrt{3}$?

14. Find the coefficient of x in the expansion of $(x - 4)^2$.

15. If $x - 3$ is the factor of $ax^2 + 5x + 12$ find the value of a.

Higher Order Thinking Skills (HOTS)

1. If x, y, z are all different real numbers and

$$\frac{1}{(x-y)^2} + \frac{1}{(y-z)^2} + \frac{1}{(z-x)^2} = \left(\frac{1}{x-y} + \frac{1}{y-z} + \frac{1}{z-x}\right)^2 + \lambda$$

then the value of λ is :

(A) 0 (B) 1
(C) 2 (D) 3

2. If $(x - 2)$ is a common factor of $x^3 - 4x^2 + ax + b$ and $x^3 - ax^2 + bx + 8$, then the values of a and b are respectively:

(A) 3 and 5 (B) 2 and -4
(C) 4 and 0 (D) 0 and 4

3. Let $x = (2008)^{1004} + (2008)^{-1004}$ and $y = (2008)^{1004} - (2008)^{-1004}$ then the value of $(x^2 - y^2)$ is equal to:

(A) 4 (B) -4
(C) 0 (D) None

4. If $(a^2 + b^2)^3 = (a^3 + b^3)^2$ then $\frac{a}{b} + \frac{b}{a} =$

(A) $\frac{2}{3}$ (B) $\frac{3}{2}$
(C) $\frac{5}{6}$ (D) $\frac{6}{5}$

5. If $\frac{(\sqrt{a} - \sqrt{b})^2 + 4\sqrt{ab}}{a - b} = \frac{5}{3}$, then the value of $a : b$ is:

(A) 1 : 16 (B) 1 : 4
(C) 4 : 1 (D) 16 : 1

6. If the polynomial $P(x) = 2x^4 + x^3 - 5x^2 - x + 1$ is divided by the polynomial $Q(x) = x^2 - x$ then the remainder is a linear polynomial $R(x) = ax + b$. Then $(a + b)$ equals:

(A) -2 (B) -1
(C) 1 (D) 2

7. If $\frac{x^3 + x^2 + x + 1}{x^3 - x^2 + x - 1} = \frac{x^2 + x + 1}{x^2 - x + 1}$, then the number of real value of x satisfying are

(A) 0 (B) 1
(C) 2 (D) 3

8. If $2x^3 - 5x^2 + x + 2 = (x - 2)(ax^2 - bx - 1)$, then a & b are respectively:

(A) 2, 1 (B) 2, -1
(C) 1, 2 (D) -1, 1/2

9. Let $f(x)$ be a polynomial function. If $f(x)$ is divided by $x-1$, $x+1$ & $x+2$, then remainders are 5, 3 and 2 respectively. When $f(x)$ is divided by $x^3 + 2x^2 - x - 2$, then remainder is :

(A) $x - 4$ (B) $x + 4$
(C) $x - 2$ (D) $x + 2$

10. If $x = \sqrt{2 + \sqrt{2}}$, then $x^4 + \frac{4}{x^4}$ is:

(A) $2(3 - \sqrt{2})$ (B) $6\sqrt{2} - 2$
(C) $6 - \sqrt{2}$ (D) 12

11. The factors of $x^2 + xy - 2xz - 2yz$ are:

(A) $(x + y)(x + 2z)$
(B) $(x + y)(x - 2z)$
(C) $(x - y)(x - 2z)$
(D) $(x - y)(x + 2z)$

12. If $x = 3 + \sqrt{8}$ and $y = 3 - \sqrt{8}$ then $\frac{1}{x^2} + \frac{1}{y^2} =$

(A) -34 (B) 34
(C) $12\sqrt{8}$ (D) $-12\sqrt{8}$

13. How much does $-4x^2 - 3xy + 5y^2$ is less than $3x^2 - 9y^2 + 14xy$?
(A) $-7x^2 - 17xy + 14y^2$ (B) $-x^2 + 11xy - 4y^2$
(C) $7x^2 + 17xy - 14y^2$ (D) None of these

14. The polynomial $p(x) = 2x^4 - x^3 - 7x^2 + ax + b$ is divisible by $x^2 - 2x - 3$ for certain values of a and b. The value of $(a + b)$, is:
(A) −34 (B) −30
(C) −26 (D) −18

15. If $\frac{x}{y} + \frac{y}{x} = -1$, where $x \neq 0$, then the value of $(x^3 - y^3)$ is:
(A) 1 (B) −1
(C) 0 (D) $\frac{1}{2}$

16. The polynomials $ax^3 + 3x^2 - 3$ and $2x^3 - 5x + a$ when divided by $(x - 4)$ leave the remainder R_1 and R_2 respectively. Find the value of a if $R_1 + R_2 = 0$.
(A) $\frac{153}{65}$ (B) $\frac{-153}{65}$
(C) $\frac{135}{65}$ (D) $\frac{-135}{65}$

17. If $abx^2 = (a - b)^2 (x + 1)$, then the value of $1 + \frac{4}{x} + \frac{4}{x^2}$ is:
(A) $\left(\frac{a-b}{a+b}\right)^2$ (B) $\left(\frac{a+b}{a-b}\right)^2$
(C) $\left(\frac{a}{a+b}\right)^2$ (D) $\left(\frac{b}{a+b}\right)^2$

18. The value of $(s - a)^3 + (s - b)^3 + (s - c)^3 - 3(s - a)(s - b)(s - c)$, when $3s = a + b + c$, is _______.
(A) 0 (B) 1
(C) 2 (D) 3

19. If $a + b + c = 9$ and $ab + bc + ca = 26$, then the value of $a^3 + b^3 + c^3 - 3abc$ is:
(A) 8 (B) 27
(C) 64 (D) 216

20. The GCD of the polynomial $(3x - 5)(2x + 6)$ and $(3x - 5)(x + 8)$ is:
(A) $(2x + 6)$ (B) $(3x - 5)$
(C) $(x + 8)$ (D) $(x - 8)$

Free Response Type

Very Short Answer Type Questions

1. What is the degree of polynomial 2^5?

2. Simplify : $\frac{x}{x-y} - \frac{y}{x+y} - \frac{2xy}{x^2-y^2}$

3. If $p(x) = x^2 - 2\sqrt{2}x + 1$, then find the value of $p(2\sqrt{2})$

4. If $x^2 + kx + 6 = (x + 2)(x + 3)$ for all x, then find the value of k.

5. If $x + \frac{1}{x} = 2$, then $x^2 + \frac{1}{x^2}$ is equal to
(A) 0 (B) 1
(C) 2 (D) 3

6. If $\left(a + \frac{1}{a}\right)^2 = 3$, then $a^3 + \frac{1}{a^3}$ equals:
(A) 0 (B) $3\sqrt{3}$
(C) $7\sqrt{7}$ (D) $6\sqrt{3}$

7. If $49x^2 - b = \left(7x + \frac{1}{2}\right)\left(7x - \frac{1}{2}\right)$, then find the value of b.

8. If $a + b + c = 0$, then find the value of $a^3 + b^3 + c^3$.

9. If $x + 1$ is a factor of $ax^3 + x^2 - 2x + 4a - 9$, find the value of a.

10. Factorise:
(i) $x^2 + 9x + 18$ (ii) $6x^2 + 7x - 3$
(iii) $2x^2 - 7x - 15$ (iv) $84 - 2r - 2r^2$

Short Answer Type Questions

1. By actual division, find the quotient and the remainder when the first polynomial is divided by the second polynomial: $x^4 + 1; x - 1$

2. Show that:
(i) $x + 3$ is a factor of $69 + 11x - x^2 + x^3$.
(ii) $2x - 3$ is a factor of $x + 2x^3 - 9x^2 + 12$.

3. If $x = \sqrt{3} + \sqrt{2}$, then find $x + \frac{1}{x}$, $x^2 + \frac{1}{x^2}$, $x^3 + \frac{1}{x^3}$, $x^4 + \frac{1}{x^4}$

4. (i) Check whether $p(x)$ is a multiple of $g(x)$ or not, where $p(x) = x^3 - x + 1$, $g(x) = 2 - 3x$
(ii) Check whether $g(x)$ is a factor of $p(x)$ or not, where $p(x) = 8x^3 - 6x^2 - 4x + 3$, $g(x) = \frac{x}{3} - \frac{1}{4}$

ASSESSMENT CORNER

5. Find the value of a, if $x - a$ is a factor of $x^3 - ax^2 + 2x + a - 1$.

6. (i) Without actually calculating the cubes, find the value of $48^3 - 30^3 - 18^3$.
   (ii) Without finding the cubes, factorise $(x - y)^3 + (y - z)^3 + (z - x)^3$.

7. For the polynomial $\frac{x^3 + 2x + 1}{5} - \frac{7}{2}x^2 - x^6$, write
   (i) The degree of the polynomial
   (ii) The coefficient of x^3
   (iii) The coefficient of x^6
   (iv) The constant term

8. Give an example of a polynomial, which is:
   (i) Monomial of degree 1
   (ii) binomial of degree 20
   (iii) Trinomial of degree 2

9. If $a + b + c = 2$, $a^2 + b^2 + c^2 = 1$ and $abc = 3$ then $\frac{1}{a} + \frac{1}{b} + \frac{1}{c}$ is equal to
   (A) 0 (B) 1/2
   (C) 1 (D) 2

10. Without actually calculating the cubes, evaluate the expression $10^3 + (-8)^3 + (-2)^3$.

11. If $x - 3$ is the factor of $ax^2 + 5x + 12$ find the value of a.

12. Determine whether $x - 3$ is a factor of polynomial $p(x) = x^3 - 3x^2 + 4x - 12$.

Long Answer Type Questions

1. Factorise:
   (i) $a^3 - 8b^3 - 64c^3 - 24abc$
   (ii) $2\sqrt{2}a^3 + 8b^3 - 27c^3 + 18\sqrt{2}abc$.

2. Find the value of
   (i) $x^3 + y^3 - 12xy + 64$, when $x + y = -4$
   (ii) $x^3 - 8y^3 - 36xy - 216$, when $x = 2y + 6$

3. If $x + y = 12$ and $xy = 27$, find the value of $x^3 + y^3$.

4. If the polynomials $az^3 + 4z^2 + 3z - 4$ and $z^3 - 4z + a$, leave the same remainder when divided by $z - 3$, find the value of a.

5. Multiply $x^2 + 4y^2 + z^2 + 2xy + xz - 2yz$ by $(-z + x - 2y)$.

6. If $a + b + c = 5$ and $ab + bc + ca = 10$, then prove that $a^3 + b^3 + c^3 - 3abc = -25$.

7. Simplify $(2x - 5y)^3 - (2x + 5y)^3$.

8. Without actual division, prove that $2x^4 - 5x^3 + 2x^2 - x + 2$ is divisible by $x^2 - 3x + 2$.

ARCHIVE CORNER

1. If $(x - 2y)^6 = A_0x^6 - A_1x^5.y^1 + A_2x^4.y^2 - A_3x^3.y^3 + A_4x^2.y^4 - A_5x.y^5 + A_6y^6$, find the $A_0 - A_1 + A_2 - A_3 + A_4 - A_5 + A_6$.
(A) 0 (B) 2
(C) 1 (D) −3, 9

2. What must be added to $x^4 + 2x^3 - 2x^2 + x - 2$ so that the result is exactly divisible by x^2?
(A) $-x + 2$ (B) 3
(C) $x - 2$ (D) $4x - 3$

3. The expression $(a + b + c)^2 + (a + b - c)^2 + (a - b + c)^2 + (b + c - a)^2$ equals:
(A) $4(ab + bc + ca)$
(B) $2(a^2 + b^2 + c^2 + ab + bc + ca)$
(C) $4(a^2 + b^2 + c^2)$
(D) $(a^2 + b^2 + c^2)$

4. Remainder when $a^2 + b^2 + 2(ab + bc + ca)$ is divided by $(a + b + 2c)$ is:
(A) $a + b$ (B) ab
(C) $a - b$ (D) 0

5. If $2^x = 4^y = 8^z$ and $\left(\frac{1}{2x}+\frac{1}{4y}+\frac{1}{6z}\right)=\frac{24}{7}$, then the value of z is:
(A) $\frac{7}{16}$ (B) $\frac{7}{32}$
(C) $\frac{7}{48}$ (D) $\frac{7}{64}$

6. If $a - b = 3$, $a + b + x = 2$, then the value of $(a - b)[x^3 + 3(a + b)x^2 + 3x(a + b)^2 + (a + b)^3]$ is:
(A) 84 (B) 48
(C) 32 (D) 24

7. If $x = 2\sqrt{2} + \sqrt{7}$, identify the value of $\frac{1}{2}\left(x+\frac{1}{x}\right)$
(A) $2\sqrt{2} - \sqrt{7}$ (B) $\sqrt{7}$
(C) $2\sqrt{2}$ (D) $\sqrt{2} + \sqrt{7}$

8. Which among the options is one of the factors of $x^2 + \frac{x}{6} - \frac{1}{6}$?
(A) $3x + 1$ (B) $2x + 1$
(C) $x - \frac{1}{5}$ (D) $x - \frac{1}{2}$

9. If $x^2 + 2x = 45$, what is the value of $x^4 + 4x^3 + 4x^2 - 13$?
(A) 2013 (B) 1986
(C) 2012 (D) 32

10. Identify the zeros of the given polynomial. $p(z) = 4z^2 - 15z\pi - 4\pi^2$
(A) $4\pi, -\frac{\pi}{4}$ (B) $-4\pi, \frac{\pi}{4}$
(C) $4\pi, \frac{\pi}{4}$ (D) $-4\pi, \frac{\pi}{4}$

11. Identify the remainder when $1 + x + x^2 + x^3 + \dots + x^{2012}$ is divided by $x - 1$.
(A) 2012 (B) 1
(C) 2013 (D) 0

12. If p and q are the roots of the equation $x^2 + px + q$ then:
(A) $p = 1, q = 0$ (B) $p = 0, q = 1$
(C) $p = -2, q = 0$ (D) None of these

13. The degree of the polynomial
$3x^2 + 12 - \left(\sqrt{3} + \sqrt{12}\right)^2 + 12x + 4$ is:
(A) 1 (B) 2
(C) 4 (D) 0

14. Find the remainder when $2x^3 - 9x^2 + x + 12$ is divided by $2 + 3x$.
(A) 0 (B) $\frac{116}{9}$
(C) −2 (D) $\frac{182}{27}$

15. Find the numerical value of $A : B$ where
$A=\left(\frac{x^m}{x^n}\right)^{m+n-l}\times\left(\frac{x^n}{x^l}\right)^{n+l-m}\times\left(\frac{x^l}{x^m}\right)^{l+m-n}$ and
$B = (x^{1/a-b})^{1/a-c} \times (x^{1/b-c})^{1/b-a} \times (x^{1/c-a})^{1/c-b}$; a, b, c being all different
(A) 1 : 1 (B) 2 : 1
(C) 1 : 2 (D) 3 : 1

16. If $(x - 1)$, $(x + 1)$ and $(x - 2)$ are factors of $x^4 + (p - 3)x^3 - (3p - 5)x^2 + (2p - 9)x + 6$, then the value of p is:
(A) 1 (B) 2
(C) 3 (D) 4

17. $8(a - 2b)^2 - 2a + 4b - 1 =$
(A) $(2a - 4b - 1)(4a - 8b + 1)$
(B) $(2a + 4b + 1)(4a - 8b + 1)$
(C) $(2a - 4b - 1)(4a - 8b - 1)$
(D) $(2a + 4b - 1)(4a + 8b + 1)$

18. If $p = x + \frac{1}{x}$ then the value of $p - \frac{1}{p}$ will be:

(A) $3x$ (B) $\frac{3}{x}$

(C) $\frac{x^4 + x^2 + 1}{x^3 + x}$ (D) $\frac{x^4 + 3x^2 + 1}{x^3 + x}$

19. Factors of $\frac{1}{3}c^2 - 2c - 9$ are:

(A) $\left(\frac{1}{3}c + 3\right)(c + 3)$ (B) $\left(\frac{1}{3}c - 3\right)(c - 3)$

(C) $\left(\frac{1}{3}c - 3\right)(c + 3)$ (D) $\left(c - \frac{1}{3}\right)(3c + 1)$

20. If a polynomial $x^4 - 4x^2 + x^3 + 2x + 1$ is divided by $x - 1$, then remainder will be :

(A) 0 (B) 1
(C) 9 (D) –1

21. If $x^2 + 4y^2 + 9z^2 - 4xy - 12yz + 6xz = 0$, then:

(A) $x = 2y - 3z$ (B) $x = y - 3z$
(C) $2x = y - 3z$ (D) $x = 3y - 2z$

22. A polynomial which divided by $x + 2$, the quotient is $2x^2 - 3x + 1$ and the remainder is 5. The polynomial will be:

(A) $2x^3 + x^2 - 5x + 7$
(B) $2x^3 - x^2 + 5x + 7$
(C) $2x^3 + x^2 + 5x + 7$
(D) $2x^3 + x^2 - 5x - 7$

23. If $a^2 + b^2 = 234$ and $ab = 108$, find the value of $\frac{a+b}{a-b}$

(A) 10 (B) 8
(C) 5 (D) 4

24. Zero of the polynomial $p(x) = 2x + 1$ is:

(A) $-\frac{1}{2}$ (B) $\frac{1}{2}$

(C) 0 (D) ∞

25. Remainder on dividing polynomial $3x^2 - x^3 - 3x + 5$ by $x - 1 - x^2$ is:

(A) 7 (B) –3
(C) 0 (D) $2x + 5$

ARCHIVE CORNER

ANSWER KEY

Check Points

Check Point 1

1. (a) binomial (b) trinomial (c) binomial (d) monomial (e) trinomial (f) monomial (g) binomial (h) trinomial
2. (a) quadratic (b) cubic (c) linear (d) quadratic (e) cubic (f) cubic (g) linear
3. (a) $x = 2$ (b) $x = -\frac{1}{8}$ (c) $x = -1$ or 6 (d) $x = -\frac{1}{2}$ or -1
4. $q = 3x + 2, r = 10$
5. 37

Check Point 2

6. $4x^2 + 9y^2 + 4z^2 + 12\,xy - 12\,yz - 8\,xz$
7. 91
8. 23
9. 52

Check Point 3

11. $(xy + 5)\,(x^2 - 2y^2)$
12. $(x + 2)\,(3x + 2)$
13. $(2 - c)\,(a + 2b)$
14. $(3a - b + c)\,(9a^2 + b^2 + c^2 + 3ab + bc - 3ac)$
15. $4\,(2x - d)\,(4x^2 + 2xd + d^2)$

Assessment Corner

Fixed Response Type

Fill in the Blanks

1. Zero 2. $P(b/a)$ 3. -8 4. $a = b$ 5. 0 6. 2007

True/False

1. True 2. False 3. False 4. True 5. False

Single Correct Type Questions

1. D 2. A 3. D 4. D 5. A 6. D 7. B 8. C 9. C
10. A 11. A 12. C 13. C 14. D 15. C 16. D 17. A 18. B
19. B 20. 0 21. C 22. B 23. A 24. A 25. C

Multiple Correct Type Questions

1. BD 2. BC 3. BD 4. AC 5. C 6. AC 7. ABCD 8. D 9. AC
10. AB 11. A 12. A 13. C 14. C 15. C 16. A 17. D 18. C
19. B 20. B 21. B 22. B 23. B 24. B 25. A

Match Type Questions

1. (i)-(B, C), (ii)-(C), (iii)-(A), (iv)-(B)
2. (i)-(A, B, C), (ii)-(A, B), (iii)-(A, D), (iv)-(A, C)
3. (i)-(B, D), (ii)-(B, C), (iii)-(A, C), (iv)-(A)
4. (i)-(D), (ii)-(A), (iii)-(C), (iv)-(B)
5. (i)-(C), (ii)-(A), (iii)-(B), (iv)-(D)

Assertion and Reason Type Questions

1. A 2. B 3. A

Comprehension Type Questions

1. B 2. D 3. C

Numerical Type Questions

1. 108 2. −63 3. 8 4. 3 5. 33/8 6. 20 7. 3842 8. 1 9. 2
10. 13 11. 1 12. 10 13. 0 14. −8 15. −3

Higher Order Thinking Skills (HOTS)

1. A 2. C 3. A 4. A 5. D 6. A 7. A 8. A 9. B
10. D 11. B 12. B 13. C 14. A 15. C 16. B 17. B 18. A
19. B 20. B

Free Response Type

Very Short Answer Type Questions

1. 0 2. $\frac{x-y}{x+y}$ 3. 1 4. 5 5. C 6. A 7. ¼ 8. $3abc$
9. 2 10. (i) $(x+3)(x+6)$ (ii) $(3x-1)(2x+3)$ (iii) $(x-5)(2x+3)$ (iv) $-2(r+7)(r-6)$

Short Answer Type Questions

1. Remainder = 2 & Quotient = x^3+x^2+x+1
2. (i) 0 (ii) 0
3. $2\sqrt{3}$, 10, $18\sqrt{3}$, 98
4. (i) Not a factor (ii) Yes $g(x)$ is a factor of $f(x)$
5. 1/3
6. (i) 7760 (ii) $3(x-y)(y-z)(z-x)$
7. (i) 6 (ii) 1/5 (iii) −1 (iv) 1/5
8. (i) $2x$ (ii) $x^{20}-20x$ (iii) $x^2+5x+12$
9. B 10. 480 11. −3 12. Yes

Long Answer Type Questions

2. (i) 0 (ii) 0 3. 756 4. −1 7. $(10y)(12x^2+25y^2)$

Archive Corner

1. C 2. A 3. C 4. D 5. C 6. B 7. C 8. B 9. C
10. A 11. C 12. D 13. B 14. D 15. A 16. D 17. A 18. C
19. C 20. B 21. A 22. B 23. C 24. A 25. B

ANSWER KEY

CHAPTER 3

Coordinate Geometry

Learning Outcomes

After reading this chapter, you would be able to:

- understand introduction to coordinate systems.
- explain co-ordinates of a point.
- describe points on axes.
- understand plotting the points.

Geekspeak

- Coordinate axis
- X-axis
- Y-axis
- Rectangular axis
- Coordinate
- Ordinates
- Abscissa
- Quadrant

Introduction

For describing the position of a point in a plane, the branch of mathematics which is used to know as co-ordinate geometry, inverted by Rene Descartes.

A pair of two numbers x and y listed in a specific order, is called an ordered pair (x, y) where x at the first place and y at the second place such that $(x, y) \neq (y, x)$.

Coordinate Geometry

Coordinate geometry, also known as analytic geometry, is a branch of mathematics that uses a coordinate system to define geometric figures and analyze their properties.

Co-ordinate System

Two-dimensional coordinate geometries commonly use two types of coordinate systems.

- **Cartesian or Rectangular co-ordinate system:** In Cartesian co-ordinate system we represent any point by **ordered pair (x, y)**, where x and y are called X and Y co-ordinates of that point respectively.
- **Polar co-ordinate system:** In polar co-ordinate system, we represent any point by ordered pair **(r, θ)** where **'r'** is called **radius vector** and 'θ' is called **vectorial angle** of that point.

Rectangular Coordinates

Take two perpendicular lines $X'OX$ and $Y'OY$ intersecting at the point O. $X'OX$ and $Y'OY$ are called the coordinate axes. $X'OX$ is called the **X-axis**, $Y'OY$ is called the **Y-axis** and O is called the origin. Lines $X'OX$ and $Y'OY$ are also called rectangular axes.

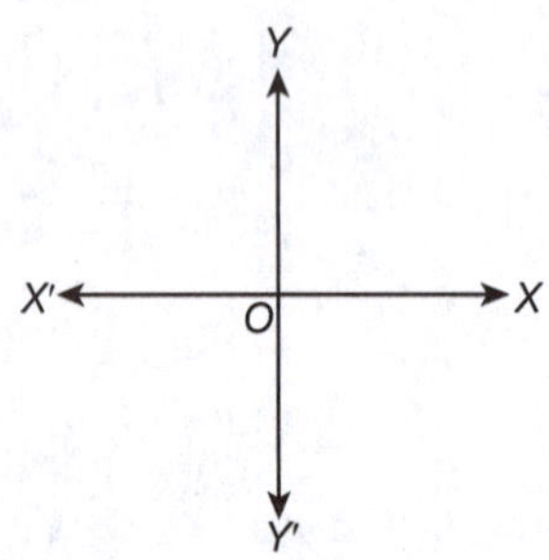

Figure 3.1

Co-ordinates of a Point

Let P be any point as shown in the figure. Draw PL and PM perpendiculars on **Y-axis** and **X-axis**, respectively.

The algebraic length LP **(or OM)** is called x-**coordinate** or the **abscissa of point P** and MP is called the **y-coordinate** or the **ordinate of point P**. A point whose abscissa is x and ordinate is y is named as the point **(x, y) or $P(x, y)$**.

The two lines $X'OX$ and $Y'OY$ divide the plane into four parts called **quadrants.** XOY, YOX', $X'OY$. and $Y'OX$ are, respectively, called the first, second, third and fourth quadrants. The following table 3.1 shows the signs of the coordinates of points situated in different quadrants:

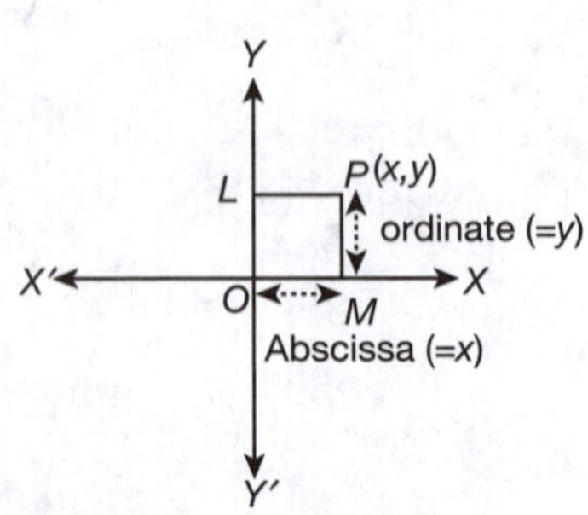

Figure 3.2

Table 3.1 Signs of the Coordinates of Points Situated in Different Quadrants

Quadrant	*x*-coordinate	*y*-coordinate	Point
First quadrant	+	+	(+, +)
Second quadrant	–	+	(–, +)
Third quadrant	–	–	(–, –)
Fourth quadrant	+	–	(+, –)

Competition Corner

Abscissa is the algebraic perpendicular distance of a point from **y-axis**. (i.e., positive to the right of **y-axis** or negative to the left of **y-axis**)

Ordinate is positive above **x-axis** or negative below **x-axis**.
Abscissa of any point on **y-axis** is zero.
Ordinate of any point on **x-axis** is zero.
Co-ordinates of the **origin** are **(0, 0)**.

Points on Axes

If point *P* lies on **X-axis** then clearly its distance from **X-axis** will be **zero**, therefore we can say that its **Y-coordinate** will be **zero**. Similarly, if any point *Q* lies on **Y-axis**, then its distance from **Y-axis** will be **zero** therefore we can say its **X-coordinate** will be **zero**.

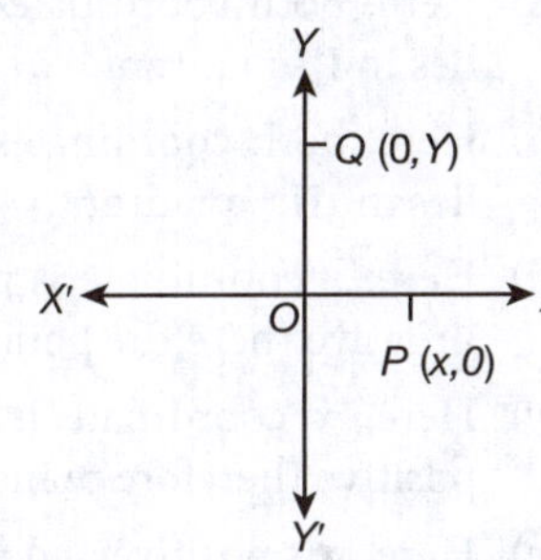

Figure 3.3

Plotting the Points

In order to plot the points in a plane, we may use the following algorithm.

Step I: Draw two mutually perpendicular lines on the graph paper, one horizontal and the other vertical.
Step II: Mark their intersection point as **O** (origin).
Step III: Choose a suitable scale on **X-axis** and **Y-axis** and mark the points on both axes.
Step IV: Obtain the coordinates of the point which is to be plotted. Let the point be **P(*a*, *b*)**. To plot this point start from the origin and move **'*a*'** units along *X*-axis or ***OX***. According to position of point **'*a*'** is positive or negative respectively.

Suppose we arrive at point ***M***. From point ***M*** moving vertically upward or downward **'*b*'** through units according to **'*b*'** is positive or negative. The point where we arrive finally is the required point ***P* (*a*, *b*)**.

Illustration 3.1

Plot the point (3, 4) on a graph paper.

Solution: Let *X.OX* and *Y.OY* be the coordinate axis. Here given point is *P*(3, 4), first we move 3 units along *OX* as 3 is positive then we arrive at point *M*. Now from *M* we move vertically upward as 4 is positive. Then we arrive at *P*(3, 4).

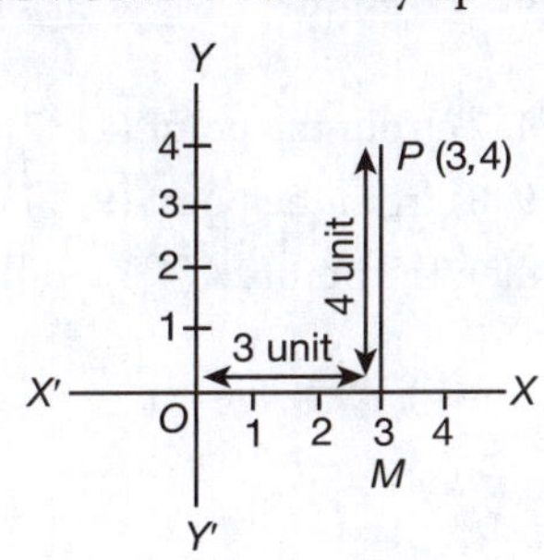

Illustration 3.2

Write the quadrants for the following points.

(i) A (3, 4) **(ii)** B (–2, 3) **(iii)** C (–5, –2) **(iv)** D (4, –3) **(v)** E (–5, –5)

Solution:

(i) Here, both coordinates are positive therefore point A lies in I[st] quadrant.
(ii) Here, x is negative and y is positive therefore point B lies in IInd quadrant.
(iii) Here, both coordinates are negative therefore point C lies in IIIrd quadrant.
(iv) Here, x is positive and y is negative therefore point D lies in IVth quadrant.
(v) Here, both coordinates are negative therefore point E lies in IIIrd quadrant.

Illustration 3.3

Plot the following points on the graph paper and also specify the quadrants or co-ordinate axes in which they lie:

(i) A (2, 5) **(ii)** B (–5, –7) **(iii)** C (3, –2) **(iv)** D (0, 5) **(v)** E (5, 0)

Solution:

Let XOX and YOY be the coordinate axis. Then the given points may be plotted as given below:

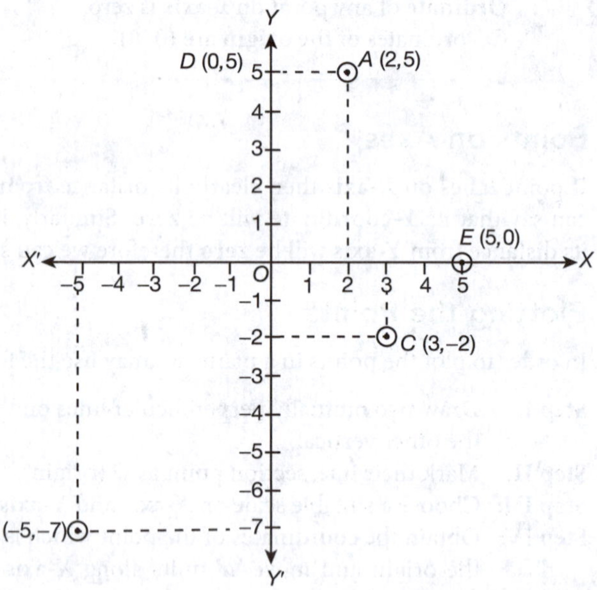

(i) Here, both coordinates are positive therefore point A lies in I[st] quadrant.
(ii) Here, both coordinates are negative therefore point B lies in IIIrd quadrant.
(iii) Here, x coordinate is positive and the y coordinate is negative therefore point C lies in the quadrant.
(iv) Here, x coordinate is zero and the y coordinate is positive therefore point D lies on the positive y-axis.
(v) Here, x is positive and y is zero therefore point E lies on the positive x-axis.

Check Point 1

1. Write down the quadrants in which the following points lie.
   (a) (3, –7) (b) (–3, 7) (c) (–2, –9) (d) (6, 0) (e) (–2, 0) (f) (0, 8) (g) (4, 7)
2. What is the distance of the point (8, 3) from the
   (i) x-axis? (ii) y-axis?
3. What is the distance of the point (4, 7) from the point (11, 7)?
4. What is the distance of the point (9, 8) from the point (9, –1)
5. What will be the figure obtained when the points A(4, 3), B(4, –3), C(–2, –3) and D(–2, 3) are connected in order? Plot the points.

STRUCTURAL OUTLINE

Coordinate Geometry

Co-ordinates of a Point

Abscissa is the algebraic perpendicular distance of a point from **y-axis**. (i.e., positive to the right of **y-axis** or negative to the left of **y-axis**)

Ordinate is positive above **x-axis** or negative below **x-axis**.

Abscissa of any point on **y-axis** is zero.

Ordinate of any point on **x-axis** is zero.

Co-ordinates of the **origin** are **(0, 0)**.

Rectangular Coordinates

Take two perpendicular lines **X'OX** and **Y'OY** intersecting at the point **O. X'OX** and **Y'OY** are called the coordinate axes. **X'OX** is called the **X-axis**, **Y'OY** is called the **Y-axis** and **O** is called the origin. Lines **X'OX** and **Y'OY** are also called rectangular axes.

Co-ordinate system

(i) Cartesian or Rectangular co-ordinate system : In Cartesian co-ordinate system we represent any point by **ordered pair (x, y)**, where **x** and **y** are called **x** and **y** co-ordinate of that point respectively.

(ii) Polar co-ordinate system : Inpolar co-ordinate system we represent any point by ordered pair **(r, θ)** where **'r'** is called **radius vector** and 'θ' is called **vectorial angle** of that point.

ASSESSMENT CORNER

Fixed Response Type

Fill in the Blanks

1. Point (–5, 8) lies in ______ quadrant.
2. ______ are the signs of the abscissa and ordinate of a point in the second quadrant.
3. Abscissa of all the points on the *y*-axis is ______.
4. In ______ quadrant of a point whose both the coordinates are negative.
5. If *x* coordinate of a point is zero, then this point always lies in ______.

True/False

1. If the coordinates of the two points are *P* (–2, 3) and Q(–3, 5), then find (abscissa of *P*) – (abscissa of Q) is 1.
2. The points whose abscissa and ordinate have different signs will lie in the second quadrant.
3. (0, 4) is the point whose ordinate is 4 and which lies on the *y*-axis.
4. 4 is the perpendicular distance of the point *P*(3, 4) from the *y*-axis.

Single Correct Type Questions

1. The abscissa of a point is the distance of that point from:
   (A) *X*-axis (B) *Y*-axis
   (C) Origin (D) None of these
2. Abscissa of a point is positive in:
   (A) 1st and 2nd Quadrant
   (B) 1st and 3rd Quadrant
   (C) 2nd and 3rd Quadrant
   (D) 1st and 4th Quadrant
3. If both co-ordinates of any point are negative then that point will lie in:
   (A) First quadrant
   (B) Second quadrant
   (C) Third quadrant
   (D) Fourth quadrant
4. If the abscissa of any point is zero then that point will lie:
   (A) on *X*-axis (B) on *Y*-axis
   (C) at origin (D) None of these
5. The distance of the point (3, 5) from the *X*-axis is:
   (A) $\sqrt{34}$ (B) 3
   (C) 5 (D) None of these
6. Position of point (–6, 0) on graph paper is:
   (A) *OY′*
   (B) *OX′*
   (C) in the second quadrant
   (D) in the fourth quadrant
7. Points (1, -1), (3, -2), (5, -5), (3, -4)
   (A) lie in II quadrant
   (B) lie in III quadrant
   (C) lie in IV quadrant
   (D) Does not lie in the same quadrant
8. The points (–5, 2) and (2, –5) lie in the:
   (A) same quadrants
   (B) II and III quadrants respectively
   (C) II and IV quadrants respectively
   (D) IV and III quadrants respectively
9. Which of the following points lie on the negative side of the *x*-axis?
   (A) (–4, 0) (B) (–3, 2)
   (C) (0, –4) (D) (5, –7)
10. Ordinate of a point is negative in:
    (A) III and IV quadrants
    (B) III quadrant only
    (C) II and III quadrants
    (D) IV quadrant only
11. If *x* coordinate of a point is zero, then the point lies on:
    (A) First quadrant (B) Second quadrant
    (C) X-axis (D) Y-axis
12. If coordinates of point *P* are (*x*, *y*) such that $x < 0$, $y = 0$, then *P* lies on:
    (A) positive *x*-axis (B) positive *y*-axis
    (C) negative *y*-axis (D) negative *x*-axis
13. To find the abscissa of a point in the first quadrant, which of the given steps is correct:
    (A) Join the point with the *x*-axis
    (B) Draw perpendicular on the *x*-axis from the point.
    (C) Find the perpendicular distance of that point with the *y*-axis.
    (D) None of these

14. To locate a point $(-a, -b)$ in the third quadrant if $a > 0, b > 0$.
    (A) Move only in the negative direction of the x-axis.
    (B) Move 'a' units in the negative direction of the x-axis then b units vertically downward in the negative direction of the y-axis parallel to the y-axis.
    (C) Move 'b' units along the x-axis
    (D) None of these.

15. Signs of the abscissa and ordinate of a point in the second quadrant are respectively
    (A) +, +   (B) +, –
    (C) –, +   (D) –, –

Multiple Correct Type Questions

1. The points in which abscissa and ordinate have different signs will lie in
   (A) I and II quadrants
   (B) II and III quadrants
   (C) I and III quadrants
   (D) II and IV quadrants
2. Mark the correct answer:
   (A) Any point in the second quadrant can be written in the form $(-x, y)$ for all x, y
   (B) Any point in the third quadrant can be written in the form $(-x, -y)$ for all x, y
   (C) Any point in the fourth quadrant can be written in the form $(x, -y)$ for all x, y
   (D) Any point in the first quadrant can be written in the form (x, y), where $x > 0, y > 0$.
3. Which of the points $P(0, 3)$, $Q(1, 0)$, $R(0, -1)$, $S(-5, 0)$ and $T(1, 2)$ do not lie on the X-axis?
   (A) P and R only   (B) Q and S
   (C) P, R and T (D) Q, S and T
4. The distance between the points A $(C, 0)$ and B $(0, -C)$ is:
   (A) $\sqrt{2C}$ (B) $\sqrt{2}C$
   (C) $\sqrt{2C^2}$ (D) $2C^2$
5. If the perpendicular distance of a point P from the X-axis is 5 units and the foot of the perpendicular lies in the negative direction of the X-axis, then the point P has:
   (A) x co-ordinate = –5
   (B) y co-ordinate = 5 only 16.
   (C) y co-ordinate = –5 only
   (D) y co-ordinate = 5 or –5.
6. If the coordinates of point A are (a, b) with $ab > 0$, then A lies in:
   (A) I quadrant   (B) II quadrant
   (C) III quadrant   (D) IV quadrant
7. Which of the following statements is/are correct?
   (A) The coordinate axes are mutually perpendicular to each other.
   (B) The y-axis is also called ordinate.
   (C) The point of intersection of the x-axis and y-axis is called origin.
   (D) The x-axis is also called abscissa.
8. The perpendicular distance of point $P(x, y)$ from y-axis is known as:
   (A) x coordinate   (B) ordinate
   (C) y-coordinate   (D) abscissa
9. The perpendicular distance of point $P(x, y)$ from x-axis is known as:
   (A) x-coordinate   (B) abscissa
   (C) ordinate   (D) y-coordinate

Match Type Questions

Direction: Column-I and Column-II contain four entries each. Entries of Column-I are to be matched with some entries of Column-II. Only one entry of Column-I may have the matching with the one entry of Column-II and one entry of Column-II may have only one matching with one entry of Column-I

1.

Column-I [Point (x, y)]	Column-II [Point (x, y) lines in]
(i) $x > 0, y > 0$	(P) Q_2
(ii) $x < 0, y > 0$	(Q) Q_1
(iii) $x < 0, y < 0$	(R) Q_4
(iv) $x > 0, y < 0$	(S) Q_3

2.

Column-I [Point (x, y)]	Column-II [Point (x, y) lines on]
(i) $x > 0, y = 0$	(P) –ve x-axis
(ii) $x < 0, y = 0$	(Q) –ve y-axis
(iii) $x = 0, y < 0$	(R) +ve y-axis
(iv) $x = 0, y > 0$	(S) +ve x-axis

3.

Column-I [Point $P(a, b)$]	Column-II (Quadrant)
(i) $a > 0, b \geq 0$	(P) III quadrant
(ii) $a < 0, b < 0$	(Q) I quadrant
(iii) $a > 0, b = 0$	(R) Positive x-axis
(iv) $a < 0, b \leq 0$	(S) Negative x-axis

ASSESSMENT CORNER

Assertion and Reason Type Questions

Directions: In the following questions as Assertion (A) is given followed by a Reason (R). Mark your responses from the following options.

(A) Both Assertion and Reason are true and Reason is the correct explanation of 'Assertion'.

(B) Both Assertion and Reason are true and Reason is not the correct explanation of 'Assertion'.

(C) Assertion is true but Reason is false.

(D) Assertion is false but Reason is true.

1. **Assertion:** Point $P(-2, 3)$ is at a distance of 3 units from x-axis.
   Reason: Ordinate gives the perpendicular distance of point from the x-axis.
2. **Assertion:** The distance of point $R(3, 4)$ from origin is 3 units.
   Reason: The distance between two points is given by $\sqrt{(x_2 - x_1)^2 + (y_2 - y_1)^2}$

Comprehension Type Questions

Comprehension 1: Plot the points $A(-2, 0)$ $B(2, 0)$, $C(2, 2)$, $D(0, 4)$, $E(-2, 2)$ on the graph paper and join them in order.

Now answer the following questions according to the figure obtained.

1. What is the figure obtained by joining the points $ABCDE$?
   (A) Square
   (B) Rectangle
   (C) Triangle
   (D) Pentagon
2. What is the area of the figure so formed?
   (A) 12 sq. units (B) 8 sq. units
   (C) 4 sq. units (D) 2 sq. units
3. What is the distance of point E from x-axis?
   (A) −2 units (B) 4 units
   (C) −4 units (D) 2 units

Numerical Type Questions

1. If the co-ordinates of the two points are $P(-2, 3)$ and $Q(-3, 5)$, then (abscissa of P) −(abscissa of Q) is:
2. The perpendicular distance of the point P (3, 4) from the Y-axis is:
3. The area of the triangle formed by joining the points (1, 0), (0, 0) and (0, 1) is:
4. The distance between the points $\left(\frac{-8}{5}, 2\right)$ and $\left(\frac{2}{5}, 2\right)$ is:
5. The perimeter of the triangle formed by the points (0, 0), (1, 0) and (0, 1) is:
   (A) $1 \pm \sqrt{2}$ (B) $\sqrt{2} + 1$
   (C) 3 (D) $2 + \sqrt{2}$
6. The point (2, 3) is at a distance of what units from x-axis:
7. Ordinate of all the points on the x-axis is
8. The point (4, 3) is at a distance of what units from origin:

Higher Order Thinking Skills (HOTS)

1. Points (1, -1), (2, -2), (4, -5), (-3, -4)
   (A) lie in II quadrant
   (B) lie in III quadrant
   (C) lie in IV quadrant
   (D) Does not lie in the same quadrant
2. Point (10, −7) lies
   (A) First quadrant
   (B) Third quadrant
   (C) Second quadrant
   (D) Fourth quadrant
3. The point of intersection of horizontal and vertical lines determining the position of a point in a cartesian plane is called:
   (A) Origin (B) X-axis
   (C) Y-axis (D) Quadrants

Free Response Type

Very Short Answer Type Questions

1. Point (−3, 5) lies in which quadrant?
2. What are the signs of the abscissa and ordinate of a point in the second quadrant?
3. The abscissa of a point is distance of that point from
   (A) x-axis (B) y-axis
   (C) Origin (D) None of these
4. Find the quadrant of a point whose both coordinates are negative.

5. If the y coordinate of a point is zero, then this point always lies?

6. If $P(-1, 1)$, $Q(3, -4)$, $R(1, -1)$, $S(-2, -3)$ and $T(-4, 4)$ are plotted on the graph paper, then find the point(s) which lies in the fourth quadrant?

7. The point (4, 2) is at a distance of __________ units from y-axis

8. The points whose abscissa and ordinate have different signs will lie in which quadrant?

9. Find the point whose ordinate is 4 and which lies on the y-axis?

10. Find the perpendicular distance of the point $P(3, 4)$ from the y-axis?

Short Answer Type Questions

1. Plot the point $P(-6, 2)$ and from it draw PM and PN as perpendiculars to the x-axis and y-axis, respectively.
   Write the coordinates of the points M and N.

2. Plot the following points and write the name of the figure obtained by joining them in order: $P(-3, 2)$, $Q(-7, -3)$, $R(6, -3)$, $S(2, 2)$

3. Plot the points (x, y) given by the following table:

x	2	4	−3	−2	3	0
y	4	2	0	5	−3	0

4. Plot the following points and check whether they are collinear or not:
   (i) (1, 3), (−1, −1), (−2, −3)
   (ii) (1, 1), (2, −3), (−1, −2)
   (iii) (0, 0), (2, 2), (5, 5)

5. If we join the points (−2, 0), (0, 1), (2, 0) and (0, −1) then name of the figure formed is:
   (A) square (B) rectangle
   (C) rhombus (D) parallelogram

6. Which of the following points lie on the y-axis? $A(1, 1)$, $B(1, 0)$, $C(0, 1)$, $D(0, 0)$, $E(0, -1)$, $F(-1, 0)$, $G(0, 5)$, $H(-7, 0)$, $I(3, 3)$.

7. Which of the points P(0, 3), Q(1, 0), R(0, −1), S(−5, 0) and T(1, 2) do not lie on the x-axis?

8. If the co-ordinates of the two points are P(−2, 3) and Q(−4, 5), then (abscissa of P)−(abscissa of Q) is

9. Taking 0.5 cm as 1 unit, plot the following points on the graph paper:
   $A(1, 3)$, $B(-3, -1)$, $C(1, -4)$, $D(-2, 3)$, $E(0, -8)$, $F(1, 0)$

10. Write the coordinates of the vertices of a rectangle whose length and breadth are 5 and 3 units respectively, one vertex at the origin, the longer side lying on the x-axis and one of the vertices lying in the third quadrant.

11. Plot the points $P(1, 0)$, $Q(4, 0)$ and $S(1, 3)$. Find the coordinates of the point R such that $PQRS$ is a square.

12. Three vertices of a rectangle are (3, 2), (−4, 2) and (−4, 5). Plot these points and find the coordinates of the fourth vertex.

Long Answer Type Questions

1. Plot the points in the plane if their co-ordinates are given as $A(5, 0)$, $B(0, 3)$, $C(7, 2)$, $D(-4, 3)$, $E(-3, -2)$ and $F(3, -2)$. Also, find the quadrant or co-ordinate axes on which they lie.

2. Plot the following pairs of numbers as points in the Cartesian plane.
   (4, 8), (8, 35), (−3, 5), (−2.5 ,0), (−5, 1), (0, −2)

3. Plot the points and find out the quadrants or axis on which the following point lies:
   (i) $P(-7, 6)$ (ii) $Q(0, 5.5)$
   (iii) $R\left(-\frac{3}{2}, -2.5\right)$ (iv) $S(6, -9)$

4. In the figure given below, determine:

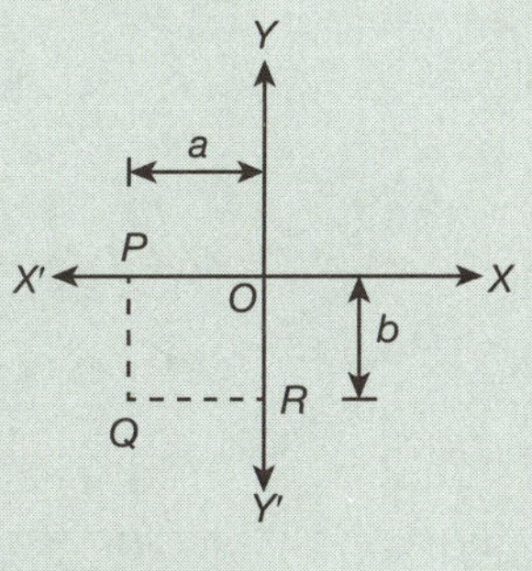

   (i) Abscissa of point Q
   (ii) Ordinate of point Q
   (iii) Coordinate of point Q

5. Write the coordinates of a point.
   (a) above the x-axis, lying on the y-axis and at a distance of 6 units.
   (b) lying on the x-axis to the left of the origin and at a distance of 3 units.

ARCHIVE CORNER

1. The foot of the perpendicular from $P(-3, 2)$ to the Y-axis is M. Co-ordinates of M are _______.
   (A) (3, 0) (B) (0, 2)
   (C) $\left(\frac{3}{2}, -1\right)$ (D) (–3, 2)

2. Number of straight lines passing through the point (1, 2) is:
   (A) 1 (B) 2
   (C) 3 (D) ∞

3. The distance of the point $P(-6, 8)$ from the origin is:
   (A) 8 (B) 10
   (C) $2\sqrt{2}$ (D) 6

ANSWER KEY

CHECK POINTS

Check Point 1

1. (a) IV quadrant (b) II quadrant (c) III quadrant (d) on positive x axis
   (e) on Negative x axis (f) on Positive y axis (g) I quadrant
2. (i) 3 (ii) 8
3. 7
4. 20
5. Rectangle

Assessment Corner

FIXED RESPONSE TYPE

Fill in the Blanks

1. 2 2. –, + 3. 0 4. 3 5. y-axis

True/False

1. True 2. True 3. True 4. False

Single Correct Type Questions

1. B 2. D 3. C 4. B 5. C 6. B 7. C 8. C 9. A
10. A 11. D 12. D 13. C 14. B 15. C

Multiple Correct Type Questions

1. D 2. D 3. AC 4. B 5. D 6. AC 7. ABCD 8. AD 9. CD

Match Type Questions

1. (i)-Q; (ii)-P; (iii)-S; (iv)-R
2. (i)-S; (ii)-P; (iii)-Q; (iv)-R
3. (i)-Q, R; (ii)-P; (iii)-R; (iv)-P, S

Assertion and Reason Type Questions

1. A 2. D

Comprehension Type Questions

1. D 2. A 3. D

Numerical Type Questions

1. 1 2. 3 3. 1/2 4. 2 5. $2+\sqrt{2}$ 6. 3 units 7. 0 8. 5 units

Higher Order Thinking Skills (HOTS)

1. **D** 2. D 3. D

FREE RESPONSE TYPE

Very Short Answer Type Questions

1. II
2. –ve and +ve
3. B
4. III
5. On X axis
6. P-(II), Q-(IV), R-(IV), S-(III) and T-(II)
7. 4
8. II or IV
9. (0, 4)
10. 3

Short Answer Type Questions

1. *M* (–6, 0), *N* (0, 2)
2. Let *X′OX* and *Y′OY* be the coordinate axes. *PQRS* is trapezium
4. (i, iii)
5. (C)
6. C(0, 1), D(0, 0), E(0, –1), F(0, 5)
7. P, R and T
8. 2
10. D(0, 0), A(–5, 0), C(0, –3) & B(–5, –3)
11. (4, 3)
12. (3, 5)

Long Answer Type Questions

1.

Point	(5, 3)	(0, 3)	(7, 2)	(–4, 3)	(–3, –2)	(3, –2)
Location	I quadrant	Y axis	I Quadrant	II Quadrant	III Quadrant	IV Quadrant

4. (i) $-a$ (ii) $-b$ (iii) $(-a, -b)$
5. (a) (0, 6) (b) (–3, 0)

Archive Corner

1. B
2. D
3. B

ANSWER KEY

CHAPTER 4

Linear Equations

Learning Outcomes

After reading this chapter, you would be able to:

- various forms of linear equation in two variables.
- solution of linear equation in variables.
- graph of linear equation in two variables.

Geekspeak

- Linear equation
- Variables
- Solution
- Infinite
- Graphical method

Introduction

In earlier classes, we have learnt that a linear equation in one variable x is an equation of the form $ax + b = 0$, where a, b are real numbers such that $a \neq 0$. The value of the variable which satisfies a given linear equation is known as its solution. The solution of a linear equation is also known as its root. If $ax - b = 0$ is a linear equation, then $x = \frac{b}{a}$ is its solution or root. In this section, we shall introduce the notion of a linear equation in two variables, x and y.

Linear Equations

A linear equation is an algebraic equation in which the highest power of the variable(s) is one. These equations describe straight lines when graphed on a coordinate plane.

Linear Equation in One Variable

An equation of the form $\boldsymbol{ax + b = 0}$ where $\boldsymbol{a}$ and $\boldsymbol{b}$ are real numbers, $a \neq 0$ and **'x'** is a variable, is called a **linear equation in one variable**. Here **'a'** is called **coefficient** of x and **'b'** is called a **constant term**. i.e., $3x + 5 = 0$, $7x - 2 = 0$, etc.

Linear Equation in Two Variables

An equation of the form $Ax + By + C = 0$ is called a linear equation.

Where A is called coefficient of x, B is called coefficient of y and C is the constant term (free from x and y).

$A, B, C \in R$ [$\in \rightarrow$ belongs to, $R \rightarrow$ Real No.]

But A and B cannot be simultaneously zero.

If $A \neq 0$, $B = 0$, the equation will be of the form $Ax + C = 0$. [Line || to Y-axis]

If $A = 0$, $B \neq 0$, the equation will be of the form $By + C = 0$. [Line || to X-axis]

If $A \neq 0$, $B \neq 0$, $C = 0$ equation will be of the form $Ax + By = 0$. [Line passing through origin]

If $A \neq 0$, $B \neq 0$, $C \neq 0$, the equation will be of the form $Ax + By + C = 0$.

It is called a linear equation in two variables because the two unknowns (x and y) occur only in the first power and the product of two unknown quantities does not occur. Since it involves two variables, therefore, a single equation will have infinite set of solutions, i.e., indeterminate solution. So, we require a pair of equations, i.e., simultaneous equations.

Solution of a Linear Equation

A linear equation in two variables has infinitely many solutions. A solution means an ordered pair (x, y) of values which satisfy the given equation. To find solutions, we express one variable in terms of another variable.

Then, we put the values of the first variable to get the values of the second variable.

Important Points About Linear Equation

- The graph of an equation of the type $x = k$ (where k is a constant) is a straight line parallel to the y-axis at a distance of k units from the y-axis.
- The graph of an equation of the type $y = k$ (where k is a constant) is a straight line parallel to the x-axis at a distance of k units from the x-axis.
- The points of intersection of the two lines give the solution of the two equations.
- A single linear equation in two variables has infinite number of solutions.

Illustration 4.1

Prove that $x = 3$, $y = 2$ is a solution of $3x - 2y = 5$.

Solution: $x = 3$, $y = 2$ is a solution of $3x - 2y = 5$, because L.H.S. $= 3x - 2y = 3 \times 3 - 2 \times 2 = 9 - 4 = 5 =$ R.H.S.

i.e., $x = 3$, $y = 2$ satisfied the equation $3x - 2y = 5$.

$\therefore$ It is a solution to the given equation.

Illustration 4.2

Find three solutions of the equation, $5x - 6y + 6 = 0$.

Solution: To make calculations easier, we rewrite the equation as, $y = (5x + 6)/6$

Now we may substitute any value for x and calculate the corresponding value of y.

Take $x = 0$, then $y = 1$.

Take $x = 6$, then $y = 6$

Take $x = -6$, then $y = -4$

Therefore three solutions are, $x = 0, y = 1$; $x = 6, y = 6$ and $x = -6, y = -4$

Illustration 4.3

Find three solutions of the equation, $2x = 6 - 5y$.

Solution: Rewrite the equation as $x = (6 - 5y)/2$

Take $y = 0$, then $x = 3$

Take $y = -2$, then $x = 8$

Take $y = 2$, then $x = -2$

Therefore three solutions are: $x = 3, y = 0$; $x = 8, y = -2$; $x = -2, y = 2$

Check Point 1

1. Which of the following equations are linear?
   (a) $4x + y^2 - 1 = 0$ (b) $x - y = 0$ (c) $y^2 = 4x - 1$ (d) $9x + 5 = 4y - 1$ (e) $3x - 5 = 0$
2. Express the following equations in the form $ax + by + c = 0$ and write the values of a, b and c.
   (a) $5x = 7y + 1$ (b) $8y - 3x = 1$ (c) $3x = 5y$ (d) $9x - 4 = 0$ (e) $7y + 4 = 0$
3. Express the following equations in the form $y = mx + c$ and write the values of m and c.
   (a) $6x + 7y = 3$ (b) $3x - 4y + 2 = 0$ (c) $6y + 7x - 2 = 0$ (d) $3x - 5y - 2 = 0$
4. Write down any 3 solutions of the following equations.
   (a) $4x - 7y + 2 = 0$ (b) $2x - y = 6$ (c) $x + 3y - 6 = 0$ (d) $10x - 9y + 5 = 0$
5. Rahul purchased some red T-shirts and some white T-shirts at ₹150 and ₹225 respectively. If the number of red T-shirts is x and the number of white T-shirts is y, then write a linear expression in x and y to denote his total bill which came out to be ₹900.

Graph of a Linear Equation in Two Variables

So far, you have obtained the solutions of a linear equation in two variables algebraically. Now, let us look at their geometric representation. You know that each such equation has infinitely many solutions. How can we show them in the coordinate plane? You may have got some indication in which we write the solution as pairs of values.

The solutions of the linear equation in the following example, namely, $x + 2y = 6$ (1) can be expressed in the form of a table as follows by writing the values of y below the corresponding values of x:

x	0	2	4	6	.	.	.
y	3	2	1	0	.	.	.

In the previous chapter, you studied how to plot the points on a graph paper. Let us plot the points (0, 3), (2, 2), (4, 1) and (6, 0) on a graph paper. Now join any two of these points and obtain a line. Let us call this line AB (*see* Fig. 4.1 below).

Do *you* see that the other two points also lie on line *AB*? Now, pick another point on this line, say (8, −1). Is this a solution? In fact, 8 + 2(−1) = 6. So, (8, −1) is a solution. Pick any other point on this line *AB* and verify whether its coordinates satisfy the equation or not. Now, take any point not lying on the line *AB*, say (2, 0). Do its coordinates satisfy the equation? Check and see that they do not.

Let us list your observations:

1. Every point whose coordinates satisfy Equation (1) lies on the line *AB*.
2. Every point (a, b) on the line *AB* gives a solution $x = a$, $y = b$ of Equation (1).
3. Any point, which does not lie on the line *AB*, is not a solution of Equation (1).

So, *you* can conclude that every point on the line satisfies the equation of the line and every solution of the equation is a point on the line. In fact, a linear equation in two variables is represented geometrically by a line whose points make up the collection of solutions of the equation. This is called the graph of the linear equation. So, to obtain the graph of a linear equation in two variables, it is enough to plot two points corresponding to two solutions and join them by a line. However, it is advisable to plot more than two such points so that *you* can immediately check the correctness of the graph.

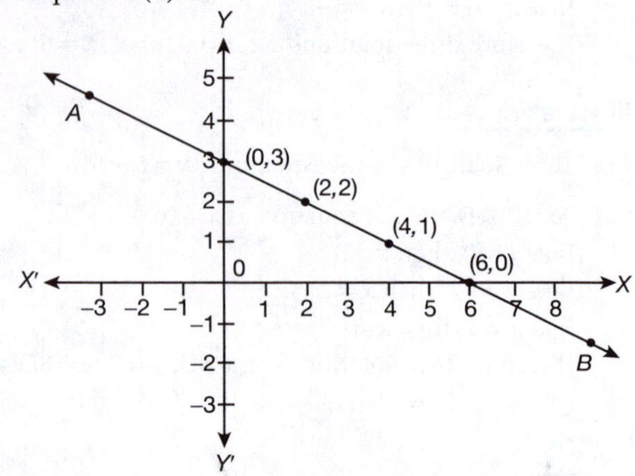

Figure 4.1

Illustration 4.4

Solve the equation $2x + 1 = x - 3$, and represent the solution(s) on

(i) the number line,

(ii) the Cartesian plane

Solution: We solve $2x + 1 = x - 3$, to get

$$2x - x = -3 - 1$$

i.e., $x = -4$

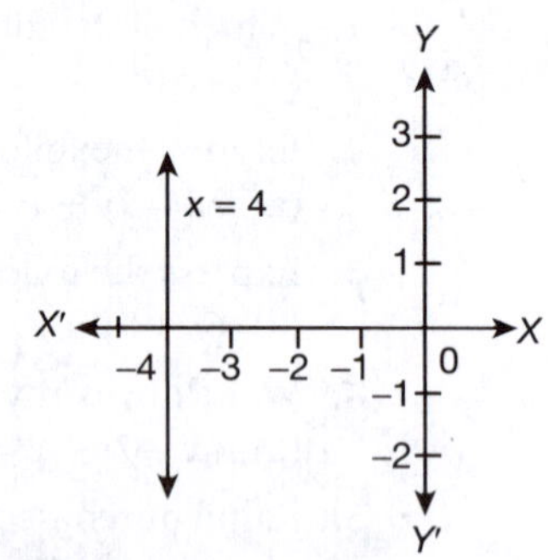

(i) The representation of the solution on the number line is shown in figure, where $x = -4$ is treated as an equation in one variable.

(ii) We know that $x = -4$ can be written as $x + 0\,y = -4$ which is a linear equation in the variables x and y.

This is represented by a line. Now all the values of y are permissible because $0.y$ is always 0. However, x must satisfy the equation $x = -4$. Hence, two solutions of the given equation are $x = -4$, $y = 0$ and $x = -4$, $y = 2$. Note that the graph *AB* is a line parallel to the *y*-axis and at a distance of 4 units to the left of it (*see* Figure).

Illustration 4.5

Draw the graph of the following:

(i) $x = 2$ **(ii)** $2x = 1$ **(iii)** $x + 4 = 0$ **(iv)** $x = 0$

Solution:

(i) $x = 2$

$x + 0, y = 2$

x	2	2	2
y	−1	0	2

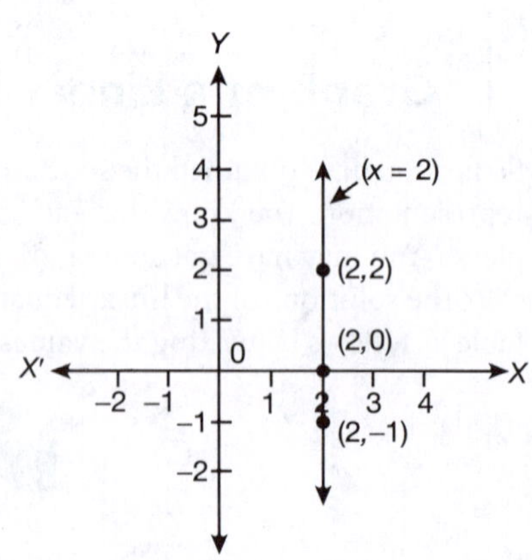

(ii) $2x = 1$

$x + 0.y = \frac{1}{2}$

x	0.50	0.50	0.50
y	–1	0	2

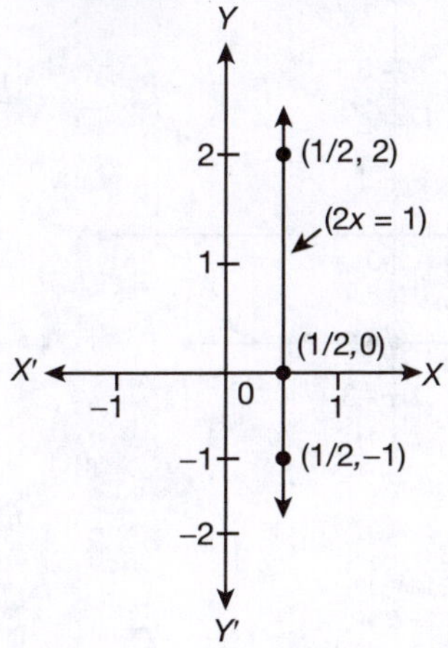

(iii) $x + 4 = 0$

$x + 0.y = -4$

x	–4	–4	–4
y	–1	0	2

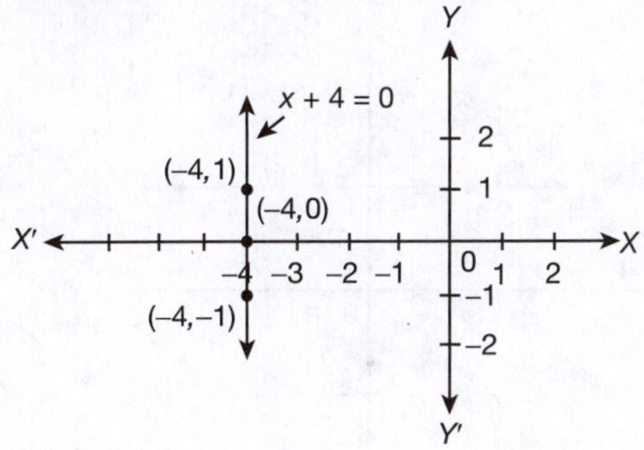

(iv) $x = 0$

$x + 0.y = 0$

x	0	0	0
y	0	1	2

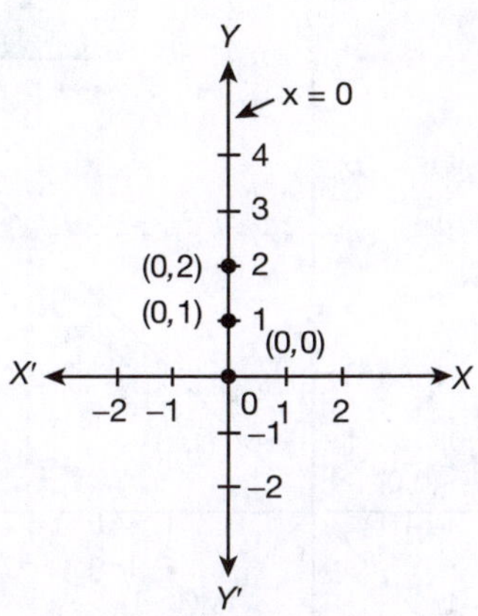

Illustration 4.6

Draw the graph of the following:

(i) $y = 0$ **(ii)** $y - 2 = 0$ **(iii)** $2y + 4 = 0$

Solution:

(i) $y = 0$

$x.0 + y = 0$

x	0	1	2
y	0	0	0

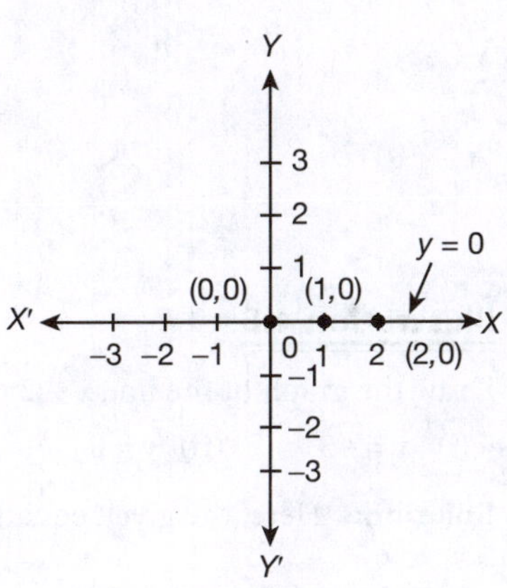

(ii) $y - 2 = 0$

$x.0 + y = 2$

x	−2	−1	1
y	2	2	2

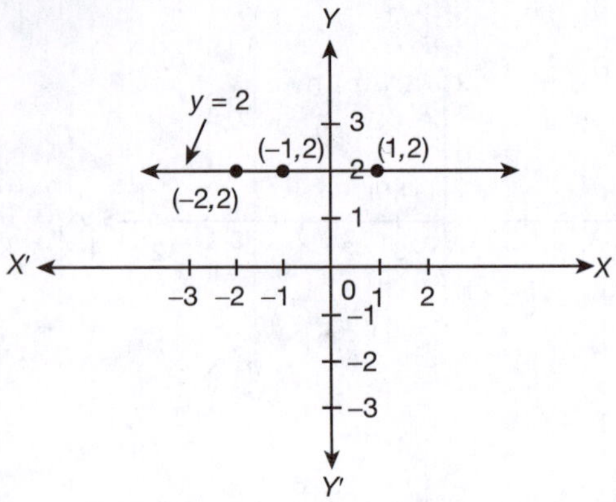

(iii) $2y + 4 = 0$

$y = -2$

x	0	2	−2
y	−2	−2	−2

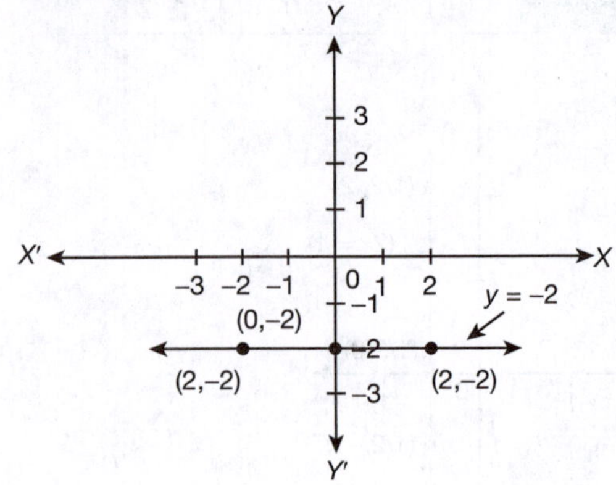

Illustration 4.7

Draw the graph of the following:

(i) $x = y$ **(ii)** $x = -y$

Solution:

(i) $x = y$

x	1	−3	0
y	1	−3	0

(ii) $x = -y$

x	1	−2	0
y	−1	2	0

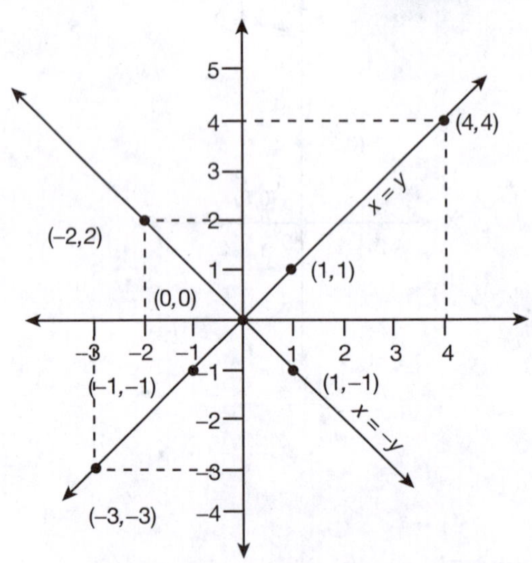

Illustration 4.8

Draw the graph of the line $x - 2y = 3$, from the graph, find the coordinate of the point when

(i) $x = -5$ **(ii)** $y = 0$

Solution: Here, the given equation is $x - 2y = 3$.

Solving it for y we get $2y = x - 3 \Rightarrow y - \dfrac{x-3}{2}$

Let, $x = -1$, then $y = \dfrac{-1-3}{2} = -2$

$x = 1$, then $y = \dfrac{1-3}{2} = -1$

$x = 3$, then $y = \dfrac{3-3}{2} = 0$

Hence, we get

x	-1	1	3
y	-2	-1	0

Clearly, when $x = -5$ then $y = -4$ and when $y = 0$ then $x = 3$.

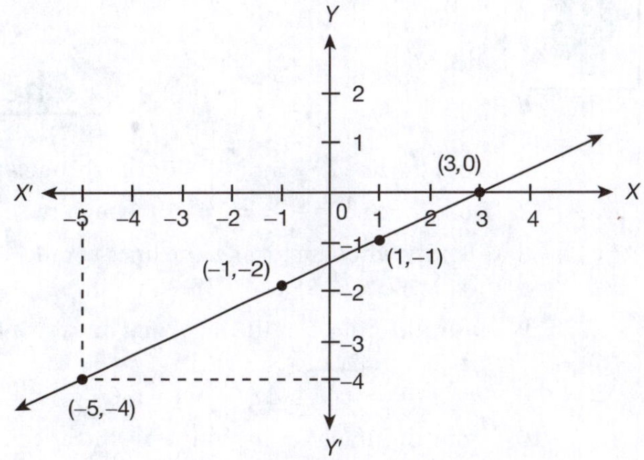

Illustration 4.9

Draw the graphs of the lines represented by the equations $x + y = 4$ and $2x - y = 2$ in the same graph. Also, find the coordinate of the point where the two lines intersect.

Solution: Given equations are:

$$x + y = 4 \qquad \ldots\text{(i)}$$

$$2x - y = 2 \qquad \ldots\text{(ii)}$$

(i) We have $y = 4 - x$

x	0	2	4
y	4	2	0

(ii) We have $y = 2x - 2$

x	1	0	3
y	0	-2	4

By drawing the lines on a graph paper, clearly, we can say that P is the point of intersection where coordinates are $x = 2$, $y = 2$.

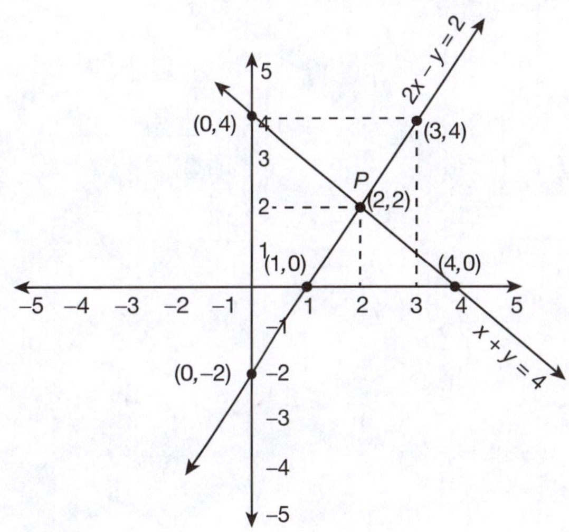

Illustration 4.10

Draw the graph of the equation $3x + 2y = 6$. Find the co-ordinates of the point where the graph cuts the x-axis and y-axis.

Solution: $3x + 2y = 6$

$$2y = 6 - 3x$$

$$y = \frac{6-3x}{2}$$

x	-2	0	2
y	6	3	0

Line cuts the x-axis at $(2, 0)$ and y-axis at $(0, 3)$.

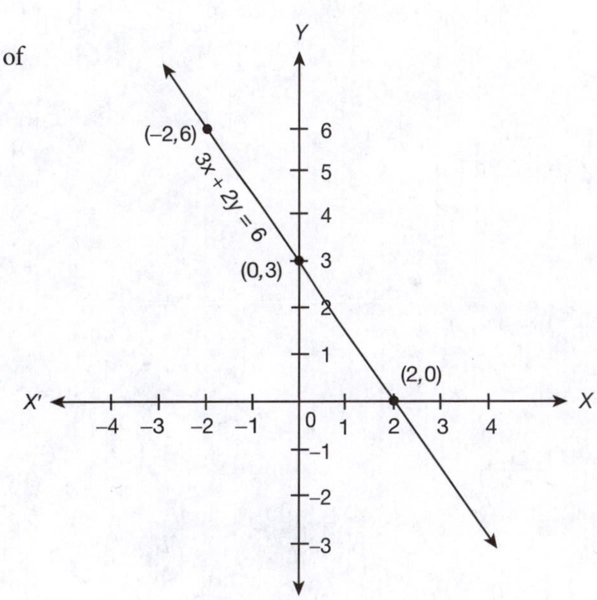

Check Point 2

6. Does the line $2x - 5y + 31 = 0$ pass through the point $(-3, 5)$?

7. Does the line $7y + 3x = 0$ pass through the origin?

8. Identify without plotting, the lines parallel to the x or y axis:
(a) $5x + 3 = 0$ (b) $3 - 7y = 0$ (c) $10x - 1 = 0$ (d) $4x + 9 = 0$

9. Draw the graphs of the following linear equations.
(a) $x = 7 + 2y$ (b) $3x - y = 0$ (c) $5x + 6 = 0$ (d) $4y - 12 = 0$
(e) $x - 7 = 0$ (f) $y + 4 = 0$

10. Draw the graphs of the following linear equations.
(a) $5x - 6y + 3 = 0$ (b) $x - 6y = 12$ (c) $3y + 5x = 9$ (d) $4x - 5y = 0$

STRUCTURAL OUTLINE

Linear Equation in 2 variable

An equation of the form $Ax + By + C = 0$ is called a linear equation.

Solution of a Linear equation

A linear equation in two variables has infinitely many solutions. A solution means an ordered pair (x, y) of values which satisfy the given equation. To find solutions we express one variable in terms of another variable.

If $A \neq 0$, $B = 0$

Then equation will be of the form $Ax + C = 0$. [Line || to y-axis]

If $A = 0$, $B \neq 0$,

Then equation will be of the form $By + C = 0$. [Line || to x-axis]

If $A \neq 0$, $B \neq 0$, $C = 0$

Then equation will be of the form $Ax + By = 0$. [Line passing through origin]

Important points about linear equation in two variables

(i) The graph of an equation of the type $x = k$ (where k is a constant) is a straight line parallel to the y-axis at a distance of k units from the y-axis.

(ii) The graph of an equation of the type $y = k$ (where k is a constant) is a straight line parallel to the x-axis at a distance of k units from the x-axis.

(iii) The points of intersection of the two lines gives the solution of the two equations.

(iv) A single linear equation in two variables has infinite no. of solutions.

ASSESSMENT CORNER

Fixed Response Type

Fill in the Blanks

1. A rectangle is 8 cm long and 5 cm wide. Its perimeter is doubled when each of its sides is increased by x cm, then its new length is _______.

2. The graph of a linear equation in one or two variables is _______.

3. If the graph intersects at one point, then the number of solutions of two linear equations in two variables have _______.

4. If $5x - 2y = k$ one of answer is (2, –2), then $k =$ _______.

5. How many solutions, does a linear equation in two variables have _______.

6. Solve equation: $\frac{2x}{5}+1=\frac{x}{3}+3$, then $x =$ _______.

True/False

1. Determine whether $x = 5, y = 4$ is a solution of the equation $x - 2y = -3$.

2. $x = 0$ represents the equation of the y-axis.

3. $y = 2$ represents a line parallel to the x-axis.

4. (2, –3) is the solution of the linear equation $2x + 4y = -8$

5. If $x = 1$, $y = 1$ is a solution of equation $9ax + 12ay = 63$ then, the value of a is 3.

Single Correct Type Questions

1. Which of the following equations is not linear equation?
(A) $2x + 3 = 7x - 2$
(B) $\frac{2}{3}x + 5 = 3x - 4$
(C) $x^2 + 3 = 5x - 3$
(D) $(x - 2)^2 = x^2 + 8$

2. Solution of equation $\sqrt{3}x - 2 = 2\sqrt{3} + 4$ is:
(A) $2(\sqrt{3} - 1)$
(B) $2(1 - \sqrt{3})$
(C) $1 + \sqrt{3}$
(D) $2(1 + \sqrt{3})$

3. The value of x which satisfy $\frac{6x+5}{4x+7}=\frac{3x+5}{2x+6}$ is:
(A) –1
(B) 1
(C) 2
(D) –2

4. The graph of the linear equation $2x + 3y = 6$ cuts the y-axis at the point
(A) (2, 0)
(B) (0, 2)
(C) (3, 0)
(D) (0, 3)

5. A linear equation in two variables has maximum:
(A) only one solution
(B) two solution
(C) infinite solution
(D) None of these

6. The equation $x = 7$, in two variables can be written as
(A) $1 \times x + 1 \times y = 7$
(B) $1 \times x + 0 \times y = 7$
(C) $0 \times x + 1 \times y = 7$
(D) $0 \times x + 0 \times y = 7$

7. The linear equation 3x-11y=10 has:
(A) Unique solutions
(B) Two solutions
(C) Infinitely many solutions
(D) No solutions

8. The graph of line $5x + 3y = 4$ cuts y-axis at the point:
(A) $\left(0,\frac{4}{3}\right)$
(B) $\left(0,\frac{3}{4}\right)$
(C) $\left(\frac{4}{5},0\right)$
(D) $\left(\frac{5}{4},0\right)$

9. The linear equation $2x - 5y = 7$ has
(A) No solutions
(B) Unique solutions
(C) Two solutions
(D) Infinitely many solutions

10. The graph of linear equation $x+2y = 2$, cuts the y-axis at:
(A) (2,0)
(B) (0,2)
(C) (0,1)
(D) (1,1)

11. Which is an equation of the line with the coefficient of x is $\frac{2}{3}$ and that passes through the point (4, –1)?
(A) $y=-\frac{1}{4}x+\frac{2}{3}$
(B) $y=-4x+\frac{2}{3}$
(C) $y=\frac{2}{3}x-\frac{5}{3}$
(D) $y=\frac{2}{3}x-\frac{11}{3}$

12. Geometric representation of $y = 4$ as an equation in one variable is:

(A) 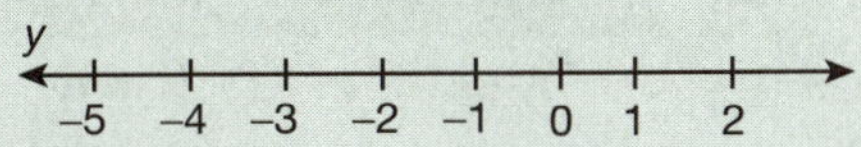

(B) 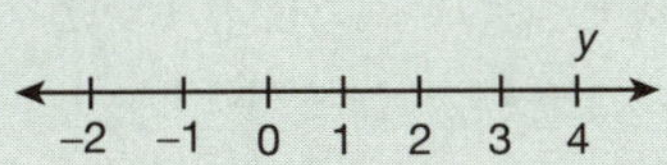

(C) 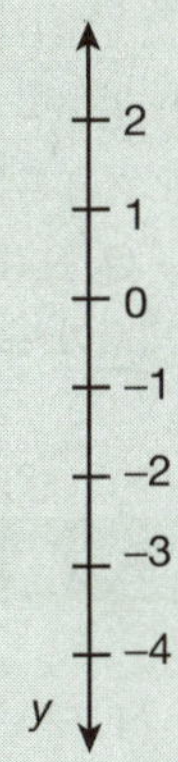

(D) Both (A) and (B) are correct

13. The set of equations representing the given graph is:

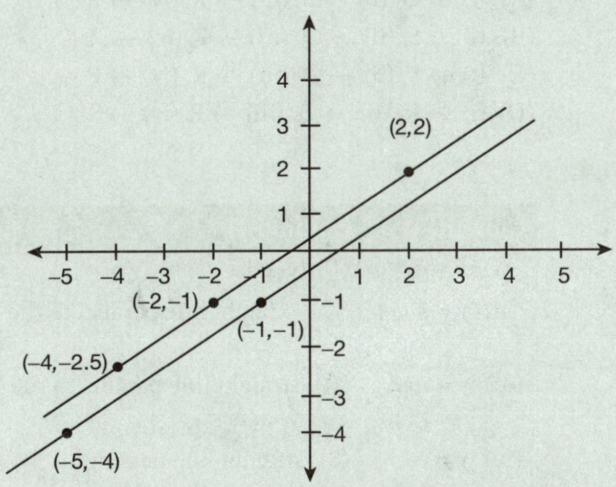

(A) $2x + 7y = 11; 5x + \frac{35y}{2} = 25$

(B) $3x - 4y = 1; 8y - 6x = 4$

(C) $7x + 2y = 11; y - 2x = 3$

(D) $3x - 7y = 10; 8y - 6x = 4$

14. Which of the following statement is correct?

(A) $x = 0$ represents the equation of the y-axis

(B) $y = 2$ represents a line parallel to the x-axis

(C) (2, –3) is the solution of linear equation $2x + 4y = -8$

(D) All of these

Multiple Correct Type Questions

1. Which of the following is the solution of $2x + 3y = 6$?

(A) (3, 0) (B) (0, 2)

(C) (–3, 4) (D) (1, 1)

2. The solution of the given equation $3x - 2y = 4$ is:

(A) (0, –2) (B) (–2, –5)

(C) (0, 3) (D) (2, 1)

3. Which of the following is/are correct?

(A) Solutions of the equation $4x + 3y = 12$ are (0, 4) and (3, 0)

(B) $\left(0, -\frac{4}{3}\right)$ and $\left(1, -\frac{4}{3}\right)$ are solutions of equation $3y + 4 = 0$

(C) (0, 0) is a solution of the equation $2x + 5y = 0$

(D) (2, 3) is one of the solution of the equation $x + 2y = 6$

4. Which of the following is/are not correct?

(A) Any point on the y-axis is of the form $(x, 0)$

(B) The equation of x-axis is of the form $x + y = 0$

(C) Any point on the x-axis is of the form $(0, y)$

(D) The equation $y + 3 = 0$ represents a line

5. Which of the following is/are not the solutions of the equation $x - 2y = 4$?

(A) (4, 0) (B) $(\sqrt{2}, 4\sqrt{2})$

(C) (1, 1) (D) (2, 0)

6. The graph of the linear equation $2x + 3y = 6$ cuts the y-axis at the point :

(A) (2, 0) (B) (0, 2)

(C) (3, 0) (D) (0, 3)

7. Which of the following is *a* linear equation?

(A) $2x + 17 = 0$

(B) $3y + 3x = 4$

(C) $5x - 2y = 3xy$

(D) $6x + y = 8$

Match Type Questions

Direction: Column-I and Column-II contains four entries each. Entries of Column-I are to be matched with some entries of Column-II. Only one entry of Column-I may have the matching with the one entry of Column-II and one entry of Column-II may have matching with one entry of Column-I.

1.

Column-I (Equation)	Column-II (Graph)
(i) $x = 2$	(P)

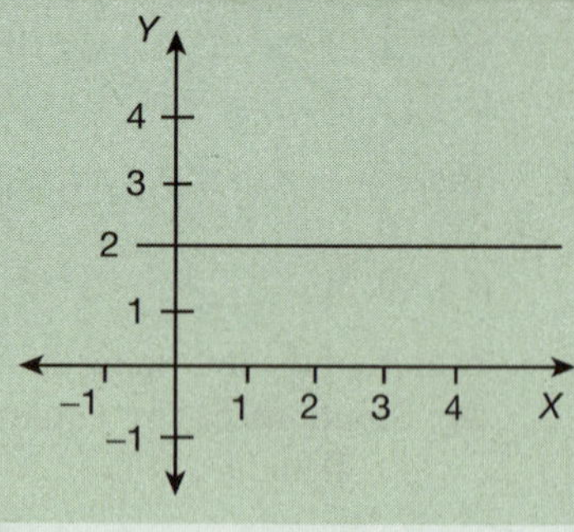

(ii) $y + 2 = 0$	(Q)

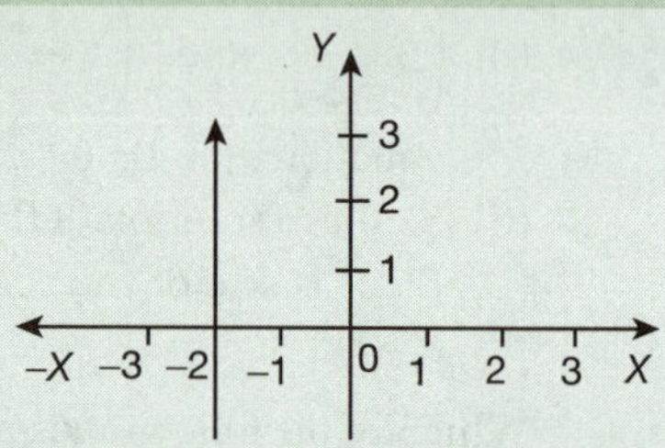

(iii) $2y - 4 = 0$	(R)

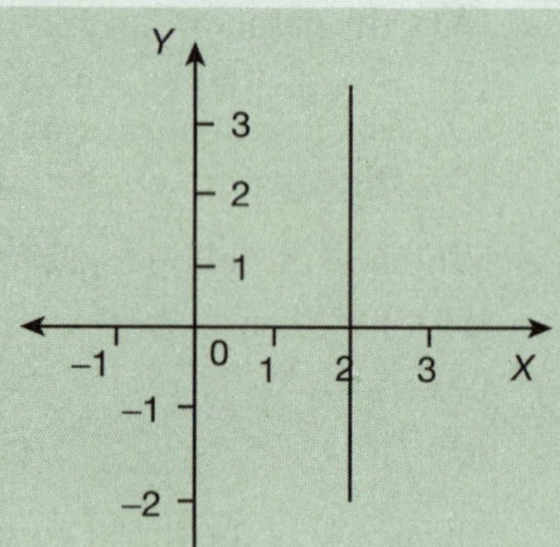

(iv) $8x + 16 = 0$	(S)

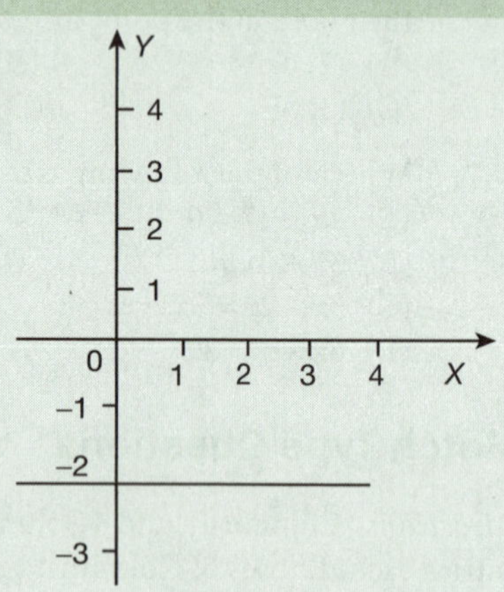

(A) (i) → R, (ii) → S, (iii) → P, (iv) → Q
(B) (i) → S, (ii) → Q, (iii) → P, (iv) → R
(C) (i) → R, S (ii) → Q, (iii) → Q, R, (iv) → P
(D) (i) → R, (ii) → Q, (iii) → P, (iv) → S

2.

Column-I (Equation)	Column-II (Solution)
(i) $2x + 3y = 11$	(P) (0, 0)
(ii) $3x + 7y = 16$	(Q) (3, 1)
(iii) $x + y = 4$	(R) (1, 3)
(iv) $x - y = 0$	(S) (4, 1)

(A) (i) → Q, (ii) → S, (iii) → R, (iv) → P
(B) (i) → S, (ii) → Q, (iii) → P, (iv) → R
(C) (i) → R, S (ii) → Q, (iii) → Q, R (iv) → P
(D) (i) → R, (ii) → Q, (iii) → P, (iv) → S

3.

Column-I	Column-II
(i) $2x + y = 7$	(P) (0, 9)
(ii) $x - 2y = 4$	(Q) (1, 5)
(iii) $x - 4y = 0$	(R) (0, 0)
(iv) $px + y = 9$	(S) (4, 0)

(A) (i) → Q, (ii) → S, (iii) → R, (iv) → P
(B) (i) → S, (ii) → Q, (iii) → P, (iv) → R
(C) (i) → S, (ii) → Q, (iii) → R, (iv) → P
(D) (i) → R, (ii) → Q, (iii) → P, (iv) → S

4.

Column-I	Column-II
(i) $x = a$	(P) x-axis
(ii) $y = a$	(Q) straight line parallel to the x-axis
(iii) $y = mx$	(R) straight line parallel to the y–axis
(iv) $y = 0$	(S) straight line passing through the origin

(A) (i) → Q, (ii) → S, (iii) → R, (iv) → P
(B) (i) → S, (ii) → Q, (iii) → P, (iv) → R
(C) (i) → R, (ii) → Q, (iii) → S, (iv) → P
(D) (i) → R, (ii) → Q, (iii) → P, (iv) → S

5. If the temperature of a liquid can be measured in Kelvin units as xK or in Fahrenheit units as y°F, find the relation between the two systems of measurement of temperature given by the linear equation $y = \frac{9}{5}(x - 273) + 32$

Column-I	Column-II
(i) 26°C in Fahrenheit	(P) 104°
(ii) 64°F in Celsius	(Q) 8.9°
(iii) 48°F in Celsius	(R) 78.8°
(iv) 40°C in Fahrenheit	(S) 17.8°

(A) (i) → Q, (ii) → S, (iii) → R, (iv) → P
(B) (i) → S, (ii) → Q, (iii) → P, (iv) → R
(C) (i) → R, (ii) → Q, (iii) → S, (iv) → P
(D) (i) → R, (ii) → S, (iii) → Q, (iv) → P

6.

Column-I	Column-II
(i) $x + y = 0$	(P) (3/2, 3)
(ii) $y - 2x = 0$	(Q) (–5, 5)
(iii) $3x + 5y = 0$	(R) (5, –2)
(iv) $2x - y = 12$	(S) (0, 0)
	(T) (–5, 3)
	(U) (5, –3)

(A) (i) → Q, R (ii) → S, (iii) → R, (iv) → P
(B) (i) → Q, S (ii) → P (iii) → T, U (iv) → R
(C) (i) → R, (ii) → Q, T (iii) → S, (iv) → P, U
(D) (i) → R, (ii) → S, (iii) → Q, (iv) → P, S

Assertion and Reason Type Questions

Directions: In the following questions Assertion (A) is given followed by a Reason (R). Mark *your* responses from the following options.

(A) Both Assertion and Reason are true and Reason is the correct explanation of 'Assertion'.
(B) Both Assertion and Reason are true and Reason is not the correct explanation of 'Assertion'.
(C) Assertion is true but Reason is false.
(D) Assertion is false but Reason is true.

1. **Assertion:** The graph of equation $y + 1 = x + 1$ passes through origin.
   Reason: The graph of a linear equation with its constant term = 0 always passes through the origin.
2. **Assertion:** The linear equation in two variables has a unique solution.
   Reason: Every point on the graph of a linear equation in two variables is a solution of the linear equation.
3. **Assertion:** There are infinite number of lines which pass through (2, 14).
   Reason: A linear equation in two variables has infinitely many solutions.
4. **Assertion:** For all values of k, $\left(\frac{-3}{2}, k\right)$ is a solution of the linear equation $2x + 3 = 0$.
   Reason: The linear equation $ax + b = 0$ can be expressed as a linear equation in two variables as $x = b/a$.
5. **Assertion:** The graph of the two linear equations $x - 2y = 1$ and $2x + 3y = 9$ intersect at (3, 1).
   Reason: Every point lying on $x - 2y = 1$ is a solution of $2x + 3y = 9$.

Comprehension Type Questions

Comprehension 1: The ratio of incomes of Ram and Shyam are in the ratio of 9 : 7 and the ratio of their expenditures are 4 : 3 If both of them save ₹200 per month, then answer the following questions.

1. Monthly income of Shyam
   (A) ₹18000 (B) ₹1400
   (C) ₹2400 (D) ₹2100
2. How much percentage of Ram's total expenditure is more than that of Shyam's total expenditure?
   (A) $33\frac{1}{3}\%$ (B) 25%
   (C) 20% (D) $22\frac{2}{9}\%$
3. How much percentage of Shyam's total income is his expenditure?
   (A) $28\frac{2}{7}\%$ (B) $33\frac{1}{3}\%$
   (C) 67% (D) $85\frac{5}{7}\%$

Numerical Type Questions

1. If $\frac{2x+7}{x+2} = \frac{4x+3}{2x-7}$, find the value of $x^3 + x^2 + x + 1$.
2. For what value of c, the linear equation $2x + cy = 8$ has equal values of x and y for its solution.
3. If the point (–3, 4) lies on the linear equation $ay = 5x + 11$, then find the value of a.
4. If $\frac{3x+6}{8} - \frac{11x-8}{24} + \frac{x}{3} = \frac{3x}{4} - \frac{x+7}{24}$, then the value of x is:
5. If $x = 1$, $y = 1$ is a solution of equation $9ax + 12ay = 63$ then, the value of a is:
6. Point (3, 4) lies on the graph of the equation $3y = kx + 7$. The value of $3k$ is:

ASSESSMENT CORNER

7. Solve the following system of linear equation graphically:
$4x - 3y + 4 = 0$
$4x + 3y - 20 = 0$
Find the area bounded by the x-axis and these lines.

Higher Order Thinking Skills (HOTS)

1. If x and y are both positive solutions of equation $ax + by + c = 0$, always lie in the:
(A) First quadrant
(B) Second quadrant
(C) Third quadrant
(D) Fourth quadrant

2. If the point (–1, –5) lies on the graphs of $3x = ay + 7$ and $y = bx + 7$, then the value of $a + b$ is:
(A) 10 (B) 11
(C) 12 (D) 14

3. A class has 36 boys. If $\frac{1}{4}$ of the boys sitting inside go outside, the number of boys sitting inside and outside will be the same. Find the initial number of students sitting inside.
(A) 20 (B) 30
(C) 24 (D) 50

4. Divide ₹380 between A, B and C so that B may have ₹30 more than A, and C may have ₹20 more than B.
(A) A = ₹100, B = ₹130, C = ₹150
(B) A = ₹120, B = ₹150, C = ₹130
(C) A = ₹100, B = ₹150, C = ₹130
(D) A = ₹150, B = ₹100, C = ₹120

5. How many solutions, two linear equations in two variables representing coincident lines, have?
(A) One solution (B) Two solution
(C) Three solution (D) Infinite solution

6. The area of the triangle formed by the lines $y = x$, $x = 6$ and $y = 0$ is:
(A) 36 sq. unit (B) 18 sq. unit
(C) 9 sq. unit (D) 72 sq. unit

7. The area of the triangle formed by the lines $x = 3$, $y = 4$ and $x = y$ is:
(A) 1/2 sq. unit (B) 1 sq. unit
(C) 2 sq. unit (D) None of these

8. The equations $2x + y - 5 = 0$ and $6x + 3y - 15 = 0$ show:
(A) Coincident lines (B) Infinite solutions
(C) Unique solution (D) No solution

FREE RESPONSE TYPE

Very Short Answer Type Questions

1. If (2, 0) is a solution of the linear equation $2x + 3y = k$, then find the value of k.

2. The graph of the linear equation $2x + 3y = 6$ cuts the y-axis at which point?

3. Lines $x = a$ and $y = b$ will intersect at
(A) (a, a) (B) (b, b)
(C) (a, b) (D) (b, a)

4. Any point on the line $y = x$ is of which form?

5. The equation of the x-axis is of which form?

6. The graph of the linear equation $2x + 3y = 6$ is a line which meets the x-axis at which point?

7. Determine whether $x = 5$, $y = 4$ is a solution of the equation $x - 2y = -3$.

8. Find the value of k if (3, 4) is a solution of the equation $5x - 2y = k$. Find one more solution to the equation.

9. Write the equations of the line parallel to the x-axis at a distance of 3 units.

Short Answer Type Questions

1. At what point does the graph of the linear equation $x + y = 5$ meet a line which is parallel to the y-axis, at a distance 2 units from the origin and in the positive direction of the x-axis?

2. Find four solution of the following linear equation $2x + 3y = 16$.

3. Draw the graph of the equation represented by the straight line which is parallel to the x-axis and is 4 units above it.

4. Determine the point on the graph of the linear equation $2x + 5y = 19$, whose ordinate is $1\frac{1}{2}$ time its abscissa.

5. How many solution(s) of the equation $2x + 1 = x - 3$ are there on the:
(i) Number line (ii) Cartesian plane

6. Find the solution of the linear equation $x + 2y = 8$ which represents a point on
(i) x-axis (ii) y-axis

7. If $(a + b, a - b)$ is the solution of the equations $3x + 2y = 20$ and $4x - 5y = 42$, then find the value of b

8. If $p = 3x + 1$, $q = \frac{1}{3}(9x + 13)$ and $p : q = 6 : 5$ then find x.

9. I am three times as old as my son. Five years later, I shall be two and a half times as old as my son. Taking my age as x year and my son's age as y year, write the linear equation so formed.

10. The following linear equation converts Fahrenheit to Celsius, $F = \frac{9}{5}C + 32$
    (i) If the temperature is 30°C, what is the temperature in Fahrenheit?
    (ii) If the temperature is 95°F, what is the temperature in Celsius?
    (iii) Find the temperature which is numerically the same in both the scales of temperature.

Long Answer Type Questions

1. The Autorikshaw fare in a city is charged ₹10 for the first kilometre and at ₹4 per kilometre for subsequent distances covered. Write the linear equation to express the above statement. Draw the graph of the linear equation.

2. Draw the graph of the linear equation $3x + 4y = 6$. At what points, the graph cuts the x-axis and the y-axis.

3. The force exerted to pull a cart is directly proportional to the acceleration produced in the body. Express the statement as a linear equation of two variables and draw the graph of the same by taking the constant mass equal to 6 kg. Read from the graph, the force required when the acceleration produced is (i) 5 m/sec², (ii) 6 m/sec².

4. The linear equation that converts Fahrenheit (F) to Celsius (C) is given by the relation $C = \frac{5F - 160}{9}$.
    (i) If the temperature is 86°F, what is the temperature in Celsius?
    (ii) If the temperature is 35°C, what is the temperature in Fahrenheit?
    (iii) If the temperature is 0°C what is the temperature in Fahrenheit and if the temperature is 0°F, what is the temperature in Celsius?
    (iv) What is the numerical value of the temperature which is same in both the scales?

5. If the temperature of a liquid can be measured in Kelvin units as x°K or in Fahrenheit units as y°F, the relation between the two systems of measurement of temperature is given by the linear equation

$$y = \frac{9}{5}(x - 273) + 32$$

    (i) Find the temperature of the liquid in Fahrenheit if the temperature of the liquid is 313°K.
    (ii) If the temperature is 158° F, then find the temperature in Kelvin.

6. A man hires an auto rickshaw to cover a certain distance. The fare is ₹10 for the first kilometre and ₹7 for subsequent kilometres. Taking total distance covered as x km and total fare as ₹y,
    (i) Write a linear equation for this.
    (ii) The man covers a distance of 16 km and gave ₹120 to the auto driver. The auto driver said, 'It is not the correct amount' and returned him the balance. Find the correct amount paid back by the auto driver.

7. Draw the graph of the equation, $2x + 3y = 6$. Find the length of intercept on both co-ordinate axes.

8. Express y in terms of x, given that $2y - 4x = 7$. Check whether $(-1, -1)$ is a solution of the line.

ARCHIVE CORNER

1. If $\frac{15}{x}+\frac{2}{y}=17$ and $x=3$, then the value of y is:
   (A) $\frac{1}{6}$ (B) $\frac{1}{5}$
   (C) $-\frac{1}{6}$ (D) $-\frac{1}{5}$

2. Age of Ramesh is x. Ramesh is 5 years older than Mahesh, but 3 years younger than Suresh, then Suresh's age is _______ years.
   (A) $x+3$ (B) $x+5$
   (C) $x-5$ (D) $8-x$

3. A farmer divides his herd of x cows among his 4 sons such that the first son gets one-half of the herd, the second son gets one-fourth, the third son gets one-fifth and the fourth son gets 7 cows, then the value of x is:
   (A) 100 (B) 140
   (C) 160 (D) 180

4. In three given numbers the second number is twice than the first number and thrice than the third number. If the average of the three numbers is 44, what is the largest number?
   (A) 24 (B) 72
   (C) 36 (D) 8

5. If $\frac{x}{3}+7=15-\frac{x}{5}$ then find the solution?
   (A) $x=20$ (B) $x=15$
   (C) $x=21$ (D) $x=18$

6. Line $x + y = 2$ passes through the _______ quadrants.
   (A) 1st and 3rd both (B) 2nd and 3rd both
   (C) 3rd and 4th both (D) 1st, 2nd, 4th

7. 3 years ago, the sum of the ages of the father and his son was 40 years. After 2 years, the sum of the ages of the father and his son will be:
   (A) 40 (B) 46
   (C) 50 (D) 60

8. A father is 7 times as old as his son. Two years ago, the father was 13 times as old as his son. Father's present age is:
   (A) 24 years (B) 28 years
   (C) 30 years (D) 32 years

ANSWER KEY

CHECK POINTS

Check Point 1

1. (b), (d), (e)
2. (a) $5x - 7y - 1 = 0$; $a = 5, b = -7, c = -1$
   (b) $-3x + 8y - 1 = 0$; $a = -3, b = 8, c = -1$
   (c) $3x - 5y = 0$; $a = 3, b = -5, c = 0$
   (d) $9x - 4 = 0$; $a = 9, b = 0, c = -4$
   (e) $7y + 4 = 0$; $a = 0, b = 7, c = 4$
3. (a) $y = \frac{-6}{7}x + \frac{3}{7}; m = \frac{-6}{7}, c = \frac{3}{7}$ (b) $y = \frac{3}{4}x + \frac{1}{2}; m = \frac{3}{4}, c = \frac{1}{2}$
   (c) $y = \frac{-7}{6}x + \frac{1}{3}; m = \frac{-7}{6}, c = \frac{1}{3}$ (d) $y = \frac{3}{5}x - \frac{2}{5}; m = \frac{2}{5}, c = \frac{-2}{5}$
4. (a) $x = 3, y = 2; x = -4, y = -2; x = 10, y = 6$
   (b) $x = 3, y = 0; x = 4, y = 2; x = 5, y = 4$
   (c) $x = 6, y = 0; x = 3, y = 1; x = 0, y = 2$
   (d) $x = 4, y = 5; x = -5, y = -5; x = 13, y = 15$
5. $150x + 225y = 900$

Check Point 2

6. Yes 7. Yes
8. (a) parallel to the y-axis (b) parallel to the x-axis
   (c) parallel to the y- axis (d) parallel to the y-axis

Assessment Corner

FIXED RESPONSE TYPE

Fill in the Blanks

1. $\frac{29}{2}$ 2. a straight line 3. 1 4. 14 5. infinite 6. 30

True/False

1. True 2. True 3. True 4. True 5. True

Single Correct Type Questions

1. C 2. D 3. B 4. B 5. C 6. B 7. C 8. A 9. D
10. C 11. D 12. D 13. B 14. D

Multiple Correct Type Questions

1. ABC 2. ABD 3. ABC 4. ABC 5. BCD 6. B 7. ABD

Match Type Questions

1. A 2. D 3. A 4. C 5. D 6. B

Assertion and Reason Type Questions

1. A 2. D 3. B 4. A 5. C

Comprehension Type Questions

1. B 2. A 3. D

Numerical Type Questions

1. –104 2. $c=\frac{8-2x}{x}$ 3. –1 4. 3 5. 3 6. 5 7. 12

Higher Order Thinking Skills (HOTS)

1. A 2. D 3. C 4. A 5. D 6. B 7. A 8. AB

Free Response Type

Very Short Answer Type Questions

1. 4 2. (0, 2) 3. C 4. (a, a) 5. $y = 0$ 6. (3, 0) 7. YES 8. 7
9. 3

Short Answer Type Questions

1. (2, 3) 3. (1, 4) (2, 4) (3, 4) 4. (2, 1.5) 5. (i) 1 (ii) Infinite
6. (i) x-axis: $y = 0$ then $x = 8$ point is (8, 0) (ii) y-axis: $x = 0$ then $2y = 8$ then point is (0, 4)
7. $a = 3$ and $b = 5$ 8. 7 9. My present age is 45 years and my son's present age is 15 years.
10. (i) 86 (ii) 35 (iii) –40

Long Answer Type Questions

1. Therefore, the linear equation is $y = 6 + 4x$
2. The point at which the graph cuts x-axis = (2, 0).
   The point at which the graph cuts the x-axis = (0, 1.5).
3. (i) The force is 30 N (ii) The force is 36 N
4. (i) 30°C (ii) 95°F (iii) (–160/9)°C (iv) –40
6. (i) $y=10+7(x-1)=7x+3$ (ii) $y=16\times7+3=115.$ 7. (0, 2) and (3, 0) 8. not solution

Archive Corner

1. A 2. A 3. B 4. B 5. B 6. D 7. C 8. B

ANSWER KEY

CHAPTER 5

Introduction to Euclid's Geometry

Learning Outcomes

After reading this chapter, you would be able to:

- Euclid's Postulates and Axioms of Geometry.

Geekspeak

- Euclid's definitions
- Postulates
- Axioms
- Geometry
- Theorem

Introduction

The word 'geometry' comes from the Greek words 'geo' meaning 'earth' and 'metre in' meaning 'to measure'. The Greek mathematician Thales is credited with providing the first known proof. This proof was his statement that a circle is bisected by its diameter (i.e., cut into two equal parts). One of his most famous students of Thales was Pythagoras (572 BC). Pythagoras and his group his discovered many geometric properties and extensively developed the theory of geometry. This process continued till 300 BC. At that time Euclid, a teacher of mathematics at Alexandria in Egypt, collected all the known work and arranged it in his famous treatise called 'Elements'. He divided the 'Elements' into 13 chapters, each of which he called a book.

Euclid Geometry

Euclidean geometry is the study of plane and solid figures based on axioms and theorems formulated by the ancient Greek mathematician Euclid around 300 BCE.

Euclid's Definitions

- A point is that which has no part.
- A line is breadthless length.
- The ends of a line segment are points.
- A straight line is that which has length only.
- A surface is that which has length and breadth only.
- The edges of a surface are lines.
- A plane surface is that which lies evenly with straight lines on itself.

Basic Term and Definition

There are three basic concepts in geometry, namely, 'point', 'line' and 'plane'. It is not possible to define these three concepts precisely. We can, however, have a good idea of these concepts by considering the examples given below

Point: A point is represented by a fine dot made by a sharp pencil on a sheet of paper. A Point is denoted by capital letter A, B, P, Q, R, etc.

Plane: The surface of a smooth wall or the surface of a sheet of paper or the surface of a smooth blackboard are close examples of a plane.

Line: If we fold a piece of paper, the crease in the paper represents a geometrical straight line. The edge of the ruler, the edge of the top of a table, the meeting place of two walls of a room are close examples of a geometrical straight line.

Geometrical Concepts

Axioms: The basic facts which are taken for granted, without proof, are called axioms.
E.g., Halves of equal are equal.

Statements: A sentence which can be judged to be true or false is called a sentence.
E.g., The sum of the angles of a triangle is 180°, is a true statement.

Theorems: A statement that requires a proof, is called a theorem. Establishing the truth of a theorem is known as proving the theorem.
E.g., The sum of all angles around a point is 360°

Corollary: A statement whose truth can easily be decided from a theorem, is called its corollary.

Conjecture: In mathematics, a **conjecture** is a conclusion or proposition based on incomplete information, for which no proof has been found, for example, the **Goldbach Conjecture** state that every even integer greater than two is the sum of two prime numbers.

Point: A point is an exact location. A fine dot represents a point. Point is denoted by capital letter *A*, *B*, *P*, *Q*, *R*, etc.

Line segment: The straight path between two points *A* and *B* is called the line segment $\overline{AB}$. Points *A* and *B* are called the endpoints of the line segment $\overline{AB}$. A line segment has a definite length.

Line: A line segment $\overline{AB}$ when extended indefinitely in both directions is called the line $\overleftrightarrow{AB}$. A line has no endpoints. A line has no definite length. Sometimes, we label lines with small letters *l*, *m*, *n*, etc.

Figure 5.1

Interior point of a line segment: Point *R* is called an interior point of a line segment *PQ* if *R* lies between *P* and *Q* but *R* is neither *P* nor *Q*.

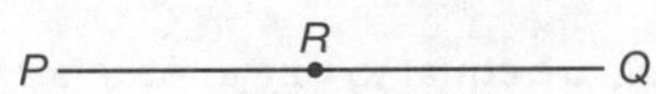

Figure 5.2

Congruence of line segment: Two line segments *AB* and *CD* are congruent if trace copy of one can be superposed on the other so as to cover it completely and exactly in this case we write $AB \cong CD$. In other words, we can say two lines are congruent if their length is the same.

Distance between two points: The distance between two points *P* and *Q* is the length of line segment *PQ*.

Ray: Directed line segment is called a ray. If *AB* is a ray then it is denoted by $\overrightarrow{AB}$. Point *A* is called initial point of the ray.

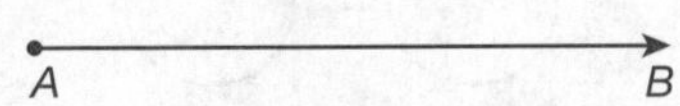

Figure 5.3

Opposite rays: Two rays *AB* and *AC* are said to be opposite rays if they are collinear and point *A* is the only common point of the two rays.

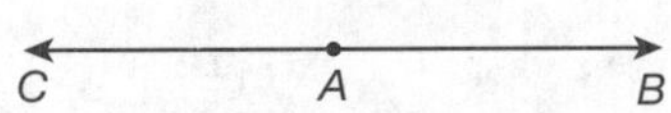

Figure 5.4

Collinear points: Three or more points are said to be collinear if there is a line which contains all of them.

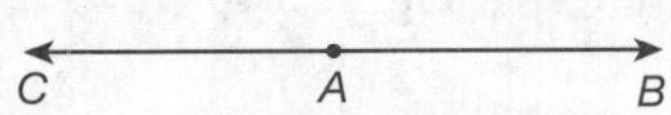

Figure 5.5

Concurrent Lines: Three or more lines are said to be concurrent if there is a point which lies on all of them (Fig 5.6).

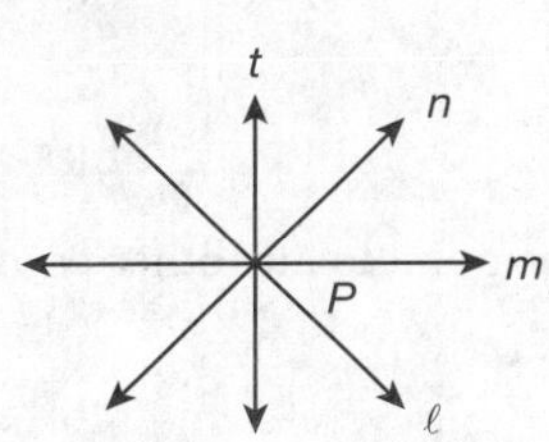

Figure 5.6

Intersecting lines: Two lines are intersecting if they have a common point. The common point is called the **'point of intersection'**.

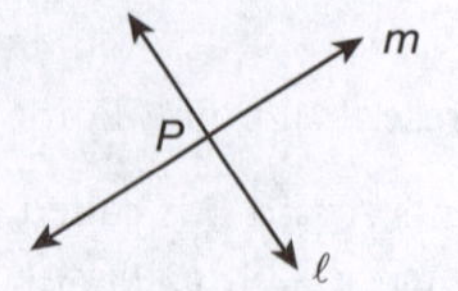

Figure 5.7

Parallel lines: Two lines l and m in a plane are said to be parallel lines if they do not have a common point.

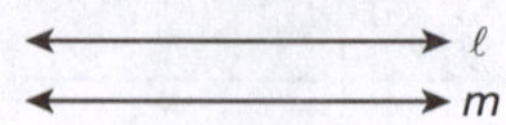

Figure 5.8

Plane: A plane is a surface such that every point of the line joining any two points on it lies on it.

Euclid's Axioms

(i) Things which are equal to the same thing are equal to one another.
If $b = a$ and $c = a$ then, $b = c$

(ii) If equals are added to equals, the wholes are equal.
If $a = b$ and $c = d$ then $a + c = b + d$

(iii) If equals are subtracted from equals, the remainders are equal.
If $a = b$ and $c = d$ then $a - c = b - d$

(iv) The things which coincide with one another are equal to one another.

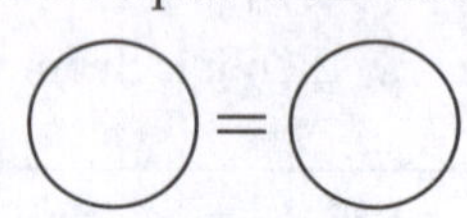

Figure 5.9

Circles with the same radii

(v) The whole is greater than the part.

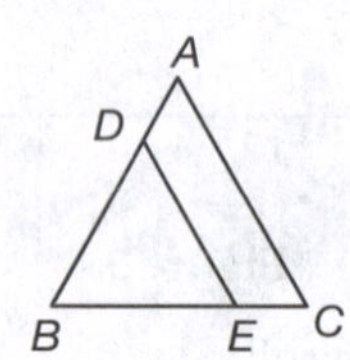

Figure 5.10

Area of $\Delta DBE <$ Area of ΔABC

(vi) The things which are double of the same thing are equal to one another.
If $y = 2x$ and $z = 2x$, then $y = z$

(vii) The things which are halves of the same thing are equal to one another.
If $y = x/2$ and $z = x/2$, then $y = z$

Euclid's Five Postulates

(i) A straight line may be drawn from any one point to any other point.

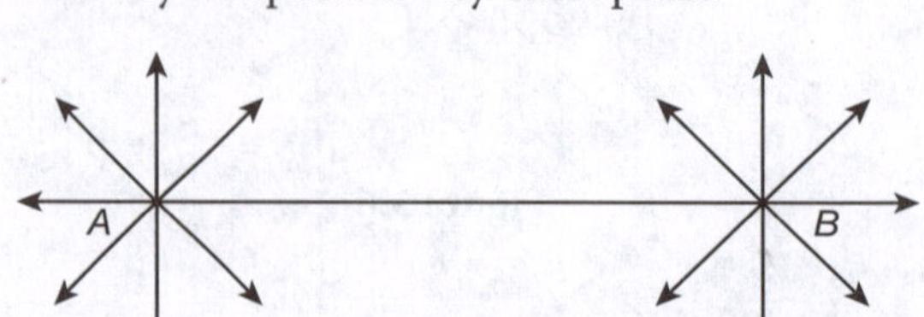

Figure 5.11

(ii) A terminated line or a line segment can be produced infinitely.

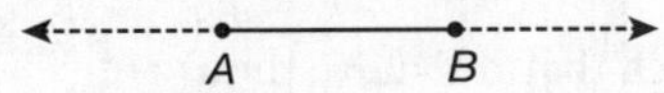

Figure 5.12

(iii) A circle can be drawn with any centre and of any radius.

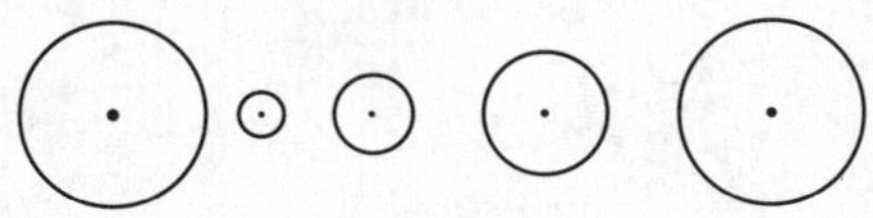

Figure 5.13

(iv) All right angles are equal to one another.

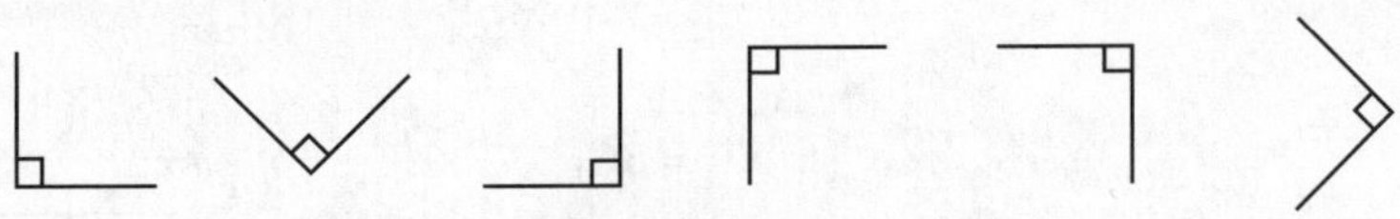

Figure 5.14

(v) If a straight line falling on two straight lines makes the interior angles on the same side of it taken together less than two right angles, then the two straight lines if produced infinitely meet on that side on which the sum of angles is less than two right angles.

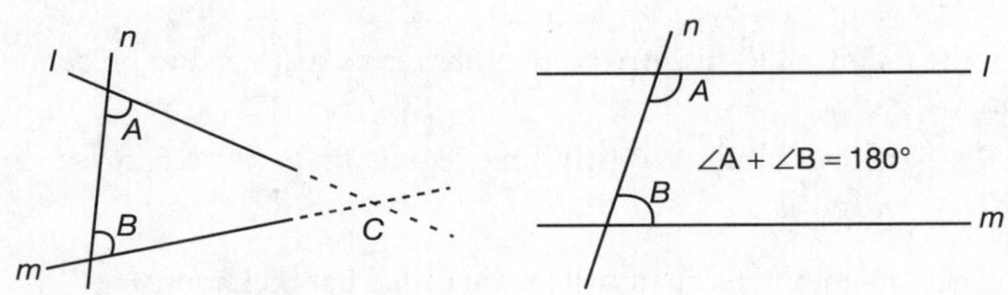

Figure 5.15

If $\angle A + \angle B < 2 \times (90^\circ) = 180^\circ$, then l and m meet at some point on the side in which $\angle A$ and $\angle B$ lie. However, if $\angle A + \angle B = 180^\circ$, then the lines l and m will never meet. In other words lines, l and m will be parallel.

$\angle A + \angle B < 180^\circ$, l and m intersect each other $\angle A + \angle B = 180^\circ$, $l \parallel m$

Incidence Axioms

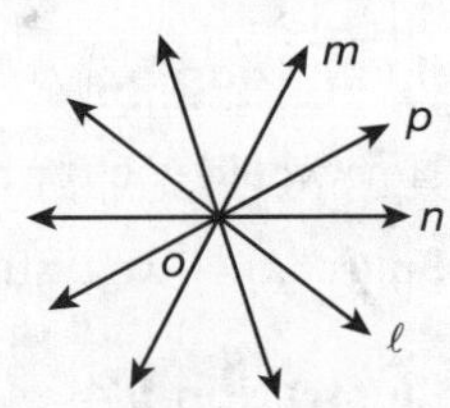

Figure 5.16

(i) A line is the collection of infinite number of points.
(ii) Through a given point, an infinite line can be drawn.
(iii) Given two distinct points, there is one and only one line that contains both points.

Parallel Axioms

If P is a point outside a line λ, then one and only one line can be drawn through P which is parallel to λ.

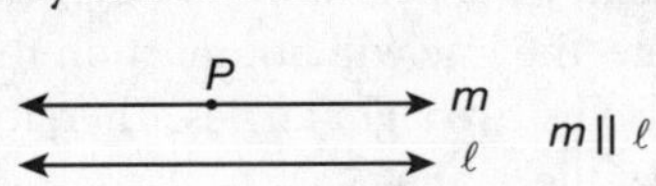

Figure 5.17

The above axioms may also be re-stated as follows: Two intersecting lines cannot both be parallel to the same line.

Illustration 5.1

If point C lies between two points A and B such that $AC = BC$, then prove that $AC = \frac{1}{2}AB$. Explain by drawing the figure.

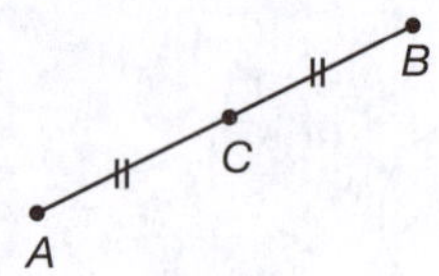

Solution: According to the given statement, the figure will be as shown alongside in which point C lies between two points A and such that $AC = BC$.

Clearly, $AC + BC = AB$

$\Rightarrow$ $AC + AC = AB$ [$\because AC = BC$]

$\Rightarrow$ $2AC = AB$

And, $AC = BC = \frac{1}{2}AB$

Keystone

- Two distinct lines cannot have more than one point in common.

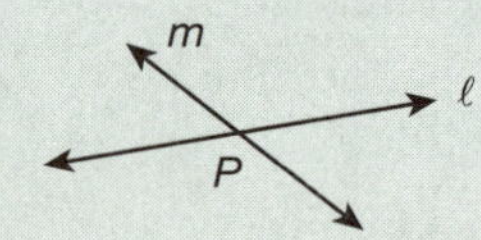

- Two lines which are both parallel to the same line are parallel to each other.
  i.e., $l \parallel n,\ m \parallel n \Rightarrow l \parallel m$

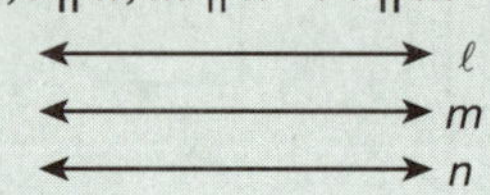

Illustration 5.2

Give a definition for each of the following terms. Are there other terms that need to be defined first? What are they, and how might you define them?

(i) Parallel lines **(ii)** Perpendicular lines **(iii)** Line segment **(iv)** Radius

Solution:

(i) Parallel lines: Lines which do not intersect anywhere are called parallel lines.

(ii) Perpendicular lines: Two lines which are at a right angle to each other are called perpendicular lines.

(iii) Line segment: It is a terminated line.

(iv) Radius: The length of the line segment joining the centre of a circle to any point on its circumference is called its radius.

Illustration 5.3

How would you rewrite Euclid's fifth postulate so that it would be easier to understand?

Solution: Two distinct intersecting lines cannot be parallel to the same line.

Illustration 5.4

Does Euclid's fifth postulate imply the existence of parallel lines? Explain.

Solution: If a straight line l falls on two straight lines m and n such that the sum of the interior angles on one side of l is two right angles, then by Euclid's fifth postulate, the line will not meet on this side of l. Next, we know that the sum of the interior angles on the other side of the line l also be two right angles. Therefore they will not meet on the other side. So, the lines m and n never meet and are, therefore parallel.

Theorem: If l, m, n are lines in the same plane such that l intersects m and $n \parallel m$, then l intersects n also.

Given:-Three lines l, m, n in the same plane show that l intersects m and $n \parallel m$.

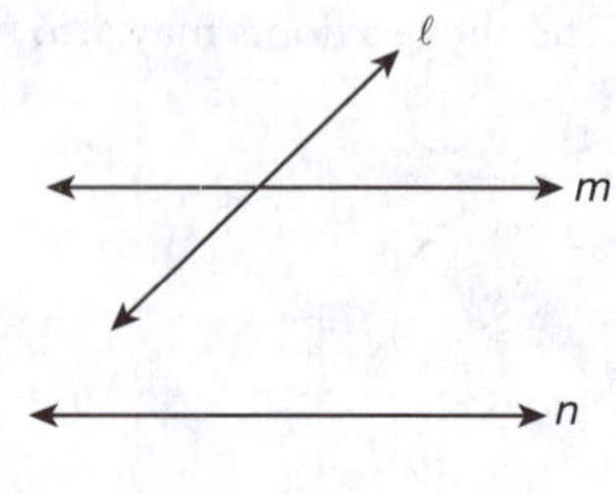

To prove: Lines l and n are intersecting lines.

Proof: Let l and n be non-intersecting lines. Then, $l \parallel n$.

But, $n \parallel m$ [Given]

$\therefore$ $l \parallel n$ and $n \parallel m \Rightarrow l \parallel m$

$\Rightarrow$ l and m are non-intersecting lines.

This is a contradiction to the hypothesis that l and m are intersecting lines.
So our supposition is wrong.
Hence, l intersects line n.

Illustration 5.5

If lines AB, AC, AD and AE are parallel to a line l, then prove that points A, B, C, D and E are collinear.

Solution: Lines AB, AC, AD and AE are parallel to a line l.

To prove: A, B, C, D, E are collinear.

Proof: Since AB, AC, AD and AE are all parallel to a line l. Therefore, point A is outside l and lines AB, AC, AD, AE are drawn through A and each line is parallel to l.

But by parallel lines axiom, one and only one line can be drawn through the point A outside it and parallel to l.

This is possible only when A, B, C, D and E all lie on the same line. Hence, A, B, C, D and E are collinear.

Check Point 1

1. Define:
   (i) Axiom (ii) Theorem
2. Define:
   (i) Collinear point (ii) Concurrent lines
3. How many lines can be drawn through two points?
4. In the figure below $CA = BD$. Show that $CB = AD$.

5. If a line segment can be drawn through 3 points A, B and C, what can you say about these points?

STRUCTURAL OUTLINE

Euclid's Geometry

Euclid's Definitions

(i) A point is that which has no part.
(ii) A line is breadthless length.
(iii) The ends of a line segment are points.
(iv) A straight line is that which has length only.
(v) A surface is that which has length and breadth only.
(vi) The edges of asurface are lines.
(vii) A plane surface is that which lies evenly with the straight lines on itself.

Geometrical concepts

Axioms: The basic facts which are taken for granted, without proof, are called axioms.

Statements: A sentence which can be judged to be true or false is called a sentence.

Theorems: A statement that requires a proof, is called a theorem. Establishing the truth of a theorem is known as proving the theorem.

Corollary: A statement whose truth can easily be decided from a theorem, is called its corollary.

Conjecture: In mathematics, a conjecture is a conclusion or proposition based on incomplete information.

Euclid's Five Postulates

(i) A straight line may be drawn from any one point to any other point.
(ii) A terminated line or a line segment can be produced infinitely.
(iii) A circle can be drawn with any centre and of any radius.
(iv) All right angles are equal to one another.
(v) If a straight line falling on two straight lines makes the interior angles on the same side of it taken together less than two right angles, then the two straight lines if produced infinitely meet on that side on which the sum of angles are less than two right angles.

Euclid's Axioms

(i) Things which are equal to the same thing are equal to one another.
(ii) If equal are added to equals, the wholes are equal.
(iii) If equal are subtracted from equals, the remainders are equal.
(iv) The things which coincide with one another are equal to one another.
(v) The whole is greater than the part.
(vi) The thing which are double of the same thing are equal to one another.
(vii) The thing which are halves of the same thing are equal to one another.

ASSESSMENT CORNER

Fixed Response Type

Fill in the Blanks

1. Two lines intersect each other at a ______.
2. The number of line segments determined by three non-collinear points is ______.
3. If equals be added to equals, then wholes are ______.
4. All right angles are equal, is stated in the form of ______.
5. 'Whole is greater than the part'. Is stated as in the form of ______.

True/False

1. In figure, if $AB = PQ$ and $PQ = XY$, then $AB = XY$.

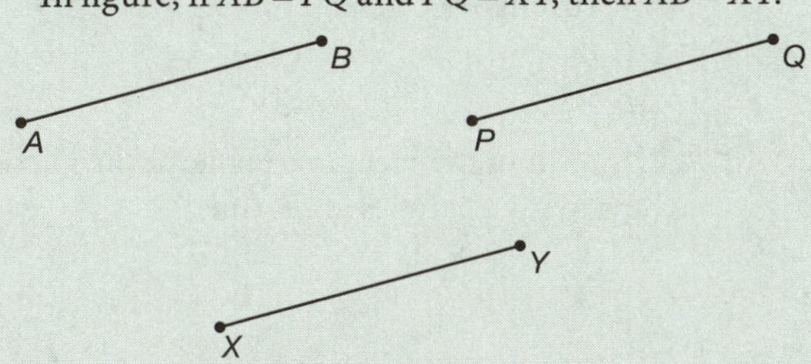

2. Only one line can pass through a single point.
3. If two circles are equal, then their radii are equal.
4. A terminated line can be produced indefinitely on both sides.
5. There are an infinite number of lines which pass through two distinct points.
6. A line segment has one end-point only

Single Correct Type Questions

1. A proof is required for:
   (A) Postulate (B) Axiom
   (C) Theorem (D) Definition
2. How many number of lines does pass through two distinct points?
   (A) 1 (B) 2
   (C) 3 (D) 4
3. Which of the following is an example of a geometrical line?
   (A) Black Board
   (B) Sheet of paper
   (C) Meeting place of two walls
   (D) Tip of the sharp pencil
4. Given four points such that no three of them are collinear, then the number of lines that can be drawn through any of the two points is:
   (A) 2 lines (B) 4 lines
   (C) 6 lines (D) 8 lines
5. Two planes intersect each other to form a:
   (A) Plane (B) point
   (C) Straight line (D) angle
6. 'Lines are parallel if they do not intersect' is stated in the form of:
   (A) An axiom (B) a definition
   (C) A postulate (D) a proof
7. Select the wrong statement.
   (A) Only one line can pass through a single point
   (B) Only one line can pass through two distinct points
   (C) A line consists of infinite number of points.
   (D) If two circles are equal, then their radii are equal
8. Number of dimension(s) a surface has:
   (A) 0 (B) 1
   (C) 2 (D) 3
9. The number of line segments determined by three collinear points is:
   (A) Two (B) Three
   (C) Only one (D) Four
10. If the point P lies in between M and N and C is the midpoint of MP, then:
    (A) $MC + PN = MN$ (B) $MP + CP = MN$
    (C) $MC + CN = MN$ (D) None of these
11. If equals be added to equals, then whole are:
    (A) Unequal (B) twice of each other
    (C) Half of the other (D) equal
12. A circle can be drawn with any Centre and any radius, is stated in the form of:
    (A) An axiom (B) a postulate
    (C) A definition (D) a theorem
13. Euclid's first axiom is:
    (A) If equals are added to equals, the wholes are equal
    (B) The whole is greater than part
    (C) Things which are equal to the same things are equal to one another

(D) Things which coincide with another are equal to one another.

14. Euclid's third postulate is:
(A) A circle can be drawn with any centre and any radius
(B) A straight line may be drawn from any one point to any other point
(C) All right angles are equal to one another
(D) A terminated line can be produced infinitely

15. 'Whole is greater than the part'. Is stated in the form of:
(A) A postulate (B) a definition
(C) An axiom (D) a theorem

16. Euclid stated that all right angles are equal to one another in the form of a/an _______.
(A) Axiom (B) Definition
(C) Postulate (D) Proof

17. If P, Q and R are three points on a line, and Q lies between P and R, then:
(A) $PQ + QR = PR$ (B) $PR + RQ = PQ$
(C) $RP + QR = PQ$ (D) None of these

Multiple Correct Type Questions

1. Which of the following is/are correct?
(A) A plane surface is a surface which lies evenly with a straight line on itself.
(B) A surface is that which has length and breadth only.
(C) A line is breadthless length.
(D) A point is that which has no part.

2. Which of the following is/are Euclid's axioms?
(A) Things which are equal to the same thing are never equal to one another.
(B) If equals are added to equals, the wholes are equal.
(C) The whole is greater than the part.
(D) Things which are halves of the same things are equal to one another.

3. Which of the following is/are Euclid's postulates?
(A) A straight line may be drawn from any one point to any other point.
(B) A circle can be drawn with any centre and any radius.
(C) A terminated line cannot be produced indefinitely.
(D) All right angles are never equal to one another.

4. Which of the following is/are incorrect?
(A) A triangle whose sides are equal is called a scalene triangle.
(B) A triangle, each of whose angles is less than 90°, is called an acute triangle.
(C) If all sides of a polygon are different, it is called a regular polygon.
(D) A triangle with one of its angles greater than 90°, is known as an obtuse triangle.

5. Which postulate of Euclid states that a terminated line can be produced indefinitely?
(A) 4 (B) 3
(C) 2 (D) 1

6. How many lines can be drawn parallel to a given line through the given point?
(A) 4 (B) 3
(C) 2 (D) 1

7. If four lines intersect in a plane, at the maximum how many triangles are formed?
(A) 1 (B) 2
(C) 3 (D) 4

8. If $x = y$, then which of the following is correct?
(A) $x + y = y - z$ (B) $x - z = y + z$
(C) $x - z = y - z$ (D) All of these

9. In a plane, two straight lines have at the most _________ point(*s*) in common
(A) one (B) two
(C) three (D) infinite

10. If two circles are congruent, then their _________ are equal
(A) radii (B) diameters
(C) circumferences (D) All of these

11. A line segment has _________ endpoints.
(A) no (B) one
(C) two (D) infinite

Free Response Type

Very Short Answer Type Questions

1. Find the number of dimensions, a point has.

2. A pyramid is a solid figure, which plane figure forms the base of it?

3. It is known that if $x + y = 10$ then $x + y + z = 10 + z$. Write Euclid's axiom that illustrates this statement.

4. Write whether the following statements are True or False? Justify your answer.

ASSESSMENT CORNER

(i) Euclidean geometry is valid only for curved surfaces.
(ii) The boundaries of the solids are curves.
(iii) The edges of a surface are curves.
(iv) The things which are double of the same thing are equal to one another.
(v) If a quantity B is a part of another quantity A, then A can be written as the sum of B and some third quantity C.
(vi) The statements that are proved are called axioms.
(vii) 'For every line l and for every point P not lying on a given line l, there exists a unique line m passing through P and parallel to l' is known as Play fair's axiom.

5. How many lines can pass through:
(i) One point (ii) Two distinct points

6. Find the number of points in which two distinct straight lines may intersect.

7. A, B and C are three collinear points such that point A lies between B and C. Name all the line segments determined by these points and write the relation between them.

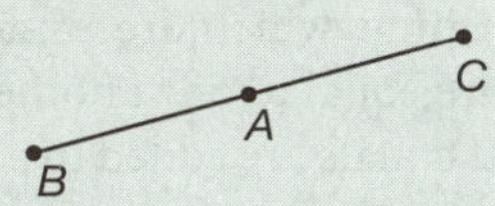

8. (i) How many lines can be drawn to pass through three given points if they are not collinear?
(ii) How many line segments can be drawn to pass through two given points?

9. Define
(a) line segment (b) radius of a circle

10. Define
(a) square (b) perpendicular lines

Short Answer Type Questions

1. If point C lies between two points A and B such that $AC = BC$, then prove that $AC = \frac{1}{2}AB$. Explain by drawing the figure.

2. Prove that every line segment has one and only one midpoint.

3. L, M, N are three lines in the same plane such that L intersect M and $M \parallel N$. Show that L also intersects N

4. Using Euclid axiom find x, if $3x + 5 = 17$

5. If AB is a line and P is a fixed point, outside AB, how many lines can be drawn through P which are:
(i) Parallel to AB
(ii) Not parallel to AB.

6. Out of the three lines AB, CD and EF, if AB is parallel to EF and CD is also parallel to EF, then what is the relation between AB and CD?

7. If A, B and C are three points on a line, and B lies between A and C, then prove that $AB + BC = AC$.

8. In the given figure, if $AB = CD$; prove that $AC = BD$.

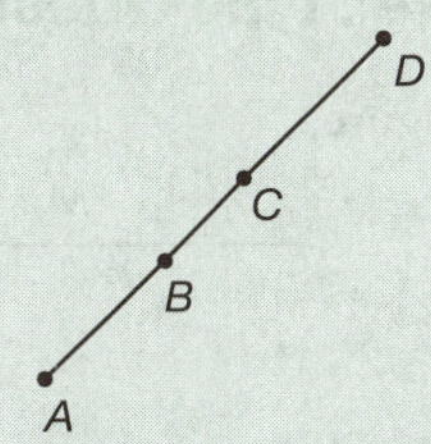

9. Solve the equation $a - 15 = 25$ and state which axiom do you use here.

10. In the figure, we have: $AC = XD$, C is the midpoint of AB and D is the midpoint of XY. Using an Euclid's axiom, show that $AB = XY$.

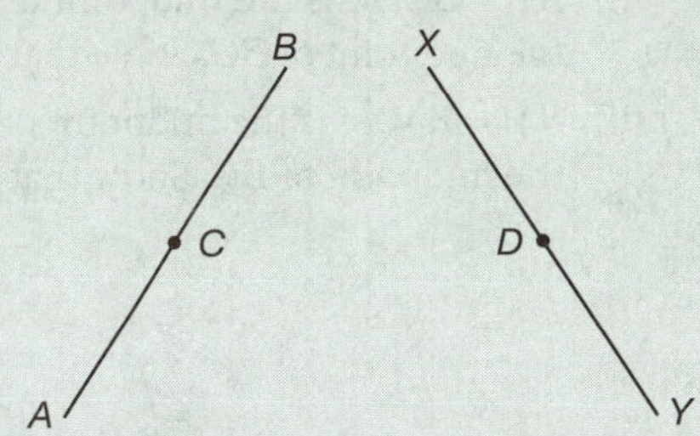

11. In the figure, we have:

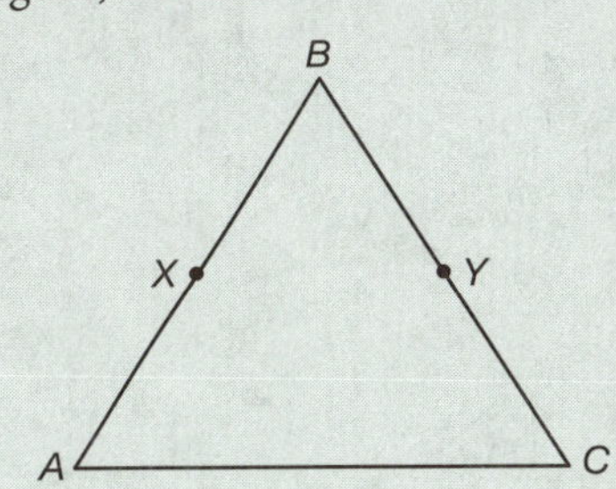

$BX = \frac{1}{2}AB$, $BY = \frac{1}{2}BC$ and $AB = BC$. Show that $BX = BY$.

12. In the figure, we have $\angle 1 = \angle 3$ and $\angle 2 = \angle 4$. Show that $\angle A = \angle C$.

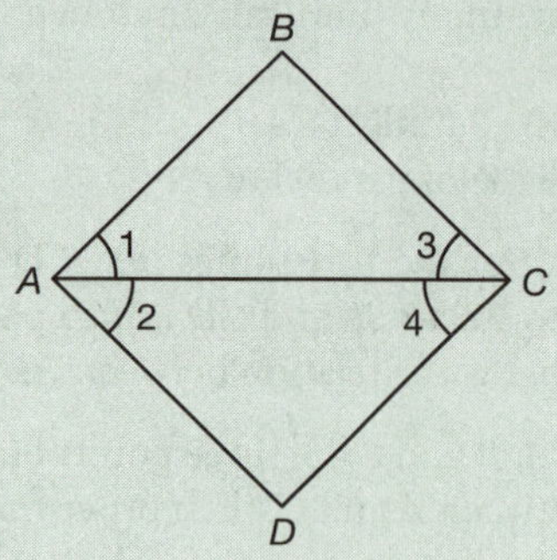

Long Answer Type Questions

1. In the figure,

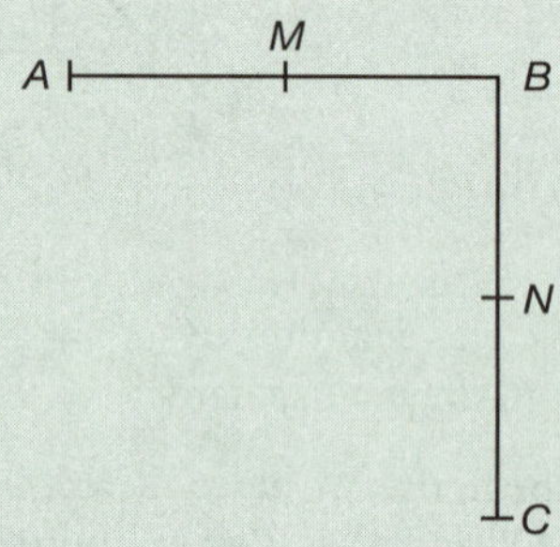

(i) $AB = BC$, M is the midpoint of AB and N is the midpoint of BC. Show that $AM = NC$.

(ii) $BM = BN$, M is the midpoint of AB and N is the midpoint of BC. Show that $AB = BC$.

2. Read the following statement:
An equilateral triangle is a polygon made up of three line segments out of which two line segments are equal to the third one and all its angles are 60° each.
Define the terms used in this definition which you feel necessary. Are there any undefined terms in this? Can you justify that all sides and all angles are equal in an equilateral triangle?

3. Study the following statement:
"Two intersecting lines cannot be perpendicular to the same line".
Check whether it is an equivalent version to Euclid's fifth postulate.

4. Read the following two statements which are taken as axioms:
   (i) If two lines intersect each other, then the vertically opposite angles are not equal.
   (ii) If a ray stands on a line, then the sum of two adjacent angles so formed is equal to 180°.
Is this system of axioms consistent? Justify your answer.

5. Read the following axioms:
   (i) Things which are equal to the same thing are equal to one another.
   (ii) If equals are added to equals, the wholes are equal.
   (iii) Things which are double of the same thing are equal to one another.
Check whether the given system of axioms is consistent or inconsistent.

ANSWER KEY

CHECK POINTS

Check Point 1

3. 1 **5.** Points A, B, C are collinear points

Assessment Corner

FIXED RESPONSE TYPE

Fill in the Blanks

1. Point **2.** 3 **3.** Equal **4.** Postulate **5.** Axioms

True/False

1. True **2.** False **3.** True **4.** False **5.** False **6.** False

Single Correct Type Questions

1. C **2.** A **3.** C **4.** C **5.** C **6.** B **7.** A **8.** C **9.** B
10. C **11.** D **12.** B **13.** C **14.** A **15.** C **16.** C **17.** A

Multiple Correct Type Questions

1. ABCD **2.** ABCD **3.** ABC **4.** AC **5.** C **6.** D **7.** D **8.** C
9. AD **10.** ABCD **11.** C

FREE RESPONSE TYPE

Very Short Answer Type Questions

1. 1 **2.** Triangle or Rectangle
3. If equal are added to equals, the wholes are equal.
4. (i) False (ii) False (iii) False (iv) True (v) True (vi) True (vii) True
5. (i) Infinite (ii) One **6.** 1
7. AB, AC, BC then $BC = BA + AC$ **8.** (i) 0 (ii) 1
9. (a) A Part of a line (b) Distance between circumference and centre of a circle
10. (a) A quadrilateral in which all sides and angles are equal.
(b) Angle between two lines is 90°

Short Answer Type Questions

4. $x = 4$ **5.** (i) 1 (ii) Infinite **6.** AB and CD are parallel **9.** $a = 40$

Long Answer Type Questions

3. Yes for that they should be parallel. **4.** (i) False (ii) Yes. **5.** (i) Yes (ii) Yes (iii) Yes

CHAPTER 6

Lines and Angles

Learning Outcomes

After reading this chapter, you would be able to:

- angles and their types.
- angles made by transversal.
- angles in a triangle.

Geekspeak

- Points
- Line
- Angles
- Acute angle
- Obtuse angle
- Right angle
- Straight line
- Reflex angle
- Complete angle
- Vertical opposite angle
- Alternate interior angle
- Corresponding angle
- Co-interior angle
- Exterior angle
- Complementary angle
- Supplementary angle
- Linear pair of angles
- Adjacent angles

Introduction

You have already studied about points, lines and angles in our earlier classes. In this chapter, you will study the properties of the angle formed when two lines intersect each other, and also the properties of the angles formed when a line intersects two or more parallel lines at distinct points.

Line

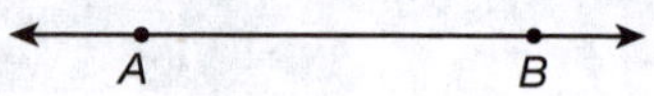

Figure 6.1

A geometrical line is a set of points that extends endlessly in both directions i.e., a line has no endpoints. It has only length. The arrowheads show that the line goes on endlessly on either side (Fig 6.1). Lines are denoted by small letters *l*, *m*, *n*

Basic term and definition

Some basic terms related to line are described below

Point

A point is represented by a dot. It has no dimensions like length, breadth or thickness. It has only position.

Points are denoted by capital letters *A*, *B*, *C*, *D*, etc.

A dot made by a sharp pencil is a point.

Line Segment

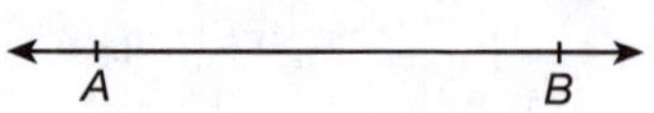

Figure 6.2

A line segment is a line which has endpoints. In the figure, the part of the line between the points '*A*' and '*B*', including '*A*' and '*B*' is a line segment. The line segment *AB* is represented as *AB* or segment *AB*.

Plane

A plane is a set of points. It is a flat surface with length and breadth. A geometrical plane extends endlessly in all directions. Small letters are used to denote a plane.

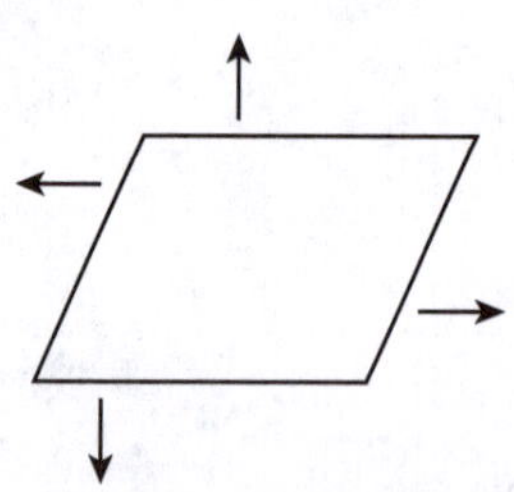
Figure 6.3

E.g., the surface of a sheet of paper and the surface of a wall.

Coplanar Points

The points that belong to the same plane are called coplanar points.

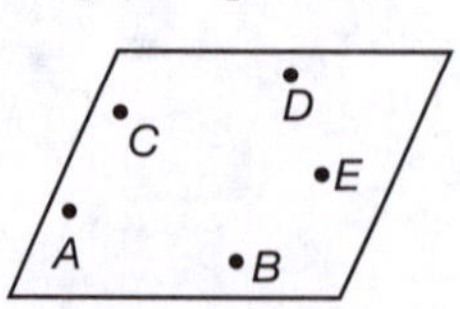

Figure 6.4

Coplanar Lines

The lines that lie in the same plane are called coplanar lines.

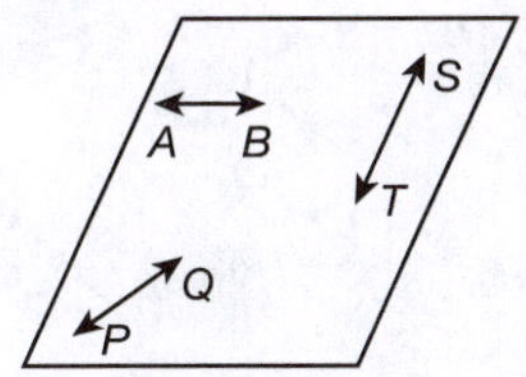

Figure 6.5

Space

The universal set of points, lines and planes is called a space. It has no end.

Distance Between Two Points

The distance between two points A and B is the length of the line segment joining them. The distance between A and B is denoted by $d(A, B)$ or AB.

Midpoint

Given a line segment AB, a point M is said to be the midpoint of AB, if M is an interior point of AB, such that $AM = MB$.

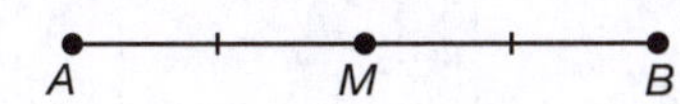

Figure 6.6

Perpendicular Bisector

A line 'l' passing through the midpoint 'M' of a line segment $\overline{AB}$ and perpendicular to AB is called the perpendicular bisector of the line segment $\overline{AB}$.

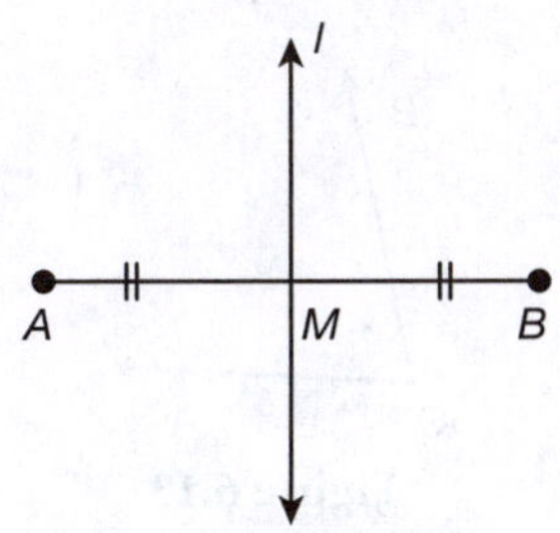

Figure 6.7

Collinear Points

If three or more points lie on a straight line, then those points are called collinear points.

In Fig 6.8, A, B, C, D and E are collinear.

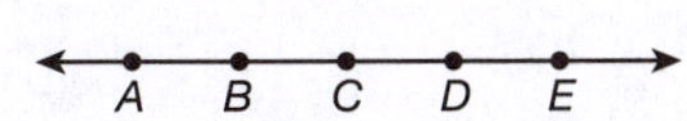

Figure 6.8

Non-collinear Points

The points which do not lie on a straight line are called non-collinear points.

In Fig. 6.9, G, H, I do not lie on the straight line 'l'.

Hence, they are non-collinear points.

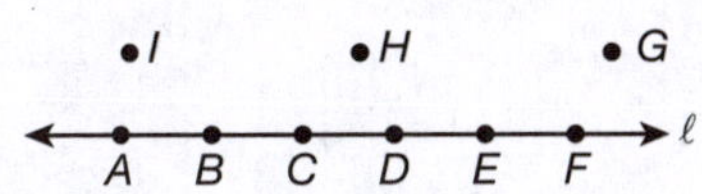

Figure 6.9

Angles

An angle is the union of two non-collinear rays with a common initial point. The common initial point is called the **'vertex'** of the angle and two rays are called the **'arms'** of the angle.

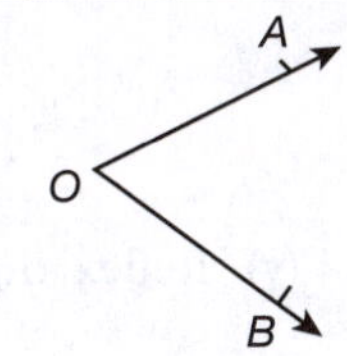

Figure 6.10

Angle addition axiom: If X is a point in the interior of $\angle BAC$ (Fig 6.11), then $m\ \angle BAC = m\ \angle BAX + m\ \angle XAC$.

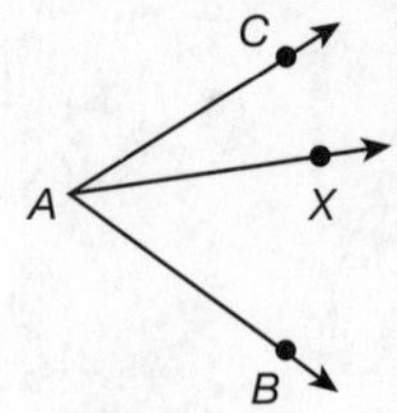

Figure 6.11

> **Keystone**
>
> Every angle has a measure and the unit of measurement is degree.
>
> One right angle = 90°
>
> 1° = 60′ (minutes)
>
> 1′ = 60″ (Seconds)

Types of Angles

(i) **Right angle:** An angle whose measure is 90° is called a **right angle.**

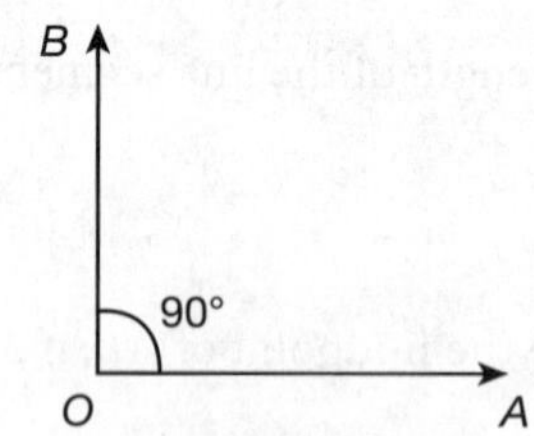

Figure 6.12

(ii) **Acute angle:** An angle whose measure is less than 90° is called an **acute angle.**

$$0° < \angle BOA < 90°$$

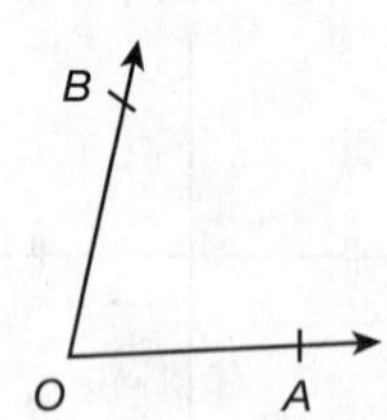

Figure 6.13

(iii) **Obtuse angle:** An angle whose measure is more than 90° but less than 180° is called an **obtuse angle.**

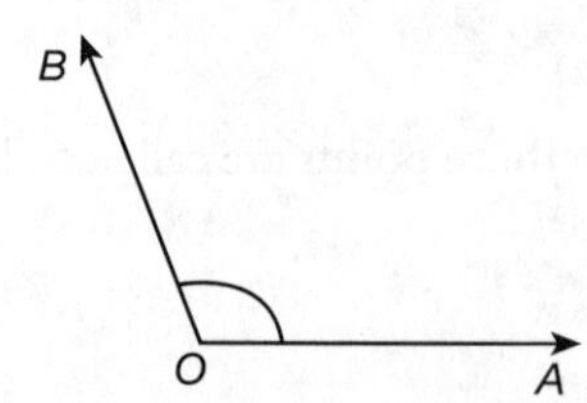

$$90° < \angle AOB < 180°.$$

Figure 6.14

(iv) **Straight angle:** An angle whose measure is 180° is called a **straight angle.**

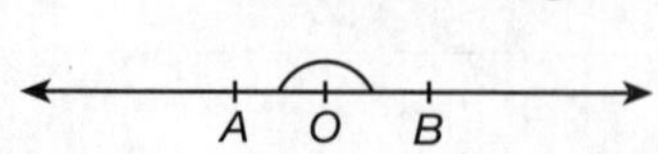

Figure 6.15

(v) **Reflex angle:** An angle whose measure is more than 180° is called a **reflex angle.**

$$180° < \angle AOB < 360°.$$

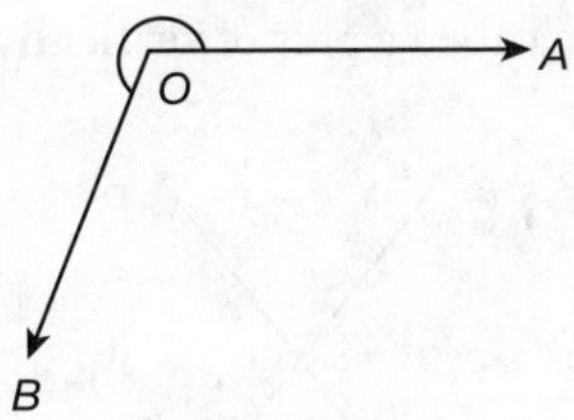

Figure 6.16

(vi) Complementary angles: Two angles, the sum of whose measures is 90° are called **complementary angles**.

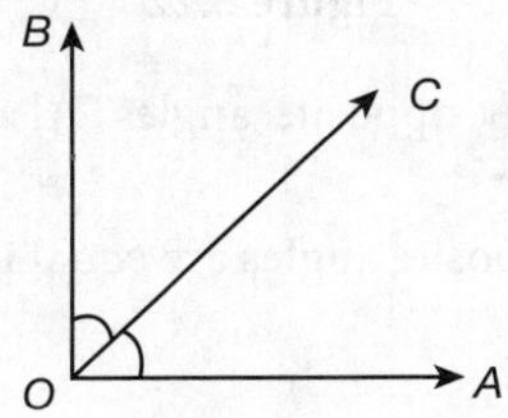

Figure 6.17

$\angle AOC$ and $\angle BOC$ are complementary as their sum is 90°.

(vii) Supplementary angles: Two angles, the sum of whose measures is 180°, are called the **supplementary angles**.

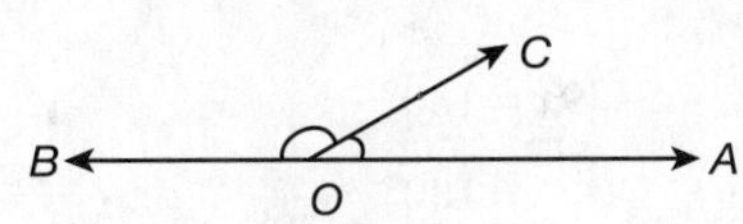

Figure 6.18

$\angle AOC$ and $\angle BOC$ are supplementary as their sum is 180°.

(viii) Angle Bisectors: A ray OX is said to be the bisector of $\angle AOB$, if X is a point in the interior of $\angle AOB$ (Fig. 6.19), and $\angle AOX = \angle BOX$.

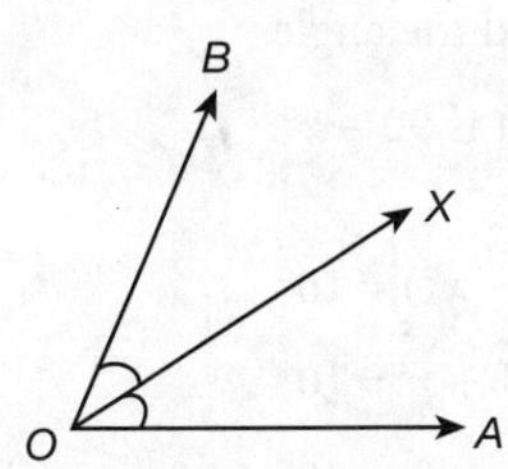

Figure 6.19

(ix) Adjacent angles: Two angles are called **adjacent angles**, if:

(I) They have the same vertex,

(II) They have a common arm,

(III) Non-common arms are on either side of the common arm.

$\angle AOX$ and $\angle BOX$ are adjacent angles, OX is a common arm, OA and OB are non-common arms and lie on either side of OX (Fig. 6.20).

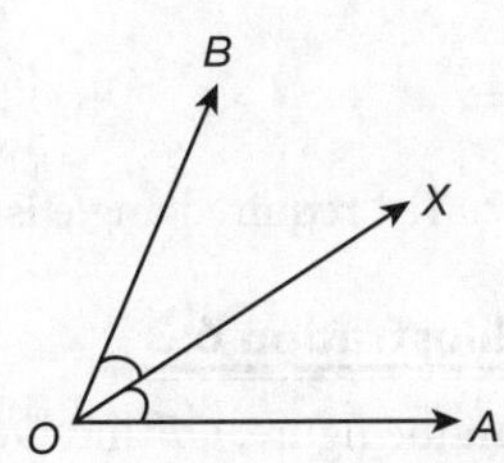

Figure 6.20

(x) Linear pair of angles: Two adjacent angles are said to form a linear pair of angles, if their non-common arms are two opposite rays.

$$\angle AOC + \angle BOC = 180°.$$

Figure 6.21

(xi) Vertically opposite angles: Two angles are called a pair of **vertically opposite angles**, if their arms form two pairs of opposite rays.

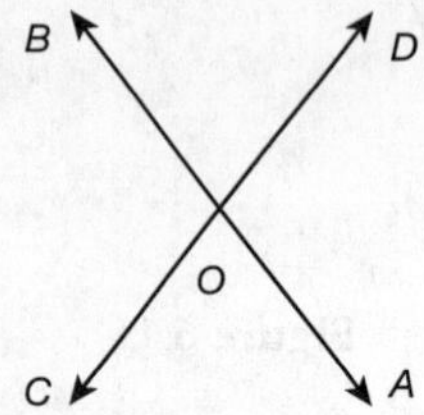

Figure 6.22

$\angle AOC$ and $\angle BOD$ form a pair of vertically opposite angles. Also, $\angle AOD$ and $\angle BOC$ form a pair of vertically opposite angles.

If two lines intersect, then the vertically opposite angles are equal i.e., $\angle AOC = \angle BOD$ and $\angle BOC = \angle AOD$.

Illustration 6.1

Two supplementary angles are in ratio 4 : 5, find the angles.

Solution: Let angles be $4x$ and $5x$.

$\therefore$ Angles are supplementary.

So, $4x + 5x = 180°$

$$\Rightarrow \quad 9x = 180°$$

$$\Rightarrow \quad x = \frac{180°}{9} = 20°$$

$\therefore$ Angles are $4 \times 20°$, $5 \times 20° \Rightarrow 80°$ and $100°$.

Illustration 6.2

If an angle differs from its complement by 10°, find the angle.

Solution: Let the angle is $x°$ then its complement is $90 - x°$.

Now given,

$$x° - (90 - x°) = 10°$$

$$\Rightarrow \quad x° - 90° + x° = 10°$$

$$\Rightarrow \quad 2x° = 10° + 90° = 100°$$

$$\Rightarrow \quad x° = \frac{100°}{2} = 50°$$

$\therefore$ The required angle is 50°.

Illustration 6.3

In the figure, OP and OQ bisect $\angle BOC$ and $\angle AOC$ respectively. Prove that $\angle POQ = 90°$.

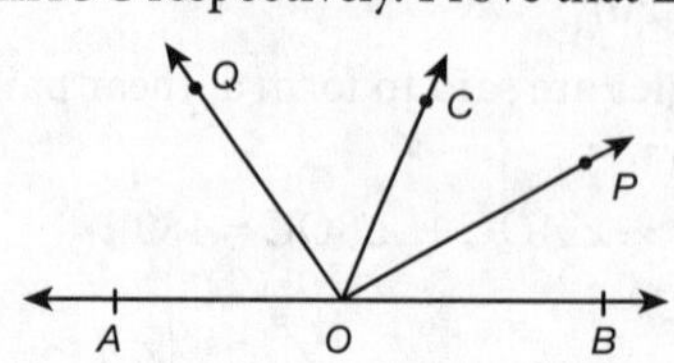

Solution: $\because$ OP bisects $\angle BOC$

$$\therefore \quad \angle POC = \frac{1}{2} BOC \quad \ldots(i)$$

Also, OQ bisects $\angle AOC$

$\therefore \quad \angle COQ = \frac{1}{2}\angle AOC \quad \ldots(ii)$

$\because \quad OC$ stands on AB

$\therefore \quad \angle AOC + \angle BOC = 180^\circ \quad$ [Linear pair]

$\Rightarrow \quad \frac{1}{2}\angle AOC + \frac{1}{2}\angle BOC = \frac{1}{2}\times 180^\circ$

$\Rightarrow \quad \angle COQ + \angle POC = 90^\circ \quad$ [Using (i) and (ii)]

$\Rightarrow \quad \angle POQ = 90^\circ \quad$ [By angle sum property]

Hence, Proved.

Illustration 6.4

In the figure, lines AB, CD and EF intersect at O. Find the measures of $\angle AOC$, $\angle DOE$ and $\angle BOF$.

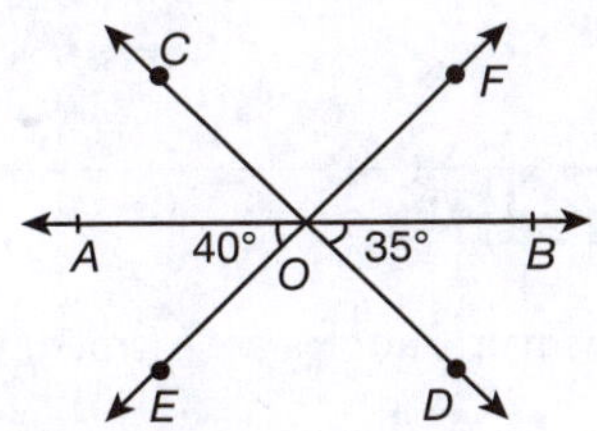

Solution: Given $\angle AOE = 40^\circ$ and $\angle BOD = 35^\circ$

Clearly $\quad \angle AOC = \angle BOD \quad$ [Vertically opposite angles]

$\Rightarrow \quad \angle AOC = 35^\circ$

$\angle BOF = \angle AOE \quad$ [Vertically opposite angles]

$\Rightarrow \quad \angle BOF = 400$

Now, $\quad \angle AOB = 180^\circ \quad$ [Straight angles]

$\Rightarrow \quad \angle AOC + \angle COF + \angle BOF = 180^\circ \quad$ [Angles sum property]

$\Rightarrow \quad 35^\circ + \angle COF + 40^\circ = 180^\circ$

$\Rightarrow \quad \angle COF = 180^\circ - 75^\circ = 105^\circ$

Now, $\quad \angle DOE = \angle COF \quad$ [Vertically opposite angles]

$\therefore \quad \angle DOE = 105^\circ.$

Check Point 1

1. Find the supplement of $100^\circ\ 48'$.
2. Find the angle such that an angle is equal to its supplement.
3. Find the angle such that an angle is equal to its complement.
4. In the given figure below, find the value of y.

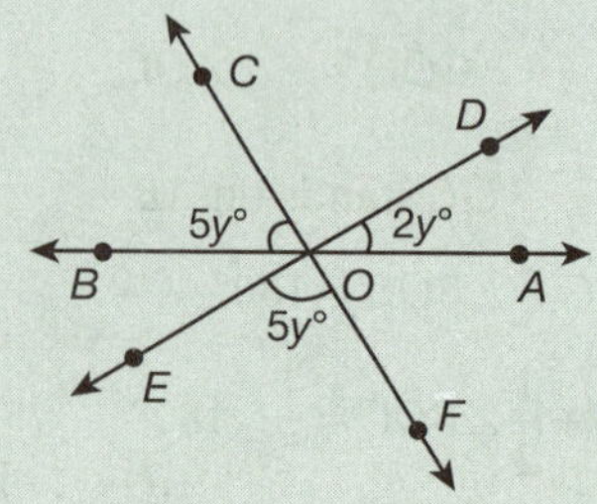

5. In the figure PQR is a straight line and $\angle PQS : \angle SQR = 7 : 5$. Find $\angle SQR$.

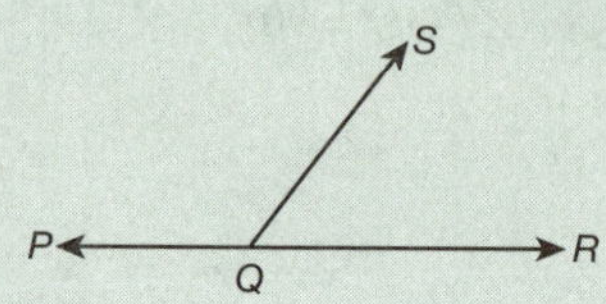

Angles Made by Transversal

When a transversal intersects two parallel lines, several angles are formed, which can be categorized into different types.

Basic Term and Definition

Some basic terms related to parallel line are described below.

Parallel Lines

Two lines l and m in the same plane are said to be parallel lines if they do not intersect when produced indefinitely in either direction and we write $l \parallel m$ which is read as l is parallel to m.

Clearly, when $l \parallel m$, we have $m \parallel l$.

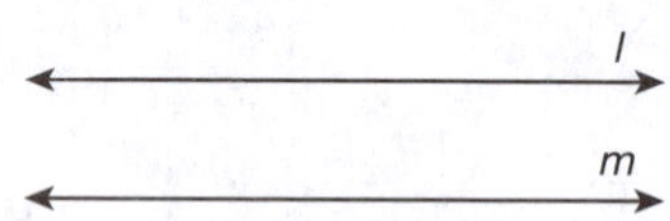

Figure 6.23

Parallel Rays

Two rays are parallel if the corresponding lines determined by them are parallel. In other words, two rays in the same plane are parallel. If they do not intersect each other even if extended indefinitely beyond their initial points.

In figure 6.24, ray $OA \parallel$ ray PQ.

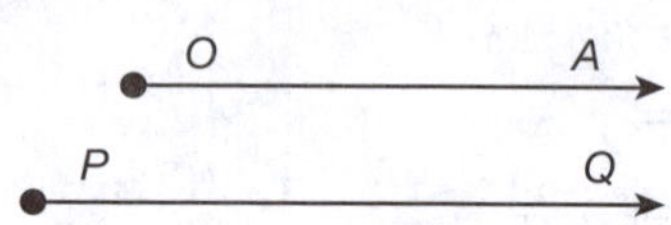

Figure 6.24

Parallel Segments

Two segments are parallel if the corresponding lines determined by them are parallel.

In other words, two segments which are in the same plane and do not intersect each other even if extended indefinitely in both directions are said to be parallel.

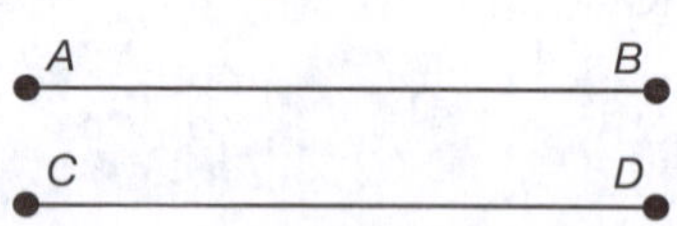

Figure 6.25

Angles Made by a Transversal

A line which intersects two or more given lines at distinct points is called a transversal to the given lines.

- **Exterior angles:** The angles whose arms do not include the line segment PQ are called **exterior angles**. In figure, angles 1, 2, 7 and 8 are exterior angles.
- **Interior angles:** The angles whose arms include line segment PQ are called **interior angles**. In figure, angles 3, 4, 5 and 6 are interior angles.

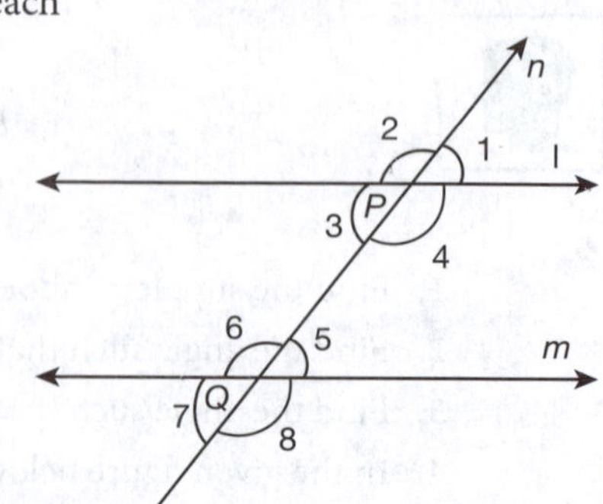

Figure 6.26

- **Corresponding angles:** A pair of angles in which one arm of both the angles is on the same side of the transversal and their other arms are directed in the same sense is called a pair of **corresponding angles**.
  In the figure $\angle 1, \angle 5; \angle 2, \angle 6; \angle 3, \angle 7$ and $\angle 4, \angle 8$ are four pairs of corresponding angles.
- **Alternate interior angles:** A pair of angles in which one arm of each of the angles is on the opposite side of the transversal and whose other arm includes the segment *PQ* is called a pair of **alternate interior angles**. In the figure $\angle 3, \angle 5; \angle 4$ and $\angle 6$ are alternate interior angles.
- **Alternate exterior angles:** A pair of angles in which one arm of each of the angles is on opposite sides of the transversal and whose other arms are directed in opposite directions and do not include segment *PQ* is called a pair of **alternate exterior angles**. In figure, $\angle 2, \angle 8; \angle 1$ and $\angle 7$ are alternate exterior angles.

Keystone

- Lines in a plane are parallel, if they do not intersect when produced indefinitely in either direction.
- The distance between two intersecting lines is zero.
- The distance between two parallel lines is the same everywhere and is equal to the perpendicular distance between them.

Transversal to Two Parallel Lines

If two parallel lines are intersected by a transversal, then:

- Pairs of alternate (interior or exterior) angles are equal.
- Pairs of corresponding angles are equal.
- Interior angles on the same side of the transversal are supplementary.

If two non-parallel lines are intersected by transversal then none of (i), (ii) and (iii) hold true.

If two lines are intersected by a transversal, then they are parallel if anyone of the following is true:

(i) Pair of corresponding angles are equal.

(ii) Pair of alternate interior angles are equal.

(iii) Pair of interior angles on the same side of the transversal are supplementary.

Illustration 6.5

In figure if $l \parallel m$, $n \parallel p$ and $\angle 1 = 85°$ find $\angle 2$.

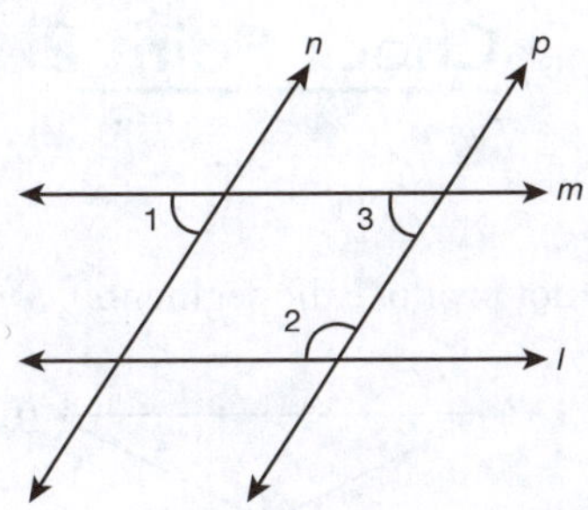

Solution: $\because n \parallel p$ and m are transversal.

$\therefore$ $\angle 1 = \angle 3 = 85°$ [Corresponding angles]

Also $l \parallel m$ and p are transversal.

$\therefore$ $\angle 2 + \angle 3 = 180°$ [Co-interior angles]

$\Rightarrow$ $\angle 2 + 85° = 180°$

$\Rightarrow$ $\angle 2 = 180° - 85°$

$\Rightarrow$ $\angle 2 = 95°$.

Illustration 6.6

In the given figure, $AB \parallel CD$ and $AC \parallel BD$. If $\angle EIC = 40°$, $\angle FDG = 55°$, $\angle HIB = x°$, then the value of x is:

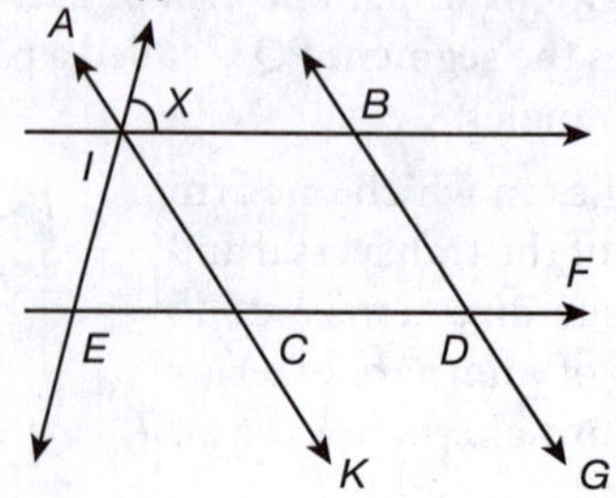

Solution:

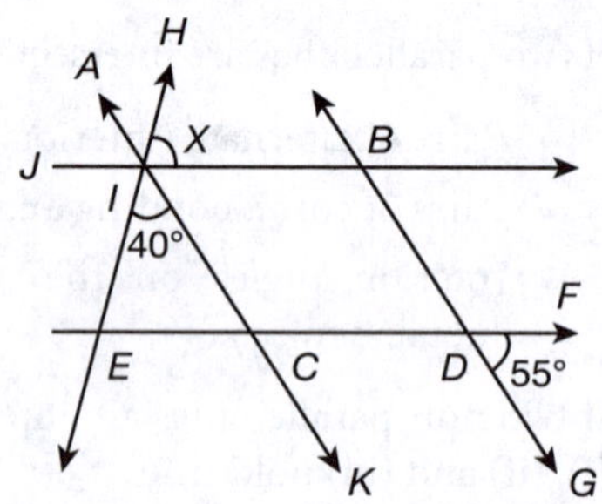

(i) $\angle AIH = \angle EIC$ (Vertically opp $\angle s$)

$\angle AIH = 40°$

(ii) $\angle BDC = \angle FDG$ (Vertically opp $\angle s$)

$\therefore \angle BDC = 55°$

$\angle ICE = \angle BDC$ (Corresponding $\angle s$)

$\therefore \angle ICE = 55°$

$\angle AIJ = \angle ICE$ (Corresponding $\angle s$)

$\therefore \angle AIJ = 55°$

$\angle x = 180° - (\angle AIJ + \angle HIA)$ {Linear pair}

$\angle x = 180° - (55° + 40°)$

$\angle x = 180° - 95° = 85°$

Check Point 2

6. In the following diagram, list out:

(i) Pairs of corresponding angles.

(ii) Pairs of alternate angles (Do not produce the segments).

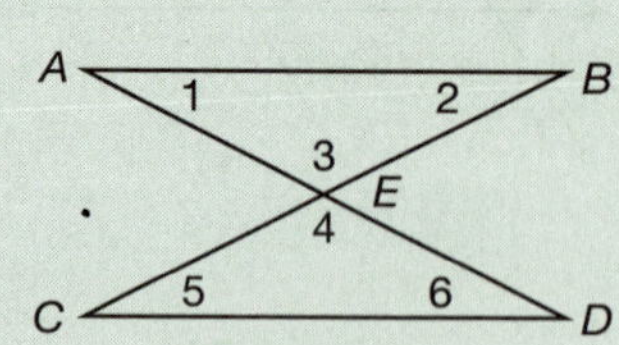

7. In the figure, $\angle 4 = 4x$, $\angle 3 = 2.5x + 24°$, find the value of x, given that $AD \parallel CB$.

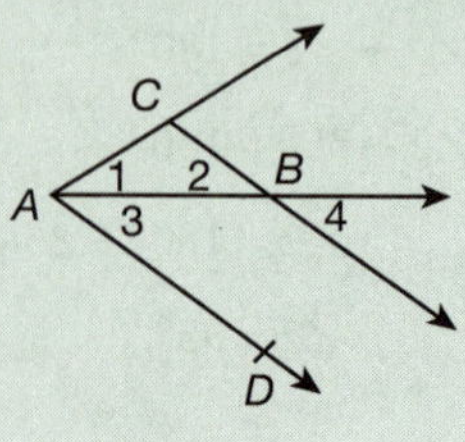

8. In the given figure find x, if $m \parallel n$.

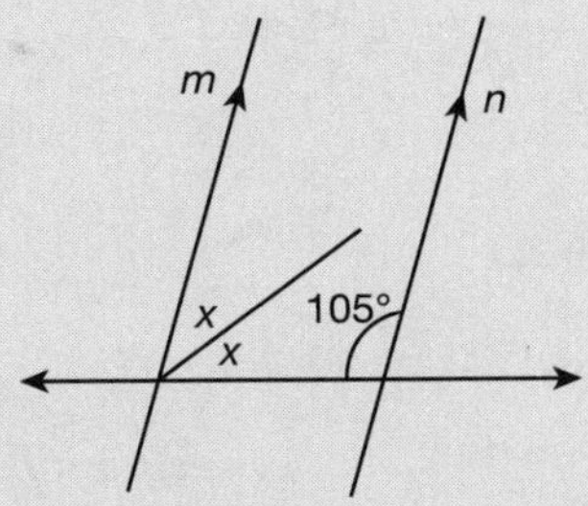

9. In the figure, $AB \parallel CD \parallel EF$, find x and y.

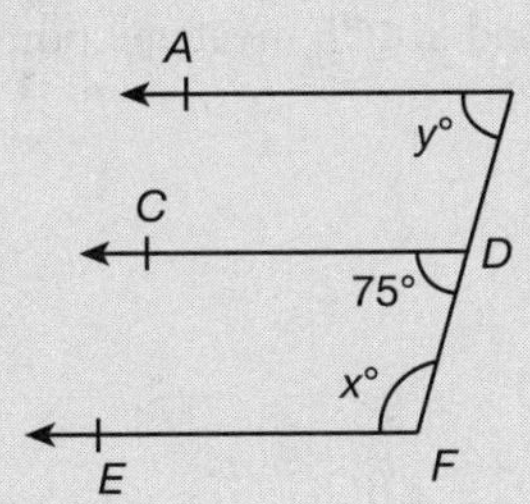

10. In the given figure $AB \parallel CD$. Find $\angle FXE$.

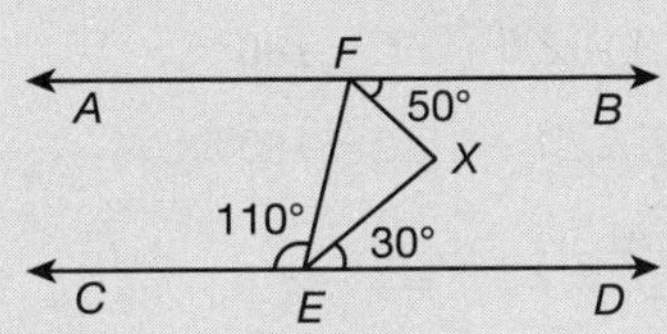

Triangles

A plane figure bounded by three lines in a plane is called a **triangle**. Every triangle has three sides and three angles. If ABC is any triangle then AB, BC and CA are three sides and $\angle A$, $\angle B$ and $\angle C$ are three angles.

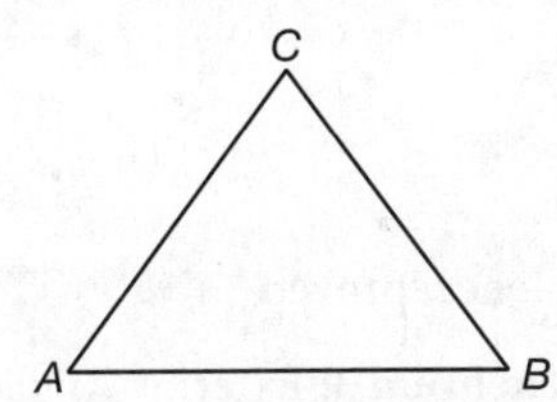

Figure 6.27

Types of Triangles

(i) On the basis of sides we have three types of triangles:
Scalene triangle: A triangle in which no two sides are equal is called a **scalene triangle.**
Isosceles triangle: A triangle having two sides equal is called an **isosceles triangle.**
Equilateral triangle: A triangle in which all sides are equal is called an **equilateral triangle.**

(ii) On the basis of angles we have three types:
Right triangle: A triangle in which any one angle is a right angle is called **right triangle.**
Acute triangle: A triangle in which all angles are acute is called an **acute triangle.**
Obtuse triangle: A triangle in which any one angle is obtuse is called an **obtuse triangle.**

Theorems

Theorem 1: The sum of interior angles of a triangle is 180°.

To Prove: $\angle A + \angle B + \angle C = 180°$ or $\angle 1 + \angle 2 + \angle 3 = 180°$.

Construction: Through A, draw a line l parallel to BC.

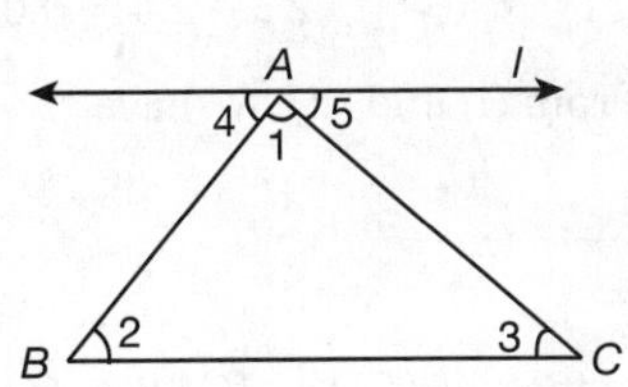

Figure 6.28

Proof: Since $l \parallel BC$. Therefore,

$$\angle 2 = \angle 4 \quad \text{[Alternate interior angles]}$$

$$\angle 3 = \angle 5 \quad \text{[Alternate interior angles]}$$

$$\therefore \quad \angle 2 + \angle 3 = \angle 4 + \angle 5$$

$$\angle 1 + \angle 2 + \angle 3 = \angle 1 + \angle 4 + \angle 5$$

[Adding $\angle 1$ both sides] $\angle 1 + \angle 2 + \angle 3 = 180°$

[$\because$ Sum of angles at a point on a line is 180°]

$$\angle A + \angle B + \angle C = 180°.$$

Theorem 2: If the bisectors of angles $\angle ABC$ and $\angle ACB$ of a triangle ABC meet at a point O, then $\angle BOC = 90° + \frac{1}{2}\Delta A$.

Given: A ΔABC such that the bisectors of $\angle ABC$ and $\angle ACB$ meet at a point O.

To Prove: $\angle BOC = 90° + \frac{1}{2}\angle A$.

Proof: In ΔBOC, we have

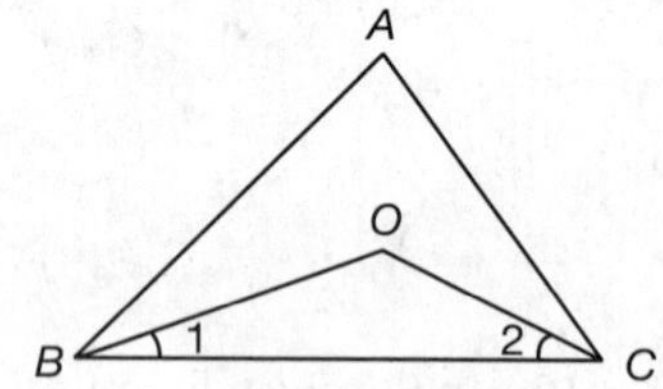

Figure 6.29

$$\angle 1 + \angle 2 + \angle BOC = 180°$$

$$\angle 1 + \angle 2 = 180° - \angle BOC \quad \text{...(i)}$$

In ΔABC, we have

$$\Rightarrow \quad \angle A + \angle B + \angle C = 180°$$

$$\Rightarrow \quad \angle A + 2\angle 1 + 2\angle 2 = 180°$$

$$\Rightarrow \quad \frac{\angle A}{2} + \angle 1 + \angle 2 = 90°$$

$$\Rightarrow \quad \angle 1 + \angle 2 = 90° - \frac{1}{2}\angle A \quad \text{...(ii)}$$

From (i) and (ii)

$$180° - \angle BOC = 90° - \frac{1}{2}\angle A$$

$$\angle BOC = 90° + \frac{1}{2}\angle A.$$

Hence, proved

Theorem 3: Exterior Angle of a Triangle

If the side of the triangle is produced, the exterior angle so formed is equal to the sum of two interior opposite angles.

Given: A triangle ABC. D is a point on BC produced, forming exterior angle $\angle 4$.

To Prove: $\angle 4 = \angle 1 + \angle 2$ i.e. $\angle ACD = \angle CAB + \angle CBA$.

Proof: In triangle ABC, we have

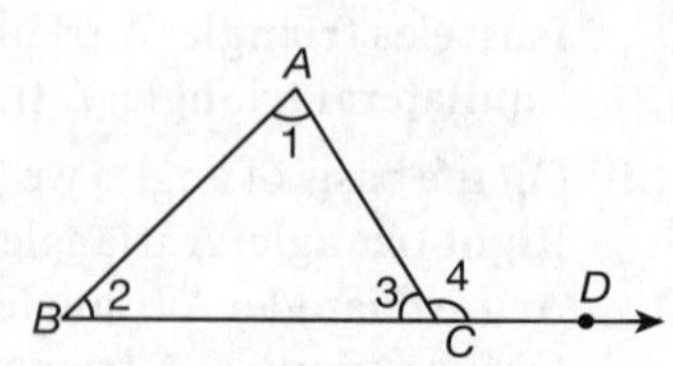

Figure 6.30

$$\angle 1 + \angle 2 + \angle 3 = 180° \quad \text{...(i)}$$

Also,

$$\angle 3 + \angle 4 = 180° \quad [\because \angle 3 \text{ and } \angle 4 \text{ form a linear pair}] \quad \text{...(ii)}$$

From (i) and (ii), we have

$$\angle 1 + \angle 2 + \angle 3 = \angle 3 + \angle 4$$

$$\Rightarrow \quad \angle 1 + \angle 2 = \angle 4$$

Hence, $\angle ACD = \angle CAB + \angle CBA$.

Corollary: An exterior angle of a triangle is greater than either of the interior opposite angles.

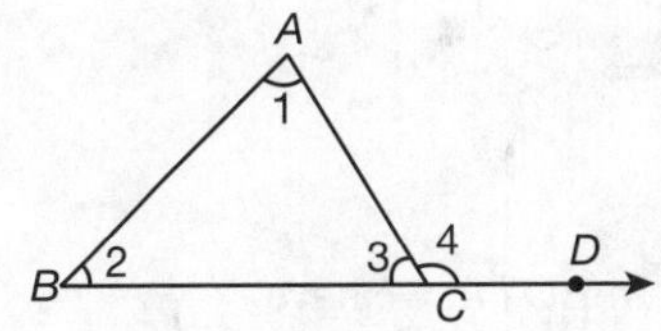

Figure 6.31

Proof: Let ABC be a triangle whose side BC is produced to form exterior angle $\angle A$.

Then, $\quad \angle 1 + \angle 2 = \angle 4 \Rightarrow \angle 4 > \angle 1$ and $\angle 4 > \angle 2$

i.e., $\quad \angle ACD > \angle CAB$ and $\angle ACD > \angle CBA$

Theorem 4: The sides AB and AC of a ΔABC are produced to P and Q respectively. If the bisectors of $\angle PBC$ and $\angle QCB$ intersect at O, then $\angle BOC = 90° - \frac{1}{2}\angle A$.

Given: A ΔABC in which sides AB and AC are produced to P and Q respectively. The bisectors of $\angle PBC$ and $\angle QCB$ intersect at O.

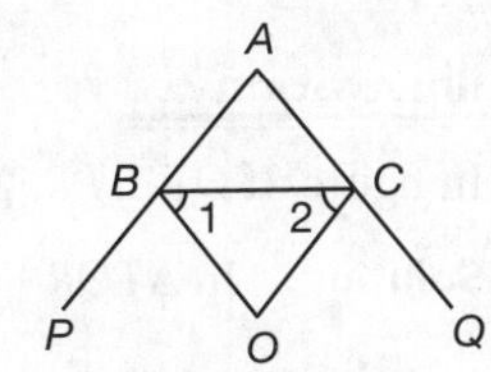

Figure 6.32

To Prove: $\angle BOC = 90° - \frac{1}{2}\angle A$

Proof: Since $\angle ABC$ and $\angle CBP$ form a linear pair.

$\therefore \quad \angle ABC + CBP = 180°$

$\Rightarrow \quad \angle B + 2\angle 1 = 180°$ $\quad$ [BO is the bisector of $\angle CBP$ $\quad \because \angle CBP = 2\angle 1$]

$\Rightarrow \quad 2\angle 1 = 180° - \angle B$

$\Rightarrow \quad \angle 1 = 90° - \frac{1}{2}\angle B$ $\quad$ ...(i)

Again, $\angle ACB$ and $\angle QCB$ form a linear pair.

$\therefore \quad \angle ACB + \angle QCB = 180°$

$\Rightarrow \quad \angle C + 2\angle 2 = 180°$ $\quad$ [$\because$ OC is the bisector of $\angle QCB$ $\quad \because \angle QCB = 2\angle 2$]

$\Rightarrow \quad 2\angle 2 = 180° - \frac{1}{2}\angle C$

$\Rightarrow \quad \angle 2 = 90° - \frac{1}{2}\angle C$ $\quad$ ...(ii)

In ΔBOC, we have

$$\angle 1 + \angle 2 + \angle BOC = 180°$$

$\Rightarrow \quad 90° - \frac{1}{2}\angle B + 90° - \frac{1}{2}\angle C + \angle BOC = 180°$ $\quad$ [Using (i) and (ii)]

$\Rightarrow \quad 180° - \frac{1}{2}(\angle B + \angle C) + \angle BOC = 180°$

$\Rightarrow \quad \angle BOC = \frac{1}{2}(\angle B + \angle C)$

$\Rightarrow \quad \angle BOC = \frac{1}{2}(180° - \angle A)$ $\quad$ [$\because \angle A + \angle B + \angle C = 180°$ $\quad \therefore \angle B + \angle C = 180° - \angle A$]

$\Rightarrow \quad \angle BOC = 90° - \frac{1}{2}\angle A.$

Illustration 6.7

In the figure, TQ and TR are the bisectors of $\angle Q$ and $\angle R$ respectively. If $\angle QPR = 80°$ and $\angle PRT = 30°$, determine $\angle TQR$ and $\angle QTR$.

Solution: Since, the bisectors of $\angle Q$ and $\angle R$ meet at T.

$\therefore \quad \angle QTR = 90° + \frac{1}{2}\angle QPR$

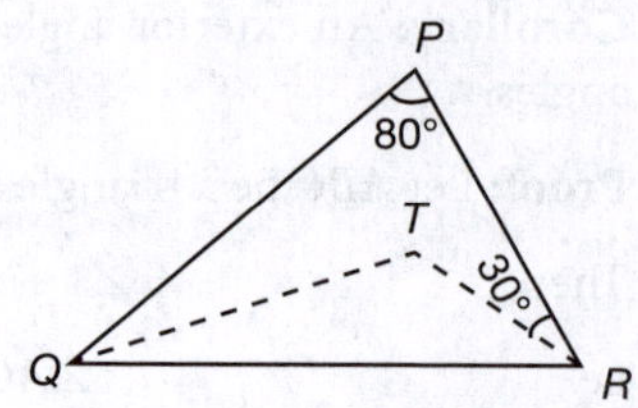

$$\Rightarrow \quad \angle QTR = 90° + \frac{1}{2}(80°)$$

$$\Rightarrow \quad \angle QTR = 90° + 40° = 130°$$

In ΔQTR, we have

$$\angle TQR + \angle QTR + \angle TRQ = 180°$$

$$\Rightarrow \quad TQR + 130° + 30° = 180° \quad [\because \angle TRQ = \angle PRT = 30°]$$

$$\Rightarrow \quad \angle TQR = 20°$$

Thus, $\angle TQR = 20°$ and $\angle QTR = 130°$.

Illustration 6.8

In figure, If $QT \perp PR$, $\angle TQR = 40°$ and $\angle SPR = 30°$, find x and y.

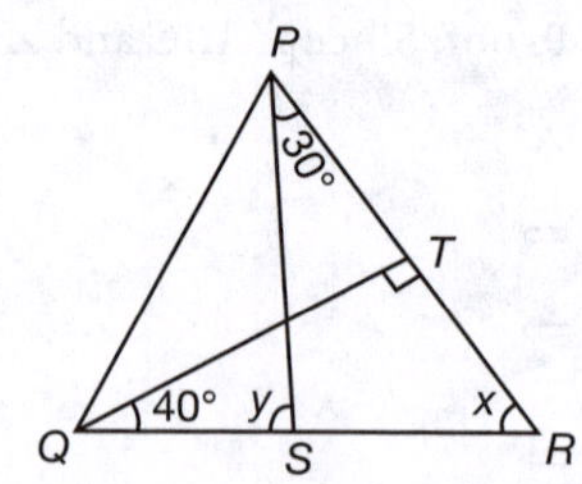

Solution: In ΔTQR

$$\angle TQR + \angle QTR + \angle TRQ = 180°$$

$$\Rightarrow \quad 40° + 90° + \angle TRQ = 180°$$

$$\Rightarrow \quad \angle TRQ = 180° - 130° = 50°$$

$$\Rightarrow \quad x = 50°$$

In ΔPSR, using exterior angle property, we have

$$\angle PSQ = \angle PRS + \angle RPS$$

$$\Rightarrow \quad y = x + 30°$$

$$\Rightarrow \quad y = 50° + 30° = 80°.$$

Illustration 6.9

The side BC of a ΔABC is produced, such that D is on ray BC. The bisector of $\angle A$ meets BC in L as shown in the figure. Prove that $\angle ABC + \angle ACD = 2\angle ALC$.

Solution: In ΔABC, we have

$$\text{ext. } \angle ACD = \angle B + \angle A$$

$$\Rightarrow \quad \text{ext. } \angle ACD = \angle B + 2\angle 1 \quad \ldots\text{(i)}$$

$[\because AL$ is the bisector of $\angle A \quad \because \angle A = 2\angle 1]$

$$\Rightarrow \quad \angle ACD = \angle B + 2\angle 1$$

In ΔABL, we have

$$\text{ext. } \angle ALC = \angle B + \angle BAL$$

$$\Rightarrow \quad \text{ext. } \angle ALC = \angle B + \angle 1$$

$$\Rightarrow \quad 2\angle ALC = 2\angle B + 2\angle 1 \quad \ldots\text{(ii)}$$

[Multiplying both sides by 2]

Subtracting (i) from (ii), we get

$$2\angle ALC - \angle ACD = \angle B$$

$$\Rightarrow \quad \angle ACD + \angle B = 2\angle ALC$$

$$\Rightarrow \quad \angle ACD + \angle ABC = 2\angle ALC.$$

Check Point 3

11. The sum of the acute angles of an obtuse triangle is 70° and their difference is 10°. Find the bigger acute angle.
12. If one angle of a triangle is equal to the sum of the other two, then determine the type of triangle.
13. In ΔABC, $2A = 3B$, $5B = 2C$ then determine the angles of the triangle.
14. If one angle of a triangle is equal to half the sum of the other two equal angles, then determine the type of triangle.
15. In the figure if $AB = AC$, $CH = CB$ and $HK \parallel BC$ then find $\angle HCK$.

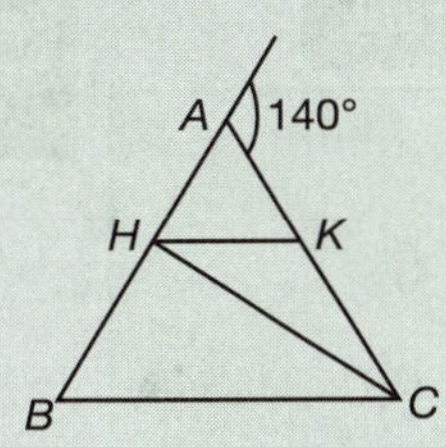

Competition Corner

- Internal angle sum of an n-sided polygon $= (n-2)\times 180°$
- External angle sum of an n-sided polygon $= 360°$.
- Each interior angle of a regular polygon of n-side $= \dfrac{(n-2)\times 180°}{n}$.
- Each exterior angle of a regular polygon of n-side $= \dfrac{360°}{n}$.

STRUCTURAL OUTLINE

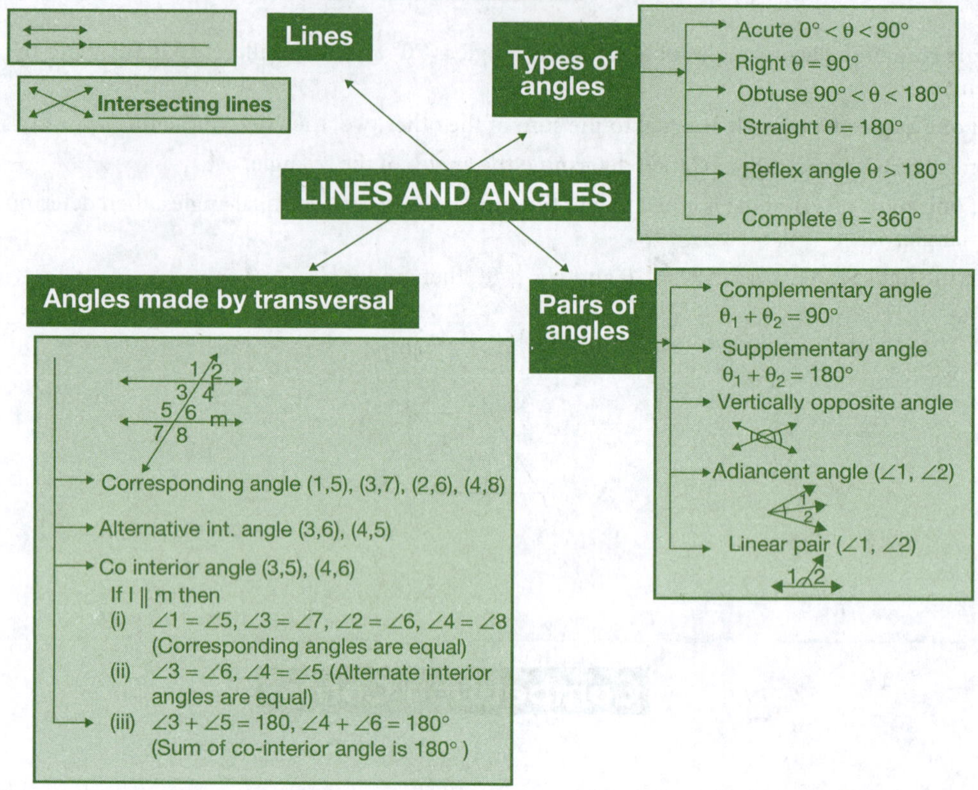

ASSESSMENT CORNER

Fixed Response Type

Fill in the Blanks

1. If a, b are complementary angles and b, c are supplementary angles. If the average of a and c is 85°, then $a + b + c$ is _______.
2. The supplement of an angle and the complement of another have the sum equal to half of a complete angle. If the greater angle is 10° more than the smaller, then the smaller angle is _______.
3. If the difference between an angle and its supplement is 100°, then the ratio of the larger and the smaller angles _______.
4. There are two angles a and b such that $a = b + 15°$. If the supplement of $3b$ is twice the complement of $b + 15°$ then the value of a is _______.
5. The ratio between the complement and the supplement of an angle is 1 : 2. The angle is _______.
6. In ΔABC, $m\ \angle B = 90°$, $AB = BC$. Then $AB : AC =$ _______.

True/False

1. All Linear pairs angles are supplementary angles.
2. All supplementary angles are adjacent angles.
3. Alternative interior angles are always equal.
4. In a triangle sum of two angles is equal to the third angle then the triangle is right angled triangle.
5. In an equilateral triangle all angles are 60°.

Single Correct Type Questions

Level 1

1. Two parallel lines have:
   (A) A common point
   (B) two common points
   (C) No common point
   (D) infinite common points
2. An angle is 14° more than its complementary angle then the angle is:
   (A) 38° (B) 52°
   (C) 50° (D) None of these
3. The angle between the bisectors of two adjacent supplementary angles is:
   (A) Acute angle (B) Right angle
   (C) Obtuse angle (D) None of these
4. X lies in the interior of $\angle BAC$. If $\angle BAC = 70°$ and $\angle BAX = 42°$ then $\angle XAC =$
   (A) 28° (B) 29°
   (C) 27° (D) 30°
5. If the supplement of an angle is three times its complement, then the angle is:
   (A) 40° (B) 35°
   (C) 50° (D) 45°
6. Two angles forms a linear pair whose measures are a and b are such that $2a - 3b = 60°$, then $\frac{4a}{5b} = ?$
   (A) 0 (B) $\frac{8}{5}$
   (C) $\frac{1}{2}$ (D) $\frac{2}{3}$
7. The complement of $(90° - a)$ is:
   (A) $-a°$ (B) $90° + a$
   (C) $90° - a$ (D) $a°$
8. If two lines intersected by a transversal, then each pair of corresponding angles so formed is:
   (A) Equal (B) Complementary
   (C) Supplementary (D) None of these
9. In the given figure, $AB \parallel CD$, $\angle ABF = 45°$and $\angle CFD = 110°$. Then, $\angle FDC$ is:

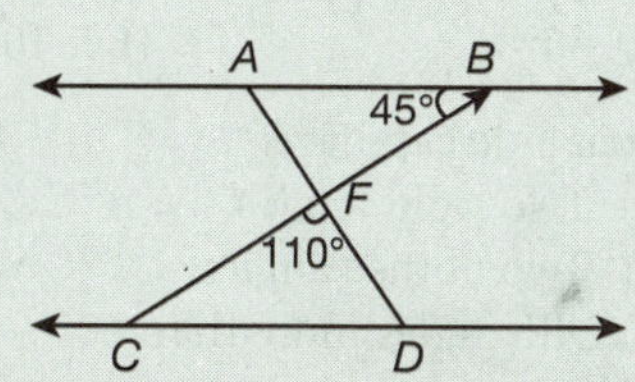

   (A) 25° (B) 45°
   (C) 35° (D) 30°
10. In the given figure $PQ \parallel RS$, $\angle QPR = 70°$, $\angle ROT = 20°$. Then, find the value of x.

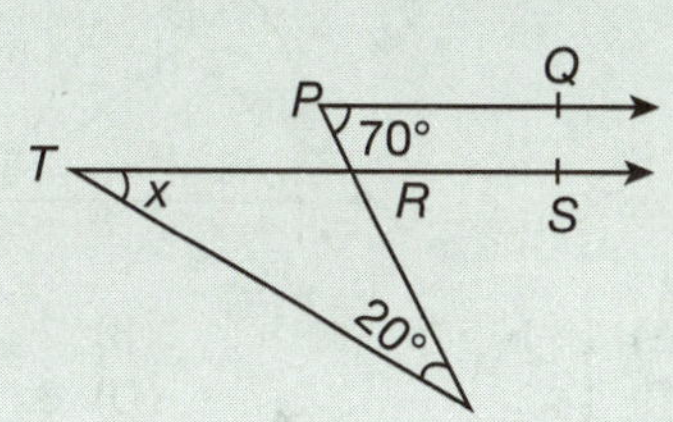

ASSESSMENT CORNER

(A) 20° (B) 70°
(C) 110° (D) 50°

11. If one angle of the triangle is equal to the sum of the other two then the triangle is:
(A) Acute a triangle
(B) Obtuse triangle
(C) Right triangle
(D) None

12. In the adjoining figure, $AD = BD = AC$; $\angle CAE = 75°$ and $\angle ACD = x°$. Then the value of x is:

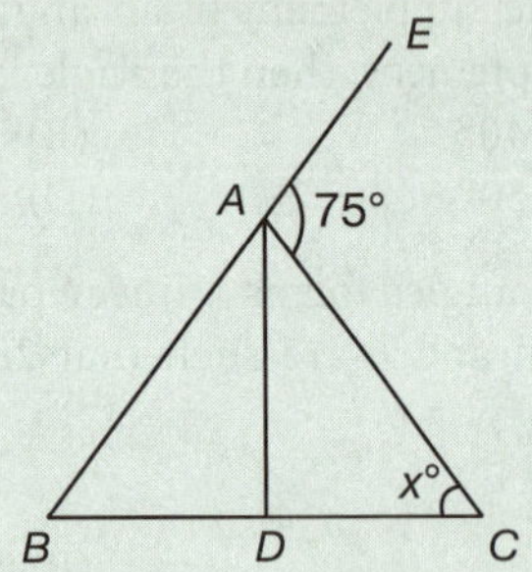

(A) 45° (B) 50°
(C) 60° (D) $37\frac{1}{2}°$

13. In the given figure, $\angle PQR$ is:

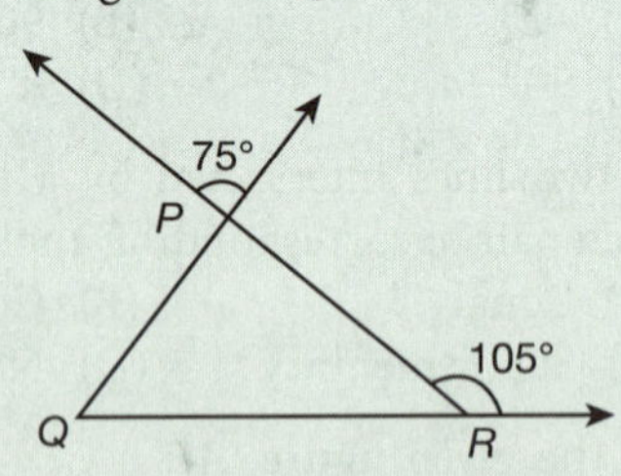

(A) 40° (B) 50°
(C) 30° (D) 105°

14. A triangle can have:
(A) Two right angles
(B) Two obtuse angles
(C) All angles more than 60°
(D) Two acute angles

15. In the given figure, the ratio $\angle ABD$: $\angle ACD$ is:

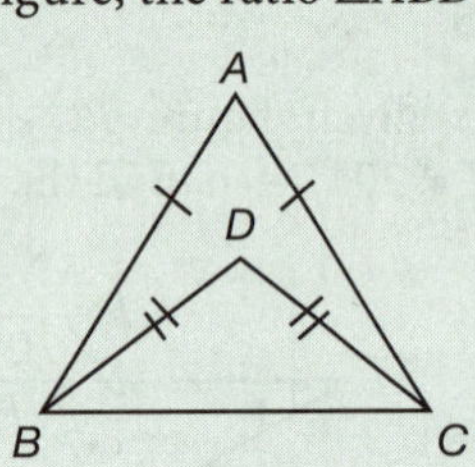

(A) 1 : 1 (B) 2 : 1
(C) 1 : 2 (D) 3 : 1

Level 2

16. If one angle of a triangle is 72° and the difference between the other two angles is 12°, Find the ratio of the other two angles.
(A) 4 : 5 (B) 2 : 1
(C) 3 : 4 (D) 5 : 3

17. An angle is 18° less than its complementary angle. The measure of this angle is:
(A) 36° (B) 48°
(C) 83° (D) 81°

18. In ΔABC, $\angle A : \angle B : \angle C = 2 : 3 : 5$, then the angle at B is:
(A) 54° (B) 126°
(C) 136° (D) 64°

19. If two interior angles on the same side of a transversal intersecting two parallel lines are in the ratio 5: 4, then the greatest angle is:
(A) 54° (B) 100°
(C) 120° (D) 136°

20. If angles with measures x and y form a complementary pair, then angles with which of the following measures will form a supplementary pair?
(A) $(x + 47°), (y + 43°)$
(B) $(x - 23°), (y + 23°)$
(C) $(x - 43°), (y - 47°)$
(D) No such pair is possible

21. If one angle of a triangle is equal to the sum of the other two angles, then the triangle is a/an:
(A) Acute angled triangle
(B) Obtuse angled triangle
(C) Right-angled triangle
(D) None of these

22. In the figure, lines AB and CD intersect at O. If $\angle AOC + \angle BOE = 100°$ and $\angle BOD = 60°$, Find $\angle BOE$ and reflex $\angle COE$ respectively.

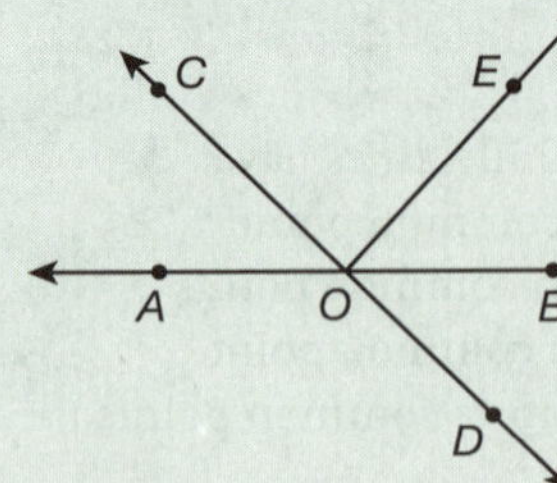

(A) 40°, 280°
(B) 40°, 260°
(C) 30°, 260°
(D) 30°, 250°

ASSESSMENT CORNER

23. In the diagram if ΔABC and ΔPQR are equilateral. The $\angle CXY$ equals:

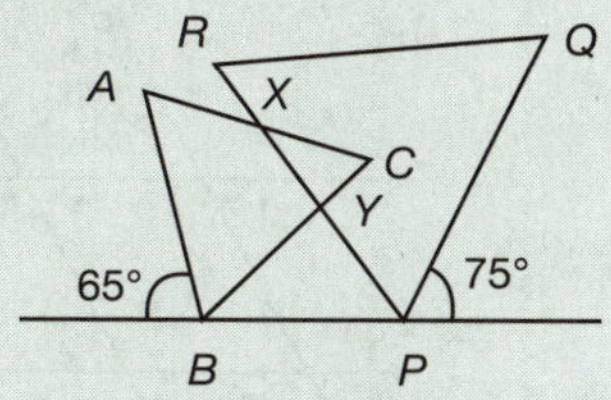

(A) 35° (B) 40°
(C) 45° (D) 50°

24.

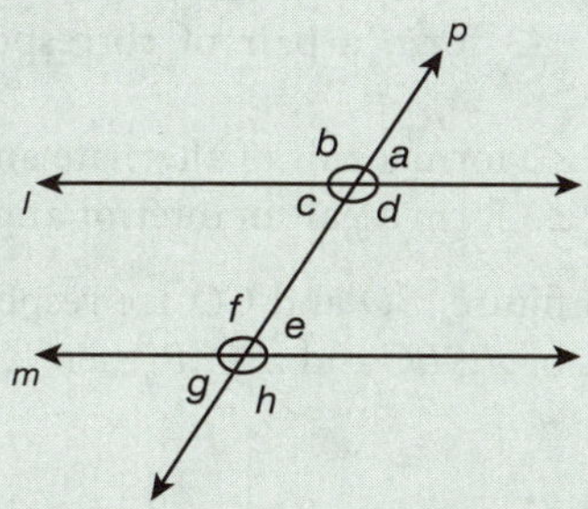

In the above figure (not to scale), l and m are parallel lines and p is a transversal. If $c = 45°$, then f is:

(A) 45° (B) 135°
(C) 145° (D) 170°

25.

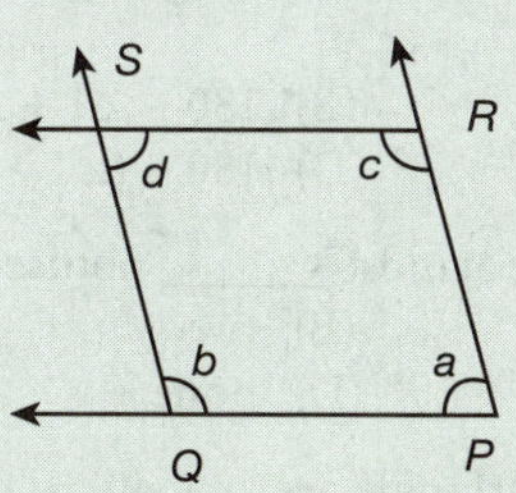

In the above figure (not to scale), $\overrightarrow{PQ} \parallel \overrightarrow{RS}$ and $\overrightarrow{PR} \parallel \overrightarrow{QS}$. Each pair of parallel rays is intersecting the other pair and a, b, c and d are the angles formed. If $c = 120°$, then a is:

(A) 80° (B) 70°
(C) 60° (D) 90°

Multiple Correct Type Questions

1. Which of the following statement is false?
   (A) If two angles form a linear pair, then each of these angles is 90°.
   (B) Angles forming a linear pair can both be acute angles.
   (C) Both of the angles forming a linear pair can be obtuse.
   (D) Bisectors of the adjacent angles forming a linear pair form a right angle.

2. If $x°$ is the measure of an angle which is equal to its complement and $y°$ is the measure of the angle which is equal to its supplement, then $x°/y°$ is:
   (A) 1 (B) 3
   (C) 0.5 (D) 2

3. In the figure below $\overline{AB} \parallel \overline{FC}$, $\overline{AE} \parallel \overline{BC}$ and $\overline{AF} \parallel \overline{BD}$. If $\angle F = x$, $\angle C = y$, $\angle EAB = k$ and $\angle ABD = p$, then which of the following is incorrect?

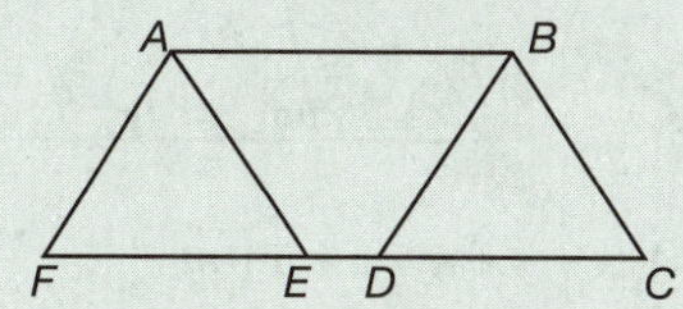

   (A) $x = k$ and $y = p$ (B) $x = p$ and $y = k$
   (C) Both (A) and (B) (D) None of the above

4. In the figure below, $AD \parallel \overline{GE}$, $\overline{GB} \parallel \overline{FC} \parallel \overline{ED}$ and $\overline{BF} \parallel \overline{CE}$ (not to scale). If $\angle ABG = x$, $\angle GBF = y$, $\angle CED = p$ and $\angle CDE = q$, then $x - y$ is:

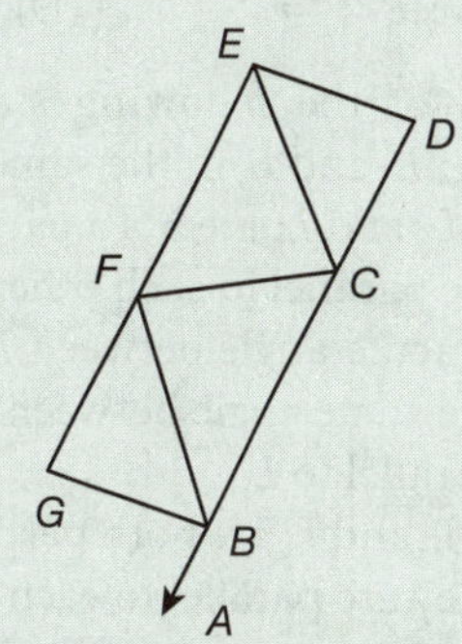

   (A) $p - q$
   (B) $q - p$
   (C) Cannot be determined
   (D) None of these

5. For triangle ADE as shown in the figure. Which of the following angle relation is/are correct?

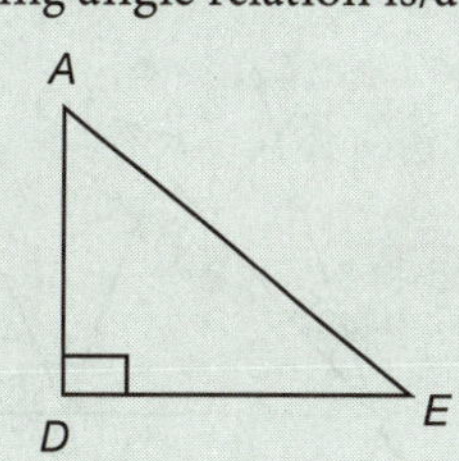

   (A) Of the 12 angles formed at the three vertices by adjoining lines, four are acute, four obtuse and four are right angles.
   (B) The mean measure of the above 12 angles is 90°.
   (C) The measure of the above twelve angles will generally have 3 or 5 distinct values.
   (D) Of the 12 angles formed, the greatest angle formed is the right angle.

6. For triangle ADE as shown in the figure. Which of the following angle relation is/are correct?

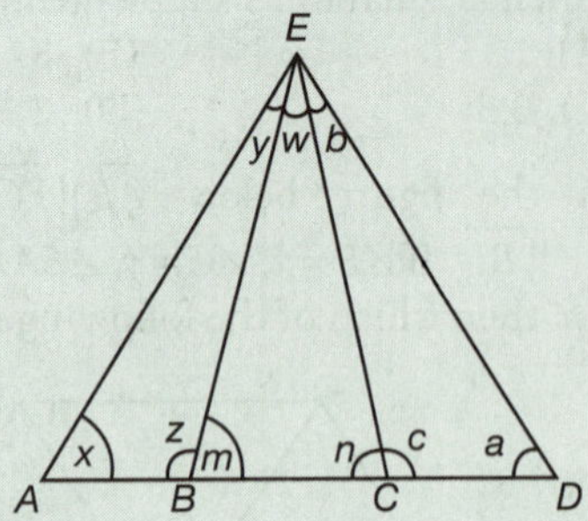

(A) $x+y+n=a+b+m$
(B) $x+z+n=w+c+m$
(C) $x+y=m$
(D) $y+z=a+b$

7. A triangle can have at most _______ Obtuse angles.
(A) One (B) Two
(C) Three (D) None

8. Which of the following statements relating 3 lines L_1, L_2 and L_3 in the same plane is correct?
(A) If L_2 and L_3 are both parallel to L_1, then they are parallel to each other.
(B) If acute angle between L_1 and L_2 is equal to the acute angle between L_1 and L_3, then L_2 is parallel to L_1.
(C) If L_2 and L_3 are both perpendicular to L_1 then they are parallel to each other.
(D) If the perpendicular distance between L_1 and L_3 is equal to the perpendicular distance between L_1 and L_2 then L_1, L_2 and L_3 are always parallel to each other.

9. In the give figure, $AC \parallel BD$, $\angle CAF = 25°$, $\angle DBG = 65°$ and $BF = BA$. Then which of the following statements is correct?

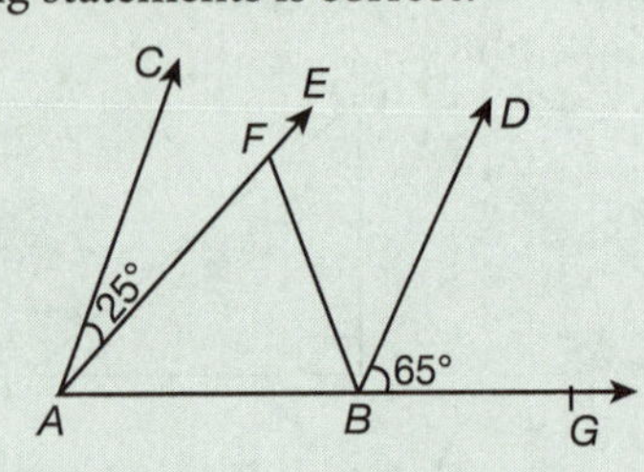

(A) $\angle FBD = 15°$ (B) $\angle FAB = \angle BCA$
(C) $\angle BFE = 140°$ (D) $\angle FBG = 80°$

10. In the given figure, $l \parallel m$ and $p \parallel n$, if $\angle 1 = 75°$, then

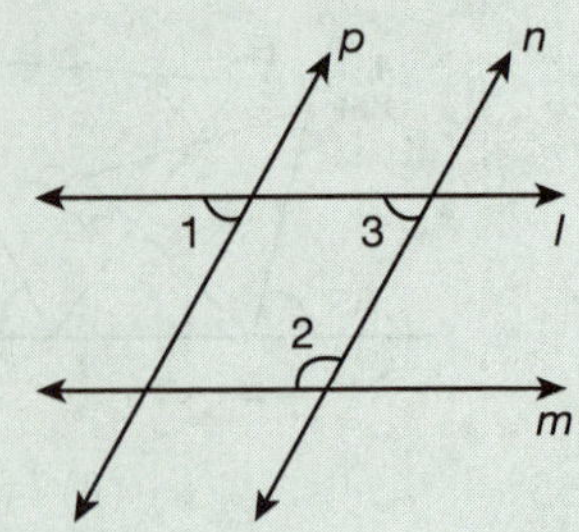

(A) $\angle 2 = \angle 1 + 1/3$ (of a right angle)
(B) $\angle 1$ and $\angle 3$ form a pair of corresponding angles
(C) $\angle 2$ and $\angle 3$ form a pair of alternate angles.
(D) $\angle 2$ and $\angle 3$ form a pair of interior angles.

11. In the given figure, BO and CO are respectively the bisectors of $\angle ABC$ and $\angle ACB$, then $\angle BOC$ is equal to:

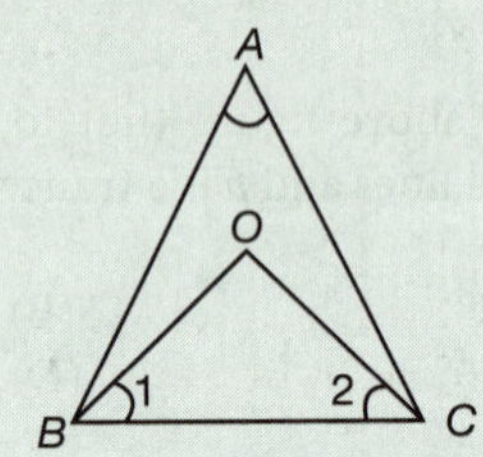

(A) $90 - {}^1/_2\angle A$ (B) $180 - \angle 1 + \angle 2$
(C) $90 + {}^1/_2\angle A$ (D) $180 - (\angle 1 + \angle 2)$

12. A triangle can have at most _______ obtuse angles.
(A) one (B) two
(C) three (D) none

13. If the angles of a triangle are $(x - 40)°$, $(x - 20)°$ and $\left(\frac{1}{2}x - 10\right)°$, then the smallest angle is:
(A) $(x - 40°)$ (B) $\left(\frac{1}{2}x - 10°\right)$
(C) $(x - 40°)$ (D) $(180 - x°)$

Match Type Questions

Direction: Column-I and Column-II contain four entries each. Entries of Column-I are to be matched with some entries of Column-II. One or more than one entries of Column-I may have the matching with some entries of Column-II and one entry of Column-II may have one or more than one matching with entries of Column-I.

1.

Column-I	Column-II
(i) Complement of 13°	(P) 13
(ii) 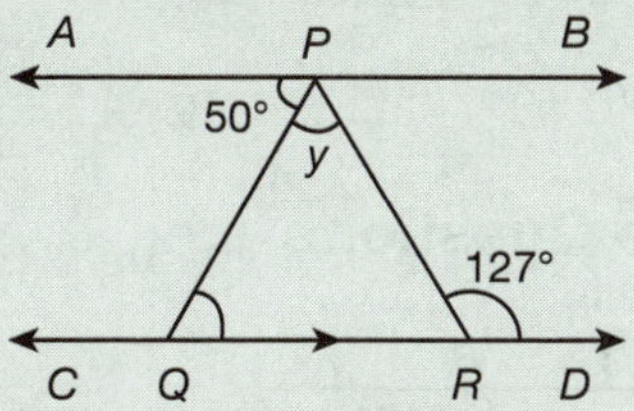 Given $AB \parallel CD$. Then y	(Q) 167°
(iii) 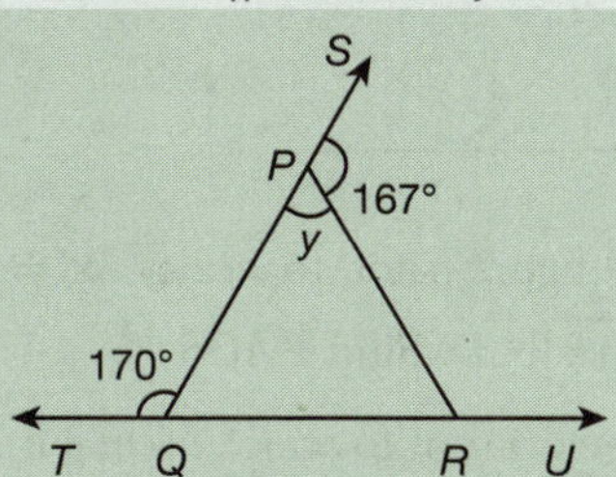 Find y	(R) 77°
(iv) Supplement of 13°	(S) right angle $+ 11 \times 7°$

2.

Column-I	Column-II
(i) 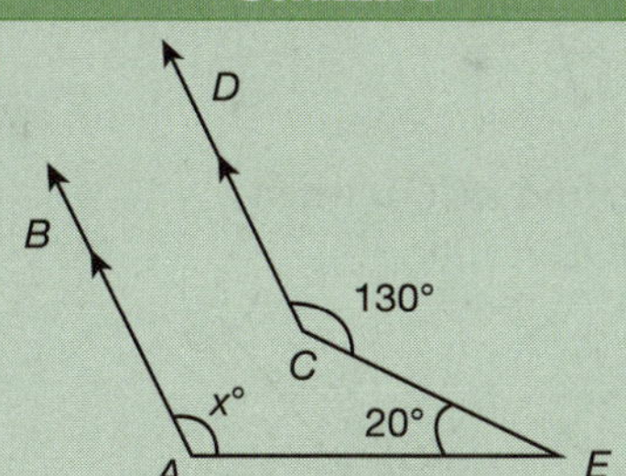 Find x.	(P) 75°
(ii) 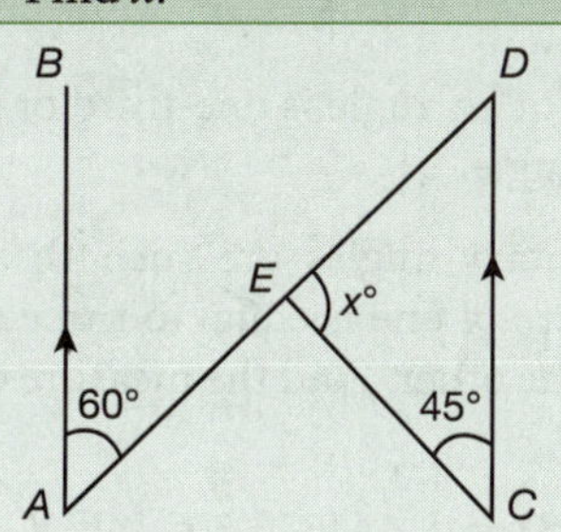 Find x.	(Q) 110°
(iii) 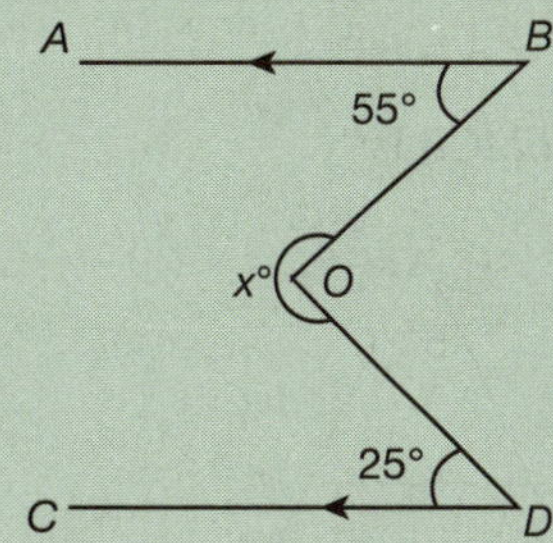 Find x	(R) 45°
(iv) 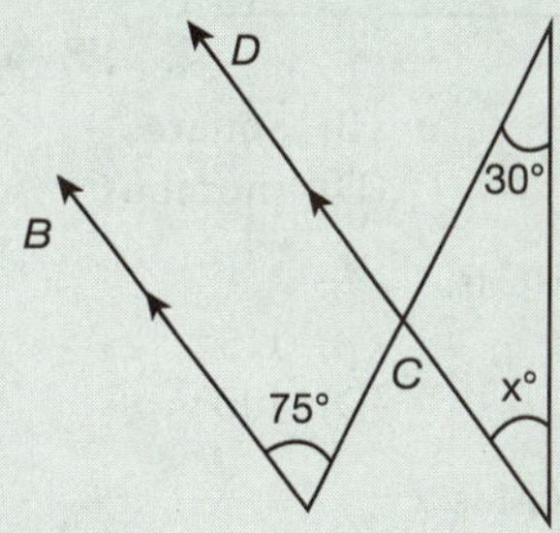 Find x	(S) 280°

(Continued)

3.

Column-I (Regular plane figure)	Column-II (Measure of interior angles)
(i) Triangle	(P) 108°
(ii) Square	(Q) 120°
(iii) Pentagon	(R) 90°
(iv) Hexagon	(S) 60°

Assertion and Reason Type Questions

Directions: In the following questions an Assertion (A) is given followed by a Reason (R). Mark your responses from the following options.

(A) Both Assertion and Reason are true and Reason is the correct explanation of 'Assertion'.

(B) Both Assertion and Reason are true and Reason is not the correct explanation of 'Assertion'.

(C) Assertion is true but Reason is false.

(D) Assertion is false but Reason is true.

1. **Assertion:** If one angle of a linear pair is acute, then its other angle will be obtuse.
   Reason: The sum of two angles of a linear pair is always 180°.

2. **Assertion:** Line L_1 is parallel to line L_2 and L_2 is parallel to line L_3, then L_1 parallel to L_3.
   Reason: Two lines parallel to the same line are parallel to each other.

ASSESSMENT CORNER

Comprehension Type Questions

Comprehension-1: ΔABC is an isosceles triangle in which $\angle B = \angle C$ and $LM \parallel BC$. If $\angle A = 50°$.

1. The quadrilateral $LMCB$ is:

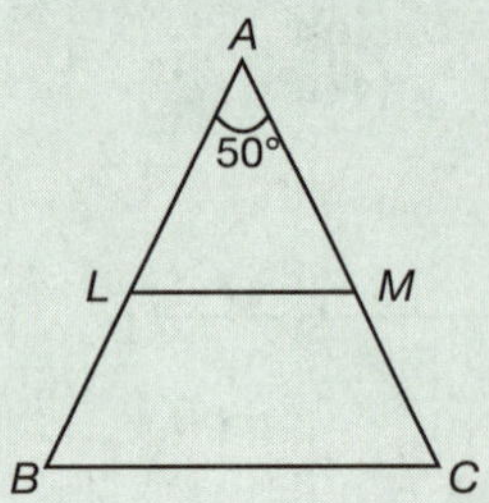

(A) Trapezium (B) Square
(C) rectangle (D) rhombus

2. The value of $\angle LMC$ is:
(A) 65° (B) 115°
(C) 130° (D) 100°

3. The value of $\angle ALM$ is:
(A) 130° (B) 80°
(C) 65° (D) 100°

Comprehension-2: The sides AB and ΔABC are produced to points E and D respectively. If bisectors BO and CO of $\angle CBE$ and $\angle BCD$ respectively meet at point O.

4. The value of $\angle CBO$ is:
(A) $(180 - y)/2$ (B) $90/2 - y$
(C) $\frac{1}{2}(90 - y)$ (D) $(90° - y)/2$

5. The value of $\angle BOC$ is:
(A) $\frac{1}{2}(y + z)$ (B) $\frac{1}{2}\left(\frac{y}{z} + \frac{z}{2}\right)$
(C) $180° - x$ (D) $180° - x/2$

6. Which of the following relation is correct?

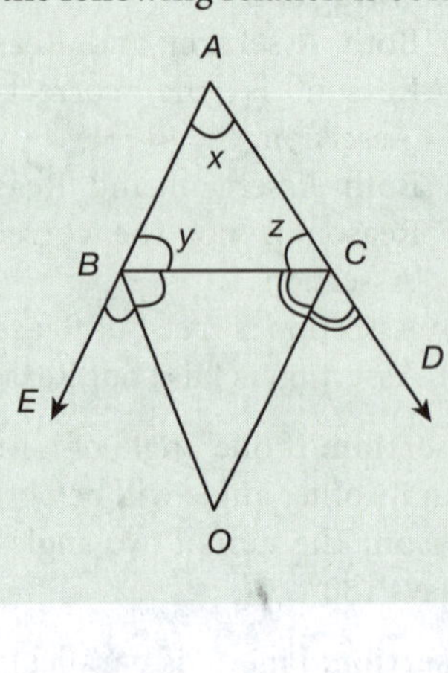

(A) $x + y = 180° - z$

(B) $\angle BOC = 90° - \frac{1}{2}\angle BAC$

(C) $\angle BOC = 90° + \frac{1}{2}\angle BAC$

(D) $x + z = 180° - y$

Numerical Type Questions

1.

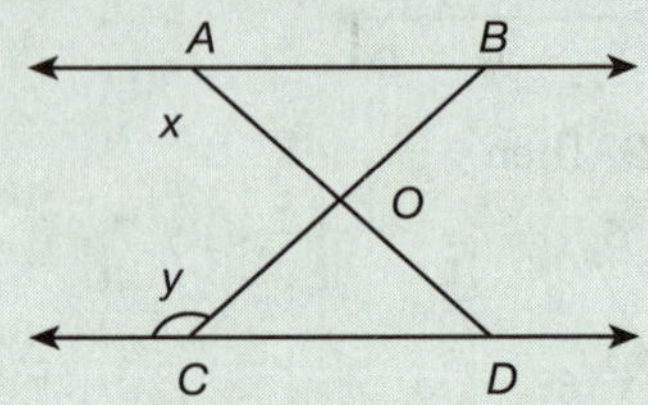

In the above figure (not to scale), $x = 125°$, $y = 135°$ and $\overleftrightarrow{AB} \parallel \overleftrightarrow{CD}$. Find $\angle AOB$.

2. In the figure below (not to scale), $l \parallel m \parallel n$, p and q are transversals. AB: $BC = 2$: 1 and $DE = 5$ cm. Find EF.

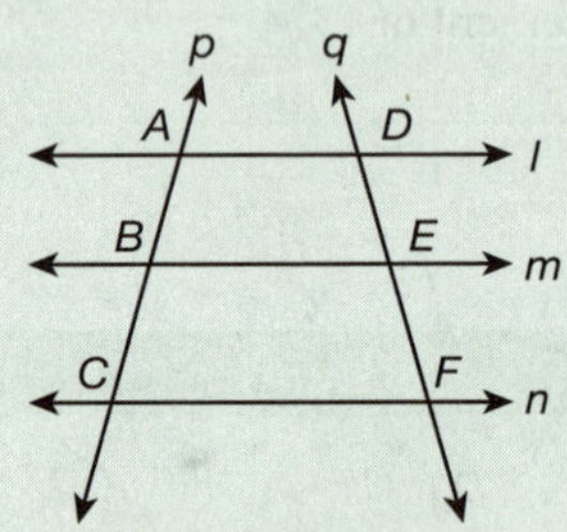

3. In the figure, find $\angle COD$ when $\angle AOC + \angle BOD = 100°$.

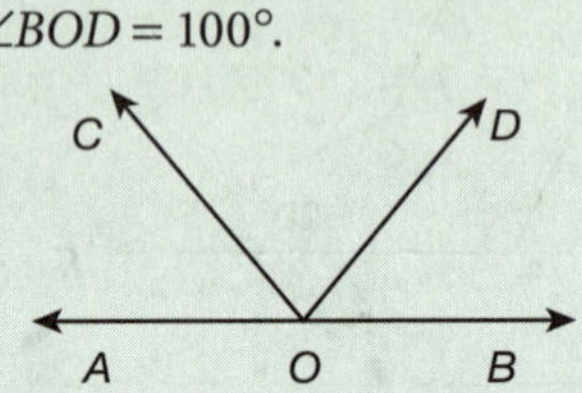

4. The supplement of an angle is one-third of itself. Determine the angle.

5. Two complementary angles are such that two times the measure of one is equal to three times the measure of the other. Find the measure of the larger angle.

6. In figure, $AB \parallel ED$ and $\angle ABC = 30°$, $\angle EDC = 70°$ then find $x°$.

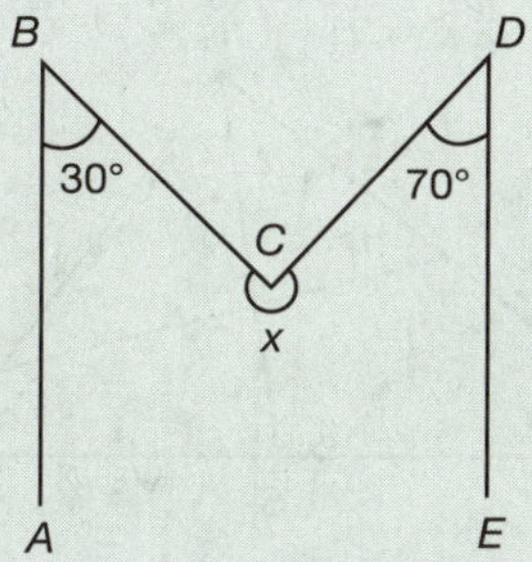

7. In figure, $AB \parallel CD$ and $CD \parallel EF$. Also, $EA \perp AB$, if $\angle BEF = 55°$, find the values of x, y and z.

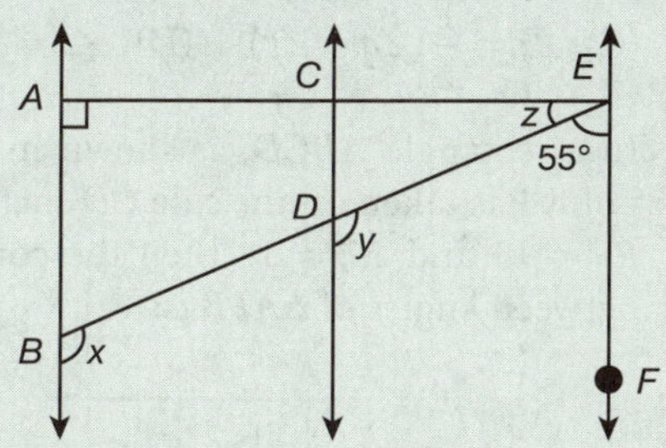

8. In the diagram, If $AB = AD = BD = DC$, then find $x°$.

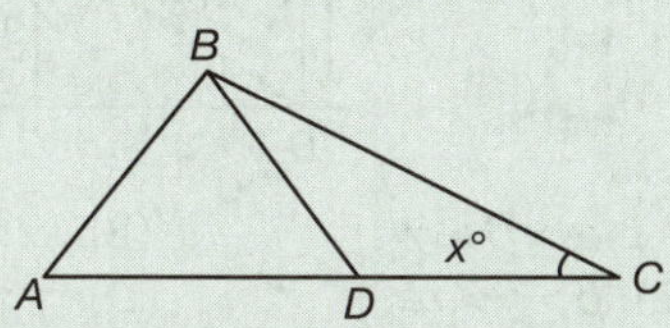

9. In figure, if $AB \parallel CD \parallel EF$ and $y: z = 3: 7$, find x.

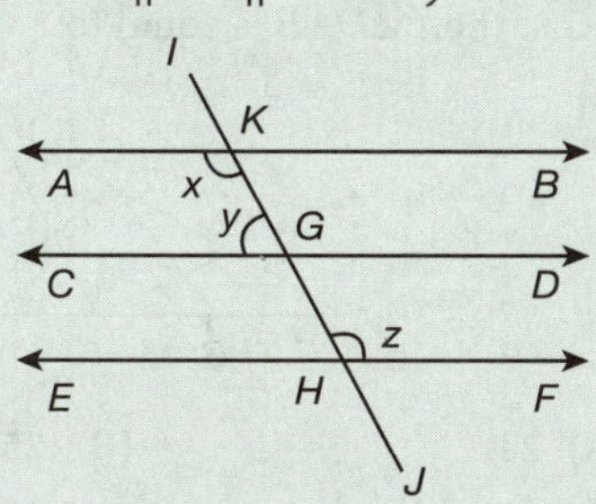

10. In figure, if $AB \parallel CD$, $EF \perp CD$ and $\angle GED = 126°$, find $\angle AGE$, $\angle GEF$ and $\angle FGE$.

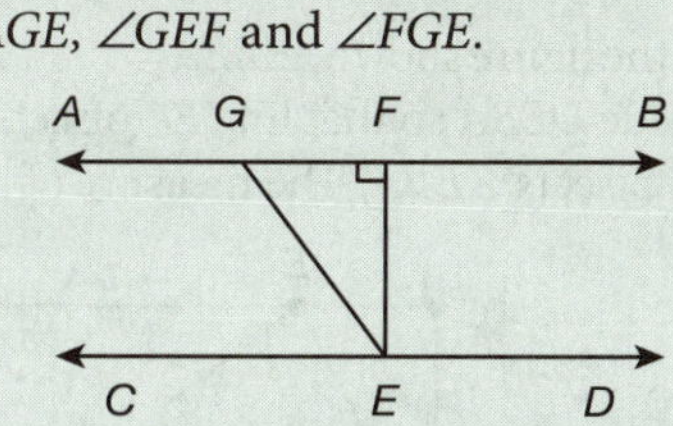

11. ΔABC is an isosceles triangle in which $\angle B = \angle C$ and L and M are points on AB and AC respectively such that $LM \parallel BC$. If $\angle A = 50°$ find $\angle LMC$.

12. In figure if $AB \parallel DF$, $AD \parallel FG$, $\angle BAC = 65°$, $\angle ACB = 55°$ Find $\angle FGH$.

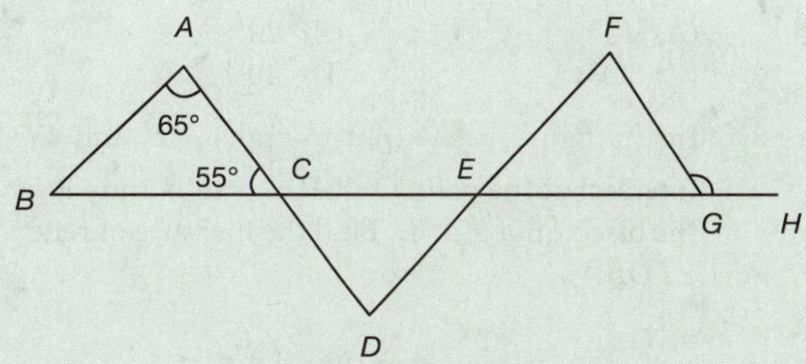

13. In figure, if $PQ \perp PS$, $PQ \parallel SR$, $\angle SQR = 28°$ and $\angle QRT = 65°$, then find the value of x and y.

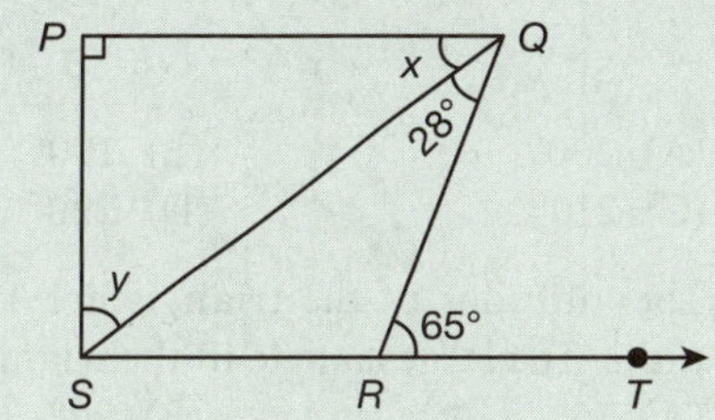

14. In the figure given below (not to scale), MN and OP intersect at right angles.
If $(\angle MAB : \angle BAP) = 2 : 1 = (\angle PAC : \angle CAN)$, then $(\angle MAB + \angle PAC)$ is:

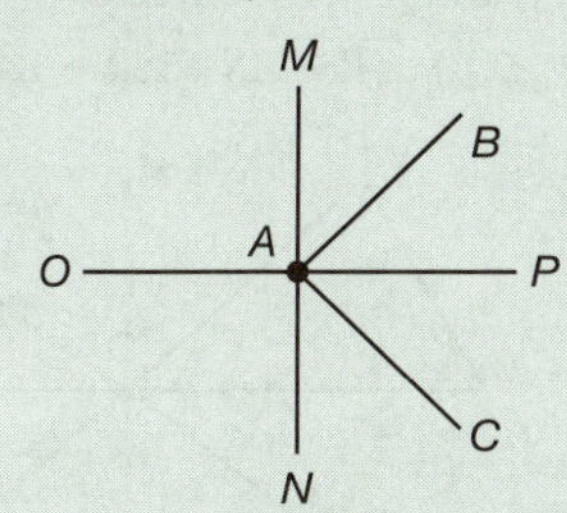

15.

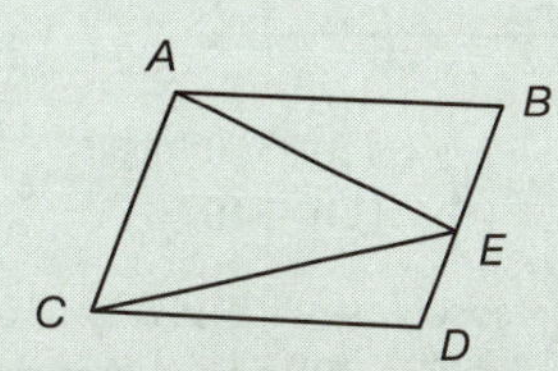

In the above figure (not to scale), $\overline{AB} \parallel \overline{CD}$. If $\angle BAE = 25°$ and $\angle DCE = 30°$, then find $\angle AEC$.

Higher Order Thinking Skills (HOTS)

1. In the figure below (not to scale), $\overline{AB} \parallel \overline{CD}$, $\angle AHF = 50°$ and $\angle DEG = 140°$. If $\angle BHJ = 2\angle HGE$ then find $\angle BHJ$.

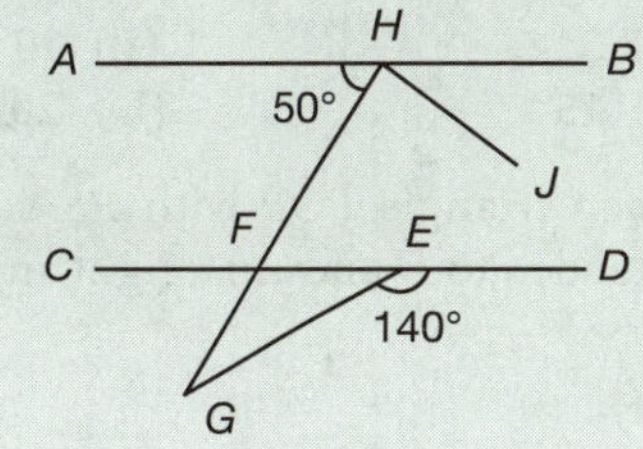

ASSESSMENT CORNER

(A) 10° (B) 20°
(C) 30° (D) 40°

2. In the figure below (not to scale), $\overline{AB}$ and $\overline{CD}$ intersect at the point O. $\angle AOC = 100°$ and $\overrightarrow{OP}$ is the bisector of $\angle AOD$. Find the measure of reflex $\angle POB$.

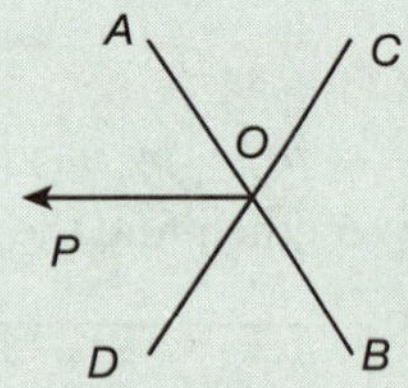

(A) 200° (B) 190°
(C) 210° (D) 220°

3. The altitudes of the triangle are 12, 15 and 20 units. The largest angle in the triangle is:
(A) 75° (B) 90°
(C) 120° (D) 135°

4. Lines PS, QT and RU intersect at a common point O, as shown P is joined to Q, R to S and T to U, to form triangles. The value of $\angle P + \angle Q + \angle R + \angle S + \angle T + \angle U$ is:

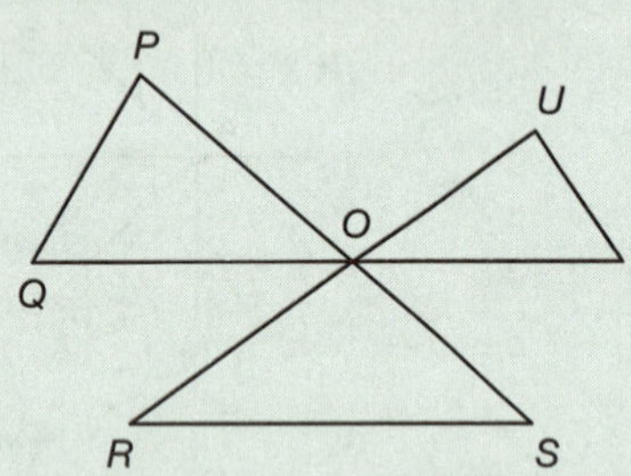

(A) 270° (B) 360°
(C) 450° (D) 540°

5. Triangle ABC is isosceles with $AB = AC$. The measure of angle BAD is 30° and $AD = AE$. The measure of angle EDC, is:

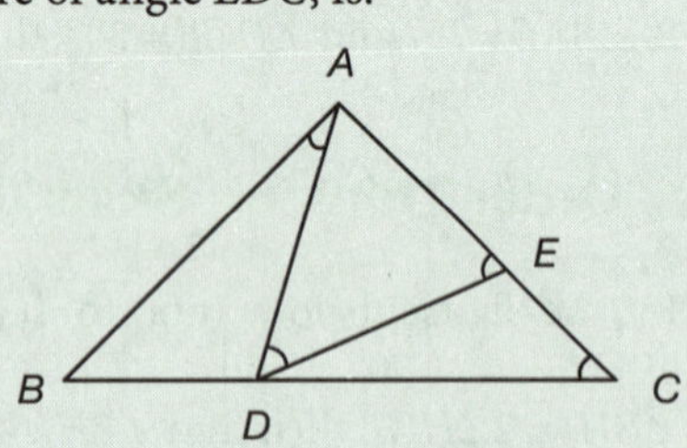

(A) 5° (B) 10°
(C) 15° (D) 20°

6. Given triangle PQR with RS bisecting $\angle R$, PQ extended to D and $\angle n$ a right angle, then:

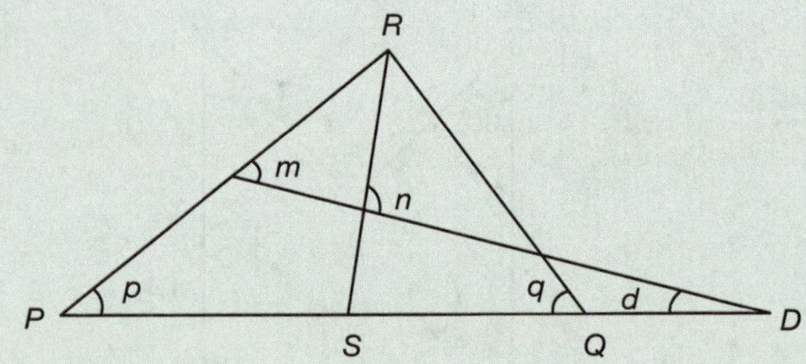

(A) $\angle m = \frac{1}{2}(\angle p - \angle q)$ (B) $\angle m = \frac{1}{2}(\angle p + \angle q)$

(C) $\angle d = \frac{1}{2}(\angle q + \angle p)$ (D) $\angle d = \frac{1}{2}\angle m$

7. In a rectangle $ABCD$, as shown in the figure, a point P is taken on the side CD such that $PC = 9$, $BP = 15$ and $AB = 14$ then the correct relation between angles of ΔAPB is:

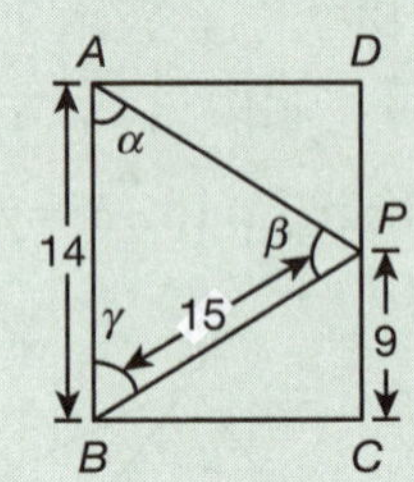

(A) $\alpha > \beta > \gamma$ (B) $\alpha > \gamma > \beta$
(C) $\beta > \gamma > \alpha$ (D) $\gamma > \alpha > \beta$

8. In the figure, $AB = BC = CD = DE = EF = FG = GA$, then $\angle DAE$ is equal to:

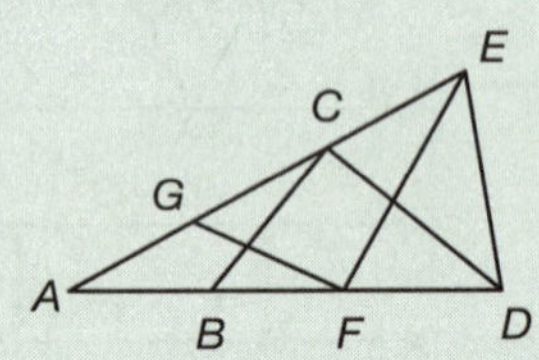

(A) 24° (B) 25°

(C) 27° (D) $\frac{180°}{7}$

9. In the figure shown, $\angle BEA = 100°$. Point F is chosen inside $DEBA$ so that line FA bisects $\angle EAB$ and line FB bisects $\angle EBA$. The measure of $\angle BFA$, is:

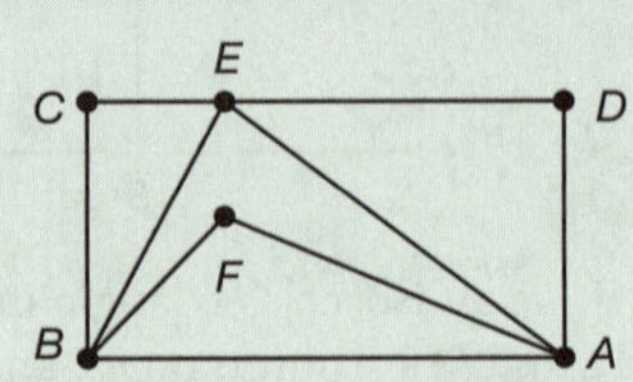

(A) 140° (B) 145°
(C) 150° (D) 155°

10. In the figure (not to scale), $\angle ABC$ is a straight line. If $\angle FBE = 60°$, $\angle CBG = 120°$, $\angle ABG = x°$, $\angle ABF = y°$ and $\angle CBE = z° = 2y°$, then $(x° + z°) : y°$ is:

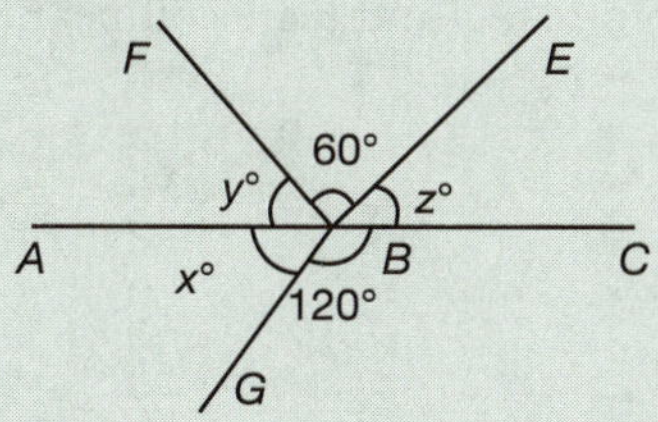

(A) 2 : 7 (B) 1 : 1
(C) 1 : 2 (D) 7 : 2

11.

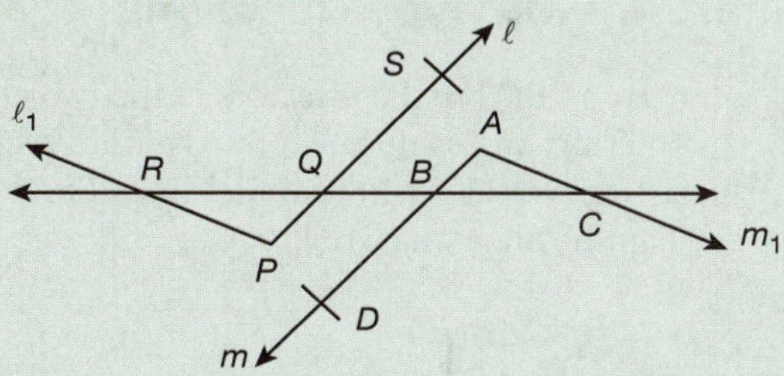

In the above figure, $\ell \| m$ and $l_1 \| m_1$. If $\angle ACB = 40°$ and $\angle DBC = 110°$, then find $\angle QPR$.

(A) 60° (B) 70°
(C) 80° (D) 110°

12.

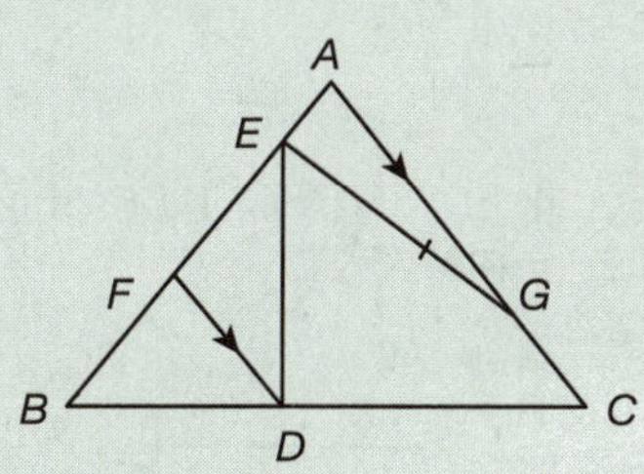

In the above ΔABC, $\overline{AC} \| \overline{DE}$ and $\overline{DF} \| \overline{EG}$. If $\angle FDE = 65°$ then find $\angle EGA$.

(A) 65° (B) 70°
(C) 115° (D) 150°

13.

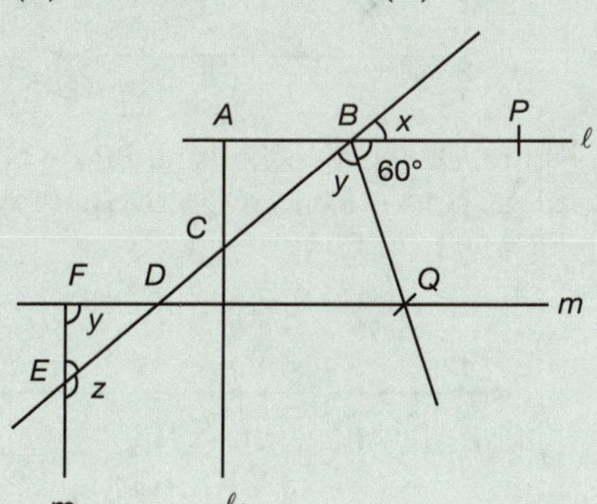

In the above figure $l \| m$ and $l_1 \| m_1$. If $x = y$ and $\angle PBQ = 60°$, then find $\angle z$.

(A) 60°
(B) 80°
(C) 100°
(D) 120°

14.

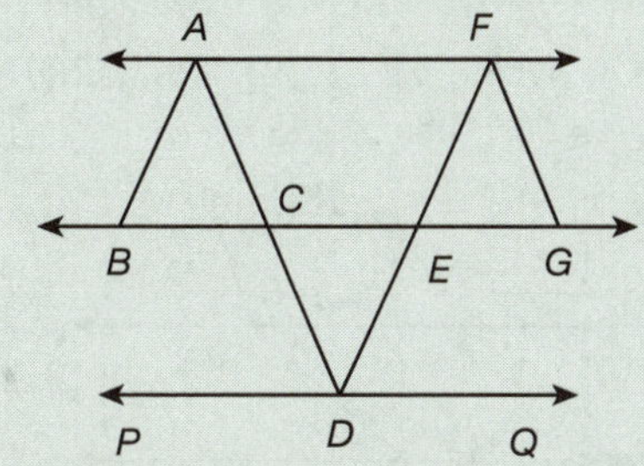

In the figure above (not to scale), $\overrightarrow{AF} \| \overrightarrow{BG} \| \overrightarrow{PQ}$, $\overline{AB} \| \overline{EF}$ and $\overline{AD} \| \overline{FG}$. $\angle ABC = 30°$ and $\angle FGE = 70°$ Find $\angle CDE$.

(A) 20°
(B) 40°
(C) 60°
(D) 80°

15. In the figure below (not to scale), $\overline{AB} \| \overline{CD}$ and $\overline{BD} \| \overline{EF}$. If $\angle ABD = \angle DBC = x$, $\angle BDC = \angle ADB = y$, $\angle BCF = s$ and $\angle DCE = t$, then which of the following is correct?

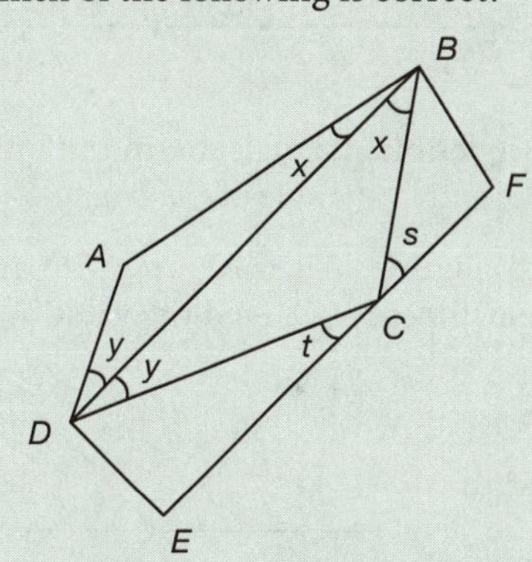

(A) $x = t$ and $y = s$
(B) $x = s$ and $y = t$
(C) $x = y = t = S$
(D) None of the above

ASSESSMENT CORNER

FREE RESPONSE TYPE

Very Short Answer Type Questions

1. If two interior angles on the same side of a transversal intersecting two parallel lines are in the ratio 2: 3, then the greater of the two angles?

2. In Figure, if $AB \parallel CD \parallel EF$, $PQ \parallel RS$, $\angle RQD = 25°$ and $\angle CQP = 60°$, then $\angle QRS$ =?

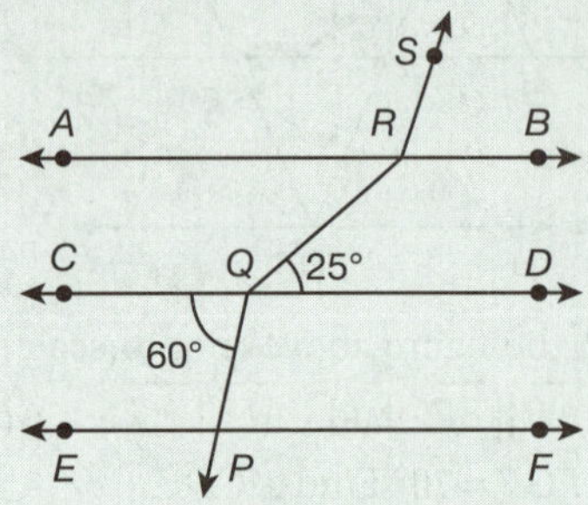

3. An exterior angle of a triangle is 105° and its two interior opposite angles are equal. What is the measure of each of these equal angles?

4. In Figure, POQ is a line. Find the value of x is:

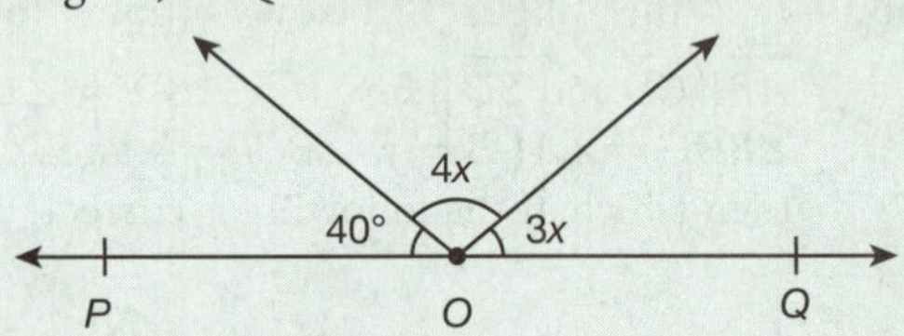

5. Angles of a triangle are in the ratio 2: 4: 3. Find the smallest angle of the triangle.

6. In Figure, AB, CD and EF are three lines concurrent at O. Find the value of y.

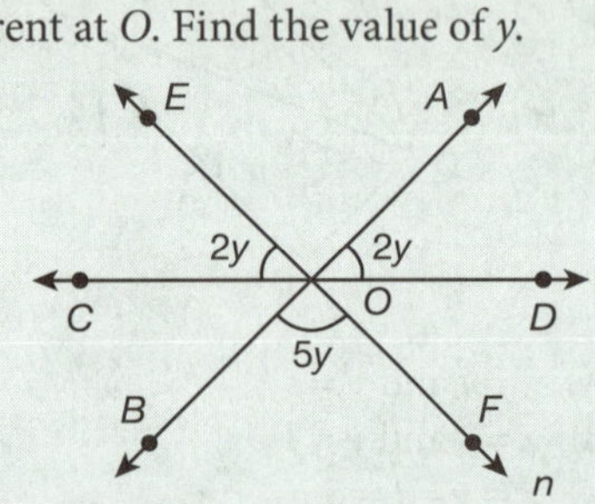

7. In Figure, $x = y$ and $a = b$. Prove that $l \parallel n$.

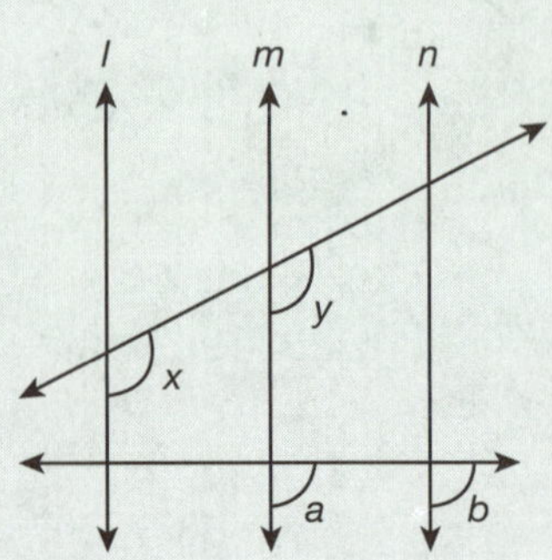

8. In Figure, OD is the bisector of $\angle AOC$, OE is the bisector of $\angle BOC$ and $OD \perp OE$. Show that points A, O and B are collinear.

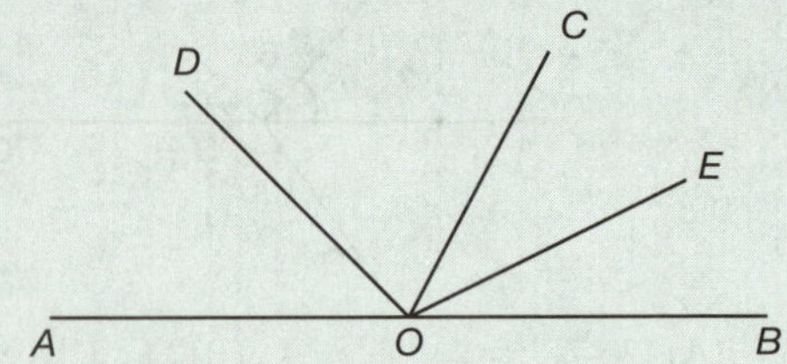

Short Answer Type Questions

1. AP and BQ are the bisectors of the two alternate interior angles formed by the intersection of a transversal t with parallel lines l and m (see Figure). Show that $AP \parallel BQ$.

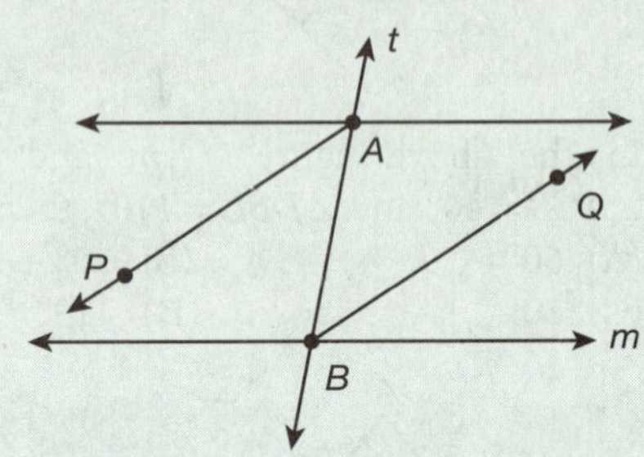

2. In Figure, $BA \parallel ED$ and $BC \parallel EF$. Show that $\angle ABC + \angle DEF = 180°$.

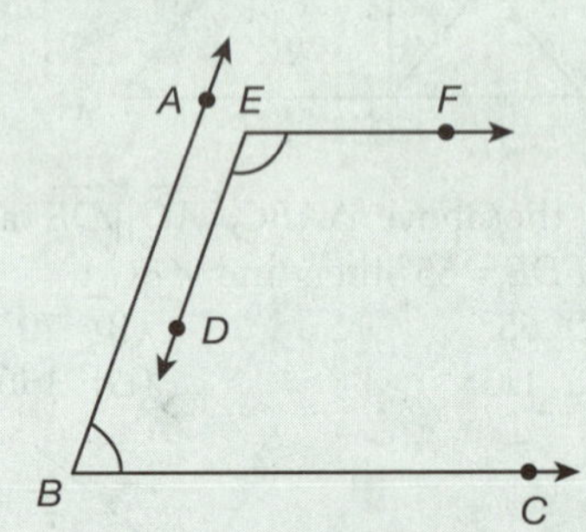

3. In Figure, $DE \parallel QR$ and AP and BP are bisectors of $\angle EAB$ and $\angle RBA$, respectively. Prove that $\angle APB = 90°$.

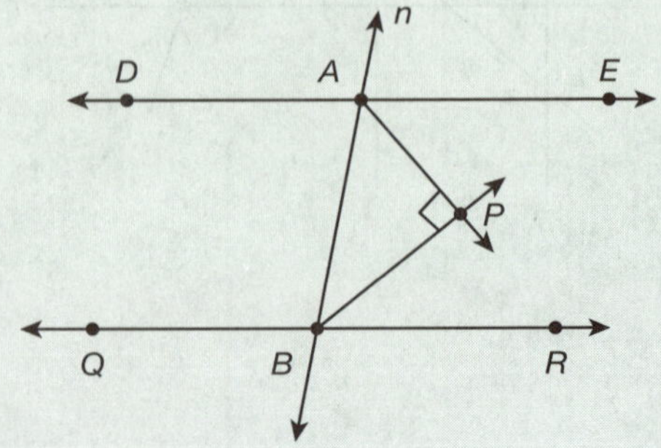

4. The angles of a triangle are in the ratio 2 : 3 : 4. Find the angles of the triangle.

5. In figure, if $x + y = w + z$ then prove that AOB is a straight line.

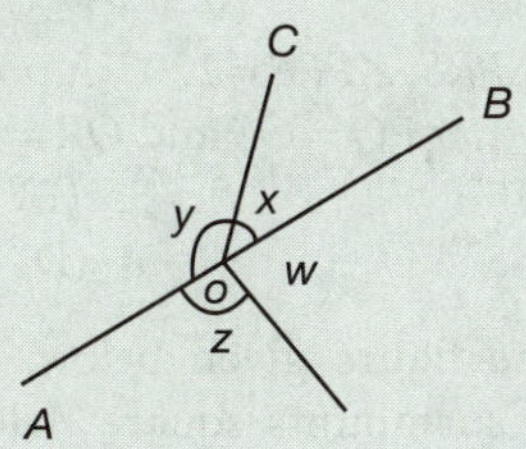

6. In the figure, $x : y : z = 5 : 4 : 6$. If XOY is a straight line find the values of x, y and z.

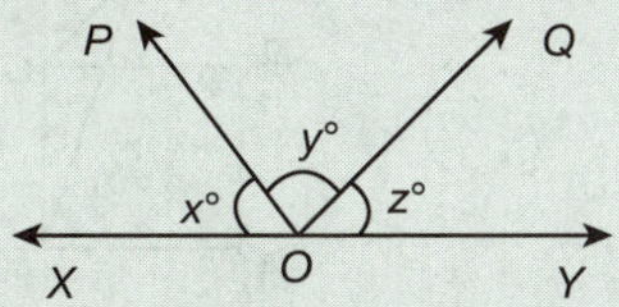

7. In the given figure, AB is a mirror, PO is the incident ray and OR is the reflected ray. If $\angle POR = 112°$ find $\angle POA$.

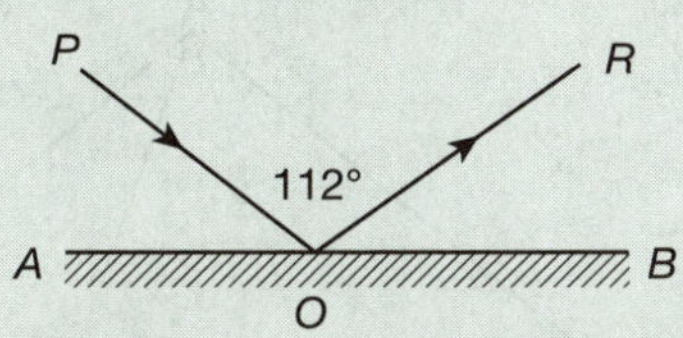

8. If two complementary angles are in the ratio 13 : 5, then find the angles.

9. Find the complement of each of the following angles:
   (i) $36° 40'$ (ii) $42° 25' 36''$

10. Write the supplementary angles of the following angles.
   (i) $54°28'$ (ii) $98°35' 20''$

Long Answer Type Questions

1. In the figure, POQ is a line. Ray OR is perpendicular to line PQ. OS is another ray lying between rays OP and OR. Prove that $\angle ROS = \frac{1}{2}(\angle QOS - \angle POS)$.

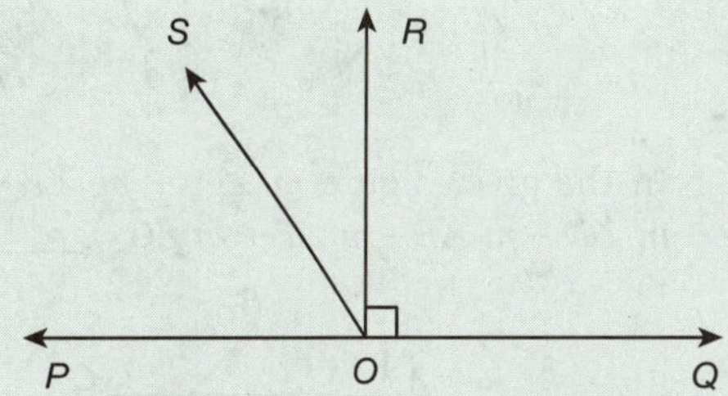

2. In Figure, m and n are two plane mirrors perpendicular to each other. Show that incident ray CA is parallel to reflected ray BD.

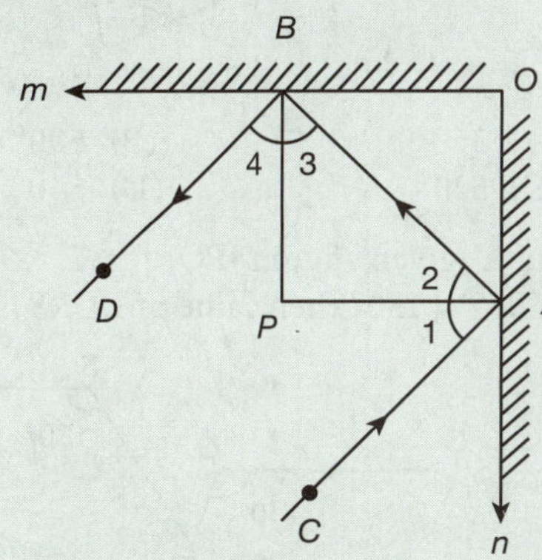

3. Bisectors of angles B and C of a triangle ABC intersect each other at point O. Prove that $\angle BOC = 90° + \frac{1}{2}\angle A$.

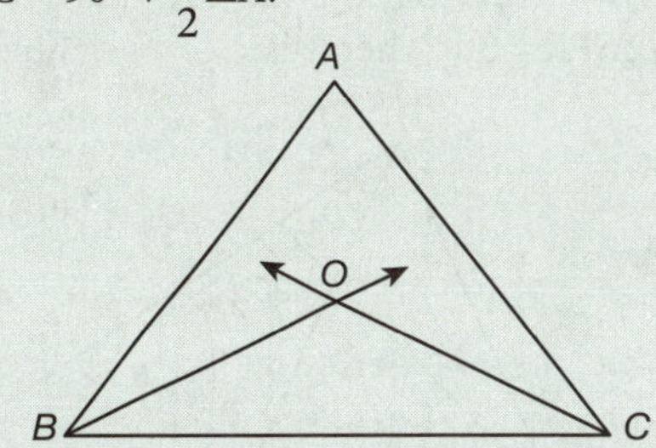

4. Bisectors of interior $\angle B$ and exterior $\angle ACD$ of a ΔABC intersect at point T. Prove that $\angle BTC = \frac{1}{2}\angle BAC$.

5. If two parallel lines are intersected by a transversal, prove that the bisectors of the interior angles on the same side of the transversal intersect each other at right angles.

6. If two parallel lines are intersected by a transversal, prove that the bisectors of the two pairs of interior angles enclose a rectangle.

ARCHIVE CORNER

1. In the given figure $m\angle A + m\angle B + m\angle C + m\angle D + m\angle E + m\angle F + m\angle G =$ _______.

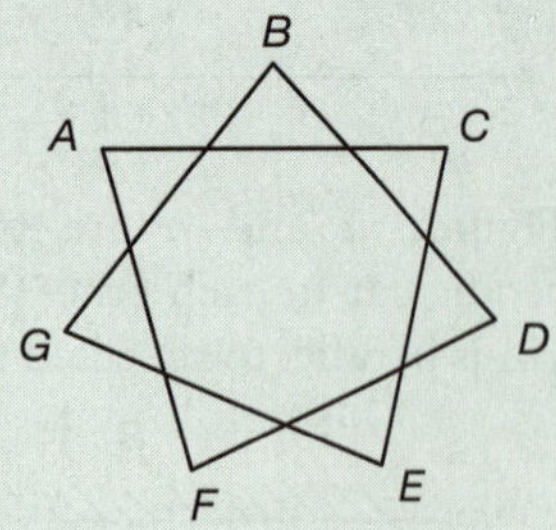

(A) 360° (B) 500°
(C) 520° (D) 540°

2. In a given figure $PQ \parallel ST$, $\angle PQR = 110°$, $\angle RST = 130°$ then value of $\angle QRS$ is:

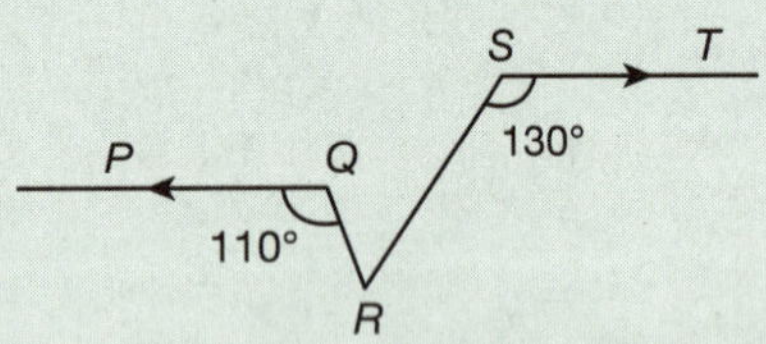

(A) 20° (B) 50°
(C) 60° (D) 70°

3. In figure, if $QT \perp PR$, $\angle TQR = 40°$ and $\angle SPR = 30°$, then y is:

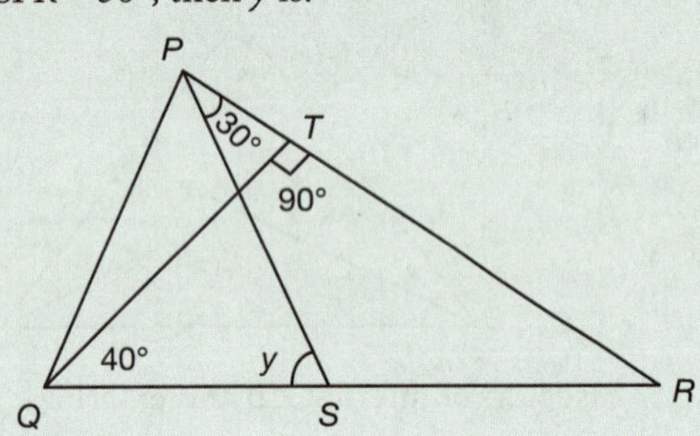

(A) 70° (B) 110°
(C) 90° (D) 80°

4. In given figure $AB \parallel CD$, $\angle ABE = 120°$ $\angle DCE = 110°$ and $\angle BEC = x°$ then $x°$ will be:

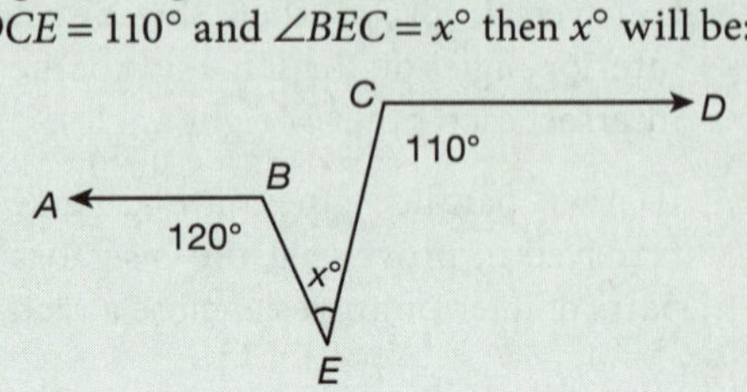

(A) 60° (B) 50°
(C) 40° (D) 70°

5. In a ΔPRS, $\angle PRS = 120°$. A point Q is taken on PR such that $PQ = QS$ and $QR = RS$ then $\angle QPS =$
(A) 15° (B) 30°
(C) 45° (D) 12°

6. In the figure given below, equilateral triangle *EDC* surmounts square *ABCD*. Find the angle *DEB* represented by *x*:

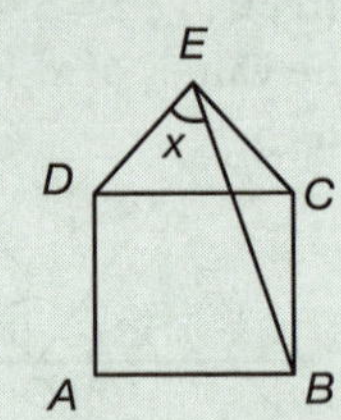

(A) 60° (B) 15°
(C) 30° (D) 45°

7.

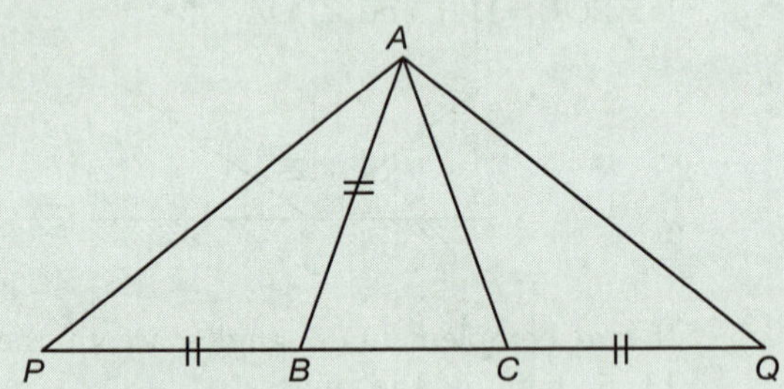

In the above figure ΔAPQ, $P - B - C - Q$ and $AB = AC = PB = CQ$. Find the angle congruent to $\angle PAQ$.
(A) $\angle ACP$ (B) $\angle ABP$
(C) $\angle APC$ (D) $\angle BAQ$

8. In ΔABC, $m\angle B = 90°$, $AB = BC$. Then $AB : AC =$ _______.
(A) 1 : 3 (B) 1 : 2
(C) $1 : \sqrt{2}$ (D) $\sqrt{2} : 1$

ARCHIVE CORNER

ANSWER KEY

Check Points

Check Point 1

1. 79° 12′ 2. 90° 3. 45° 4. 15° 5. 75°

Check Point 2

6. (i) No pair of corresponding angles (ii) ∠1 and ∠6, ∠2 and ∠5
7. 16° 8. 37.5° 9. $x = 105°$, $y = 75°$ 10. 80°.

Check Point 3

11. 40° 12. Right angle triangle 13. $A = 54°$, $B = 36°$, $C = 90°$
14. Equilateral triangle 15. 30°

Assessment Corner

Fixed Response Type

Fill in the Blanks

1. 220 2. 95, 85 3. $\frac{7}{2}$ 4. 30, 45 5. 0 6. 1 : 1

True/False

1. True 2. False 3. False 4. True 5. True

Single Correct Type Questions

Level 1

1. C 2. B 3. B 4. A 5. D 6. B 7. B 8. D 9. A
10. D 11. C 12. B 13. C 14. D 15. A

Level 2

16. A 17. A 18. A 19. B 20. A 21. C 22. A 23. B 24. B
25. C

Multiple Correct Type Questions

1. ABC 2. C 3. AC 4. B 5. AB 6. A 7. A 8. AC 9. ACD
10. ABD 11. D 12. A 13. B

Match Type Questions

1. (i) → (R); (ii) → (R); (iii) → (P); (iv) → (Q, S)
2. (i) → (Q); (ii) → (P); (iii) → (S); (iv) → (R)
3. (i) → (S); (ii) → (R); (iii) → (P); (iv) → (Q)

Assertion and Reason Type Questions

1. A 2. A

Comprehension Type Questions

1. A 2. B 3. C 4. A 5. A 6. ABD

Numerical Type Questions

1. 80° 2. 2.5 3. 80° 4. 135° 5. 54° 6. 260° 7. 35° 8. 30° 9. 126°
10. 126° 11. 115° 12. 125° 13. 53° 14. 120° 15. 55°

Higher Order Thinking Skills (HOTS)

1. B 2. D 3. B 4. B 5. C 6. B 7. A 8. D 9. A
10. D 11. B 12. C 13. D 14. D 15. C

FREE RESPONSE TYPE

Very Short Answer Type Questions

1. 72° and 108° 2. 145° 3. 52.5° 4. 60 and 80 5. 40°, 60° and 80° 6. 20
7. Corresponding angles are equal so lines are parallel 8. *A*, *O*, *B* are collinear

Short Answer Type Questions

4. 40°, 60° and 80° 5. 180° 6. 60°, 48° and 72° 7. 34° 8. 65° and 25°
9. (i) 53°20′ (ii) 47°34′24″ 10. (i) 125°32′ (ii) 81°24′40″

Archive Corner

1. D 2. C 3. D 4. B 5. A 6. D 7. B 8. C

CHAPTER 7

Triangles

Learning Outcomes

After reading this chapter, you would be able to understand:

- classification of triangles.
- congruency of triangles.
- sufficient conditions for congruence of two triangles.
- some inequality relations in a triangle.

Geekspeak

- Triangle
- Isosceles triangle
- Equilateral triangle
- Congruent
- Median
- Altitude
- Angle bisector
- Inequality
- SAS
- ASA
- AAS
- RHS
- SSS

Introduction

Every figure has a shape, size and a position. If we are given two figures then by simply looking at them carefully, we can decide whether they are of the same shape or not. If two figures cover each other exactly then clearly they are of the same shape and same size. Then these two figures are called congruent figures. This method of comparing two figures is known as the method of superposition. In this chapter we will study the basic criteria for congruency of special figures.

Triangle

A triangle is a three-sided polygon characterized by three edges (sides) and three vertices (corners). Triangles are fundamental shapes in geometry and have various properties and classifications.

Scalene Triangle

(i) A triangle in which none of the three sides are equal is called a scalene triangle.

(ii) All three angles are also different.

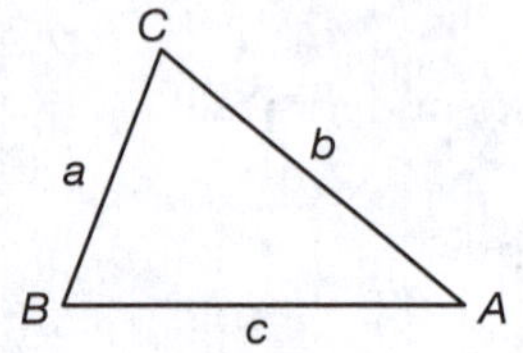

$a \neq b \neq c$

Figure 7.1

Isosceles Triangle

(i) A triangle in which at least two sides are equal is called an isosceles triangle.

(ii) In this triangle, the angles opposite to the congruent sides are also equal.

(iii) 2 medians, 2 altitudes equal.

(iv) Internal bisectors of 2 angles are equal.

(v) Bisector of vertical angle bisects the base and is perpendicular to the base.

(vi) May be acute, obtuse or right-angled triangle.

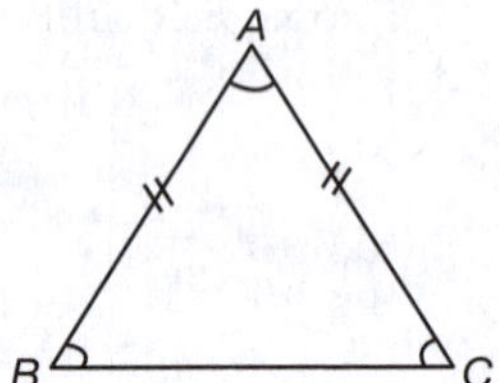

$AB = AC$

$\angle B = \angle C$

Equilateral Triangle

(i) A triangle in which all three sides are equal is called an equilateral triangle.

(ii) In this triangle each angle is congruent and equal to 60°.

(iii) Always acute-angled.

(iv) Incentre, circumcentre, orthocentre and centroid coincide.

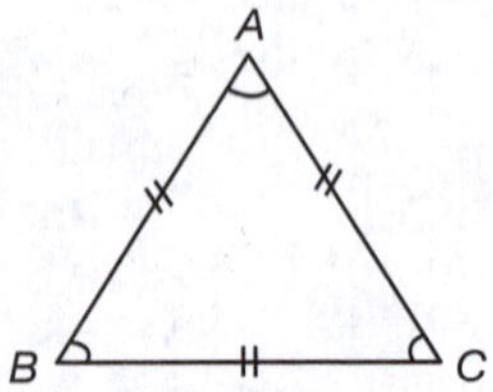

$AB = BC = AC$

$\angle A = \angle B = \angle C = 60°$

Isosceles Right-angled Triangle

(i) Two sides are equal.

(ii) Angle included by the equal sides is 90°.

(iii) Side opposite to 90° is the hypotenuse and is the greatest side.

(iv) Median to the hypotenuse is half of the hypotenuse.

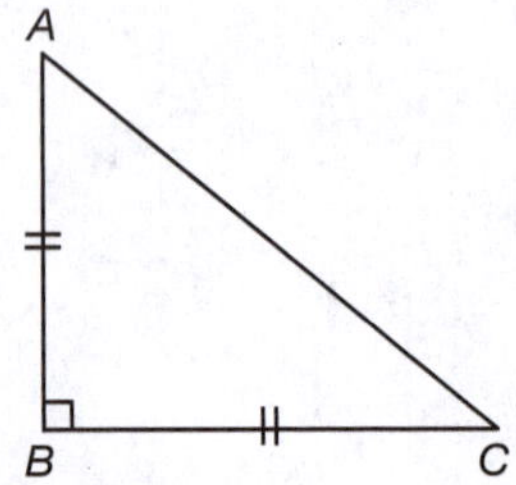

Fundamental Properties of Triangles

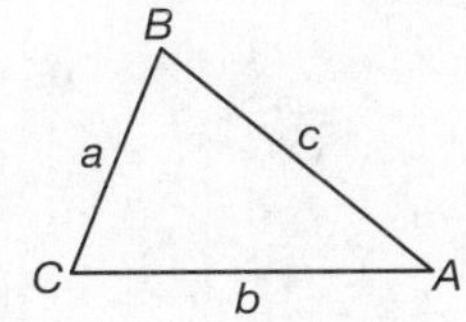

1. Sum of any two sides is always greater than the third side.
2. The difference between any two sides is always less than the third side.
3. Greater angle has a greater side opposite to it and a smaller angle has a smaller side opposite to it i.e., if two sides of the triangle are not congruent then the angle opposite to the greater side is greater.
4. Let a, b, and c be the three sides of a ΔABC and c is the largest side, then:
   (i) if $c^2 < a^2 + b^2$, the triangle is acute angle triangle
   (ii) if $c^2 = a^2 + b^2$, the triangle is right angled triangle
   (iii) If $c^2 > a^2 + b^2$, the triangle is obtuse angle triangle
5. The sum of all the three interior angles is always 180° i.e., $\angle CAB + \angle ABC + \angle BCA = 180°$

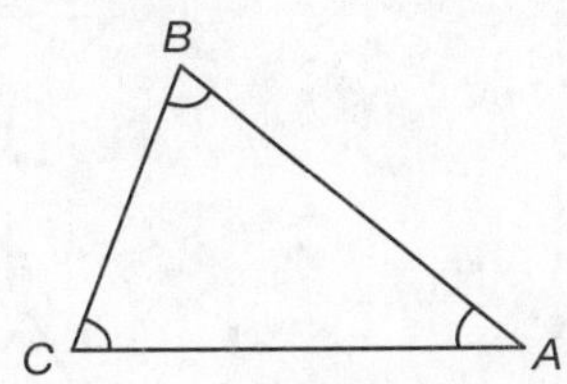

6. The sum of three (ordered) exterior angles of a triangle is 360°.

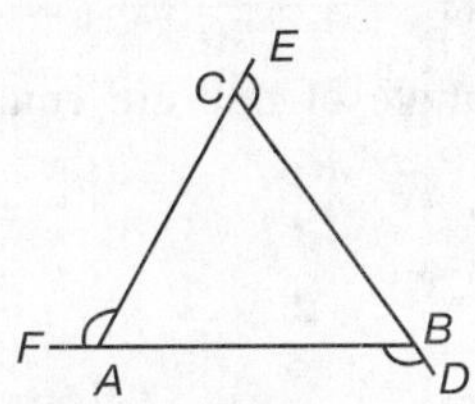

Fig. (i)

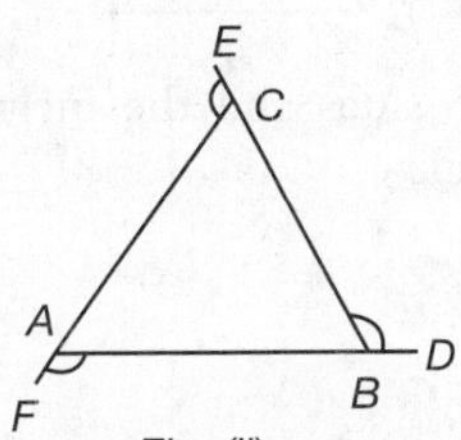

Fig. (ii)

In fig (i): $\angle FAC + \angle ECB + \angle DBA = 360°$
In fig (ii): $\angle FAB + \angle DBC + \angle ECA = 360°$

7. A triangle must have at least two acute angles.
8. In a triangle, the measure of an exterior angle equals the sum of the measures of the interior opposite angles.
9. The measure of an exterior angle of a triangle is greater than the measure of each of the opposite interior angles.

Congruent Figures

The figures are called congruent if they have the same shape and same size. In other words, two figures are called congruent if they are having equal length, width and height.

Fig. (i)

Fig. (ii)

In the above figures {fig.(i) and fig.(ii)} both are equal in length, width and height, so these are congruent figures.

Congruent Triangles

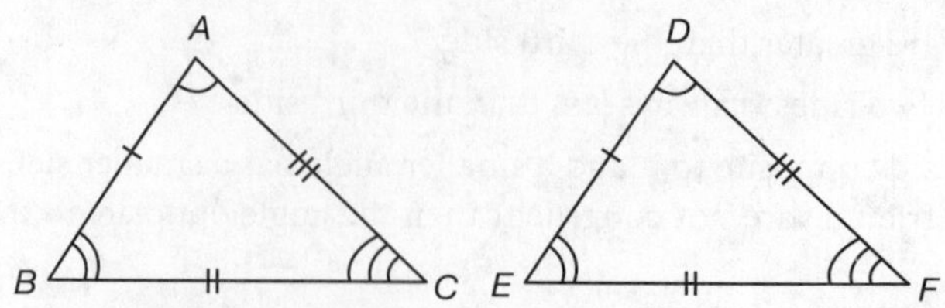

Two triangles are congruent if and only if one of them can be made to superimpose on the other, so as to cover it exactly.

If two triangles ΔABC and ΔDEF are congruent then $\angle A = \angle D$, $\angle B = \angle E$, $\angle C = \angle F$ and $AB = DE$, $BC = EF$, $AC = DF$.

If two ΔABC and ΔDEF are congruent then we write $\Delta ABC \cong \Delta DEF$, we cannot write as $\Delta ABC \cong \Delta DFE$ or $\Delta ABC \cong \Delta EDF$.

Hence, we can say that two triangles are congruent if and only if there exists a one-one correspondence between their vertices such that the corresponding sides and the corresponding angles of the two triangles are equal.

Sufficient Conditions for Congruence

SAS Congruence Criterion

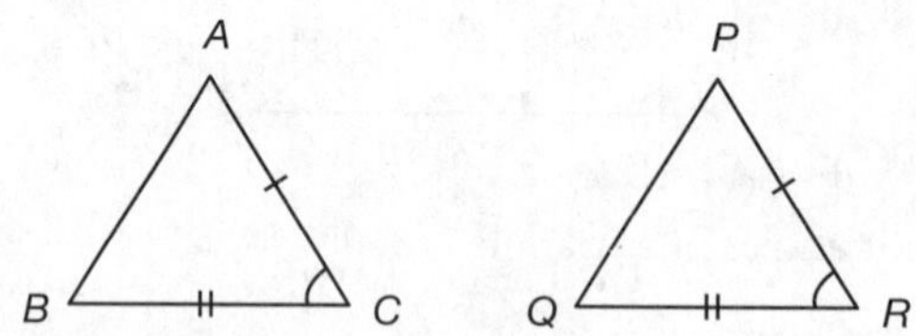

Two triangles are congruent if two sides and the included angle of one are equal to the corresponding sides and the included angle of the other triangle.

ASA Congruence Criterion

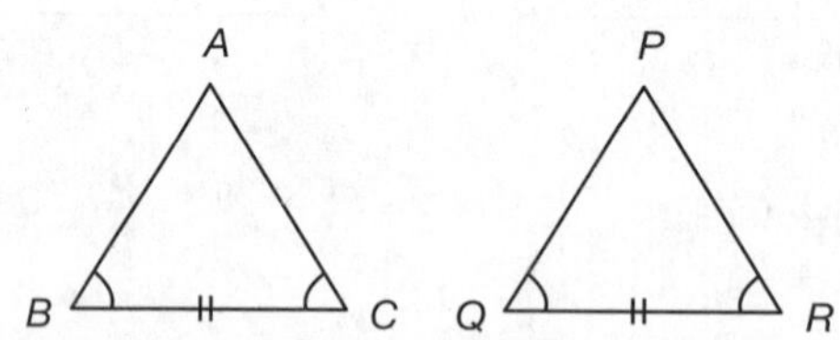

Two triangles are congruent if two angles and the included side of one triangle are equal to the corresponding two angles and the included side of the other triangle.

AAS Congruence Criterion

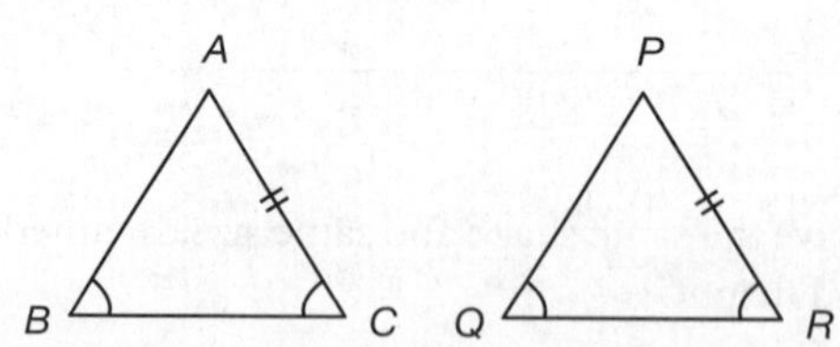

If any two angles and a non-included side of one triangle are equal to the corresponding angles and side of another triangle, then the two triangles are congruent.

SSS Congruence Criterion

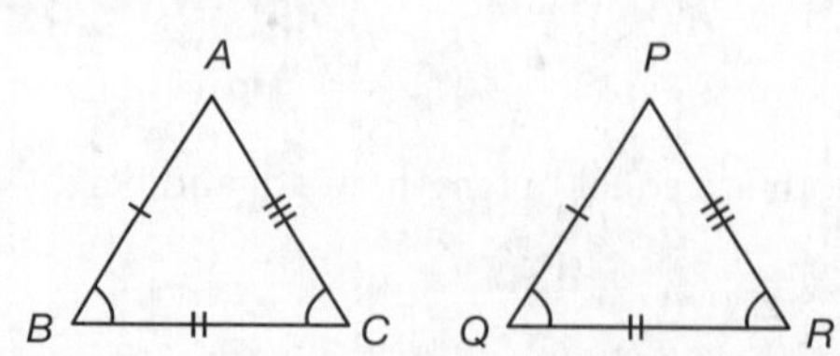

Two triangles are congruent if the three sides of one triangle are equal to the corresponding three sides of the other triangle.

RHS Congruence Criterion

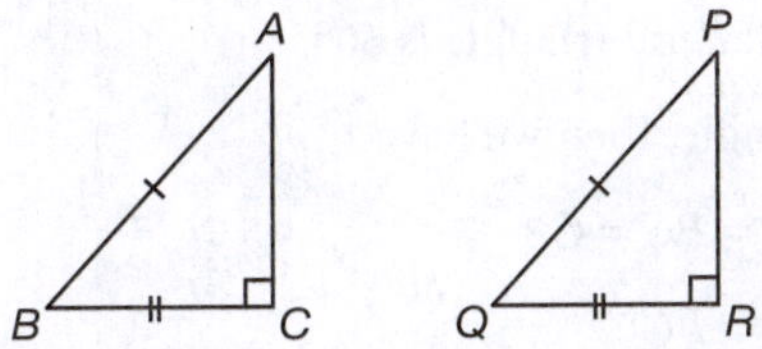

Two right triangles are congruent if the hypotenuse and one side of one triangle are respectively equal to the hypotenuse and one side of the other triangle.

Keystone

If two triangles are congruent then their corresponding sides and angles are also congruent by **CPCT** (corresponding parts of congruent triangles are also congruent).

Theorem 1: Angles opposite to equal sides of an isosceles triangle are equal.

Given: ΔABC in which $AB = AC$.

To prove: $\angle B = \angle C$.

Construction: We draw the bisector AD of $\angle A$ which meets BC in D.

Proof: In ΔABD and ΔACD we have

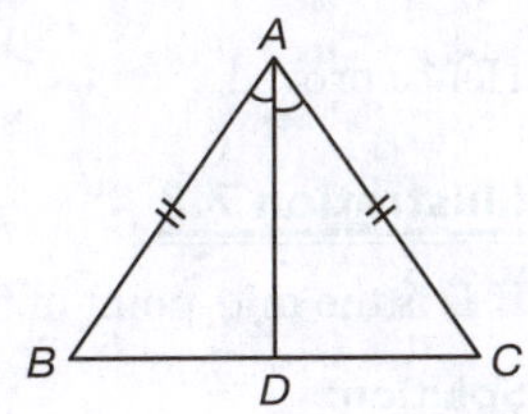

$AB = AC$ [Given]

$\angle BAD = \angle CAD$ [$\because$ AD is the bisector of $\angle A$]

And, $AD = AD$ [Common side]

$\therefore$ By SAS criterion of congruence, we have

$\Delta ABD \cong \Delta ACD$

$\Rightarrow$ $\angle B = \angle C$ [By CPCT]

Hence Proved.

Converse: If two angles of a triangle are equal, then sides opposite to them are also equal.

Theorem 2: If the bisector of the vertical angle bisects the base of the triangle, then the triangle is isosceles.

Given: A ΔABC in which AD is the bisector of $\angle A$ meeting BC in D such that $BD = CD$.

To prove: ΔABC is an isosceles triangle.

Construction: We produce AD to E such that $AD = DE$ and join EC.

Proof: In ΔADB and ΔEDC we have

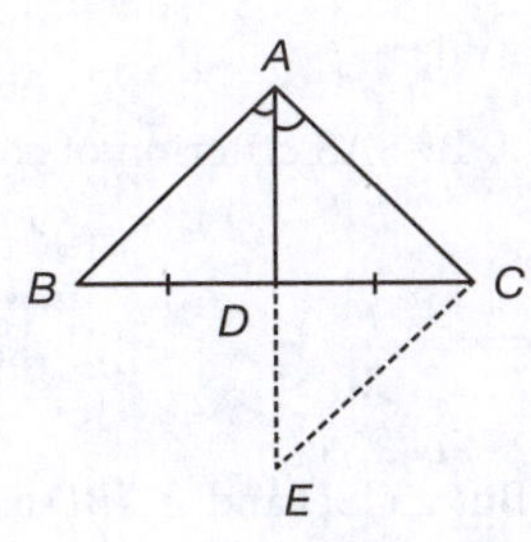

$AD = DE$ [By construction]

$\angle ADB = \angle CDE$ [Vertically opposite angles]

$BD = DC$ [Given]

$\therefore$ By SAS criterion of congruence, we get

$\Delta ADB \cong \Delta EDC$

$\Rightarrow$ $AB = EC$ and $\angle BAD = \angle CED$ [By CPCT]

But, $\angle BAD = \angle CAD$

$\therefore$ $\angle CAD = \angle CED$ [AD is the bisector of $\angle A$]

$\Rightarrow$ $AC = EC$ [Sides opposite to equal angles are equal]

$\Rightarrow$ $AC = AB$. [By equation (i)]

Hence proved.

Illustration 7.1

Prove that measure of each angle of an equilateral triangle is 60°.

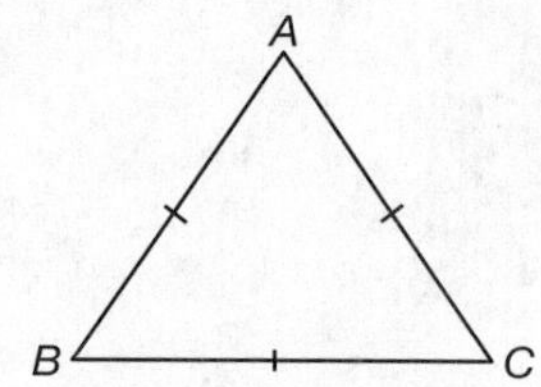

Solution: Let ΔABC be an equilateral triangle, then we have

$$AB = BC = CA \quad \ldots(i)$$

$\because$ $AB = BC$

$\therefore$ $\angle C = \angle A$ ...(ii)

[Angles opposite to equal sides are equal]

Also, $BC = CA$

$\therefore$ $\angle A = \angle B$ ...(iii)

[Angles opposite to equal sides]

By (ii) and (iii) we get $\angle A = \angle B = \angle C$

Now in ΔABC

$$\angle A + \angle B + \angle C = 180°$$

$\Rightarrow$ $3\angle A = 180°$ $[\therefore \angle A = \angle B = \angle C]$

$\Rightarrow$ $\angle A = 60° = \angle B = \angle C.$

Hence proved.

Illustration 7.2

If D is the mid-point of the hypotenuse AC of a right triangle ABC, prove that $BD = AC$.

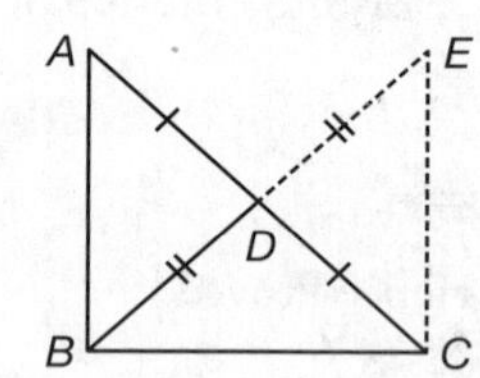

Solution:

Given: ΔABC is a right triangle such that $\angle B = 90°$ and D is the midpoint of AC.

To prove: $BD = \frac{1}{2}AC.$

Construction: Produce BD to E such that $BD = DE$ and join EC.

Proof: In ΔADB and ΔCDE

$AD = DC$ [Given]

$BD = DE$ [By construction]

And, $\angle ADB = \angle CDE$ [Vertically opposite angles]

$\therefore$ By SAS criterion of congruence, we have

$$\Delta ADB \cong \Delta CDE$$

$\Rightarrow$ $EC = AB$ and $\angle CED = \angle AB$ ...(i)

[By CPCT]

But $\angle CED$ and $\angle ABD$ are alternate interior angles

$\therefore$ $CE \parallel AB$

$\Rightarrow$ $\angle ABC + \angle ECB = 180°$ [Consecutive interior angles]

$\Rightarrow$ $90 + \angle ECB = 180°$

$\Rightarrow$ $\angle ECB = 90°.$

Now, In ΔABC and ΔECB we have

$AB = EC$ [By (i)]

$BC = BC$ [Common]

And, $\angle ABC = \angle ECB = 90°$

∴ By SAS criterion of congruence

$$\Delta ABC \cong \Delta ECB$$

$\Rightarrow$ $AC = EB$ [By CPCT]

$\Rightarrow$ $\frac{1}{2} AC = \frac{1}{2} EB$

$\Rightarrow$ $BD = \frac{1}{2} AC.$

Hence Proved.

Illustration 7.3

In a right-angled triangle, one acute angle is double the other. Prove that the hypotenuse is double the smallest side.

Solution:

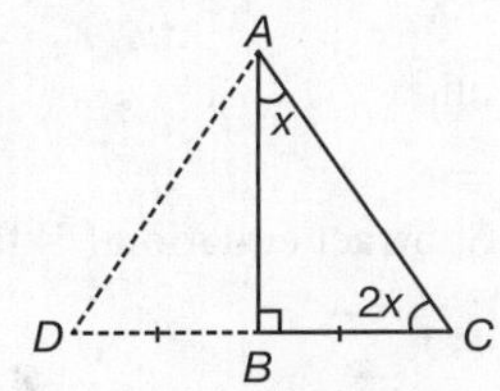

Given: ΔABC is a right triangle such that $\angle B = 900$ and $\angle ACB = 2\angle CAB$.

To prove: $AC = 2BC.$

Construction: Produce CB to D such that $BD = CB$ and join AD.

Proof: In ΔABD and ΔABC we have

$BD = BC$ [By construction]

$AB = AB$ [Common]

$\angle ABD = \angle ABC = 90°$

∴ By SAS criterion of congruence, we get

$$\Delta ABD \cong \Delta ABC$$

$\Rightarrow$ $AD = AC$ and $\angle DAB = \angle CAB$ [By CPCT]

$\Rightarrow$ $AD = AC$ and $\angle DAB = x$ [$\because \angle CAB = x$]

Now, $\angle DAC = \angle DAB + \angle CAB = x + x = 2x$

∴ $\angle DAC = \angle ACD$

$\Rightarrow$ $DC = AD$ [Side Opposite to equal angles]

$\Rightarrow$ $2BC = AD$ [$\because$ $DC = 2BC$]

$\Rightarrow$ $2BC = AC$ [$AD = AC$].

Hence proved.

Illustration 7.4

Prove that the medians of an equilateral triangle are equal.

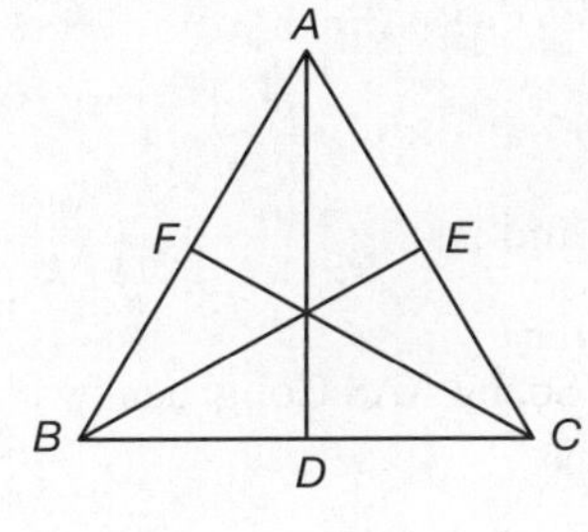

Solution:

Given: A ΔABC in which $AB = BC = AC$, and AD, BE and CF are its medians.

To prove: $AD = BE = CF.$

Prove: In ΔADC and BEA, we have:

$$DC = EA \qquad [BC = AC \Rightarrow \frac{1}{2}BC = \frac{1}{2}AC]$$

$$\angle ACD = \angle BAE \qquad \text{[Each equal to 60°]}$$

$$AC = AB \qquad \text{[Given]}$$

$\therefore$ $$\Delta ADC \cong \Delta BEA \qquad \text{[SAS criteria]}$$

So, $$AD = BE \qquad \text{[By CPCT]}$$

Similarly, $$BE = CF$$

Hence, $AD = BE = CF$.

Illustration 7.5

In the given figure, $AB = AC$ and $OB = OC$. Prove that $\angle ABO = \angle ACO$.

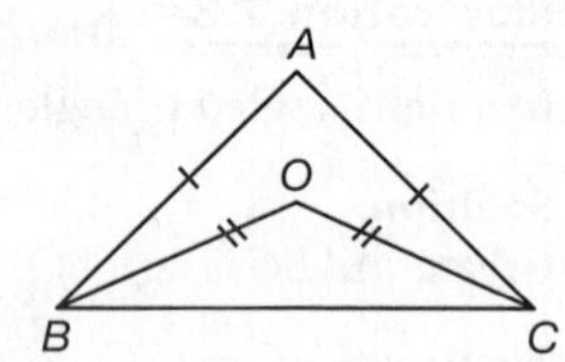

Solution: $AB = AC$

So, $$\angle B = \angle C \qquad \ldots\text{(i)}$$

and $$OB = OC$$

$\Rightarrow$ $$\angle OBC = \angle OCB \qquad \ldots\text{(ii)}$$

Subtract equation (ii) from (i)

$\therefore$ $$\angle B - \angle OBC = \angle C - \angle OCB$$

$$\angle ABO = \angle ACO.$$

Illustration 7.6

In the adjoining figure, X and Y are respectively two points on equal sides AB and AC of ΔABC such that $AX = AY$. Prove that $CX = BY$.

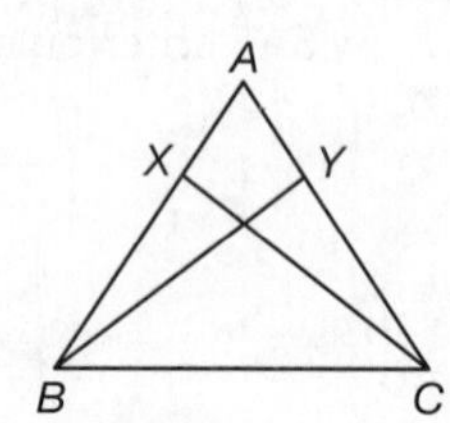

Solution: In ΔAXC and ΔAYB

$$AX = AY \qquad \text{[Given]}$$

$$AC = AB \qquad \text{[Given]}$$

$$\angle A = \angle A \qquad \text{[Common]}$$

So, by SAS congruency

$$\Delta AXC \cong \Delta AYB$$

So, by CPCT

$$CX = BY.$$

Illustration 7.7

In the given figure, if $x = y$ and $AB = CB$, then prove that $AE = CD$.

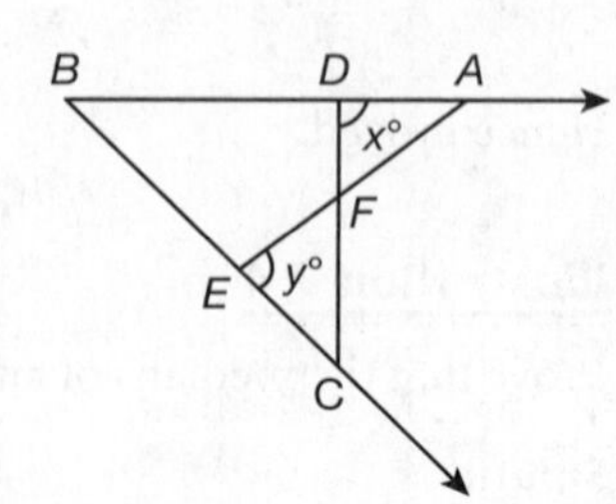

Solution: In ΔABE and ΔCDB

$$AB = CB \qquad \text{[Given]}$$

$$\angle ABE = \angle CBD \qquad \text{[Common]}$$

and $$\angle AEB = \angle CDB$$

$$[\because x° = y° \Rightarrow 180° - x° = 180° - y° \Rightarrow \angle CDB = \angle AEB]$$

So, by AAS Congruency

$$\Delta ABE \cong \Delta CBD$$

$\therefore$ By CPCT,

$$AE = CD.$$

Illustration 7.8

In the given figure, ABC is an equilateral triangle; $PQ \parallel AC$ and AC are produced to R such that $CR = BP$. Prove that QR bisects PC.

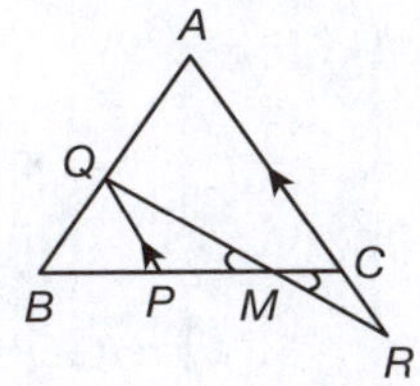

Solution: Let QR intersect PC at M.

$\therefore$ $\angle BPQ = \angle BCA$ [Alternate interior angles $PQ \parallel AR$]

So, $\angle B = \angle BPQ = \angle BQP = 60°$

$\therefore$ ΔBQP is an equilateral triangle.

So, $PQ = BP = CR.$

In ΔPMQ and ΔCMR

$\angle QMP = \angle RMC$ [Vertically opposite angles]

$\angle MQP = \angle MRC$ Alternate angles]

$PQ = CR$ [$CR = BP$ and $BP = PQ$]

So, $\Delta PMQ \cong \Delta CMR$ [By AAS congruency]

$\therefore$ By CPCT

$$PM = MC.$$

Hence, QR bisects PC.

Check Point 1

1. In the following example the data is marked on the diagrams. Write a criterion of congruence that supports your conclusion. If more than one criterion is involved state all.

(i)
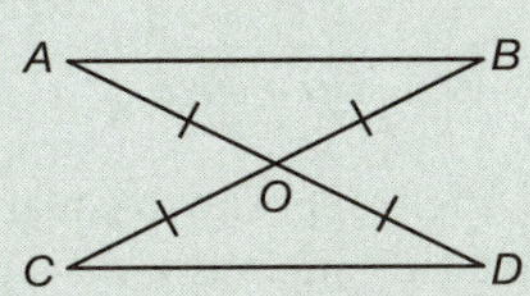

(ii)
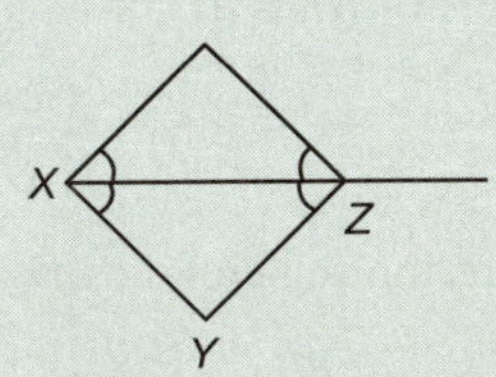

(iii)
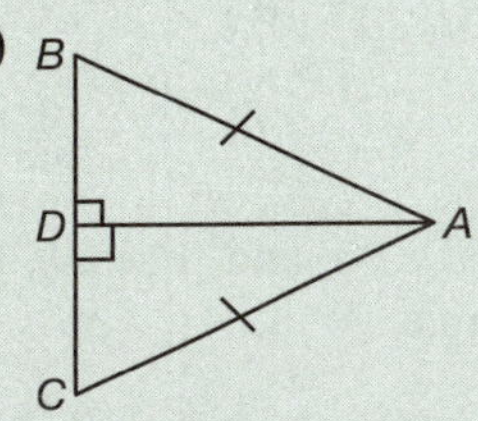

2. Given $AB = 4$ cm, $DC = 4$ cm, $AD = BC$. Prove $\Delta ABC \cong \Delta ADC$.

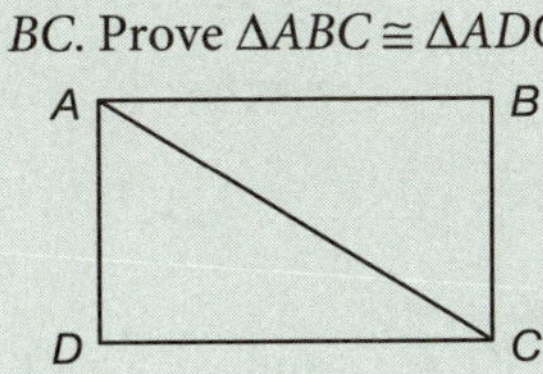

3. Given AD bisects BC and $AB = AC$. Prove $\Delta ADB \cong \Delta ADC$.

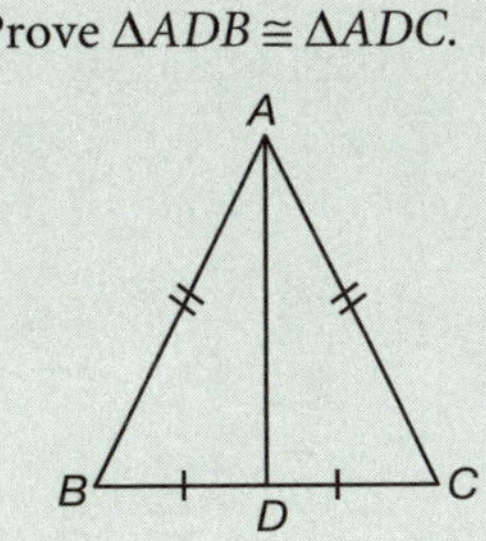

4. Given $AB = CF$, $EF = BD$ and $\angle AFE = \angle DBC$ Prove $\Delta AFE \cong \Delta CBD$.

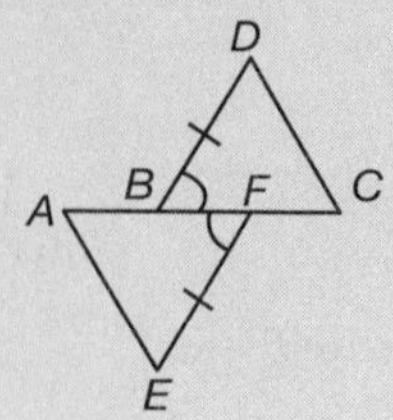

5. Given $\angle P = \angle R$, $PQ = RQ$. Prove $\Delta PQT \cong \Delta RQS$

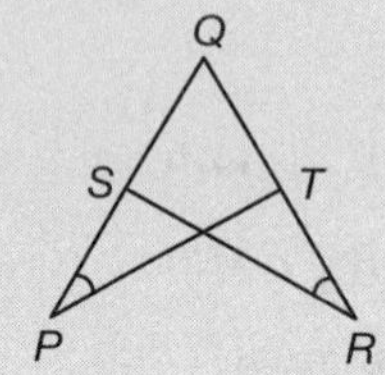

Inequality Relations in a Triangle

Theorem 3: If two sides of a triangle are unequal, the longer side has a greater angle opposite to it.

Given: A ΔABC in which $AC > AB$.

To Prove: $\angle ABC > \angle ACB$.

Construction: Mark a point D on AC such that $AB = AD$. Join BD.

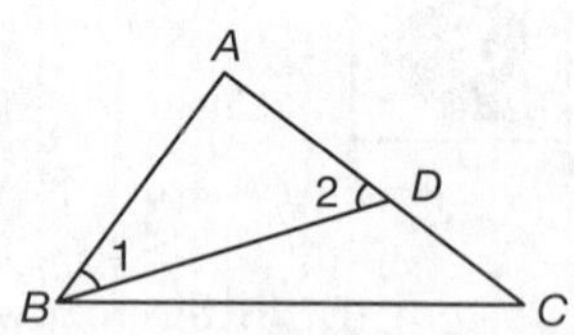

Proof: In ΔABD, we have

$$AB = AD \quad \text{[By construction]}$$

$$\Rightarrow \quad \angle 1 = \angle 2 \quad \ldots\text{(i)}$$

[Angle opposite to equal sides are equal]

Now, consider ΔBCD. We find that $\angle 2$, is the exterior angle of ΔBCD and an exterior angle is always greater than the interior opposite angle.

Therefore, $$\angle 2 > \angle DCB$$

$$\Rightarrow \quad \angle 2 > \angle ACB \quad \ldots\text{(ii)}$$

$[\because \angle ACB = \angle DCB]$

From (i) and (ii), we have

$$\angle 1 = \angle 2 \text{ and } \angle 2 > \angle ACB$$

$$\Rightarrow \quad \angle 1 > \angle ACB \quad \ldots\text{(iii)}$$

But, $\angle 1$ is a part of $\angle ABC$.

$$\therefore \quad \angle ABC > \angle 1 \quad \ldots\text{(iv)}$$

From (iii) and (iv), we get

$$\angle ABC > \angle ACB.$$

Theorem 4: The sum of any two sides of a triangle is greater than the third side.

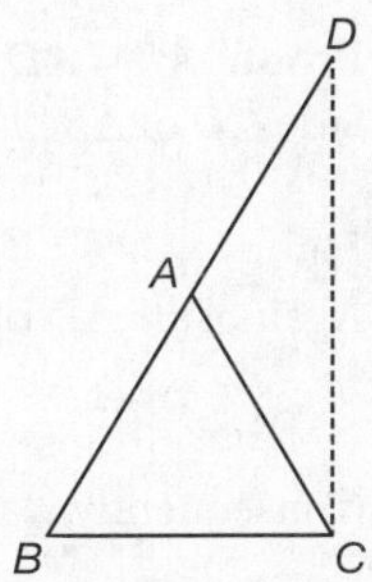

Given: A ΔABC.

To Prove: $AB + AC > BC$, $AB + BC > AC$ and $BC + AC > AB$.

Construction: Produce side BA to D such that $AD = AC$. Join CD.

Proof: In ΔACD, we have

$AC = AD$ [By construction]

$\Rightarrow \angle ADC = \angle ACD$ [Angles opposite to equal sides are equal]

$\Rightarrow \angle ACD = \angle ADC$

$\Rightarrow \angle BCA + \angle ACD > \angle ADC$ [$\because \angle BCA + \angle ACD > \angle ACD$]

$\Rightarrow \angle BCD > \angle ADC$

$\Rightarrow \angle BCD > \angle BDC$ [$\because \angle ADC = \angle BDC$]

$\Rightarrow BD > BC$ [$\because$ Side opposite to greater angle is larger]

$\Rightarrow BA + AD > BC$

$\Rightarrow BA + AC > BC$ [$\because AC = AD$ (By construction)]

$\Rightarrow AB + AC > BC$

Thus, $AB + AC > BC$

Similarly, $AB + BC > AC$ and $BC + AC > AB$.

Theorem 5: Of all the line segments that can be drawn to a given line, from a point, not lying on it, the perpendicular line segment is the shortest.

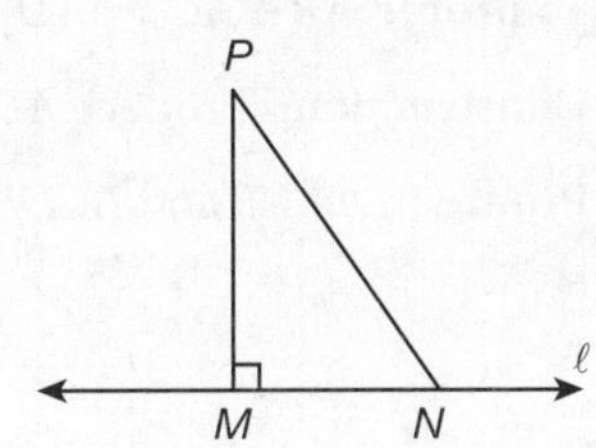

Given: A straight line l and a point P not lying on l. $PM \perp l$ and N is any point on l other than M.

To prove: $PM < PN$.

Proof: In ΔPMN,

we have $\angle M = 90°$

$\Rightarrow \angle N < 90°$ [$\because \angle M = 90° \Rightarrow \angle MPN + \angle PNM = 90°$]

$\Rightarrow \angle P + \angle N = 90° \Rightarrow \angle N < 90°$

$\Rightarrow \angle N < \angle M$

$\Rightarrow PM < PN$ [Side opposite to greater angle is larger]

Thus, $PM < PN$.

Hence, PM is the shortest of all line segments from P to l.

Theorem 6: Prove that the difference between any two sides of a triangle is less than its third side.

Given: A ΔABC.

To prove:

(i) $AC - AB < BC$

(ii) $BC - AC < AB$

(iii) $BC - AB < AC$

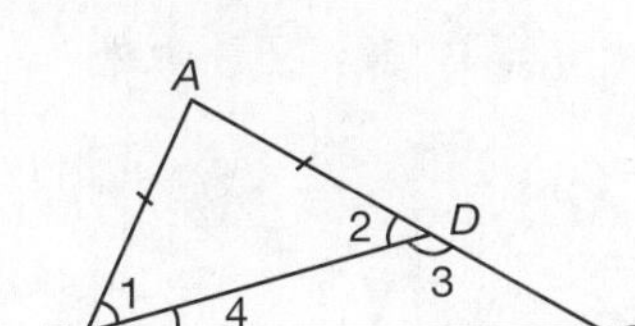

Construction: Let $AC > AB$. Then, along AC, set off $AD = AB$. Join BD.

Proof: $AB = AD \Rightarrow \angle 1 = \angle 2$.

Side CD of ΔBCD has been produced to A.

$\therefore \quad \angle 2 > \angle 4$ [$\because$ exterior angle > each interior opposite angle]

Again, side AD of ΔABD has been produced to C.

$\therefore \quad \angle 3 > \angle 1$ [$\because$ exterior angle > each interior opposite angle]

Consequently, $\angle 3 > \angle 2$ [$\because \angle 1 = \angle 2$]

Now, $\angle 3 > \angle 2$ and $\angle 2 > \angle 4$

$\Rightarrow \quad \angle 3 > \angle 4.$

$\therefore \quad BC > CD$ [side opposite to greater angle is longer]

$\Rightarrow \quad CD < BC$

$\Rightarrow \quad AC - AD < BC$

$\Rightarrow \quad AC - AB < BC$ [$\because AD = AB$]

Hence, $AC - AB < BC.$

Similarly, $BC - AC < AB$ and $BC - AB < AC.$

Illustration 7.9

Prove that any two sides of the triangle are together greater than twice the median drawn to the third side.

Solution:

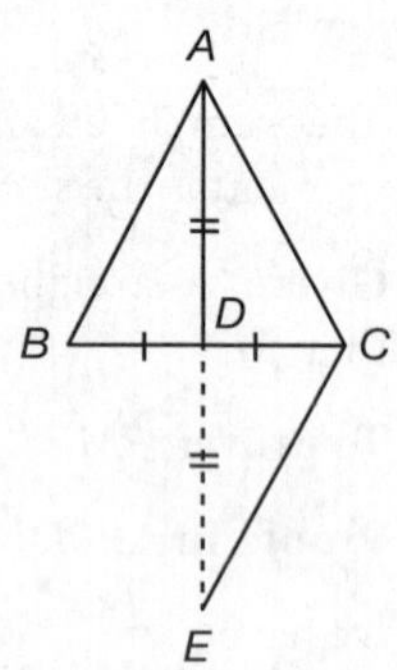

Given: ΔABC and AD is the median.

To prove: $AB + AC > 2AD$

Construction: Produce AD to E such that $AD = DE$. Join EC.

Proof: In ΔADB and ΔCDE

$AD = DE$ [By construction]

$BD = DC$ AD is the median]

$\angle ADB = \angle CDE$ [Vertically opposite angles]

$\Delta ADB \cong \Delta CDE$ [By SAS congruency]

So, by CPCT

$$AB = EC$$

In ΔAEC

$AC + EC > 2AD.$ [Sum of two sides of a triangle is always greater than the third side]

So, $AC + AB > 2AD.$ [As $EC = AB$].

Illustration 7.10

In the figure, T is a point on the side QR of ΔPQR and S is a point such that $RT = ST$. Prove that $PQ + PR > QS$.

Solution: In ΔPQR we have:

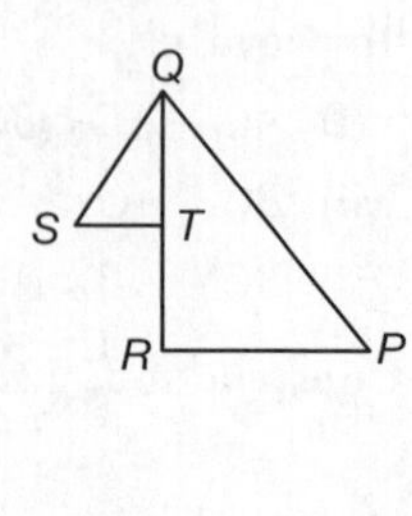

$PQ + PR > QR$

$\Rightarrow \quad PQ + PR > QT + TR$

$\Rightarrow \quad PQ + PR > QT + S$ ...(i)

[$\therefore RT = ST$] ST

In ΔQST

$$QT + ST > SQ \quad \text{...(ii)}$$

From (i) and (ii)

$$\therefore \quad PQ + PR > SQ$$

Hence proved.

Check Point 2

6. In the figure, compare $\angle BCD$ with $\angle A$.

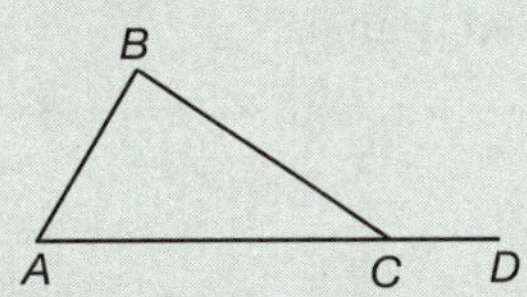

7. If $\Delta ABC \cong \Delta CDE$, compare $\angle FED$ with $\angle B$.

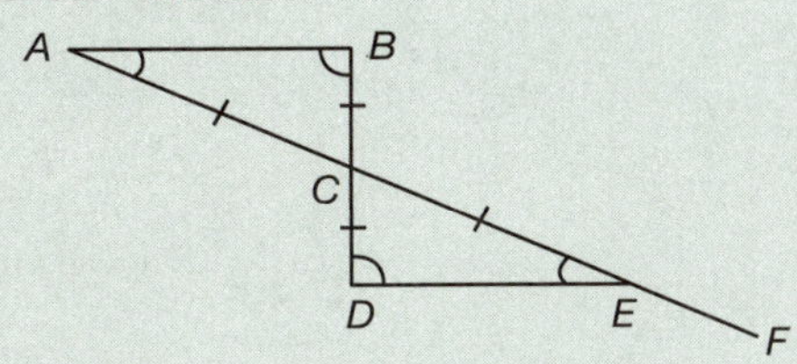

8. If $AB = BC$ and $\angle B = \frac{1}{2}\angle A$, prove that $AB > AC$.

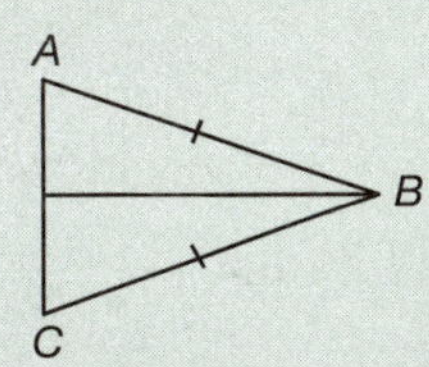

9. List all sides of ΔABC in the increasing order of their length.

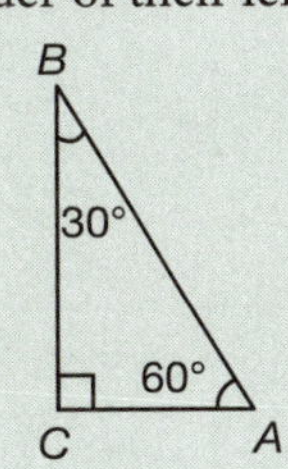

10. List the angles of the triangle ABC in the increasing order of their magnitude.

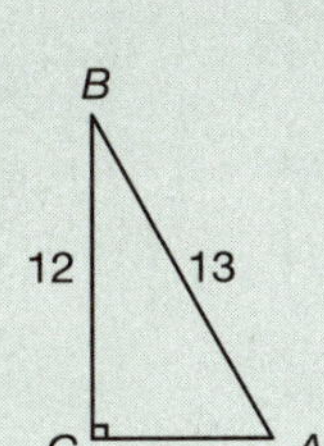

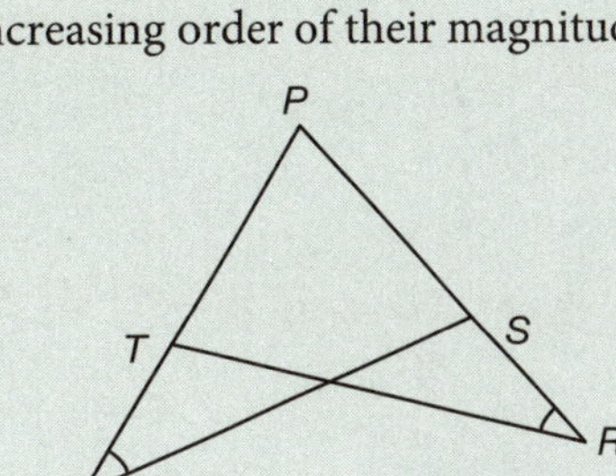

Competition Corner

- Intersection Point of medians of triangle is called median of the triangle.
- Intersection Point of altitudes of triangle is called orthocenter of the triangle.
- Intersection Point of perpendicular bisector of triangle is called circumcenters of the triangle.
- Intersection Point of angle bisector of triangle is called incentre of the triangle.
- In an Equilateral triangle median, incentre, circumcenter and orthocenter are the same.

If a, b and c are the sides of a triangle then

(a) If $a^2 > b^2 + c^2$ then triangle is obtuse-angled triangle.

(b) If $a^2 = b^2 + c^2$ then triangle is right-angled triangle.

(c) If $a^2 < b^2 + c^2$ then triangle is acute angled triangle.

STRUCTURAL OUTLINE

Triangle

Fundamental properties of triangles

1. Sum or any two sides is always greater than the third side.
2. The difference of any two sides is always less than the third side.
3. Greater angle has a greater side opposite to it.
4. Let a, band c be the three sides of a AABC and cis the largest side, then
   - (i) if $c^2 < a^2 + b^2$, the triangle is acute angle triangle
   - (ii) if $c^2 = a^2 + b^2$, the triangle is right angled triangle
   - (iii) if $c^2 > a^2 + b^2$, the triangle is obtuse angle triangle
5. The sum of all the three interior angles is alwayss 180°.
6. The sum of three (ordered) exterior angles of a triangle is 360°.
7. A triangle must have at least two acute angles.
8. In a triangle, the measure of an exterior angle equals the sum of the measure of the interior angle equals the sum of the measures of the interior opposite angle.
9. The measure of an exterior angle of a triangle is greater than the measure of each of the opposite interior angles.

Sufficient conditions for congruence of two triangle

(i) SAS Congruence criterion
(ii) ASA Congruence criterion
(iii) AAS Congruence criterion
(iv) SSS Congruence criterion
(v) RHS Congruence criterion

Scalene triangle

(i) A triangle in which none of the three sides are equal is called a scalene triangle

(ii) All the three angles are also different

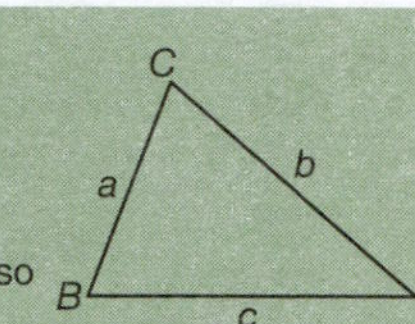

$a \neq b \neq c$

Isosceles triangle

(i) A triangle in which at leat two least two sides are equal is called an isosceles triangle.
(ii) In this triangle, the angles opposite to the congruent sides are also equal
(iii) 2 medians, 2 altitudes equal.
(iv) Internal bisectors of 2 angles are equl.
(v) Bisector of vertical angle bisects the base and perpendicular to the base.
(vi) May be acute, obtuse or right-angled triangle.

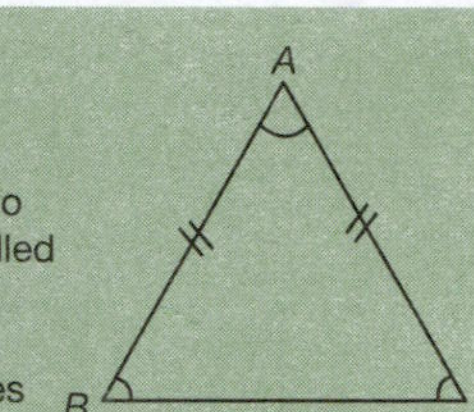

$AB = AC$
$\angle B = \angle C$

Isosceles right-angled triangle

(i) 2 sides are equal
(ii) Angle included by the equal sides is 90°.
(iii) Side opposite to 90° is hypotenuse and is the greatest side.
(iv) Median to the hypotenuse is half of the hypotenuse.

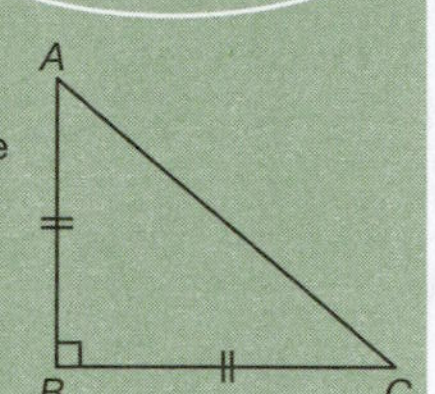

Equilateral triangle

(i) A triangle in which all the three sides are equal is called an equilateral triangle.

(ii) In this triangle each angle is congruent and equal to 60°

(iii) Always acute angled.

(iv) Incentre, circumcentre, orthocentre and centroid coincide.

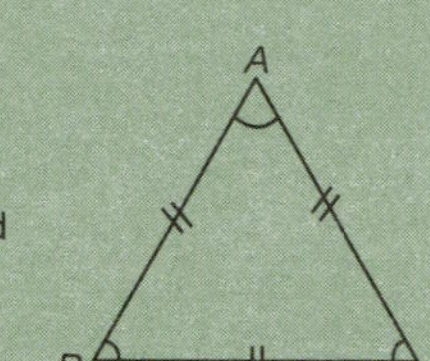

$AB = BC = AC$
$\angle A = \angle B = \angle C = 60°$

EXEMPLIFICATION

1. In figure, two sides AB and BC and the median AM of a ΔABC are respectively equal to sides DE and EF and the median DN of ΔDEF. Prove that $\Delta ABC \cong \Delta DEF$.

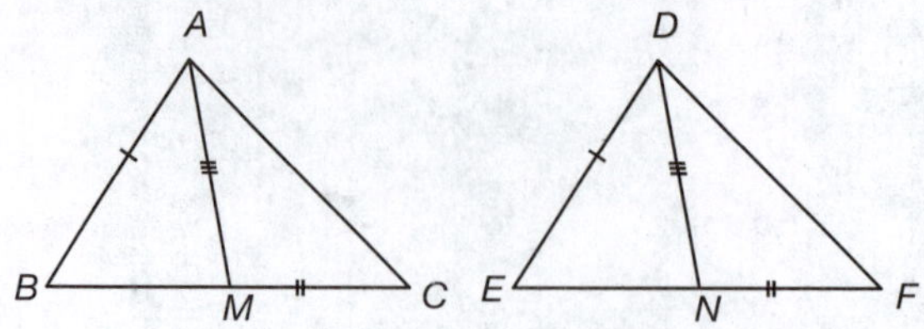

Solution: $\because$ AM and DN are medians of ΔABC and ΔDEF respectively

$\therefore$ $$BM = MC \text{ and } EN = NF$$

$\Rightarrow$ $$BM = \frac{1}{2} BC \text{ and } EN = \frac{1}{2} EF$$

But, $$BC = EF$$

$\therefore$ $$BM = EN \quad \ldots\text{(i)}$$

In ΔABM and ΔDEN we have

$$AB = DE \quad \text{[Given]}$$

$$AM = DN \quad \text{[Given]}$$

$$BM = EN \quad \text{[By (i)]}$$

$\therefore$ By SSS criterion of congruence we have

$$\Delta ABM \cong \Delta DEN$$

$\Rightarrow$ $$\angle B = \angle E \quad \ldots\text{(ii)}$$

[By CPCT]

Now, In ΔABC and ΔDEF

$$AB = DE \quad \text{[Given]}$$

$$\angle B = \angle E \quad \text{[By (ii)]}$$

$$BC = EF \quad \text{[Given]}$$

$\therefore$ By SAS criterion of congruence, we get

$$\Delta ABC \cong \Delta DEF$$

Hence proved.

2. In the given figure, $AY \perp ZY$ and $BY \perp XY$ such that $AY = ZY$ and $BY = XY$. Prove that $AB = ZX$.

Solution: $\angle BYX = 90°$ and $\angle AYZ = 90°$.

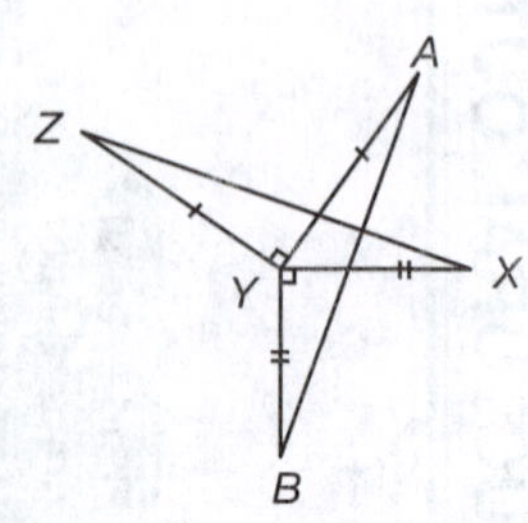

$$\angle BYX = \angle AYZ$$

$\Rightarrow$ $$\angle BYX + \angle AYX = \angle AYZ + \angle AYX$$

$\Rightarrow$ $$\angle AYB = \angle ZYX$$

Now, in ΔAYB and ΔZYX

$$AY = ZY \quad \text{[Given]}$$

$$BY = XY \quad \text{[Given]}$$

$$\angle AYB = \angle ZYX \quad \text{[proved above]}$$

$\therefore$ $\Delta AYB \cong \Delta ZYX$ [By SAS congruency]

Hence, $AB = ZX$ [By CPCT]

3. In ΔABC, D is the midpoint of BC. If $DL \perp AB$ and $DM \perp AC$ such that $DL = DM$, prove that $AB = AC$.

Solution: In ΔBDL and ΔDMC

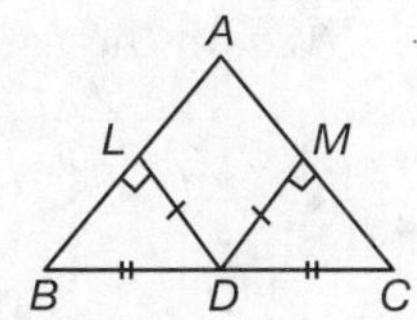

$DL = DM$ [Given]

$\angle DLB = \angle DMC$ [Each 90°]

$BD = DC$ [D is the midpoint of BC]

$\therefore$ $\Delta DLB \cong \Delta DMC$ [By RHS congruency]

So, by CPCT

$\angle B = \angle C$

Hence, $AB = AC$.

4. In figure, $PQ = PR$, show that $PS > PQ$.

Solution: In ΔPQR

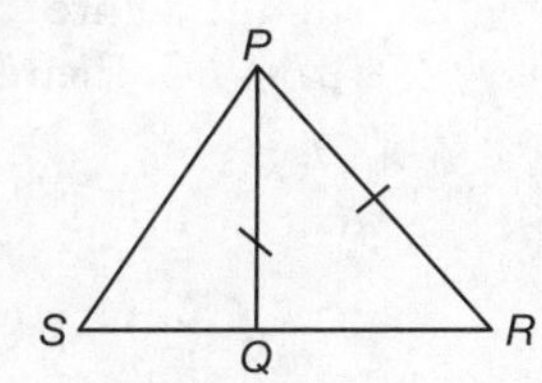

$\therefore$ $PQ = PR$

$\Rightarrow$ $\angle PRQ = \angle PQR$ ...(i)

In ΔPSQ, SQ is produced to R

$\therefore$ Ext. $\angle PQR > \angle PSQ$ ...(ii)

$\Rightarrow$ $\angle PRQ > \angle PSQ$ [From equation (i) and (ii)]

$\Rightarrow$ $\angle PRS > \angle PSR$

$\Rightarrow$ $PS > PR$ [Side opposite to greater angle is larger]

But, $PR = PQ$

$\therefore$ $PS > PQ$

Hence proved.

ASSESSMENT CORNER

FIXED RESPONSE TYPE

Fill in the Blanks

1. In the figure, it is given that $AB = CF$, $EF = BD$ and $\angle AFE = \angle CBD$. then $\Delta AFE \cong \Delta$ _______

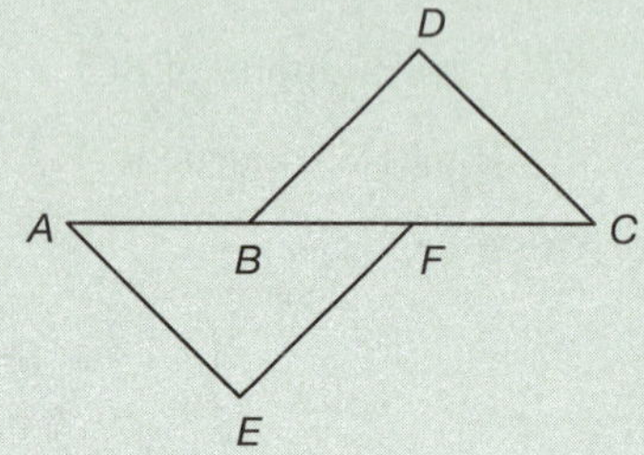

2. In the figure, it is given that $\angle A = \angle C$ and $AB = EC$. Then $\Delta ABD \cong \Delta$ _______

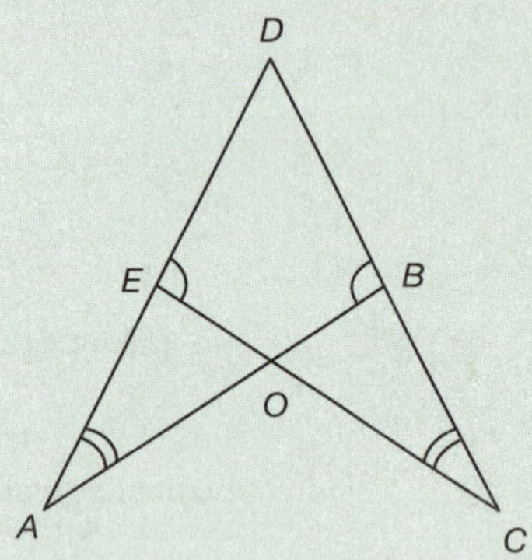

3. In the figure, $AB = AC = AD$, then $\angle BCD$ is a _______ angle.

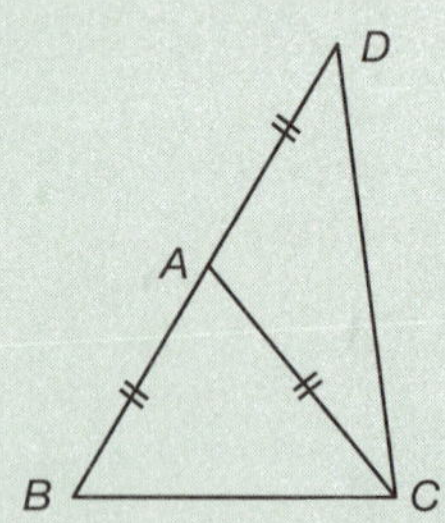

4. ABC is a triangle and D is the midpoint of BC. The perpendiculars from D to AB and AC are equal. Then the triangle is _______

5. If D is any point on the base BC produced, of an isosceles triangle ABC, then AD _______ AB. (Use <, > and =)

6. In ΔPQR, S is any point on the side QR. Show that $PQ + QR + RP$ _______ $2\,PS$. (Use <, > and =)

True/False

1. In the figure $AC = BC$, $\angle DCA = \angle ECB$ and $\angle DBC = \angle EAC$. Then triangles DBC and EAC are congruent, and hence $DC = EC$ and $BD = AE$.

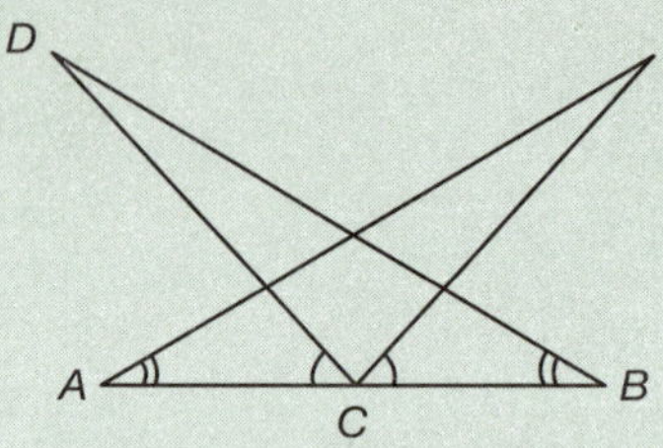

2. In the figure, BD and CE are altitudes. If $BE = CD$, then $BD = DE$.

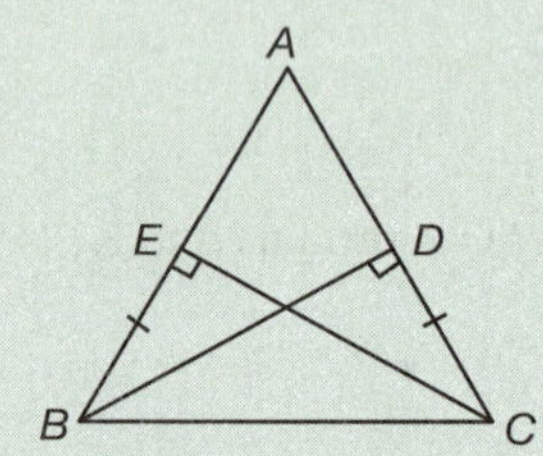

3. In the figure, ΔABC is a right-angled triangle at B. $ADEC$ and $BCFG$ are squares. Then $AF = BE$.

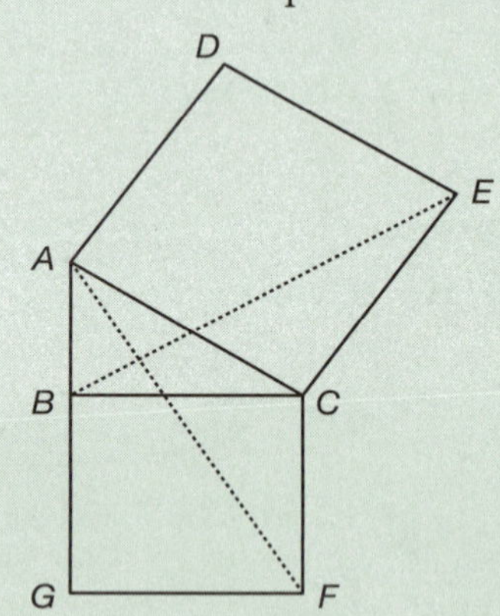

4. ΔABC and ΔDBC are two isosceles triangles on the same base BC, and vertices A and D are on the same side of BC. If AD is extended to intersect BC at P, Then AP bisects $\angle A$ as well as $\angle D$.

5. Perimeter of a triangle is greater than the sum of its three medians.

Single Correct Type Questions

Level 1

1. $ABCD$ is a square and P, Q, R are points on AB, BC and CD respectively such that $AP = BQ = CR$ and $\angle PQR = 90°$, then $\angle QPR =$
   (A) 45° (B) 50°
   (C) 60° (D) 70°

2. In a ΔXYZ, $LM \parallel YZ$ and bisectors YN and ZN of $\angle Y$ and $\angle Z$ respectively meet at N on LM. Then $YL + ZM =$
   (A) YZ (B) XY
   (C) XZ (D) LM

3. In ΔAOC and ΔXYZ, $\angle A = \angle X$, $AO = XZ$, $AC = XY$, then by which congruence rule is $\Delta AOC \cong \Delta XZY$
   (A) SAS (B) ASA
   (C) SSS (D) RHS

4. Two equilateral triangles are congruent when:
   (A) Their angles are equal
   (B) Their sides are equal
   (C) Their sides are proportional
   (D) Their areas are proportional

5. In the given figure, if $AB = AC$ and $BD = DC$. ΔABD and ΔACD are congruent by which criterion?

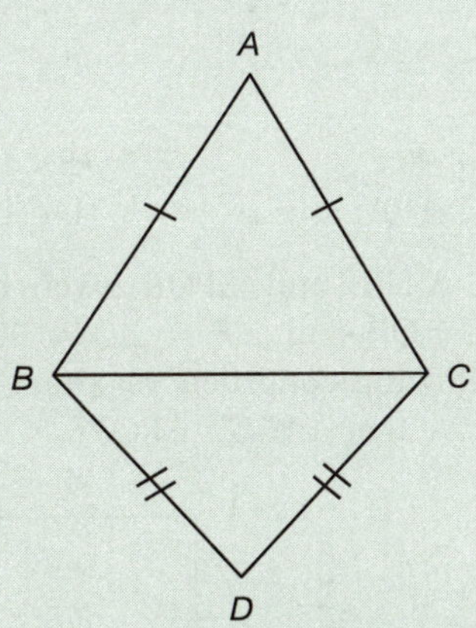

   (A) SSS (B) ASA
   (C) SAS (D) RHS

6. In the given figure, AD is the median, then $\angle BAD$ is:

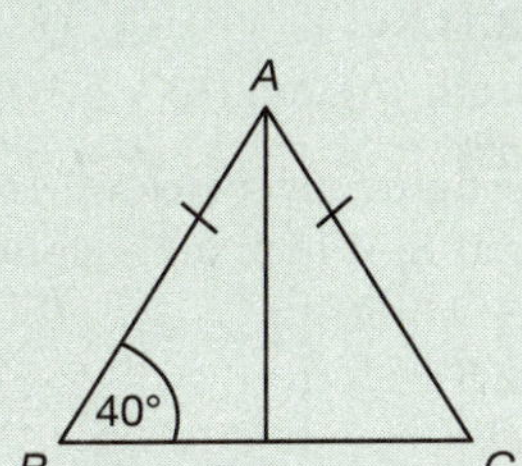

   (A) 55° (B) 50°
   (C) 100° (D) 40°

7. $\Delta ABC \cong \Delta PQR$. If $AB = 5$cm, $\angle B = 40°$ and $\angle A = 80°$, then which of the following is true?
   (A) $QP = 5$ cm, $\angle P = 60°$
   (B) $QP = 5$ cm, $\angle R = 60°$
   (C) $QR = 5$ cm, $\angle R = 80°$
   (D) $QR = 5$ cm, $\angle Q = 40°$

8. If the three altitudes of a Δ are equal then the triangle is:
   (A) Isosceles (B) Equilateral
   (C) Right angled (D) None

9. In a ΔPQR, PS is the bisector of $\angle P$ and $\angle Q = 70°$ $\angle R = 30°$, then:
   (A) $QS > PQ > PR$ (B) $QS < PQ < PR$
   (C) $PQ > QS > SR$ (D) $PQ < QS < SR$

10. If D is any point on the side BC of a ΔABC, then:
    (A) $AB + BC + CA > 2\,AD$
    (B) $AB + BC + CA < 2AD$
    (C) $AB + BC + CA > 3\,AD$
    (D) None

11. If the length of the largest side of a triangle is 12 cm, then the other two sides of the triangle can be:
    (A) 4.8 cm, 8.2 cm (B) 3.2 cm, 7.8 cm
    (C) 6.4 cm, 2.8 cm (D) 7.6 cm, 3.4 cm

12. It is not possible to construct a triangle when its sides are:
    (A) 8.3 cm, 3.4 cm, 6.1 cm
    B) 5.4 cm, 2.3 cm, 3.1 cm
    (C) 6 cm, 7 cm, 10 cm
    (D) 3cm, 5 cm, 5cm

13. P is the point on side BC of ΔABC such that AP bisects $\angle BAC$. Then:
    (A) $BP = CP$ (B) $BA > BP$
    (C) $BP > BA$ (D) $CP < CA$

14. In the given figure, which of the following statement is true?

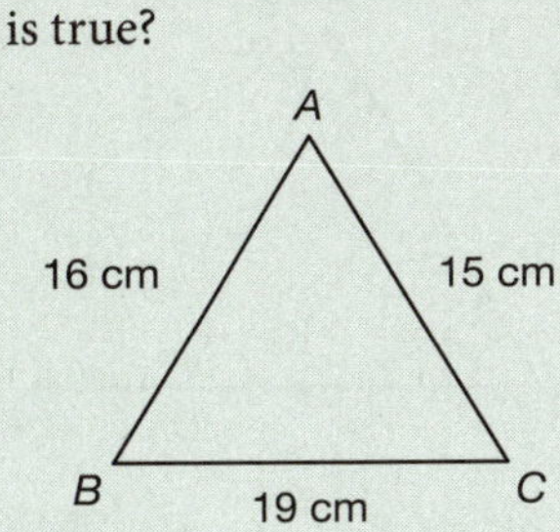

    (A) $\angle B = \angle C$
    (B) $\angle B$ is the greatest angle in the triangle
    (C) $\angle B$ is the smallest angle in the triangle
    (D) $\angle A$ is the smallest angle in the triangle

15. In a right-angled triangle ABC, P is the midpoint of AC. Which one is true?

(A) $PA = \frac{AC}{2}$ (B) $PB = \frac{AC}{2}$
(C) $PA = PB$ (D) All of these

Level 2

16. In the given figure $AC = CB$, $\angle PCA = \angle QCB$ and $\angle PBC = \angle QAC$, then the true statement is:

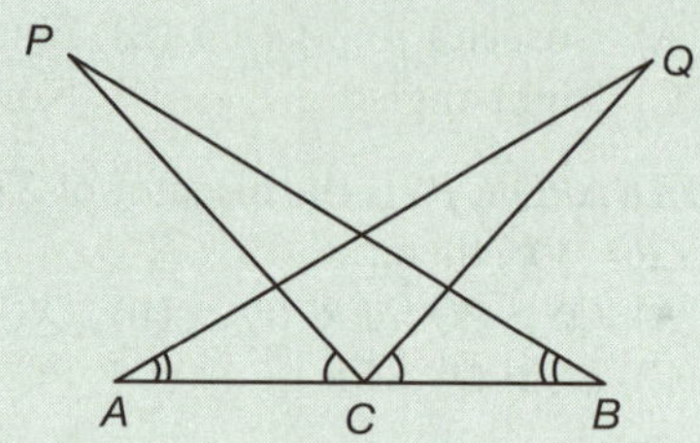

(A) $PB > QA$ (B) $\angle CPB \neq \angle CQA$
(C) $PC \neq QC$ (D) $\Delta PCB \cong \Delta QCA$

17. For given figure, which one is correct?

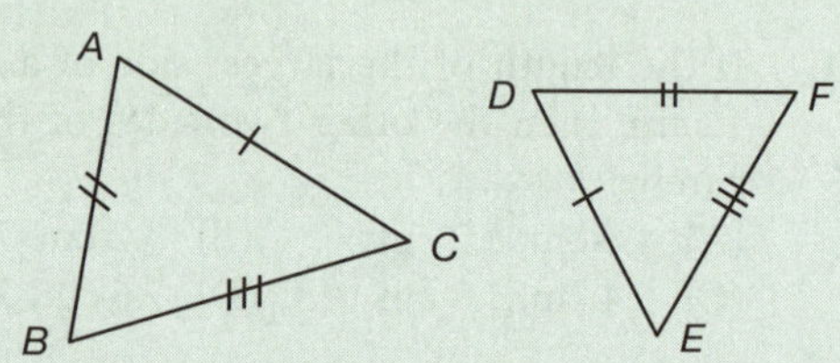

(A) $\Delta ABC \cong \Delta DEF$ (B) $\Delta ABC \cong \Delta FED$
(C) $\Delta ABC \cong \Delta DFE$ (D) $\Delta ABC \cong \Delta EDF$

18. The perimeter of a triangle is:
(A) greater than the sum of its altitudes
(B) less than the sum of its altitudes
(C) equal to the sum of its altitudes
(D) None of these

19. In the given diagram $\angle B = \angle C = 65°$ and $\angle D = 30°$, then the true statement is:

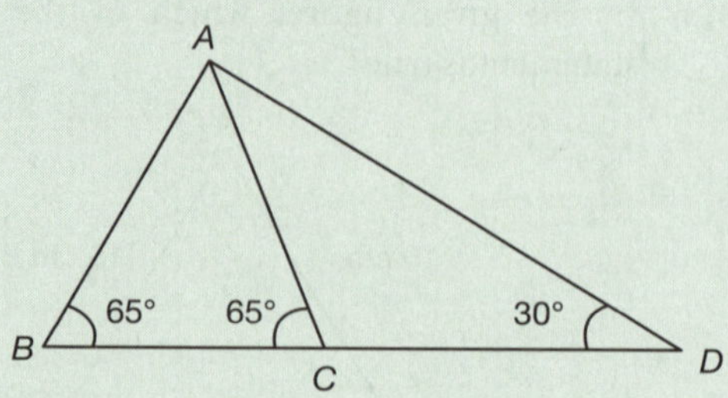

(A) $BC = CA$ (B) $CA > CD$
(C) $BD > AD$ (D) $AC = AD$

20. In a ΔPQR, PS is the bisector of $\angle P$, $\angle Q = 70°$ and $\angle R = 30°$, then:

(A) $QS < PQ > PR$ (B) $QR > PR > PQ$
(C) $QR = PR = PQ$ (D) $QR < PR = PQ$

21. A In the figure above, ABC is a triangle and $\overline{AB} \| \overline{DE}$. Find $\angle BAC$ and $\angle EDC$ when $\angle DCE = 80°$.

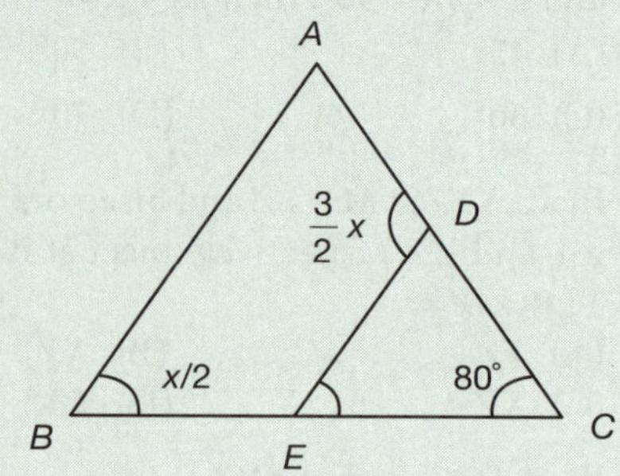

(A) 30°, 30° (B) 60°, 60°
(C) 60°, 50° (D) 40°, 40°

22. In the above triangle ABC, $AB = AC$, $\overline{AC}$ is produced to E and $\overline{BC}$ produced to D. What is the measure of $\angle BAC$?

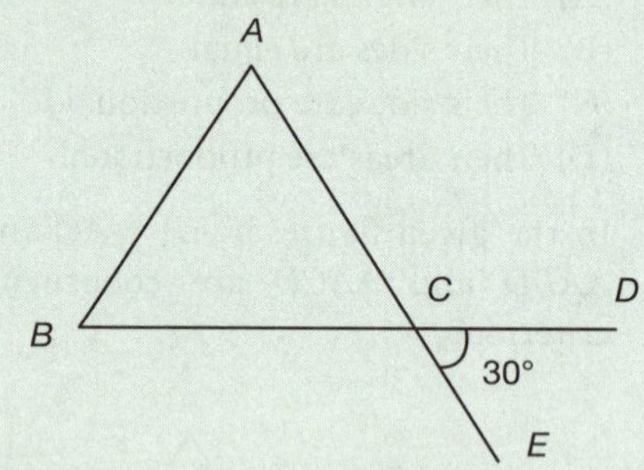

(A) 90° (B) 100°
(C) 110° (D) 120°

23. In ΔABC and ΔPQR given below, $AB = PQ$, $BC = QR$ and $\angle B = \angle Q = 90°$. Which of the following congruency axioms is/are suitable to prove that $\Delta ABC \cong \Delta PQR$?

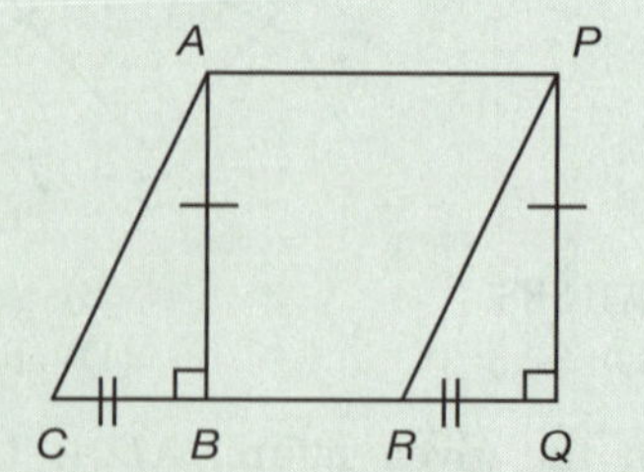

(A) R.H.S (B) S.A.S
(C) both (A) and (B) (D) None of these

24. In the figure given below, $\overline{AB}$ and $\overline{CD}$ bisect each other at E. Which of the following is/are true?
(a) $AD = BC$ (b) $\angle A = \angle C$
(c) $\angle B = \angle D$

ASSESSMENT CORNER

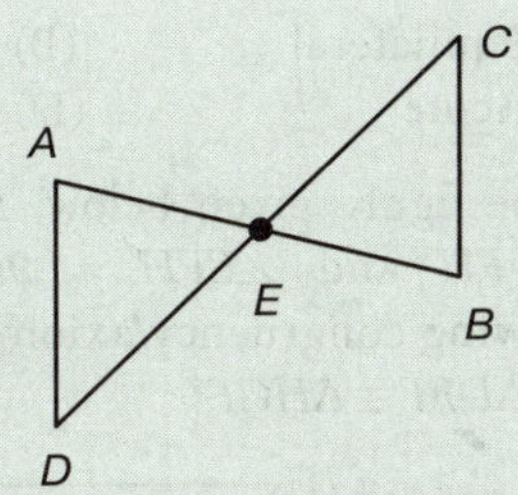

(A) Only (a) (B) Only (b)
(C) Only (c) (D) All (a), (b) and (c)

25. In the figure given below, $\overline{PT} \perp \overline{QR}$, where PT is the median drawn to $\overline{QR}$. Which of the following is/are sufficient to prove that $\Delta PQT \cong \Delta SRT$?

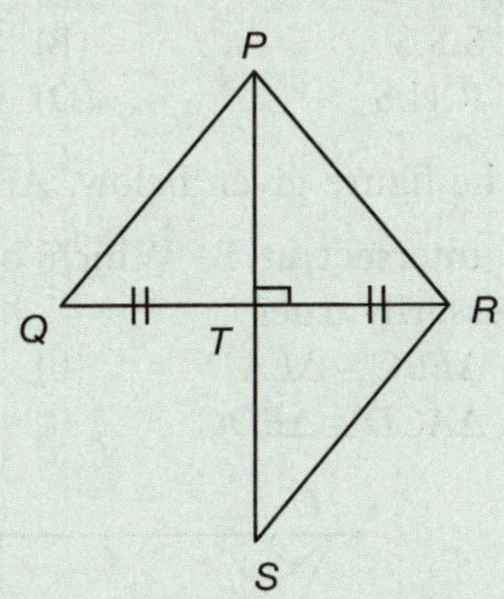

(A) P, T and S are collinear points
(B) $PT = TS$
(C) $PR = RS$
(D) [(A) and (C)] or [(A) and (B)] or [(B) and (C)]

Multiple Correct Type Questions

1. In the figure, $AC > AB$ and D is the point on AC such that $AB = AD$. Then which of the following is/are correct?

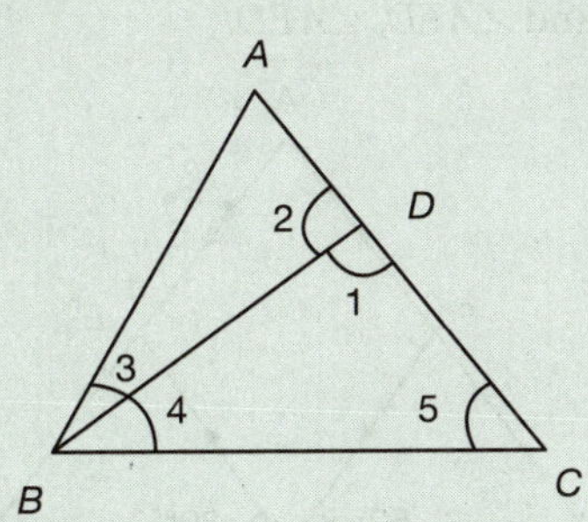

(A) $\angle 4 > \angle 5$ (B) $\angle 2 > \angle 5$
(C) $\angle 1 > \angle 4$ (D) $\angle 1 > \angle 3$

2. Which of the following statements relating to triangles ABC and DEF is/ are correct?
(A) If $AB = DE$, $BC = EF$ and the areas of the two triangles are equal, then they are congruent.
(B) If $\angle ABC = \angle DEF = 90°$, $AB = DE$, $AC = DF$ then the triangles are congruent.
(C) If $\angle ABC = \angle DEF$, $\angle ACB = \angle DFE$ and the areas of the triangles are equal, then they are congruent.
(D) If $\angle ABC = \angle DEF$. $\angle ACB = \angle DFE$ and $\angle BAC = \angle EDF$, then the triangles are congruent.

3. In figure $AD = AE$, D and E are points on BC such that $BD = EC$. Then which of the following is correct?

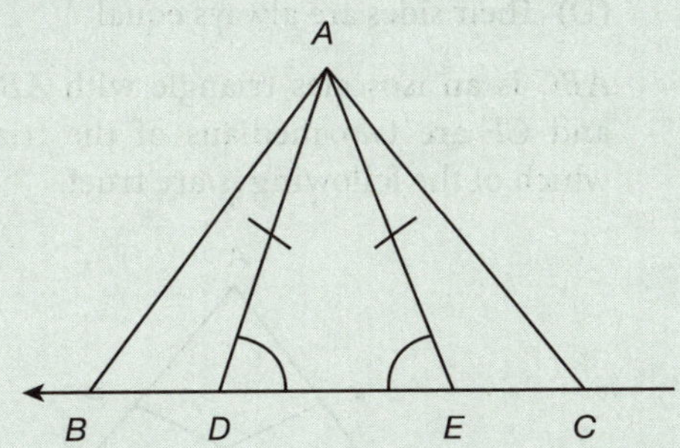

(A) $AB = AD$ (B) $CD = BE$
(C) $\angle ADE = \angle AED$ (D) $AB = AC$

4. In figure, $AD = BC$ and $BD = CA$. Then which of the following is true?

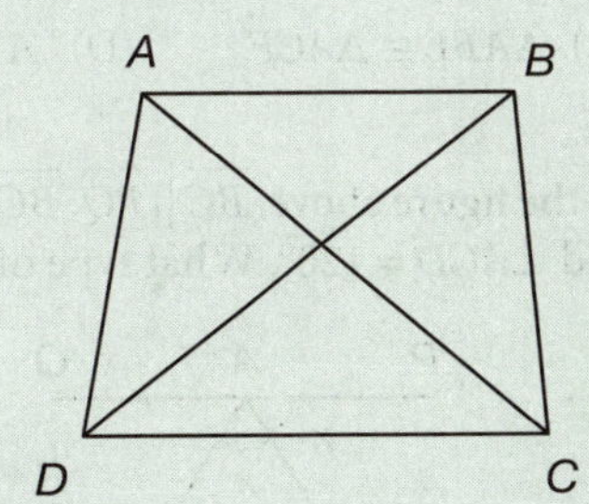

(A) $\angle ADB = \angle BCA$ (B) $\Delta ADB \cong \Delta BCA$
(C) $AD = AC$ (D) $\angle DAB = \angle CBA$

5. AD is the bisector of $\angle A$ of $\angle ABC$, where D lies on BC. Then

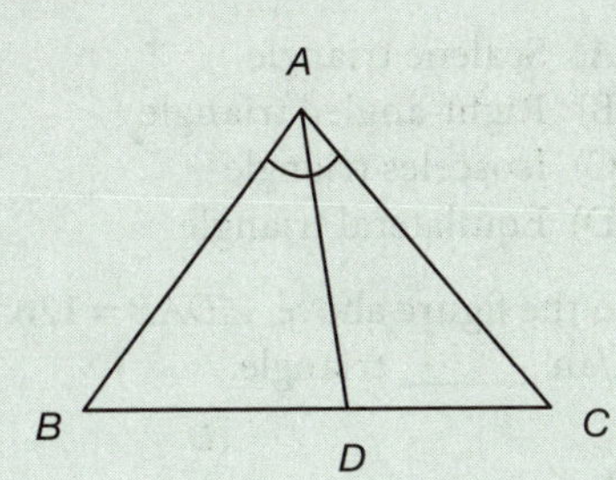

(A) $AB > BD$ (B) $\angle ADB < \angle BAD$
(C) $\angle ADC > \angle DAC$ (D) $AC > CD$

6. Which of the following statements is/are true?
(A)Any two similar figures are congruent.
(B) Any two congruent figures are similar.
(C) Two polygons are similar, if their corresponding sides are proportional.
(D) Two triangles are similar if their corresponding sides are proportional.

7. Any two squares are always:
(A) Congruent
(B) Similar
(C) Their angles are equal to 90°
(D) Their sides are always equal

8. ABC is an isosceles triangle with $AB = AC$, BE and CF are two medians of the triangle then which of the following is/are true?

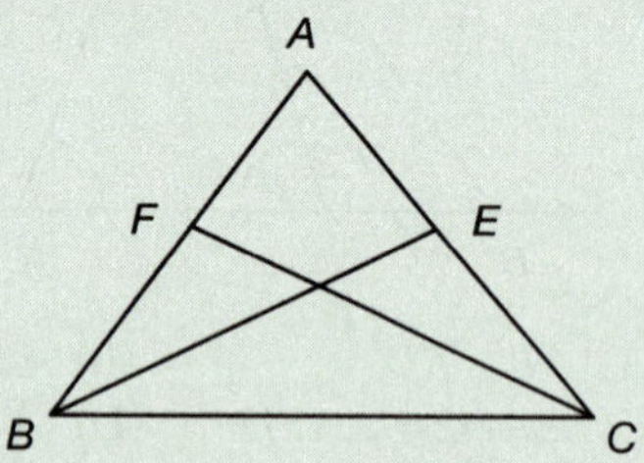

(A) $BE = CF$ (B) $AB = AC$

(C) $\Delta ABE \cong \Delta ACF$ (D) $AE = \frac{1}{2}AC$

9. In the figure above, $\overline{BC} \parallel \overline{PQ}$, $\overline{BC}$ is produced to D and $\angle ACD = 120°$. What type of triangle is ABC?

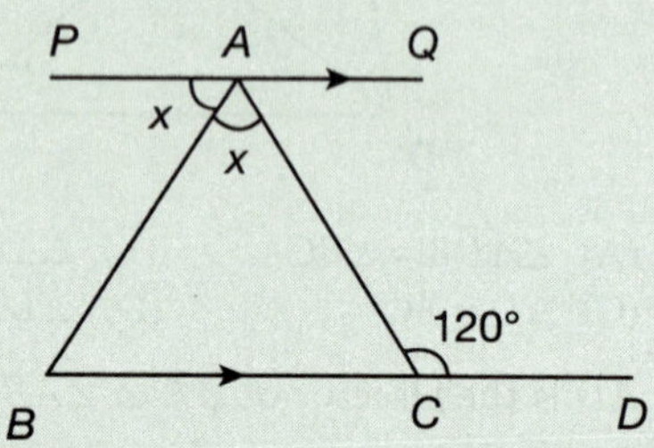

(A) Scalene triangle
(B) Right-angled triangle
(C) Isosceles triangle
(D) Equilateral triangle

10. In the figure above, $\angle DAB = 120°$. Then ΔABC is a/an ______ triangle.

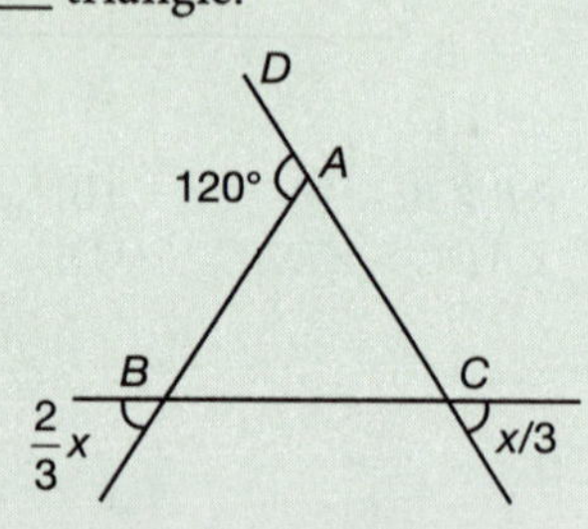

(A) Equilateral (B) Isosceles
(C) Acute (D) Right-angled

11. In the figure given below, $DE = GH$, $FE = FG$, $FD = FH$ and $\angle EFH = 90°$. Which of the following congruency/axiom is suitable to prove that $\Delta DEF \cong \Delta HGF$?

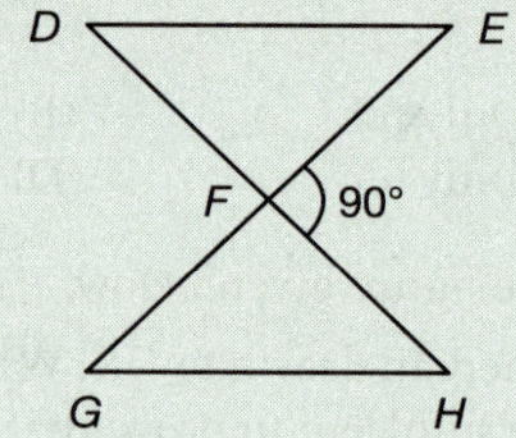

(A) S.S.S (B) S.A.S
(C) R.H.S (D) All of the above

12. In the figure given below, $\overleftrightarrow{AB} \parallel \overleftrightarrow{CD}$ and $\overline{AC}$ and $\overline{BD}$ intersect at E. Which of the following is necessarily true?
(a) $\Delta EBC \cong \Delta EAD$ (b) $\Delta ABC \cong \Delta BAD$
(c) $\Delta ACD \cong \Delta BDC$

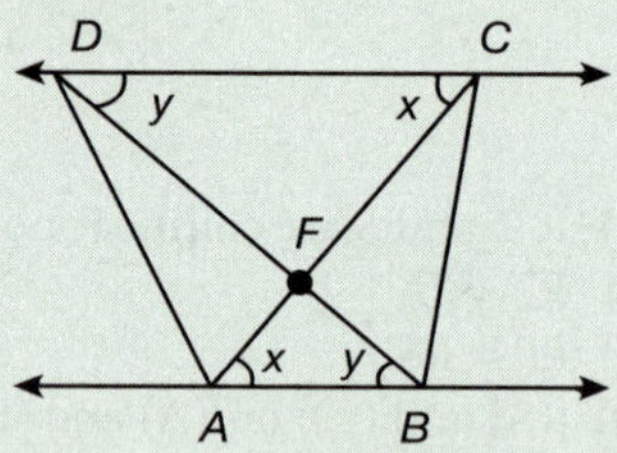

(A) Only (a) (B) Both (b) and (c)
(C) Both (a) and (c) (D) None of the above

13. In the above figure, $\overline{AB}$ is parallel to $\overline{DE}$, $\overline{AC}$ is parallel to $\overline{FD}$, $\angle EDC = 30°$ and $\angle BDF = 50°$. Find $\angle AFD$, $\angle AED$.

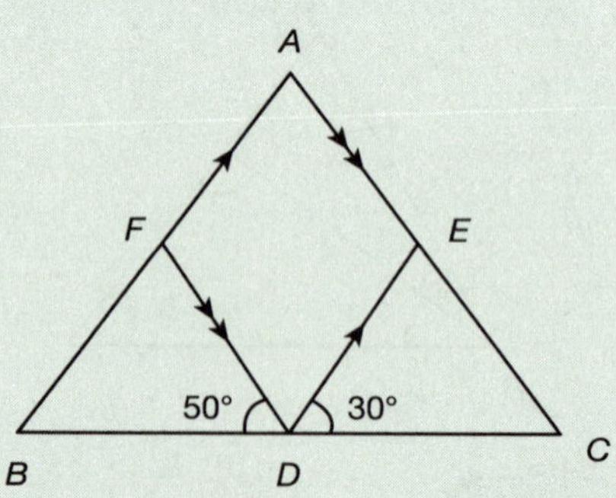

(A) 100°, 80° (B) 80°, 80°
(C) 100°, 100° (D) 50°, 30°

14. In the figure above (not to scale), $\overline{AD}$ is the angle bisector of $\angle EAF$, $\angle AFC = 110°$ and $\angle DCF = 20°$. If $\angle DAF = 30°$ and $\angle EBD = 10°$, then find $\angle AEB$.

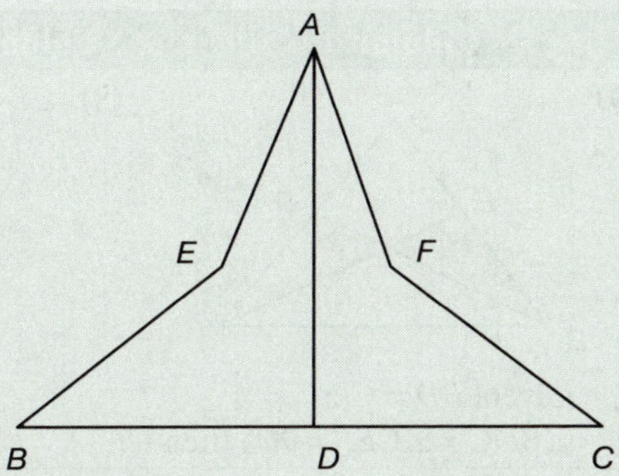

(A) 110° (B) 120°
(C) 150° (D) 160°

15. In the triangle above, if $\angle DCE = \frac{1}{2}\angle BCD = \frac{1}{3}\angle DBC = \frac{1}{4}\angle BDC$, then find $\angle BAC$.

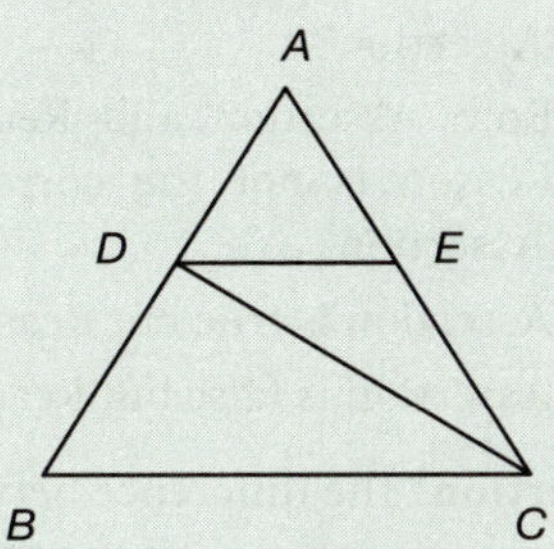

(A) 90° (B) 80°
(C) 120° (D) 60°

Match Type Questions

Directions: **Column-I** and **Column-II** contain four entries each. Entries of Column-I are to be matched with some entries of Column-II. Only one entry of Column-I may have the matching with the one entry of Column-II and one entry of Column-II may have only one matching with one entry of Column-I.

1.

Column-I	Column-II
(A) 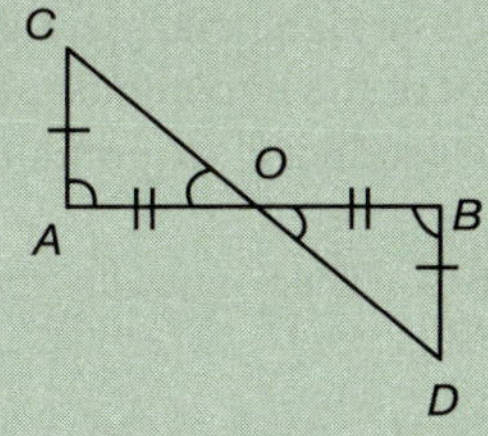 ($AC \perp AB$; $BD \perp AB$)	(P) ASA
(B) 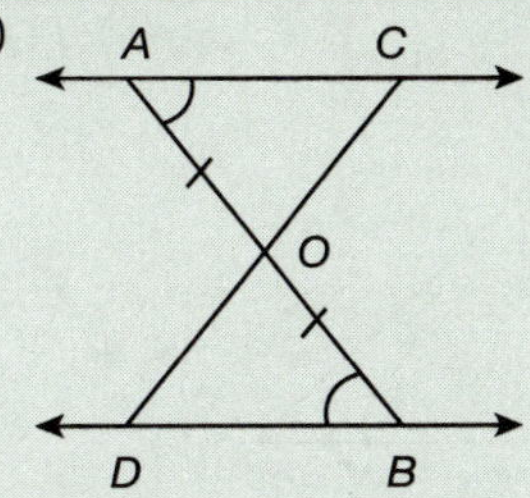 ($l \parallel m$)	(Q) SAS
(C) 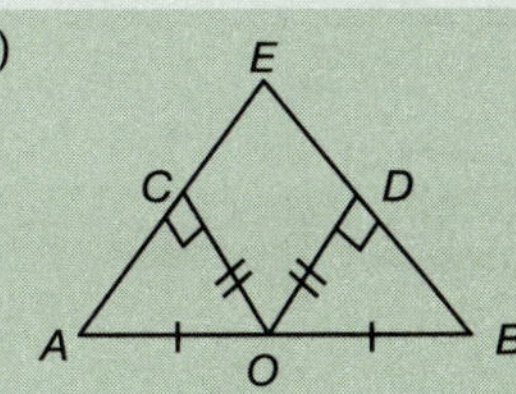	(R) AAS
(D) 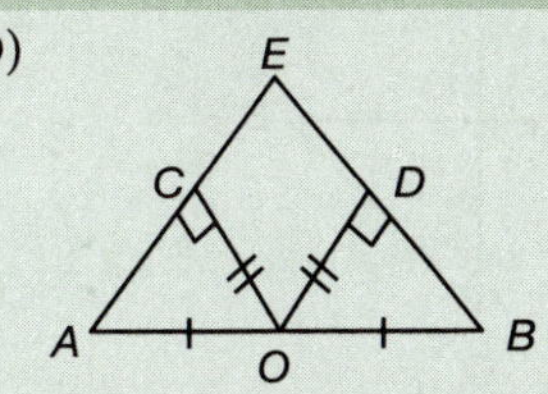 ($OA = OB$; BD and AC are medians)	(S) RHS

2.

Column-I	Column-II
(A) 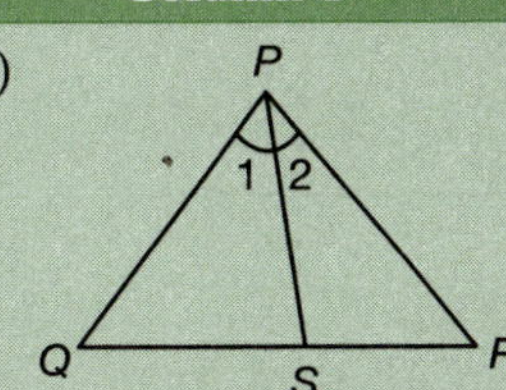 If $PR > PQ$, $\angle 1 = \angle 2$, then	(P) $PR > SR$
(B) 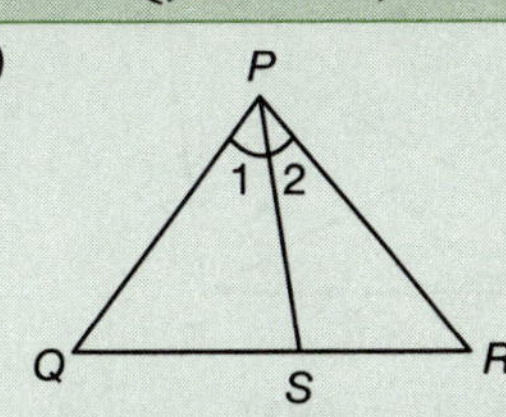 If $\angle 1 = \angle 2$, then	(Q) $PR > PQ$
(C) 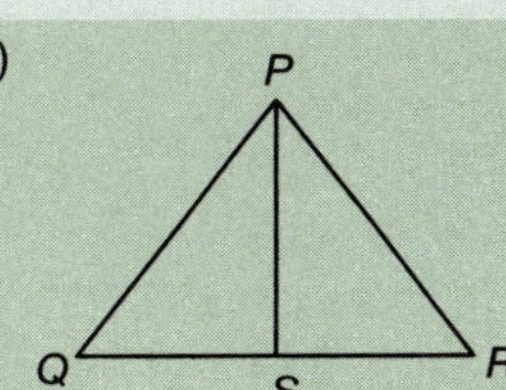 If $PQ > PR$,.then	(R) $\angle PSR > \angle PSQ$

(Continued)

Column-I	Column-II
(D) 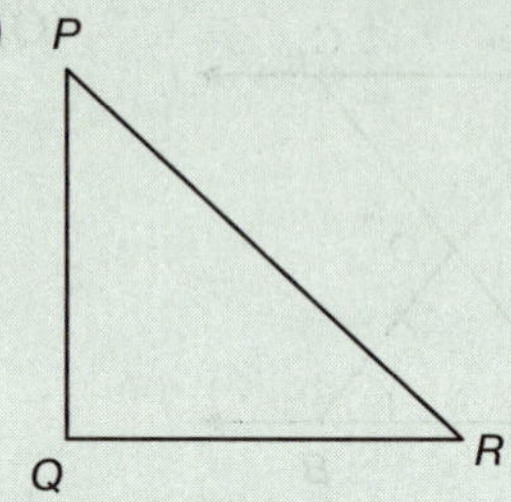 If $\angle Q = 90°$, then	(S) $PQ > PS$

3.

Column-I	Column-II
(A) 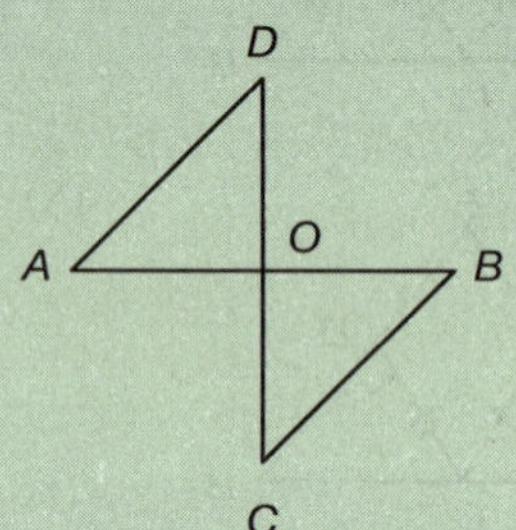 Given: $DO = CO$; $AO = BO$, then	(P) $AB = AC$
(B) 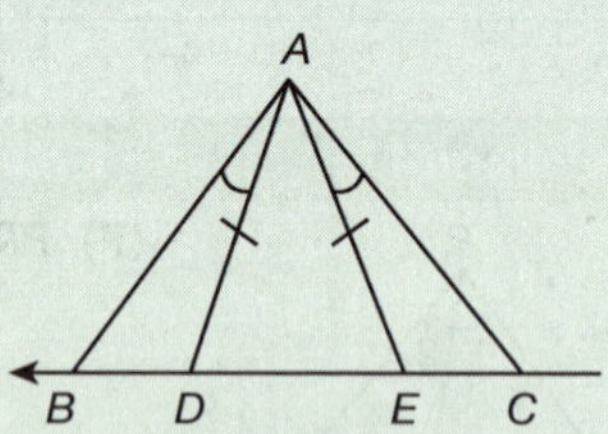 Given; $AD = AE$; $\angle BAD = \angle CAE$, then	(Q) $\angle C = \angle D$
(C) 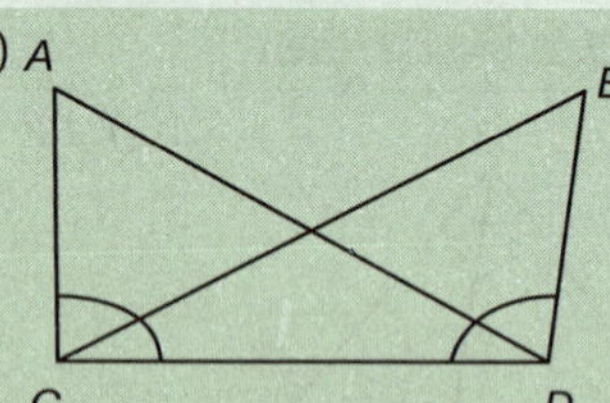 Given; $\angle BCD = \angle ADC$; $\angle ACB = \angle BFA$ then	(R) $AD = BC$

(*Continued*)

Column-I	Column-II
(D) 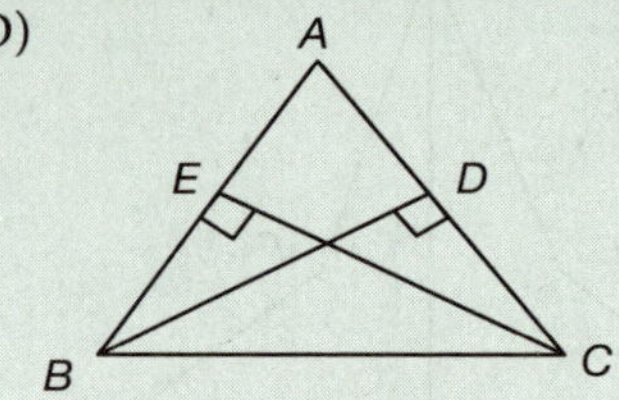 Given; $BD = CE$; $\angle BDC = \angle CEF = 90°$, then	(S) $\angle B = \angle C$

Assertion and Reason Type Questions

Directions: In the following questions Assertion (A) is given followed by a Reason (R). Mark your responses from the following options.

(A) Both Assertion and Reason are true and Reason is the correct explanation of 'Assertion'.

(B) Both Assertion and Reason are true and Reason is not the correct explanation of 'Assertion'.

(C) Assertion is true but Reason is false.

(D) Assertion is false but Reason is true.

1. **Assertion:** The difference between any two sides of a triangle is less than the third side.
   Reason: The sum of any two sides of a triangle is greater than the third side.

2. **Assertion:** In a right triangle, the hypotenuse is the largest side.
   Reason: If two angles of a triangle are unequal the greater angle has the larger side opposite to it.

3. **Assertion:** If each angle of a triangle is equal to 60°, then the triangle is equilateral.
   Reason: An equilateral triangle has all its angles equal.

Comprehension Type Questions

Comprehension 1: *ABC* is a right triangle, right angled at *C* and *M* is the midpoint of the hypotenuse *AB*.
C is joined to *M* and produced to point *D* such that $DM = CM$. The point
D is joined to point *B*. Then answer the following questions.

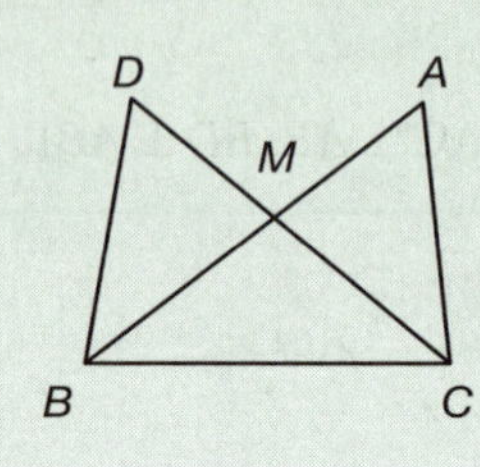

1. Which of the following is correct?
   (A) $\Delta ACM \cong \Delta BMD$ (B) $\Delta BDC \cong \Delta ACM$
   (C) $\Delta AMC \cong \Delta BMD$ (D) $\Delta ABC \cong \Delta CBD$

2. Which of the following statement is not true?
   (A) Area of ΔABC is twice the area of ΔDBC
   (B) Area of ΔBMD is equal to the area of ΔDMC
   (C) Area of ΔAMC is equal to the area of ΔBMC
   (D) Area of ΔABC is equal to the area of ΔDBC

3. $\angle DBC$ is a right-angled triangle, why?
   (A) Because the area of ΔAMC is equal to the area of ΔDBM
   (B) Because $\angle DBC \angle CBM$
   (C) Because $AC \parallel DB$
   (D) Because $\angle DMB = \angle AMC$

Numerical Type Questions

1. In the above diagram, $\angle CAB = 30°$, $\angle BCA = 50°$. If $x°$ and $y°$ are exterior angles, then find $x + y$.

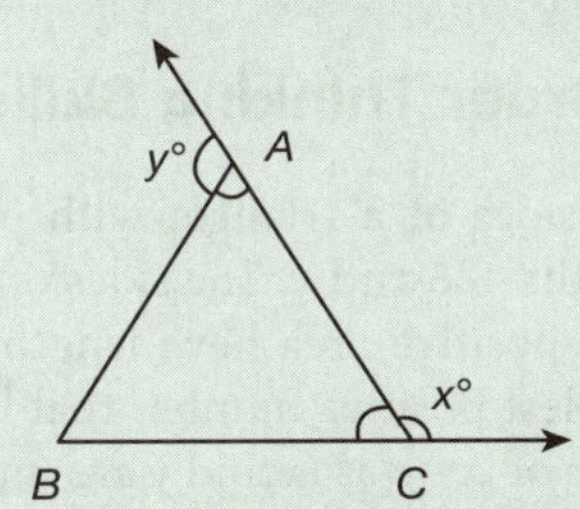

2. In the figure above, ABE is a triangle and $AC = AD$. What is the measure of $\angle CBA$?

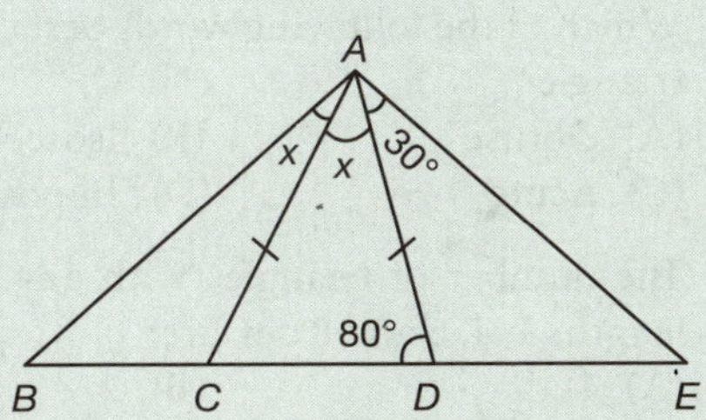

3. In the figure above, DEG is a triangle and F is lying on EG. $DE = EF$ and $DF = FG$. If $\angle DGF = 25°$ then $\angle EDG =$ ______.

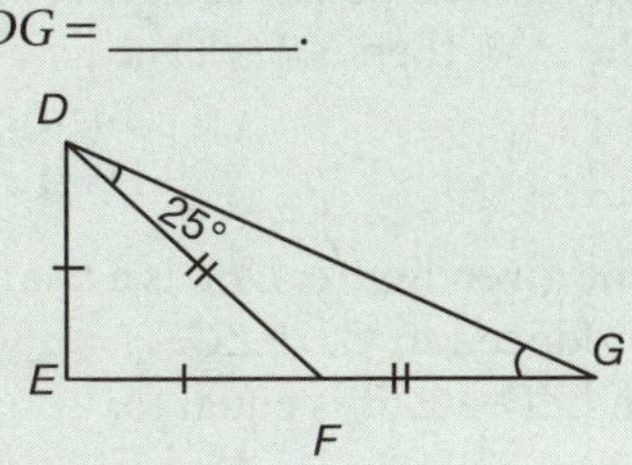

4. In the above triangle, ABC, $\overline{EF} \parallel \overline{DC}$ and $\overline{AC} \parallel \overline{FD}$. $\angle EFD = \frac{1}{3}\angle BAC$ and $\angle ABC = 40°$. Find $\angle FEA$.

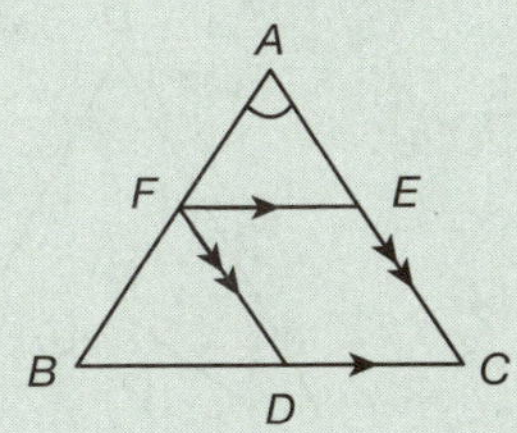

5. In the figure above, ABC and DEC are two triangles. $\angle BAC = 40°$, $\angle CDE = 30°$ and $\angle AFD = 100°$. Find $\angle ACB$.

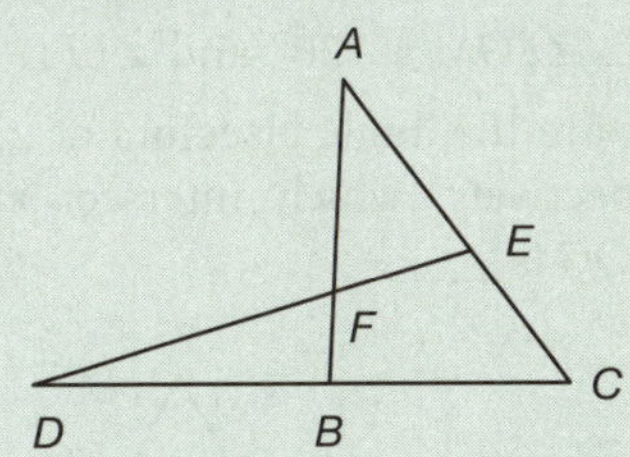

6. In the figure above (not to scale), ABC is a triangle. $\overline{AE}$ is bisector of $\angle BAC$, $\angle ACD = 150°$.

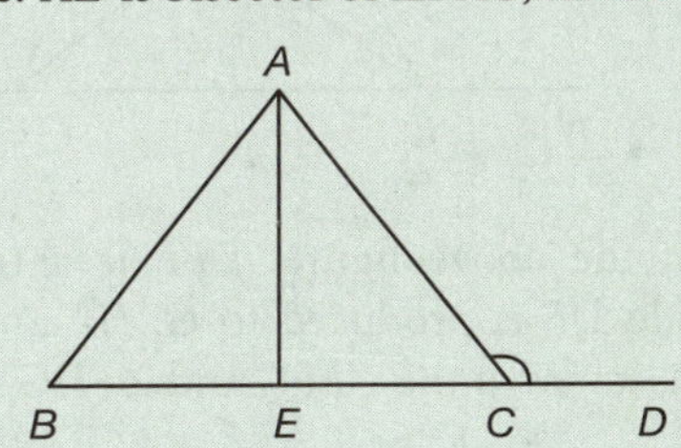

$\angle BAE = \frac{1}{2}(\angle BEA)$. If $\overline{BC}$ is produced to D, then find $\angle ABE$.

7. In ΔABC, AD is the median. If $\overline{AD}$ produced to F, $\overline{AC}$ produced to E, $\angle DCE = \frac{3}{2}\angle CDF$ and $\angle DAC = 20°$, then find $\angle BDA$.

8. In a triangle PQR, D is a point on QR such that $\angle PRD = \angle QPD$. If $\angle QPR = 122\frac{1}{2}°$, then $\angle PDQ =$ ______?

9. In a triangle ABC, if $\angle A > \angle B > \angle C$ and $\angle A$, $\angle B$ and $\angle C$ are integers, then the least possible value for $\angle A$ is:

10. In the above triangle DEF, the bisectors of the angles E and F intersect each other at a point G. If angle $EDF = 63\frac{1}{2}°$, then angle $EGF =$ _______.

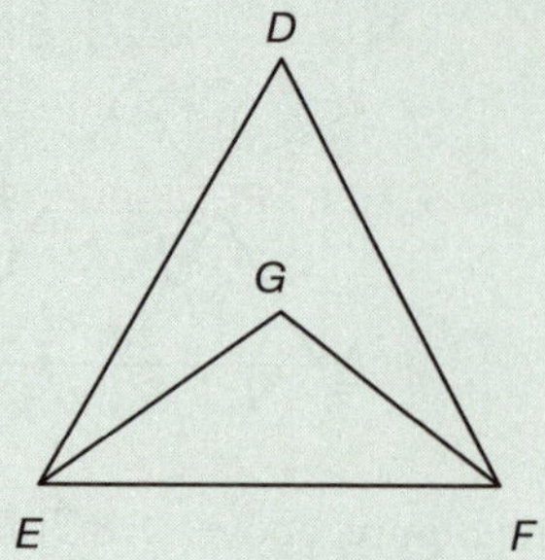

11. In the above ΔEFG, side FG is produced on either side. $\angle EGM = 120°$ and $\angle EFN = 110°$. $\overline{OF}$ and $\overline{OG}$ are the angle bisectors of $\angle EFG$ and $\angle EGF$ respectively, which intersect at point O. The $\angle FOG$ is _______.

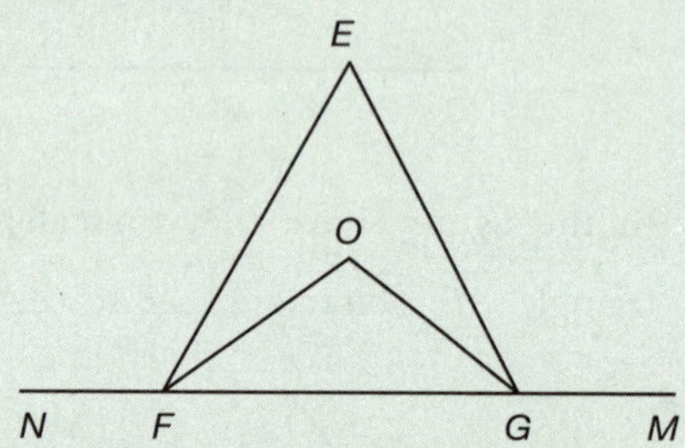

12. In the above figure, DEF is a triangle whose side DF is produced to G. HF and HD are the bisectors of the $\angle EFG$ and $\angle EDG$ respectively. If $\angle DEF = 23\frac{1°}{2}$, then $\angle DHF$ in degrees is equal to:

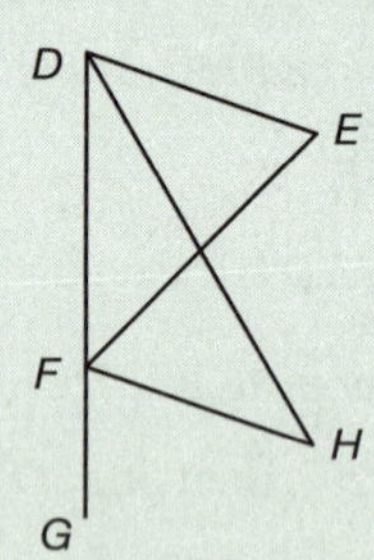

13. In ΔPQR, PD is perpendicular to QR and PO is the bisector of the angle QPR. If $\angle PQR = 65°$ and $\angle PRQ = 23\frac{1°}{2}$, then $\angle DPO$ in degrees is equal to:

14. In the figure above, $\angle ABD = 20°$, $\angle BDC = 110°$ and $\angle DCA = 30°$. What is the value of $\angle BAC$?

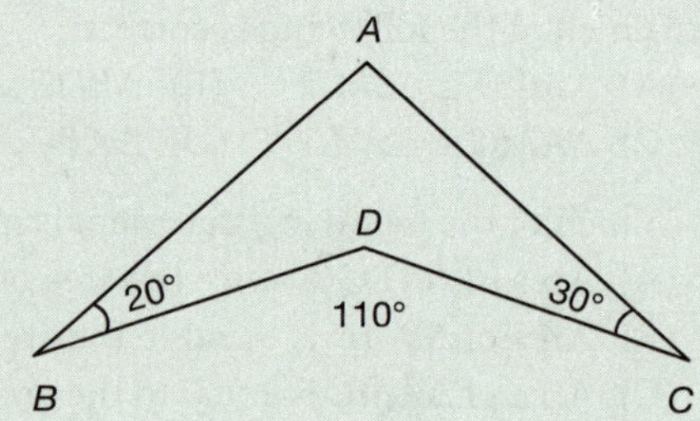

15. In the figure above (not to scale), $\angle ABE = \angle ECD$ and $\angle EBD = \angle ACE$. If $\angle BAC = 80°$ and $\angle BEC = 100°$, then $\angle BDC =$ _______.

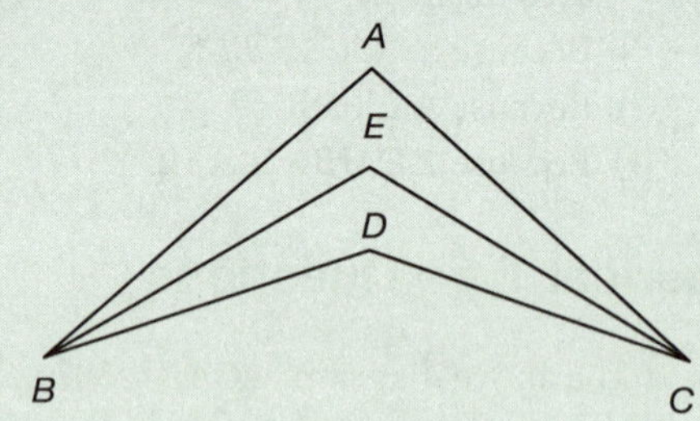

Higher Order Thinking Skills (HOTS)

1. The sides of a triangle with positive area have lengths 4, 6 and x. The sides of a second triangle with positive area have lengths 4, 6 and y. The smallest positive number that is not the possible value of $|x \cdot y|$ is (x and y are integers):

(A) 2 (B) 4
(C) 6 (D) 8

2. The sides of a triangle are in the ratio 4 : 6 : 11. Which of the following words best described the triangle?

(A) Obtuse (B) Isosceles
(C) Acute (D) Impossible

3. The number of triangles with any three of the lengths 1, 4, 6 and 8 cm, are:

(A) 4 (B) 2
(C) 1 (D) 0

4. In an isosceles triangle MNO, $MN = OM$. If P is a point on the side ON such that MP is the bisector of the $\angle M$, then $NP : PO$ is:

(A) 1 : 1 (B) 1 : 2
(C) 2 : 1 (D) 1 : 3

5. In the given figure, DEF is a triangle. The side DF is produced to G. If $\angle GFH = x°$ and $\angle HFE = y°$, then $(\angle D + \angle E)$ is equal to:

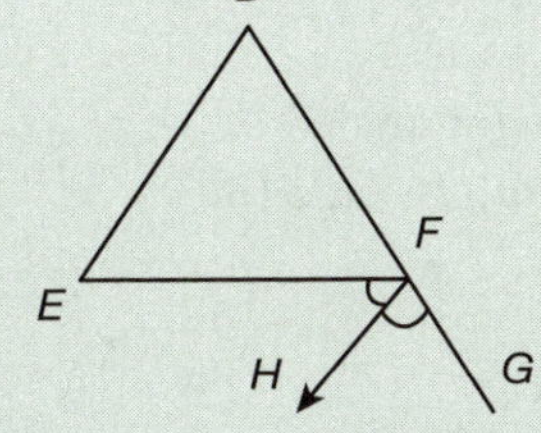

(A) $x^\circ + y^\circ$ (B) $2x^\circ + y^\circ$
(C) $x^\circ + 2y^\circ$ (D) $2x^\circ - y^\circ$

6. In ΔABC, $AB = AC$ and $\overline{AD}$ is the median. If $\overline{AC}$ produced' to E and $\angle DAC = 20^\circ$, then find $\angle DCE$.
(A) 30° (B) 60°
(C) 70° (D) 110°

7. In the figure above, $\overline{AC}$ and $\overline{BF}$ intersect at E, $\angle CAB = 80^\circ$, $\angle ABD = 20^\circ$, $\angle BDC = 120^\circ$ and $\angle FCA = 30^\circ$. Find $\angle DCE$ and $\angle EFC$.

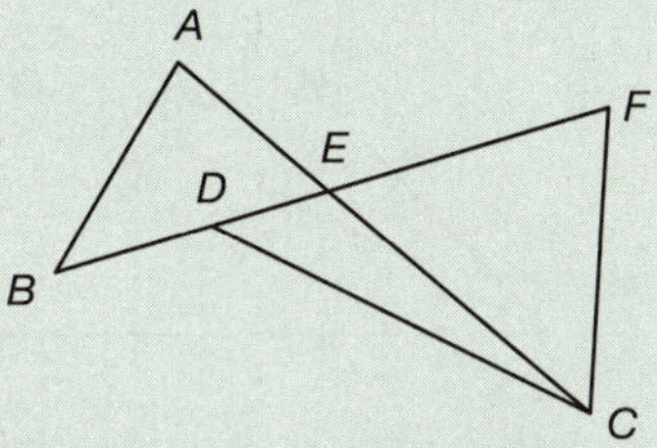

(A) $20^\circ, 70^\circ$ (B) $20^\circ, 80^\circ$
(C) $30^\circ, 70^\circ$ (D) $30^\circ, 60^\circ$

8. In ΔPQR, $PQ = 6$ cm, $PR = 8$ cm and P is the orthocentre. What is the length of $\overline{QR}$?
(A) 9 cm
(B) 8 cm
(C) 10 cm
(D) Cannot be determined

9. In the triangle above, $AB = AC$ and I is the incentre. Then $\angle BAC =$ __________.

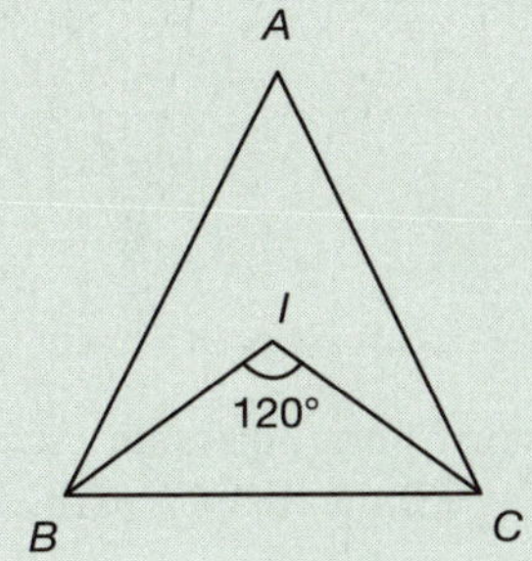

(A) 30° (B) 60°
(C) 90° (D) 120°

10. In ΔABC, $\angle A = 70^\circ$, $\angle B = 60^\circ$ and I is incentre then $\angle BIC =$ ________.
(A) 110° (B) 120°
(C) 125° (D) 135°

11. In a triangle ABC, if $\angle B = 90^\circ$, $AB = 5$ cm and $BC = 12$ cm, then the length of the altitude drawn from B to the side AC (in cm) is:

(A) $\frac{120}{5}$ (B) $\frac{120}{13}$

(C) $\frac{60}{13}$ (D) $\frac{60}{5}$

12.

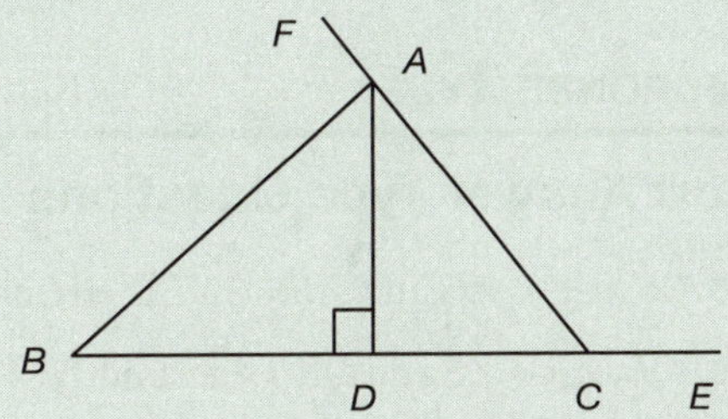

In ΔABC, AD is the altitude from A to the side BC. $\overline{BC}$ is produced to E, and $\overline{CA}$ is produced to F. If $\angle ACE = \frac{5}{2}\angle DAC$ and $\angle BAF = \frac{5}{3}\angle DAC$, then find $\angle ABC$.

(A) 35° (B) 45°
(C) 70° (D) 90°

13.

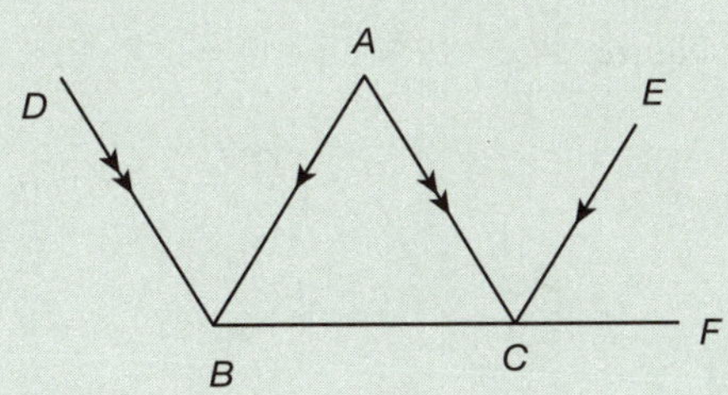

In the figure above (not to scale)

$\overline{AB} \parallel \overline{CE}$, $\overline{DB} \parallel \overline{AC}$,

$\angle DBA = 40^\circ$ and $\angle ECF = 50^\circ$,

find $\angle ABC + \angle ACB$.
(A) 140° (B) 90°
(C) 100° (D) 135°

14. In the figure given below, $AB = AC$ and $\overline{AD}$ bisects $\angle A$. Which of the following is true?
(a) $\angle ADB = 90^\circ$ (b) $BD = CD$
(c) $AB = BC$

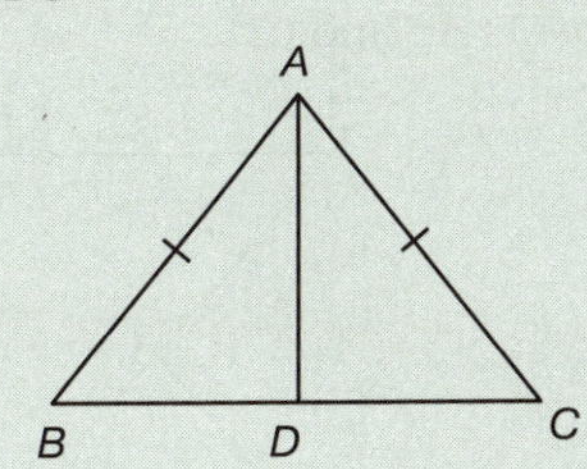

(A) Only (a) (B) Only (b)
(C) Both (a) and (b) (D) All (a), (b) and (c)

15. In the above figure, ΔABC is ______.

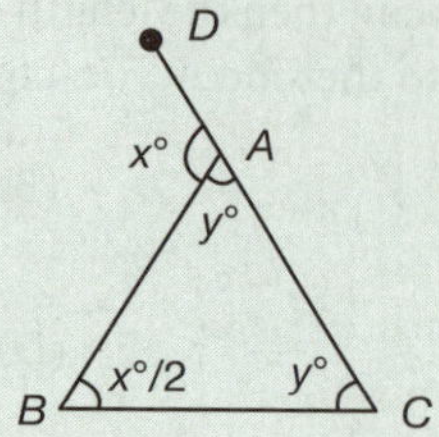

(A) Equilateral
(B) Isosceles
(C) Right-angled
(D) Both (A) and (B)

Free Response Type

Very Short Answer Type Questions

1. In ΔABC, $AB = AC$ and $\angle B = 50°$. Then find $\angle C$.
2. In ΔPQR, $\angle R = \angle P$ and $QR = 4$cm and $PR = 5$ cm. Find the length of PQ.
3. It is given that $\Delta ABC \cong \Delta FDE$ and $AB = 5$ cm, $\angle B = 40°$ and $\angle A = 80°$. Then find DF.
4. In ΔPQR, if $\angle R > \angle Q$, then which is longer between PQ and PR?
5. In triangles ABC and DEF, $AB = FD$ and $\angle A = \angle D$. The two triangles will be congruent by SAS axiom then find the side corresponding to AC.
6. In Figure, $PQ = PR$ and $\angle Q = \angle R$. Prove that $\Delta PQS \cong \Delta PRT$.

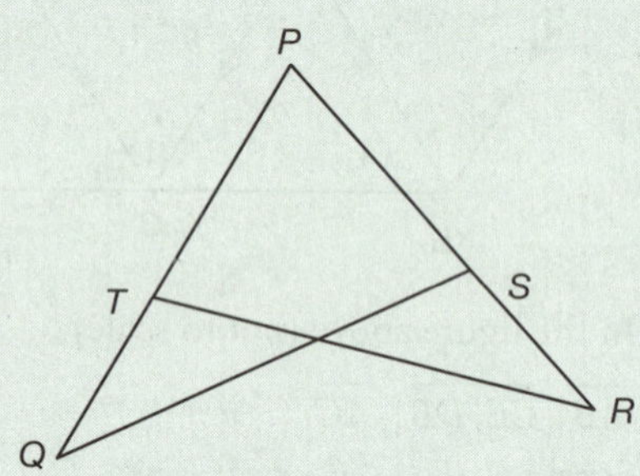

7. In triangles ABC and PQR, $\angle A = \angle Q$ and $\angle B = \angle R$. Which side of ΔPQR should be equal to side AB of ΔABC so that the two triangles are congruent? Give reason for your answer.
8. In Figure, two lines AB and CD intersect each other at point O such that $BC \parallel DA$ and $BC = DA$. Show that O is the mid-point of both the line segments AB and CD.

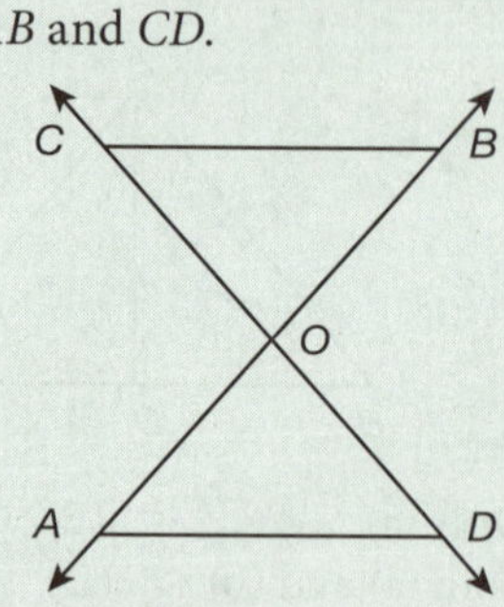

Short Answer Type Questions

1. In Figure, $PQ > PR$ and QS and RS are the bisectors of $\angle Q$ and $\angle R$, respectively. Show that $SQ > SR$.

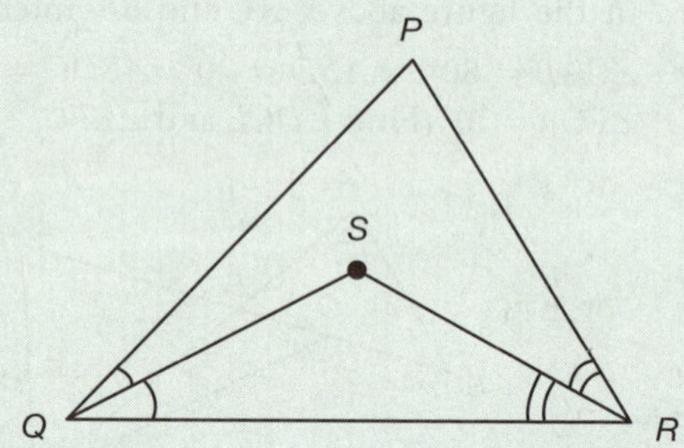

2. ABC is an isosceles triangle with $AB = AC$ and BD and CE are its two medians. Show that $BD = CE$.
3. CDE is an equilateral triangle formed on a side CD of a square $ABCD$ (according to figure). Show that $\Delta ADE \cong \Delta BCE$.

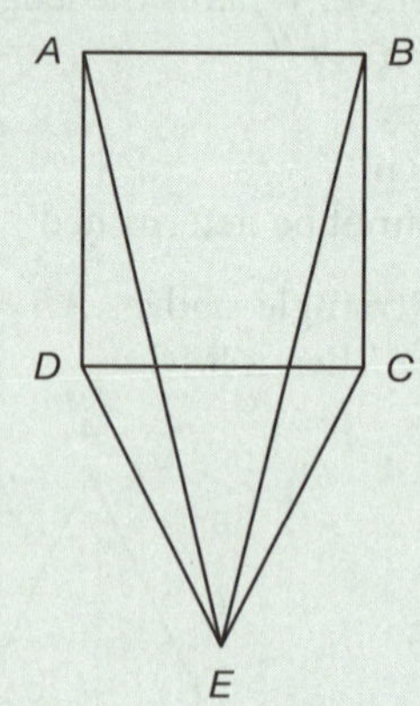

4. D is any point on side AC of a ΔABC with $AB = AC$. Show that $CD < BD$.
5. In Figure, $l \parallel m$ and M is the mid-point of a line segment AB. Show that M is also the mid-point of any line segment CD, having its endpoints on l and m, respectively.

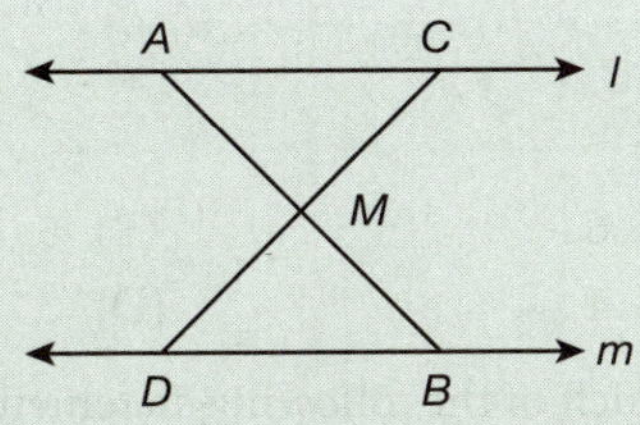

6. In Figure, AD is the bisector of $\angle BAC$. Prove that $AB > BD$.

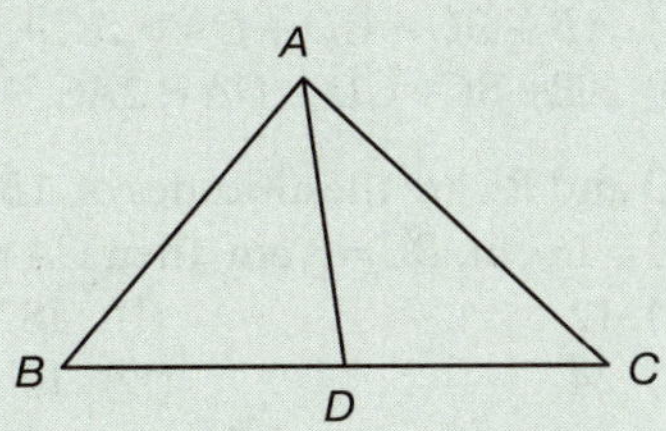

7. In Figure, ABC is a right triangle and right-angled at B such that $\angle BCA = 2\ \angle BAC$. Show that hypotenuse $AC = 2\ BC$.

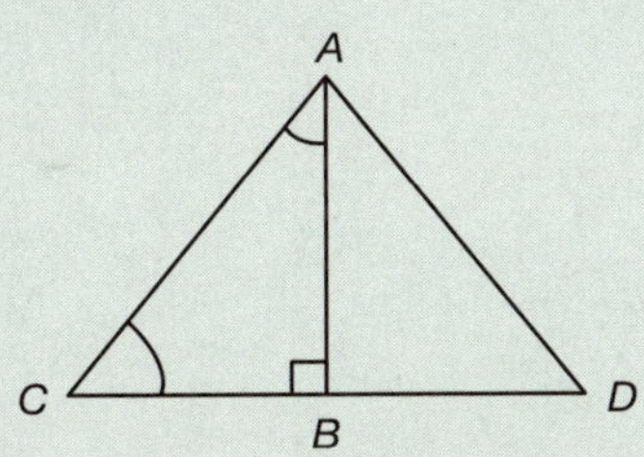

8. Prove that if in two triangles two angles and the included side of one triangle are equal to two angles and the included side of the other triangle, then the two triangles are congruent.

9. If the bisector of an angle of a triangle also bisects the opposite side, prove that the triangle is isosceles.

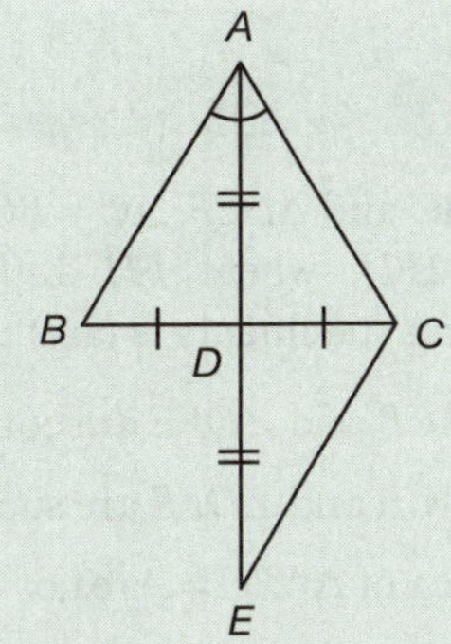

10. S is any point in the interior of ΔPQR. Show that $SQ + SR < PQ + PR$.

Long Answer Type Questions

1. O is a point in the interior of a square $ABCD$ such that OAB is an equilateral triangle. Show that ΔOCD is an isosceles triangle.
2. In a right triangle, prove that the line segment joining the midpoint of the hypotenuse to the opposite vertex is half the hypotenuse.
3. $ABCD$ is quadrilateral such that $AB = AD$ and $CB = CD$. Prove that AC is the perpendicular bisector of BD.
4. Show that in a quadrilateral $ABCD$, $AB + BC + CD + DA < 2\ (BD + AC)$.
5. Line segment joining the midpoints M and N of parallel sides AB and DC, respectively of a trapezium $ABCD$ is perpendicular to both the sides AB and DC. Prove that $AD = BC$.
6. ABC is a right triangle such that $AB = AC$ and the bisector of angle C intersects the side AB at D. Prove that $AC + AD = BC$.

ARCHIVE CORNER

1. In ΔABC and ΔDEF, $AC = BC = DF = EF$, length $AB = 2FH$, where $FH \perp DE$. Which of the following statements is (are) true?

   I. $\angle ACB$ and $\angle DFE$ are complementary

   II. $\angle ACB$ and $\angle DFE$ are supplementary

   III. Area of ΔABC = Area of ΔDEF

   IV. Area of $\Delta ABC = 1.5x$ (Area of ΔDEF)

   (A) II only (B) III only
   (C) I and III only (D) II and III only

2. The lengths of the sides of the triangle are integers and its perimeter is 14. How many such distinct triangles are possible?

   (A) 6 (B) 5
   (C) 4 (D) 3

3. Which of the following statements is false for the quadrilateral $ABCD$?

   (A) $AB + BC + CD + DA > AC$
   (B) $AB + BC + CD + DA > AB + AC$
   (C) $AB + BC + CD + DA > AC + BD$
   (D) $AB + BC + CD + DA < 2AC$.

4. AD and BE are the altitudes of ABC. If $AD = 6$ cm, $BC = 16$ cm, $BE = 8$ cm, then CA = ________ cm.

   (A) 12 (B) 18
   (C) 24 (D) 10

ANSWER KEY

CHECK POINTS

Check Point 1

1. **(i)** SAS **(ii)** ASA **(iii)** RHS

Check Point 2

6. $\angle BCD > A$ (Exterior angle of a triangle is greater than either of the two interior opposite angles).
7. $\angle FED > \angle B$ 9. $CA < BC < AB$ 10. $\angle B < \angle A < \angle C$

Assessment Corner

FIXED RESPONSE TYPE

Fill in the Blanks

1. ΔCBD 2. ΔCED 3. 90 4. Isosceles 5. > 6. >

True/False

1. True 2. False 3. True 4. True 5. True

Single Correct Type Questions

Level 1

1. A 2. D 3. A 4. B 5. A 6. B 7. B 8. B 9. B
10. A 11. A 12. B 13. B 14. C 15. D 16. D 17. C 18. A
19. B 20. A 21. B 22. D 23. B 24. A 25. D

Multiple Correct Type Questions

1. BCD 2. ABC 3. BC 4. ABD 5. ACD 6. BDC 7. BC 8. ABCD
9. D. 10. C 11. ABCD 12. D 13. B 14. D 15. D

Match Type Questions

1. A → Q, B → P, C → S, D → S
2. A → PR, B → PR, C → S, D → Q
3. A → R, B → P, C → Q, D → PS

Assertion and Reason Type Questions

1. A 2. A 3. A

Comprehension Type Questions

1. C 2. B 3. C

Numerical Type Questions

1. 280 2. 20 3. 75 4. 35 5. 70 6. 90 7. 80 8. 122.5 9. 61
10. 121.75 11. 115 12. 11.75 13. 22.25 14. 60 15. 120

Higher Order Thinking Skills (HOTS)

1. D 2. D 3. C 4. A 5. A 6. D 7. A 8. C 9. B
10. C. 11. C. 12. C 13. A 14. C 15. A

Free Response Type

Very Short Answer Type Questions

1. 50 2. 4 cm 3. 5 cm 4. $PQ > PR$ 5. $AC = DE$
7. Then $PQ = AB$ or $PR = AC$ or $QR = BC$.

Archive Corner

1. C 2. C 3. C 4. A

CHAPTER 8

Quadrilaterals

Learning Outcomes

After reading this chapter, you would be able to understand:

- classification of quadrilateral.
- properties of quadrilaterals.
- important theorems related to quadrilaterals and parallelogram.
- intercept theorem.
- midpoint theorem and its converse and application of midpoint theorem.

Geekspeak

- Convex quadrilaterals
- Concave quadrilaterals
- Quadrilaterals
- Diagonal
- Parallelogram
- Rhombus
- Square
- Rectangle
- Kite
- Trapezium
- Isosceles trapezium
- Midpoint
- Bisect
- Perpendicular
- Intercept

Introduction

A quadrilateral is a closed figure obtained by joining four points in a plane (with no three points collinear) in an order.

Since, 'quad' means 'four' and 'lateral' means 'sides', therefore 'quadrilateral' means 'a figure bounded by four sides'.

Quadrilaterals

A **quadrilateral** is a four sided closed figure.

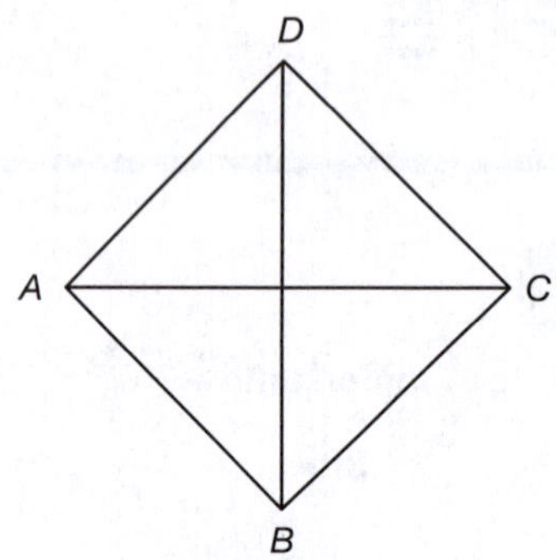

Figure 8.1

Let ***A***, ***B***, ***C*** and ***D*** be four points in a plane such that:

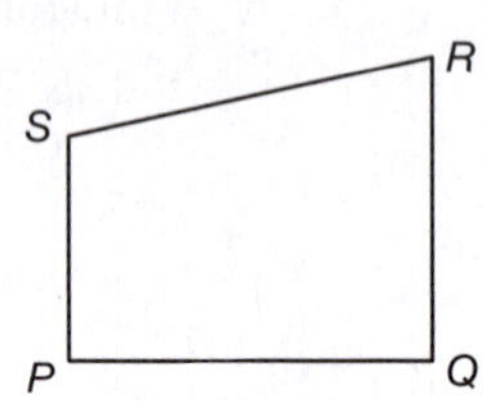

Figure 8.2

(i) No three of them are collinear.

(ii) The line segments AB, BC, CD and DA do not intersect except at their endpoints, then the **figure** obtained by joining A, B, C and D is called a **quadrilateral**.

Properties of Quadrilaterals

(i) Sum of four interior angles is 360°.

(ii) The figure formed by joining the midpoints of a quadrilateral is a parallelogram.

(iii) The sum of opposite sides of a quadrilateral circumscribed about a circle, is always equal.

(iv) Area of quadrilateral $= \frac{1}{2} \times$ one of the diagonals $\times$ sum of the perpendiculars drawn to the diagonals from the opposite vertices.

i.e., $Ar\ (\Delta ABCD) = \frac{1}{2} \times AC \times (DE + BF)$

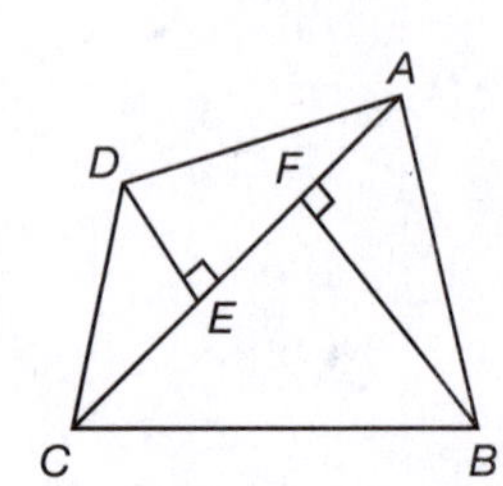

Figure 8.3

Types of Quadrilaterals

Quadrilaterals are classified based on the length of their sides and the measures of their angles.

Parallelogram

A **parallelogram** is a quadrilateral in which both pairs of opposite sides are parallel.

In the figure, $AB \parallel DC$, $AD \parallel BC$, therefore, $ABCD$ is a parallelogram.

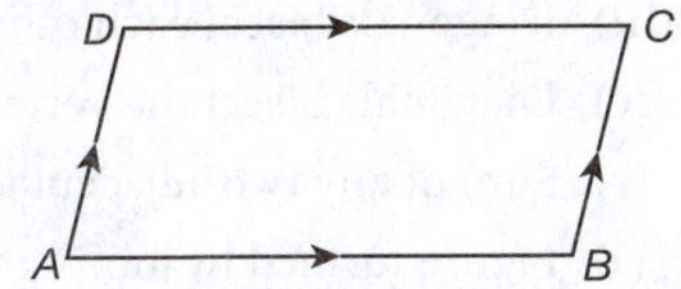

Figure 8.4

Properties of Parallelogram

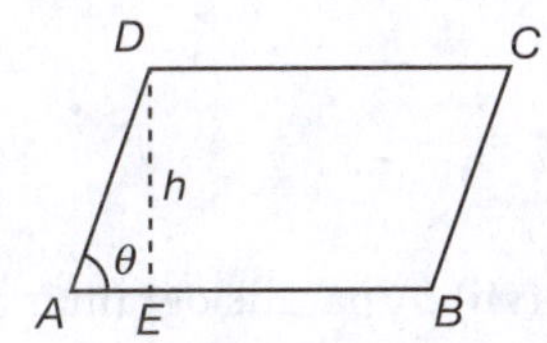

Figure 8.5

(i) The opposite sides are parallel and equal.

(ii) Opposite angles are equal.

(iii) Sum of any two adjacent angles is 180°.

(iv) Diagonals bisect each other.

(v) Diagonals need not be equal in length

(vi) Diagonals need not be bisected at the right angle.

(vii) Diagonals need not bisect angles at the vertices.

(viii) Each diagonal divides a parallelogram into two congruent triangles.

(ix) Lines joining the midpoints of the adjacent sides of a quadrilateral form a parallelogram.

(x) Lines joining the midpoints of the adjacent sides of a parallelogram is a parallelogram.

(xi) The parallelogram that is inscribed in a circle is a rectangle.

(xii) The parallelogram that is circumscribed about a circle is a rhombus.

(xiii) $(AC)^2 + (BD)^2 = (AB)^2 + (BC)^2 + (CD)^2 + (AD)^2 = 2(AB^2 + BC^2)$

(xiv) Parallelogram that lies on the same base and between the same parallel lines are equal in area.

(xv) A parallelogram is a rectangle if its diagonals are equal.

Rectangle

A **rectangle** is a parallelogram, in which each of its angles is a right angle. If $ABCD$ is a rectangle then $\angle A = \angle B = \angle C = \angle D = 90°$, $AB = CD$, $BC = AD$ and diagonals $AC = BD$.

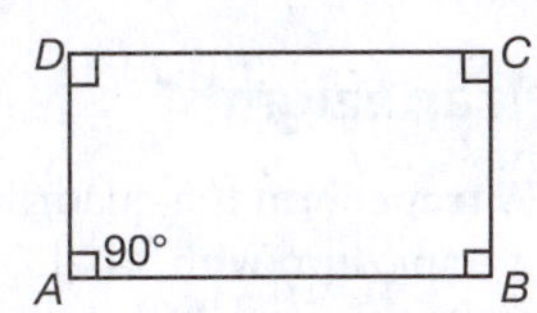

Figure 8.6

Properties of Rectangle

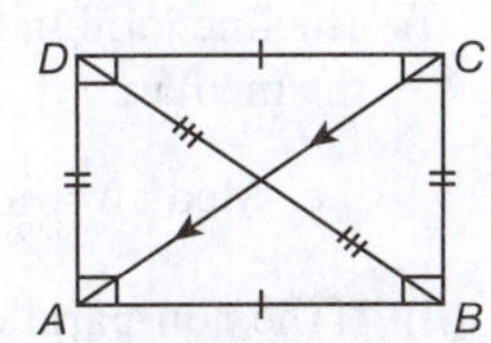

Figure 8.7

(i) Opposite sides are parallel and equal.

(ii) Opposite angles are equal and of 90°.

(iii) Diagonals are equal and bisect each other, but not necessarily at right angles,

(iv) When a rectangle is inscribed in a circle, the diameter of the circle is equal to the diagonal of the rectangle.

(v) For the given perimeter of rectangles, a square has maximum area.

(vi) The figure formed by joining the midpoints of the adjacent sides of a rectangle is a rhombus.

(vii) The quadrilateral formed by joining the midpoints of the intersection of the angle bisectors of a parallelogram is a rectangle.

(viii) Every rectangle is a parallelogram.

Rhombus

A **rhombus** is a parallelogram in which all its sides are equal in length. If $ABCD$ is a rhombus then, $AB = BC = CD = DA$.

The diagonals of a rhombus are perpendicular to each other.

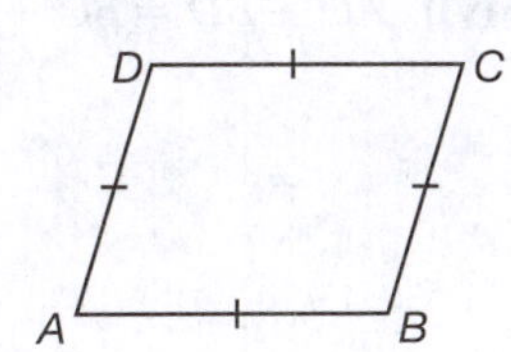

Figure 8.8

Properties of Rhombus

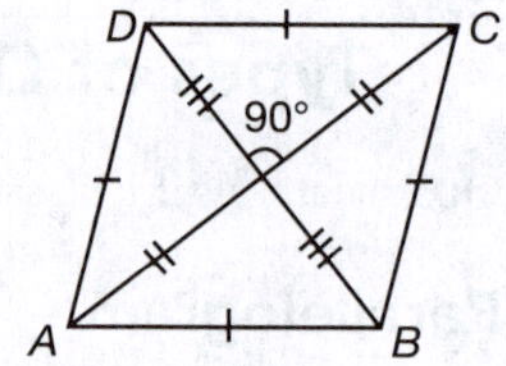

Figure 8.9

(i) Opposite sides are parallel and equal.
(ii) Opposite angles are equal.
(iii) Diagonals bisect each other at right angle, but they are not necessarily equal.
(iv) Diagonals bisect the vertex angles.
(v) Sum of any two adjacent angles is 180°.
(vi) Figure formed by joining the midpoints of the adjacent sides of a rhombus is a rectangle.

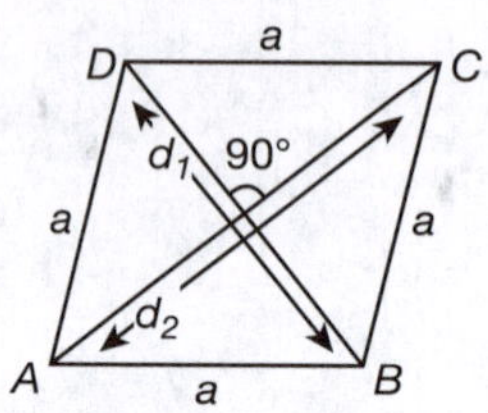

Figure 8.10

(vii) A parallelogram is a rhombus if its diagonals are perpendicular to each other.

Square

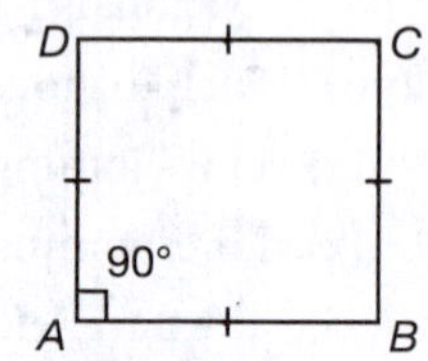

Figure 8.11

A **square** is a parallelogram having all sides equal and each angle equal to the right angle. If $ABCD$ is a square then $AB = BC = CD = DA$, diagonal $AC = BD$ and $\angle A = \angle B = \angle C = \angle D = 90°$.
The diagonals of a square are perpendicular to each other.

Properties of Square

(i) All sides are equal and parallel.
(ii) All angles are right angles.
(iii) Diagonals are equal and bisect each other at right angle.
(iv) The figure formed by joining the midpoints of the adjacent sides of a square is a square.

Trapezium

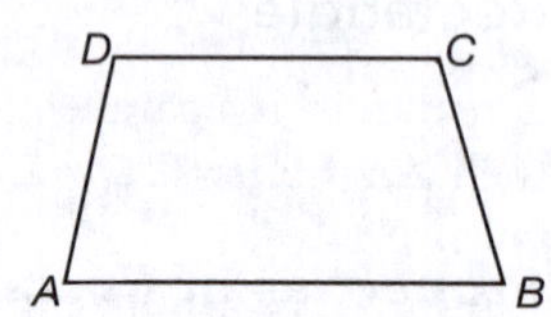

Figure 8.12

A **trapezium** is a quadrilateral with only one pair of opposite sides parallel. In figure, $ABCD$ is a trapezium with $AB \parallel DC$.

Properties of Trapezium

(i) The line joining the midpoints of the oblique (non-parallel) sides is half the sum of the parallel sides and is called the median.

[i.e., Median $= \frac{1}{2} \times$ sum of parallel sides $= \frac{1}{2} \times (AB + DC) = EF$]

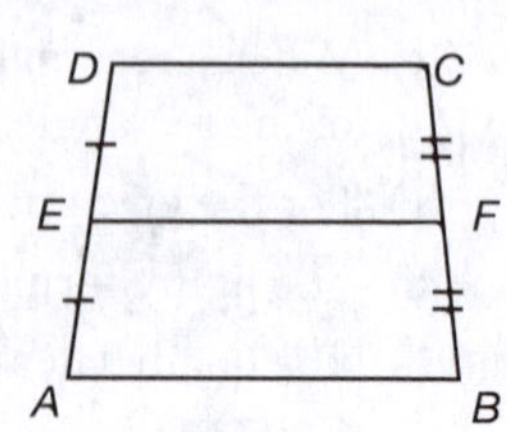

Figure 8.13

(ii) If the non-parallel sides are equal, then the diagonals will also be equal to each other.
(iii) Diagonals intersect each other proportionally in the ratio of lengths of parallel sides.
(iv) By joining the midpoints of adjacent sides of a trapezium, four similar triangles are obtained.
(v) If a trapezium is inscribed in a circle, then it is an isosceles trapezium with equal oblique sides.
(vi) $AC^2 + BD^2 = BC^2 + AD^2 + 2ABCD$

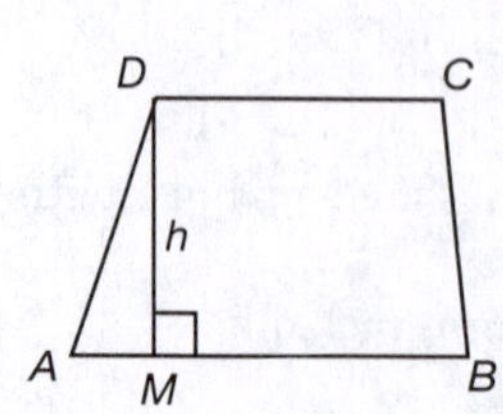

Figure 8.14

Isosceles Trapezium

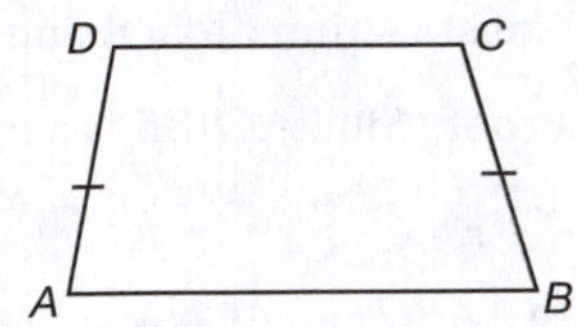

Figure 8.15

A trapezium is said to be an **isosceles trapezium**, if its non-parallel sides are equal. Thus a quadrilateral $ABCD$ is an isosceles trapezium, if $AB \parallel DC$ and $AD = BC$.

In isosceles trapezium $\angle A = \angle B$ and $\angle C = \angle D$.

Kite

A **kite** is a quadrilateral in which two pairs of adjacent sides are equal. If $ABCD$ is a kite then $AB = AD$ and $BC = CD$.

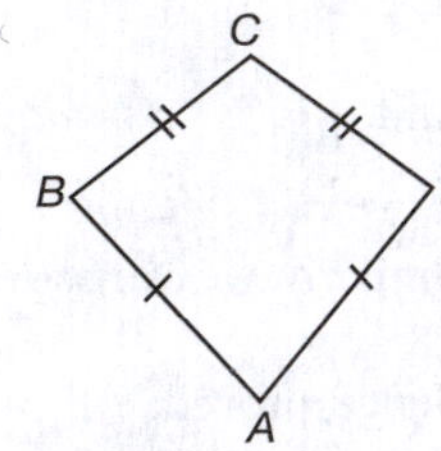

Figure 8.16

Properties of Kite

(i) $AB = BC$ and $AD = CD$.

(ii) Diagonals intersect at right angles.

(iii) Shorter diagonal is bisected by the longer diagonal.

Properties of all quadrilaterals are sum up in table 8.1.

Table 8.1 Properties of Quadrilaterals

Property	Parallelogram	Rectangle	Rhombus	Square
Opposite sides are equal	✓	✓	✓	✓
All sides are equal	✗	✗	✓	✓
Opposite is equal and right angle	✓	✓	✓	✓
All angles are equal and right angle	✗	✓	✗	✓
Diagonals bisect each other	✓	✓	✓	✓
Diagonals bisect each other at right angles	✗	✗	✓	✓
Diagonals are equal	✗	✗	✓	✓
Diagonals form four triangles of equal area	✗	✓	✗	✓
Diagonals from four congruent triangles	✓	✓	✓	✓
Diagonals from four triangles	✗	✗	✓	✓

Keystone

(i) Square, rectangle and rhombus are all parallelograms.

(ii) Kite and trapezium are not parallelograms.

(iii) A square is a rectangle.

(iv) A square is a rhombus.

(v) A parallelogram is a trapezium.

Theorems of Quadrilaterals

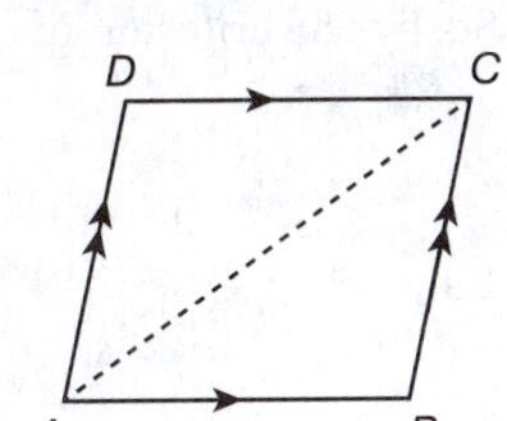

Figure 8.17

Theorem 1: A diagonal of a parallelogram divides the parallelogram into two congruent triangles.

Given: A parallelogram $ABCD$.

To Prove: A diagonal divides the parallelogram into two congruent triangles.

i.e., if diagonal AC is drawn then $\Delta ABC \cong \Delta CDA$ and if diagonal BD is drawn then $\Delta ABD \cong \Delta CDB$.

Construction: Join A and C.

Proof: Since, $ABCD$ is a parallelogram.

$\therefore$ $AB \parallel DC$ and $AD \parallel BC$.

In ΔABC and ΔCDA

$\angle BAC = \angle DCA$ [Alternate angles]

$\angle BCA = \angle DAC$ [Alternate angles]

And, $AC = AC$ [Common side]

$\therefore$ $\Delta ABC \cong \Delta CDA$ [By ASA congruency]

Similarly, we can prove that

$\Delta ABD \cong \Delta CDB$

Hence, proved.

Theorem 2: The diagonals of a parallelogram bisect each other.

Given: A parallelogram $ABCD$. Its diagonals AC and BD intersect each other at point O.

To Prove: Diagonals AC and BD bisect each other

i.e., $OA = OC$ and $OB = OD$.

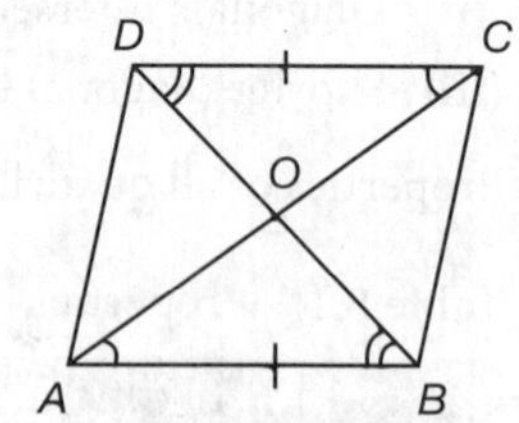

Figure 8.18

Proof: In ΔAOB and ΔCOD

$\because$ $AB \parallel DC$ and BD is a transversal line.

$\therefore$ $\angle ABO = \angle CDO$ [Alternate angles]

$\because$ $AB \parallel DC$ and AC is a transversal line.

$\therefore$ $\angle BAO = \angle DCO$ [Alternate angles]

And, $AB = DC$

$\Rightarrow$ $\Delta AOB \cong \Delta COD$ [By ASA congruency]

$\Rightarrow$ $OA = OC$ and $OB = OD$ [By CPCT]

Hence, Proved.

Theorem 3: The diagonals of a rhombus are perpendicular to each other.

Given: A rhombus $ABCD$ whose diagonals AC and BD intersect at O.

To prove: $\angle BOC = \angle DOC = \angle AOD = \angle AOB = 90°$.

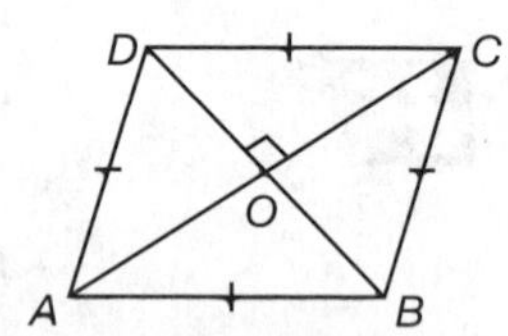

Figure 8.19

Proof: Parallelogram is a rhombus, if all of its sides are equal.

$AB = BC = CD = DA$ ...(i)

Since the diagonals of a parallelogram bisect each other.

$\therefore$ $OB = OD$ and $OA = OC$ ...(ii)

In ΔBOC and ΔDOC

$BO = OD$ [From (ii)]

$BC = DC$ [From (i)]

$OC = OC$

So, by SSS criterion of congruence

$\Delta BOC \cong \Delta DOC$

$\angle BOC = \angle DOC$ [By CPCT]

But, $\angle BOC + \angle DOC = 180°$ [Linear pair]

$\angle BOC = \angle DOC = 90°$

Similarly, $\angle AOD = \angle AOB = 90°$

Hence, $\angle BOC = \angle DOC = \angle AOD = \angle AOB = 90°$.

Illustration 8.1

The angles of a quadrilateral are in the ratio 3: 5: 9: 13. Find all the angles of the quadrilateral.

Solution: Let the angles be $3x$, $5x$, $9x$ and $13x$.

$$\therefore \quad 3x + 5x + 9x + 13x = 360°$$

$$\Rightarrow \quad 30x = 360° \text{ and } x = \frac{360°}{30} = 12°$$

$$\therefore \quad 1^{st} \text{ angle} = 3x = 3 \times 12° = 36°,$$

$$2^{nd} \text{ angle} = 5x = 5 \times 12° = 60°,$$

$$3^{rd} \text{ angle} = 9x = 9 \times 12° = 108°,$$

And, $$4^{th} \text{ angle} = 13 \times 12° = 156°.$$

Illustration 8.2

Use the information given in the adjoining figure to calculate the value of x.

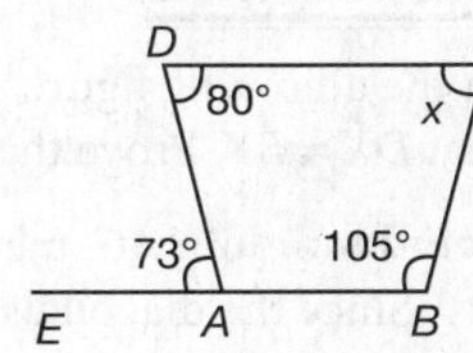

Solution: Since, EAB is a straight line.

$$\therefore \quad \angle DAE + \angle DAB = 180°$$

$$\Rightarrow \quad 73° + \angle DAB = 180°$$

$$\Rightarrow \quad \angle DAB = 180° - 73° = 107°.$$

Since, the sum of the angles of quadrilateral $ABCD$ is 360°.

$$\therefore \quad 107° + 105° + x + 80° = 360°$$

$$\Rightarrow \quad 292° + x = 360°$$

$$\Rightarrow \quad x = 360° - 292°$$

$$\Rightarrow \quad x = 68°.$$

Illustration 8.3

Prove that the angle bisectors of a parallelogram form a rectangle.

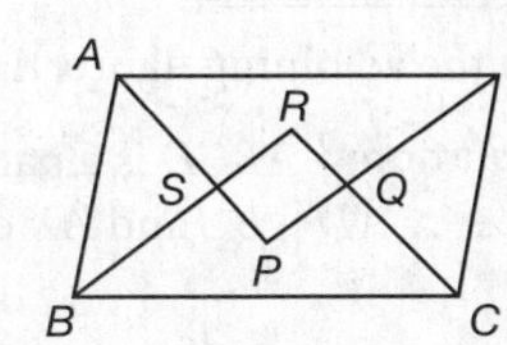

Solution: A parallelogram $ABCD$ in which bisectors of angles A, B, C, D intersect at P, Q, R, S to form a quadrilateral $PQRS$.
Since, $ABCD$ is a parallelogram, so $AD \parallel BC$ and transversal AB intersect them at A and B respectively.

$$\angle A + \angle B = 180°$$

$$\Rightarrow \quad \frac{1}{2}\angle A + \frac{1}{2}\angle B = 90°$$

$$\Rightarrow \quad \angle BAS + \angle ABS = 90° \qquad \ldots\text{(i)}$$

[AS and BS are bisectors of $\angle A$ and $\angle B$ respectively]

$$\angle BAS + \angle ABS + \angle ASB = 180°$$

$$\Rightarrow \quad 90° + \angle ASB = 180°$$

$$\Rightarrow \quad \angle ASB = 90°$$

$$\Rightarrow \quad \angle RSP = 90°$$

[$\angle ASB$ and $\angle RSP$ are vertically opposite angles]

Similarly, $\angle SRQ = 90°$, $\angle RQP = 90°$ and $\angle SPQ = 90°$.

Hence, $PQRS$ is a rectangle.

Illustration 8.4

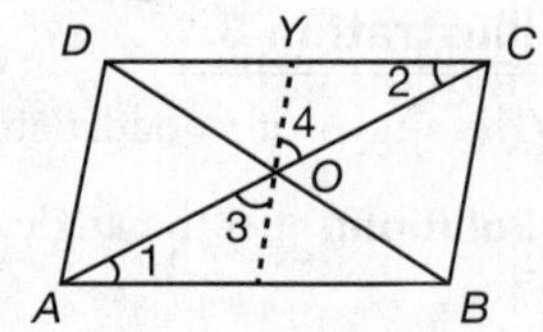

The diagonals of a parallelogram $ABCD$ intersect at O. A line through O intersects AB at X and DC at Y. Prove that $OX = OY$.

Solution: Since $AB \parallel CD$.

In ΔOAX and ΔOCY

$$\angle 1 = \angle 2 \quad \text{[Alternate angles]}$$

$$OA = OC$$

and $$\angle 3 = \angle 4 \quad \text{[Vertically opposite angles]}$$

So, by ASA criterion of congruence,

$$\Delta OAX \cong \Delta OCY \Rightarrow OX = OY \quad \text{[By CPCT]}$$

Illustration 8.5

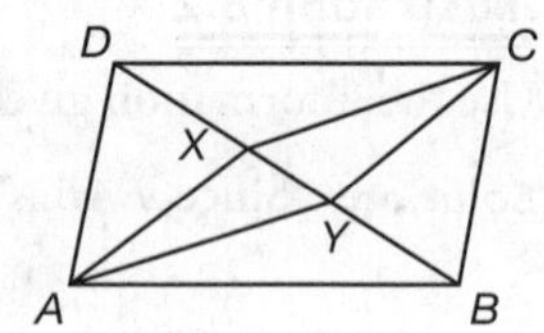

In the adjoining figure, $ABCD$ is a parallelogram and X, Y are the points on diagonal BD such that $DX = BY$. Prove that $CXAY$ is a parallelogram.

Solution: Join AC, meeting BD at O.

Since the diagonals of a parallelogram bisect each other.

$$OA = OC \text{ and } OD = OB$$

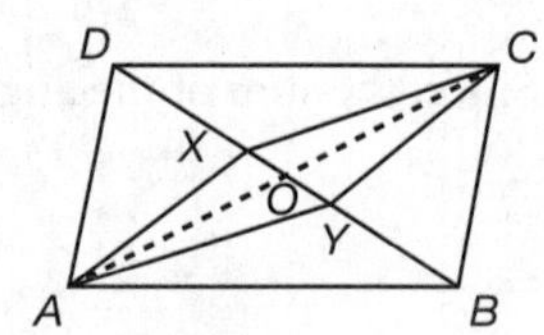

Now, $$OD = OB \text{ and } DX = BY$$

$\Rightarrow$ $$OD - DX = OB - BY$$

$\Rightarrow$ $$OX = OY$$

Now, $$OA = OC \text{ and } OX = OY.$$

$\therefore$ $CXAY$ is a quadrilateral whose diagonals bisect each other.

$\therefore$ $CXAY$ is a parallelogram.

Illustration 8.6

In the adjoining figure, $ABCD$ is a parallelogram and the bisector of $\angle A$ bisects BC at X. Prove that $AD = 2AB$.

Solution: $ABCD$ is a parallelogram.

$\therefore$ $AD \parallel BC$ and AX cuts them.

$\therefore$ $$\angle BXA = \angle DAX = \frac{1}{2}\angle A \quad \text{[Alternate interior angles]}$$

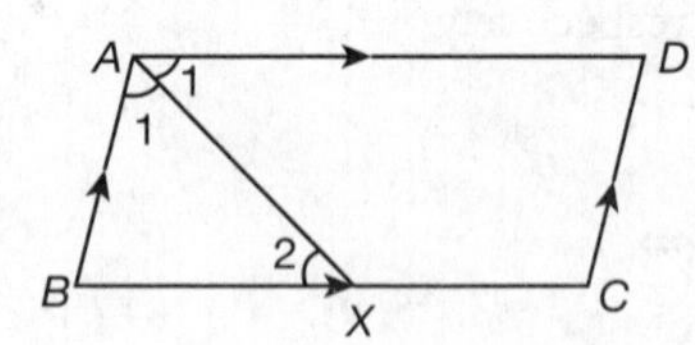

$\therefore$ $$\angle 2 = \frac{1}{2}\angle A$$

Also, $$\angle 1 = \frac{1}{2}\angle A$$

$\therefore$ $$\angle 2 = \angle 1$$

$\Rightarrow$ $$AB = BX$$

$\Rightarrow$ $$AB = BC$$

$\Rightarrow$ $$AB = AD$$

$\Rightarrow$ $$AD = 2\,AB.$$

Illustration 8.7

$ABCD$ is a trapezium in which $AB \parallel CD$ and $AD = BC$. Show that:

(i) $\angle A = \angle B$ **(ii)** $\angle C = \angle D$

(iii) $\Delta ABC \cong \Delta BAD$ **(iv)** diagonal AC = diagonal BD.

Solution:

(i) Extend AB and draw a line through C parallel to DA intersecting AB produced at E.

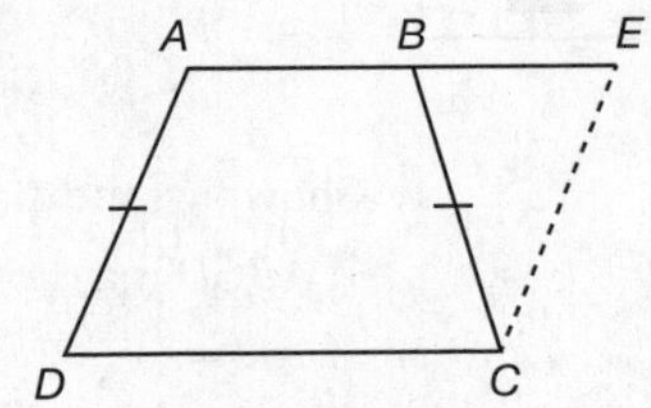

Since, $AD \parallel CE$ and transversal AE cuts them at A and E respectively.

$\therefore \quad \angle A + \angle E = 180°$

$\Rightarrow \quad 180° - \angle E = \angle A$

Since, $AB \parallel CD$ and $AD \parallel CE$

$\therefore \quad AECD$ is a parallelogram.

$\Rightarrow \quad AD = CE$

$\Rightarrow \quad BC = CE$

Thus, in ΔBCE

$BC = CE$

$\Rightarrow \quad \angle CBE = \angle CEB$

$\Rightarrow \quad 180° - \angle B = \angle E$

$\Rightarrow \quad 180° - \angle E = \angle B$

$\Rightarrow \quad \angle A = \angle B.$

(ii) Consecutive interior angles on the same side of a transversal are supplementary.

$\therefore \quad \angle A + \angle D = 180°$ and $\angle E + \angle C = 180°$

$\Rightarrow \quad \angle A + \angle D = \angle E + \angle C$

$\Rightarrow \quad \angle B + \angle D = \angle E + \angle C$

$\Rightarrow \quad \angle D = \angle C \qquad [\angle B = \angle E]$

(iii) In ΔABC and ΔBAD

$AB = BA$

$\angle B = \angle A$ and $BC = AD$

So, by SAS congruence criterion

$\Delta ABC \cong \Delta BAD$

(iv) Since, $\Delta ABC \cong \Delta BAD$

$AC = BD$

Hence, diagonal AC = diagonal BD.

Illustration 8.8

In ΔABC, lines are drawn through A, B and C parallel respectively to the sides BC, CA and AB, forming ΔPQR. Show that $BC = \frac{1}{2} QR$.

Solution: $AQ \parallel CB$ and $AC \parallel QB$

$\Rightarrow \quad AQCB$ is parallelogram.

$\Rightarrow \quad BC = AQ \qquad$ [$\because$ Opposite sides of *a* || *gm* is equal] Q A R

$AR \parallel CB$ and $AB \parallel RC$

$\Rightarrow \quad ARCB$ is parallelogram.

$\Rightarrow \quad BC = AR \qquad$ [$\because$ Opposite sides of *a* || *gm* are equal]

So, $\quad AQ = AR$

$\Rightarrow \quad AQ = AR = \frac{1}{2} QR$

$\Rightarrow \quad BC = \frac{1}{2} QR.$

Check Point 1

1. Show that the diagonals of a rhombus are perpendicular to each other.
2. If *ABCD* is a rhombus, find $\angle AOD$, where *O* is the point of intersection of the diagonals.
3. If $AD = (x + 2y)$ cm, $BC = (2x + 3)$ cm, $DC = (x + 7)$ cm and $AB = (3y + 2)$ cm find *AB* and *BC* in parallelogram *ABCD*.
4. Given a parallelogram *ABCD*. *DE* perpendicular to *AC* and *BF* perpendicular to *AC*. Prove that: $DE = BF$

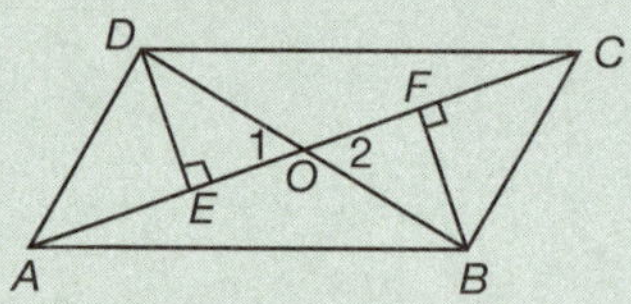

5. Given a parallelogram *ABCD*, $EF \parallel AD$, $GH \parallel CB$. Prove that *EFHG* is a parallelogram.

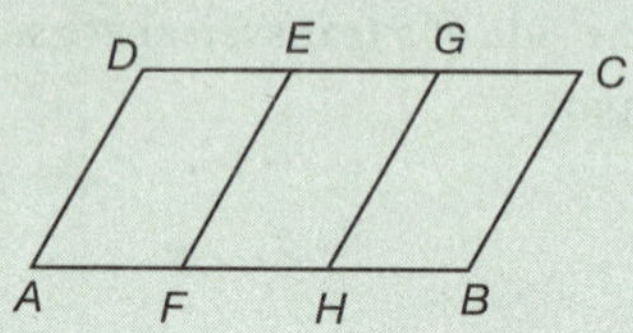

Midpoint Theorem

In a triangle, the line segment joining the midpoints of any two sides is parallel to the third side and is half of it.

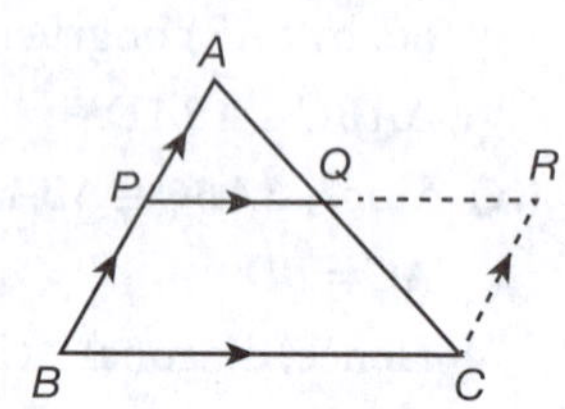

Figure 8.20

Given: A triangle *ABC* in which *P* is the midpoint of side *AB* and *Q* is the midpoint of side *AC*.

To Prove: *PQ* is parallel to *BC* and is half of it i.e., $PQ \parallel BC$ and $PQ = \frac{1}{2} BC$.

Construction: Produce *PQ* up to point *R* such that $PQ = QR$. Join *R* and *C*.

Proof: In ΔAPQ and ΔCRQ

$PQ = QR$ [By construction]

$AQ = QC$ [Given]

And, $\angle AQP = \angle CQR$ [Vertically opposite angles]

So, $\Delta APQ \cong \Delta CRQ$ [By SAS]

$\therefore$ $AP = CR$ [By CPCT]

And, $\angle APQ = \angle CRQ$ [By CPCT]

But, $\angle APQ$ and $\angle CRQ$ are alternate angles and whenever the alternate angles are equal, the lines are parallel.

$\Rightarrow$ $AP \parallel CR$

$\Rightarrow$ $AB \parallel CR$

$\Rightarrow$ $BP \parallel CR$

$AP = BP$ [Given, *P* is the midpoint of *AB*]

$\Rightarrow$ $CR = BP$ [As, $AP = CR$]

Now, $BP = CR$ and $BP \parallel CR$

$\Rightarrow$ $BCRP$ is a parallelogram.

[When any pair of opposite sides are equal and parallel, the quadrilateral is a parallelogram]

$BCRP$ is a parallelogram and opposite sides of a parallelogram are equal and parallel.

$\therefore$ $$PR = BC \text{ and } PR \parallel BC$$

Since, $PQ = QR$

$\Rightarrow$ $$PQ = \frac{1}{2} PR = \frac{1}{2} BC \qquad [\text{As, } PR = BC]$$

Also, $$PQ \parallel BC \qquad [\text{As, } PR \parallel BC]$$

$\therefore$ $$PQ \parallel BC \text{ and } PQ = \frac{1}{2} BC$$

Hence, Proved.

Converse of Midpoint Theorem

The line drawn through the midpoint of one side of a triangle parallel to the another side; bisects the third side.

Given: A triangle ABC in which P is the midpoint of side AB and PQ is parallel to BC.

To prove: PQ bisects the third side AC i.e., $AQ = QC$.

Construction: Through C, draw CR parallel to BA, which meets PQ produced at point R.

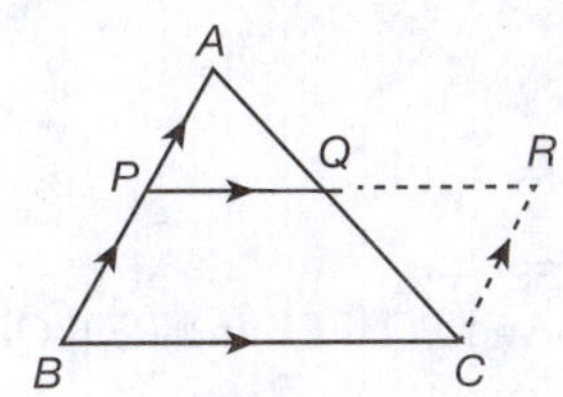

Figure 8.21

Proof: Since, $PQ \parallel BC$ i.e., $PR \parallel BC$ [Given]

and $$CR \parallel BA \text{ i.e., } CR \parallel BP. \qquad [\text{By construction}]$$

$\therefore$ Opposite sides of quadrilateral $PBCR$ are parallel.

$\Rightarrow$ $PBCR$ is a parallelogram

$\Rightarrow$ $$BP = CR$$

Also, $BP = AP$ [As, P is the midpoint of AB]

$\therefore$ $$CR = AP$$

$\because$ $$AB \parallel CR \text{ and } AC \text{ is transversal, } \angle PAQ = \angle RCQ \qquad [\text{Alternate angles}]$$

$\therefore$ $$AB \parallel CR \text{ and } PR \text{ is transversal, } \angle APQ = \angle CRQ \qquad [\text{Alternate angles}]$$

In ΔAPQ and ΔCRQ

$$CR = AP, \angle PAQ = \angle RCQ \text{ and } \angle APQ = \angle CRQ$$

$\Rightarrow$ $$\Delta APQ \cong \Delta CRQ \qquad [\text{By ASA}]$$

$\Rightarrow$ $$AQ = QC \qquad [\text{By CPCT}]$$

Hence, proved.

Keystone

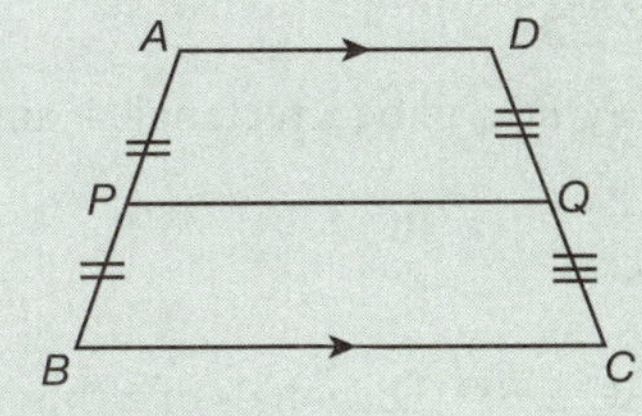

In quadrilateral $ABCD$, if side AD is parallel to side BC; $ABCD$ is a trapezium.

Now, P and Q are the midpoints of the non-parallel sides of the trapezium;

then $PQ = \frac{1}{2}(AD + BC)$.

i.e., The length of the line segment joining the midpoints of the two non-parallel sides of a trapezium is always equal to half of the sum of the length of its two parallel sides.

Intercept Theorem

Theorem: If there are three or more parallel lines and the intercepts made by them on a transversal are equal, then the corresponding intercepts on any other transversal are also equal.

Given: Three parallel lines *l*, *m* and *n* i.e., $l \parallel m \parallel n$. A transversal ***p*** meets these parallel lines at points *A*, *B* and *C* respectively such that $AB = BC$. Another transversal ***q*** also meets parallel lines ***l, m*** and ***n*** at points *D*, *E* and *F* respectively.

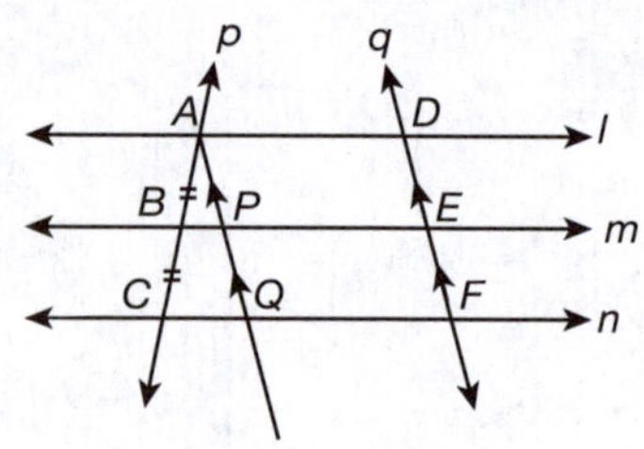

Figure 8.22

To Prove: $DE = EF$

Construction: Through point *A*, draw a line parallel to *DEF*; which meets *BE* at point *P* and *CF* at point *Q*.

Proof: In ΔACQ, *B* is the midpoint of *AC* and *BP* is parallel to *CQ* and we know that the line through the midpoint of one side of the triangle and parallel to another side bisects the third side.

$\therefore$ $AP = PQ$ ... (i)

When the opposite sides of a quadrilateral are parallel, it is a parallelogram and so its opposite sides are equal.

$\therefore$ $AP \parallel DE$ and $AD \parallel PE$

$\Rightarrow$ *APED* is a parallelogram.

$\Rightarrow$ $AP = DE$ ... (ii)

And $PQ \parallel EF$ and $PE \parallel QF$

$\Rightarrow$ *PQFE* is a parallelogram

$\Rightarrow$ $PQ = EF$ ... (iii)

From the above equations, we get

$DE = EF$

Hence, proved.

Illustration 8.9

ABCD is a rhombus and *P*, *Q*, *R* and *S* are the midpoints of the sides *AB*, *BC*, *CD* and *DA* respectively. Prove that the quadrilateral *PQRS* is a rectangle.

Solution:

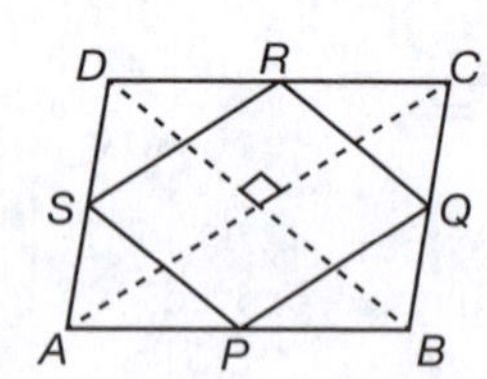

In ΔABC, $PQ \parallel AC$ and $PQ = \frac{1}{2} AC$ ... (i)

[By midpoint theorem]

In ΔADC, $SR \parallel AC$ and $SR = \frac{1}{2} AC$ ... (ii)

[By midpoint theorem]

$\therefore$ $PQ = SR$ and $PQ \parallel SR$ [From (i) and (ii)]

$\Rightarrow$ *PQRS* is a parallelogram.

Now, *PQRS* will be a rectangle if any angle of the parallelogram *PQRS* is 90°.

$PQ \parallel AC$ [By midpoint theorem]

$QR \parallel BD$ [By midpoint theorem]

But, $AC \perp BD$ [Diagonals of a rhombus are perpendicular to each other]

$\therefore$ $PQ \perp QR$

[Angle between two lines = angle between their parallels]

$\Rightarrow$ *PQRS* is a rectangle.

Hence, proved.

Illustration 8.10

ABCD is a trapezium in which $AB \parallel DC$, *BD* is a diagonal and *E* is the midpoint of *AD*. A line is drawn through *E* parallel to *AB* intersecting *BC* at *F* (Figure). Prove that *F* is the midpoint of *BC*.

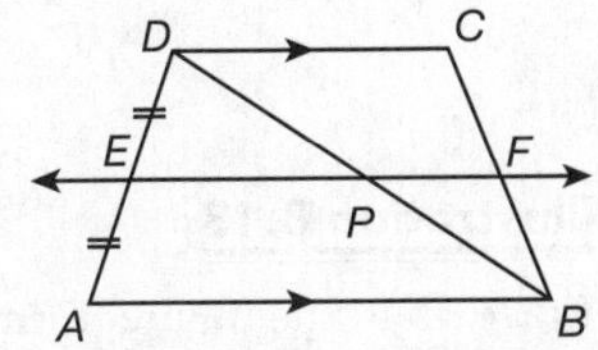

Solution: Given line *EF* is parallel to *AB* and $AB \parallel DC$.

$\therefore$ $$EF \parallel AB \parallel DC.$$

According to the converse of the midpoint theorem, in ΔABD, *E* is the midpoint of *AD* and *EP* is parallel to *AB*. [As $EF \parallel AB$]

$\therefore$ *P* is the midpoint of side *BD*.

[The line through the midpoint of a side of a triangle and parallel to the other side, bisects the third side]

Now, in ΔBCD, *P* is the midpoint of *BD* and, *PF* is parallel to *DC*. [As $EF \parallel DC$]

$\therefore$ *F* is the midpoint of *BC*

[The line through the midpoint of a side of a triangle and parallel to the other side, bisects the third side]

Hence, proved.

Illustration 8.11

In the given figure, *E* and *F* are respectively, the midpoints of non-parallel sides of a trapezium *ABCD*. Prove that:

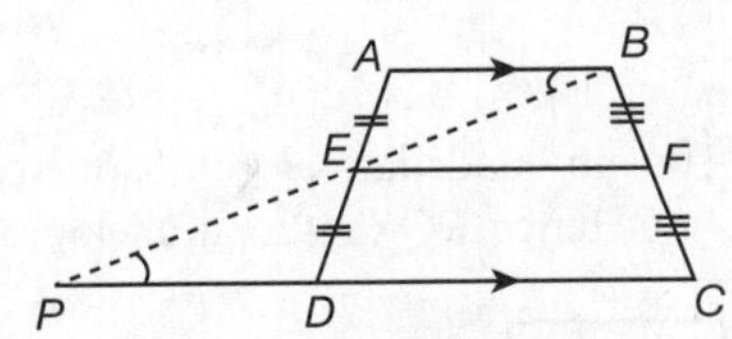

(i) $EF \parallel AB$ (ii) $EF = \frac{1}{2}(AB + DC)$.

Solution: Join *BE* and produce it to intersect *CD* produced at point *P*. In ΔAEB and ΔDEP, $AB \parallel PC$ and *BP* are transversal.

$$\angle ABE = \angle DPE \quad \text{[Alternate interior angles]}$$

$$\angle AEB = \angle DEP \quad \text{[Vertically opposite angles]}$$

And $$AE = DE \quad \text{[E is the midpoint of AD]}$$

So, $$\Delta AEB \cong \Delta DEP \quad \text{[By AAS congruency]}$$

$$BE = PE \quad \text{[By CPCT]}$$

And $$AB = DP \quad \text{[By CPCT]}$$

Since, the line joining the midpoints of any two sides of a triangle is parallel and half of the third side, Therefore, in ΔBPC, *E* is the midpoint of *BP* [As, $BE = PE$] and *F* is the midpoint of *BC* [Given]

$\Rightarrow$ $$EF \parallel PC \text{ and } EF = \frac{1}{2} PC$$

$\Rightarrow$ $$EF \parallel DC \text{ and } EF = \frac{1}{2}(PD + DC)$$

$\Rightarrow$ $$EF \parallel AB \text{ and } EF = \frac{1}{2}(AB + DC) \quad \text{[As, } DC \parallel AB \text{ and } PD = AB]$$

Hence, proved.

Illustration 8.12

AD and *BE* are medians of ΔABC and $BE \parallel DF$. Prove that $CF = \frac{1}{4} AC$.

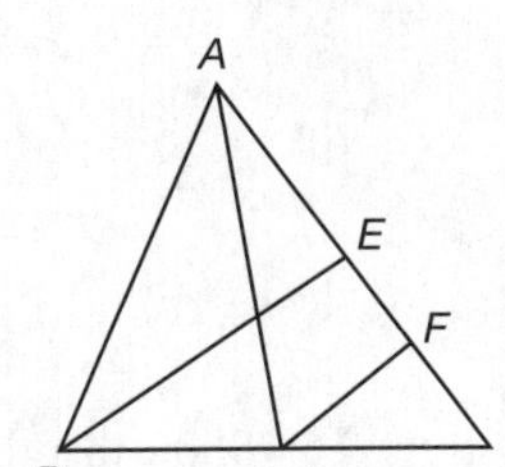

Solution: In ΔBEC, *DF* is a line through the midpoint *D* of *BC* and parallel to *BE* intersecting *CE* at *F*. Therefore, *F* is the midpoint of *CE*. Because the line drawn through the midpoint of one side of a triangle and parallel to another side bisects the third side.

Now, F is the midpoint of CE

$$\Rightarrow \qquad CF = \frac{1}{2}CE \Rightarrow CF = \frac{1}{2}\left(\frac{1}{2}AC\right) \Rightarrow CF = \frac{1}{2}AC.$$

Illustration 8.13

Prove that the figure formed by joining the midpoints of the pairs of consecutive sides of a quadrilateral is a parallelogram.

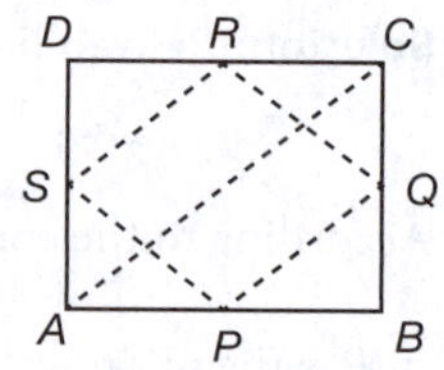

Solution: $ABCD$ is a quadrilateral in which P, Q, R and S are the midpoints of the sides AB, BC, CD and DA respectively.

Join A and C.

In ΔABC, P and Q are the midpoints of sides AB and AC respectively.

$$\therefore \qquad PQ \parallel AC \text{ and } PQ = \frac{1}{2}AC \qquad \text{[By midpoint theorem]}$$

In ΔABC, P and Q are the midpoints of sides AB and AC respectively.

$$\therefore \qquad RS \parallel AC \text{ and } RS = \frac{1}{2}AC \qquad \text{[By midpoint theorem]}$$

$$\therefore \qquad PQ = RS \text{ and } PQ \parallel RS.$$

Thus in quadrilateral $PQRS$, one pair of opposite sides are equal and parallel.

Hence, $PQRS$ is a parallelogram.

Check Point 2

6. Prove that the median to the hypotenuse of a right-angled triangle is half the length of the hypotenuse.
7. The diagonals of a quadrilateral $ABCD$ are perpendicular to each other. Show that the quadrilateral, formed by joining the middle points of its sides is a rectangle.

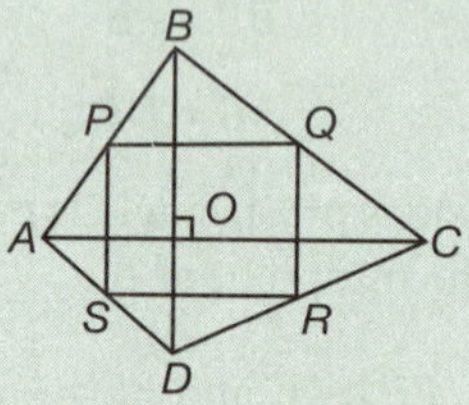

8. Perpendiculars dropped from the midpoints of two sides of a triangle to the third side are equal.

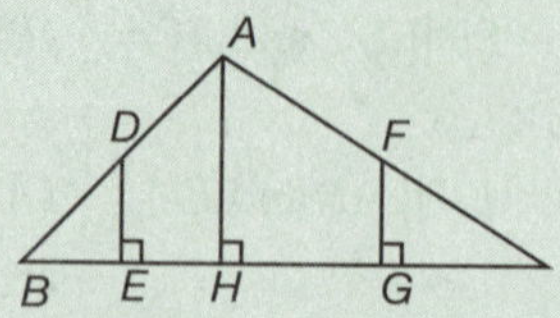

9. In ΔABC, the medians CD and BE are produced to X and Y such that $CD = DX$ and $BE = EY$. Prove that the points X, A, Y are collinear.

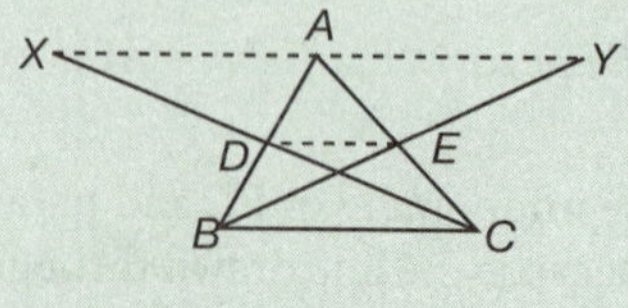

10. Show that the three line segments which join the middle points of the sides of a triangle, divide it into four triangles which are congruent to each other.

Polygon

A closed plane figure bounded by line segments is called a polygon.

The line segments are called its sides and the points of intersection of consecutive sides are called its vertices. An angle formed by two consecutive sides of a polygon is called an interior angle or simply an angle of the polygon.

Table 8.2 Number of Sides of a Polygon

Number of sides	Name
3	Triangles
4	Quadrilateral
5	Pentagon
6	Hexagon
7	Heptagon
8	Octagon
9	Nonagon
10	Decagon

A polygon is named according to the number of sides it has.

In general, a polygon of "*n*" sides is called *n*-gon. Thus, a polygon having 18 sides is called 18-gon.

The line segment joining any two non-consecutive vertices of a polygon is called its diagonal.

Convex Polygon

If all (interior) angles of a polygon are less than 180°, it is called a convex polygon.

In the figure given below, *ABCDEF* is a convex polygon.

In other words, a polygon is a convex polygon if the line segment joining any two points inside it lies completely inside the polygon.

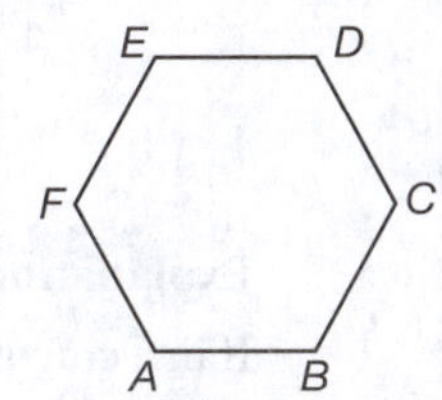

Figure 8.23

Exterior Angle of Convex Polygon

If we produce a side of polygon, the angle it makes with the next side is called an exterior angle. In the diagram given below, *ABCDE* is a pentagon. Its side *AB* has been produced to *P*, then $\angle CBP$ is an exterior angle.

Corresponding to each interior angle, there is an exterior angle. Also, an exterior angle and its adjacent interior angle make a straight line, i.e., an exterior angle + adjacent interior angle = 180°

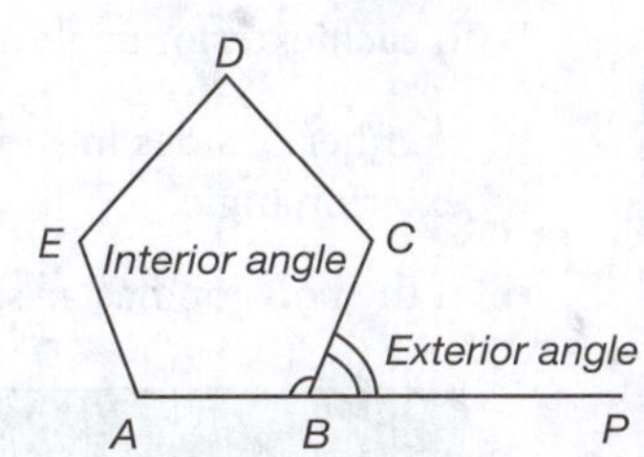

Figure 8.24

Concave Polygon

If one or more of the (interior) angles of a polygon is greater than 180° i.e., reflex, it is called concave (or re-entrant) polygon. In the figure given below, *ABCDEFG* is a concave polygon.

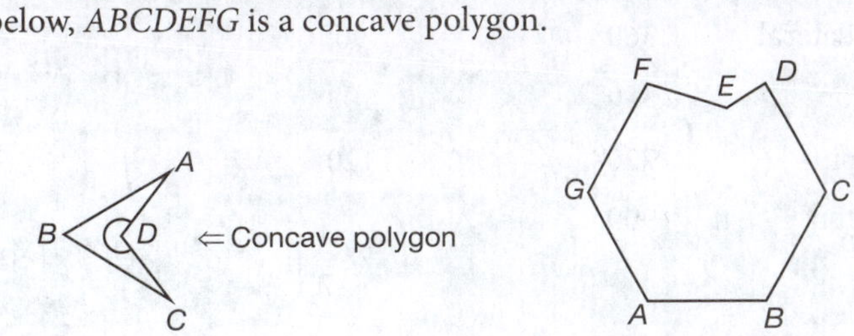

Figure 8.25

Regular Polygon

A polygon is called a regular polygon if all its sides have equal length and all its angles have equal size.

Thus, in a regular polygon

(i) All sides are equal in length **(ii)** All interior angles are equal in size **(iii)** All exterior angles are equal in size

All regular polygons are convex.

Competition Corner

- (i) If there is a polygon of 'n' sides ($n \geq 3$), we can cut it into (n – 2) triangles with a common vertex and so the sum of the interior angles of a polygon of 'n' sides would be: $(n-2) \times 180° = (n-2) \times 2$ right-angles $= (2n-4)$ right angles

  (ii) If there is a regular polygon of 'n' sides ($n \geq 3$), then its each interior angle is equal to $\left(\frac{2n-4}{n} \times 90\right)^{\circ}$.

  (iii) Each exterior angle of a regular polygon of 'n' sides is equal to $\left(\frac{360}{n}\right)^{\circ}$.

- The sum of all the exterior angles formed by producing the sides of a convex polygon in the same order is equal to four right angles.

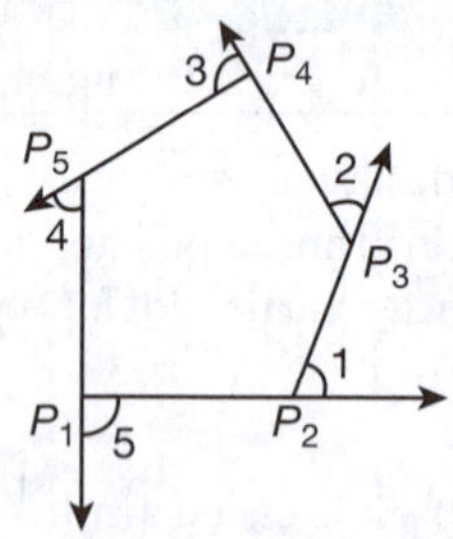

Explanation

If in a convex polygon $P_1P_2P_3P_4P_5$, all the sides are produced in order, forming exterior angles ∠1, ∠2, ∠3, ∠4 and ∠5, then ∠1 + ∠2+ ∠3 + ∠4 + ∠5 = 4 right angles = 360°

- If each exterior angle of a regular polygon is $x°$, then the number of sides in the polygon $= \frac{360°}{x}$. Greater the number of sides in a regular polygon, greater the value of its each interior angle and smaller the value of each exterior angle.
- If the polygon has 'n' sides, then the number of diagonals of the polygon $= \frac{n(n-1)}{2} - n$

No. of sides	Polygon	Sum of all the angles	Each interior angle (Regular Polygon)	Each exterior angle (Regular Polygon)	No. of diagonals
3	Triangle	180°	60°	120°	0
4	Quadrilateral	360°	90°	90°	2
5	Pentagon	540°	108°	72°	5
6	Hexagon	720°	120°	60°	9
7	Heptagon	900°	$\left(128\frac{4}{7}\right)^{\circ}$	$\left(51\frac{3}{7}\right)^{\circ}$	14
8	Octagon	1080°	135°	45°	20
9	Nonagon	1260°	140°	40°	27
10	Decagon	1440°	144°	36°	35

Check Point 3

11. The difference between an exterior angle of $(n - 1)$ sided regular polygon and an exterior angle of $(n + 2)$ sided regular polygon is $6°$, then the value of 'n' is:

(A) 14 (B) 15

(C) 13 (D) 12

12. How many diagonals are there in a decagon?

(A) 19 (B) 29

(C) 35 (D) 45

STRUCTURAL OUTLINE

QUADRILATRALS

Parallelogram

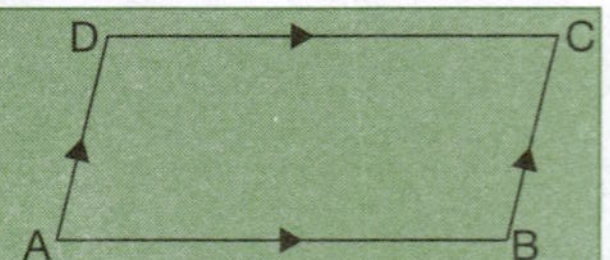

- The opposite sides are parallel and equal.
- Opposite angles are equal.
- Sum of any two adjacent angles is 180°.
- Diagonals bisect each other.
- Diagonals need not bisect angles at the vertices.
- Each diagonal divides a parallelogram into two congruent triangles.
- Lines joining the mid-points of the adjacent sides of a quadrilateral form a parallelogram.
- Lines joining the mid-points of the adjacent sides of a parallelogram is a parallelogram.
- The parallelogram that is inscribed in a circle is a rectangle.
- The parallelogram that is circumscribed about a circle is a rhombus.
- $(AC)^2 + (BD)^2 = 2(AB^2 + BC^2)$

Definition and Properties

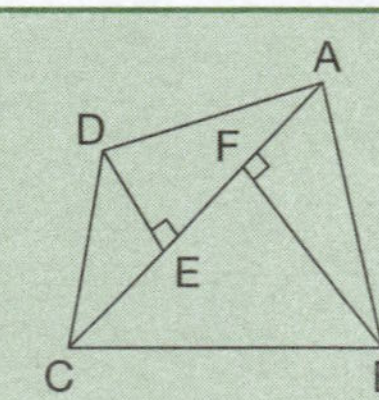

A **quadrilateral** is a four sided closed figure.

Let **A**, **B**, **C** and **D** be four points in a plane such that :

(i) No three of them are collinear.

(ii) The line segments AB, BC, CD and DA do not intersect except at their end points, then **figure** obtained by joining A, B, C & D is called a **quadrilateral**.

Properties : –

(i) Sum of four interior angles is 360°.

(ii) The sum of opposite sides of a quadrilateral circumscribed about a circle, is always equal.

(iii) Area of quadrilateral = $\frac{1}{2}$ × one of the diagonals × sum of the perpendiculars drawn to the diagonals from the opposite vertices.

i.e, Ar (ABCD) = $\frac{1}{2} \times AC \times (DE + BF)$

Rectangle

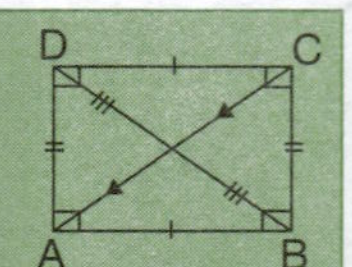

- Opposite angles are equal and of 90°.
- Diagonals are equal and bisect each other.
- When a rectangle is inscribed in a circle, the diameter of the circle is equal to the diagonal of the rectangle.
- For the given perimeter of rectangles, a square has maximum area.
- The figure formed by joining the mid-points of the adjacent sides of a rectangle is a rhombus.
- The quadrilateral formed by joining the mid-points of intersection of the angle bisectors of a parallelogram is a rectangle.
- Every rectangle is a parallelogram.

Rhombus

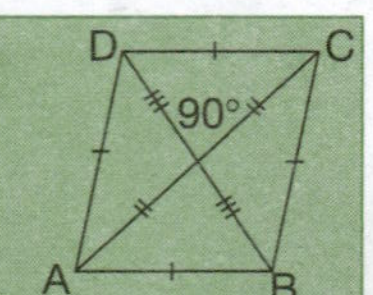

- All sides are equal.
- Diagonals bisect each other at right angle.
- Diagonals bisect the vertex angles.
- Figure formed by joining the mid-points of the adjacent sides of a rhombus is a rectangle.
- A parallelogram is a rhombus if its diagonals are perpendicular to each other.

Square

A **square** is a parallelogram having all sides equal and each angle equal to right angle.

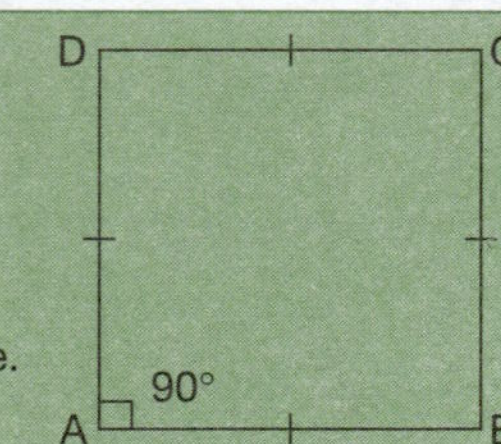

QUADRILATRALS

Trapezium

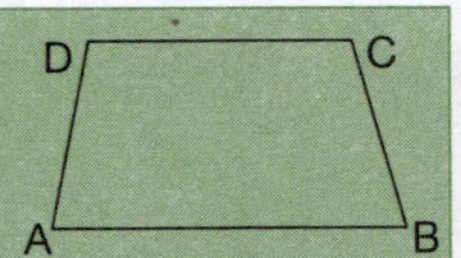

Trapezium : A **trapezium** is a quadrilateral with only one pair of opposite sides parallel. In figure, ABCD is a trapezium with AB || DC.

Properties : –

- The line joining the mid-points of the oblique (non-parallel) sides is half the sum of the parallel sides and is called the median.

[i.e., Median = $\frac{1}{2}\times$ sum of parallel sides = $\frac{1}{2}\times$ (AB + DC) = EF]

- If the non-parallel sides are equal, then the diagonals will also be equal to each other.
- Diagonals intersect each other proportionally in the ratio of lengths of parallel sides.
- By joining the mid-points of adjacent sides of a trapezium, four similar triangles are obtained.
- If a trapezium is inscribed in a circle, then it is an isosceles trapezium with equal oblique sides.
- $AC^2 + BD^2 = BC^2 + AD^2 + 2AB.\ CD$

Mid-Point Theorem

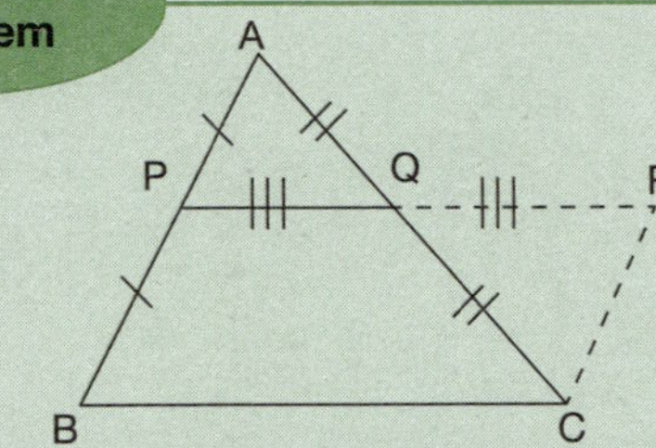

In a triangle, the line segment joining the mid-points of any two sides is parallel to the third side and is half of it.

If P is the mid-point of side AB and Q is the mid-point of side AC. Then PQ || BC and PQ = $\frac{1}{2}$ BC.

Isosceles Trapezium

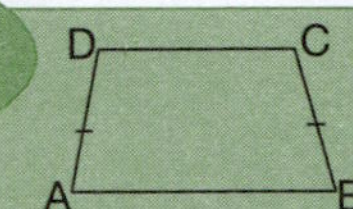

- A trapezium is said to bean **isosceles trapezium**, if its non-parallel sides are equal. Thus a quadrilateral ABCD is an isosceles trapezium, if AB || DC and AD = BC.
- In isosceles trapezium **∠A = ∠B and ∠C = ∠D.**

Kite

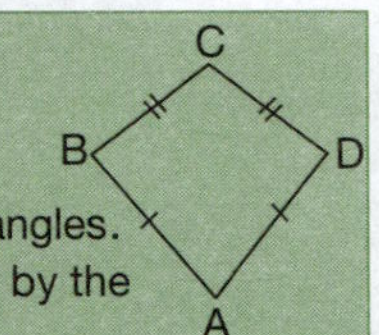

- AB = BC and AD = CD.
- Diagonals intersect at right angles.
- Shorter diagonal is bisected by the longer diagonal.

ASSESSMENT CORNER

FIXED RESPONSE TYPE

Fill in the Blanks

1. If in a quadrilateral diagonals bisect each other, then the quadrilateral must be a ________.
2. The diagonals of a rectangle are ________.
3. If the diagonals of a parallelogram intersect at right angles, then the parallelogram must be a ________.
4. The quadrilateral formed by joining the midpoints of consecutive sides of a square is a ________.
5. The triangle formed by joining the midpoints of an equilateral triangle is ________.
6. If there are three or more parallel lines and the intercepts made by them on a transversal are equal then their intercepts on any other transversal are also ________.

True/False

1. A diagonal of a parallelogram divides it into two congruent triangles.
2. The opposite sides of a parallelogram are equal.
3. The diagonals of a parallelogram never bisect each other.
4. The opposite angles of a parallelogram are complementary.
5. A rhombus is a quadrilateral, whose all the sides are equal and each angle is 90°.

Single Correct Type Questions

Level 1

1. In a parallelogram *ABCD*, $\angle D = 105°$, then the $\angle A$ and $\angle B$ will be:
   (A) 105°, 75° (B) 75°, 105°
   (C) 105°, 105° (D) 75°, 75°
2. Which is not correct about rectangle *EFGH*?
   (A) $\angle E = \angle F = \angle G = \angle H = 90°$
   (B) $EG = FH$
   (C) $EF = GH$ and $HE = FG$
   (D) *EG* and *FH* are angle bisectors.
3. The measure of all the angles of a parallelogram, if an angle is 24° less than twice the smallest angle, is:
   (A) 37°, 143°, 37°, 143°
   (B) 108°, 72°, 108°, 72°
   (C) 68°, 112°, 68°, 112°
   (D) None of these
4. In the adjoining figure, *AP* and *BP* are angle bisectors of $\angle A$ and $\angle B$ which meets at *P* on the parallelogram *ABCD*. Then $2\angle APB =$

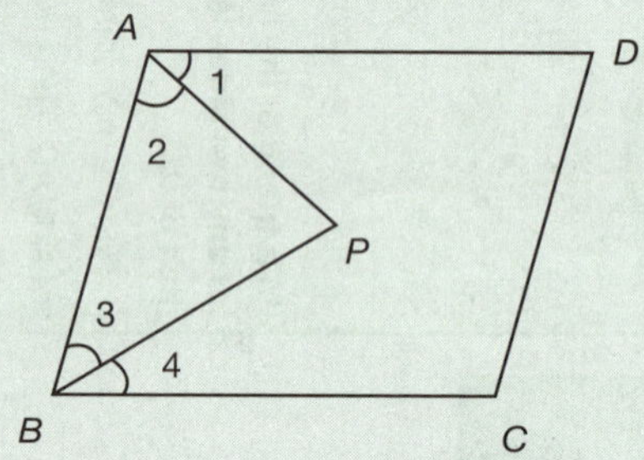

   (A) $\angle C + \angle D$ (B) $\angle A + \angle C$
   (C) $\angle B + \angle D$ (D) $2\angle C$
5. The measures of the angles of a quadrilateral *ABCD* are respectively in the ratio 1 : 2 : 3 : 4. Then which of the following is true?

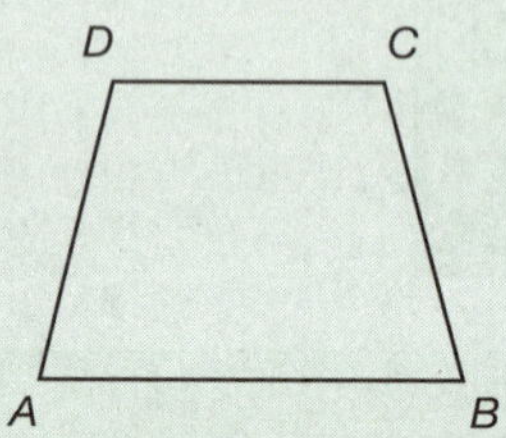

   (A) $AC = BD$ (B) $AD \parallel BC$
   (C) $AB \parallel DC$ (D) None of these
6. From the figure, find the value of $\angle SQP$ and $\angle QSP$ of parallelogram *PQRS*.

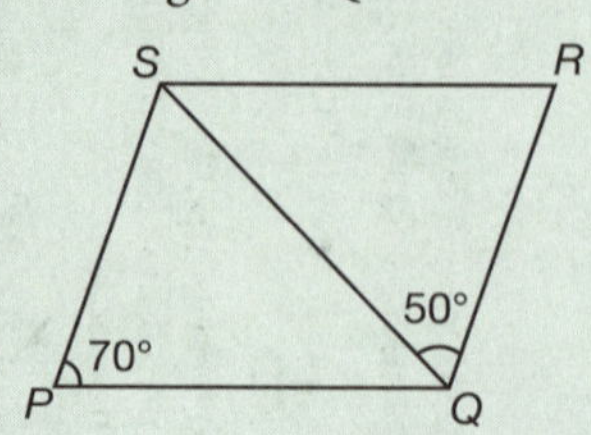

   (A) 60°, 50° (B) 60°, 45°
   (C) 70°, 35° (D) 35°, 70°

7. In a quadrilateral $ABCD$, the line segments bisecting $\angle C$ and $\angle D$ meet at E. Then $\angle A + \angle B$ is equal to:

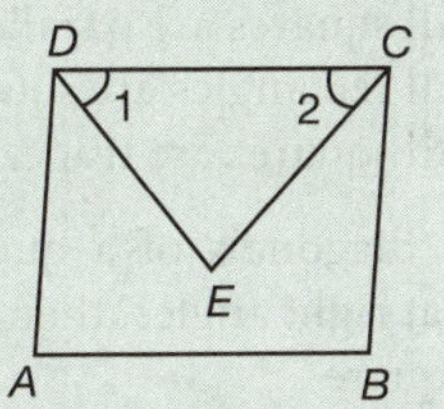

(A) $\angle CED$ (B) $\frac{1}{2} \angle CED$

(C) $2\angle CED$ (D) None of these

8. Which of the following properties are not true for parallelogram?
(A) Its diagonals are perpendicular to each other.
(B) The diagonals divide the figure into four congruent triangles.
(C) Its diagonals are equal.
(D) All of the above

9. If the diagonals of a parallelogram are equal then it is a:
(A) rectangle (B) trapezium
(C) rhombus (D) square

10. $ABCD$ is a trapezium and P, Q are the midpoints of the diagonal's AC and BD. Then PQ is equal to:

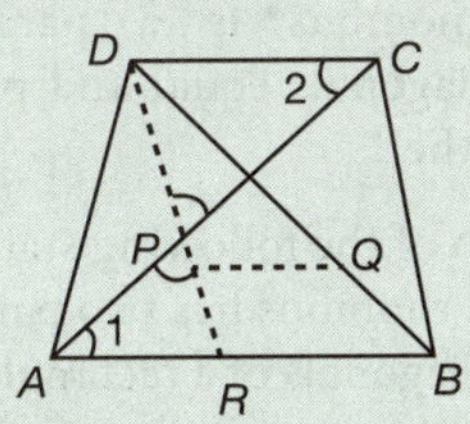

(A) $\frac{1}{2}(AB)$ (B) $\frac{1}{2}(CD)$

(C) $\frac{1}{2}(AB - CD)$ (D) $\frac{1}{2}(AB + CD)$

11. If $ABCD$ is a trapezium in which $AB \parallel CD$ and $AD = BC$, then $\angle A$ is equal to:
(A) 180° (B) 90°
(C) $\angle B$ (D) None of these

12. A point X inside a rectangle $PQRS$ is joined to the vertices then, which of the following is true?
(A) Area (ΔPSX) = Area (ΔRXQ)
(B) Area (ΔPSX) + Area (ΔPXQ) = Area (ΔRSX) + Area (ΔRQX)
(C) Area PXS + Area (ΔRXQ) = Area (ΔSRX) + Area (ΔPXQ)
(D) None of the above

13. $ABCD$ is a parallelogram and AP and CQ are the perpendiculars from A and C on its diagonal BD, respectively. Then AP is equal to:
(A) DP (B) CQ
(C) PQ (D) AB

14. In the figure, $ABCD$ is a parallelogram. P and Q are midpoints of the sides AB and CD, respectively. Then $PRQS$ is:

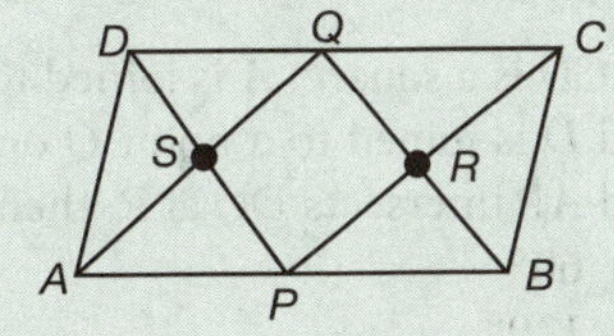

(A) parallelogram (B) trapezium
(C) rectangle (D) none of these

15. In a triangle, P, Q and R are the midpoints of the sides BC, CA and AB respectively. If $AC = 16$ cm, $BC = 20$ cm and $AB = 24$ cm, then the perimeter of the quadrilateral $ARPQ$ will be:
(A) 60 cm (B) 30 cm
(C) 40 cm (D) none of these

Level 2

16. $LMNO$ is a trapezium with $LM \parallel NO$. If P and Q are the midpoints of LO and MN respectively and $LM = 5$ cm and $ON = 10$ cm, then $PQ =$
(A) 2.5 cm (B) 5 cm
(C) 7.5 cm (D) 15 cm

17. In a right-angle triangle ABC is right-angled at B. Given that $AB = 9$ cm, $AC = 15$ cm and D, E are the midpoints of the sides AB and AC respectively, then the area of $\Delta ADE =$
(A) 67.5 cm^2 (B) 13.5 cm^2
(C) 27 cm^2 (D) data insufficient

18. In ΔABC, AD is the median through A and E is the midpoint of AD. BE produced meets AC in F. Then

(A) $AF = \frac{1}{4}AC.$ (B) $AF = \frac{1}{3}AC.$

(C) $AF = \frac{1}{2}AC.$ (D) None of these

19. The bisectors of the angles of a parallelogram encloses a

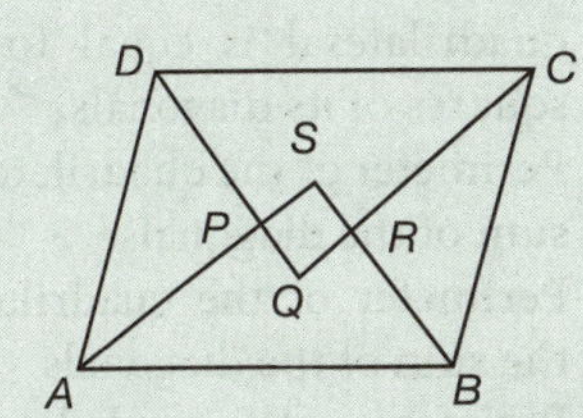

(A) Rhombus (B) Rectangle
(C) Square (D) None of these

20. Two regular polygons are such that the ratio between their number of sides is 1 : 2 and the ratio of measures of their interior angles is 3 : 4. The number of sides of each polygon is:
(A) 5, 10 (B) 6, 12
(C) 4, 8 (D) 2, 3

21. *ABCD* is a square, *A* is joined to a point *P* on *BC* and *D* is joined to a point *Q* on *AB*. If $AP = DQ$ and *AP* intersects *DQ* at *R*, then $\angle DRP$ is:
(A) 60°
(B) 120°
(C) 90°
(D) can't be determined

22. When the diagonals of a parallelogram are perpendicular to each other then it is called:
(A) Square (B) rectangle
(C) rhombus (D) parallelogram

23. In the given figure, *ABCD* is a parallelogram. Compute the values of *x* and *y*.

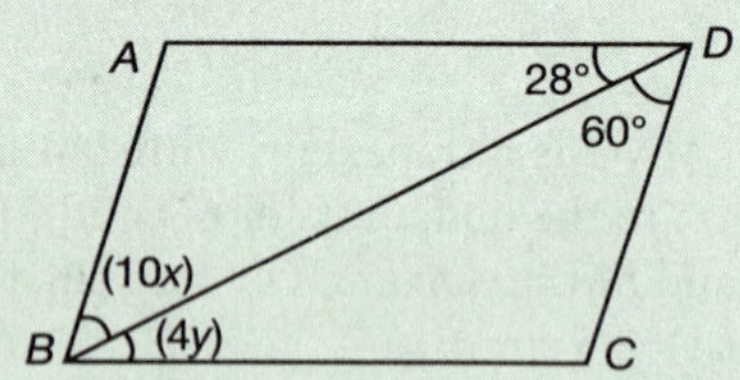

(A) $x = 6°$ and $y = 7°$ (B) $x = 3°$ and $y = 2°$
(C) $x = 5°$ and $y = 6°$ (D) None of these

24. If an angle of a parallelogram is two-thirds the adjacent angles, Then both angles of a parallelogram:
(A) 60°, 120° (B) 36°, 144°
(C) 72°, 108° (D) None of these

25. A quadrilateral having only one pair of opposite sides parallel is called a
(A) Square (B) Rhombus
(C) Trapezium (D) Parallelogram

Multiple Correct Type Questions

1. *ABCD* is quadrilateral. If *AC* and *BD* are its diagonals then the incorrect statement/s is/are:
(A) Sum of the squares of the sides of the quadrilateral is equal to the sum of the squares of its diagonals.
(B) Perimeter of the quadrilateral is equal to the sum of the diagonals
(C) Perimeter of the quadrilateral is less than the sum of the diagonals
(D) Perimeter of the quadrilateral is greater than the sum of the diagonals

2. Which of the following statements is correct?
(A) All rhombuses are parallelograms
(B) All squares are parallelograms
(C) All rectangles are square
(D) All squares are trapezium

3. If the diagonals of a quadrilateral bisect each other at right angles, then the figure is:
(A) Square (B) Parallelogram
(C) Rectangle (D) Rhombus

4. Which of the following statements is/are not true?
(A) In a parallelogram, the diagonals are equal.
(B) In a parallelogram, the diagonals bisect each other.
(C) In a parallelogram, the diagonals intersect each other at right angles.
(D) In any quadrilateral, if a pair of opposite sides are equal, it is parallelogram.

5. Which of the following statements is/ are true?
(A) Diagonals of a rectangle are equal and bisect each other at 90°
(B) Diagonals of a square are equal and bisect each other at 90°
(C) Rhombus is a parallelogram with a pair of adjacent sides equal
(D) Rhombus is a parallelogram with its diagonals equal and perpendicular to each other.

6. Which of the following statements is/are true?
(A) A rhombus has two pairs of equal angles.
(B) Diagonals of a rectangle are equal and bisect each other
(C) Two angles of a rhombus are right angles
(D) The diagonals of a square are of equal length

7. *ABCD* is a rhombus and *P*, *Q*, *R*, *S* are the midpoints of sides *AB*, *BC*, *CD* and *DA* respectively, then
(A) $\angle A = \angle C = \angle B = \angle D$
(B) $QS = PR$
(C) $\Delta APS \cong \Delta CQR$
(D) $\angle PSR = \angle PQR = 90°$

8. If in triangle *XYZ*, $XY = XZ$ and *M*, *N* are the midpoints of *XY*, *YZ*, then which of the following is correct?
(A) $MN = \frac{1}{2}YZ$
(B) $MN = \frac{1}{2}XZ$
(C) $MX = MY = NY$
(D) $MN = MX = MY$

9. Find the incorrect statements:
(A) A trapezium is a quadrilateral, having one pair of opposite sides parallel
(B) A parallelogram is a quadrilateral with both pairs of opposite sides parallel
(C) A rhombus is a quadrilateral, whose all the sides are equal and each angle is 90°
(D) A square is a quadrilateral, whose all sides are equal

10. Which of the following is/are not false?
(A) A diagonal of a parallelogram divides it in two congruent triangles.
(B) The opposite sides of a parallelogram are equal.
(C) The diagonals of a parallelogram never bisect each other
(D) The opposite angles of a parallelogram are complementary

11. Choose the correct statements among the following given options
(A) Area of a parallelogram is the product of any of its sides and the corresponding altitude.
(B) The area of a triangle is half the product of any of its sides and the corresponding altitude.
(C) The area of a trapezium is half the product of its height and the sum of the parallel sides.
(D) A diagonal of a parallelogram divides it into two triangles of distinct area.

12. In the figure, if E and F are the midpoints of the sides of AB and CD of parallelogram $ABCD$ respectively then which one of the following is/are true?

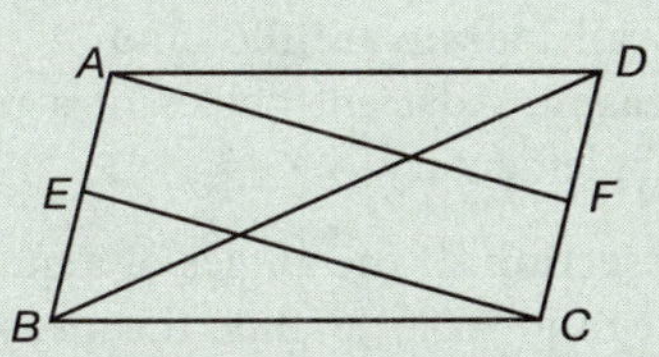

(A) Line segments CE and AF trisects BD
(B) $AE = CF$
(C) $\Delta ADF \cong \Delta CBE$
(D) $AE = CD$

13. $ABCD$ is a parallelogram, BM and DN both are perpendiculars to the segments AC and BM = DN, then which of the following is/are true?

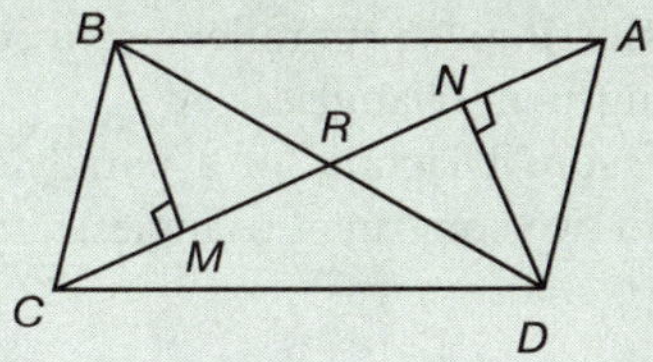

(A) $BR = DR$
(B) $\Delta BRC \cong \Delta DRA$
(C) $\Delta BMR \cong \Delta DNR$
(D) $\Delta BMC \cong \Delta DNA$

14. In triangle ABC, a line l is drawn parallel to BC cutting AB and AC at D and E respectively. If $\angle A = 60°$ and $\angle B = 70°$

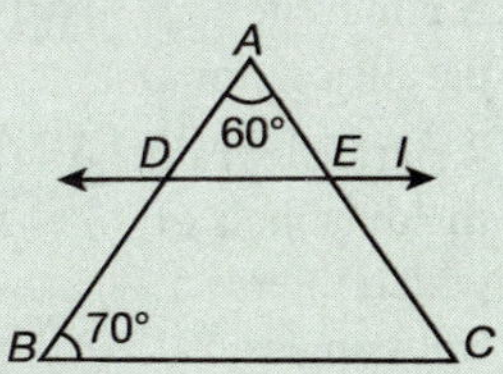

(A) $\angle C = 50°$
(B) D and E are midpoints of sides AB and AC respectively
(C) $\angle D = \angle B$
(D) $\angle D = \angle E$

15. In the adjacent figure, $ABCD$ is a parallelogram in which $\angle DAO = 40°$, $\angle BAO = 35°$, and $\angle COD = 65°$, then:

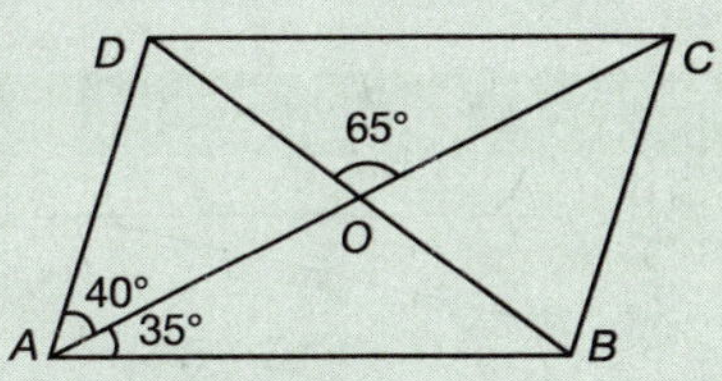

(A) $\angle OBC + \angle OCB = 65°$
(B) $\angle ADC + \angle OAD = 180°$
(C) $\angle ODC = 80°$
(D) $\angle CBD = 25°$

16. In the figure, L, M and N are the midpoints of AP, BP and CP respectively, then:

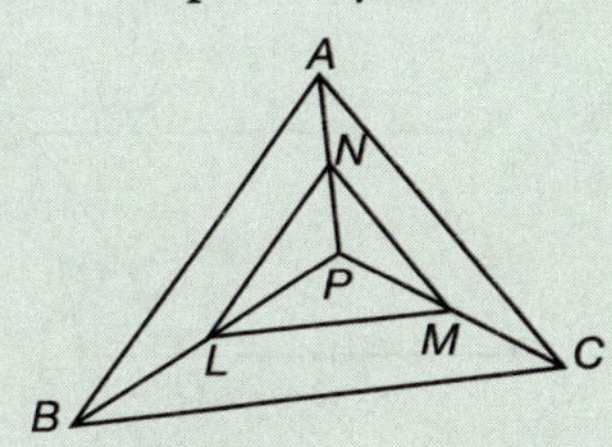

(A) $\angle CAP = \angle MNP$
(B) $\angle ABP = \angle NLP$
(C) $\angle CAP = \angle NMP$
(D) $\angle PBC = \angle PCB$

Match Type Questions

Directions: Match the following (one to one) Column-I and Column-II contain four entries each. Entries of Column-I are to be matched with some entries of Column-II. Only One entry of Column-I may have the matching with the one entry of Column-II and one entry of Column-II may have only one matching with one entry of Column-I.

1.

Column-I	Column-II
(i) Quadrilateral with opposite sides parallel	(P) A square
(ii) A concyclic parallelogram	(Q) A rhombus
(iii) A parallelogram, the diagonals of which intersect at right angles	(R) A rectangle
(iv) A quadrilateral, the diagonals of which bisect each other at right angles	(S) A parallelogram

(A) (i)-(S), (ii)-(R), (iii)-(P), (iv)-(Q)
(B) (i)-(S, Q), (ii)-(R), (iii)-(P), (iv)-(Q, R)
(C) (i)-(R), (ii)-(S), (iii)-(P), (iv)-(Q)
(D) (i)-(S, Q), (ii)-(R, P), (iii)-(P, Q), (iv)-(Q, R)

2.

Column-I	Column-II
(i) 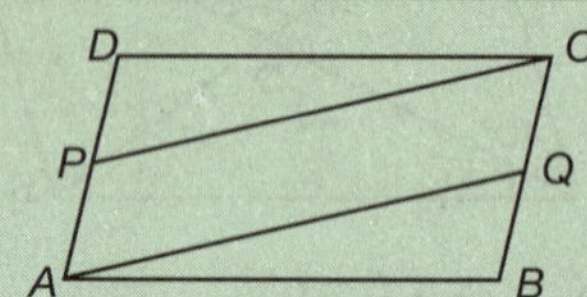	(P) $CP = AQ$
(ii) 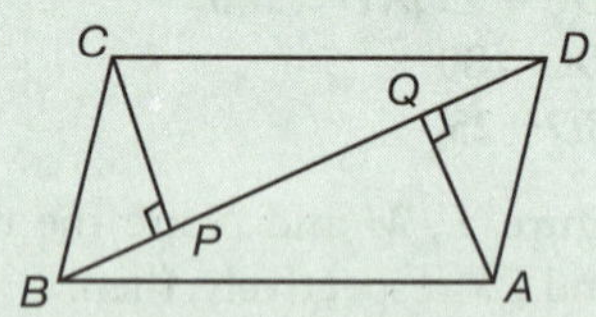	(Q) $PAQC$ is a parallelogram
(iii) 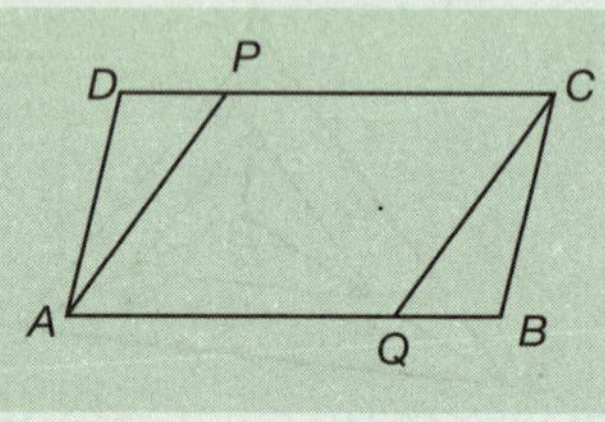	(R) $AD = BC$
(iv) 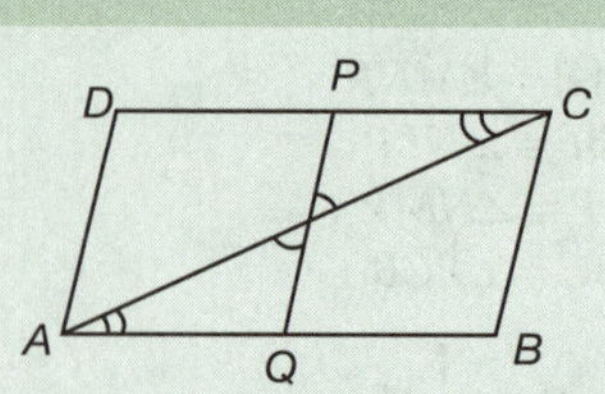	(S) $PC \parallel AQ$

(A) (i)-(S), (ii)-(R), (iii)-(P), (iv)-(P, Q, R)
(B) (i)-(S, Q), (ii)-(R), (iii)-(P), (iv)-(Q, R, S)
(C) (i)-(P, Q, R, S), (ii)-(P, S, R), (iii)-(P, Q, R, S), (iv)-(P, R, S)
(D) (i)-(S, Q), (ii)-(R, P), (iii)-(P, Q), (iv)-(Q, R, S)

Assertion and Reason Type Questions

Directions: In the following questions as Assertion (A) is given followed by a Reason (R). Mark your responses from the following options.

(A) Both Assertion and Reason are true and Reason is the correct explanation of 'Assertion'
(B) Both Assertion and Reason are true and Reason is not the correct explanation of 'Assertion'.
(C) Assertion is true but Reason is false
(D) Assertion is false but Reason is true

1. If in a quadrilateral *ABCD*, the diagonals *AC* and *BD* bisect each other at *O*, then:
Assertion: *ABCD* is necessarily a square
Reason: Triangles *AOD* and *BOC* are congruent

2. If midpoints of a rectangle are joined, then
Assertion: The quadrilateral formed is necessarily a parallelogram.
Reason: Area of the quadrilateral so formed is half the area of the rectangle.

3. If the diagonals of a parallelogram are equal, then
Assertion: Parallelogram is a rectangle
Reason: Each angle of the parallelogram is 90°.

4. **Assertion:** Two opposite angles of a parallelogram are $(3x - 2)°$ and $(50 - x)°$. The measure of one of the angles is 37°.
Reason: Opposite angles of a parallelogram are equal.

5. **Assertion:** If an angle of a parallelogram is two-thirds the adjacent angle, the two angles of the parallelogram are 106° and 74°.
Reason: Adjacent angles of a parallelogram are supplementary.

6. **Assertion:** If the angles of a quadrilateral are in the ratio 2: 3: 7: 6, then the measure of angles are 40°, 60°, 140°, 120° respectively.
Reason: The sum of the angles of a quadrilateral is 360°.

7. **Assertion:** If the diagonals of a parallelogram *ABCD* are equal, then $\angle ABC = 90°$.
Reason: If the diagonals of a parallelogram are equal, it becomes a rectangle.

8. **Assertion:** A parallelogram consists of two congruent triangles.
Reason: Diagonal of a parallelogram divides it into two congruent triangles.

Comprehension Type Questions

Rama draws a rectangular-shaped figure and named its vertices as A, B, C, and D. She marked P, Q, R and S as the midpoints of the side AB, BC, CD and DA respectively.

1. The quadrilateral $PQRS$ is a
   (A) Rectangular (B) Square
   (C) Rhombus (D) Trapezium
2. The perimeter of quadrilateral $PQRS$ is:
   (A) $\frac{1}{2}BD$ (B) $2\,BD$
   (C) $4\,BD$ (D) $\frac{1}{4}BD$
3. Which of the following relations holds true for the diagonal of quadrilateral $PQRS$?
   (A) $PR = AD$ (B) $PR = \frac{1}{2}AD$
   (C) $PR = AB$ (D) $PR = SQ$

Numerical Type Questions

1. The angles of a quadrilateral are $x°$, $(x - 10)°$, $(x + 30°)$ and $(2x)°$, the smallest angle is equal to:
2. In the given figure, $ABCD$ is a rhombus. If $\angle A = 70°$, then $\angle CDB$ is equal to:

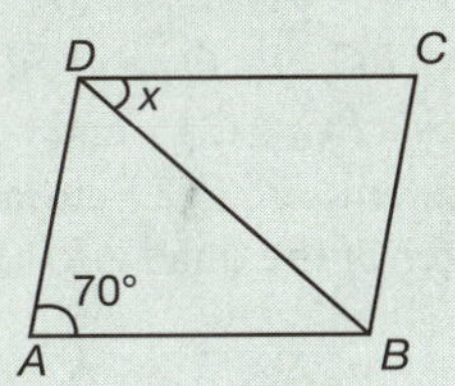

3. $PQRS$ is a square, PR and SQ intersect at O. The measure of $\angle POQ$ is
4. $ABCD$ is a quadrilateral whose diagonals intersect each other at point O such that $OA = OB = OD$. If $\angle OAB = 30°$, then the measure of $\angle ODA$ is:
5. A quadrilateral $ABCD$ has four angles $x°$, $2x°$, $\frac{5x°}{2}$ and $\frac{7x°}{2}$ respectively. What is the difference between the value of biggest and the smallest angles?
6. $ABCD$ is a parallelogram, E is the midpoint of AB and CE bisects $\angle BCD$. The $\angle DEC$ is:

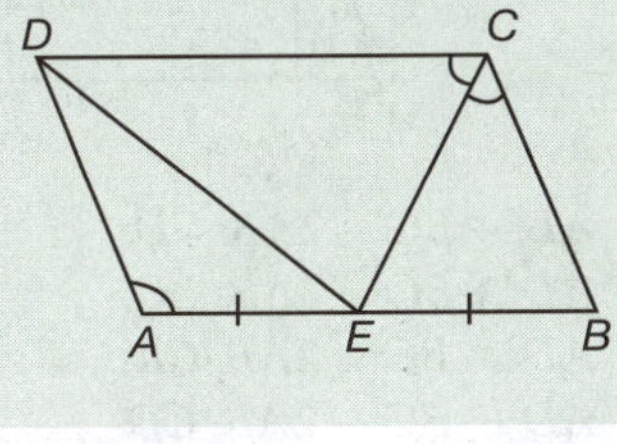

7. $PQRS$ is a square. The $\angle SRP$ is equal to

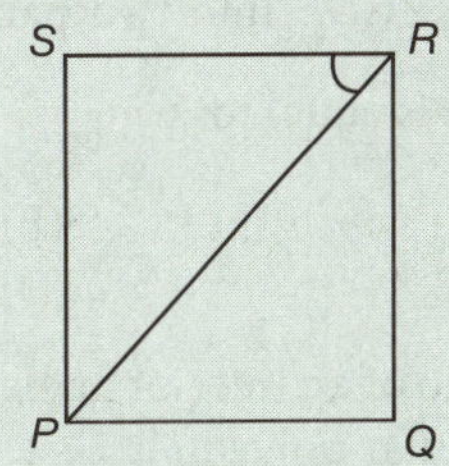

8. Each interior angle of a regular polygon is 144°. Find the interior angle of a regular polygon which has double the number of sides as the first polygon.
9. One angle of a pentagon is 140°. If the remaining angles are in the ratio 1 : 2 : 3 : 4. The size of the greatest angle is:
10. Two opposite angles of a parallelogram are $(3x - 2)°$ and $(50 - x)°$ then the value of x will be:
11. $ABCD$ is a rhombus with $\angle ABC = 56°$, then the $\angle ACD$ will be:
12. In an Isosceles trapezium $ABCD$ if $\angle A = 45°$ then $\angle C$ will be:
13. In a quadrilateral $ABCD$, AO & DO are angle bisectors of $\angle A$ and $\angle D$ and given that $\angle C = 105°$, $\angle B = 70°$, then the $\angle AOD$ is:
14. The diagonals of a rectangle $ABCD$ meet at O. If $\angle BOC = 44°$, then $\angle OAD$ is:
15. In the adjoining figure $ABCD$ is a parallelogram, then the measure of x is:

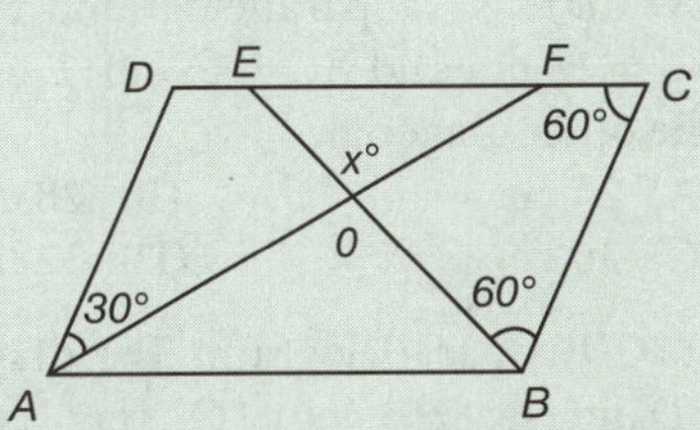

Higher Order Thinking Skills (HOTS)

1. The ratio of the measure of an angle of a regular octagon to the measure of its exterior angle is:
   (A) 3 : 1 (B) 2 : 1
   (C) 1 : 3 (D) 1 : 2
2. The exterior angle of a regular polygon is one-third of its interior angle. The number of sides of the polygon is:
   (A) 9 (B) 8
   (C) 10 (D) 12

3. *ABCDE* is a regular pentagon, Diagonal *AD* divides $\angle CDE$ into two parts, then the ratio of $\frac{\angle ADE}{\angle ADC}$ is equal to:

(A) 3 : 1 (B) 1 : 4
(C) r : 3 (D) 1 : 2

4. The ratio of an interior angle to the exterior angle of a regular polygon is 7 : 2. The number of sides of the polygon is:

(A) 9 (B) 19
(C) 7 (D) 8

5. Find $\angle P + \angle Q + \angle R + \angle S + \angle T$.

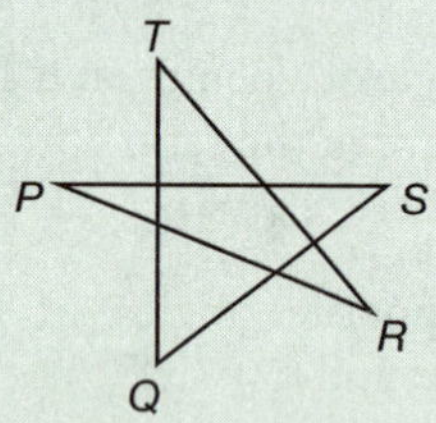

(A) 90° (B) 60°
(C) 45° (D) 180°

6. *ABCDE* is a regular pentagon. The bisector of $\angle A$ of the pentagon meets the side *CD* in *M*. Then the measure of $\angle AMC$ is:

(A) 54° (B) 45°
(C) 90° (D) 100°

7. Diagonals of a parallelogram are 8 m and 6 m respectively. If one of the sides is 5 m, then the area of the parallelogram is:

(A) 18 m^2 (B) 30 m^2
(C) 24 m^2 (D) 48 m^2

8. (*ABCD*) is a parallelogram, *AB* = 14 cm, *BC* = 18 cm and *AC* = 16 cm. Find the length of the other diagonal.

(A) 24 cm (B) 28 cm
(C) 36 cm (D) 32 cm

9. *ABCD* is parallelogram. The diagonals *AC* and *BD* intersect at a point "O". If *E*, *F*, *G* and *H* are the midpoints of *AO*, *DO*, *CO* and *BO* respectively, then the ratio of (*EF* + *FG* + *GH* + *HE*) to (*AD* + *DC* + *CB* + *BA*) is:

(A) 1 : 1 (B) 1 : 2
(C) 1: 3 (D) 1 : 4

10. In a rectangle *ABCD*, *P* and *Q* are the midpoints of *BC* and *AD* respectively and *R* is any point on *PQ*, then ar(ΔARB) equals:

(A) $\frac{1}{2}$ (□*ABCD*) (B) $\frac{1}{3}$ (□*ABCD*)
(C) $\frac{1}{4}$ (□*ABCD*) (D) None of these

11. In the trapezium shown, *AB* || *DC*, and *E* and *F* are the midpoints of the two diagonals. If *DC* = 60 and *EF* = 5 then the length of *AB* is equal to :

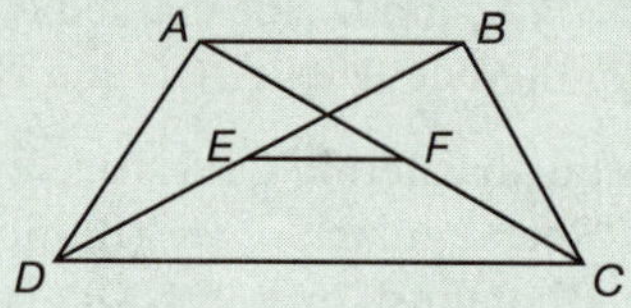

(A) 40 (B) 45
(C) 50 (D) 55

12. The line joining the midpoints of the diagonals of a trapezium has a length of 3. If the longer base is 97, then the shorter base is:

(A) 94 (B) 92
(C) 91 (D) 90

13. *ABCD* is a trapezium in which *AB* || *DC* and *AD* = *BC*. If *P*, *Q*, *R*, *S* be respectively the midpoints of *BA*, *BD*, *CD* and *CA*. Then *PQRS* is a

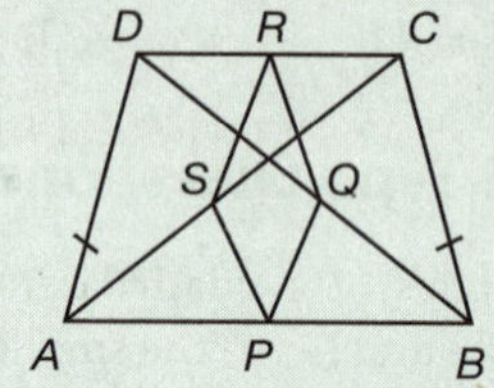

(A) Rhombus (B) Rectangle
(C) Parallelogram (D) Square

14. In a ΔABC, *P*, *Q* and *R* are the midpoints of sides *BC*, *CA* and *AB* respectively. If *AC* = 21 cm, *BC* = 29 cm and *AB* = 30 cm. The perimeter of the quad *ARPQ* is:

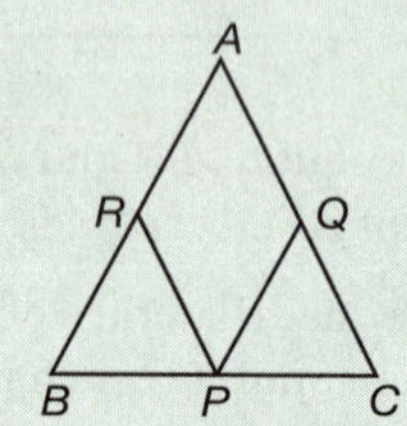

(A) 91 cm (B) 60 cm
(C) 51 cm (D) 70 cm

15. *ABCD* is a trapezium in which *AB* || *CD*. Then $AC^2 + BD^2$ is equal to:

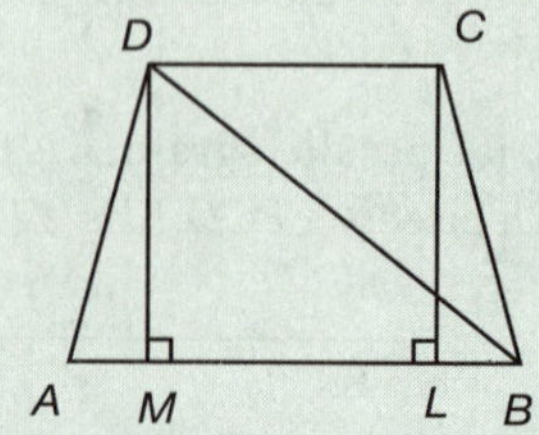

(A) $AD^2 + BC^2 - 2AB.\ CD.$
(B) $AD^2 + BC^2 + 2AB.\ CD.$
(C) $AD^2 - BC^2 + 2AB.\ CD.$
(D) $AD^2 - BC^2 - 2AB.\ CD.$

Free Response Type

Very Short Answer Type Questions

1. Diagonals of a parallelogram *ABCD* intersect at *O*. If $\angle BOC = 90°$ and $\angle BDC = 50°$, then find $\angle OAB$.

2. Three angles of a quadrilateral are 75°, 90° and 75°. Find the fourth angle.

3. A diagonal of a rectangle is inclined to one side of the rectangle at 25°. Find the acute angle between the diagonals.

4. *ABCD* is a rhombus such that $\angle ACB = 40°$. Then find $\angle ADB$.

5. If angles *A*, *B*, *C* and *D* of the quadrilateral *ABCD*, taken in order, are in the ratio 3 : 7 : 6 : 4, then identify the type of quadrilateral *ABCD*.

6. If *APB* and *CQD* are two parallel lines, then find the type of quadrilateral formed by the bisectors of the angles *APQ*, *BPQ*, *CQP* and *PQD*.

7. Diagonals *AC* and *BD* of a parallelogram *ABCD* intersect each other at *O*. If *OA* = 3 cm and *OD* = 2 cm, determine the lengths of *AC* and *BD*.

8. One angle of a quadrilateral is of 108° and the remaining three angles are equal. Find each of the three equal angles.

Short Answer Type Questions

1. The angle between two altitudes of a parallelogram through the vertex of an obtuse angle of the parallelogram is 60°. Find the angles of the parallelogram.

2. *ABCD* is a rhombus in which altitude from *D* to side *AB* bisects *AB*. Find the angles of the rhombus.

3. *E* and *F* are points on diagonal *AC* of a parallelogram *ABCD* such that *AE* = *CF*. Show that *BFDE* is a parallelogram.

4. *D*, *E* and *F* are the midpoints of the sides *BC*, *CA* and *AB*, respectively of an equilateral triangle *ABC*. Show that ΔDEF is also an equilateral triangle.

5. Points *P* and *Q* have been taken on opposite sides *AB* and *CD*, respectively of a parallelogram *ABCD* such that *AP* = *CQ* (*see* figure). Show that *AC* and *PQ* bisect each other.

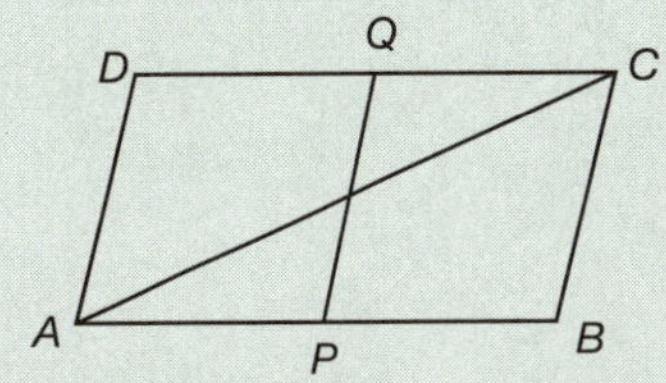

6. A diagonal of a parallelogram bisects one of its angles. Prove that it will bisect its opposite angle also.

7. Show that the quadrilateral formed by joining the midpoints of the sides of a rhombus, taken in order, forms a rectangle.

8. In a parallelogram *ABCD*, *AB* = 10 cm and *AD* = 6 cm. The bisector of $\angle A$ meets *DC* in *E*. *AE* and *BC* produced meet at *F*. Find the length of *CF*.

9. *P*, *Q*, *R* and *S* are respectively the midpoints of the sides *AB*, *BC*, *CD* and *DA* of a quadrilateral *ABCD* in which *AC* = *BD*. Prove that *PQRS* is a rhombus.

10. *ABCD* is a quadrilateral in which $AB \parallel DC$ and *AD* = *BC*. Prove that $\angle A = \angle B$ and $\angle C = \angle D$.

Long Answer Type Questions

1. *E* is the midpoint of a median *AD* of ΔABC and *BE* is produced to meet *AC* at *F*. Show that $AF = \frac{1}{3} AC$.

2. *PQ* and *RS* are two equal and parallel line segments. Any point *M* not lying on *PQ* or *RS* is joined to *Q* and *S* and lines through *P* parallel to *QM* and through *R* parallel to *SM* meet at *N*. Prove that line segments *MN* and *PQ* are equal and parallel to each other.

3. *P*, *Q*, *R* and *S* are respectively the midpoints of sides *AB*, *BC*, *CD* and *DA* of quadrilateral *ABCD* in which *AC* = *BD* and $AC \perp BD$. Prove that *PQRS* is a square.

4. Prove that the line joining the midpoints of the diagonals of a trapezium is parallel to the parallel sides of the trapezium.

5. *P* is the midpoint of the side *CD* of a parallelogram *ABCD*. A line through *C* parallel to *PA* intersects *AB* at *Q* and *DA* produced at *R*. Prove that *DA* = *AR* and *CQ* = *QR*.

6. $ABCD$ is a parallelogram and X and Y are points on the diagonal BD such that $DX = BY$. Prove that:

(i) $AXCY$ is a parallelogram
(ii) $AX = CY$, $AY = CX$
(iii) $\Delta AYB \cong \Delta CXD$
(iv) $\Delta AXD \cong \Delta CYB$

ARCHIVE CORNER

1. In the given diagram, $ABCD$ is a parallelogram. Bisectors of $\angle A$ and $\angle B$ meet at the point X. Then the value of $\angle AXB$ is:

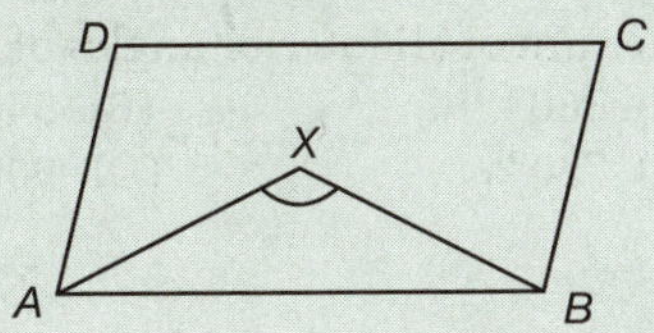

(A) 150° (B) 120°
(C) 90° (D) 60°

2. The short diagonal of a rhombus is equal to its side, then the value of the angle opposite to its longer diagonal is:
(A) 30° (B) 60°
(C) 90° (D) 120°

3. The bisectors of angles of a parallelogram make a figure which is:
(A) Rectangle (B) Circle
(C) Pentagon (D) Octagon

4. $PQRS$ is a parallelogram and M, N are the midpoints of PQ and RS respectively. Which of the following is not true?

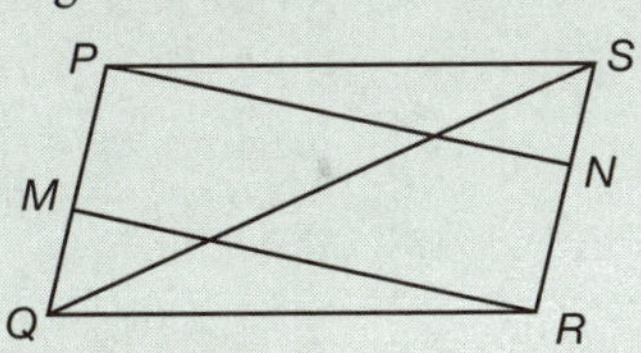

(A) RM trisects QS
(B) PN trisects QS
(C) $\Delta PSN \cong \Delta RQM$
(D) MS is not parallel to QN

5. An obtuse angle of a rhombus is greater than twice the acute angle by 30°. Find the measure of each angle.
(A) 50° (B) 130°
(C) 80° (D) 60°

6. $ABCD$ is a rhombus and P, Q, R, S are respectively midpoints of sides AB, BC, CD and DA. Then $\angle RSP$ is:
(A) 120° (B) 90°
(C) 60° (D) 30°

7. If the angle bisectors of $\angle DAB$ and $\angle CBA$ of any quadrilateral $ABCD$ intersect at Point P, then find $2m\angle APB$.

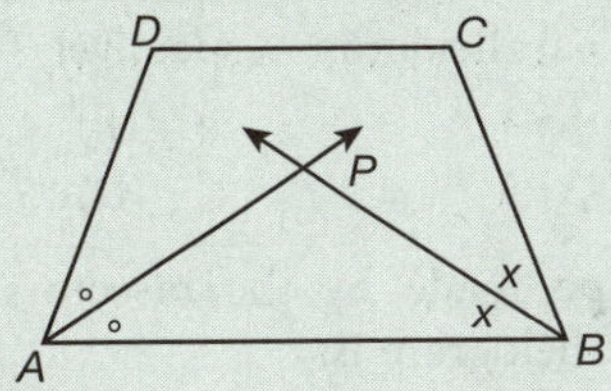

(A) $\angle C + \angle D$ (B) $\angle C + \angle B$
(C) $\angle A + \angle B$ (D) $\angle A + \angle D$

8. The side of a rhombus is 10 cm. The smaller diagonal is $\frac{1}{3}$of the greater diagonal. Find the length of the greater diagonal.
(A) $6\sqrt{10}$ cm (B) $10\sqrt{6}$ cm
(C) $6\sqrt{5}$ cm (D) $5\sqrt{6}$ cm

9. Sides AB and CD of a quadrilateral. $ABCD$ are extended as in the figure. Then $a + b$ is equal to:
(A) $x + 2y$ (B) $x - y$
(C) $x + y$ (D) $2x + y$.

10. Angle at A in trapezium $ABCD$ if $AB = 18$ cm, $BC = 10$ cm, $CD = 12$ cm, $DA = 8$cm, $AB \parallel CD$, will be:
(A) 80° (B) 45°
(C) 90° (D) None of these

11. The line segment joining the midpoints of the adjacent sides of a quadrilateral form:
(A) Parallelogram
(B) Square
(C) Rhombus
(D) Rectangle

12. In a rhombus of side 10 cm, one of the diagonals is 12 cm long and the length of the second diagonal will be:
(A) 4 cm (B) 8 cm
(C) 12 cm (D) 16 cm

13. The length of the side of a rhombus is 4 cm. If one of the diagonals is equal to the side of the rhombus, then the length of the other diagonal in cm will be:
(A) $\frac{\sqrt{3}}{2}$ (B) $\sqrt{3}$
(C) $2\sqrt{3}$ (D) $4\sqrt{3}$

ARCHIVE CORNER

14. The difference between the two adjacent angles of a parallelogram is 20°. What would be the ratio between the smaller and longer angles of the parallelogram respectively?
(A) 5 : 4 (B) 4 : 7
(C) 3 : 5 (D) 5 : 6

15. Shape made by the bisectors of angles of a parallelogram is:
(A) Rectangle (B) Square
(C) Circle (D) Straight line

16. Which of the following statements is false for the quadrilateral $ABCD$?
(A) $AB + BC + CD + DA > AC$
(B) $AB + BC + CD + DA > AB + AC$
(C) $AB + BC + CD + DA > AC + BD$
(D) $AB + BC + CD + DA < 2AC$.

17. The sum of all interior angles of a Heptagon is:
(A) 360° (B) 540°
(C) 720° (D) 900°

ANSWER KEY

Check Points

Check Point 1

2. 90° 3. $AB = 8$ cm, $BC = 5$ cm.

Check Point 2

6. (i) No pair of corresponding angles (ii) $\angle 1$ and $\angle 6$, $\angle 2$ and $\angle 5$
7. 16° 8. 37.5° 9. $x = 105°$, $y = 75°$ 10. 80°.

Check Point 3

11. C 22. C

Assessment Corner

Fixed Response Type

Fill in the Blanks

1. Parallelogram 2. Equal 3. Rhombus 4. Square 5. Equilateral triangle 6. Equal

True/False

1. True 2. True 3. False 4. False 5. False

Single Correct Type Questions

1. B 2. D 3. C 4. A. 5. D. 6. A 7. C 8. D 9. A
10. B 11. C 12. C 13. B 14. A 15. C 16. C 17. B 18. B
19. B 20. A 21. C 22. C 23. A 24. C 25. C

Multiple Correct Type Questions

1. ABC 2. ABD 3. ABCD 4. ACD 5. BC 6. ABD 7. BCD 8. BD 9. CD
10. AB 11. ABC 12. ABC 13. ABCD 14. AC 15. ACD 16. AB

Match Type Questions

1. A 2. C

Assertion and Reason Type Questions

1. D 2. B 3. C 4. A 5. D 6. A 7. A 8. A

Comprehension Type Questions

1. C 2. B 3. A

Numerical Type Questions

1. 58 2. 55 3. 90 4. 60 5. 100 6. 90 7. 45 8. 162 9. 160
10. 13. 11. 62 12. 135 13. 87.5 14. 68 15. 90

Higher Order Thinking Skills (HOTS)

1. A 2. B 3. D 4. A 5. D 6. C 7. C 8. B 9. B
10. C 11. C 12. C 13. C 14. C 15. B

FREE RESPONSE TYPE

Very Short Answer Type Questions

1. 40 2. 120 3. 50 4. 100 5. Not specific quadrilateral
6. Quadrilateral formed by the bisectors of the angles *APQ*, *BPQ*, *CQP* and *PQD* is rectangle
7. 4unit 8. 84

Short Answer Type Questions

1. 60°, 120°, 60° and 120°
2. The angles of the rhombus are ∠A = ∠C = 60° and ∠B = ∠D = 120°
8. *CF* = 4 cm

Archive Corner

1. C 2. D 3. A 4. D 5. AB 6. B 7. A 8. A 9. C
10. C 11. A 12. D 13. D 14. A 15. A 16. C 17. D

ANSWER KEY

CHAPTER 9

Circles

Learning Outcomes

After reading this chapter, you would be able to:

- circle definition and terminology.
- properties and theorem of circle.
- results on angles subtended by arcs and cyclic quadrilateral.

Geekspeak

- Circle
- Chord
- Diameter
- Radius
- Subtends
- Segment
- Major segment
- Minor segment
- Sector
- Minor sector
- Major sector
- Arc
- Circumference
- Cyclic quadrilaterals

Introduction

We may have come across many objects in daily life, which are round in shape, such as wheels of a vehicle, bangles, coins of 50 p, ₹1, ₹5, buttons of shirts and etc. In a clock you might have observed that the second's hand goes round the dial of the clock rapidly and its tip moves in a round path. This path traced by the tip of the second's hand is called a circle. In this chapter, we will study about circles, other related terms and some properties of a circle.

Circle

The collection of all the points in a plane, which are at a fixed distance from a fixed point in the plane, is called a **circle**.

The fixed point is called the **centre** of the circle and the fixed distance is called the **radius** of the circle.

In the figure, ***O*** is the **centre** and the length ***OP*** is the **radius** of the circle. So the line segment joining the centre and any point on the circle is called a radius of the circle.

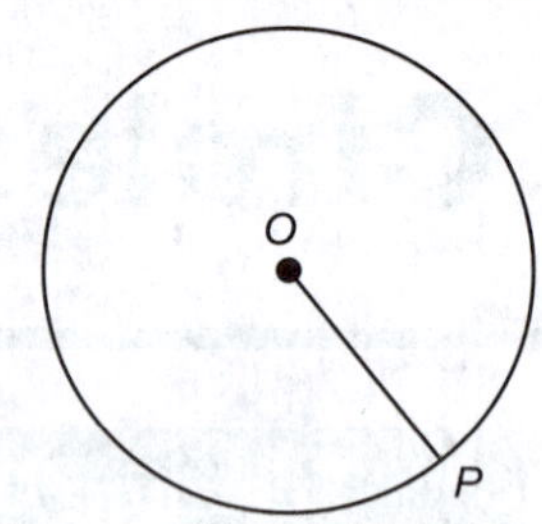

Figure 9.1

Chord

If we take two points P and Q on a circle, then the line segment PQ is called a **chord** of the circle.

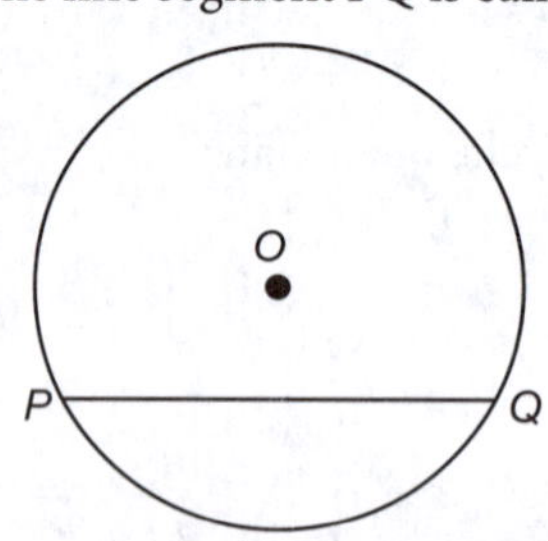

Figure 9.2

Diameter

The chord which passes through the centre of the circle is called the **diameter** of the circle.

A diameter is the longest chord and all diameters of the same circle have the same length, which is equal to two times the radius. In the figure, AOB is the **diameter** of the circle.

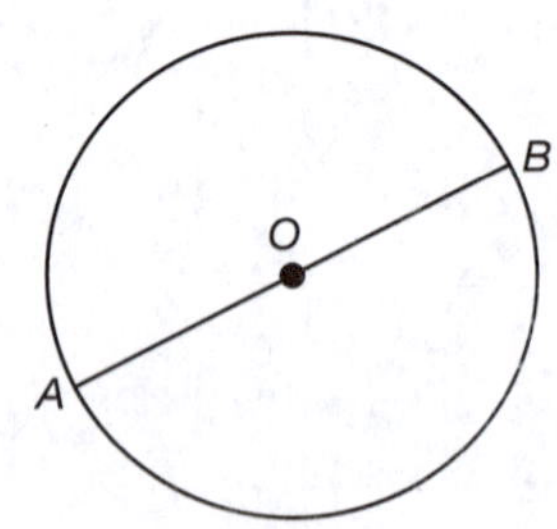

Figure 9.3

Arc

A piece of a circle between two points is called an **arc**. The longer one is called the **major arc *PQ*** and the shorter one is called the **minor arc *PQ***. The minor arc PQ is also de-remarked by $\overset{\frown}{PQ}$ and the major arc PQ by $\overset{\frown}{QP}$. When P and Q are ends of a diameter, then both arcs are equal and each is called a **semi-circle**.

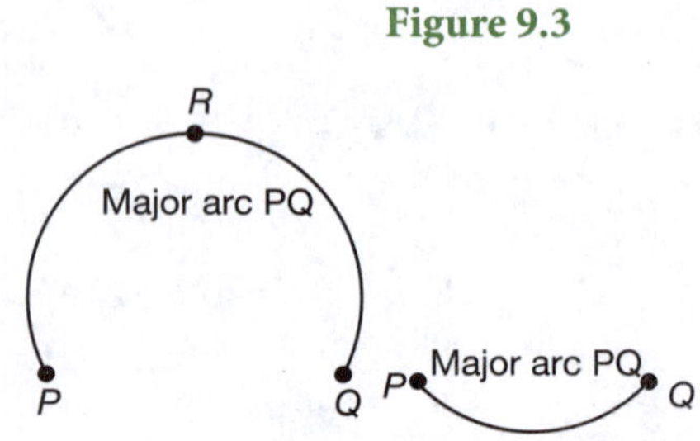

Figure 9.4

Circumference

The length of the complete circle is called its **circumference**.

Segment

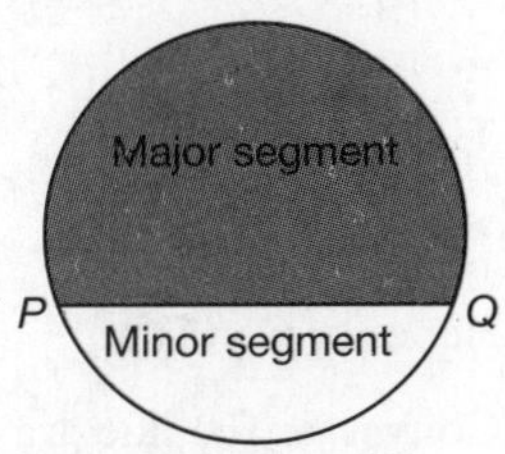

Figure 9.5

The region between a chord and either of its arcs is called a **segment** of the circular region or simply a segment of the circle. There are two types of segments which are the **major segment** and the **minor segment** (as in the **Fig 9.5**).

Sector

The region between an arc and the two radii, joining the centre to the end points of an arc is called a **sector**. Minor arc corresponds to the **minor sector** and the major arc corresponds to the **major sector**.

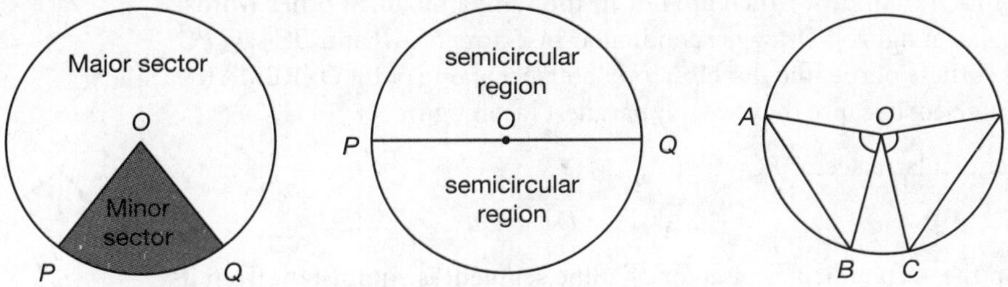

Figure 9.6

When two arcs are equal, then both segments and both sectors become the same and each is known as a **semi-circular region**.

Theorems Related to Chords

Theorem 1: Equal chords of a circle subtend equal angles at the centre.

Given: AB and CD are the two equal chords of a circle with centre O.

To prove: $\angle AOB = \angle COD$.

Proof: In ΔAOB and ΔCOD,

$$OA = OC \quad \text{[Radii of a circle]}$$
$$OB = OD \quad \text{[Radii of a circle]}$$
$$AB = CD \quad \text{[Given]}$$
$$\therefore \quad \Delta AOB \cong \Delta COD \quad \text{[By SSS congruency]}$$
$$\therefore \quad \angle AOB = \angle COD. \quad \text{[By CPCT]}$$

Hence proved.

Converse: If the angles subtended by the chords of a circle at the centre are equal, then the chords are equal.

Theorem 2: The perpendicular from the centre of a circle to a chord bisects the chord.
Given: A circle with centre O. AB is a chord of this circle. $OM \perp AB$.

To prove: $MA = MB$.

Construction: Join OA and OB.

Proof: In the right triangles OMA and OMB,

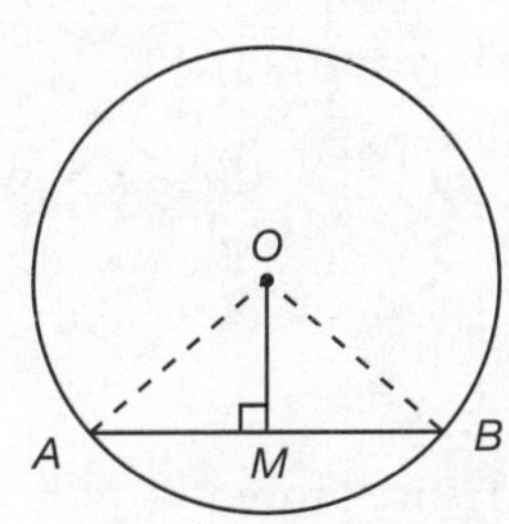

Figure 9.7

$$OA = OB \quad \text{[Radii of a circle]}$$
$$OM = OM \quad \text{[Common]}$$

$$\angle OMA = \angle OMB \quad \text{[90° each]}$$

$\therefore$ $$\Delta OMA \cong \Delta OMB \quad \text{[By RHS]}$$

$\therefore$ $$MA = MB \quad \text{[By CPCT]}$$

Hence proved.

Converse: The line drawn through the centre of a circle to bisect a chord is perpendicular to the chord.

Theorem 3: There is one and only one circle passing through three given non-collinear points.

Proof: Take three points A, B and C, which are not in the same line, or in other words, they are not collinear [as in figure]. Draw perpendicular bisectors of AB and BC say, PQ and RS respectively. Let these perpendicular bisectors intersect at one point O.(REMARK that PQ and RS will intersect because they are not parallel) [as in figure 9.8].

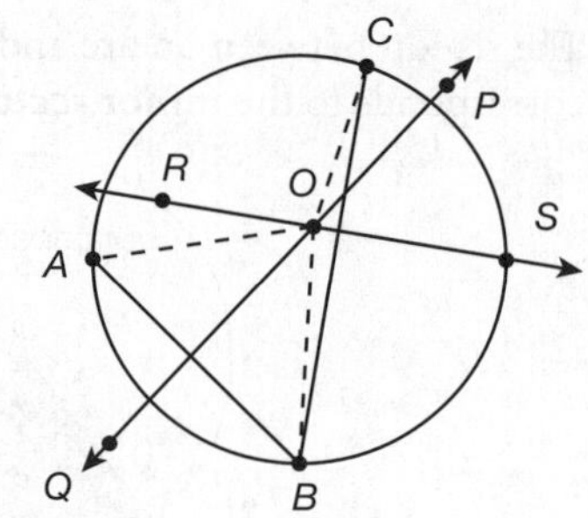

Figure 9.8

$\because$ O lies on the perpendicular bisector PQ of AB.

$\therefore$ $$OA = OB$$

[$\because$ Every point on the perpendicular bisector of a line segment is equidistant from its end points]

Similarly,

$\because$ O lies on the perpendicular bisector RS of BC.

$\therefore$ $$OB = OC$$

[$\because$ Every point on the perpendicular bisector of a line segment is equidistant from its end points]

So, $$OA = OB = OC$$

i.e., points A, B and C are at equal distances from point O.

So, if we draw a circle with centre O and radius OA it will also pass through B and C. This shows that there is a circle passing through the three points A, B and C. We know that two lines (perpendicular bisectors) can intersect at only one point, so we can draw only one circle with a radius OA. In other words, there is a unique circle passing through A, B and C.

Hence proved.

Illustration 9.1

In the figure, $AB = CB$ and O is the centre of the circle. Prove that BO bisects $\angle ABC$.

Solution:

Given: In the figure, $AB = CB$ and O is the centre of the circle.

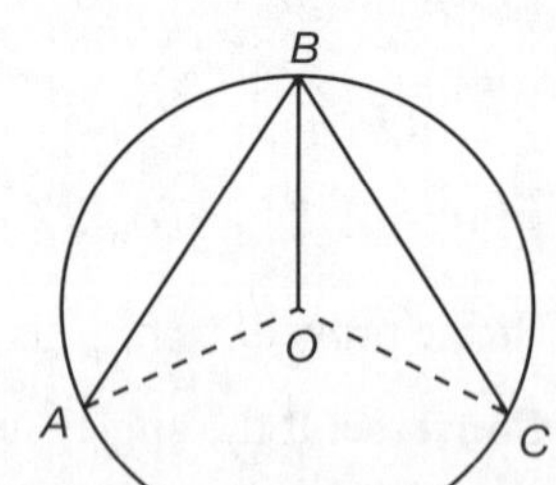

To prove: BO bisects $\angle ABC$.

Construction: Join OA and OC.

Proof: In ΔOAB and ΔOCB,

$$OA = OC \quad \text{[Radii of the same circle]}$$

$$AB = CB \quad \text{[Given]}$$

$$OB = OB \quad \text{[Common]}$$

$\therefore$ $$\Delta OAB \cong \Delta OCB \quad \text{[By SSS congruency]}$$

$\therefore$ $$\angle ABO = \angle CBO \quad \text{[By CPCT]}$$

$\Rightarrow$ BO bisects $\angle ABC$.

Hence proved.

Illustration 9.2

Two circles with centres A and B intersect at C and D. Prove that $\angle ACB = \angle ADB$.

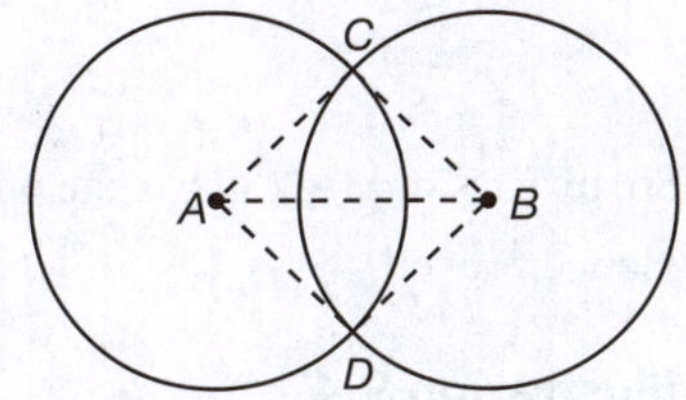

Solution:

Given: Two circles with centres A and B intersect at C and D.

To prove: $\angle ACB = \angle ADB$.

Construction: Join AC, AD, BC, BD and AB.

Proof: In ΔACB and ΔADB,

$AC = AD$ [Radii of the same circle]

$BC = BD$ [Radii of the same circle]

$AB = AB$ [Common]

$\therefore$ $\Delta ACB \cong \Delta ADB$ [By SSS congruency]

$\therefore$ $\angle ACB = \angle ADB$. [By CPCT].

Hence proved.

Illustration 9.3

In the figure, $\overset{\frown}{AB} \cong \overset{\frown}{AC}$ and O is the centre of the circle. Prove that OA is the perpendicular bisector of BC.

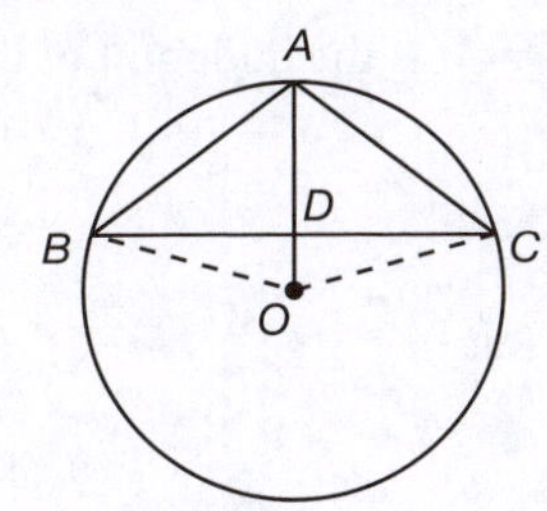

Solution:

Given: In the figure, $\overset{\frown}{AB} \cong \overset{\frown}{AC}$ and O is the centre of the circle.

To prove: OA is the perpendicular bisector of BC.

Construction: Join OB and OC.

Proof:

$\because$ $\overset{\frown}{AB} \cong \overset{\frown}{AC}$ [Given]

$\therefore$ chord AB = chord AC.

[$\because$ If two arcs of a circle are congruent, then their corresponding chords are equal]

$\therefore$ $\angle AOB = \angle AOC$ ...(i)

[$\because$ Equal chords of a circle subtend equal angles at the centre]

In ΔOBD and ΔOCD,

$\angle DOB = \angle DOC$ [From (i)]

$OB = OC$ [Radii of the same circle]

$OD = OD$ [Common]

$\therefore$ $\Delta OBD \cong \Delta OCD$ [By SAS congruency]

$\therefore$ $\angle ODB = \angle ODC$ ...(ii) [By CPCT]

And, $BD = CD$ ...(iii) [By CPCT]

But $\angle BDC = 180°$

$\therefore$ $\angle ODB + \angle ODC = 180°$

$\Rightarrow$ $\angle ODB + \angle ODB = 180°$ [From equation (ii)]

$\Rightarrow$ $2\angle ODB = 180°$

$$\Rightarrow \qquad \angle ODB = 90°$$

$$\therefore \qquad \angle ODB = \angle ODC = 90° \qquad \text{...(iv)}$$

[From (ii)]

So, by (iii) and (iv), *OA* is the perpendicular bisector of *BC*.

Hence proved.

Illustration 9.4

Prove that the line joining the midpoints of the two parallel chords of a circle passes through the centre of the circle.

Solution: Let *AB* and *CD* be two parallel chords of a circle whose centre is *O*.

Let *L* and *M* be the midpoints of the chords *AB* and *CD* respectively. Join *OL* and *OM*.

Draw *OX* || *AB* or *CD*.

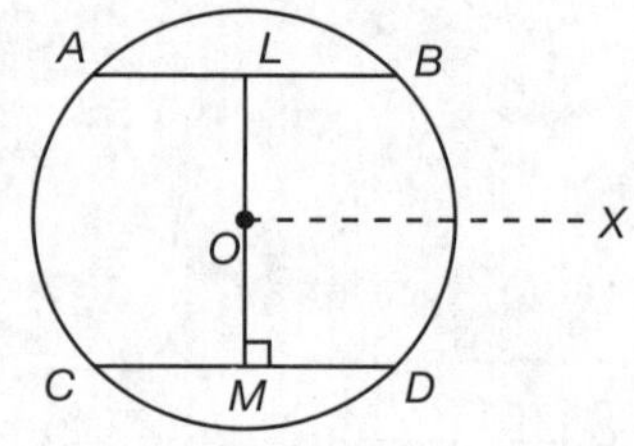

∵ L is the midpoint of the chord *AB* and *O* is the centre of the circle.

$$\therefore \qquad \angle OLB = 90°$$

[∵ The perpendicular drawn from the centre of a circle to a chord bisects the chord]

But, $$OX \parallel AB$$

$$\therefore \qquad \angle LOX = 90° \qquad \text{...(i)}$$

[∵ Sum of the consecutive interior angles on the same side of a transversal is 180°]

∵ *M* is the midpoint of the chord *CD* and *O* is the centre of the circle.

$$\therefore \qquad \angle OMD = 90°$$

[∵ The perpendicular drawn from the centre of a circle to a chord bisects the chord]

But $$OX \parallel CD \qquad \text{...(ii)}$$

[∵ Sum of the consecutive interior angles on the same side of a transversal is 180°]

$$\therefore \qquad \angle MOX = 90°$$

From the above equations, we get:

$$\angle LOX + \angle MOX = 90° + 90° = 180°$$

$$\Rightarrow \qquad \angle LOM = 180°$$

⇒ *LM* is a straight line passing through the centre of the circle.

Hence proved.

Illustration 9.5

l is a line which intersects two concentric circles (i.e., circles with the same centre) with common centre *O* at *A*, *B*, *C* and *D* (as in the figure). Prove that *AB* = *CD*.

Solution:

Given: *l* is a line which intersects two concentric circles (i.e., circles with the same centre) with common centre *O* at *A*, *B*, *C* and *D*.

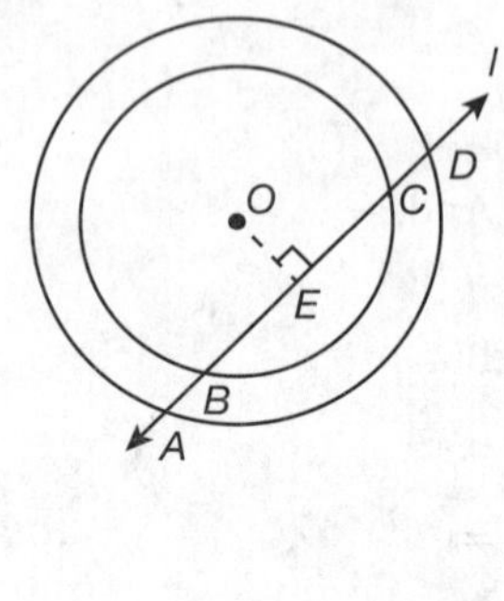

To prove: *AB* = *CD*.

Construction: Draw $OE \perp l$.

Proof: ∵ The perpendicular drawn from the centre of a circle to a chord bisects the chord.

$$\therefore \qquad AE = ED \qquad \text{...(i)}$$

And $$BE = EC \qquad \text{...(ii)}$$

Subtracting (ii) from (i), we get:

$$AE - BE = ED - EC$$

$\Rightarrow \qquad AB = CD.$

Hence proved.

Illustration 9.6

PQ and RS are two parallel chords of a circle whose centre is O and radius is 10 cm. If $PQ = 16$ cm and $RS = 12$ cm, find the distance between PQ and RS, if they lie:

(i) on the same side of the centre O.

(ii) on the opposite sides of the centre O.

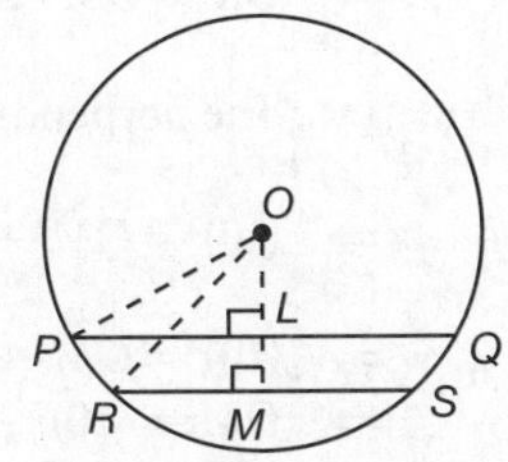

Solution:

(i) Draw the perpendicular bisectors OL and OM of PQ and RS respectively.

$\because \quad PQ \parallel RS$

$\therefore \quad OL$ and OM are in the same line.

$\Rightarrow \quad O, L$ and M are collinear.

Join OP and OR.

In the right triangle OLP,

$OP^2 = OL^2 + PL^2$ [By Pythagoras Theorem]

$$\Rightarrow \quad (10)^2 = OL^2 + \left(\frac{1}{2} \times PQ\right)^2$$

[$\because$ The perpendicular drawn from the centre of a circle to a chord bisects the chord]

$$\Rightarrow \quad 100 = OL^2 + \left(\frac{1}{2} \times 16\right)^2$$

$\Rightarrow \quad 100 = OL^2 + (8)^2 \Rightarrow 100 = OL^2 + 64$

$\Rightarrow \quad OL^2 = 100 - 64 \Rightarrow OL^2 = 36 = (6)^2$

$\Rightarrow \quad OL = 6$ cm

In the right triangle OMR,

$OR^2 = OM^2 + RM^2$ [By Pythagoras Theorem]

$$\Rightarrow \quad OR^2 = OM^2 + \left(\frac{1}{2} \times RS\right)^2$$

[$\because$ The perpendicular drawn from the centre of a circle to a chord bisects the chord]

$$\Rightarrow \quad (10)^2 = OM^2 + \left(\frac{1}{2} \times 12\right)^2 \Rightarrow (10)^2 = OM^2 + (6)^2$$

$\Rightarrow \quad OM^2 = (10)^2 - (6)2 = (10 - 6)(10 + 6) = (4)(16) = 64 = (8)^2.$

$\Rightarrow \quad OM = 8$ cm

$\therefore \quad LM = OM - OL = 8 - 6 = 2$ cm.

Hence, the distance between PQ and RS, if they lie on the same side of the centre O, is 2 cm.

(ii) Draw the perpendicular bisectors OL and OM of PQ and RS respectively.

$\because \quad PQ \parallel RS$

$\therefore \quad OL$ and OM are in the same line.

$\Rightarrow \quad L, O$ and M are collinear.

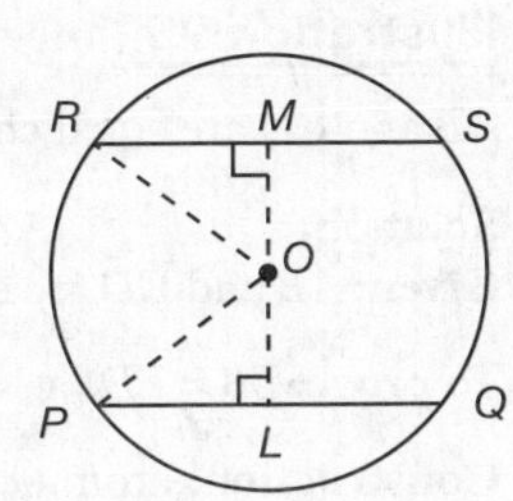

Join OP and OR.

In the right triangle OLP,

$OP^2 = OL^2 + PL^2$ [By Pythagoras Theorem]

$$\Rightarrow \quad OP^2 = OL^2 + \left(\frac{1}{2} \times PQ\right)^2$$

[$\because$ The perpendicular drawn from the centre of a circle to a chord bisects the chord]

$$\Rightarrow \quad (10)^2 = OL^2 + \left(\frac{1}{2} \times 16\right)^2$$

$\Rightarrow \quad 100 = OL^2 + (8)^2$

$\Rightarrow \quad 100 = OL^2 + 64$

$\Rightarrow \quad OL^2 = 100 - 64 \Rightarrow OL^2 = 36 = (6)^2$

$\Rightarrow \quad OL = 6$ cm.

In the right triangle OMR,

$OR^2 = OM^2 + RM^2$ [By Pythagoras Theorem]

$$\Rightarrow \quad OR^2 = OM^2 + \left(\frac{1}{2} \times RS\right)^2$$

[∵ The perpendicular drawn from the centre of a circle to a chord bisects the chord]

$$\Rightarrow \quad (10)^2 = OM^2 + \left(\frac{1}{2} \times 12\right)^2$$

$\Rightarrow \quad (10)^2 = OM^2 + (6)^2$

$\Rightarrow \quad OM^2 = (10)^2 - (6)^2$

$= (10 - 6)(10 + 6) = (4)(16) = 64 = (8)^2$.

$\Rightarrow \quad OM = 8$ cm

$\therefore \quad LM = OL + OM = 6 + 8 = 14$ cm

Hence, the distance between PQ and RS, if they lie on the opposite side of the centre O, is 14 cm.

Theorem 4: Equal chords of a circle (or of congruent circles) are equidistant from the centre (or centres).

Given: A circle have two equal chords AB and CD. i.e., $AB = CD$ and $OM \perp AB$, $ON \perp CD$.

To prove: $OM = ON$

Construction: Join OB and OD

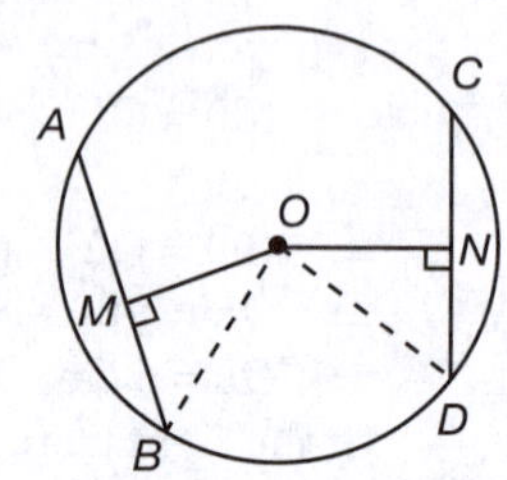

Figure 9.9

Proof: $AB = CD$ (Given)

[∵ The perpendicular drawn from the centre of a circle to a chord bisects the chord]

$\therefore \quad \frac{1}{2}AB = \frac{1}{2}CD$

$\Rightarrow \quad BM = DN$

In ΔOMB and ΔOND

$\angle OMB = \angle OND = 90°$ [Given]

$OB = OD$ [Radii of the same circle]

$BM = DN$ [Proved above]

$\therefore \quad \Delta OMB \cong \Delta OND$ [By R.H.S. congruency]

$\therefore \quad OM = ON$ [By CPCT]

Hence, proved.

Keystone

Chords equidistant from the centre of a circle are equal in length.

Illustration 9.7

AB and CD are equal chords of a circle whose centre is O. When produced, these chords meet at E. Prove that $EB = ED$.

Solution:

Given: AB and CD are equal chords of a circle whose centre is O. When produced, these chords meet at E.

To prove: $EB = ED$.

Construction: From O draw $OP \perp AB$ and $OQ \perp CD$. Join OE.

Proof: ∵ $AB = CD$ [Given]

$\therefore \quad OP = OQ$

[∵ Equal chords of a circle are equidistant from the centre]

Now in ΔOPE and ΔOQE,

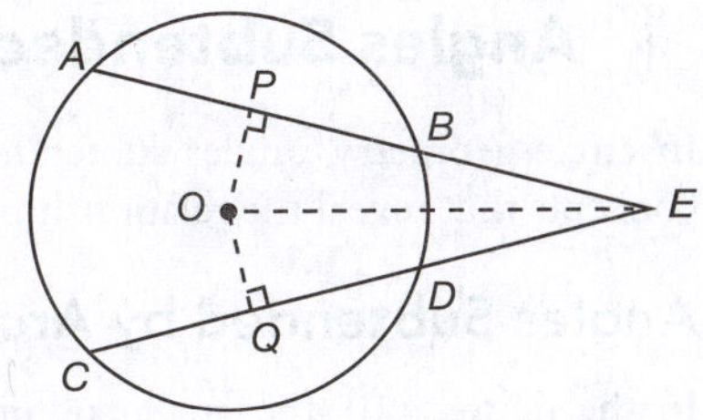

$$\angle OPE = \angle OQE \quad \text{[Each 90°]}$$

$$OE = OE \quad \text{[Common]}$$

$$OP = OQ \quad \text{[Proved above]}$$

$\therefore$ $$\Delta OPE \cong \Delta OQE \quad \text{[By RHS congruency]}$$

$\therefore$ $$PE = QE \quad \text{[By CPCT]}$$

$\Rightarrow$ $$PE - \frac{1}{2}AB = QE - \frac{1}{2}CD \quad [\because AB = CD \text{ (Given)}]$$

$\Rightarrow$ $$PE - PB = QE - QD \Rightarrow EB = ED.$$

Hence proved.

Illustration 9.8

AB and *CD* are the chords of a circle whose centre is *O*. They intersect each other at *P*. If *PO* be the bisector of $\angle APD$, prove that $AB = CD$.

OR

In the given figure, *O* is the centre of the circle and *PO* bisects the angle *APD*. Prove that $AB = CD$.

Solution:

Given: *AB* and *CD* are the chords of a circle whose centre is *O*. They intersect each other at *P*. *PO* is the bisector of $\angle APD$.

To prove: $AB = CD$.

Construction: Draw $OR \perp AB$ and $OQ \perp CD$.

Proof: In ΔOPR and ΔOPQ,

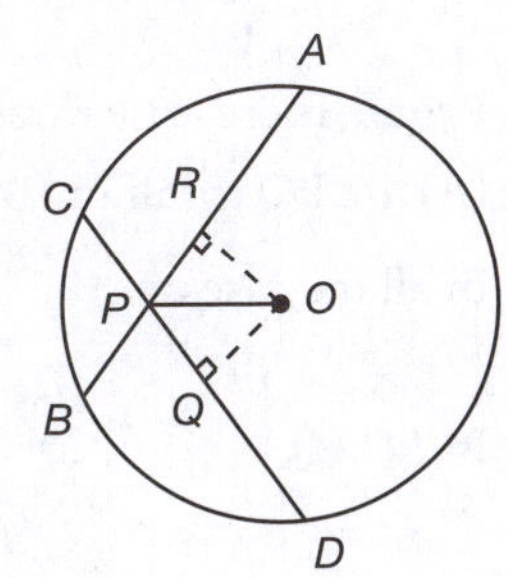

$$\angle OPR = \angle OPQ \quad \text{[Given]}$$

$$OP = OP \quad \text{[Common]}$$

And $$\angle ORP = \angle OQP \quad \text{[Each} = 90°\text{]}$$

$\therefore$ $$\Delta OPR \cong \Delta OPQ \quad \text{[By AAS congruency]}$$

$\therefore$ $$OR = OQ \quad \text{[By CPCT]}$$

$\therefore$ $$AB = CD$$

[$\because$ Chords of a circle which are equidistant from the centre are equal].

Check Point 1

1. Find the number of least non-collinear points required to draw a circle passing through them.
2. Given an arc of a circle, show how to complete the circles?
3. If two circles intersect each other, prove that the line joining their centres bisects the common chord at the right angle.
4. Find the length of a chord which is at a distance of 16 cm from the centre of a circle whose radius is 20 cm.
5. Two circles of radii 10 cm and 17 cm intersect at two points and the distance between their centres is 21 cm. Find the length of the common chord.

Angles Subtended

In circle geometry, angles subtended by arcs and properties of cyclic quadrilaterals are key concepts that reveal the relationships between angles, arcs, and segments.

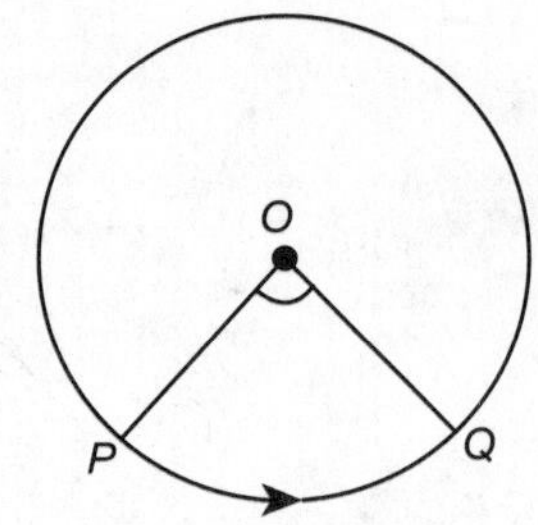

Figure 9.10

Angles Subtended by Arcs

In the figure 9.10, the angle subtended by the minor arc *PQ* at *O* is $\angle POQ$ and the angle subtended by the major arc *PQ* at *O* is reflex angle $\angle POQ$.

Theorem 1: The angle subtended by an arc at the centre is double the angle subtended by it at any point on the remaining part of the circle.

Given: An arc *PQ* of a circle subtending angles *POQ* at the centre *O* and *PAQ* at point *A* on the remaining part of the circle.

To prove: $\angle POQ = 2\angle PAQ$.

Construction: Join *AO* and extend it to point *B*.

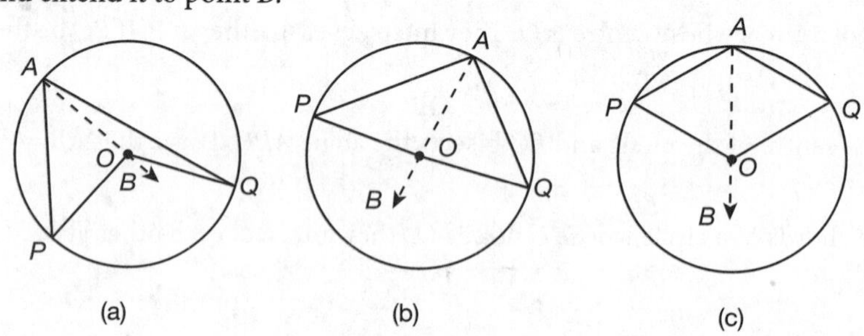

Figure 9.11

Proof: There arise three cases:

(A) arc PQ is minor (B) arc PQ is a semi-circle (C) arc PQ is major.

In all the cases, $\angle BOQ = \angle OAQ + \angle AQO$ ...(i)

[∵ An exterior angle of a triangle is equal to the sum of the two interior opposite angles]

In ΔOAQ,

$$OA = OQ \quad \text{[Radii of a circle]}$$

∴ $$\angle OQA = \angle OAQ \quad \text{...(ii)}$$

[Angles opposite equal sides of a triangle are equal]

From (i) and (ii)

$$\angle BOQ = 2\angle OAQ \quad \text{...(iii)}$$

Similarly,

$$\angle BOP = 2\angle OAP \quad \text{...(iv)}$$

Adding (iii) and (iv), we get:

$$\angle BOP + \angle BOQ = 2(\angle OAP + \angle OAQ)$$

⇒ $$\angle POQ = 2\angle PAQ. \quad \text{...(v)}$$

> **Keystone**
>
> For case (C), where *PQ* is the major arc, (v) is replaced by reflex angles.
> Thus, reflex $\angle POQ = 2\angle PAQ$.

Theorem 2: Angles in the same segment of a circle are equal.

Proof: Let *P* and *Q* be any two points on a circle to form a chord *PQ*, *A* and *C* are any other points on the remaining part of the circle and *O* is the centre of the circle. Then,

$$\angle POQ = 2\angle PAQ \quad \text{...(i)}$$

And $$\angle POQ = 2\angle PCQ \quad \text{...(ii)}$$

[Angle subtended at the centre is double the angle subtended by it on the remaining part of the circle]

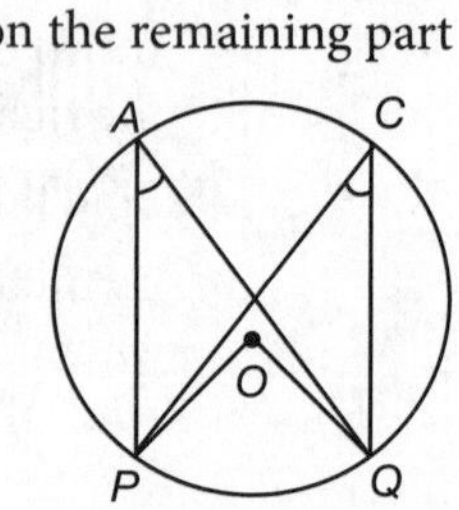

Figure 9.12

From equations (i) and (ii)

$$2\angle PAQ = 2\angle PCQ$$

$$\Rightarrow \qquad \angle PAQ = \angle PCQ.$$

Hence, proved.

Theorem 3: The angle in the semicircle is a right angle.

Proof: $\because$ $\angle PAQ$ is an angle in the segment, which is a semicircle.

$$\therefore \qquad \angle PAQ = \angle POQ = \frac{1}{2}\angle POQ = \frac{1}{2} \times 180° = 90°$$

[$\because$ POQ is straight line angle or $\angle POQ = 180°$]

If we take any other point C on the semicircle, then again, we get:

$$\angle PCQ = \frac{1}{2}\angle POQ = \frac{1}{2} \times 180° = 90°.$$

Hence, proved.

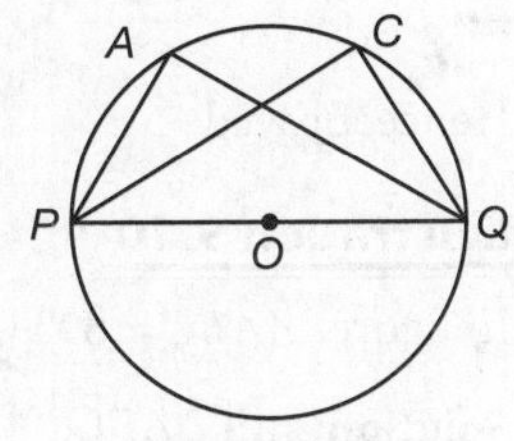

Figure 9.13

Angle subtended by Cyclic Quadrilaterals

A quadrilateral $ABCD$ is called **cyclic** if all four vertices of it lie on a circle.

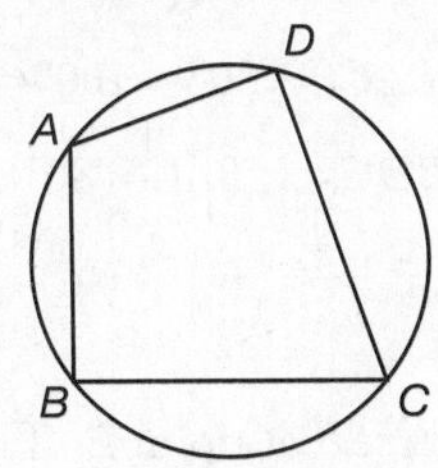

Figure 9.14

Theorem: The sum of either pair of opposite angles of a cyclic quadrilateral is 180°.

Given: A cyclic quadrilateral $ABCD$.

To prove: $\angle A + \angle C = \angle B + \angle D = 180°$.

Construction: Join AC and BD.

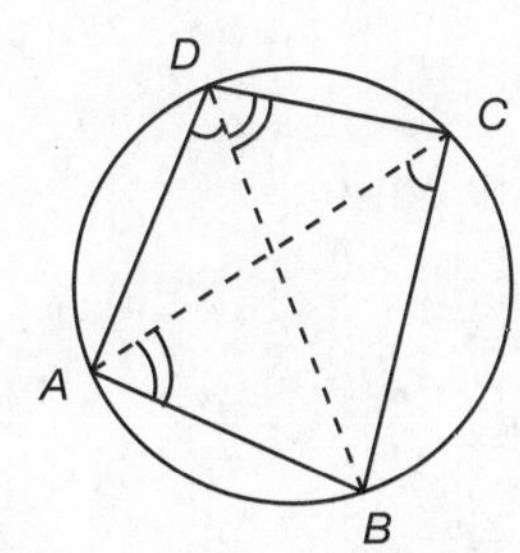

Figure 9.15

Proof: $\angle ACB = \angle ADB$ ...(i)

And $\angle BAC = \angle BDC$ ...(ii)

[Angles of the same segment of a circle are equal]

Adding equations (i) and (ii)

$$\therefore \qquad \angle ACB + \angle BAC = \angle ADB + \angle BDC$$

$$\angle ACB + \angle BAC = \angle ADC.$$

Adding $\angle ABC$ to both sides, we get:

$$\angle ACB + \angle BAC + \angle ABC = \angle ADC + \angle ABC.$$

$$\therefore \qquad \angle ADC + \angle ABC = 180°$$

i.e., $\angle D + \angle B = 180°$

$$\therefore \qquad \angle A + \angle C = 360° - (\angle B + \angle D) = 180°$$

[$\because$ $\angle A + \angle B + \angle C + \angle D = 360°$].

Hence, proved.

Illustration 9.9

If a side of a cyclic quadrilateral is produced, then the exterior angle is equal to the interior opposite angle.

Solution: Let $ABCD$ be a cyclic quadrilateral inscribed in a circle with centre O. The side AB of quadrilateral $ABCD$ is produced to E. Then, we have to prove that $\angle CBE = \angle ADC$.

Since the sum of opposite pairs of angles of a cyclic quadrilateral is 180°

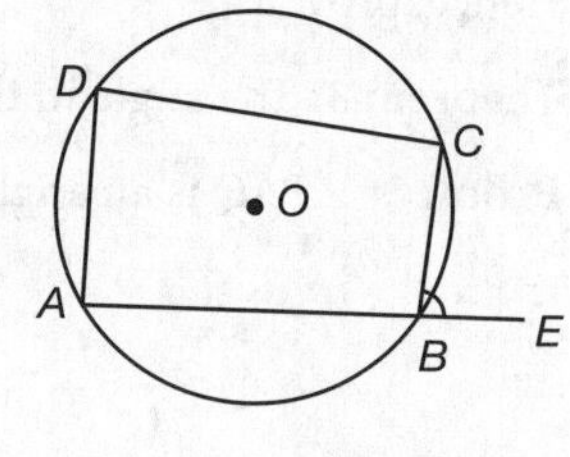

$\therefore$ $\angle ABC + \angle ADC = 180°$

But $\angle ABC + \angle CBE1 = 180°$

[$\because \angle ABC$ and $\angle CBE$ form a linear pair]

$\therefore$ $\angle ABC + \angle ADC = \angle ABC + \angle CBE$

$\Rightarrow$ $\angle ADC = \angle CBE$ or $\angle CBE = \angle ADC$.

Hence, proved.

Illustration 9.10

In figure, $\angle ABC = 69°$, $\angle ACB = 31°$, find $\angle BDC$.

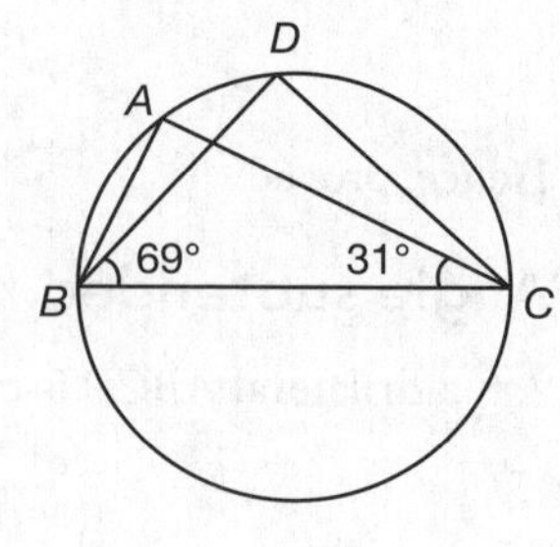

Solution: In ΔABC,

$$\angle BAC + \angle ABC + \angle ACB = 180°$$

$\Rightarrow$ $\angle BAC + 69° + 31° = 180°$

$\Rightarrow$ $\angle BAC + 100° = 180°$

$\Rightarrow$ $\angle BAC = 180° - 100° = 80°$

Now, $\angle BDC = \angle BAC = 80°$.

[Angles in the same segment of a circle are equal]

Illustration 9.11

ABCD is a cyclic quadrilateral whose diagonals intersect at point *E*. If $\angle DBC = 70°$, $\angle BAC = 30°$, find $\angle BCD$. Further, if $AB = BC$, find $\angle ECD$.

Solution: $\angle CDB = \angle BAC = 30°$ ...(i)

[Angles in the same segment of a circle are equal]

$\angle DBC = 70°$ ...(ii)

In ΔBCD,

$$\angle BCD + \angle DBC + \angle CDB = 180°$$

$\Rightarrow$ $\angle BCD + 70° + 30° = 180°$ [Using (i) and (ii)]

$\Rightarrow$ $\angle BCD + 100° = 180°$

$\Rightarrow$ $\angle BCD = 180° - 100°$

$\Rightarrow$ $\angle BCD = 80°$ ...(iii)

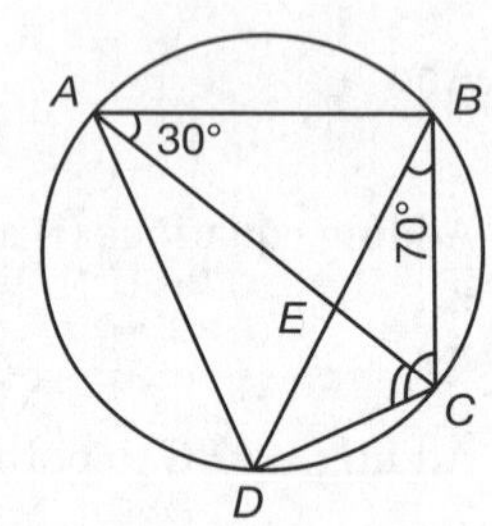

In ΔABC, $AB = BC$

$\therefore$ $\angle BCA = \angle BAC = 30°$ ...(iv)

[Angles opposite to equal sides of a triangle are equal]

$\Rightarrow$ $\angle BCA + \angle ECD = 80°$

$\Rightarrow$ $30° + \angle ECD = 80°$

$\Rightarrow$ $\angle ECD = 80° - 30°$

$\Rightarrow$ $\angle ECD = 50°$.

Illustration 9.12

In the figure, find the measures of $\angle ABD$, $\angle CDP$, $\angle PDA$, $\angle CAB$ and $\angle CBD$.

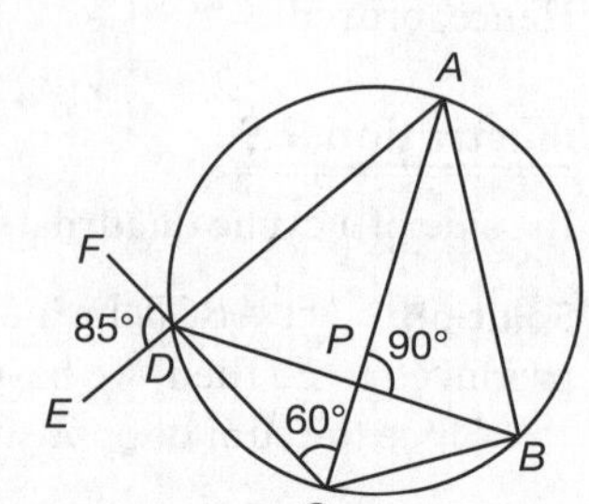

Solution: Clearly, $\angle ABD$ and $\angle ACD$ are in the same segment determined by chord *AD*.

$\therefore$ $\angle ABD = \angle ACD$

$\Rightarrow$ $\angle ABD = 60°$ [Given $\angle ACD = 60°$]

Now, $\angle CPD = \angle BPA$ [Vertically opp. angles]

$\Rightarrow$ $\angle CPD = 90°$ [Given $\angle BPA = 90°$]

In ΔCPD, we have

$$\angle CDP + \angle CPD + \angle PCD = 180°$$

$\Rightarrow$ $$\angle CDP + 60° + 90° = 180°$$

$\Rightarrow$ $$\angle CDP + 150° = 180°$$

$\Rightarrow$ $$\angle CDP = 180° - 150° = 30°$$

Since $\angle EDF$ and $\angle ADC$ are vertically opposite angles.

$\therefore$ $$\angle ADC = \angle EDF$$

$\Rightarrow$ $$\angle ADC = 85°$$

$\Rightarrow$ $$\angle PDA + \angle PDC = 85°$$

$\Rightarrow$ $$\angle PDA + 30° = 85°$$

$\Rightarrow$ $$\angle PDA = 85° - 30° = 55°$$

Since, $\angle CDB = \angle CDP$ and $\angle CAB$ are the angles in the same segment determined by chord CB.

$\therefore$ $$\angle CAB = \angle CDP$$

$\Rightarrow$ $$\angle CAB = 30°$$

In ΔACD, we have

$$\angle CAD + \angle ACD + \angle ADC = 180°$$

$$\angle CAD + 60° + 85° = 180°$$

$\Rightarrow$ $$\angle CAD = 180° - (60° + 85°) = 35°$$

Clearly, $\angle CAD$ and $\angle CBD$ are angles in the same segment determined by chord CD.

$\therefore$ $$\angle CBD = \angle CAD = 35°.$$

Illustration 9.13

If the non-parallel side of a trapezium is equal, prove that it is cyclic.

Solution:

Given: $ABCD$ is a trapezium whose two non-parallel sides AD and BC are equal.

To prove: Trapezium $ABCD$ is cyclic.

Construction: Draw $BE \parallel AD$.

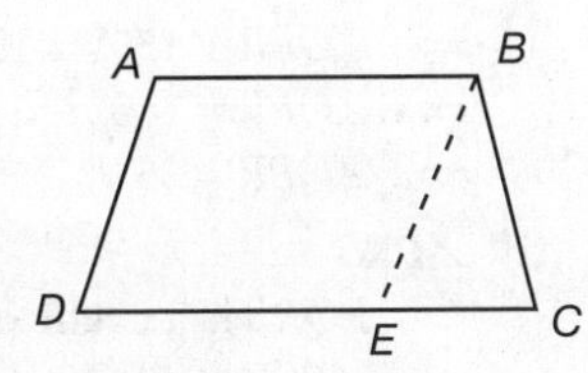

Proof: $\because$ $AB \parallel DE$ [Given]

and $AD \parallel BE$ [By construction]

$\therefore$ Quadrilateral $ABED$ is a parallelogram.

$\therefore$ $\angle BAD = \angle BED$ ...(i) [Opp. angles of *a* $\|^{gm}$]

And, $AD = BE$ ...(ii) [Opp. sides of *a* $\|^{gm}$]

But $AD = BC$ ...(iii) [Given]

From (ii) and (iii),

$$BE = BC$$

$\therefore$ $\angle BCE = \angle BEC$ ...(iv) [Angles opposite to equal sides]

$\angle BEC + \angle BED = 180°$ [Linear Pair Axiom]

$\Rightarrow$ $\angle BCE + \angle BAD = 180°$ [From (iv) and (i)]

$\Rightarrow$ Trapezium $ABCD$ is cyclic. [$\because$ If a pair of opposite angles of a quadrilateral is 180°, then the quadrilateral is cyclic]

Hence proved.

Illustration 9.14

Prove that a cyclic parallelogram is a rectangle.

Solution:

Given: $ABCD$ is a cyclic parallelogram.

To prove: $ABCD$ is a rectangle.

Proof: $ABCD$ is a cyclic quadrilateral

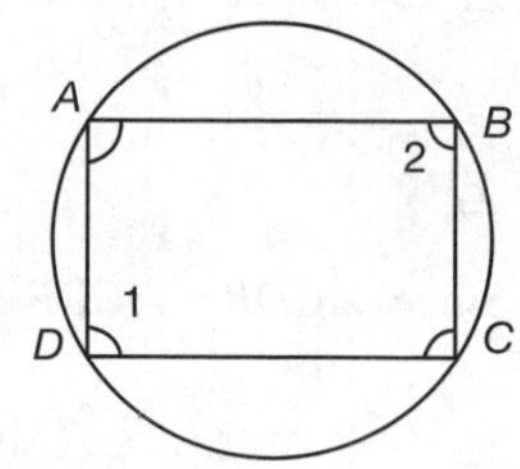

$\therefore$ $\angle 1 + \angle 2 = 180°$ ...(i)

[$\because$ Opposite angles of a cyclic quadrilateral are supplementary]

$ABCD$ is a parallelogram

$\therefore$ $\angle 1 = \angle 2$ ...(ii)

[Opp. angles of a $||^{gm}$]

From (i) and (ii),

$\angle 1 = \angle 2 = 90°$

$\therefore$ Parallelogram $ABCD$ is a rectangle.

Hence proved.

Illustration 9.15

In the figure, PQ is a diameter of a circle with centre O. If $\angle PQR = 65°$, $\angle SPR = 40°$, $\angle PQM = 50°$, find $\angle QPR$, $\angle PRS$ and $\angle QPM$.

Solution:

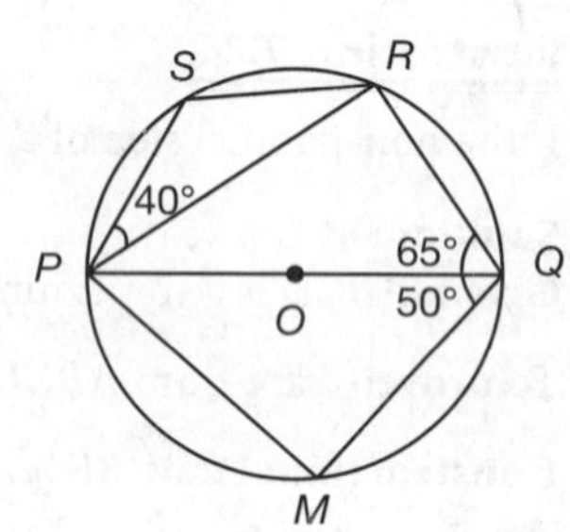

(i) $\angle QPR$

$\because$ PQ is a diameter

$\therefore$ $\angle PRQ = 90°$ [Angle in a semi-circle is 90°] In ΔPQR,

$\angle QPR + \angle PRQ + \angle PQR = 180°$

$\Rightarrow$ $\angle QPR + 90° + 65° = 180°$

$\Rightarrow$ $\angle QPR + 155° = 180°$

$\Rightarrow$ $\angle QPR = 180° - 155°$

$\Rightarrow$ $\angle QPR = 25°$.

(ii) $\angle PRS$

$\because$ $PQRS$ is a cyclic quadrilateral.

$\therefore$ $\angle PSR + \angle PQR = 180°$ [$\because$ Opposite angles of a cyclic quadrilateral are supplementary]

$\Rightarrow$ $\angle PSR + 65° = 180°$

$\Rightarrow$ $\angle PSR = 180° - 65°$

$\Rightarrow$ $\angle PSR = 115°$

In ΔPSR,

$\angle PSR + \angle SPR + \angle PRS = 180°$

$\Rightarrow$ $115° + 40° + \angle PRS = 180°$

$\Rightarrow$ $155° + \angle PRS = 180°$

$\Rightarrow$ $\angle PRS = 180° - 155°$

$\Rightarrow$ $\angle PRS = 25°$.

(iii) $\angle QPM$

$\because$ PQ is a diameter

$\therefore$ $\angle PMQ = 90°$ [$\because$ Angle in a semi-circle is 90°]

In ΔPMQ,

$\angle PMQ + \angle PQM + \angle QPM = 180°$

$\Rightarrow \quad 90° + 50° + \angle QPM = 180° \Rightarrow 140° + \angle QPM = 180°$

$\Rightarrow \quad \angle QPM = 180° - 140° \Rightarrow \angle QPM = 40°.$

Illustration 9.16

In the figure, O is the centre of the circle. Prove that $\angle x + \angle y = \angle z$.

Solution: $\angle EBF = \frac{1}{2} \angle EOF \angle z$

[∵ Angle subtended by an arc of a circle at the centre is twice the angle subtended by it at any point of the remaining part of the circle]

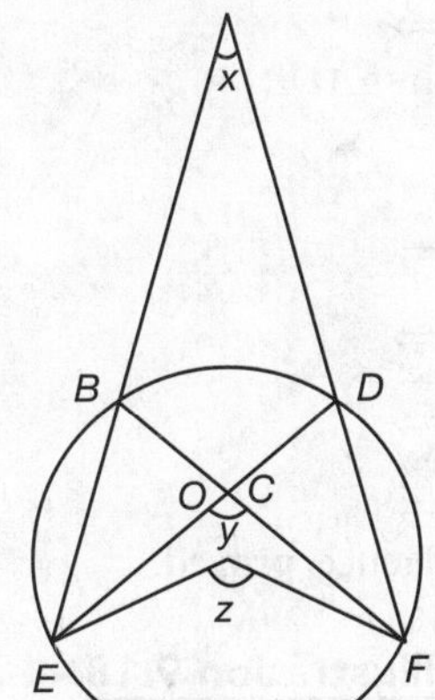

$$\therefore \quad \angle ABF = 180° - \frac{1}{2}\angle z \quad \ldots\text{(i)}$$

[Linear Pair Axiom]

$$\angle EDF = \frac{1}{2}\angle EOF = \frac{1}{2}\angle z$$

[∵ Angle subtended by any arc of a circle at the centre is twice the angle subtended by it at any point of the remaining part of the circle]

$$\therefore \quad \angle ADE = 180° - \frac{1}{2}\angle z \quad \ldots\text{(ii)}$$

[Linear Pair Axiom]

$$\angle BCD = \angle ECF = \angle y \quad \text{[Vertically Opp. Angles]}$$

$$\angle BAD = \angle x$$

In quadrilateral $ABCD$

$$\angle ABC + \angle BCD + \angle CDA + \angle BAD = 2 \times 180°$$

$$\Rightarrow \quad 180° - \frac{1}{2}\angle z + \angle y + 180° - \frac{1}{2}\angle z + \angle x = 2 \times 180° \Rightarrow \angle x + \angle y = \angle z.$$

Hence, proved.

Illustration 9.17

AB is the diameter of the circle with centre O and chord CD is equal to radius OC. AC and BD produced meet at P. Prove that $\angle CPD = 60°$.

Solution:

Given: AB is the diameter of the circle with centre O and chord CD is equal to radius OC. AC and BD produced meet at P.

To prove: $\angle CPD = 60°$.

Construction: Join AD.

Proof: In ΔOCD,

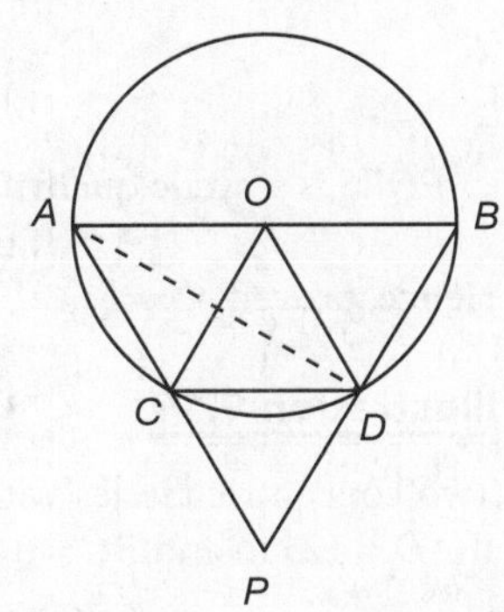

$$OC = OD \quad \ldots\text{(i)}$$

[Radii of the same circle]

$$OC = CD \quad \ldots\text{(ii)}$$

[Given]

From (i) and (ii),

$$OC = OD = CD$$

∴ ΔOCD is an equilateral triangle.

$$\therefore \quad \angle COD = 60°$$

$$\therefore \quad \angle CAD = \frac{1}{2}\angle COD = \frac{1}{2}\angle(60°) = 30°$$

$$\angle COD = \angle(60°) = 30°$$

[$\because$ Angle subtended by any arc of a circle at the centre is twice the angle subtended by it at any point of the remaining part of the circle]

$\Rightarrow$ $\angle PAD = 30°$ ...(iii)

And, $\angle ADB = 90°$ ...(iv)

[Angle in a semi-circle]

$\Rightarrow$ $\angle ADB + \angle ADP = 180°$ [Linear Pair Axiom]

$\Rightarrow$ $90° + \angle ADP = 180°$ [From (iv)]

$\Rightarrow$ $\angle ADP = 90°$ ...(v)

In ΔADP,

$$\angle APD + \angle PAD + \angle ADP = 180°$$

$\Rightarrow$ $\angle APD + 30° + 90° = 180°$ [From (iii) and (v)]

$\Rightarrow$ $\angle APD + 120° = 180°$

$\Rightarrow$ $\angle APD = 180° - 120° = 60°$

$\Rightarrow$ $\angle CPD = 60°.$

Hence, proved.

Illustration 9.18

Prove that the quadrilateral formed by angle bisectors of a cyclic quadrilateral is also cyclic.

Solution:

Given: $ABCD$ is a cyclic quadrilateral. Its angle bisectors form a quadrilateral $PQRS$.

To prove: $PQRS$ is a cyclic quadrilateral.

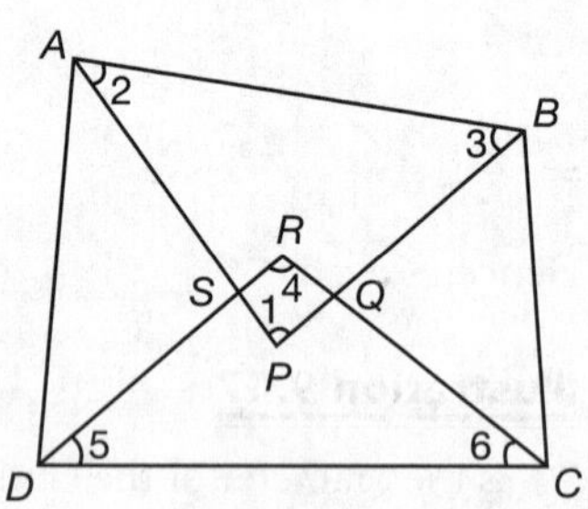

Proof: In ΔAPB

$$\angle 1 + \angle 2 + \angle 3 = 180° \quad ...(i)$$

In ΔDRC

$$\angle 4 + \angle 5 + \angle 6 = 180° \quad ...(ii)$$

$\therefore$ $\angle 1 + \angle 2 + \angle 3 + \angle 4 + \angle 5 + \angle 6 = 360°$ ...(iii)

[Adding (i) and (ii)]

But $\angle 2 + \angle 3 + \angle 6 + \angle 5 = \frac{1}{2}[\angle A + \angle B + \angle C + \angle D]$

$$= \frac{1}{2}(360°) = 180°$$

$\therefore$ $\angle 1 + \angle 4 = 360° - (\angle 2 + \angle 3 + \angle 6 + \angle 5)$

$=$ $360° - 180° = 180°.$

$\therefore$ $PQRS$ is a cyclic quadrilateral.

[$\because$ If the sum of any pair of opposite angles of a quadrilateral is 180°, then the quadrilateral is cyclic].

Hence, proved.

Illustration 9.19

Two concentric circles with centre O have A, B, C, D as the points of intersection with the line l as shown in the figure. If $AD = 12$ cm and $BC = 8$ cm, find the length of AB, CD, AC and BD.

Solution: Since $OM \perp BC$, a chord of the circle,

$\therefore$ It bisects BC.

$\therefore$ $BM = CM = \frac{1}{2}(BC) = \frac{1}{2}(8) = 4$ cm

Since, $OM \perp AD$, a chord of the circle,

$\therefore$ It bisects AD.

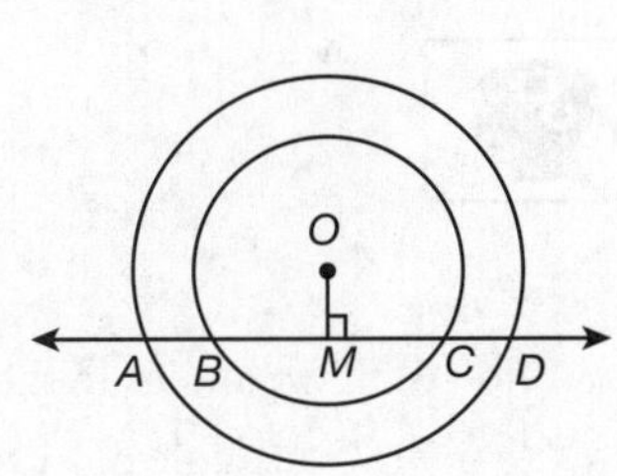

$\therefore$ $$AM = MD = \frac{1}{2} AD = \frac{1}{2}(12) = 6 \text{ cm}$$

Now, $$AB = AM - BM = 6 - 4 = 2 \text{ cm}$$

$$CD = MD - MC = 6 - 4 = 2 \text{ cm}$$

$$AC = AM + MC = 6 + 4 = 10 \text{ cm}$$

$$BD = BM + MD = 4 + 6 = 10 \text{ cm}$$

Illustration 9.20

OABC is a rhombus whose three vertices *A*, *B* and *C* lie on a circle with centre *O*. If the radius of the circle is 10 cm. Find the area of the rhombus.

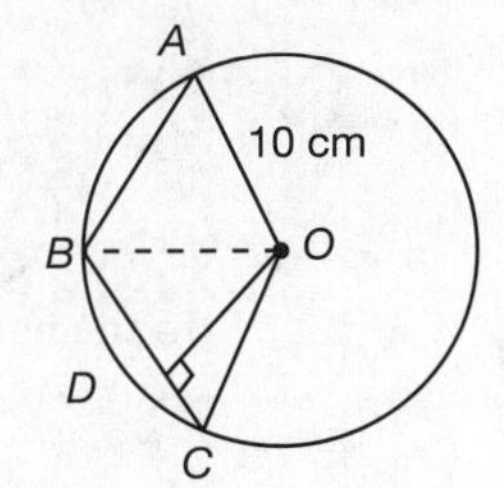

Solution: Since, *OABC* is a rhombus

$\therefore$ $$OA = AB = BC = OC = 10 \text{ cm}$$

Now, $$OD \perp BC \Rightarrow CD = \frac{1}{2} BC = \frac{1}{2}(10) = 5 \text{ cm}$$

$\therefore$ By Pythagoras theorem,

$$OC^2 = OD^2 + DC^2$$

$\Rightarrow$ $$OD^2 = OC^2 - DC^2 = (10)^2 - (5)^2 = 100 - 25 = 75$$

$\Rightarrow$ $$OD = \sqrt{75} = 5\sqrt{3}$$

$\therefore$ $$\text{Area } (\Delta OBC) = \frac{1}{2} BC \times OD = \frac{1}{2}(10) \times 5\sqrt{3} = 25\sqrt{3} \text{ sq. cm.}$$

$$\text{Area of Rhombus} = 2\,(\text{Area of } \Delta OBC) = 2(25\sqrt{3}) = 50\sqrt{3} \text{ sq. cm.}$$

Illustration 9.21

In the given figure, *AB* is the chord of a circle with centre *O*. *AB* is produced to *C* such that $BC = OB$. *CO* is joined and produced to meet the circle in *D*. If $\angle ACD = y°$ and $\angle AOD = x°$, prove that $x° = 3y°$.

Solution: Since $BC = OB$ [Given]

$\therefore$ $$\angle OCB = \angle BOC = y°$$

[$\because$ Angles opposite to equal sides are equal]

$$\angle OBA = \angle BOC + \angle OCB = y° + y° = 2y°.$$

[$\because$ Exterior angle of a Δ is equal to the sum of the opposite interior angles]

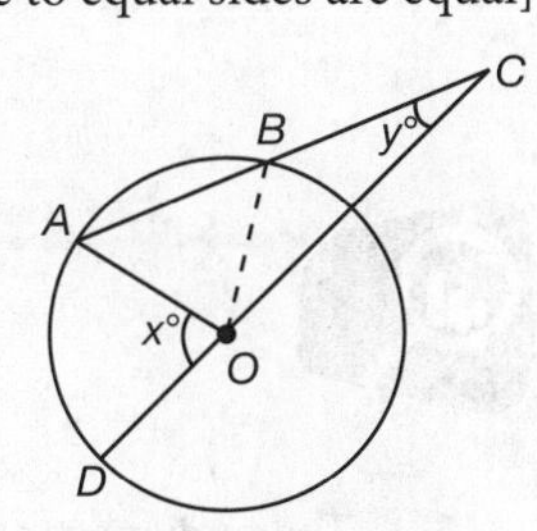

Also $OA = OB$ [Radii of the same circle]

$$\angle OAB = \angle OBA = 2y°$$

[Angles opposite to equal sides of a triangle are equal]

$$\angle AOD = \angle OAC + \angle OCA = 2y° + y° = 3y°$$

[$\because$ Exterior angle of a Δ is equal to the sum of the opposite interior angles]

Hence, $$x° = 3y°.$$

Hence proved.

Check Point 2

6. Two angles in the same segment of a circle are $(2x + 10)^\circ$ and $(x + 45^\circ)$. Then x is equal to:
7. One angle of a cyclic quadrilateral is twice its opposite angle. Then find the smaller of the two angles:
8. In the figure, O is the centre of the circle, find $\angle PQR$.

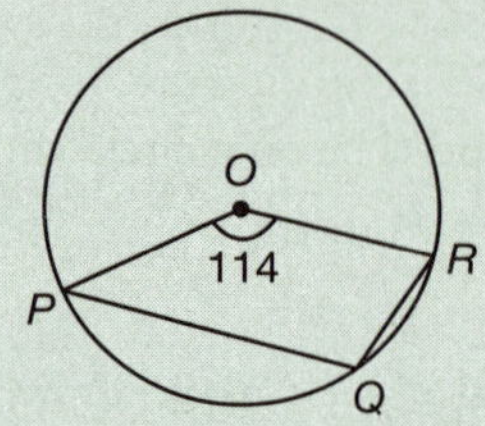

9. In the figure, O is the centre and $\angle ACB = 20^\circ$, find $\angle AOD$.

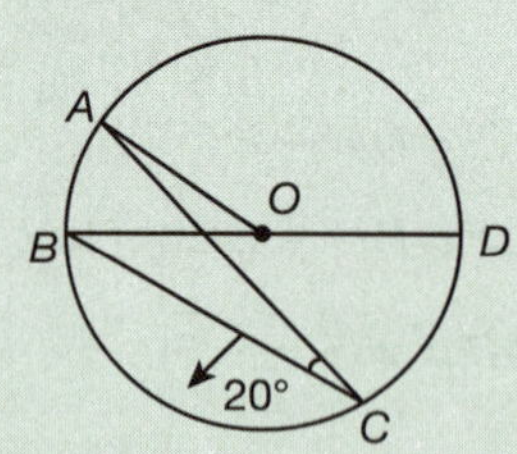

10. In this figure, find the sum of $\angle Q$ and $\angle S$.

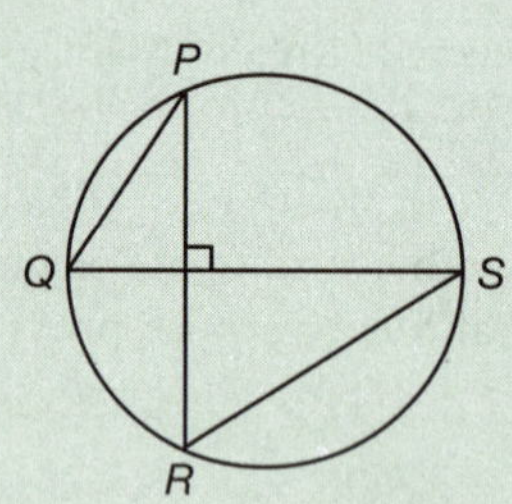

Competition Corner

- The tangent at any point of a circle and the radius through the point are perpendicular to each other.
Given: A circle with centre O. AB is a tangent to the circle at a point P and OP is the radius through P.
Then: $OP \perp AB$.

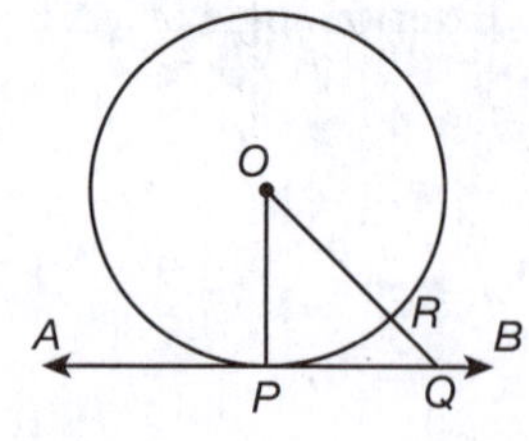

- If O be the centre of a circle and tangents are drawn to the circle at the points A and B of the circle intersect each other at P.
Then: $\angle AOB + \angle APB = 180°$.

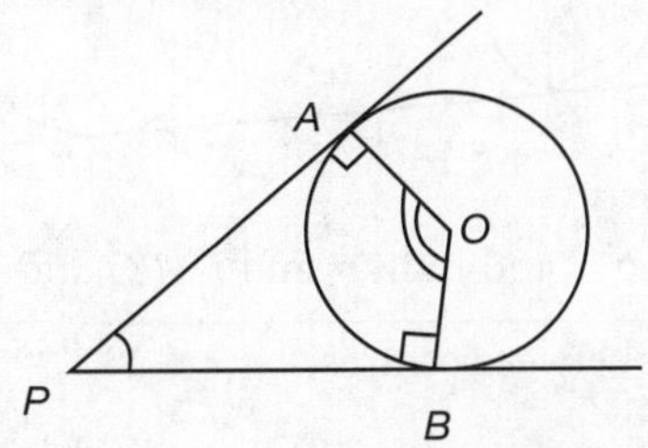

- If two tangents are drawn to a circle from an exterior point, then:
  (i) the tangents are equal in length
  (ii) the tangents subtend equal angles at the centre
  (iii) the tangents are equally inclined to the line joining the point and the centre of the circle.
Given: PA and PB are two tangents drawn to a circle with centre O, from an exterior point P.
Then: (i) $PA = PB$ (ii) $\angle AOP = \angle BOP$ (iii) $\angle APO = \angle BPO$.

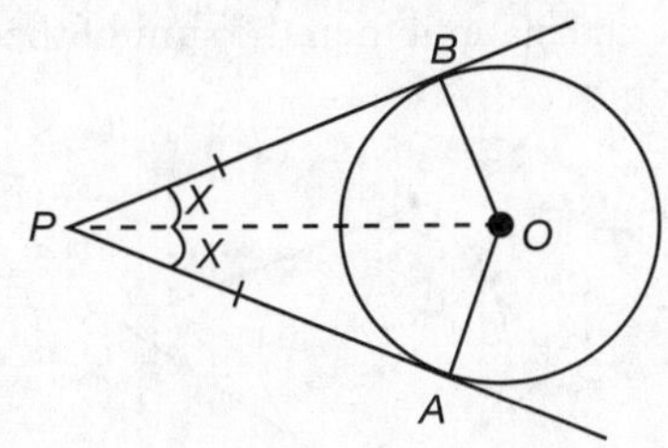

- Its I If two chords AB and CD of a circle, intersect inside a circle (outside the circle when produced at a point E).
Then: $AE \times BE = CE \times DE$.

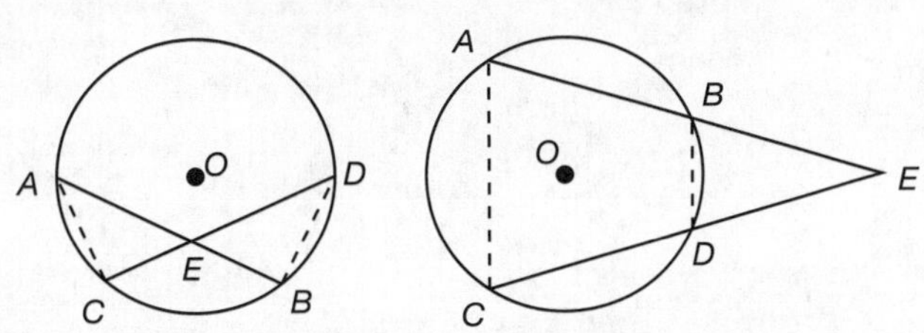

- If PB be a secant which intersects the circle at A and B and PT be a tangent at T.
Then: $PA \cdot PB = (PT)^2$.

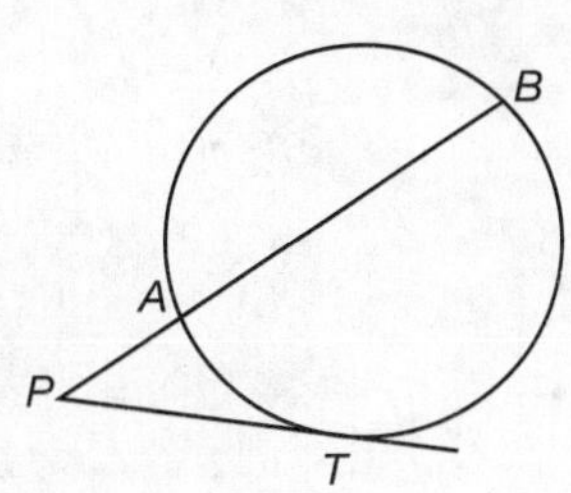

- For the two circles with centre X and Y and radii r_1 and r_2. AB and CD are two direct common tangents (OCT), then the length of $OCT = \sqrt{(\text{distance between centres})^2 - (r_2 - r_1)^2}$

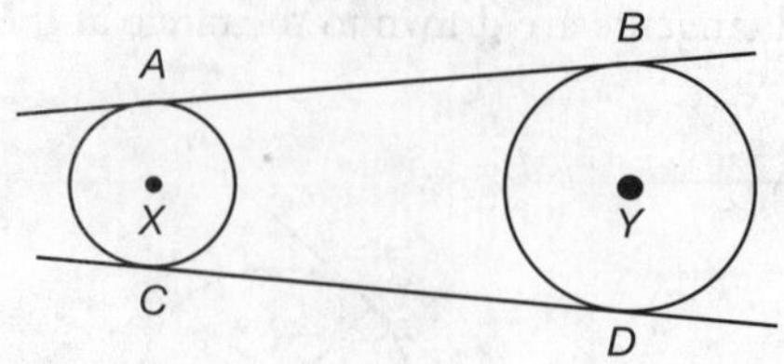

- For the two circles with centre X and Y and radii r_1 and r_2. PQ and RS are two transverse common tangents, then the length of $TCT = \sqrt{(\text{distance between centres})^2 - (r_2 + r_1)^2}$

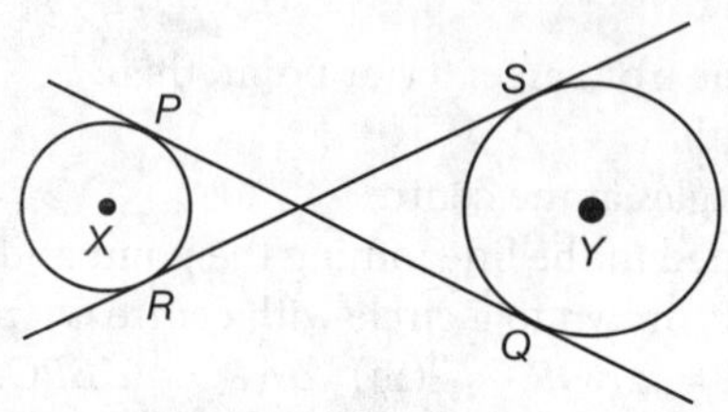

- If a circle touches all four sides of a quadrilateral then the sum of the two opposite sides is equal to the sum of the other two. $AB + DC = AD + BC$.

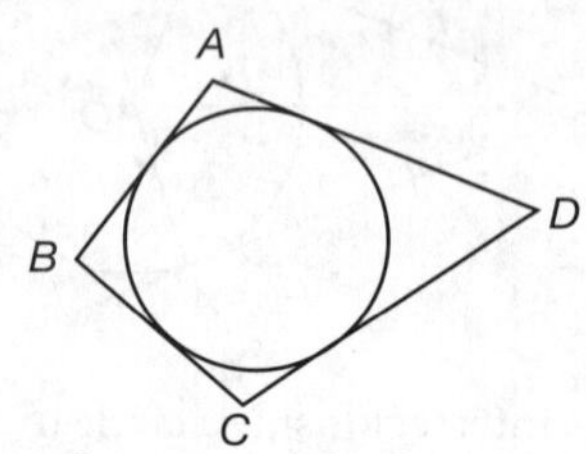

STRUCTURAL OUTLINE

Circle

Theorems

- Equal chords of a circle subtend equal angles at the centre.
- The perpendicular from the centre of a circle to a chord bisects the chord.
- There is one and only one circle passing through three given non-collinear points.
- Equal chords of a circle (or of congruent circles) are equidistant from the centre (or centres).
- The angle subtended by an arc at the centre is double the angle subtended by it at any point on the remaining part of the circle.
- Angles in the same segment of a circle are equal. Angle in the semicircle is a right angle. The sum of either pair of opposite angles of a cyclic quadrilateral is 180°.

Chord and Dimeter

Chord : If we take two points P and Q on a circle, then the line segment PQ is called a **chord** of the circle.

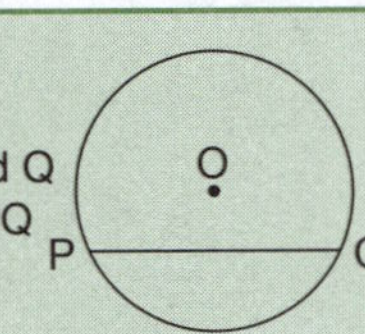

Diameter : The chord which passes through the centre of the circle, is called the **diameter** of the circle. A diameter is the longest chord

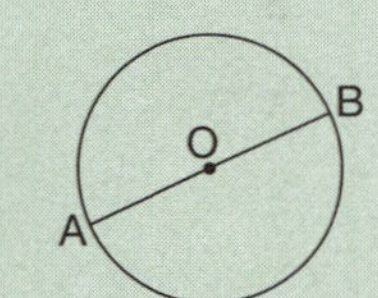

Sector and Segment

Sement : The region between a chord and either of its arcs is called a **segment** of the circular region or simply a segment of the circle. There are two types of segments which are the **major segment** and the **minor segment** (as in **figure**).

Sector : The region between an arc and the two radii, joining the centre to the end points of an arc is called a **sector**.

Minor arc corresponds to the **minor sector** and the major arc corresponds to the **major sector**.

When two arcs are equal, then both segments and both sectors become the same and each is known as a **semi-circular region**.

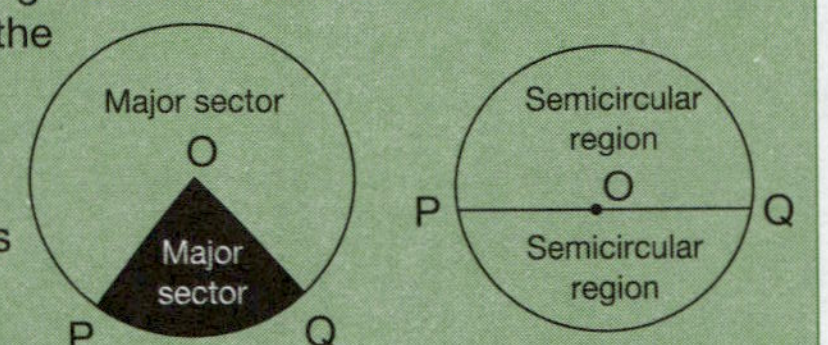

Arc and Circumference

Arc : A piece of a circle between two points is called an **arc**.
The longer one is called the **major arc PQ** and the shorter one is called the **minor arc PQ**.
The minor arc PQ is also de-remarked by $\widehat{PQ}$ and the major arc PQ by $\widehat{QP}$. When P and Q are ends of a diameter,
then both arcs are equal and each is called a **semi circle**.

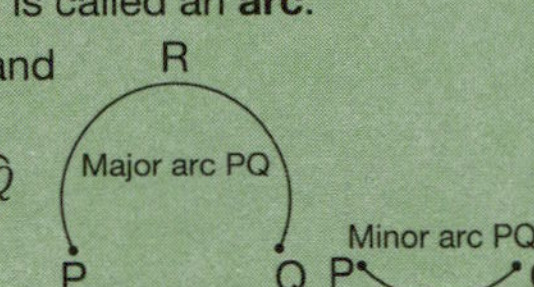

Circumference : The length of the complete circle is called its **circumference**.

ASSESSMENT CORNER

FIXED RESPONSE TYPE

Fill in the Blanks

1. _______ chords subtend equal angles at the centre.
2. The chords of a circle which are _______ from the centre are equal.
3. Chords of _______ circles which are equidistant from the corresponding centres are equal.
4. A cyclic trapezium is always _______.
5. The sum of either pair of the opposite angles of a cyclic quadrilateral is _______.
6. The longest chord of a circle is a _______ of the circle.

True/False

1. A circle has only finite number of equal chords.
2. A circle is not a plane figure.
3. Sector is the region between the diameter and its arc.
4. A chord of a circle, which is twice as long as its radius is the diameter of the circle.
5. Line segment joining the centre to any point on the circle is a radius of the circle.

Single Correct Type Questions

Level 1

1. In a circle of radius 10 cm, the length of the chord whose distance is 6 cm from the centre is:

(A) 4 cm (B) 5 cm
(C) 8 cm (D) 16 cm

2. In the diagram, O is the centre of the circle. The angles CBD is equal to:

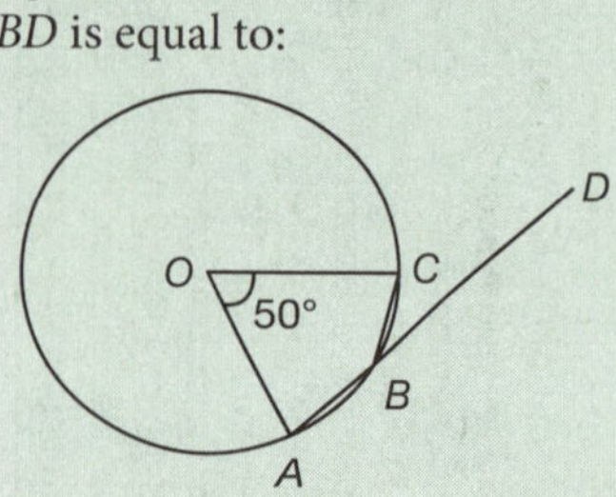

(A) 25° (B) 50°
(C) 40° (D) 130°

3. O is the centre of a circle, AB and CD are two chords of the circle. $OM \perp AB$ and $ON \perp CD$. If $OM = ON = 3$ cm and $AM = BM = 4.5$ cm, then $CD =$

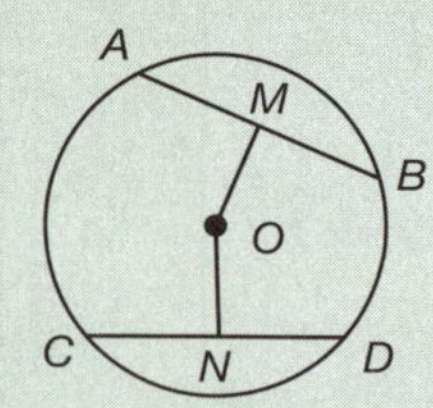

(A) 9 cm (B) 10 cm
(C) 8 cm (D) 6 cm

4. If $\overset{\frown}{AB} \cong \overset{\frown}{CD}$, then:

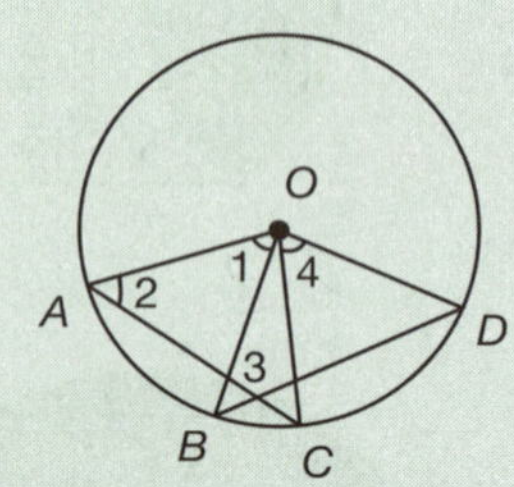

(A) $\angle 1 = \angle 2$ (B) $\angle 3 = \angle 4$
(C) $\angle 2 = \angle 3$ (D) None of these.

5. In the given circle $ABCD$, O is the centre and $\angle BDC = 42°$. The $\angle ACB$ is equal to:

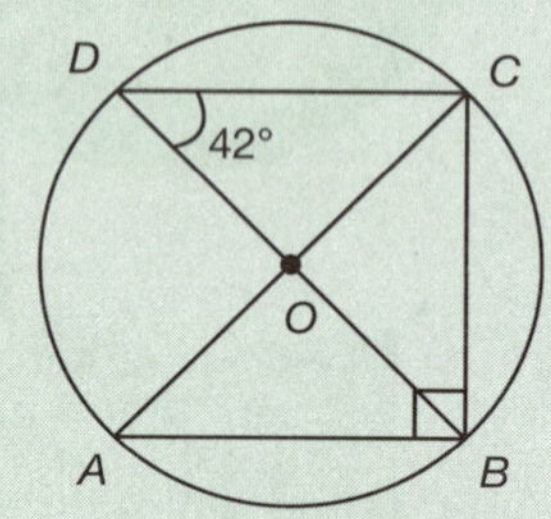

(A) 48° (B) 45°
(C) 42° (D) 60°

6. In the given figure, $\angle CAB = 80°$, $\angle ABC = 40°$. The sum of $\angle DAB + \angle ABD$ is equal to:

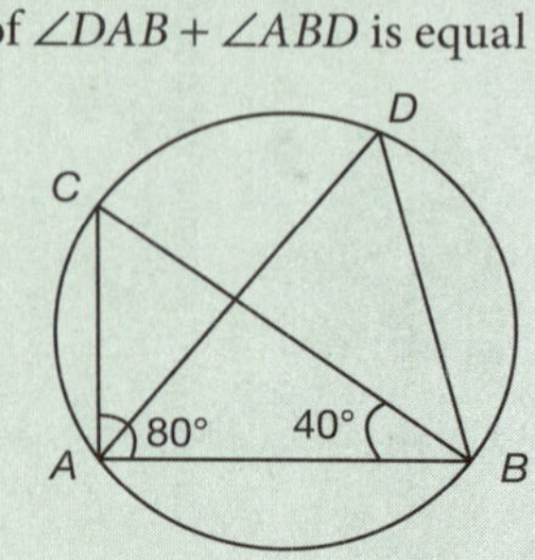

(A) 80° (B) 100°
(C) 120° (D) 140°

7. In the given figure, if C is the centre of the circle and $\angle PQC = 25°$ and $\angle PRC = 15°$, then $\angle QCR$ is equal to:

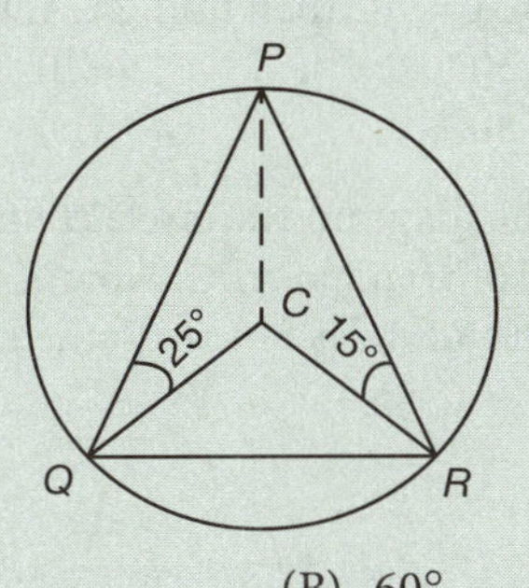

(A) 40° (B) 60°
(C) 80° (D) 120°

8. The sides BA and CD of a cyclic quadrilateral $ABCD$ are produced to meet at P, the sides DA and CB are produced to meet at Q. If $\angle ADC = 85°$ and $\angle BPC = 40°$, then $\angle CQD$ equals:
(A) 50° (B) 45°
(C) 30° (D) 75°

9. In the given figure, if $\angle ACB = 40°$, $\angle DPB = 120°$, then y will be:

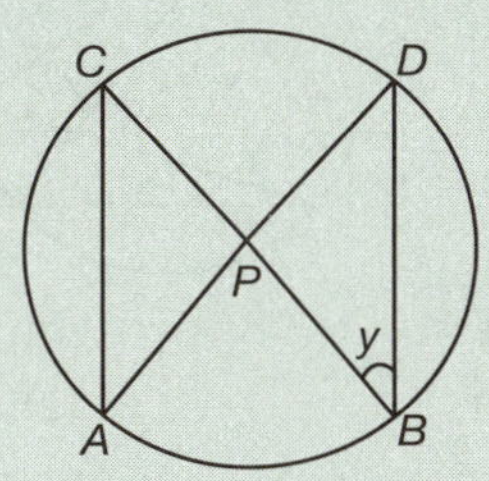

(A) 40° (B) 20°
(C) 0° (D) 60°

10. In a cyclic quadrilateral if $\angle A - \angle C = 70°$, then the greater of the angles A and C is equal to:
(A) 95° (B) 105°
(C) 125° (D) 115°

11. The length of a chord of a circle is equal to the radius of the circle. The angle at which this chord subtends on the longer segment of the circle is equal to:
(A) 30° (B) 45°
(C) 60° (D) 90°

12. In the given figure, $AB = BC = CD$, If $\angle BAC = 25°$, then value of $\angle AED$ is:

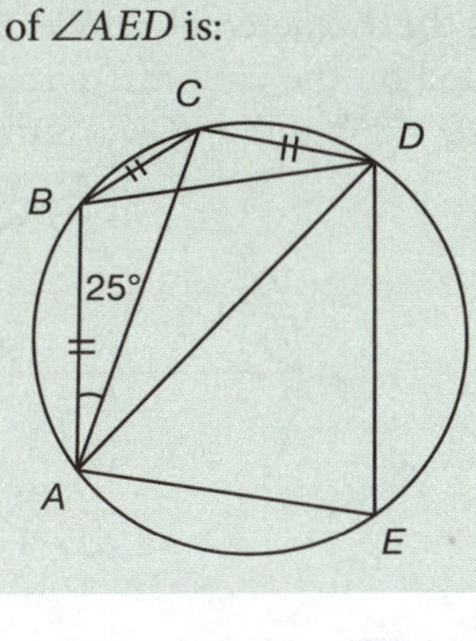

(A) 50° (B) 60°
(C) 65° (D) 75°

13. A, B and C are three points on the circle whose centre is O. If $\angle BAC = x$, $\angle CBO = \angle BCO = y$, $\angle BOC = t$, reflex $\angle BOC = z$, then:

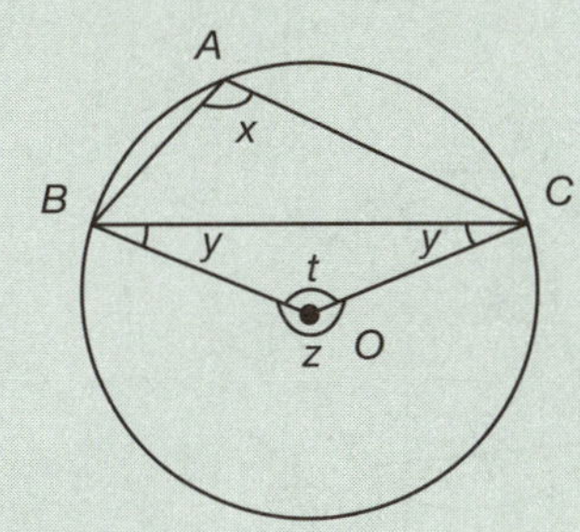

(A) $x + y = 90°$
(B) $x - y = 90°$
(C) $t + 2y° = 90°$
(D) None of these

14. O is the centre of the circle. BC is a chord of the circle and point A lies on the circle. If $\angle BAC = x$, $\angle OBC = y$, then $x + y$:

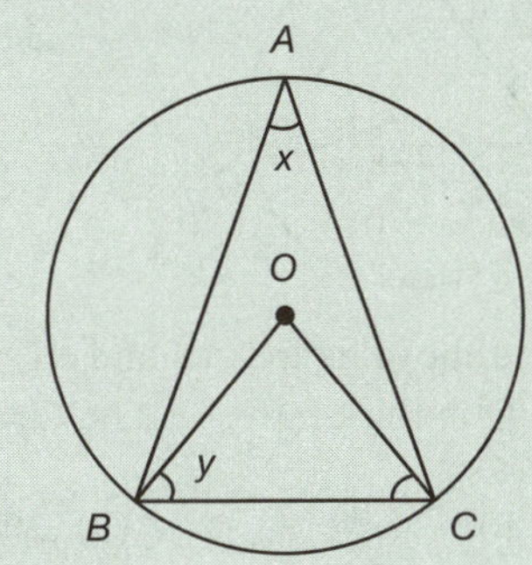

(A) $> 90°$ (B) $= 90°$
(C) $< 90°$ (D) $> 180°$

15.

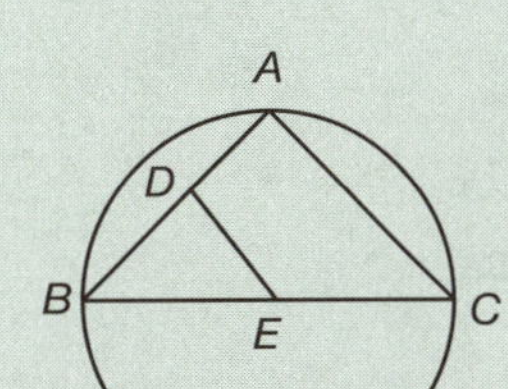

In the above figure (not to scale), $\angle ABC = 2\angle ACB$. Find the angle made by $\overline{AC}$ at the centre of the circle, if $\angle BAC = 60°$.
(A) 80° (B) 120°
(C) 160° (D) 180°

16.

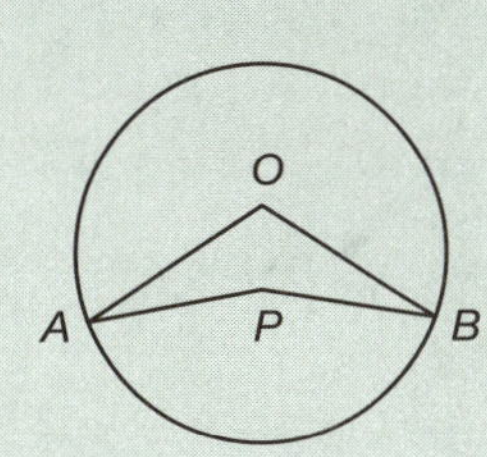

In the above figure, $AP = PB$ and O is the centre of the circle. If $\angle AOB = 80°$ and $\angle OAP = 20°$, then find $\angle APB$.

(A) 60° (B) 90°
(C) 120° (D) 160°

Level 2

17.

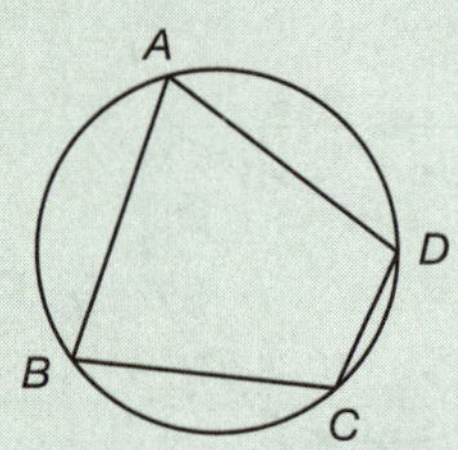

In the above figure, $ABCD$ is a cyclic quadrilateral and $\angle BCD = 2\angle BAD$, find the angle made by the diagonal BD at the centre of the circle.

(A) 60° (B) 80°
(C) 100° (D) 120°

18.

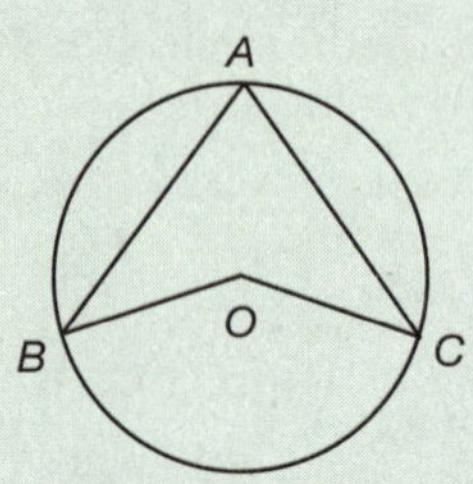

In the above figure, $\overline{AB}$ and $\overline{AC}$ are equal chords and O is the centre. If $\angle BOC = 100°$, then find $\angle ACO$.

(A) 10° (B) 20°
(C) 30° (D) 25°

19.

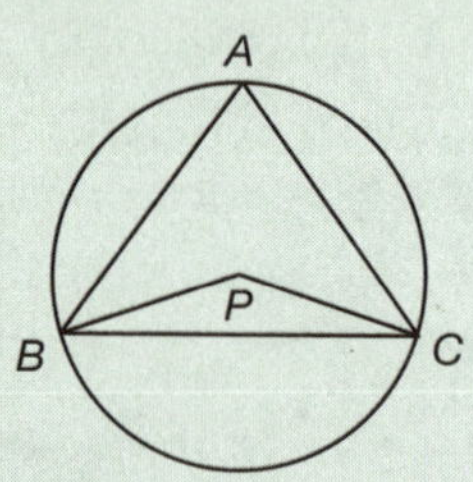

In the above figure, $\overline{AB}$ and $\overline{AC}$ are equal chords of the given circle, $BP = PC$ and $\angle ABP = \angle PBC$. If $\angle BAC = 40°$, then find $\angle BPC$.

(A) 90° (B) 100°
(C) 110° (D) 120°

20.

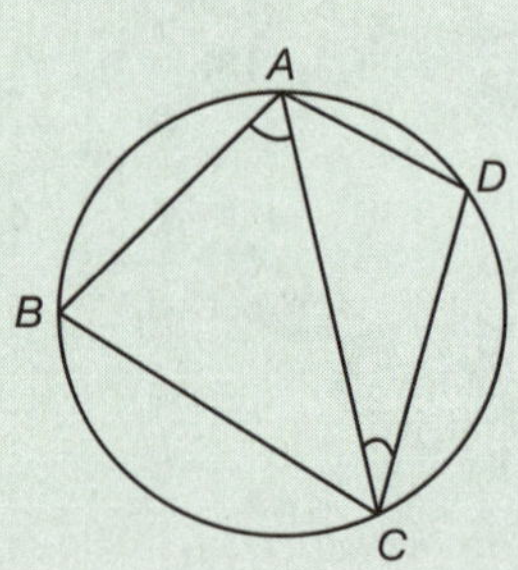

In the above figure (not to scale), $ABCD$ is a cyclic quadrilateral, $AB = BC$, $\angle BAC = 40°$ and $\angle DCA = 70°$ then find $\angle CAD$.

(A) 30° (B) 50°
(C) 80° (D) 100°

21. In the diagram the circle contains the vertices A, B, C of triangle ABC. Now $\angle ABC$ is 30° and the length of AC is 5. The diameter of the circle is:

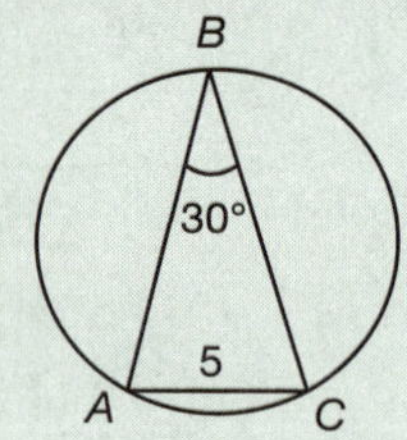

(A) $5\sqrt{3}$ (B) 8
(C) 10 (D) $5\sqrt{5}$

22. Find the measure of angle y in the figure if P is the centre of the circle:

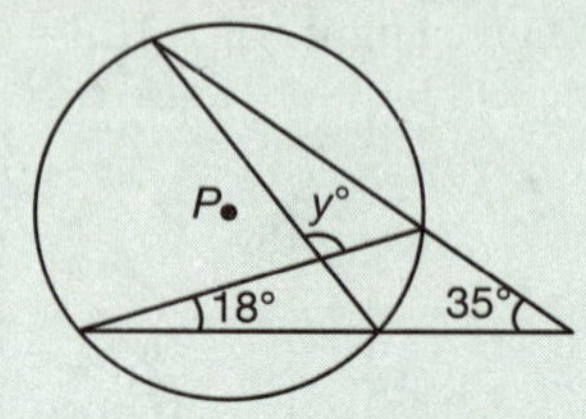

(A) 99° (B) 105°
(C) 90° (D) 109°

23. The centre of a circle is at O. AB and CD are two chords of length d and l respectively. If P is the midpoint of CD, then the length OP is:

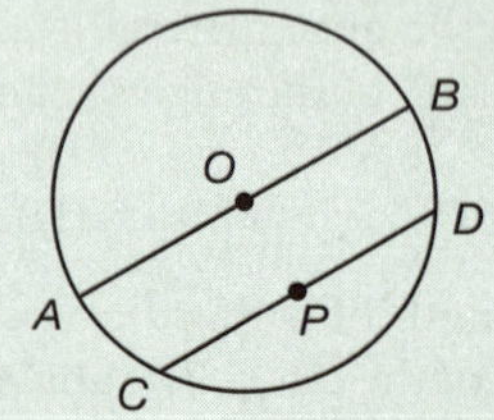

(A) $\sqrt{d^2 + \ell^2}$ (B) $\sqrt{d^2 - \ell^2}$
(C) $\frac{1}{2}\sqrt{d^2 + \ell^2}$ (D) $\frac{1}{2}\sqrt{d^2 - \ell^2}$

24. BC is the diameter of a circle. Points A and D are situated on the circumference of the semi-circle $\angle ABD = 35°$ and $\angle BCD = 60°$, $\angle ADB$ equals to:

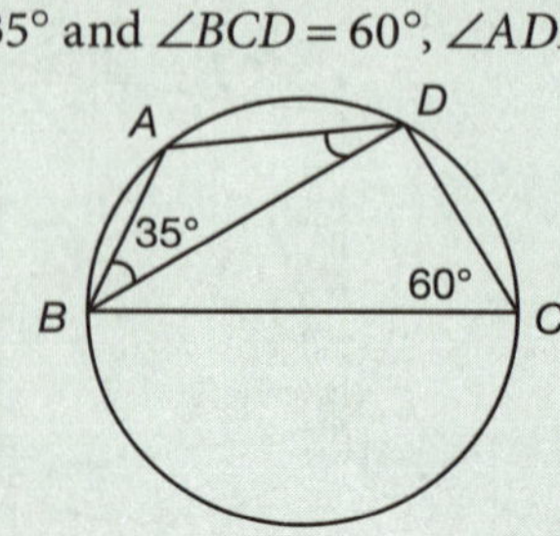

(A) 20° (B) 25°
(C) 30° (D) 115°

25. Find the value of $a + b$, if $b = 2a$.

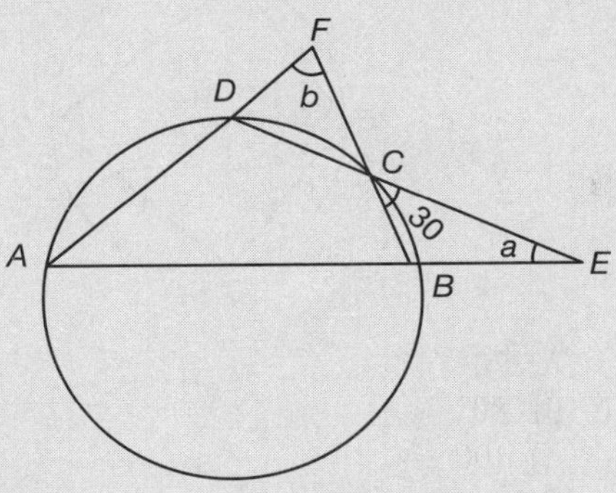

(A) 40° (B) 80°
(C) 120° (D) 160°

26. In the given figure value of 'a' is:

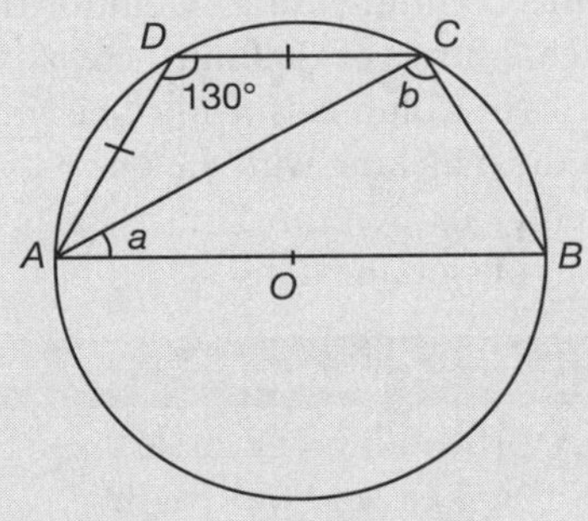

(A) 30° (B) 40°
(C) 60° (D) 90°

Multiple Correct Type Questions

1. Two circles are drawn with sides PQ and PR of a triangle PQR as diameters. Circles intersect at a point S. Then
(A) $\angle PSQ$ and $\angle PSR$ form a linear pair angles.
(B) $\angle PSQ$ and $\angle PSR$ are complementary angles.
(C) $\angle PSQ$ and $\angle PSR$ are supplementary angles.
(D) Points Q, S, R are collinear points.

2. In the given figure, $\angle R = \angle S = 30°$, then the four points P, Q, R, S

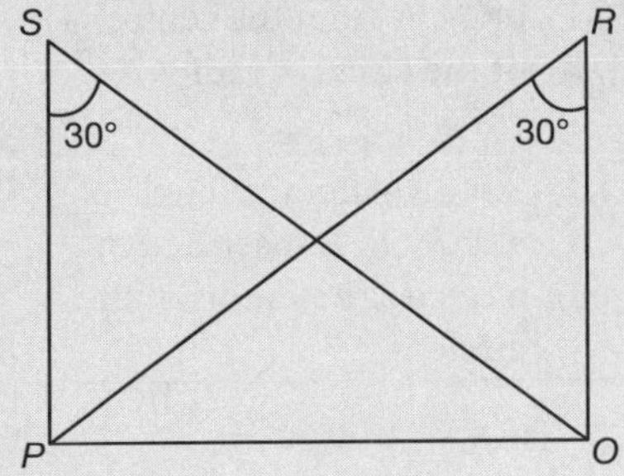

(A) are con-cyclic
(B) are collinear
(C) are not collinear
(D) lie on the same circle

3. Which of the following is /are incorrect?
(A) A circle has only finite number of equal chords
(B) A circle is not a plane figure
(C) Sector is the region between the diameter and its arc.
(D) A chord of a circle, which is twice as long as its radius is the diameter of the circle

4. If an equilateral triangle PQR is inscribed in a circle with centre O, then $\angle QOR$ is equal to
(A) 60° (B) 30°
(C) 120° (D) 90°

5. Diagonals of a cyclic quadrilateral are the diameters of that circle, Then quadrilateral can be:
(A) Parallelogram (B) Square
(C) Rectangle (D) Trapezium

6. If the radius of a circle is a rational number, then its area is given by a number which is:
(A) Rational (B) Irrational
(C) Integral (D) Real Number

7. Fill in the blanks and select the correct option. [IMO-2016]
(i) There is (are) ______P______ circle(s) passing through three non-collinear points.
(ii) A continuous piece of a circle is called the ______Q______ of the circle.
(iii) If two arcs of a circle are congruent, then their corresponding chords are ______R______.
(iv) A line segment joining the centre to any point on the circle is called its ______S______.
(v) The sum of either pair of opposite angles of a cyclic quadrilateral is ______T______.

	P	Q	R	S	T
(A)	Infinite	Chord	Not equal	Diameter	360°
(B)	Two	Arc	Equal	Diameter	360°
(C)	One	Chord	Equal	Radius	180°
(D)	One	Arc	Equal	Radius	180°

8. If two chords of a circle are equidistance from the centre of the circle, then they ______
(A) Are Equal to each other
(B) Not equal to each other.
(C) Subtend Equal Angle at the Centre.
(D) None of these

9. The chord of maximum length in a circle is called:
(A) Twice of Radius (B) Arc
(C) Diameter (D) Point

10.

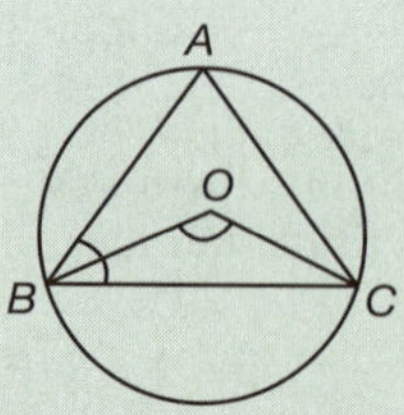

In the above diagram (not to scale), $AB = AC$. O is the centre of the circle. If $\angle ABC = 80°$, then find $\angle BOC$.

(A) 20° (B) 40°
(C) 60° (D) 80°

11. In the figure below, CD is a chord of the semi-circle with centre O.

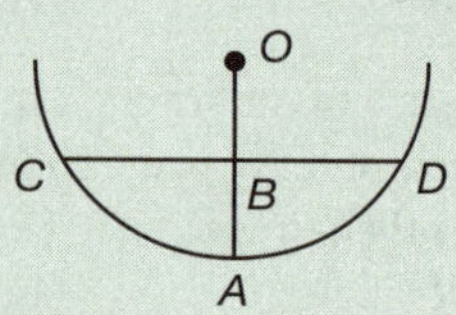

OA is the radius of the circle. If $CD = 10$ cm, $AB = 2$ cm and $\overline{OA} \perp \overline{CD}$, then find the length of OB.

(A) 3.25 cm (B) 5.25 cm
(C) 4.25 cm (D) 6.25 cm

12. O is the centre of the circle of radius 5 cm. $OP \perp AB$, $OQ \perp CD$, $AB \parallel CD$, $AB = 6$ cm and $CD = 8$ cm. Then the value of PQ can be

(A) 1 cm (B) 7 cm
(C) 4.25 cm (D) 6.25 cm

13. AB and CD are two parallel chords of a circle such that $AB = 10$ cm and $CD = 24$ cm. If the radius of circle is 13 cm then the distance between the chords can be?

(A) 10 cm (B) 7 cm
(C) 12 cm (D) 17 cm

14.

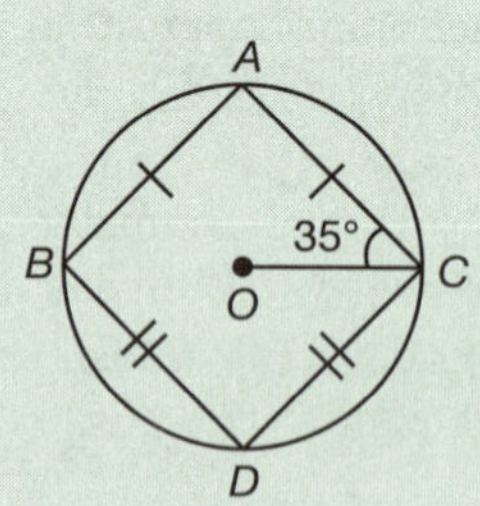

In the figure above (not to scale), $AB = AC$, $BD = DC$ and 'O' is centre of the circle. If $\angle ACO = 35°$ then find $\angle ABD$ and $\angle BDC$.

(A) 90°, 90° (B) 110°, 110°
(C) 90°, 110° (D) 80°, 90°

15. In the given figure (not to scale), O is the centre of the circle and $AB = BC$. If $\angle AQC = 80°$, then find the angle subtended by the chord AB at the centre.

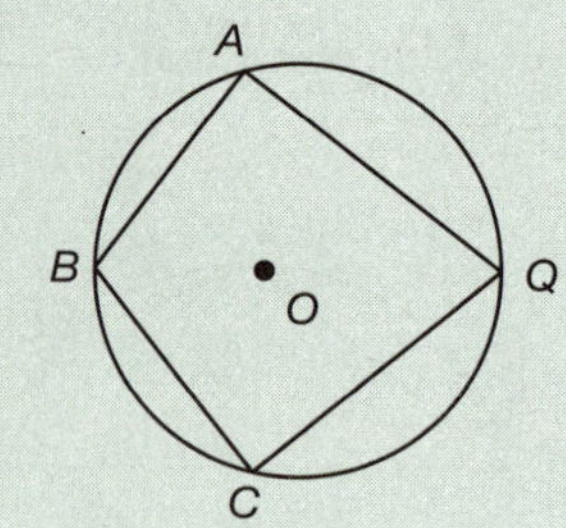

(A) 70°
(B) 80°
(C) 100°
(D) Cannot be determined

Match Type Questions

Directions: Column-I and Column-II contain four entries each. Entries of Column-I are to be matched with some entries of Column-II. Only One entry of Column-I may have the matching with the one entry of Column-II and one entry of Column-II may have Only one entry with entries of Column-I.

1.

Column-I	Column-II
(A) The radius of a circle is 8 cm and the length of one of its chords is 12 cm. The distance of the chord from the centre is	(P) 23 cm
(B) Two parallel chords of lengths 30 cm and 16 cm are drawn on the opposite sides of the centre of a circle of radius 17 cm. The distance between the chords is	(Q) 5.196 cm
(C) The length of a chord which is at a distance of 4 cm from the centre of the circle of radius 6 cm is	(R) 5.291 cm
(D) An equilateral triangle of side 9 cm is inscribed in a circle. The radius of the circle is	(S) 8.94 cm

2.

Column-I	Column-II
(A) C is a point on the minor arc AB of the circle with centre O. Given $\angle ACB = x$. Calculate x, if $ACBO$ is a parallelogram.	(P) $60°$
(B) Chord ED is parallel to the diameter AC of the circle. Given $\angle CBE = 55°$, calculate $\angle DEC$.	(Q) $120°$

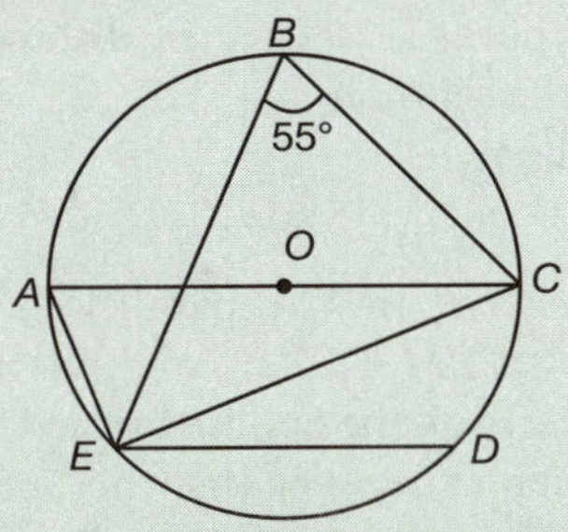

Column-I	Column-II
(C) In the given figure, O is the centre of the circle. If $\angle ACB = 60°$, find $\angle OAB$.	(R) $35°$

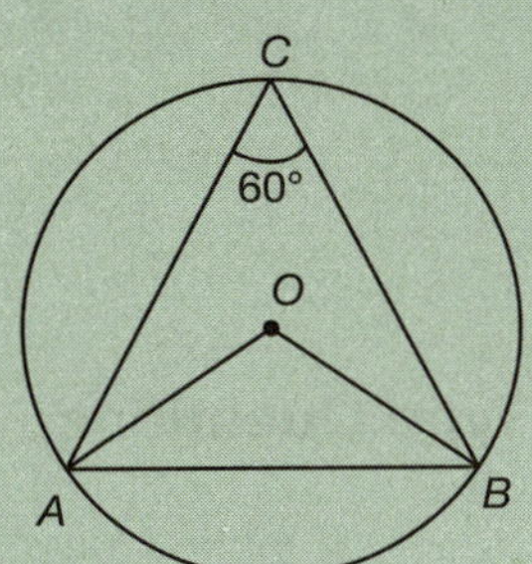

Column-I	Column-II
(D) In the given figure, O is the centre of a circle, $\angle AOB = 40°$ and $\angle BDC = 100°$, Find $\angle OBC$	(S) $30°$

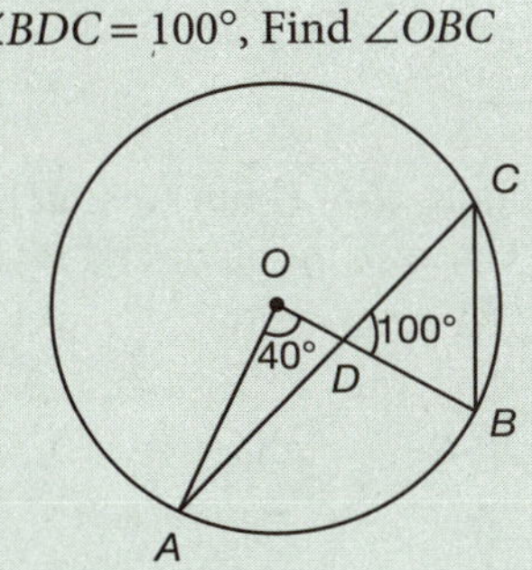

3. In the figure, AC is the diameter of a circle with centre O and chord $BD \perp AC$, intersecting each other at E. Now match the column.

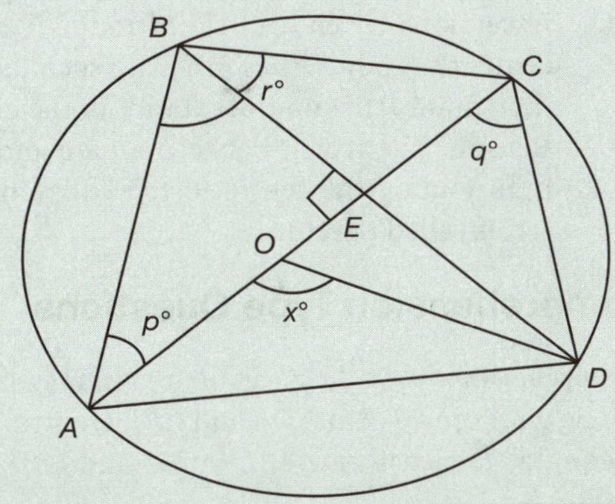

Column-I	Column-II
(A) Value of p in terms of x	(P) $\frac{x}{2}$
(B) Value of q in terms of x	(Q) $90° - \frac{x}{2}$
(C) Value of r in terms of x	(R) $90°$
(D) Value of $\angle B$	(S) $r° + q°$

Assertion and Reason Type Questions

Directions: In the following questions Assertion (A) is given followed by a Reason (R). Mark your responses from the following options.

(A) Both Assertion and Reason are true and Reason is the correct explanation of 'Assertion'.

(B) Both Assertion and Reason are true and Reason is not the correct explanation of 'Assertion'.

(C) Assertion is true but Reason is false.

(D) Assertion is false but Reason is true.

1. **Assertion:** Angle subtended at the centre by an arc is twice the size of the angle subtended by the same arc at the circumference.
Reason: Angle subtended at the circumference in a semicircle is 90°

2. **Assertion:** The circumference of a circle must be a positive real number.
Reason: If $r(>0)$ is the radius of the circle, then its circumference $2\pi r$ is a positive real…number.

3. **Assertion:** A diameter of a circle is the longest chord of the circle and all diameters have equal lengths.
Reason: length of a diameter = radius

4. **Assertion:** Given a circle of radius r and with centre O. A point P lies in a place such that $OP > r$ then point P lies on the exterior of the circle.
Reason: The region between an arc and the two radii joining the centre to the endpoints of the arc, is called a sector.

Comprehension Type Questions

Comprehension-1: In the given figure, AB is a diameter of a circle with centre O. If ADE and CBE are straight lines, meeting at E such that $\angle BAD = 35°$ and $\angle BED = 25°$. Find:

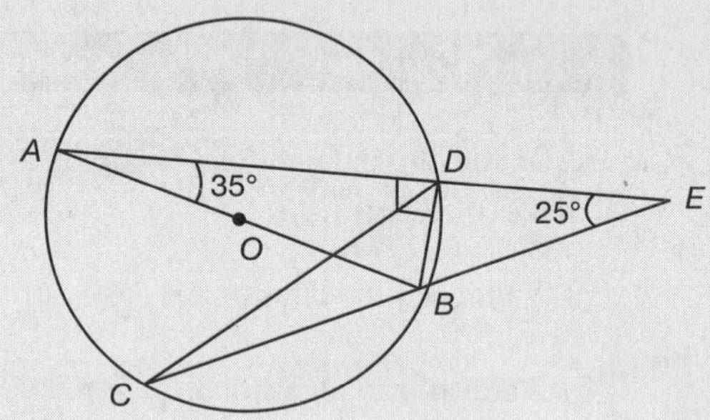

1. $\angle DBC$
(A) 35° (B) 115°
(C) 30° (D) 40°

2. $\angle DCB$
(A) 35° (B) 65°
(C) 90° (D) 45°

3. $\angle BDC$
(A) 120° (B) 105°
(C) 30° (D) 25°

Comprehension-2: In the given figure, $ABCD$ is a quadrilateral in which $\angle D = 90°$. A circle $C(O, r)$ touches the sides AB, BC, CD and DA at P, Q, R, S respectively. If $BC = 38$ cm, $CD = 25$ cm and $BP = 27$ cm. Then answer the following questions:

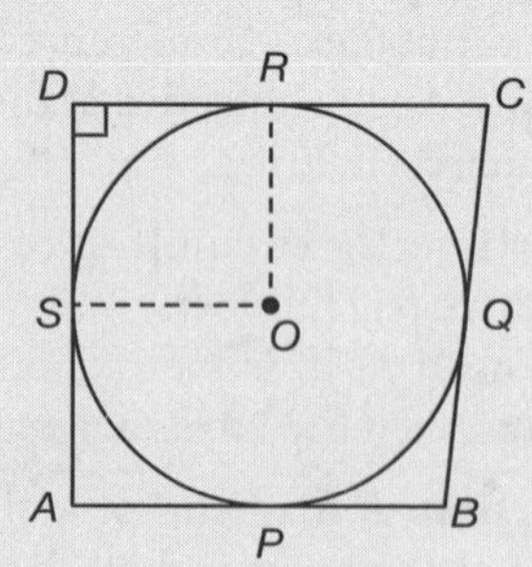

4. What is the value of r?
(A) 11 cm (B) 14 cm
(C) 13 cm (D) 12 cm

5. What is the value of CR?
(A) 14 cm (B) 13 cm
(C) 11 cm (D) 20 cm

6. Area of $DROS$?
(A) 169 cm^2 (B) 196 cm^2
(C) 121 cm^2 (D) 144 cm^2

Comprehension-3: The perpendicular from the centre of a circle to a chord bisects the chord.

7. The radius of a circle 13 cm and the length of one of its chords is 10 cm. The distance of the chord from the centre is:
(A) 11 cm (B) 12 cm
(C) 13 cm (D) 14 cm

8. LM and NP are two parallel chords of a circle such that $LM = 10$ cm and $NP = 24$ cm. If the chords are on the opposite sides of the centre and the distance between them is 17 cm, the radius of the circle is:
(A) 11 cm (B) 12 cm
(C) 13 cm (D) 14 cm

9. The radius of a circle is 10 cm and the distance of the chords from the centre is 6 cm. Then the length of one of its chords is:
(A) 12 cm (B) 13 cm
(C) 14 cm (D) 16 cm

Numerical Type Questions

1.

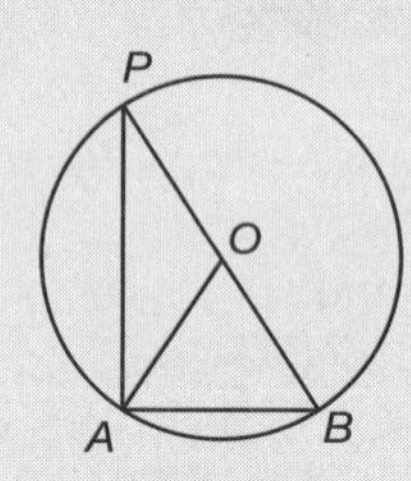

In the figure above (not to scale), $\angle PAO = 40°$, O is the centre of the circle and PB is the diameter, find $\angle OBA$.

2.

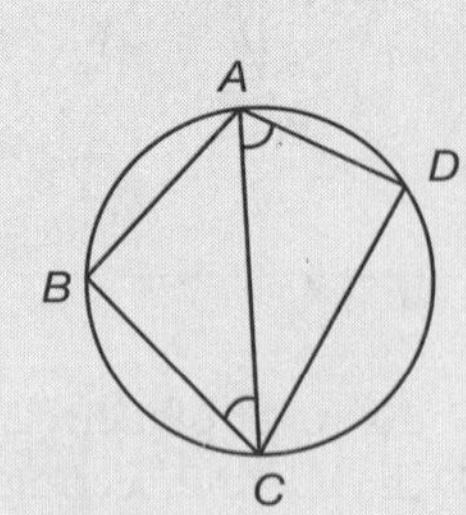

In the figure above (not to scale), $\angle CAD = 40°$, $\angle ADC = 100°$ and $\angle ACB = 20°$ then $\angle BAC$ is ________.

3. 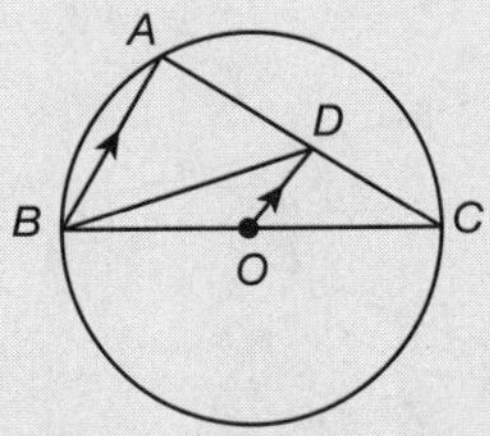

In the above figure, BC is the diameter of the circle with centre O and $\overline{AB} \| \overline{OD}$. If $\angle DOC = 40°$, then find $\angle ACB$.

4. Two equal chords of a circle intersect on the circle, make angle $x°$ and form a triangle with a diameter. What is the angle subtended by each chord at the centre?

5. 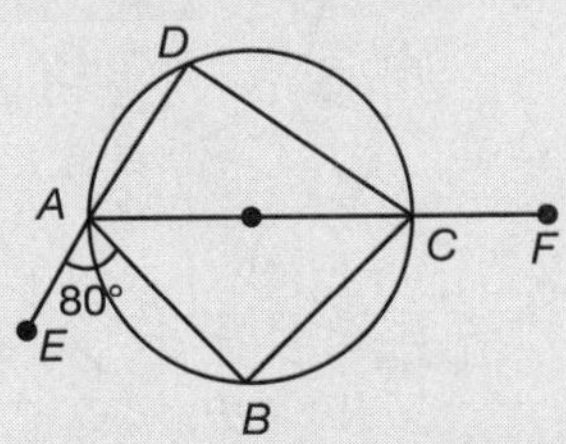

In the above figure (not to scale), AC is the diameter and $ABCD$ is the cyclic quadrilateral. If $\angle EAB = 80°$ and $\angle DCF = 110°$, then find the angle made by AB at the centre of the circle.

6. 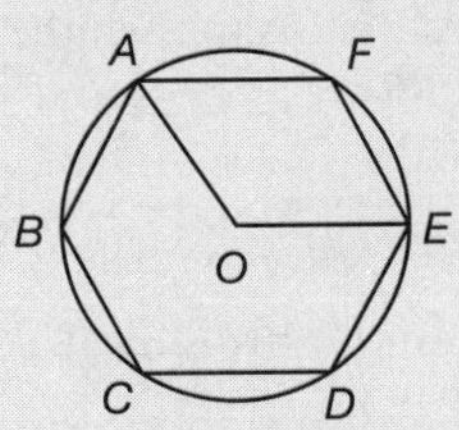

In the above figure (not to scale), $ABCDEF$ is a regular hexagon inscribed in a circle, what is $\angle AOE$?

7. 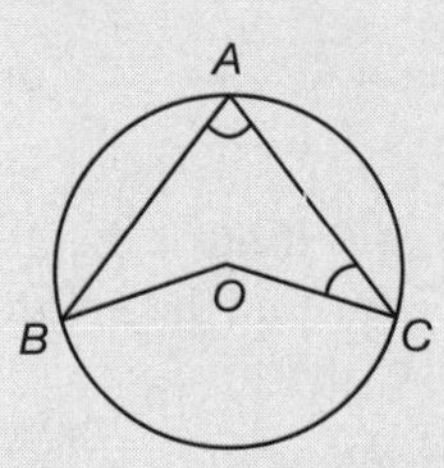

In the above figure, $AB = AC$ and O is the centre of the circle. If $\angle ACO = 40°$, then find $\angle ABO$.

8. 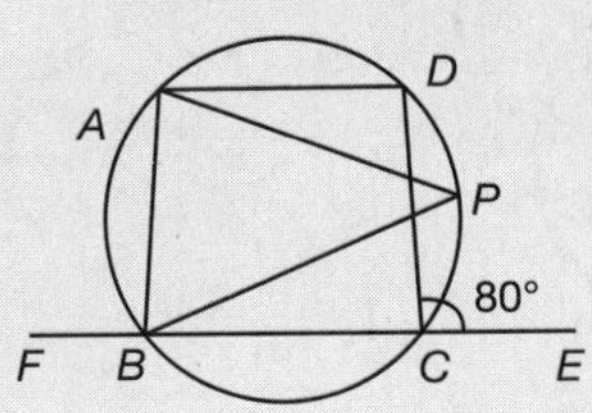

In the above figure (not to scale), $\overline{PA}$ and $\overline{PB}$ are equal chords and $ABCD$ is a cyclic quadrilateral. If $\angle DCE = 80°$, $\angle DAP = 30°$ then find $\angle APB$.

9. 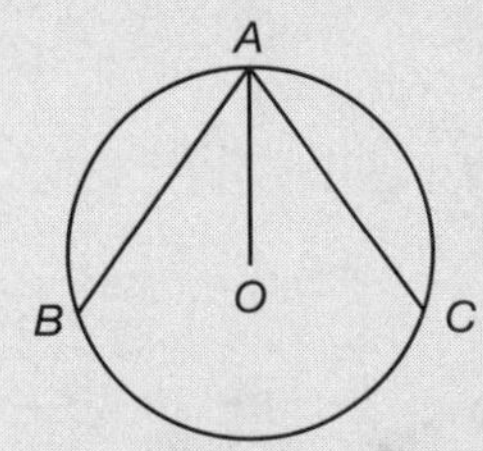

In the figure above (not to scale), chord AB = chord AC and if $\angle BAO = 25°$, then find $\angle BOC$ where 'O' is the centre.

10. 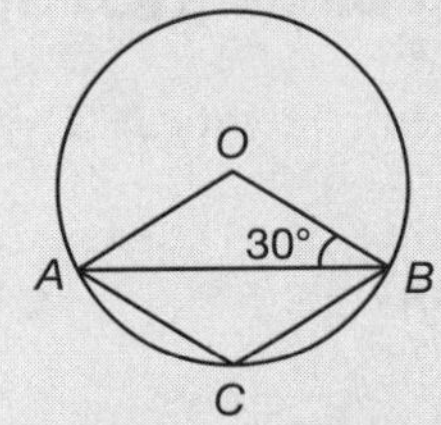

In the figure above (not to scale), O is the centre of the circle and $\angle OBA = 30°$. Find $\angle ACB$.

11. $ABCD$ is a cyclic quadrilateral inscribed in a circle with the centre O. Then $\angle OAD$ is equal to:

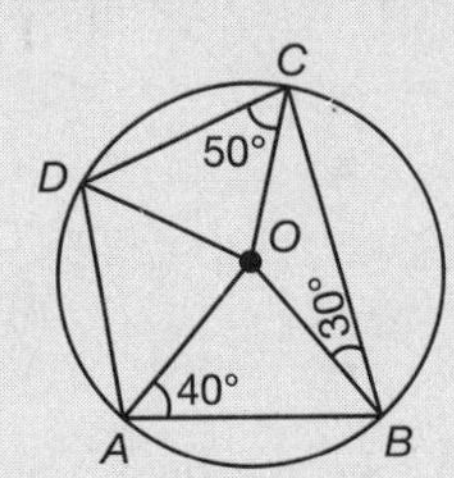

12. If the distance between two parallel chords of a circle is 6 cm and each chord is 8 cm long, then the radius of the circle is:

13. 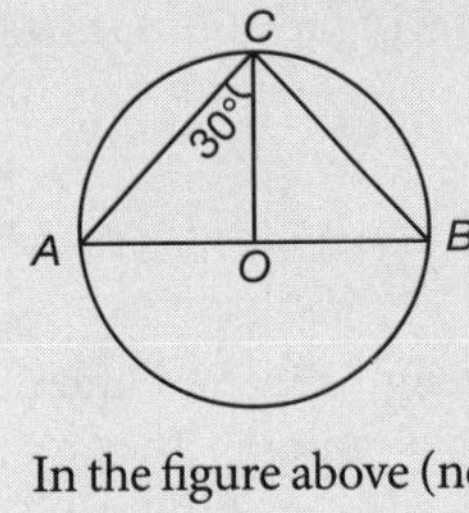

In the figure above (not to scale), AB is the diameter of the circle with centre O. If $\angle ACO = 30°$, then find $\angle BOC$.

14. 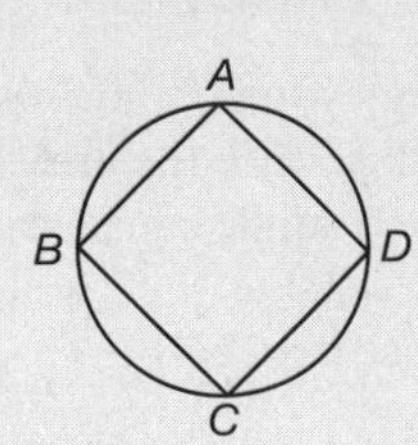

In the above figure (not to scale), if *AB, BC, CD* and *DA* are equal chords. Find the angle between any two adjacent chords.

15.

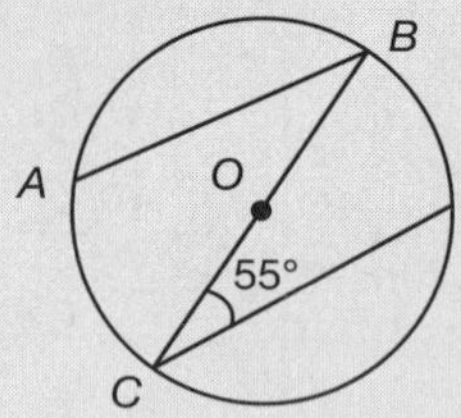

In the figure above (not to scale), $\overline{AB} \parallel \overline{CD}$, $AB = CD$ and if $\angle BCD = 55°$ and *O* is the centre of the circle, then $\angle AOB =$ _____.

Higher Order Thinking Skills (HOTS)

1. In the figure, *O* is the centre, then $\angle BXD =$

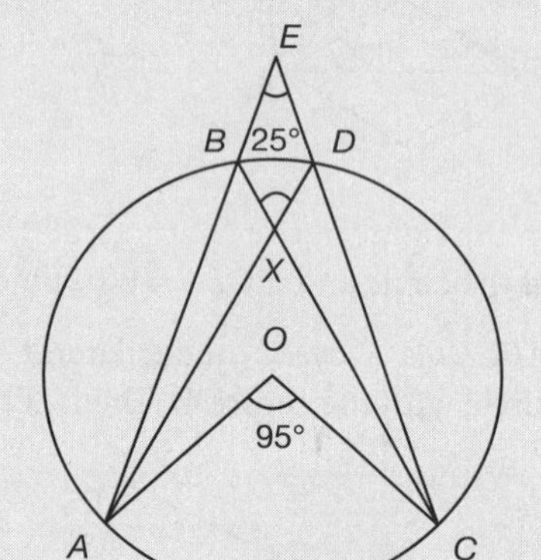

(A) 65° (B) 60°
(C) 70° (D) 55°

2. Let ΔXYZ be the right angle triangle, with the right angle at *Z*. Let A_x de-remarks the area of the circle with diameter *YZ*. Let A_y de-remark the area of the circle with diameter *XZ* and let A_z de-remarks the area of the circle with diameter *XY*. Which of the following relations is true?

(A) $A_z = A_x + A_y$ (B) $A_Z = A_x^2 + A_y^2$

(C) $A_z^2 = A_x^2 + A_y^2$ (D) $A_z^2 = A_x^2 - A_y^2$

3. A triangle with side lengths in the ratio 3 : 4 : 5 is inscribed in a circle of radius 3. The area of the triangle is equal to:
(A) 8.64 (B) 12
(C) 6 (D) 10.28

4. Two legs of a right triangle are $8\sqrt{\pi}$ and $9\sqrt{\pi}$ as shown. A circle is drawn so that the area inside the circle but outside the triangle equals the area inside the triangle but outside the circle. The radius of the circle is: (Use $\pi = 22/7$)

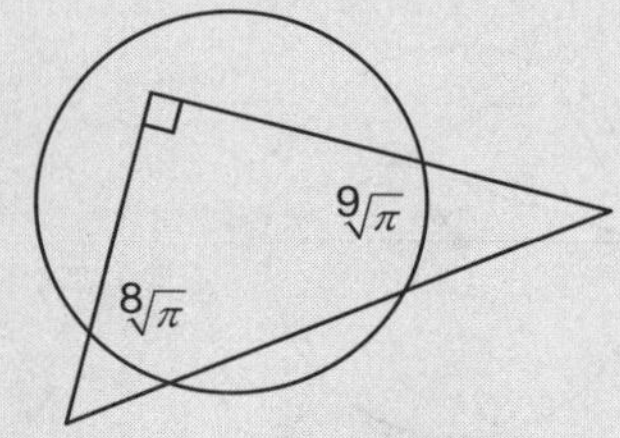

(A) $6\sqrt{\pi}$ (B) 6
(C) 5 (D) 8

5. In the diagram *O* is the centre of a circle. $AE + EB = CE + ED$. $OP \perp AB$ and $OQ \perp CD$, then the true relation between *OP* and *OQ* is:

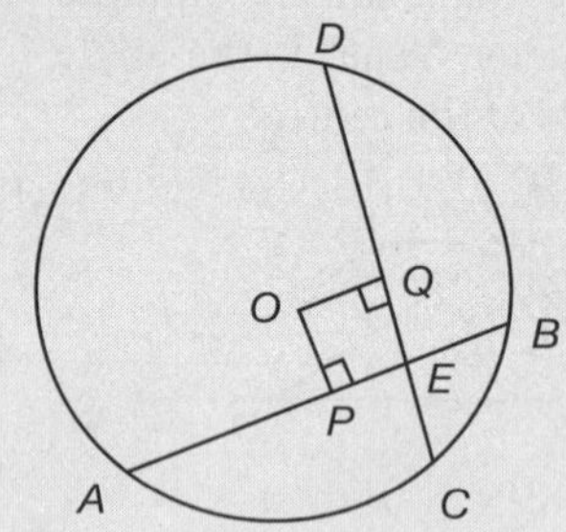

(A) $OP > OQ$ (B) $OP < OQ$

(C) $OP = \frac{1}{2}OQ$ (D) $OP = OQ$

6. *PQ* and *RS* are the chords of a circle each of which is at a distance of 5 cm from the centre. If the radius of the circle is 10 cm then the length of the chords *PQ* and *RS* are ______ and ______ respectively.

(A) $5\sqrt{3}$ cm, $10\sqrt{3}$ cm (B) $5\sqrt{3}$ cm, $5\sqrt{3}$ cm

(C) $10\sqrt{3}$ cm, $10\sqrt{3}$ cm (D) $10\sqrt{3}$ cm, $5\sqrt{3}$ cm

7. Which of the following shapes of the equal perimeter, the one having the largest area is:
(A) circle
(B) equilateral triangle
(C) square
(D) regular pentagon

8. *EF* and *FG* are two equal chords of a circle intersecting each other at *F*. If *EG* is the diameter of the circle, $EF = FG = 7$ cm, find the length of *EG*.

(A) $7\sqrt{2}$ cm (B) 49 cm

(C) $49\sqrt{2}$ cm (D) 7 cm

9.

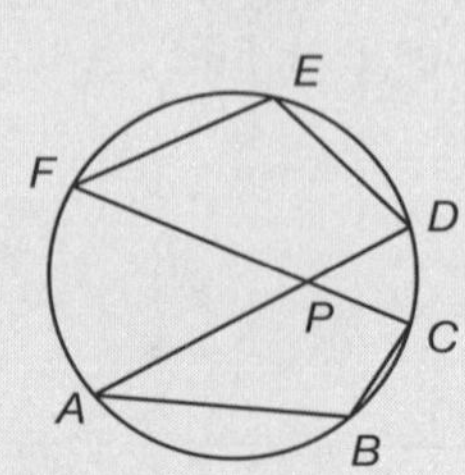

In the above figure (not to scale) $\overline{AB}, \overline{BC}, \overline{CF}, \overline{DE}$ and $\overline{FE}$ are chords of the circle. If $\angle ABC = 100°$ and $\angle FED = 110°$, then find $\angle FPA$.

(A) 20° (B) 30°
(C) 40° (D) 70°

10. There are four chords *AB, BC, CD* and *DA* in a circle making angles $\theta, 2\theta, 3\theta$ and 4θ respectively at the centre of a circle. Find the angle between *BC* and *CD*.

(A) 30° (B) 45°
(C) 60° (D) 90°

11. *MN* and *KL* are two chords of a circle of length 12 cm each, when produced they meet at point *C*. If *CM* = 20 cm, then *CL* = _______.

(A) 12 cm
(B) 10 cm
(C) 8 cm
(D) 6 cm

12.

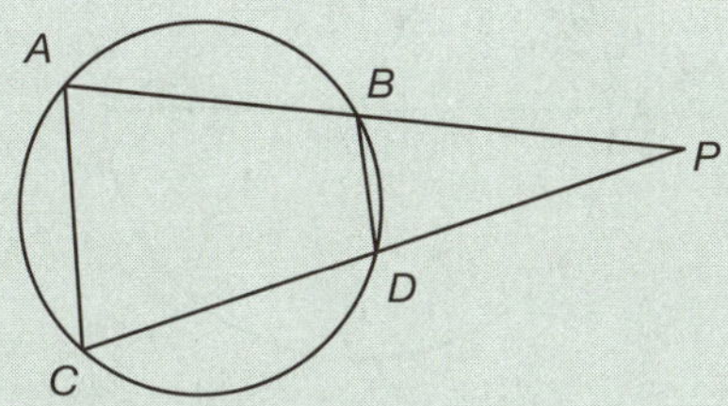

In the figure above (not to scale), *AB* = *CD* and $\overline{AB}$ and $\overline{CD}$ are produced to meet at the point *P*. If $\angle BAC = 70°$, then find $\angle P$.

(A) 30° (B) 40°
(C) 60° (D) 50°

13.

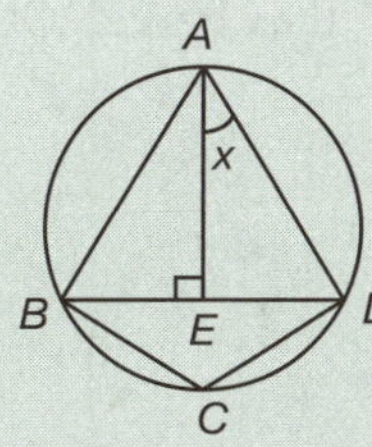

In the figure above (not to scale), *AB* = *AD*, *BC* = *CD* and $\overline{AE}$ is the perpendicular from *A* to $\overline{BD}$. If $\angle DAE = x°$, then find $\angle BCD$.

(A) $x°$ (B) $2x°$
(C) $(90 - x)°$ (D) $(180 - 2x)°$

14. A semicircle is drawn with *AB* as its diameter. From *C*, a point on *AB*, a line perpendicular to *AB* is drawn meeting the circumference of the semicircle at *D*. Given that *AC* = 2 cm and *CD* = 6 cm, the area of the semicircle is:

(A) 32π (B) 50π
(C) 40π (D) 36π

15. In the figure given above, *A* and *B* are the centres of the two congruent circles with radius of 17 units. If *AB* = 30 units, the length of the common chord *DC* is:

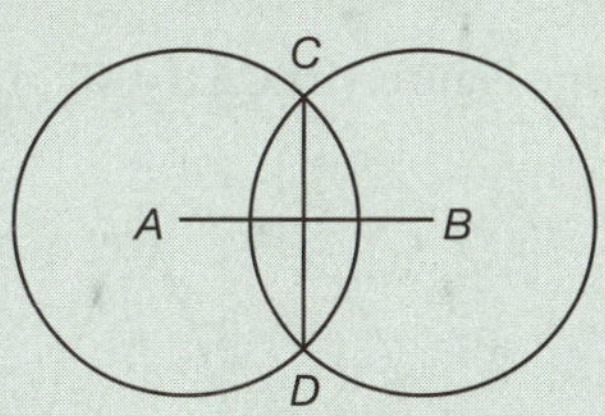

(A) 25 units (B) 18 units
(C) 10 units (D) 16 units

Free Response Type

Very Short Answer Type Questions

1. In Figure, two congruent circles have centres *O* and *O′*. Arc *AXB* subtends an angle of 75° at the centre *O* and arc *A′YB′* subtends an angle of 25° at the centre *O′*. Then the ratio of arcs *AXB* and *A′YB′* is:

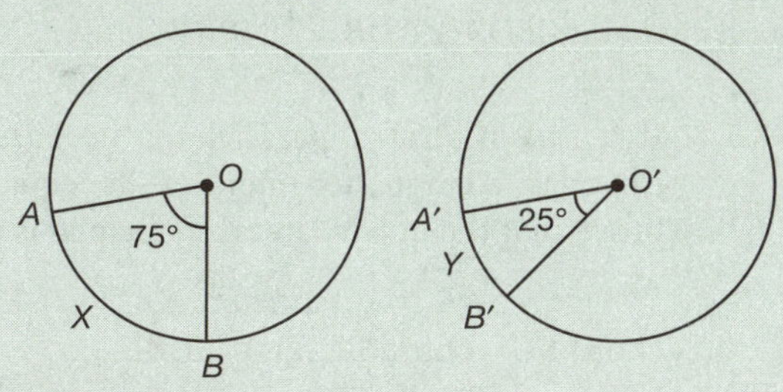

2. In Figure, *AB* and *CD* are two equal chords of a circle with centre *O*. *OP* and *OQ* are perpendiculars on chords *AB* and *CD*, respectively. If $\angle POQ = 150°$, then find $\angle APQ$?

3. In Figure, if *OA* = 5 cm, *AB* = 8 cm and *OD* is perpendicular to *AB*, then find *CD*.

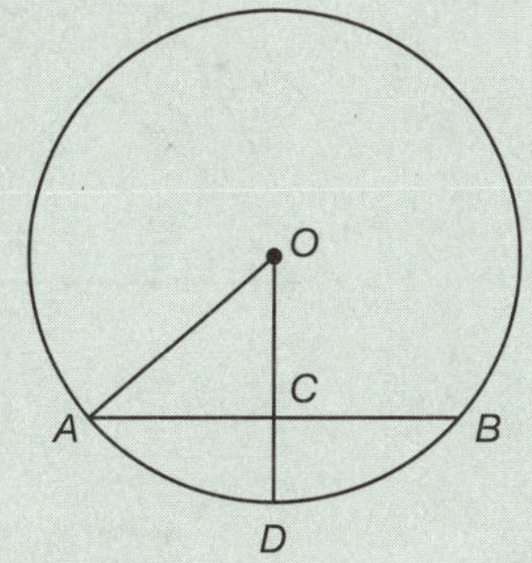

4. If *AB* = 12 cm, *BC* = 16 cm and *AB* is perpendicular to *BC*, then find the radius of the circle passing through points *A*, *B* and *C*.

5. In Figure, if $\angle ABC = 20°$, then find $\angle AOC$.

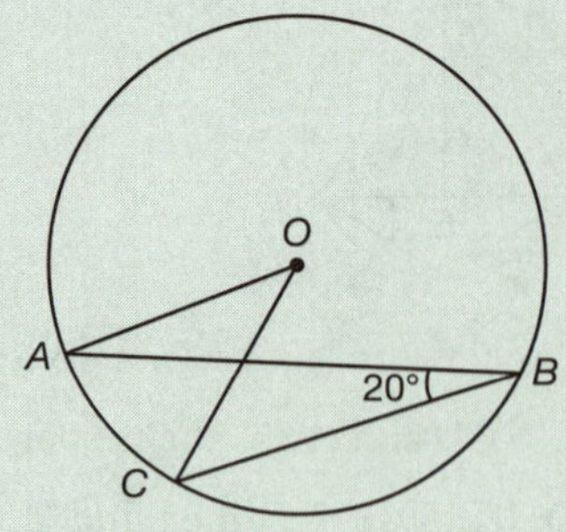

6. In the Figure, if *AOB* is the diameter of the circle and $AC = BC$, then find $\angle CAB$.

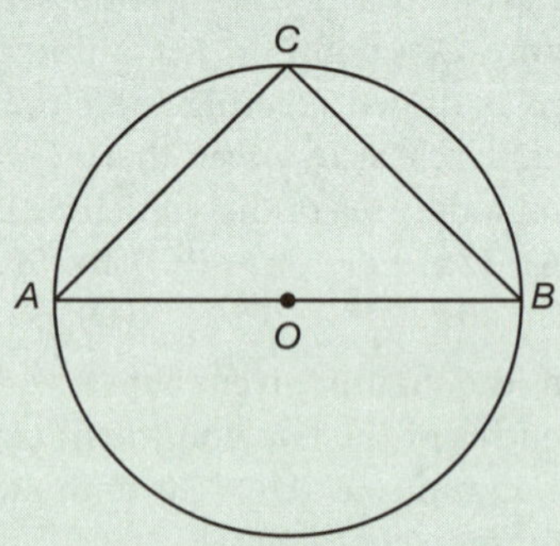

7. In the Figure, if $\angle OAB = 40°$, then find $\angle ACB$.

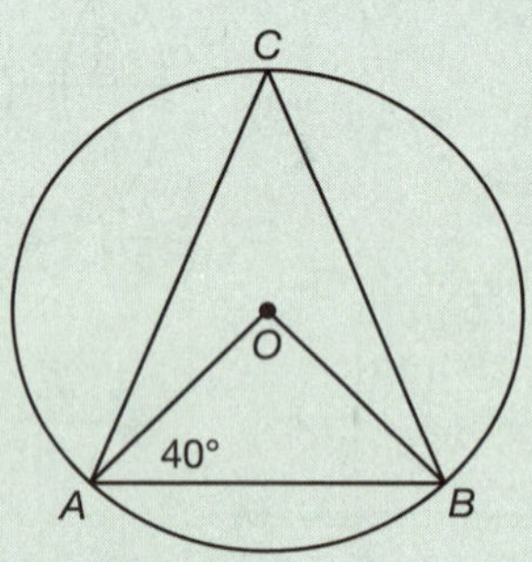

8. In the Figure, if $\angle DAB = 60°$, $\angle ABD = 50°$, then find $\angle ACB$.

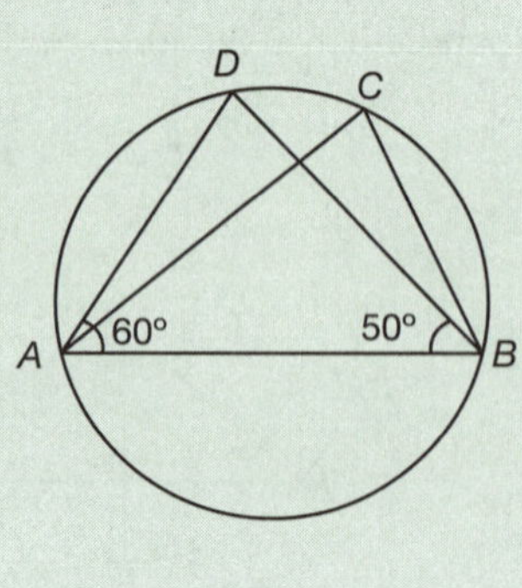

Short Answer Type Questions

1. In the Figure, *BC* is the diameter of the circle and $\angle BAO = 60°$. Then find $\angle ADC$.

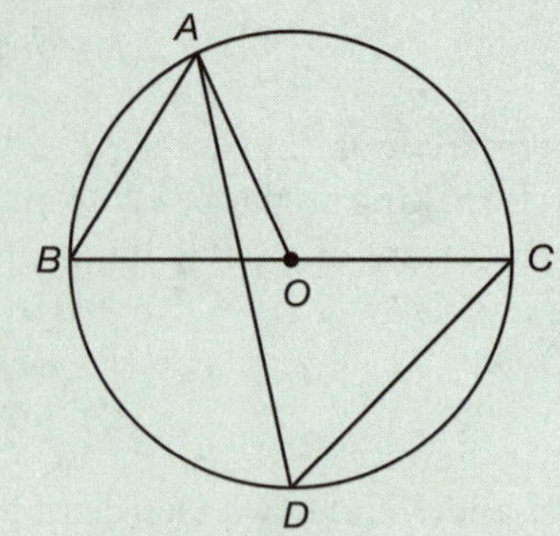

2. In the Figure, *AOC* is the diameter of the circle and arc $AXB = \frac{1}{2}$ arc *BYC*. Find $\angle BOC$.

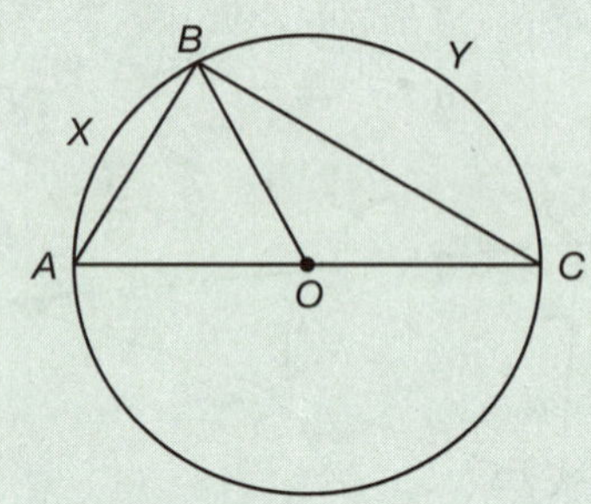

3. In Figure, $\angle ABC = 45°$, prove that $OA \perp OC$.

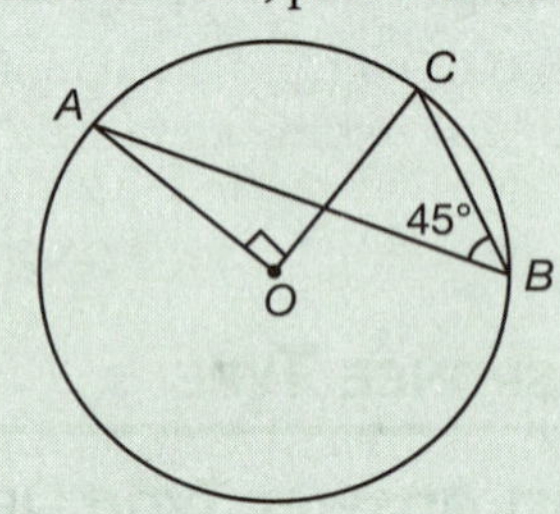

4. If a line segment joining midpoints of two chords of a circle passes through the centre of the circle, prove that the two chords are parallel.

5. *ABCD* is such a quadrilateral that *A* is the centre of the circle passing through *B*, *C* and *D*. Prove that $\angle CBD + \angle CDB = \frac{1}{2}\angle BAD$.

6. If a line is drawn parallel to the base of an isosceles triangle to intersect its equal sides, prove that the quadrilateral so formed is cyclic.

7. In Figure, *AB* is a diameter, $\angle ADC = 130°$ and chord BC = chord BE. Find $\angle CBE$.

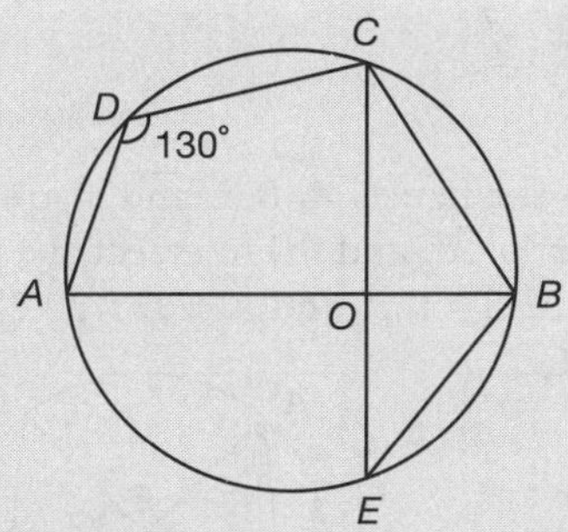

8. Two circles with centres O and O' intersect at two points A and B. A line PQ is drawn parallel to OO' through A(or B) intersecting the circles at P and Q. Prove that $PQ = 2\,OO'$.

9. In Figure, AOB is the diameter of the circle and C, D, E are any three points on the semi-circle. Find the value of $\angle ACD + \angle BED$.

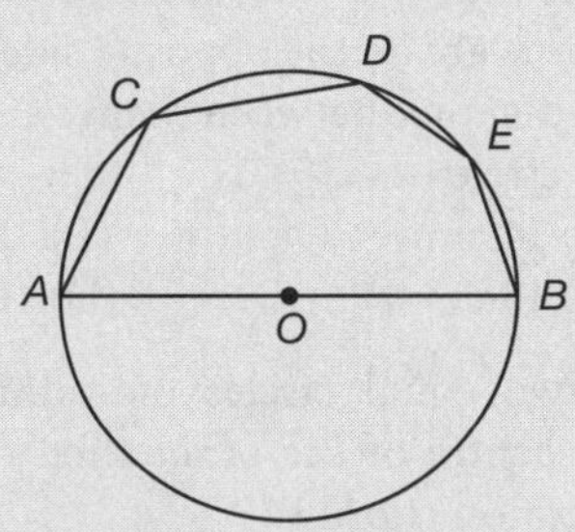

10. In the Figure, $\angle OAB = 30°$ and $\angle OCB = 57°$. Find $\angle BOC$ and $\angle AOC$.

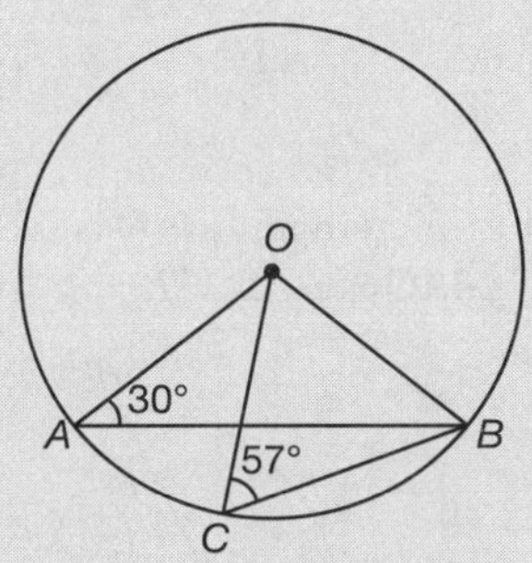

Long Answer Type Questions

1. Prove that among all the chords of a circle passing through a given point inside the circle that one is the smallest which is perpendicular to the diameter passing through the point.

2. If P, Q and R are the midpoints of the sides BC, CA and AB of a triangle and AD is the perpendicular from A on BC, prove that P, Q, R and D are concyclic.

3. Prove that angle bisector of any angle of a triangle and the perpendicular bisector of the opposite side if intersect, they will intersect on the circumcircle of the triangle.

4. If two chords AB and CD of a circle $AYDZBWCX$ intersect at right angles (see Figure), prove that arc CXA + arc DZB = arc AYD + arc BWC = semicircle.

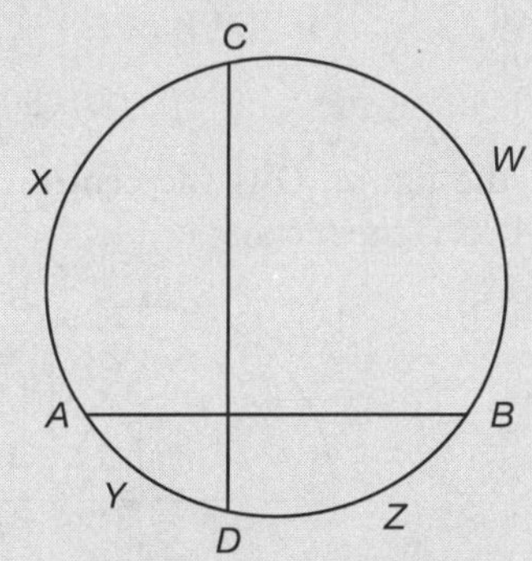

5. In Figure, AB and CD are two chords of a circle intersecting each other at point E. Prove that $\angle AEC = 2$ (Angle subtended by arc CXA at centre + angle subtended by arc DYB at the centre).

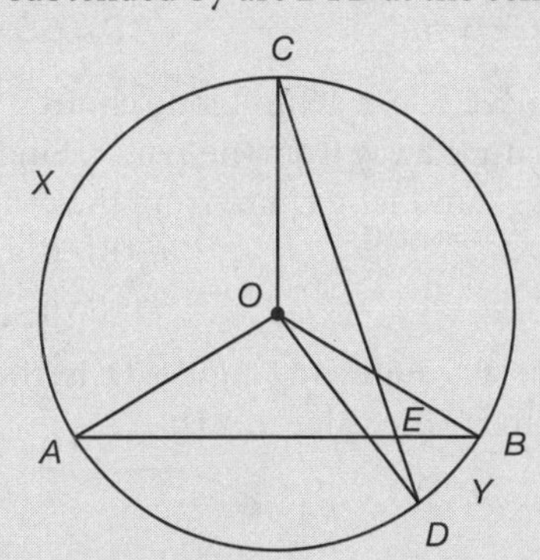

6. A circle has a radius of $\sqrt{2}$ cm. It is divided into two segments by a chord of length 2 cm. Prove that the angle subtended by the chord at a point in the major segment is 45°.

ARCHIVE CORNER

1. In the following figure, O is the centre of the circle. The value of x is:

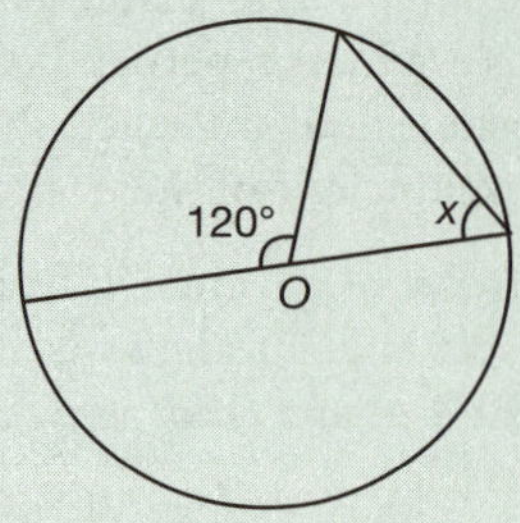

(A) 60° (B) 45°
(C) 40° (D) 80°

2. In the figure, O is the centre of the circle and $OABC$ is the rectangle:

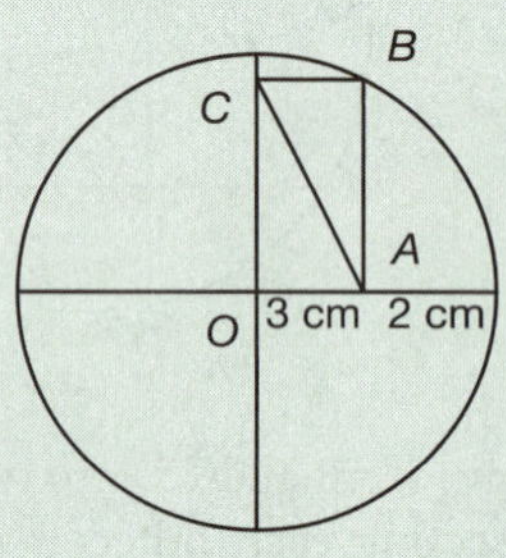

What is the length of AC?
(A) 4 cm (B) 4.5 cm
(C) 5 cm (D) 5.5 cm

3. In a circle, a 16 unit long chord is at a distance of 6 units away from the centre. Find the distance of a 12 unit long chord from the centre.
(A) 5 (B) 6
(C) 7 (D) 8

4. In the following figure O is the centre of the circle. The value of x is:

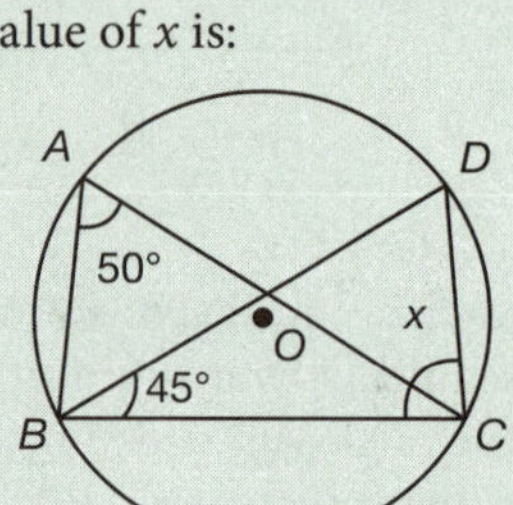

(A) 45° (B) 65°
(C) 85° (D) 95°

5. The chord of maximum length in a circle is called:
(A) Radius (B) Arc
(C) Diameter (D) Point

6. In the figure, A, B, C and D are four points on a circle. AC and BD intersect at a point E such that $\angle BEC = 125°$ and $\angle ECD = 30°$. Then $\angle BAC =$

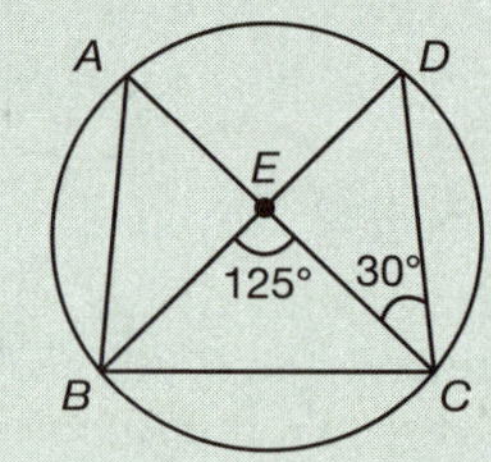

(A) 95° (B) 110°
(C) 85° (D) 105°

7. AB and CD are two parallel chords of a circle such that AB = 10 cm and CD = 24 cm. If the chords are on the opposite sides of the centre and the distance between them is 17 cm, the radius of the circle is:
(A) 14 cm (B) 10 cm
(C) 13 cm (D) 15 cm

8. If two equal circles of radius r pass through the centre of the other then the length of their common chord is:
(A) $\frac{r}{\sqrt{3}}$ (B) $r\sqrt{3}$
(C) $\frac{\sqrt{3}}{4}r$ (D) $r\sqrt{2}$

9. In the following figure O is the centre of the circle and $\angle BAC = n°$, $\angle OCB = m°$ then:

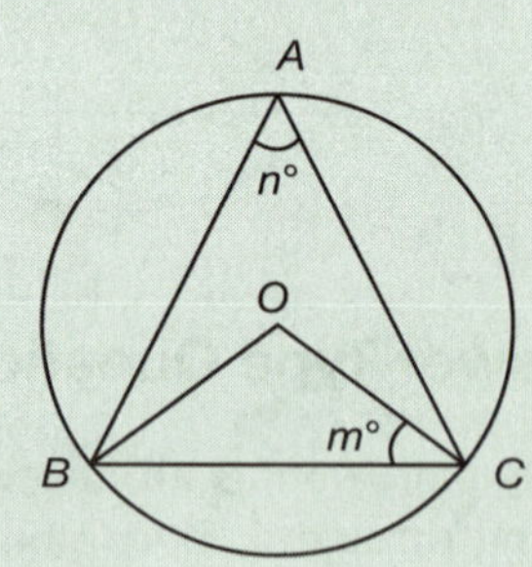

(A) $m° + n° = 90°$ (B) $m° + n° = 180°$
(C) $m° + n° = 120°$ (D) $m° + n° = 150°$

10. AB and AC are equal chords of a circle with centre O. Then by which angle OA bisects BC?
(A) 30° (B) 60°
(C) 90° (D) 120°

11. In the given figure find $\angle PQR$ (where O is the centre of the circle).

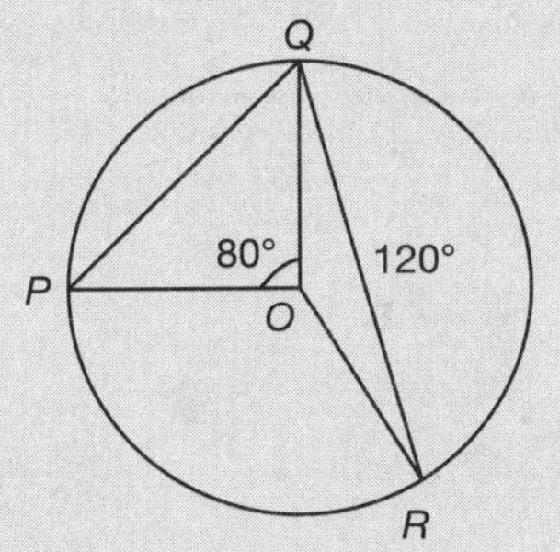

(A) 60° (B) 80°
(C) 100° (D) 120°

12. If two chords of a circle are equidistance from the centre of the circle, then they are ________
(A) Equal to each other
(B) Not equal to each other.
(C) Intersect each other.
(D) None of these

13. In the given figure, $\angle DBC = 22°$ and $\angle DCB = 78°$ then $\angle BAC$ is equal to:

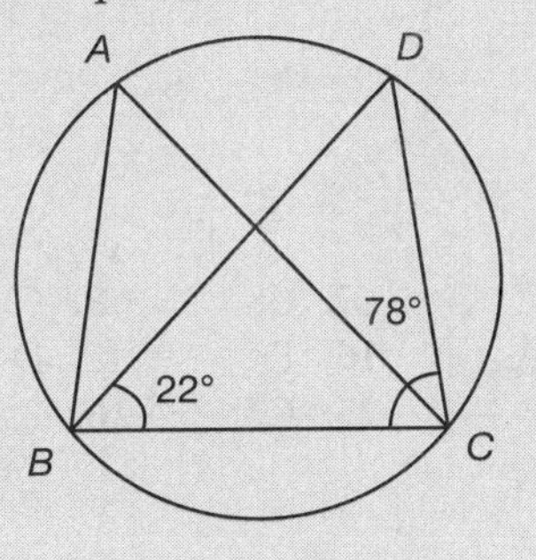

(A) 90° (B) 80°
(C) 78° (D) 22°

14. The lengths of two parallel chords of a circle are 6 cm and 8 cm. If the smaller chord is at a distance of 4 cm from the centre, then the distance of the other chord from the centre is:
(A) 5 cm (B) 4 cm
(C) 3 cm (D) 2 cm

15. In the figure, the radius of the larger circle is 2 cm and the radius of the smaller circle is 1 cm and the larger circle passes through the centre of the smaller circle. The length (in cm) of the chord AB is:

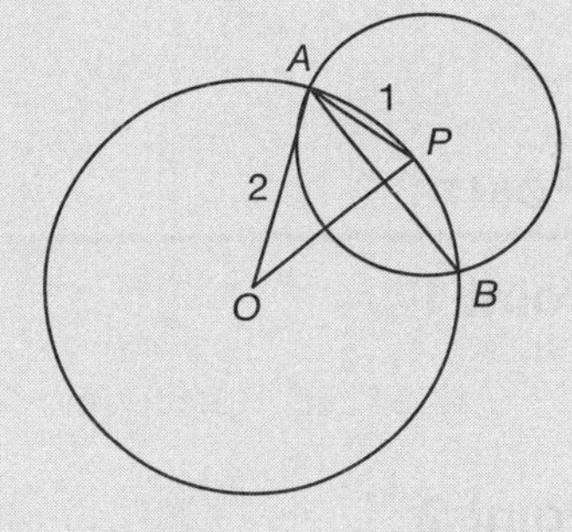

(A) $\frac{\sqrt{15}}{2}$ (B) 2
(C) $\frac{3}{2}$ (D) $\frac{5\sqrt{34}}{17}$

16. In the figure O is the centre of the circle and $\angle POR = 80°$. Then $\angle RQS$ is:

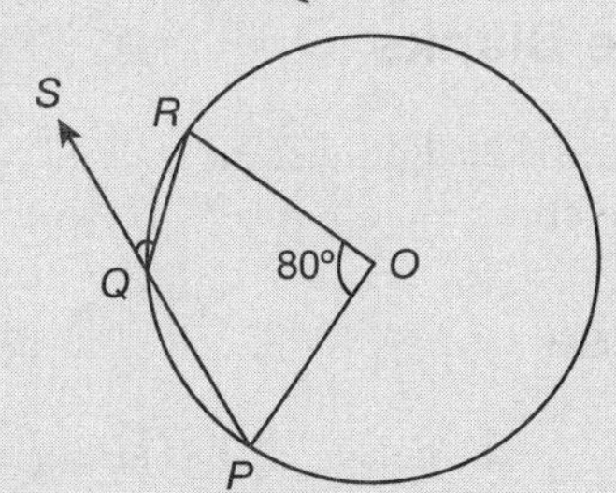

(A) 30° (B) 40°
(C) 1400 (D) 50°

17. In the figure, the semicircle centred at O has a diameter of 6 cm. The chord BC is parallel to AD and $BC = \frac{1}{3}AD$. The area of the trapezium $ABCD$ in cm², is:

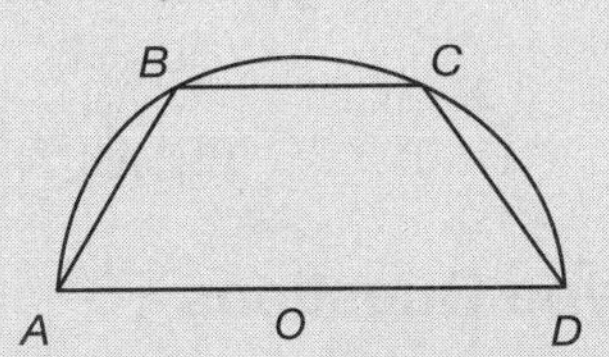

(A) 4 (B) $4\sqrt{2}$
(C) 8 (D) $8\sqrt{2}$

18. A chord of length 24 cm is situated 5 cm from the centre of a circle. The diameter of the circle will be:
(A) 24 cm (B) 29 cm
(C) 26 cm (D) 13 cm

ANSWER KEY

CHECK POINTS

Check Point 1

1. 3 **4.** 24 cm **5.** 16 cm

Check Point 2

6. 35° **7.** 60° **8.** 123° **9.** 140° **10.** 90°

Assessment Corner

FIXED RESPONSE TYPE

Fill in the Blanks

1. Equal **2.** Equidistant **3.** Congruent **4.** Isosceles Trapezium **5.** 180
6. Diameter

True/False

1 False **2.** False **3.** False **4.** True **5.** True

Single Correct Type Questions

1. D **2.** A **3.** A **4.** C **5.** A **6.** C **7.** C **8.** C **9.** B
10 C **11.** A **12.** D **13.** B **14.** B **15.** A **16.** D **17.** D **18.** D
19. C **20.** A **21.** C **22.** D **23.** D **24.** B **25.** C **26.** B

Multiple Correct Type Questions

1. ACD **2.** ACD **3.** ABC **4.** C **5.** BC **6.** BD **7.** D **8.** AC **9.** AC
10. B **11.** B **12.** AB **13.** BD **14.** C **15.** B

Match Type Questions

1. (A) → (R), (B) → (P), (C) → (S), (D) → (Q)
2. (A) → (Q), (B) → (R), (C) → (S), (D) → (P)
3. (A) → (S)(B) → (P), (C) → (Q), (D) → (R)

Assertion and Reason Type Questions

1. B **2.** A **3.** C **4.** B

Comprehension Type Questions

1. B. **2.** A. **3.** C **4.** B. **5.** C **6.** B **7.** B **8.** C **9.** D

Numerical Type Questions

1. 50 **2.** 80 **3.** 50 **4.** 45 **5.** 20 **6.** 120 **7.** 40 **8.** 80 **9.** 100
10 120 **11.** 60 **12.** 5 **13.** 60 **14.** 90° **15.** 70

Higher Order Thinking Skills (HOTS)

1. C 2. A 3. A 4. B 5. D 6. C 7. A 8. A 9. B
10. D 11. C 12. B 13. D 14. C 15. D

FREE RESPONSE TYPE

Very Short Answer Type Questions

1. 3 : 1 2. 75° 3. 2 4. 10 cm 5. 40 6. 45° 7. 50° 8. 70°

Short Answer Type Questions

1. 60° 2. 120° 7. 100° 9. 270° 10. 66° & 54°

Archive Corner

1. A 2. C 3. D 4. C 5. C 6. A 7. C 8. B 9. A
10. C 11. B 12. A 13. B 14. C 15. A 16. B 17. D 18. C

Heron's Formula

Learning Outcomes

After reading this chapter, you would be able to:

- area of triangle using Heron's formula.

Geekspeak

- Triangle
- Heron formula
- Semi Perimeter
- Area of triangle

Introduction

Heron (or **Hero**) **of Alexandria** (c10 – 70AD) was an ancient Greek mathematician and engineer who was active in his native city of Alexandria, Roman Egypt. He is considered the greatest experimenter of antiquity and his work is representative of the Hellenistic scientific tradition.

Heron's works as an inventor truly reveal his genius but he is also accredited as a mathematician who delivered a lot to the field with his practical approach. From approximations of square roots and formulating the area of a triangle to his treatise in geometry, Heron's contributions are wide-ranging. The 'Metrica' is a series of three books, found by R. Schone in Istanbul in 1896, in which Heron focuses on calculating areas and volumes of bodies such as pyramids, cones, cylinders, prisms etc. Heron's formula was found in this book which stated the area of a triangle with given sides.

Heron's Formula

If a, b, c denotes the lengths of the sides of a triangle ABC. Then,

$$\text{Area of } \Delta ABC = \sqrt{s(s-a)(s-b)(s-c)}$$

$$s = \frac{a+b+c}{2} \text{ is the semi-perimeter of } \Delta ABC.$$

Perimeter and Area of a Triangle

Heron's formula is helpful for calculating the area of various types of triangles when only the lengths of their sides are known.

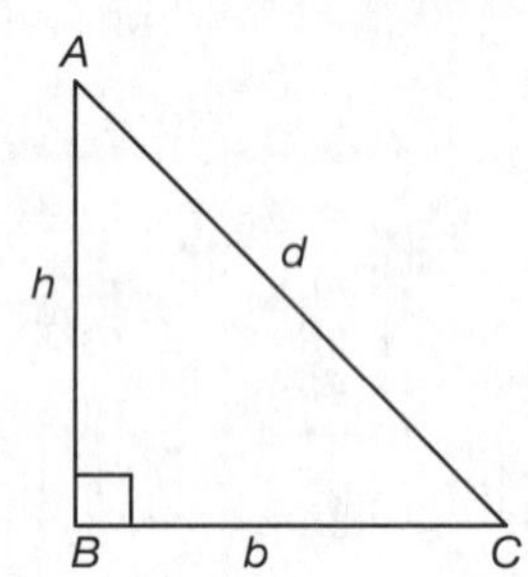

Figure 10.1

Right-angled Triangle

For a right-angled triangle, let b be the base, h be the perpendicular and d be the hypotenuse. Then

$$\text{Perimeter} = b + h + d$$

$$\text{Area} = \frac{1}{2}\,(\text{Base} \times \text{Height}) = \frac{1}{2}\,bh$$

Hypotenuse, $d = \sqrt{b^2 + h^2}$ [Pythagoras theorem]

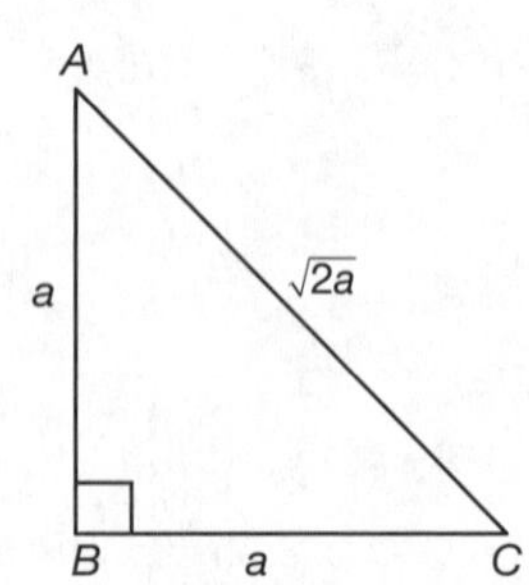

Figure 10.2

Isosceles Right-angled Triangle

For an isosceles right-angled triangle, let a be the equal sides, then

$$\text{Hypotenuse} = \sqrt{a^2 + a^2} = \sqrt{2}a$$

$$\text{Perimeter} = 2a + \sqrt{2}a$$

$$\text{Area} = \frac{1}{2}\,(\text{Base} \times \text{Height}) = \frac{1}{2}\,(a \times a) = \frac{1}{2}\,a^2.$$

Equilateral Triangle

For an equilateral triangle, let each side be a, and the height of the triangle is h, then

$$\angle A = \angle B = \angle C = 60°$$

$$\angle BAD = \angle CAD = 30°$$

$$AB = BC = AC = a \quad \text{(say)}$$

$$BD = DC = \frac{a}{2}$$

$$\left(\frac{a}{2}\right)^2 + h^2 = a^2 \Rightarrow h^2 = \frac{3a^2}{4}$$

$\therefore$ $$\text{Height } (h) = \frac{\sqrt{3}}{2}a$$

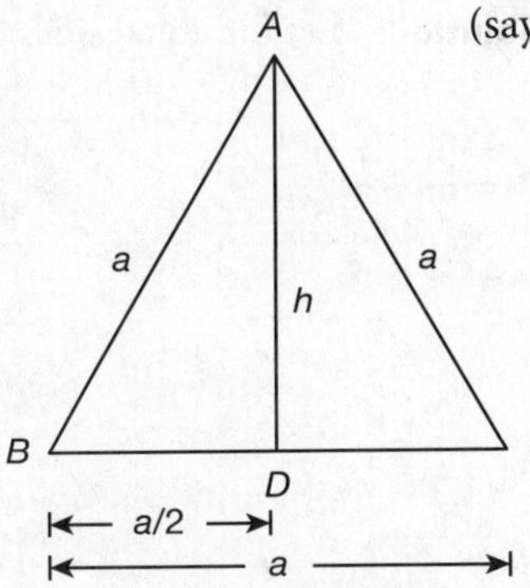

Figure 10.3

$$\text{Area} = \frac{1}{2}(\text{Base} \times \text{Height})$$

$$= \frac{1}{2} \times a \times \frac{\sqrt{3}}{2}a = \frac{\sqrt{3}}{4}a^2$$

$$\text{Perimeter} = a + a + a = 3a.$$

Application of Heron's Formula

With the help of heron's formula, we can find the area of Quadrilateral whose all side and one diagonal is given to us, Quadrilateral whose all sides and angle between any two adjacent side is the right angle, Trapezium whose all sides are given and we can find the area of Parallelogram and its types.

Illustration 10.1

The perimeter of a triangular field is 450 m and its sides are in the ratio 13 : 12 : 5. Find the area of the triangle.

Solution: Let $a = 13x$, $b = 12x$ and $c = 5x$

$\therefore$ $$\text{Perimeter} = 450$$

$$13x + 12x + 5x = 450$$

$$30x = 450$$

$$x = 15$$

So, the sides of the triangle are:

$$a = 13 \times 15 = 195 \text{ m}, \; b = 12 \times 15 = 180 \text{ m and } c = 5 \times 15 = 75 \text{ m}$$

$$2s = 195 + 180 + 75$$

$$2s = 450$$

$$s = 225 \text{ m}$$

Hence, $$\text{Area} = \sqrt{s(s-a)(s-b)(s-c)}$$

$$= \sqrt{225\,(225-195)(225-180)(225-75)}$$

$$= \sqrt{225(30)(45)(150)} = 6750 \text{ m}^2.$$

Illustration 10.2

The perimeter of an isosceles triangle is 42 cm and its base is $\frac{3}{2}$ times each of the equal sides. Find the length of each side of the triangle, area of the triangle and height of the triangle.

Solution: Let the equal sides be a and the unequal side be b.

$\therefore$ $$2a + b = 42$$

Given: $b = \frac{3}{2}a$

$$2a + \frac{3}{2}a = 42$$

$$\frac{7}{2}a = 42$$

$$a = 12 \text{ cm}$$

So $$b = \frac{3}{2}(12) = 18 \text{ cm.}$$

Also, $$\text{perimeter} = 2s = 42 \text{ cm}$$

$$s = 21 \text{ cm.}$$

$$\text{Area of triangle} = \sqrt{21(21-12)(21-12)(21-18)}$$

$$= \sqrt{21(9)(9)(3)}$$

$$= 27\sqrt{7} \text{ cm}^2$$

$$\text{Area of triangle} = \frac{1}{2} \times \text{base} \times \text{height}$$

$$27\sqrt{7} = \frac{1}{2} \times 18 \times \text{height}$$

$$\text{Height} = \frac{54\sqrt{7}}{18} = 3\sqrt{7} \text{ cm}$$

Illustration 10.3

A triangle and parallelogram have the same base and the same area. If the sides of the triangle are 26 cm, 28 cm and 30 cm, and the parallelogram stands on the base 28 cm, find the height of the parallelogram.

Solution:

$$s = \frac{26 + 28 + 30}{2} = 42 \text{ cm}$$

$\therefore$ $$\text{Area of the triangle} = \sqrt{42(42-26)(42-28)(42-30)}$$

$$= \sqrt{42(16)(14)(12)}$$

$$= 336 \text{ cm}^2$$

Let h be the height of the parallelogram.

It is given that the triangle and the parallelogram have the same base and the same area.

$\therefore$ $$\text{Area of the parallelogram} = 336 \text{ cm}^2$$

$\Rightarrow$ $$\text{Base} \times \text{height} = 336$$

$\Rightarrow$ $$28 \times h = 336$$

$\Rightarrow$ $$h = \frac{336}{28} = 12 \text{ cm}$$

Illustration 10.4

Find the area of a trapezium whose parallel sides are 25 cm, 13 cm and other sides are 15 cm and 15 cm.

Solution: Let $ABCD$ be the given trapezium in which $AB = 25$ cm, $CD = 13$ cm, $BC = 15$ cm and $AD = 15$ cm.

Draw $CE \parallel AD$.

Now, $ADCE$ is a parallelogram is which $AD \parallel CE$ and $AE \parallel CD$.

$\therefore$ $$AE = DC = 13 \text{ cm and } BE = AB - AE = 25 - 13 = 12 \text{ cm.}$$

In ΔBCE, we have

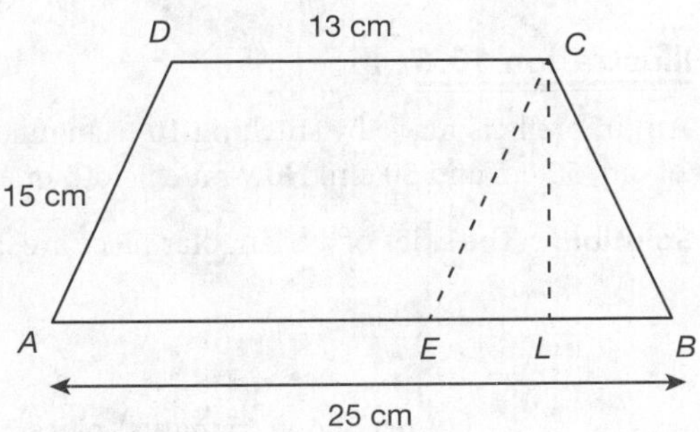

$$s = \frac{15+15+12}{2} = 21$$

$\therefore$ $$\text{Area of } \Delta BCE = \sqrt{s(s-a)(s-b)(s-c)}$$

$\Rightarrow$ $$\text{Area of } \Delta BCE = \sqrt{21(21-15)(21-15)(21-12)}$$

$\Rightarrow$ $$\text{Area of } \Delta BCE = \sqrt{21 \times 6 \times 6 \times 9}$$

$$= 18\sqrt{21} \text{ cm}^2 \quad \ldots\text{(i)}$$

Let h be the height of ΔBCE, then

$$\text{Area of } \Delta BCE = \frac{1}{2} (\text{Base} \times \text{Height})$$

$$= \frac{1}{2} \times 12 \times h = 6\,h \quad \ldots\text{(ii)}$$

From (i) and (ii), we have,

$$6h = 18\sqrt{21}$$

$\Rightarrow$ $$h = 3\sqrt{21} \text{ cm}$$

Clearly, the height of trapezium $ABCD$ is the same as that of ΔBCE.

$\therefore$ $$\text{Area of trapezium} = \frac{1}{2} (AB + CD) \times h$$

$\Rightarrow$ $$\text{Area of trapezium} = \frac{1}{2} (25 + 13) \times 3\sqrt{21} \text{ cm}^2 = 57\sqrt{21} \text{ cm}^2.$$

Illustration 10.5

Find the percentage increase in the area of a triangle if its each side is doubled.

Solution: Let a, b and c be the sides of the given triangle and s be its semi-perimeter.

$\therefore$ $$s = \frac{1}{2}(a + b + c) \quad \ldots\text{(i)}$$

The sides of the new triangle are $2a$, $2b$ and $2c$.

Let s' be its semi-perimeter.

$\therefore$ $$s' = 2\frac{1}{2}(2a + 2b + 2c) = a + b + c = 2s \quad \text{[Using (i)]}$$

Let Δ = Area of the given triangle

$$\Delta = \sqrt{s(s-a)(s-b)(s-c)} \quad \ldots\text{(ii)}$$

And, $$\Delta' = \text{Area of the new triangle}$$

$$\Delta' = \sqrt{s'(s'-2a)(s'-2b)(s'-2c)}$$

$$= \sqrt{2s\,(2s-2a)(2s-2b)(2s-2c)} \quad \text{[Using (i)]}$$

$$= \sqrt{16s\,(s-a)(s-b)(s-c)}$$

$$\Delta' = 4\,\Delta \quad \text{[Using (ii)]}$$

∴ Increase in the area of the triangle

$$= \Delta' - \Delta = 4\Delta - \Delta = 3\Delta$$

∴ $$\% \text{ increase in area} = \left(\frac{3\Delta}{\Delta}\times 100\right)\% = 300\%.$$

Illustration 10.6

An umbrella is made by stitching 10 triangular pieces of cloth of two different colours (see figure), each piece measuring 20 cm, 50 cm and 50 cm. How much cloth of each colour is required for the umbrella?

Solution: The sides of a triangular piece are 20 cm, 50 cm and 50 cm.

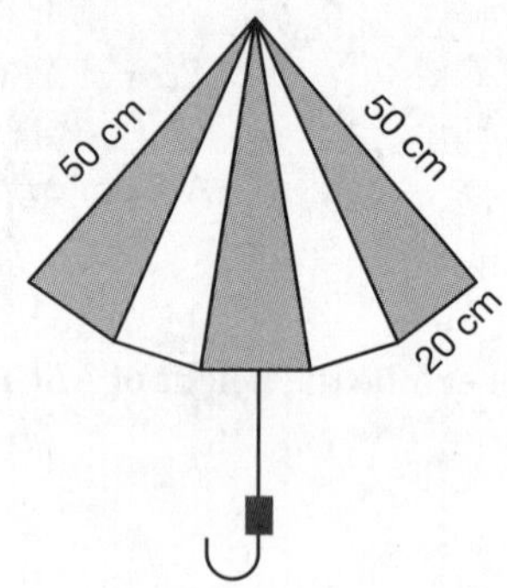

$$s = \frac{a+b+c}{2} = \frac{20+50+50}{2} = 60 \text{ cm}.$$

$$\text{Area of one triangular piece} = \sqrt{s\,(s-a)(s-b)(s-c)}$$

$$= \sqrt{60\,(60-20)(60-50)(60-50)}$$

$$= \sqrt{60 \times 40 \times 10 \times 10}$$

$$= \sqrt{240000} = 200\sqrt{6} \text{ cm}^2$$

Area of cloth of each colour for five triangular pieces $= 5 \times 200\sqrt{6} = 1000\sqrt{6}$ cm^2.

Illustration 10.7

A rhombus-shaped field has green grass for 18 cows to graze. If each side of the rhombus is 30 m and its longer diagonal is 48 m, how much area of grass field will each cow be grazing?

Solution: Clearly, triangles *ABC* and *ADC* are congruent.

∴ $$\text{Area of } \Delta ABC = \text{Area of } \Delta ADC$$

Let *s* be the semi-perimeter of ΔABC and ΔADC. Then,

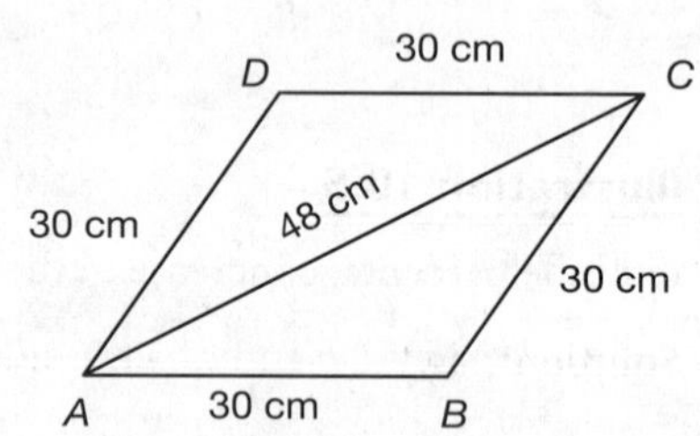

$$s = \frac{30+30+48}{2} = 54 \text{ m}.$$

∴ $$\text{Area of } \Delta ABC = \text{Area of } \Delta ADC$$

$$= \sqrt{54(54-30)\,(54-30)\,(54-48)}$$

$$= \sqrt{54\,(24)\,(24)\,(6)} = 432 \text{ m}^2$$

So, area of rhombus $ABCD = 2$ (Area of ΔABC) $= 2\,(432) = 864$ m^2

∴ $$\text{Area of grass field each cow will graze} = \frac{864}{18} = 48 \text{ m}^2.$$

Illustration 10.8

The sides of a quadrangular field, taken in order are 26 m, 27 m, 7 m and 24 m respectively. The angle contained by the last two sides is a right angle. Find its area. [Take $\sqrt{14} = 3.751$]

Solution: Area of $\Delta ADC = \frac{1}{2}\,(AD \times DC)$

$$= \frac{1}{2} \times 24 \times 7 \text{ m}^2 = 84 \text{ m}^2$$

In ΔADC, we have 90°

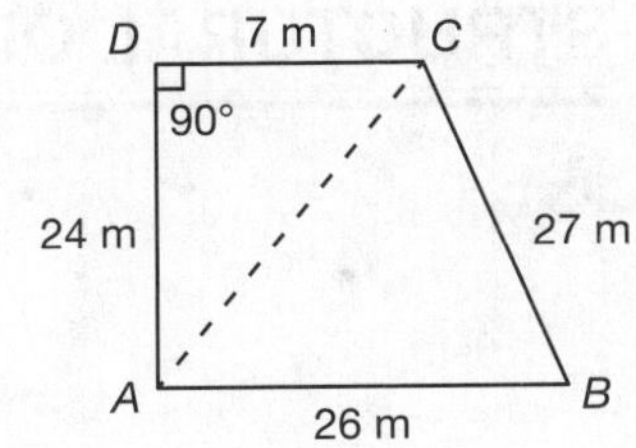

$$AC^2 = AD^2 + CD^2$$

$$\Rightarrow \quad AC^2 = 24^2 + 7^2$$

$$\Rightarrow \quad AC^2 = 25^2$$

$$\Rightarrow \quad AC = 25 \text{ m.}$$

Thus, in ΔABC, we have

$$a = BC = 27 \text{ m}, b = CA = 25 \text{ m and } c = AB = 26 \text{ m}$$

Let $2s$ be the perimeter of ΔABC. Then,

$$2s = a + b + c$$

$$2s = 27 + 25 + 26 = 78$$

$$\Rightarrow \quad s = 39 \text{ m}$$

$$\therefore \quad \text{Area of } \Delta ABC = \sqrt{s(s-a)(s-b)(s-c)}$$

$$= \sqrt{39 \times 12 \times 14 \times 13}$$

$$\Rightarrow \quad \text{Area of } \Delta ABC = \sqrt{13 \times 3 \times 3 \times 4 \times 2 \times 7 \times 13}$$

$$= 78\sqrt{14} \text{ cm}^2 = 292.57 \text{ m}^2$$

$$\text{Area of quadrilateral } ABCD = 84 + 292.57 = 376.57 \text{ m}^2.$$

Check Point 1

1. Find the area of the triangles whose sides are 25 m, 60 m and 65 m.
2. Two sides of a triangular field are 85 m and 154 m and its perimeter is 324 m. Find its area.
3. Find the area of a triangle whose sides are 50 m, 78 m and 112 m and also find the length of the perpendicular from the opposite vertex to the side of length 112 m.
4. Find the area of a trapezium whose parallel sides are 11 m and 25 m and the two non-parallel sides are 15 m and 13 m.
5. Find the area of a quadrilateral piece of land one of whose diagonals is 32 m long and the length of the perpendiculars from the other two vertices are 20 m and 12 m.

STRUCTURAL OUTLINE

Heron's Formula

Area of Triangle

If a, b, c denote the lengths of the sides of a triangle ABC. Then, Area of $\Delta ABC = \sqrt{s(s-a)(s-b)(s-c)}$

$s = \frac{a+b+c}{2}$ is the semi-perimeter of ΔABC.

Right-angled triangle

For an right-angled triangle, let **b** be the base, **h** be the perpendicular and **d** be the hypotenuse.

Then Perimeter = b + h + d

Area $= \frac{1}{2}$ (Base × Height) $= \frac{1}{2}bh$

Hypotenuse, $d = \sqrt{b^2 + h^2}$

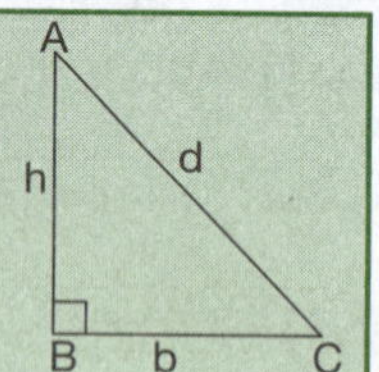

Equilateral triangle

For an equilateral triangle, let each side be **a**,

then $\angle A = \angle B = \angle C = 60°$

$\angle BAD = \angle CAD = 30°$

Area $= \frac{1}{2}$ (Base × Height) $= \frac{\sqrt{3}}{4}a^2$

Perimeter = 3a.

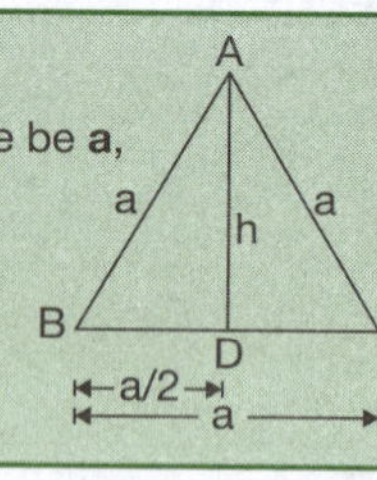

ASSESSMENT CORNER

FIXED RESPONSE TYPE

Fill in the Blanks

1. In ΔABC, $\angle B = 90°$, $AB = 3$ cm and $AC = 5$ cm, then the area of triangle ABC is __________.
2. In ΔABC, if $AB = AC = 13$ cm and $BC = 10$ cm, then the perpendicular distance between A and side BC is __________.
3. The area of an equilateral triangle whose perimeter is 12 cm is given by __________.
4. The area of a parallelogram is 392 m^2. If its base is twice the altitude, then the base is __________ and the altitude is __________.
5. The cost of levelling a rectangular ground at ₹1.25 per sq. metre is ₹900. If the length of the ground is 30 metres, then the width is __________.
6. In a trapezium $ABCD$ with bases AB and CD, where $AB = 52$, $BC = 12$, $CD = 39$ and $DA = 5$. The area of the trapezium $ABCD$, is __________.

True/False

1. The triangle has sides 35 cm, 54 cm and 61 cm long. Then the smallest altitude is 30.79 cm.
2. The sides of triangular plates are 8 cm, 15 cm and 17 cm. If its weight is 96 grams, the weight of the plate/sq. cm is 1.6 gm.
3. If the lengths of semi-diagonals of a rhombus are 5 cm and 12 cm, then the side of the rhombus is 13 cm.
4. If the altitudes of a triangle are in the ratio 2 : 3 : 4, then the lengths of the corresponding sides are in the ratio 6 : 4 : 3.
5. If the sides of a triangular plot are in the ratio of 3 : 5 : 7, its perimeter is 300 cm, then the area will be 1500 cm^2.

Single Correct Type Questions

1. If the adjacent sides of a parallelogram $ABCD$ measure 34 cm and 20 cm, and the diagonal AC measures 42 cm, then its area in cm^2 is:
   (A) 796 (B) 672
   (C) 692 (D) None of these
2. The lengths of four sides and a diagonal of the given quadrilateral are indicated in the diagram. If A denotes the area of the quadrilateral, then A in cm^2 is:

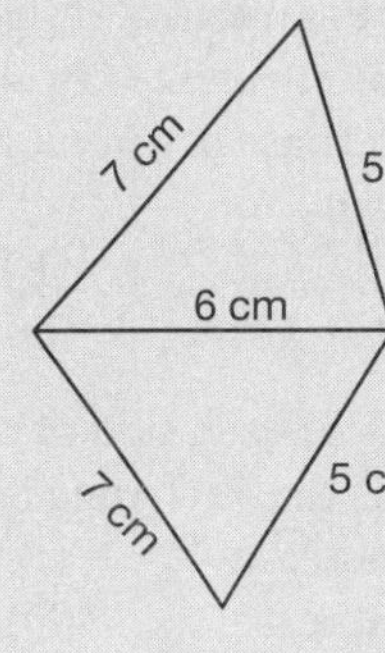

   (A) $12\sqrt{6}$ (B) $\sqrt{6}$
   (C) $6\sqrt{6}$ (D) $\sqrt{26}$
3. If the sides of a triangle are doubled, then its area:
   (A) Remains the same
   (B) Becomes doubled
   (C) Becomes three times
   (D) Becomes four times
4. Find the cost of the painting of a rhombus sheet, whose perimeter is 32 m and whose one diagonal is 10 m long is painted on both sides at the rate of ₹5 per m^2. [Use $\sqrt{39} = 6.25$]
   (A) ₹500 (B) ₹600
   (C) ₹625 (D) ₹650
5. Find the height of the trapezium in which parallel sides are 25 cm and 10 cm and non-parallel sides are 14 cm and 13 cm.
   (A) 13 cm (B) 14 cm
   (C) 11.2 cm (D) 13.2 cm
6. Calculate the area of the shaded portion.

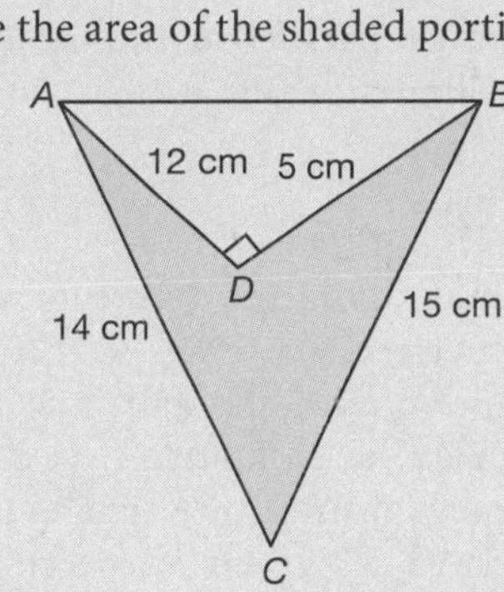

   (A) 30 cm^2 (B) 84 cm^2
   (C) 144 cm^2 (D) 54 cm^2

ASSESSMENT CORNER

7. The unequal side of an isosceles triangle is 6 cm and its perimeter is 24 cm. Find its area.

(A) $6\sqrt{2}$ cm^2 (B) $12\sqrt{2}$ cm^2
(C) $18\sqrt{2}$ cm^2 (D) $24\sqrt{2}$ cm^2

8. A triangle and a parallelogram have the same base and the same area. If the sides of the triangle are 15 cm, 14 cm and 13 cm and the parallelogram stand on the base of 15 cm, find the height of the parallelogram.

(A) 5 cm (B) 5.6 cm
(C) 6 cm (D) 6.2 cm

9. In a triangle if each side of the triangle is halved then what is the % change in its area?

(A) 75% increase (B) 75% decrease
(C) 25% increase (D) 25% decrease

10. The triangular side walls of a flyover have been used for advertisements from both sides. The sides of each wall are 120 m, 110 m and 20 m. The advertisement yield and earning of ₹100 per m^2 per year. Find the amount of revenue earned in one year. [Take $\sqrt{7} = 2.65$]

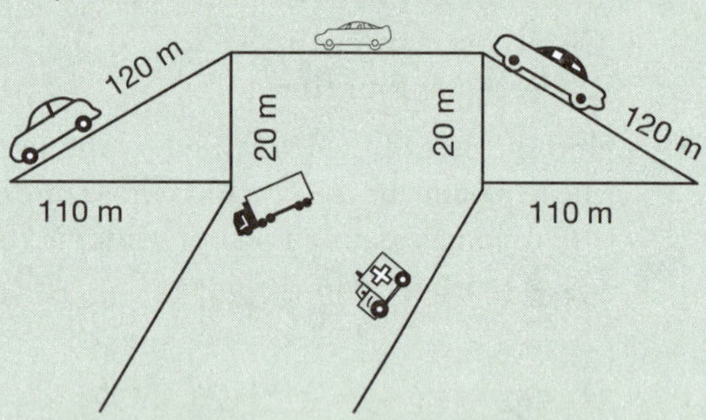

(A) ₹3,37,500 (B) ₹3,97,500
(C) ₹5,73,300 (D) ₹4,73,500

11. A rectangular lawn 60 metres by 40 metres has two roads each 5 metres wide running in the middle of it, one parallel to the length and the other parallel to the breadth. The cost of gravelling the roads at 60 paise per sq. metre is:

(A) ₹300 (B) ₹280
(C) ₹285 (D) ₹250

12. A child draws the figure of an aeroplane as given. Here the wings *EDCF* and *AGHB* are parallelograms, the tail *ADK* is an isosceles triangle, the cockpit *BLC* is a semi-circle and the portion *ABCD* is a square. Let $FP \perp CD$ and $HQ \perp AB$, $AB = 6$ cm. $KD = 5$ cm $FP = HQ = 2$ cm. The area of the figure is: [$\pi = 3.14$]

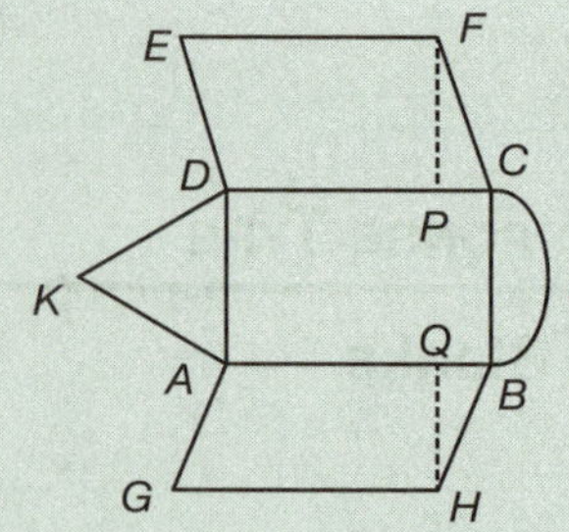

(A) 86.14 cm^2 (B) 87.25 cm^2
(C) 84.63 cm^2 (D) 91.56 cm^2

13. The area of a rhombus is 28 cm^2 and one of its diagonals is 4 cm. Its perimeter is:

(A) $4\sqrt{53}$ (B) 36 cm
(C) $2\sqrt{53}$ (D) $\sqrt{53}$ cm

14. The area of a trapezium-shaped field is 960 m^2 the distance between two parallel sides is 30 m and one of the parallel sides is 20 m. Find the length of the other parallel side.

(A) 44 m (B) 22 m
(C) 88 m (D) 11 m

Multiple Correct Type Questions

1. Find the base of an isosceles triangle whose area is 12 cm^2 and length of one of the equal sides is 5 cm.

(A) 6 cm (B) 12 cm
(C) 8 cm (D) 10 cm

2. The altitude of an equilateral triangle whose area is given by $4\sqrt{3}$ cm^2.

(A) $\frac{8\sqrt{3}}{4}$ (B) $16\sqrt{3}$ cm
(C) $8\sqrt{3}$ cm (D) $2\sqrt{3}$ cm

3. A right triangle has a hypotenuse of length q cm and one side of length p cm. If $q - p = 2$ cm, then the length of the third side is:

(A) $2\sqrt{(q-1)}$

(B) $2\sqrt{(1+p)}$

(C) $\sqrt{(q^2 - p^2)}$

(D) $\sqrt{(2(q-1))}$

4. If the side of a square is halved, then which of the following is/are true?
   (A) Area of the square becomes half.
   (B) Area of the square becomes one-fourth of the original square.
   (C) Diagonal of the square is also halved.
   (D) Diagonal of the square is one-fourth times the diagonal of the original square.

5. The area of a triangle whose two sides are 5 cm and 12 cm and angle between these two sides is 90° is given by:

   (A) $\frac{1}{2}\times 5\times 12$ (B) 5×12

   (C) $\sqrt{15\times 10\times 2\times 3}$ (D) None of these

Match Type Questions

Directions: Column-I and Column-II contain four entries each. Entries of Column-I are to be matched with some entries of Column-II. Only one entry of column-I may have the matching with one entry of Column-II and one entry of Column-II may have only one matching with the entry of Column-I.

1.

Column-I (Figure)	Column-II (Area *ABCD*)
(A) 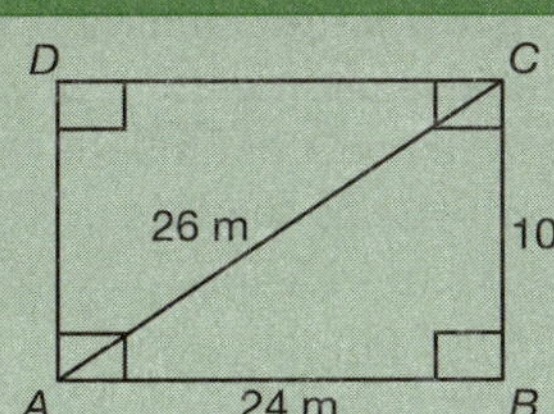	(p) 306 cm^2
(B) 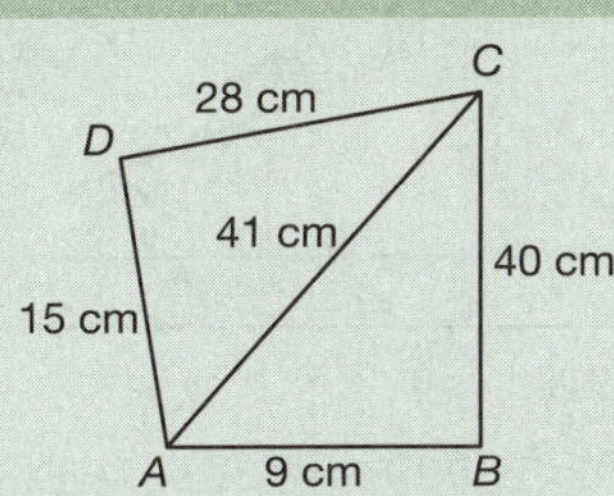	(q) 546 cm^2
(C) 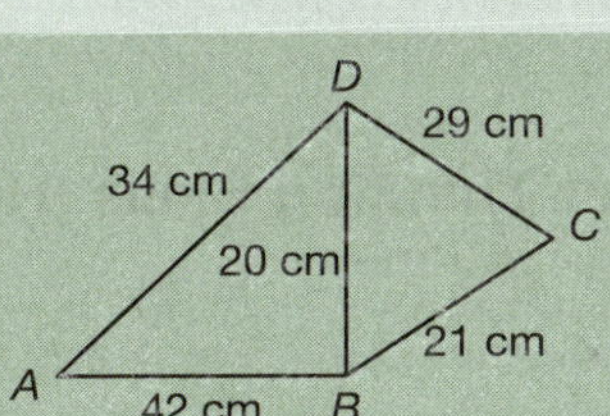	(r) 114 cm^2
(D) 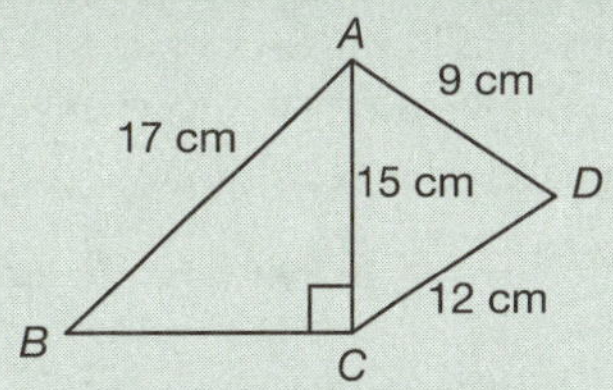	(s) 240 cm^2

(Continued)

2.

Column-I	Column-II
(A) Area of a rectangle having length = 9 cm and breadth 4 cm is	(p) 36 cm^2
(B) Area of an equilateral triangle having perimeter of 18 cm.	(q) 4.5 cm
(C) Area of the square having a diagonal length $6\sqrt{2}$ cm is	(r) $9\sqrt{3}$ cm^2
(D) Length of the altitude of an equilateral Triangle of side $3\sqrt{3}$ cm	(s) $(\sqrt{3})^5$ cm^2

Assertion and Reason Type Questions

Directions: In the following questions as Assertion (A) is given followed by a Reason (R). Mark your responses from the following options.
   (A) Both Assertion and Reason are true and Reason is the correct explanation of 'Assertion'.
   (B) Both Assertion and Reason are true and Reason is not the correct explanation of 'Assertion'.
   (C) Assertion is true but Reason is false.
   (D) Assertion is false but Reason is true.

1. **Assertion:** The area of a trapezium is directly proportional to the perpendicular distance between the parallel sides.
   Reason: The diagonal of a trapezium divides it into two triangles of equal area.

2. **Assertion:** The product of diagonals of a rhombus is equal to half the area of a rhombus.
   Reason: The area of rhombus is equal to $\frac{1}{2}\times$ Product of diagonals.

Comprehension Type Questions

Comprehension-1: A farmer has a quadrangular field *ABCD*, whose sides taken in order are 26 m, 27 m, 7 m and 24 m respectively. The angle contained by the last two sides is a right angle. He wants to grow wheat and rice on the field, so he divides the field by joining the vertices *A* and *C* with a fencing wire:

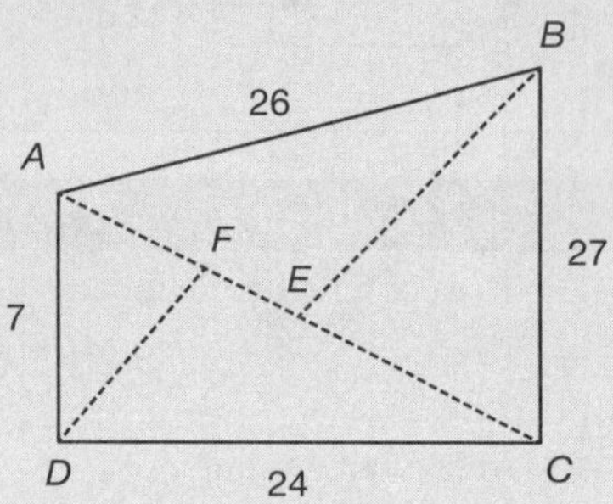

1. What is the length of wire required for dividing the field?
   (A) 18 m (B) 25 m
   (C) 39 m (D) 23 m

2. What is the length of wire required if he wants to join *BE* and *DF*?
   (A) $\frac{12}{25}\left[14+13\sqrt{14}\right]$m (B) $13\left(7\sqrt{14}\right)$m
   (C) $52\sqrt{14}$ m (D) $0.52\sqrt{14}$ m

3. What is the total area of the field on which wheat and rice are grown?
   (A) 84 m^2 (B) $6\left(14+13\sqrt{14}\right)$m^2
   (C) $7\sqrt{14}$ m^2 (D) $78\sqrt{14}$ m^2

Numerical Type Questions

1. Calculate the area of the triangle whose sides are 18 cm, 24 cm and 30 cm in length. Also, find the length of the altitude corresponding to the smallest side of the triangle.

2. The sides of a triangle are 10 cm, 24 cm and 26 cm. Find its area and the longest altitude.

3. Students of a school staged a rally for a cleanliness campaign. They walked through the lanes in two groups. One group walked through lanes *AB*, *BC* and *CA*; while the other through *AC*, *CD* and *DA* (figure). Then they cleaned the area enclosed within their lanes. If *AB* = 9 m, *BC* = 40 m, *CD* = 15 m, *DA* = 28 m and $\angle B$ = 90°. Which group cleaned more area and how much? Find the total area cleaned by the students.

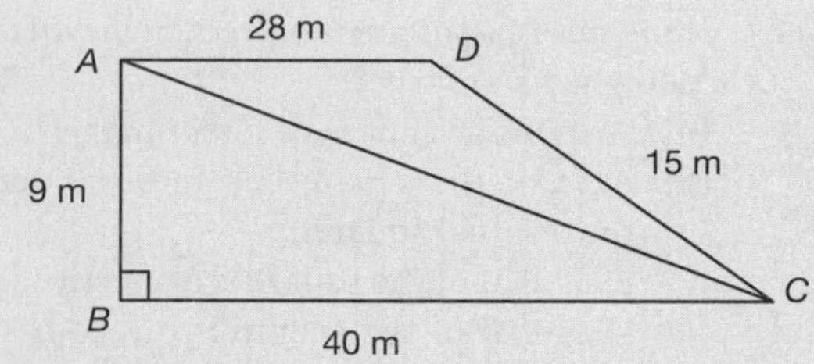

4. Find the area of the quadrilateral *ABCD* in which *AB* = 17 cm, *AD* = 9 cm, *CD* = 12 cm, $\angle ACB$ = 90° and *AC* = 15 cm.

5. Two sides of a triangular field are 85 cm and 154 cm in length, and its perimeter is 324 cm. Find the area of the field.

6. The sides of a triangular field are 165 cm, 143 cm and 154 cm. Find the cost of ploughing it at 12 paise per sq. cm.

7. If the height of an equilateral triangle is 3 cm. Then find the area of the triangle.

8. The perimeter of a right-angle triangle is 40 cm. Its hypotenuse is 17 cm. Find the area of the triangle using Heron's formula.

9. The perimeter of an isosceles triangle is 32 cm. The ratio of one of the equal sides to the base is 3 : 2. Find the area of the triangle.

10. A triangular park *ABC* has sides 120 m, 80 m and 50 m. A gardener Ramu has to put a fence all around it and also plant grass inside. How much area does he need to plant? Find the cost of fencing it with barbed wire at the rate of ₹20 per meter leaving a space 3 m wide for a gate on one side.

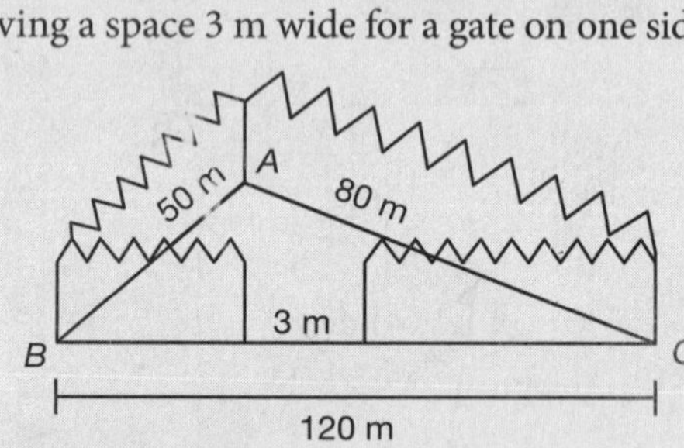

11. A field is in the shape of a trapezium whose parallel sides are 60 m and 77 m. The non-parallel sides are 25 m and 26 m. Find the area of the field.

Higher Order Thinking Skills (HOTS)

1. All the 3 sides of a right triangle are integers and one side has a length of 11 units. Area of the triangle in square units lies between:
   (A) 1 and 100 (B) 100 and 200
   (C) 200 and 300 (D) More than 300

2. In the figure given $PM = 10$ cm, $MN = 15$ cm and $PN = 17$ cm. Also $QM = QX$ and $XR = RN$. Perimeter of the ΔPQR, is:

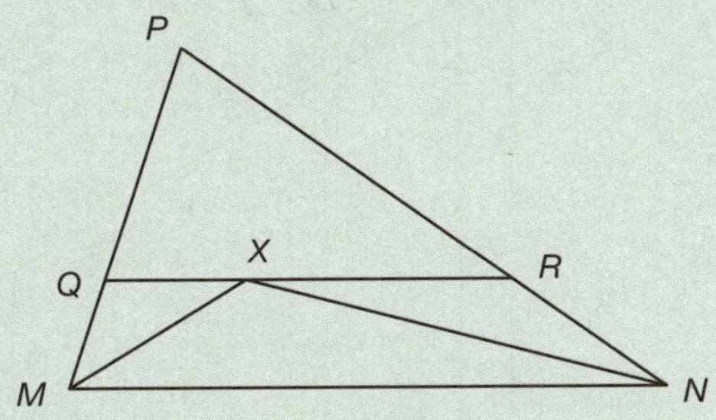

(A) 32 (B) 27
(C) 25 (D) 21

3. A triangle of area $9\,y$ cm^2 has been drawn such that its area is equal to the area of an equilateral triangle of side 6 cm. Then, the value of y is:

(A) $\sqrt{2}$ cm (B) $\sqrt{3}$ cm
(C) 2 cm (D) 3 cm

4. A plot of land is in the shape of a right-angled isosceles triangle. The length of the hypotenuse is $50\sqrt{2}$. The cost of fencing it at ₹3 per metre will be:

(A) Less than ₹300 (B) Less than ₹400
(C) More than ₹500 (D) More than ₹600

5. The perimeter of an isosceles triangle is equal to 14 cm and the lateral side is to the base in the ratio 5 : 4. The area of the triangle is:

(A) $\frac{1}{2}\sqrt{21}$ cm^2 (B) $\frac{3}{2}\sqrt{21}$ cm^2
(C) $\sqrt{21}$ cm^2 (D) $2\sqrt{21}$ cm^2

6. $ABCD$ is a rectangle with $AB = 12$ cm and $BC = 7$ cm. Point E is on AD with $DE = 2$ cm. Point P is on AB. How far to the right of point A should point P be placed so that the shaded area comprises exactly 40% of the area of the rectangle?

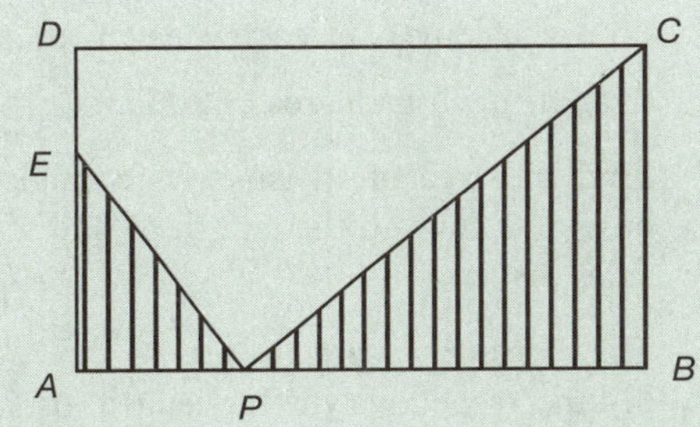

(A) 8 (B) 8.4
(C) 8.2 (D) 8.6

7. Given an isosceles trapezium $ABCD$ in order with $AB = 6$, $CD = 12$ and area 36 sq. units. Length of the side BC is:

(A) 6 (B) 5
(C) 4.5 (D) 5.5

8. The length of the side of a rhombus is 10 units and its diagonals differ by 4. The area of the rhombus is:

(A) 108 (B) 96
(C) 84 (D) 48

9. The side lengths of a trapezium are $\sqrt[4]{3}$, $\sqrt[4]{3}$, $\sqrt[4]{3}$ and $2\times\sqrt[4]{3}$. Its area is in the ratio of two relatively prime positive integers, m and n. The value of $(m + n)$ is equal to:

(A) 5 (B) 7
(C) 9 (D) 13

10. A rectangle is inscribed in a square creating four isosceles right triangles. If the total area of these four triangles is 200. The length of the diagonal of the rectangle is:

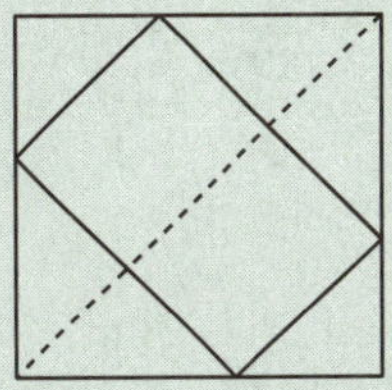

(A) 10 (B) 15
(C) 20 (D) 25

ASSESSMENT CORNER

FREE RESPONSE TYPE

Very Short Answer Type Questions

1. The base of a right triangle is 8 cm and the hypotenuse is 10 cm. Its area will be:

2. An isosceles right triangle has an area 8 cm^2. Find the length of its hypotenuse.

3. The perimeter of an equilateral triangle is 60 m. Find its area.

4. The sides of a triangle are 56 cm, 60 cm and 52 cm long. Find the area of the triangle is:

5. Find the area of an equilateral triangle with side $2\sqrt{3}$ cm

6. Find the length of each side of an equilateral triangle having an area of $9\sqrt{3}$ cm^2.

7. Find the area of an isosceles triangle having a base of 2 cm and the length of one of the equal sides of 4 cm.

8. The sides of a triangle are 35 cm, 54 cm and 61 cm, respectively. The length of its longest altitude:

Short Answer Type Questions

1. The sides of a triangular field are 41 m, 40 m and 9 m. Find the number of rose beds that can be prepared in the field, if each rose bed, on average need 900 cm^2 of space.

2. The perimeter of an isosceles triangle is 32 cm. The ratio of the equal side to its base is 3 : 2. Find the area of the triangle.

3. A field in the form of a parallelogram has sides 60 m and 40 m and one of its diagonals is 80 m long. Find the area of the parallelogram.

4. Calculate the area of the shaded region in the figure.

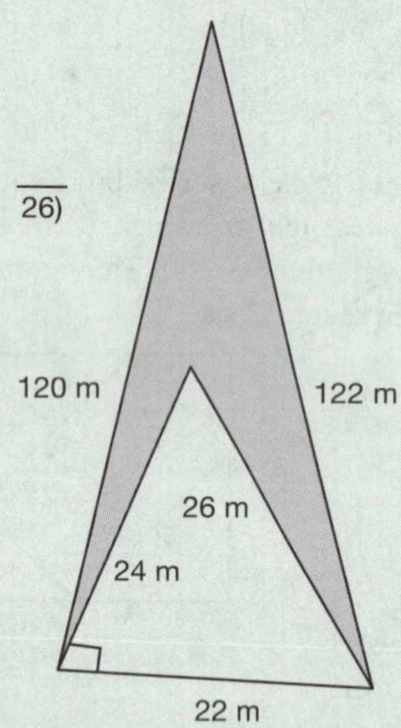

5. The perimeter of a triangular field is 420 m and its sides are in the ratio 6 : 7 : 8. Find the area of the triangular field.

6. A rhombus-shaped sheet with a perimeter of 40 cm and one diagonal of 12 cm, is painted on both sides at the rate of ₹5 per cm^2. Find the cost of painting.

7. Find the area of the trapezium *PQRS* with height *PQ* given in the Figure.

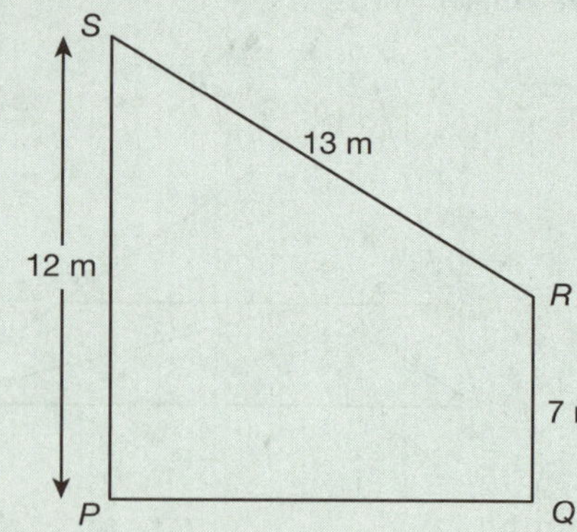

8. The perimeter of a triangle is 50 cm. One side of a triangle is 4 cm longer than the smaller side and the third side is 6 cm less than twice the smaller side. Find the area of the triangle.

9. The area of a trapezium is 475 cm^2 and the height is 19 cm. Find the lengths of its two parallel sides if one side is 4 cm greater than the other.

10. In Figure, ΔABC has sides AB = 7.5 cm, AC = 6.5 cm and BC = 7 cm. On base BC a parallelogram $DBCE$ of the same area as that of ΔABC is constructed. Find the height DF of the parallelogram.

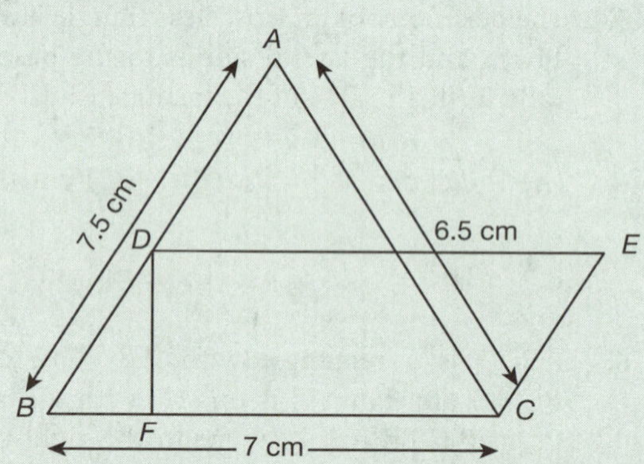

Long Answer Type Questions

1. The dimensions of a rectangle *ABCD* are 51 cm × 25 cm. A trapezium *PQCD* with its parallel sides *QC* and *PD* in the ratio 9 : 8, is cut off from the rectangle as shown in the Figure. If the area of the trapezium *PQCD* is $\frac{5}{6}$th part of the area of the rectangle, find the lengths *QC* and *PD*.

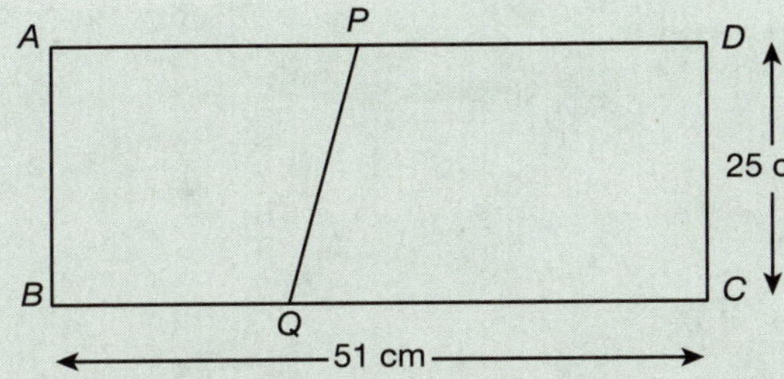

2. A design is made on a rectangular tile of dimensions 50 cm × 70 cm as shown in Figure. The design shows 8 triangles, each of sides 26 cm, 17 cm and 25 cm. Find the total area of the design and the remaining area of the tiles.

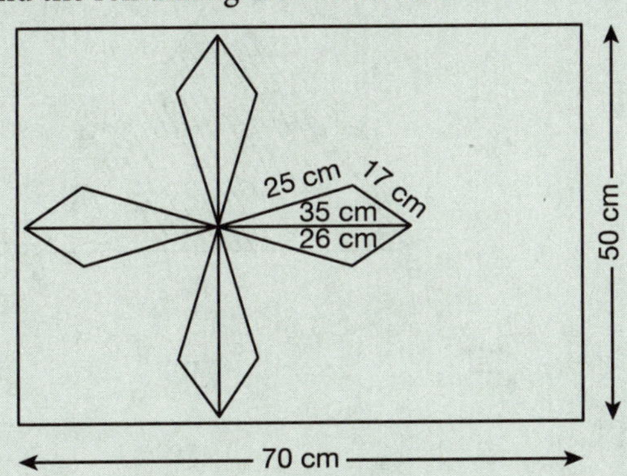

3. From a point in the interior of an equilateral triangle, perpendiculars are drawn on the three sides. The lengths of the perpendiculars are 14 cm, 10 cm and 6 cm. Find the area of the triangle.

4. If each side of a triangle is doubled, then find the ratio of the area of the new triangle thus formed and the given triangle.

5. A field is in the shape of a trapezium having parallel sides 90 m and 30 m. These sides meet the third side at right angles. The length of the fourth side is 100 m. If it costs ₹4 to plough 1 m^2 of the field, find the total cost of ploughing the field.

6. Rajesh has a triangular field with sides 240 m, 200 m and 360 m, where he grew wheat. In another triangular field with sides 240 m, 320 m and 400 m adjacent to the previous field, he wanted to grow potatoes and onions as shown in the figure. He divided the field into two parts by joining the mid-point of the longest side to the opposite vertex and grew potatoes in one part and onions in the other part. How much area (in hectares) has been used for wheat, potatoes and onions?

[$\sqrt{2} = 1.41$ and 1 hectare = 10000 m^2]

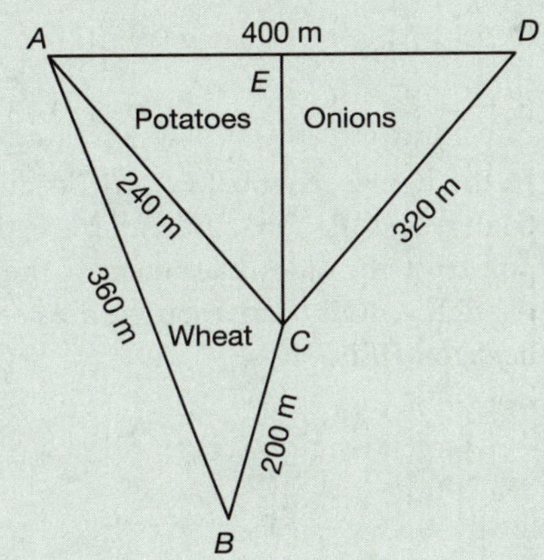

ASSESSMENT CORNER

ARCHIVE CORNER

ARCHIVE CORNER

1. A triangle with integral sides has a perimeter of 8 units. The area of the triangle is ________ sq. units.

(A) 2 (B) $2\sqrt{2}$

(C) $3\sqrt{2}$ (D) 4

2. Area of triangle *ABC* whose sides are 24 m, 40 m and 32 m is:

(A) 96 m^2 (B) 384 m^2

(C) 43 m^2 (D) 192 m^2

3. The perimeters of a regular hexagon and a square are equal. The ratio of the area of the square to the area of the hexagon is:

(A) $3:\sqrt{2}$ (B) $2:3\sqrt{3}$

(C) $1:\sqrt{3}$ (D) $3:2\sqrt{3}$

4. In the figure given below, *ABC* is an equilateral triangle. *D, E, F, G, H* and *I* are the trisector points of the sides as shown. If the side of the triangle *ABC* is 6 cm, then the area of the regular hexagon *DEFGHI* is:

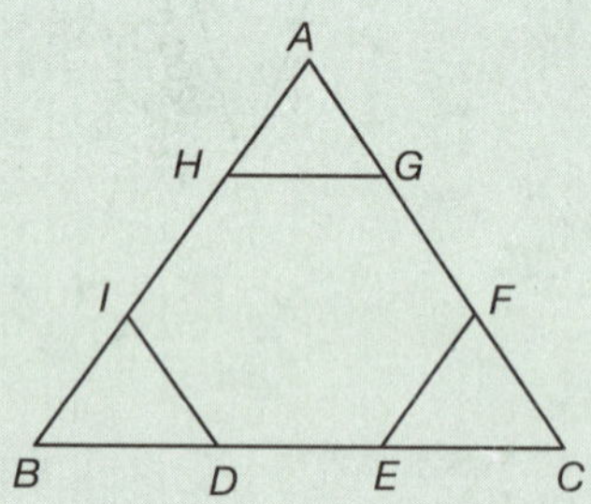

(A) $3\sqrt{3}$ cm^2 (B) $4\sqrt{3}$ cm^2

(C) $5\sqrt{3}$ cm^2 (D) $6\sqrt{3}$ cm^2

5. If every side of a triangle is doubled then a new triangle is formed. The ratio of areas of these two triangles is:

(A) 1 : 2 (B) 1 : 3

(C) 1 : 4 (D) 2 : 3

6. Equilateral triangles I, II, III and IV are such that the altitude of the triangle I is the side of triangle II, the altitude of triangle II is the side of triangle III and the altitude of the triangle is the side of triangle IV. If the area of the triangle I is 2 cm^2, then the area (in cm^2) of triangle IV is:

(A) $\frac{\sqrt{3}}{2}$ (B) $\frac{9}{16}$

(C) $\frac{27}{32}$ (D) $\frac{45}{64}$

7. ΔABC is an equilateral triangle, we have $BD = EG = DF = DE = EC$, then the ratio of the area of the shaded portion to the area of ΔABC is:

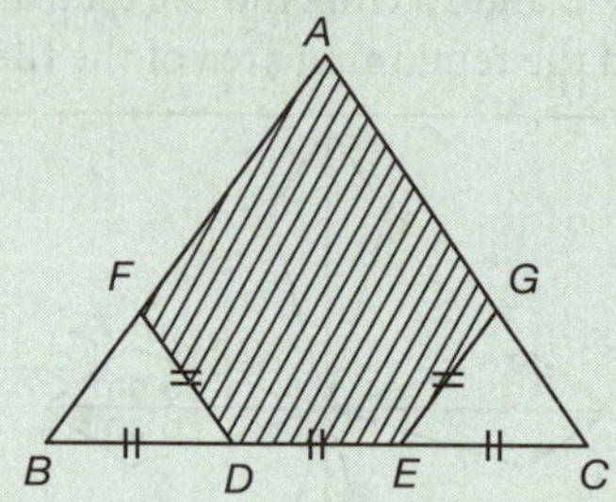

(A) $\frac{4}{11}$ (B) $\frac{7}{9}$

(C) $\frac{5}{12}$ (D) $\frac{6}{7}$

8. The height of an equilateral triangle is $\sqrt{6}$ cm. Its area is:

(A) $2\sqrt{2}$ cm^2 (B) $6\sqrt{2}$ cm^2

(C) $2\sqrt{3}$cm^2 (D) $3\sqrt{3}$cm^2

9. Heron's formula for the area of the triangle is:

(A) $\frac{1}{2}$ (Base × Height)

(B) $\sqrt{s(s-a)(s-b)(s-c)}$

(C) $\frac{a+b+c}{2}$

(D) $\sqrt{s.a.b.c}$

10. A parallelogram has sides 6 cm and 4 cm and one of its diagonals is 8 cm, then its area is:

(A) 36 cm^2 (B) $3\sqrt{15}$ cm^2

(C) $2\sqrt{15}$ cm^2 (D) $12\sqrt{210}$ cm^2

11. If the perimeter of an equilateral triangle is 24 cm, then its area will be:

(A) $16\sqrt{3}$ sq.cm (B) $32\sqrt{3}$ sq.cm

(C) $48\sqrt{3}$ sq.cm (D) $64\sqrt{3}$ sq.cm

ANSWER KEY

CHECK POINTS

Check Point 1

1. 750 m^2 2. 2772 m^2 3. 1680 m^2, 30 m 4. 216 m^2 5. 512 m^2

Assessment Corner

FIXED RESPONSE TYPE

Fill in the Blanks

1. 6 cm^2 2. 12 3. $4\sqrt{3}$ 4. 14, 28 5. 24 6. 210

True/False

1. False 2. True 3. True 4. True 5. False

Single Correct Type Questions

1. B 2. A 3. D 4. C 5. C 6. D 7. C 8. B 9. B
10. B 11. C 12. A 13. A 14. A

Multiple Correct Type Questions

1. AC 2. AD 3. C 4. BC 5. AC

Match Type Questions

1. $A \rightarrow S, B \rightarrow P, C \rightarrow Q, D \rightarrow R$
2. $P \rightarrow A, R \rightarrow B, P \rightarrow C, Q \rightarrow D$

Assertion and Reason Type Questions

1. C 2. D

Comprehension Type Questions

1. B 2. A 3. B

Numerical Type Questions

1. 24 cm 2. 24 cm 3. 306 m^2 4. 114 cm^2 5. 2772 cm^2 6. ₹1219.68
7. $3\sqrt{3} \text{ cm}^2$ 8. 60 cm^2 9. $32\sqrt{2} \text{ cm}^2$ 10. ₹4940 11. 1644 m^2

Higher Order Thinking Skills (HOTS)

1. D 2. B 3. B 4. C 5. D 6. B 7. B 8. B 9. D
10. C

Free Response Type

Very Short Answer Type Questions

1. 24 2. $4\sqrt{2}$ 3. $100\sqrt{3}$ 4. 1344 5. $3\sqrt{3}$ 6. 6 7. $\sqrt{15}$ 8. $420\sqrt{5}$

Short Answer Type Questions

1. 2000 2. $32\sqrt{2}$ 3. $600\sqrt{5}$ 4. $1320 - 24\sqrt{105}$ 5. $2100\sqrt{15}$ 6. ₹960 7. 114 sq.units
8. $20\sqrt{30}$ 9. 27 units 10. 3

Long Answer Type Questions

1. 40 2. 1868 3. $900\sqrt{3}$ 4. 4 : 1 5. 19200 6. 19200

Archive Corner

1. B 2. B 3. B 4. D 5. C 6. C 7. B 8. C 9. B
10. C 11. A

CHAPTER 11

Surface Areas and Volumes

Learning Outcomes

After reading this chapter, you would be able to understand:

- surface area and volume of cube and cuboid.
- surface area and volume of cylinder.
- surface area and volume of cone.
- surface area and volume of sphere and hemisphere.

Geekspeak

- Surface area
- Total surface area
- Lateral surface area
- Curve surface area
- Volume
- Cube
- Cuboid
- Cylinder
- Cone
- Sphere
- Hemisphere

Introduction

We had learnt how to find the surface areas and volumes of some regular solids like cuboid, cube, cylinder, cone and sphere. In our day-to-day life, we come across various solids which are combinations of two or more such solids. For example, a conical circus tent with a cylindrical base is a combination of a right circular cylinder and a right circular cone. In this chapter, we shall learn how to find the surface area and volume of such combinations.

Area and Perimeter

For quadrilaterals, area is the amount of space inside the shape, and perimeter is the total length around the shape.

Area

The area of any figure is the amount of surface enclosed within its bounding lines. Area is always expressed in square units.

Unit of Measuring Area

100 sq. millimetres = 1 sq. centimetre
100 sq. centimetres = 1 sq. decimetre
100 sq. decimetres = 1 sq. meter
100 sq. meters = 1 sq. decametre or acre
10,000 sq. meters = 1 hectare
1,000,000 sq. meters = 100 hectares = 1 sq. kilometre

Perimeter

The perimeter of a geometrical figure is the total length of the sides enclosing the figure.

Cone

A cone is a three-dimensional geometric shape with a circular base and a single vertex, and its surface area and volume are calculated as given below

(i) C.S.A. of cone = πrl

(ii) T.S.A. of cone = C.S.A. + Base area = $\pi rl + \pi r^2$

(iii) Volume of cone = $\frac{1}{3}\pi r^2 h$

Where, h = height

r = radius of base

l = slant height

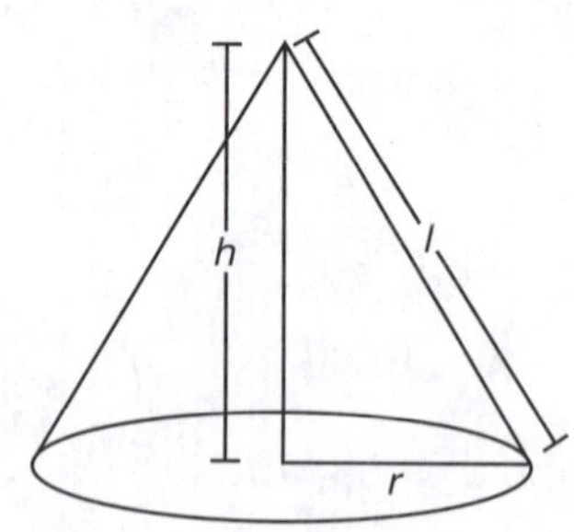

Figure 11.1

Illustration 11.1

A conical tent is 9 m high and radius of its base is 12 m.

(i) What is the cost of the canvas required to make it, if a square meter canvas costs ₹10?

(ii) How many persons can be accommodated in the tent, if each person requires 2 square meters on the ground and 15 m^3 of space to breathe in?

Solution: We have

r = Radius of the base of the conical tent = 12 m

h = Height of the conical tent = 9 m

l = Slant height of the conical tent = $\sqrt{r^2+h^2} = \sqrt{12^2+9^2}$ m = $\sqrt{225}$ m = 15 m.

(i) Area of lateral surface = $\pi r l = \frac{22}{7} \times 12 \times 15 \text{ m}^2 = 565.7 \text{ m}^2$

$\therefore$ Total cost of canvas = ₹(565.7 × 10) = ₹5657

(ii) Area of the base of the conical tent

$$\pi r^2 = \frac{22}{7} \times 12 \times 12 \text{ m}^2 = 452.57 \text{ m}^2$$

Since each person requires 2 sq. metres of floor area.

$\therefore$ Max. No. of persons who will have enough space on the ground = $\frac{452.57}{2} = 226$

Again, the volume of the conical tent

$$= \frac{1}{3} \times \text{Area of the base} \times \text{Height}$$

$$= \frac{1}{3} \times 452.57 \times 9 \text{ m}^3 = 1357.71 \text{ m}^3$$

Volume of the conical tent = 1357.71 m^3.

We have, Air space required for each person = 15 m^3

$\therefore$ No. of persons who will have enough air space to breathe in = $\frac{1357.71}{15} = 90$.

Between 226 and 90, the smaller number is 90.

Hence, 90 persons can be accommodated.

Illustration 11.2

A cylindrical vessel, without a lid, has to be tin coated on both of its surfaces (inner and outer). If the radius of its base is $\frac{1}{2}$ m and its height is 1.4 m, calculate the cost of tin-coating at the rate of ₹50 per 1000 cm^2.

Solution: Radius of the base (r) = $\frac{1}{2}$ m = $\frac{1}{2} \times 100$ cm = 50 cm

Height (h) = 1.4 m = 1.4 × 100 cm = 140 cm.

Surface area of the cylinder to be tin-coated

$$= 2\,(2\pi rh + \pi r^2) = 2\,[2 \times 3.14 \times 50 \times 140 + 3.14 \times (50)^2]$$

$$= 2\,[43960 + 7850] = 2\,(51810) = 103620 \text{ cm}^2$$

$\therefore$ Cost of tin-coating at the rate of ₹50 per 1000 cm^2 = $\frac{500}{1000} \times 103620$ = ₹5181.

Illustration 11.3

The diameter of a roller 120 cm long is 84 cm. If it takes 500 complete revolutions to level a playground, determine the cost of levelling at the rate of ₹25 per square metre. [Use $\pi = \frac{22}{7}$]

Solution: $2r = 84$ cm

$\therefore$ $$r = \frac{84}{2} \text{ cm} = 42 \text{ cm}$$

$$h = 120 \text{ cm.}$$

Area of the playground levelled in one complete revolution $= 2\pi rh$

$$= 2 \times \frac{22}{7} \times 42 \times 120 = 31680 \text{ cm}^2$$

$\therefore$ Area of the playground levelled in 500 revolutions $= 31680 \times 500 \text{ cm}^2$

$$= \frac{31680 \times 500}{100 \times 100} \text{ m}^2 = 1584 \text{ m}^2.$$

$\therefore$ Cost of levelling @ ₹25 per square metre

$$= ₹1584 \times 25 = ₹39600.$$

Illustration 11.4

A lead pencil consists of a cylinder of wood with a solid cylinder of graphite fitted into it. The diameter of the pencil is 7 mm, the diameter of the graphite is 1 mm and the length of the pencil is 14 cm. Calculate:

(i) Volume of the graphite

(ii) Volume of the wood

(iii) The weight of the whole pencil, if the specific gravity of the wood is 0.7 g/ cm^3 and that of the graphite is 2.1 g/cm^3.

Solution:

(i) We have,

Diameter of the graphite cylinder $= 1 \text{ mm} = \frac{1}{10}$ cm

$\therefore$ Radius of the graphite cylinder $= \frac{1}{20}$ cm

Length of the graphite cylinder = 14 cm

V_1 = Volume of the graphite cylinder

$$= \frac{22}{7} \times \frac{1}{20} \times \frac{1}{20} \times 14 \text{ cm}^3 = 0.11 \text{ cm}^3$$

(ii) We, have,

Diameter of pencil $= 7 \text{ mm} = \frac{7}{10}$ cm

$\therefore$ Radius of pencil $= \frac{7}{20}$ cm and Length of pencil = 14 cm

$$\therefore V_2 = \text{Volume of pencil} = \frac{22}{7} \times \frac{7}{20} \times \frac{7}{20} \times 14 \text{ cm}^2 = 5.39 \text{ cm}^3$$

Volume of wood $V_2 - V_1 = (5.39 - 0.11) \text{ cm}^3 = 5.28 \text{ cm}^3$

(iii) We have,

Specific gravity of wood = 0.7 gm/cm^3

And Specific gravity of graphite = 2.1 gm/cm^3

$\therefore$ Weight of the pencil = Volume of wood × specific gravity of wood + Volume of graphite × specific gravity of graphite

$= (5.28 \times 0.7 + 0.11 \times 2.1) \text{ gm} = 3.927 \text{ gm}.$

Illustration 11.5

How many metres of cloth of 1.1 m width will be required to make a conical tent whose vertical height is m and base radius is 16 m? Find also the cost of the cloth used at the rate of ₹14 per metre.

Solution: $h = 12$ m

$$r = 16 \text{ m}$$

$$\therefore \quad l = \sqrt{r^2 + h^2} = \sqrt{(16)^2 + (12)^2}$$

$$= \sqrt{256 + 144} = \sqrt{400} = 20 \text{ m}$$

$\therefore$ Curved surface area $= \pi r l.$

$$= \frac{22}{7} \times 16 \times 20 = \frac{7040}{7} \text{ m}^2$$

Width of cloth = 1.1 m

$$\therefore \quad \text{Length of cloth} = \frac{7040/7}{1.1} = \frac{70400}{77} = \frac{6400}{7} \text{ m}$$

$\therefore$ Cost of the cloth used at ₹14 per metre

$$= ₹\frac{6400}{7} \times 14 = ₹12800.$$

Illustration 11.6

The ratio of the volumes of the two cones is 4 : 5 and the ratio of the radii of their bases are 2 : 3. Find the ratio of their vertical heights.

Solution: Let the radii of bases, vertical heights and volumes of the two cones be r_1, h_1, v_1 and r_2, h_2, v_2 respectively. According to the question,

$$\frac{v_1}{v_2} = \frac{4}{5} \quad \text{...(i)}$$

$$\frac{r_1}{r_2} = \frac{2}{3} \quad \text{...(ii)}$$

From (i), we have

$$\frac{\frac{1}{3}\pi r_1^2 h_1}{\frac{1}{3}\pi r_2^2 h_2} = \frac{4}{5}$$

$$\Rightarrow \quad \frac{r_1^2 h_1}{r_2^2 h_2} = \frac{4}{5}$$

$$\Rightarrow \quad \left(\frac{r_1}{r_2}\right)^2 \frac{h_1}{h_2} = \frac{4}{5}$$

$$\Rightarrow \quad \left(\frac{2}{3}\right)^2 \frac{h_1}{h_2} = \frac{4}{5}$$

$$\Rightarrow \quad \frac{h_1}{h_2} = \frac{4}{5}\left(\frac{3}{2}\right)^2 \quad \text{...[Using (ii)]}$$

$$\Rightarrow \quad \frac{h_1}{h_2} = \frac{9}{5}$$

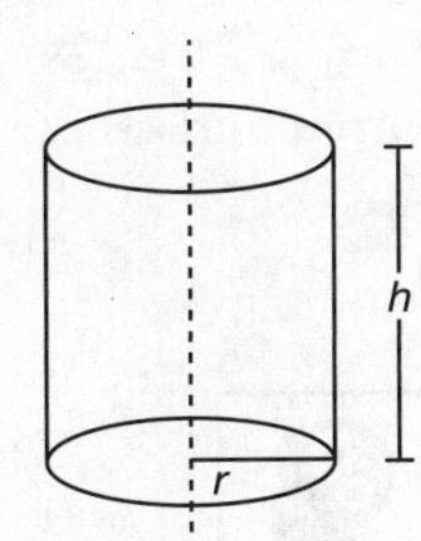

Figure 11.2

Hence the ratio of their vertical height is 9 : 5.

Illustration 11.7

If h, c and v be the height, curved surface and volume of a cone, show that $3\pi v h^3 - c^2h^2 + 9v^2 = 0$.

Solution: Let the radius of the base and slant height of the cone be r and l respectively. Then,

$$c = \text{curved surface} = \pi r l = \pi r\sqrt{r^2 + h^2} \quad \text{...(i)}$$

$$v = \text{volume} = \frac{1}{3}\pi r^2 h \quad \text{...(ii)}$$

LHS

$$3\pi v h^3 - c^2h^2 + 9v^2 = 3\pi v h^3 - c^2h^2 + 9v^2$$

$$= 3\pi\left(\frac{1}{3}\pi r^2 h\right)h^3 - \pi^2 r^2 (r^2 + h^2) h^2 + 9\left(\frac{1}{3}\pi r^2 h\right)^2 \quad \text{[Using (i) and (ii)]}$$

$$= \pi^2 r^2 h^4 - \pi^2 r^4 h^2 - \pi^2 r^2 h^4 + \pi^2 r^4 h^2 = 0.$$

Hence, proved.

Illustration 11.8

How many meters of the cloth, 5 m wide, will be required to make a conical tent, the radius of whose base is 7 m and the height is 24 m?

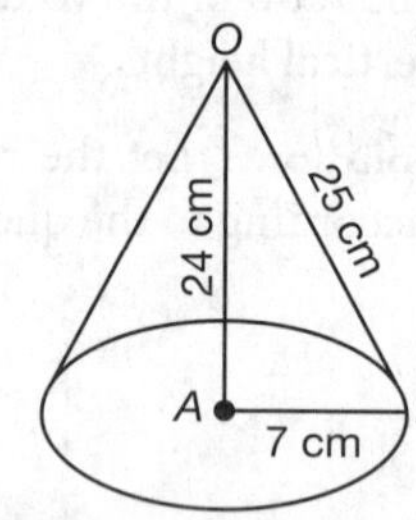

Solution: Radius of the tent, $r = 7$ m and its height, $h = 24$ m.

$\therefore$ $$\text{Slant height, } l = \sqrt{r^2 + h^2} = \sqrt{(7)^2 + (24)^2} \text{ m} = \sqrt{625} \text{ m} = 25 \text{ m}.$$

Area of the curved surface = $(\pi r l)$ sq. m

$$= \left(\frac{22}{7} \times 7 \times 25\right) \text{m}^2 = 550 \text{ m}^2.$$

Thus, the area of the cloth = 550 m^2

$$\text{Length of both required} = \left(\frac{\text{area}}{\text{width}}\right) = \left(\frac{550}{5}\right) \text{m} = 110 \text{ m}.$$

Hence, the length of the cloth required is 110 m.

Illustration 11.9

A bus stop is barricaded from the remaining part of the road, by using 50 hollow cones made of recycled cardboard. Each cone has a base diameter of 40 cm and a height of 1 m. If the outer side of each of the cones is to be painted is ₹12 per m^2, what will be the cost of painting all these cones? [Use $\pi = 3.14$ and $\sqrt{1.04} = 1.02$]

Solution: We have,

$$r = \text{radius of base} = 20 \text{ cm} = 0.2 \text{ m},$$

$$h = \text{height of cone} = 1 \text{ m}.$$

$\therefore$ $$l = \sqrt{r^2 + h^2} = \sqrt{0.04 + 1} \text{ m} = \sqrt{1.04} \text{ m} = 1.02 \text{ m}$$

Curved surface area of a cone = $\pi r l$

$$= 3.14 \times 0.2 \times 1.02 \text{ m}^2$$

$$\text{Cost of painting} = ₹[(3.14 \times 0.2 \times 1.02 \times 12) \times 50] = ₹384.34$$

Check Point 1

1. Find the volume of the cone having a radius of 7 m and a height of 12 m.
2. Find the total surface area of the cylinder having a radius of 7 m and a height of 15 m.
3. The volume of a cone is 4928 cm^3 if its height is 24 m find its radius.
4. A right triangle with sides 3, 4 and 5 is revolved about side 4 to find the volume of the solid so formed.
5. Find the volume of a hollow cylinder having inner and outer radii is 7 cm and 21 cm respectively and having a height of 14 cm.

Sphere and Hemisphere

A sphere is a perfectly round, three-dimensional object where every point on its surface is equidistant from its center. A hemisphere is simply half of a sphere, divided along a plane that passes through its center.

Sphere

(i) T.S.A. of sphere $= 4\pi r^2$

(ii) Volume of sphere $= \frac{4}{3}\pi r^3$

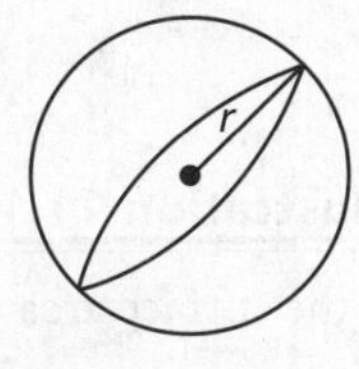

Figure 11.3

Hemisphere

(i) C.S.A. $= 2\pi r^2$

(ii) T.S.A. = C.S.A. + Base circular area

$= 2\pi r^2 + \pi r^2 = 3\pi r^2$

(iii) Volume $= \frac{2}{3}\pi r^3$

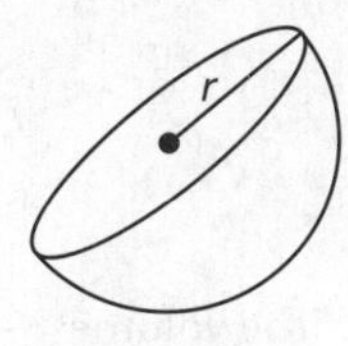

Figure 11.4

Hollow Hemisphere

(i) C.S.A. $= 2\pi (R^2 + r^2)$

(ii) T.S.A. $= 2\pi (R^2 + r^2) + \pi (R^2 - r^2)$

(iii) Volume $= \frac{2}{3}\pi (R^3 - r^3)$

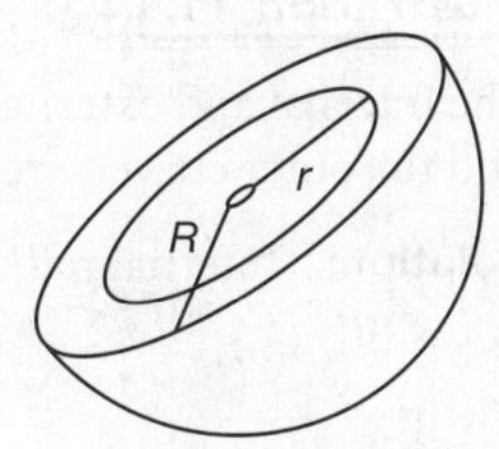

Figure 11.5

Illustration 11.10

Find the diameter of a sphere whose volume is $179\frac{2}{3}$ cubic metres

Solution: Volume $= \frac{4}{3}\pi r^3 = 179\frac{2}{3} = \frac{539}{3}$ cubic metres

$$r^3 = \frac{359}{3} \times \frac{3}{4} \times \frac{7}{22}$$

$$r^3 = \frac{343}{8}$$

$\therefore$ $$r = \frac{7}{2} \text{ metres}$$

Diameter, $2r = 7$ metres

Illustration 11.11

Find the volume and surface area of a sphere of diameter 14 cm.

Solution: Volume $= \frac{4}{3}\pi r^3 = \frac{4}{3} \times \frac{22}{7} \times \frac{14}{2} \times \frac{14}{2} \times \frac{14}{2} = 1437\frac{1}{3}$ cubic centimetres.

Surface area $= 4\pi r^2 = 4 \times \frac{22}{7} \times \frac{14}{2} \times \frac{14}{2} = 616$ square centimetres.

Illustration 11.12

Find the volume of the metal used to make a hollow sphere with an inner radius of 3.5 cm and an outer radius of 4.2 cm.

Solution: Volume of metal used

$$=\frac{4}{3}\pi(R^3-r^3)=\frac{4}{3}\times\frac{22}{7}\left[(4.2)^3-(3.5)^3\right]$$

$$=\frac{4}{3}\times\frac{22}{7}\times 31.213=130.7973 \text{ cubic centimetres}$$

Illustration 11.13

If the surface area of a sphere is 616 square centimetres, find its volume.

Solution: Let the radius of the sphere be 'r'

$$\text{Surface area} = 4\pi r^2 = 616$$

$$r^2=\frac{616}{4}\times\frac{7}{22}=49 \text{ cm}$$

$$\therefore \quad r=7 \text{ cm}$$

$\therefore$ The volume $=\frac{4}{3}\pi r^3=\frac{4}{3}\times\frac{22}{7}\times 7\times 7\times 7=1437\frac{1}{3}$ cubic centimetre

Illustration 11.14

The internal and external diameters of a hollow hemispherical vessel are 42 cm and 45.5 cm respectively. Find its capacity and the outer curved area.

Solution: Internal radius $r=\frac{42}{2}=21$ cm

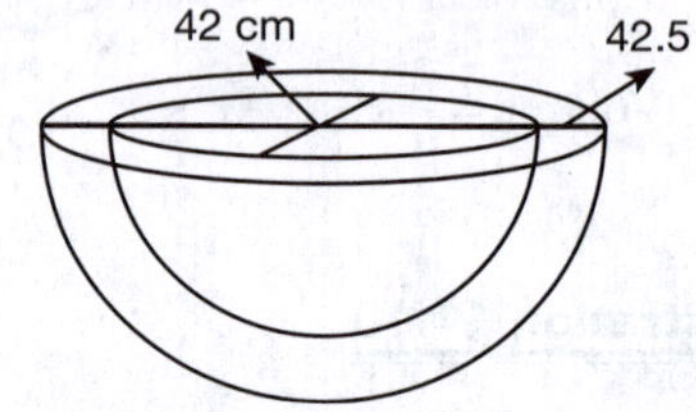

$$\text{External radius } R=\frac{45.5}{2}=22.75 \text{ cm}$$

Capacity of the vessel

$$=\frac{2}{3}\pi r^3=\frac{2}{3}\times\frac{22}{7}\times 21\times 21\times 21=19404 \text{ cm}^3$$

$$\text{Outer surface area} = 2\times\frac{22}{7}\times(22.75)^2=3253.25 \text{ cm}^2$$

Check Point 2

6. Find the surface area and volume of the sphere having a diameter of 7 cm.
7. Surface area of spheres is 154 cm^2. Find its volumes.
8. How much water will a hemispherical bowl, whose radius is 2 metres, contain?
9. A hollow hemisphere has inner radius of 5 cm and thickness of 1 cm. Find the volume of the hollow hemisphere.
10. A hemispherical dome of a building needs to be painted. If the circumference of the base of the dome is 17.6 m, find the cost of painting it, given the cost of painting is ₹5 per 100 cm^2.

Cuboid

There are six faces (rectangular), eight vertices and twelve edges in a cuboid.

Total Surface Area (T.S.A.): The area of surface from which a cuboid is formed.

(i) Total Surface Area (T.S.A.) = $2\,[l \times b + b \times h + h \times l]$ sq. units

(ii) Lateral Surface Area (L.S.A.) = $2\,[b \times h + h \times l]$
(or Area of 4 walls) = $2\,h\,[l + b]$ sq. units

(iii) Volume of Cuboid = (Area of base) × height = $(l \times b) \times h$ cubic units

(iv) Length of diagonal = $\sqrt{l^2 + b^2 + h^2}$ unit

$$= \frac{\text{Total volume objects submerged or taken out}}{\text{Cross-sectional area of container}}$$

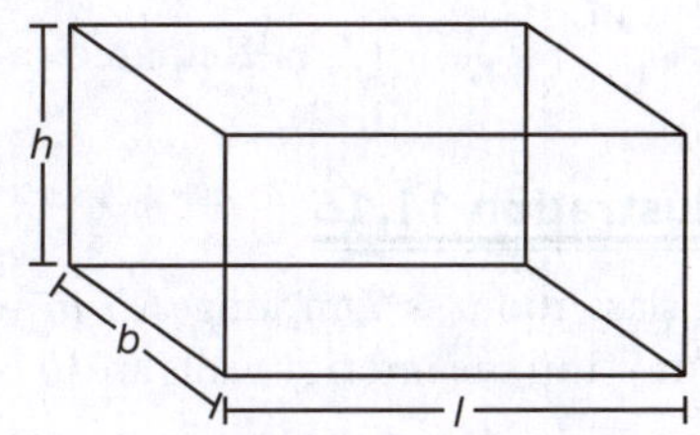

Figure 11.6

Keystone

(a) For painting the surface area of a box or to know how much tin sheet is required for making a box, we use formula (ii).

(b) To find how much a box contains or how much space a box shall occupy, we use formula (i). To find the length of the longest pole to be placed in a room, we use formula (iii).

(c) The rise or fall of liquid level in a container Total volume of objects submerged or taken out cross-sectional area of the container.

Cube

Cube has six faces. Each face is a square.

(i) T.S.A. = $2\,[x \cdot x + x \cdot x + x \cdot x] = 2\,[x^2 + x^2 + x^2] = 2\,(3x^2) = 6x^2$ sq. units

(ii) L.S.A. = $2\,[x^2 + x^2] = 4x^2$ sq. units

(iii) Volume = (Area of base) × Height = $(x^2) \times x = x^3$ cubic units

(iv) Length of diagonal = $x\sqrt{3}$ unit

(v) Total surface area of the cube = $2\,(\text{diagonal})^2 = 2d^2$

(vi) For two cubes

(a) Ratio of volumes = $(\text{Ratio of sides})^3$

(b) Ratio of surface area = $(\text{Ratio of side})^2$

(c) $(\text{Ratio of surface area})^3 = (\text{Ratio of volumes})^2$.

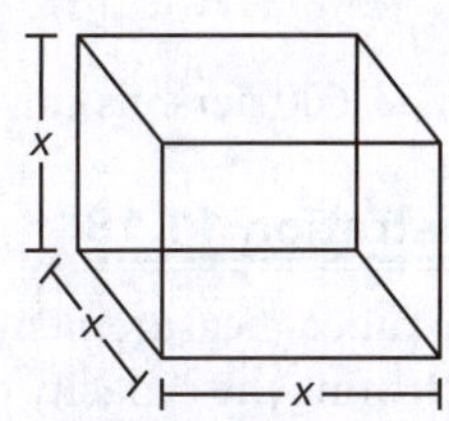

Figure 11.7

Illustration 11.15

Three equal cubes are placed adjacent in a row. Find the ratio of the total surface area of the new cuboid to that of the sum of the surface areas of three cubes.

Solution: Let the side of each of the three equal cubes be a cm.

Then, the surface area of one cube = $6a^2$ cm²

∴ Sum of the surface areas of three cubes = $3 \times 6a^2 = 18a^2$ cm².

For new cuboid

$$\text{Length } (l) = 3a \text{ cm}$$
$$\text{Breadth } (b) = a \text{ cm}$$
$$\text{Height } (h) = a \text{ cm}$$

∴ Total surface area of the new cuboid

$$= 2\,(l \times b + b \times h + h \times l) = 2\,[3a \times a + a \times a + a \times 3a] = 2\,[3a^2 + a^2 + 3a^2] = 14a^2\ \text{cm}^2$$

∴ $$\text{Required ratio} = \frac{\text{Total surface area of the new cuboid}}{\text{Sum of the surface areas of three cubes}} = \frac{14a^2}{18a^2} = \frac{7}{9} = 7:9.$$

Illustration 11.16

A class room is 7 m long, 6.5 m wide and 4 m high. It has one door 3 m × 1.4 m and three windows each measuring 2 m × 1 m the interior walls are to be colour-washed. The contractor charge ₹15 per sq. m. Find the cost of colour washing.

Solution: $l = 7$ m, $b = 6.5$ m and $h = 4$ m

∴ $$\text{Area of the 4 walls of room} = 2(l + b)\,h = 2(7 + 6.5)\,4 = 108\ \text{m}^2$$

$$\text{Area of 1 door} = 3 \times 1.4 = 4.2\ \text{m}^2$$

$$\text{Area of 1 window} = 2 \times 1 = 2\ \text{m}^2$$

∴ $$\text{Area of 3 windows} = 3 \times 2 = 6\ \text{m}^2$$

∴ Area of the walls of the room to be colour washed = 108 – (4.2 + 6) = 108 – 10.2 = 97.8 m²

∴ Cost of colour washing @ ₹15 per square metre = ₹97.8 × 15 = ₹1467.

Illustration 11.17

The dimensions of a cinema hall are 100 m, 50 m and 18 m. How many persons can sit in the hall, if each required 150 m^3 of air?

Solution: $l = 100$ m, $b = 50$ m and $h = 18$ m

∴ Volume of the cinema hall = $lbh = 100 \times 50 \times 18 = 90000\ \text{m}^3$

Volume occupied by 1 person = 150 m^3

∴ Number of persons who can sit in the hall

$$= \frac{\text{Volume of the hall}}{\text{Volume occupied by 1 person}} = \frac{90000}{150} = 600.$$

Hence, 600 persons can sit in the hall.

Illustration 11.18

The outer measurements of a closed wooden box are 42 cm, 30 cm and 27 cm. If the box is made of 1 cm thick wood, determine the capacity of the box.

Solution:

Outer dimensions

$$L = 42\ \text{cm},\ B = 30\ \text{cm and } H = 27\ \text{cm}$$

Thickness of wood = 1 cm

Inner dimensions

$$l = 42 - (1 + 1) = 40\ \text{cm}$$

$$b = 30 - (1 + 1) = 28\ \text{cm}$$

$$h = 27 - (1 + 1) = 25\ \text{cm}$$

∴ $$\text{Capacity of the box} = l \times b \times h = 40 \times 28 \times 25 = 28000\ \text{cm}^3.$$

Illustration 11.19

If v is the volume of a cuboid of dimensions a, b, and c and s is its surface area, then prove that $\frac{1}{v}=\frac{2}{s}\left(\frac{1}{a}+\frac{1}{b}+\frac{1}{c}\right)$.

Solution: Volume of cuboid $(v) = abc$ cubic unit.

Surface area of cuboid $(s) = 2\,(ab + bc + ca)$ sq. units

$$\text{L.H.S.} = \frac{1}{v} = \frac{1}{abc} \quad \ldots\text{(i)}$$

$$\text{R.H.S.} = \frac{2}{s}\left(\frac{1}{a}+\frac{1}{b}+\frac{1}{c}\right)$$

$$= \frac{2}{2\,(ab+bc+ca)}\left(\frac{bc+ca+ab}{abc}\right)$$

$$= \frac{1}{abc} \quad \ldots\text{(ii)}$$

From (i) and (ii)

$$\frac{1}{v}=\frac{2}{s}\left(\frac{1}{a}+\frac{1}{b}+\frac{1}{c}\right)$$

Hence proved.

Illustration 11.20

Three cubes of metal with edges of 3 cm, 4 cm and 5 cm respectively are melted to form a single cube. Find the lateral surface area and volume of the new cube formed.

Solution: Volume of the new cube $= (3^3 + 4^3 + 5^3)\ \text{cm}^3 = 216\ \text{cm}^3$

Let, the edge of this cube $= a$ cm.

Then, $a^3 = 216$.

$\therefore$ $a = 6$ cm.

Lateral surface area of the new cube $= 4a^2 = 4(6)^2 = 4 \times 36 = 144\ \text{cm}^2$.

Solution: External length of the box = 80 cm.

External breadth of the box = 65 cm.

External height of the box = 45 cm.

External volume of the box $= (80 \times 65 \times 45)$ cm

$= 234000\ \text{cm}^3$

Internal length of the box $= [80 - (2.5 \times 2)]$ cm

$= (80 - 5)$ cm $= 75$ cm

Internal breadth of the box $= [65 - (2.5 \times 2)]$ cm

$= (65 - 5)$ cm $= 60$ cm

Internal height of the box $= (45 - 2.5)$ cm $= 42.5$ cm

Check Point 3

11. Find the volume and total surface area of the cuboid with the following data:
Length = 80 cm breadth = 50 cm and height = 40 cm
12. Find the volume and total surface area of a cube of:
(i) Side 40 cm (ii) side 120 cm (iii) side 15 cm
13. The perimeter of a rectangular hall is 250 m. If the cost of painting the walls at the rate of ₹10 per square meter is ₹15000, find the height of the hall.
14. A village has a population of 8000. Each person needs 150 litres of water per day. The village has a tank measuring 20 m × 15 m × 6 m. The tank is full. How many days will the water last?
15. An open wooden box 80 cm long, 65 cm wide and 45 cm high, is made of 2.5 cm thick wood. Find
(i) The capacity of the box
(ii) Volume of the wood used
(iii) Weight of the box, it is being given that 100 cm^3 of wood weighs 8 g.

Cylinder

The curved surface area of the cylinder (C.S.A.): It is the area of the surface from which the cylinder is formed.
When we cut this cylinder along its height, we will find a rectangle with length $2\pi r$ and breadth h units.

(i) C.S.A. of cylinder $= (2\pi r) \times h = 2\pi r h$ sq. units

(ii) T.S.A. = C.S.A. + Area of circular top and bottom
$= 2\pi r h + (\pi r^2) + (\pi r^2)$
$= 2\pi r h + 2\pi r^2$
$= 2\pi r\,(h + r)$ sq. units

(iii) Volume of cylinder = Area of base × height
$= (\pi r^2) \times h$
$= \pi r^2 h$ cubic units

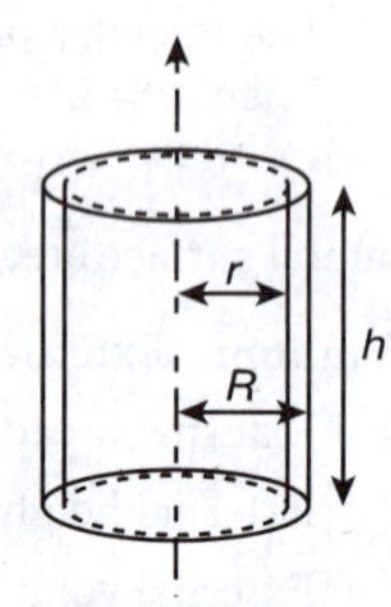

Figure 11.8

Hollow Cylinder

(i) C.S.A. of hollow cylinder $= 2\pi\,(R + r)\,h$ sq. units

(ii) T.S.A. of hollow cylinder $= 2\pi\,(R + r)\,h + 2\pi\,(R^2 - r^2)$ sq. units

(iii) Volume of hollow cylinder $= \pi\,(R^2 - r^2)\,h$ cubic units
Where, r = Inner radius of Cylinder
R = Outer radius of Cylinder
h = Height of the Cylinder

STRUCTURAL OUTLINE

Surface Area and Volume

Cuboid

T.S.A = 2 [l × b + b × h + h × l]

L.S.A. = 2 h [l + b]

Volume = (l × b) × h

Length of diagonal $= \sqrt{\ell^2 + b^2 + h^2}$

Cube

T.S.A = $6x^2$

L.S.A. = $4x^2$

Volume = x^3

Length of diagonal = $x\sqrt{3}$

Cylinder

C.S.A. = $2\pi rh$.

T.S.A. = $2\pi r(h + r)$ sq. units.

Volume = $\pi r^2 h$ cubic units

Cone

C.S.A. = πrl

T.S.A. = $\pi r(l + r)$

(iii) Volume = $\frac{1}{3}\pi r^2 h$

Where, h = height r = radius of base

l = slant height $\sqrt{h^2 + r^2}$

Sphere

T.S.A. = $4\pi r^2$

Volume = $\frac{4}{3}\pi r^3$

Hemi-Sphere

C.S.A. = $2\pi r^2$

T.S.A. = $3\pi r^2$

Volume = $\frac{2}{3}\pi r^3$

Special Points

Distance travelled by a wheel in nrevolutions (without slippage) = n × circumference

The rise or fall of liquid level in a container

$= \frac{Total volume of objectdsubmrgedorkenout}{Cross\ sec\ sectional\ area\ of\ container}$

If the given rectangular sheet of paper is rolled across its length to form a cylinder, having a height b, then Volume of the cylinder = $\frac{\ell^2 b}{4\pi}$

If the given rectangular sheet of paper is rolled across its breadth to form a cylinder, having a height ℓ, then Volume of the cylinder = $\frac{b^2 \ell}{4\pi}$

ASSESSMENT CORNER

FIXED RESPONSE TYPE

Fill in the Blanks

Complete the following statements with an appropriate word/term to be filled in the blank space(s).

1. _______ of a solid is the amount of space enclosed by the bounding surface.
2. The volume of a rectangular solid measuring 1 m by 50 cm by 0.5 m is _______ cm^3.
3. The sum of the area of the plane and curved surfaces (faces) of a solid is called its _______ Surface area.
4. The word solid sphere is used for the solid whose surface is a _______.
5. The curved surface area of a right circular cone whose slant height is 10 cm and base radius is 7 cm is _______.
6. A sphere has only _______ surface and that is curved.

True/False

1. Volume of the biggest sphere in the cube of edge 6 cm is $36\pi\, cm^3$.
2. Cuboids and cubes are special forms of right prisms.
3. A right circular cone is generated by revolving a right-angled triangle about one of the sides containing the right angle.
4. The volume of a sphere is equal to two-thirds the volume of a cylinder of the same height and diameter.
5. The volume of a rectangular solid measuring 1 m by 50 cm by 0.48 m is 24000 cm^3.

Single Correct Type Questions

Level 1

1. The percentage increase in the surface area of a cube, when each side is increased to $\frac{3}{2}$ times the original length is:
   (A) 225 (B) 200
   (C) 175 (D) 125

2. If 'l', 'b' and 'h' of a cuboid are increased, decreased and increased by 1%, 3% and 2% respectively, then the volume of the cuboid:
   (A) Increases
   (B) Decreases
   (C) Increases or decreases depending on original dimensions
   (D) Can't be calculated with given data

3. If the volume of a cube is 216 cm^3, then find its diagonals.
   (A) $6\sqrt{3}$ cm (B) 6 cm
   (C) $\frac{6}{\sqrt{3}}$ cm (D) None of these

4. The whole surface of a rectangular block is 846 cm^2. Find the length, breadth and height, if these dimensions are in the ratio 5 : 4 : 3.
   (A) 20 cm, 16 cm, 12 cm
   (B) 15 cm, 12 cm, 9 cm
   (C) 10 cm, 8 cm, 6 cm
   (D) None of these

5. The height of a conical tent at the centre is 5 m. The distance of any point on its circular base from the top of the tent is 13 m. The area of the slant surface is:
   (A) 144π sq. m
   (B) 130π sq. m
   (C) 156π sq. m
   (D) 169π sq. m

6. A rectangular sheet of paper 22 cm long and 12 cm broad can be curved to form the lateral surface of a right circular cylinder in two ways by rolling along its length and breadth. Difference between the volumes of the two cylinders thus formed is: [Use $\pi = \frac{22}{7}$]
   (A) 200 c.c (B) 210 c.c
   (C) 250 c.c (D) 252 c.c

7. The radius and height of a cone are each increased by 20%, then the volume of the cone is increased by:
   (A) 20% (B) 40%
   (C) 60% (D) 72.8%

8. Consider a hollow cylinder of inner radius r and thickness of wall t and length l. The volume of the above cylinder is given by:

(A) $2\pi l\,(r^2 - l^2)$ (B) $2\pi r l t\left(\frac{t}{2r}+1\right)$

(C) $2\pi l\,(r^2 + t^2)$ (D) $2\pi r l\,(r + t)$

9. How many meters of cloth, 5 m wide, will be required to make a conical tent, the radius of whose base is 7 m and height is 24 m?

(A) 550 m (B) 168 m

(C) 110 m (D) 33.6 m

10. Find the total surface area of a cone whose radius is $\frac{r}{2}$ and slant height is $2l$.

(A) $2\pi r\,(l + r)$ (B) $\pi r\left(\ell+\frac{r}{4}\right)$

(C) $\pi r\,(l + r)$ (D) $2\pi r l$

11. In the given figure, ΔABC is revolved about AC and a solid in the shape of the cone is formed. The volume of the cone is:

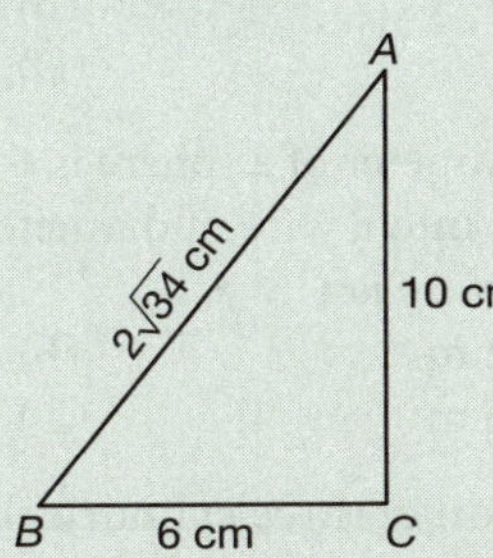

(A) $24\sqrt{34}\,\pi\,\text{cm}^3$ (B) $120\,\pi\,\text{cm}^3$

(C) $12\sqrt{34}\,\text{cm}^3$ (D) $240\,\pi\,\text{cm}^3$

12. A sphere of radius 3 cm is dropped into a cylindrical vessel of radius 4 cm. If the sphere is submerged completely, then the height (in cm) to which the water rises, is:

(A) 2.35 (B) 2.30

(C) 2.25 (D) 2.15

13. The diameter of the moon is approximately one-fourth of the diameter of the earth. What fraction of the volume of the earth is the volume of the moon?

(A) $\frac{1}{8}$ (B) $\frac{1}{64}$

(C) $\frac{1}{512}$ (D) None of these

14. Find the volume of the sphere whose surface area is 154 square cm.

(A) $\frac{77}{3}\,\text{cm}^3$ (B) $\frac{49}{3}\,\text{cm}^3$

(C) $\frac{539}{3}\,\text{cm}^3$ (D) None of these

15. A hemispherical bowl has inner diameter of 11.2 cm. Find the volume of milk it can hold.

(A) 3670.96 ml (B) 347.96 ml

(C) 337.96 ml (D) 397.96 ml

Level 2

16. There is a cylinder circumscribing the hemisphere such that their bases are common. The ratio of their volume is:

(A) 1 : 3 (B) 1 : 2

(C) 3 : 2 (D) 3 : 4

17. A cone and a cylinder have the same base area. They also have the same curved surface area. If the height of the cylinder is 3 m, then the slant height of the cone (in m) is:

(A) 3 (B) 4

(C) 6 (D) 7

18. 27 metal balls each of radius r are melted together to form one big sphere of radius R. Then the ratio of the surface area of the big sphere to that of a ball is:

(A) $\sqrt{27} : 1$ (B) $\sqrt{3} : 1$

(C) 3 : 1 (D) 9 : 1

19. The radii of two cylinders are in the ratio 2 : 3 and their heights are in the ratio of 5 : 3. The ratio of their volumes is:

(A) 10 : 17 (B) 20 : 27

(C) 17 : 27 (D) 20 : 37

20. A track is in the form of a ring whose inner circumference is 352 m and the outer circumference is 396 m. The width of the track is:

(A) 44 m (B) 14 m

(C) 22 m (D) 7 m

21. A pond 100 m in diameter is surrounded by a circular grass walk 2 m wide. How many square meters of grass are there on the walk?

(A) 98 π (B) 100 π

(C) 204 π (D) 202 π

22. A circular grassy plot of land, 42 m in diameter, has a path 3.5 m wide running around it on the outside. Find the cost of gravelling the path at ₹4 per square meter.

(A) ₹2002 (B) ₹2003

(C) ₹2004 (D) ₹2000

23. If the circumference and the area of a circle are numerically equal, then what is the numerical value of the diameter?
(A) 1 (B) 2
(C) 4 (D) *p*

24. A rhombus *OABC* is drawn inside a circle whose centre is at *O* in such a way that the vertices *A*, *B* and *C* of the rhombus are on the circle. If the area of the rhombus, is $32\sqrt{3}$ m^2, then the radius of the circle is:
(A) 64 m (B) 8 m
(C) 32 m (D) 46 m

25. Four equal circles are described about the four corners of a square so that each touches two of the others. If each side of the square is 14 cm, then the area enclosed between the circumferences of the circle is:
(A) 24 sq cm
(B) 42 sq cm
(C) 154 sq cm
(D) 196 sq cm

Multiple Correct Type Questions

1. A matchbox measures 4 cm × 2.5 cm × 1.5 cm. The volume of a packet containing 12 such boxes is:
(A) 12×15 cm^3
(B) $(12 \times 4 \times 2.5 \times 1.5)$ cm^3
(C) 180 cm^3
(D) $(4 \times 2.5 \times 1.5)$ cm^3

2. A solid cube is cut into two cuboids of equal volumes. The ratio of the total surface area of the given cube and that of one of the cuboids is:
(A) $6a^2 : 4a^2$ (B) $4a^2 : 6a^2$
(C) 3 : 2 (D) 2 : 3

3. The weight of a lead pipe 3.5 m long, if the external diameter of the pipe is 2.4 cm and the thickness of the lead is 2 mm and 1 cubic cm of lead weights 11 gm, is:
(A) (484×11) gm
(B) 5.324 kgs
(C) 5 kg
(D) $\pi(2.2)(0.2)(350)(11)$ gm

4. The base radii of two right circular cones of the same height are in the ratio 3 : 5. The ratio of their volumes is:
(A) $R_2^2 : R_1^2$ (B) $R_1^2 : R_2^2$
(C) 25 : 9 (D) 9 : 25

5. The volume of the two spheres is in the ratio 64 : 27. The difference in their surface areas, if the sum of their radii is 7, is:
(A) 28π cm^2 (B) 88 cm^2
(C) 64π cm^2 (D) 36π cm^2

6. A rectangular sheet of metal, *x* cm by *y* cm has a square of size *z* cm cut from each corner. The sheet is then bent to form a tray of depth *z* cm. The volume of the tray is not:
(A) $z(x - z)(y - z)$ cm^3
(B) xyz cm^3
(C) $z(x - 2z)(y - 2z)$ cm^3
(D) $(x + y)z$ cm^3

7. The number of solid spheres, each of diameter 6 cm that could be moulded to form a solid metal cylinder of height 45 cm and diameter 4 cm is:
(A) 3 (B) 4
(C) 5 (D) 6

8. If a solid sphere of radius *r* is melted and cast into the shape of a solid cone of height *r*, then the radius of the base of the cone is:
(A) 2*r* (B) 3*r*
(C) *r* (D) 4*r*

9. The diameter of a sphere is 6 cm. It is melted and drawn into a wire of diameter 2 mm. The length of the wire is:
(A) 12 m (B) 18 m
(C) 36 m (D) 66 m

10. The radii of three cylindrical jars of equal height are in the ratio 1 : 2 : 3. Second jar is full of water which is first poured into the first jar. After filling the first jar, water is poured into the third jar. Which of the following statements is false?
(A) Third jar is half full
(B) Third jar is one-third full
(C) Third jar is two-thirds full
(D) Third jar is four ninth full

Match Type Questions

1. Column-II gives the solid figures from the plane figure in Column-I, match them correctly:

Column-I	Column-II
(A) Rectangle rotating about axis	(p) cone
(B) Semicircle rotating about diameter	(q) cube

(Continued)

Column-I	Column-II
(C) Right-angled triangle rotating about base	(r) cylinder
(D) Six square sheet	(s) sphere

2. Match the columns correctly:

Column-I	Column-II
(A) A cylinder of radius 3 cm is inscribed in a sphere of radius 5 cm, then the volume of cylinder is	(p) 38.5 m^3
(B) A conical pit of top diameter 3.5 m is 12 m deep, the capacity of the pit is	(q) 512 cm^3
(C) The length of a diagonal of a cube is $8\sqrt{3}$ cm, then the volume of the cube is	(r) 72π cm^3
(D) The capacity of a conical vessel with a height of 12 cm and slant height of 13 cm is	(s) 100π cm^3

3. Match the columns correctly:

Column-I	Column-II
(A) A cone and a hemisphere have equal base and equal volumes, then the ratio of height to radius is	(p) 1 : 9
(B) A cone and a cylinder are of the same height. Their radii of the bases are in ratio 2: 1, then the ratio of their volumes is	(q) 1 : 1
(C) A right circular cylinder just encloses a sphere of radius *r*, then the ratio of their curved surface areas is	(r) 4 : 3
(D) Twenty seven solid iron spheres each of radius *r* and surface area *S* are melted to form a sphere with surface area *S'* then ratio of *S* and *S'* is.	(s) 2 : 1

4. Match the columns correctly:

Column-I	Column-II
(A) Ratio of the volume of a cone and sphere if each has the same diameter and same height	(p) 9 : 32
(B) The radii of two cones are in the ratio 2 : 1 and their volumes are equal, then the ratio of their heights is	(q) 1 : 2
(C) If the heights of two right circular cones are in the ratio 1: 2 and the perimeters of their bases are in the ratio 3 : 4, then ratio of their volume is	(r) 1 : 4
(D) A right circular cone and a right circular cylinder have an equal base and equal height. If the radius of the base and height are in the ratio 5 : 12, the ratio of the total surface area of the cylinder to that of the cone is	(s) 17 : 9

Assertion and Reason Type Questions

Directions: In the following questions as Assertion (A) is given followed by a Reason (R). Mark your responses from the following options.

(A) Both Assertion and Reason are true and Reason is the correct explanation of 'Assertion'.
(B) Both Assertion and Reason are true and Reason is not the correct explanation of 'Assertion'.
(C) Assertion is true but Reason is false.
(D) Assertion is false but Reason is true.

1. **Assertion:** In a cylinder, if the radius is halved and the height is doubled, the volume will be halved.
Reason: In a cylinder, the radius is doubled and the height is halved, the curved surface area will be the same.

2. **Assertion:** If the diameter of a sphere is decreased by 25% then its curved surface area is decreased by 43.75%.
Reason: Curved surface area is increased when diameter decreases.

ASSESSMENT CORNER

3. **Assertion:** A cone is a solid figure.
Reason: A cone is generated when the rectangular sheet is rotated about its axis.

Comprehension Type Questions

A sphere of radius 3 cm is given.

1. Ratio of volume of sphere to the surface area of sphere not considering units is:
(A) 1 : 2 (B) 2 : 1
(C) 1 : 1 (D) 3 : 1

2. If the sphere is cut into half, then the total surface area of half portion is:
(A) $9\pi\, cm^2$ (B) $16\pi\, cm^2$
(C) $27\pi\, cm^2$ (D) $18\pi\, cm^2$

3. Sum of the total surface areas of the two halve is:
(A) $27\pi\, cm^2$ (B) $16\pi\, cm^2$
(C) $50\pi\, cm^2$ (D) $54\pi\, cm^2$

Numerical Type Questions

1. Find the total surface area of a box whose length, breadth and height are 12 cm, 8 cm and 5 cm, respectively.

2. An iron pillar has some portion in the form of a right circular cylinder and remaining in the form of a right circular cone. The radius of the base of each of the cone and the cylinder is 8 cm. The cylindrical portion is 240 cm high and the conical part is 36 cm high. Find the weight of the pillar, if one cubic cm of iron weighs 7.8 g.

3. An open box is made of wood 3 cm thick. Its external length, breadth and height are 1.48 m, 1.16 m and 8.3 dm. Find the cost of painting the inner surface at ₹5 per m^2.

4. A room 8 m long, 6 m broad and 3 m high has two windows $1\frac{1}{2}$ m × 1 m and a door 2 m × $1\frac{1}{2}$ m. Find the cost of papering the walls with paper 50 cm wide at ₹40 per meter.

5. The dimensions of a rectangular box are in the ratio 2 : 3 : 4 and the difference between the cost of covering it with the sheet of paper at the rate of ₹8 and ₹9.50 per m^2 is ₹1248. Find the dimensions of box.

6. Find the number of bricks, each measuring 25 cm × 12.5 cm × 7.5 cm required to construct a wall 6 m long, 5 m high and 0.5 m thick, while the cement and sand mixture occupies 1/20 of the volume of the wall.

7. The circumference of the base of 9 m high wooden solid cone is 44 m. Find the slant height of the cone.

8. The curved surface area of a right circular cylinder is 4400 cm^2. If the circumference of the base is 110 cm, then find the height of the cylinder.

9. 50 circular plates, each of radius 7 cm and thickness $\frac{1}{2}$ cm, are placed one above the other to form a solid right circular cylinder. Find the total surface area.

10. The internal and external diameters of a hollow hemispherical Vessel are 24 cm and 25 cm respectively. The cost to paint 1 cm^2 the surface is ₹0.05. Find the total cost to paint the vessel all over. [Use $\pi = \frac{22}{7}$]

11. A dome of the building is in the form of a hemisphere. From inside, it was whitewashed at the cost of ₹498.96. If the cost of whitewashing is ₹2.00 per square meter, find the inside surface area of the dome and the volume of the air inside the dome.

12. Assuming the earth to be a sphere of radius 6370 km, how many square kilometres is the area of the land, if three fourth of the earth's surface is covered by water?

13. A hemispherical bowl is made of steel 0.5 cm thick. The inside radius of the bowl is 4 cm. Find the volume of steel used in making the bowl.

14. A solid metallic sphere of diameter 28 cm is melted and recast into a number of smaller cones, each of diameter $4\frac{2}{3}$ cm and height 3 cm. Find the number of cones so formed.

15. A toy is in the form of a right circular cylinder closed at one end and with a hemisphere on the other end. The height and the radius of the base are 15 cm and 6 cm respectively. The radius of the hemisphere and cylinder are the same. Calculate the total surface area and the volume of the toy. If the toy is painted at the rate of ₹2.50 per 10 cm^2, find the cost of painting the toy.

Higher Order Thinking Skills (HOTS)

1. A rectangular tin sheet is 12 cm long and 5 cm broad. It is rolled along its length to form a cylinder by making the opposite edges just

touch each other. The volume of the cylinder (in cm^3) is:

(A) $\frac{180}{\pi}$ (B) $\frac{120}{\pi}$

(C) $\frac{100}{\pi}$ (D) $\frac{60}{\pi}$

2. If the radius of the base of a right circular cylinder is halved, keeping the height of the same, what is the ratio of the volume of the reduced cylinder to that of the original one?

(A) 1 : 4 (B) 1 : 8

(C) 1 : 2 (D) 8 : 1

3. The radius of a wire is decreased to one-third. If the volume remains the same, the length will become:

(A) 1 time (B) 3 times

(C) 6 times (D) 9 times

4. Three solid spherical beads of radii 3 cm, 4 cm and 5 cm are melted into a spherical bead. Its radius is:

(A) 6 cm (B) 7 cm

(C) 8 cm (D) 9 cm

5. If a solid sphere of radius 10 cm is moulded into 8 spherical solid balls of equal radius, then the surface area of each ball (in sq. cm) is:

(A) 100π (B) 75π

(C) 60π (D) 50π

6. If the height and diameter of a right circular cylinder are 32 cm and 6 cm respectively, then the radius of the sphere whose volume is equal to the volume of the cylinder is:

(A) 3 cm (B) 4 cm

(C) 6 cm (D) None of these

7. A hollow spherical ball whose inner radius is 4 cm is full of water. Half of the water is transferred to a conical cup and it completely filled the cup. If the height of the cup is 2 cm, then the radius of the base of the cone in cm is:

(A) 4 (B) 10

(C) 8 (D) 16

8. Radius and height of a cylinder are 7 cm and 14 cm respectively. It is divided along its axis vertically into equal parts. The increase in its total surface area is:

(A) 392 sq. cm (B) 308 sq. cm

(C) 196 sq. cm (D) 154 sq. cm

9. The moon's diameter is approximately one-fourth of the diameter of the earth. The volume of the moon is what fraction of the volume of the earth?

(A) $\frac{1}{64}$ (B) $\frac{1}{8}$

(C) $\frac{1}{4}$ (D) None of these

10. The volume of a box is given by $v = x^3 - 2x^2 - 24x$. If the depth of the box be the smallest, then the depth is:

(A) $(x - 3)$ (B) $(x - 6)$

(C) $(x - 4)$ (D) $(x - 8)$

11. A cone, a right cylinder and a hemisphere stand on equal bases and have the same height. Their volumes are in the ratio:

(A) 1 : 2 : 3 (B) 1 : 3 : 2

(C) 2 : 3 : 1 (D) 2 : 1 : 3

12. The length, breadth and height of a room are in the ratio 3 : 2 : 1. If the breadth and height are halved while the length is doubled, then the total area of the four walls of the room will:

(A) Remain the same

(B) decrease by 30%

(C) Decrease by 15%

(D) decrease by 18.75%

13. If the surface area of cube A is 64% of the surface area of cube B, then the volume of cube A is 'k' per cent of the volume of cube B. The value of 'k' is:

(A) 0.64 (B) 0.512

(C) 51.2 (D) 64

14. If the radius of a right circular cylinder is increased by 50% and height is decreased by 20% then the percentage change in volume of the cylinder is:

(A) 40% (B) 50%

(C) 60% (D) 80%

15. John's birthday cake is a delightful cylinder of radius 6 inches and height of 3 inches, if these friends cut the cake into 8 equal sectors, the total surface area of a piece of birthday cake in sq. inches is:

(A) $9(\pi + 4)$ (B) $\frac{27\pi}{2}$

(C) $4(\pi + 4)$ (D) $\frac{9}{2}(3\pi + 8)$

ASSESSMENT CORNER

Free Response Type

Very Short Answer Type Questions

1. If the radius of a sphere is $2r$, find its volume.
2. If the total surface area of a cube is 96 cm^2. Find the volume of the cube.
3. Find the total surface area of a cone whose radius is $\frac{r}{2}$ and slant height is $2l$.
4. Find the length of the longest pole that can be put in a room of dimensions (10 m × 10 m × 5 m).
5. If the length of the diagonal of a cube is $6\sqrt{3}$ cm, then find the length of the edge of the cube.
6. If a sphere is inscribed in a cube, then find the ratio of the volume of the cube to the volume of the sphere will be?
7. A cone is 8.4 cm high and the radius of its base is 2.1 cm. It is melted and recast into a sphere. Find the radius of the sphere.
8. The radii of two cylinders are in the ratio of 2 : 3 and their heights are in the ratio of 5 : 3. Find the ratio of their volumes.

Short Answer Type Questions

1. The radius of a hemispherical balloon increases from 6 cm to 12 cm as air is being pumped into it. Find the ratios of the surface areas of the balloon in the two cases.
2. An edge of a cube measures r cm. If the largest possible right circular cone is cut out of this cube, then find the volume of the cone (in cm^3).
3. Find the amount of water displaced by a solid spherical ball of diameter 4.2 cm, when it is completely immersed in water.
4. How many square metres of the canvas are required for a conical tent whose height is 3.5 m and the radius of the base is 12 m?
5. The volumes of the two spheres are in the ratio 64 : 27. Find the ratio of their surface areas.
6. A cube of side 4 cm contains a sphere touching its sides. Find the volume of the gap in between.
7. The surface area of a sphere of radius 5 cm is five times the area of the curved surface of a cone of radius 4 cm. Find the height and the volume of the cone (taking $\pi = \frac{22}{7}$).
8. The radius of a sphere is increased by 10%. Prove that the volume will be increased by 33.1% approximately.
9. Metal spheres, each of radius 2 cm, are packed into a rectangular box of internal dimensions 16 cm × 8 cm × 8 cm. When 16 spheres are packed the box is filled with preservative liquid. Find the volume of this liquid. Give your answer to the nearest integer. [Use $\pi = 3.14$]
10. A right triangle with sides 6 cm, 8 cm and 10 cm is revolved about the side 8 cm. Find the volume and the curved surface of the solid so formed.

Long Answer Type Questions

1. Rainwater which falls on a flat rectangular surface of length 6 m and breadth 4 m is transferred into a cylindrical vessel of internal radius 20 cm. What will be the height of water in the cylindrical vessel if the rainfall is 1 cm? Give your answer to the nearest integer. (Take $\pi = 3.14$)
2. A cylindrical tube opened at both ends is made of iron sheet which is 2 cm thick. If the outer diameter is 16 cm and its length is 100 cm, find how many cubic centimetres of iron have been used in making the tube.
3. A semi-circular sheet of metal of diameter 28 cm is bent to form an open conical cup. Find the capacity of the cup.
4. The water for a factory is stored in a hemispherical tank whose internal diameter is 14 m. The tank contains 50 kilolitres of water. Water is pumped into the tank to fill it to its capacity. Calculate the volume of water pumped into the tank.
5. A small village, having a population of 5000, requires 75 litres of water per head per day. The village has got an overhead tank of measurement 40 m × 25 m × 15 m. For how many days will the water in this tank last?
6. A cloth having an area of 165 m^2 is shaped into the form of a conical tent of radius 5 m.
   (i) How many students can sit in the tent if a student, on an average, occupies $\frac{5}{7}$ m^2 on the ground?
   (ii) Find the volume of the cone.

ASSESSMENT CORNER

ARCHIVE CORNER

1. The dimensions of a cuboid are 18 cm × 12 cm × 9 cm. How many cubes of side 3 cm can be made by melting the cuboid?
(A) 72 (B) 69
(C) 60 (D) 55

2. If the radii of two cones are in the ratio 3 : 1 and heights are in the ratio 1 : 3, then the ratio of their volumes is:
(A) 3 : 1 (B) 2 : 1
(C) 1 : 3 (D) 1 : 2

3. Areas of six surfaces of a cuboid are 12, 12, 20, 20, and 15, 15 sq. cm respectively. Volume of this cuboid in cm^3 is:
(A) 12 (B) 15
(C) 60 (D) 94

4. On increasing each of the radii of the base and the height of a cone by 20%, its volume will be increased by ________.
(A) 20% (B) 40%
(C) 72.2% (D) 72.8%

5. If the radius of a cylinder is decreased by 50% and the height increased by 50% to form a new cylinder, then the volume will be decreased by
(A) 50% (B) 55%
(C) 62.5% (D) 63%

6. If the volume and surface area of a sphere is numerically the same, then its radius is:
(A) 4 (B) 3
(C) 2 (D) 1

7. A cone has radius r and height h. It is melted and three identical cones are formed each having the same radius as the original cone and height H. Then the value of ratio of volume is:
(A) $\frac{1}{4}$ (B) $\frac{1}{3}$
(C) $\frac{1}{2}$ (D) 1

8. From a 25 cm × 35 cm rectangular cardboard, an open box is to be made by cutting out identical squares of area 25 cm^2 from each corner and turning up the sides. The volume of the box is
(A) 3000 cm^3 (B) 1875 cm^3
(C) 21875 cm^3 (D) 1250 cm^3

9. The surface water in a swimming pool forms a rectangle with a length of 40 m and a breadth of 15 m. The depth of water increases uniformly from 1.2 m at one end to 2.4 m at the other end. The volume (in m^3) of water in the pool is:
(A) 1080 (B) 720
(C) 600 (D) 540

10. A sphere of diameter 12.6 cm is melted and cast into a right circular cone of height 25.2 cm. The diameter of the base of the cone is:
(A) 12.6 cm (B) 79.38 cm
(C) 39.69 cm (D) 69.39 cm

11. The area of adjacent faces and surface area of a cuboid with volume v and sides a, b, c are respectively x, y, z and s. Then which of the following is false?
(A) $\frac{1}{v}=\frac{2}{s}\left(\frac{1}{a}+\frac{1}{b}+\frac{1}{c}\right)$ (B) $v^2=x{\cdot}y{\cdot}z$
(C) $s=2\,(x+y+z)$ (D) $s=x+y+z$

12. The diameter of a right circular cylinder is decreased by 10%. The volume of cylinder remains the same then the percentage increase in height is:
(A) 20% (B) 23.45%
(C) 5% (D) 20.5%

13. The surface area of a cylindrical pipe, open at both ends is 628 sq. m. The difference between its radius and length is 15 m (the length being larger). If the pipe was closed at one end, the amount of water that it can hold is:
(A) 500 π cu. m (B) 525 π cu. m
(C) 550 π cu. m (D) None of these

14. How many surfaces are there in solid cylinder?
(A) 1 (B) 2
(C) 3 (D) 4

15. The area of three adjoining faces of cuboid are A, B and C respectively then its volume will be
(A) ABC (B) $\sqrt{ABC}$
(C) $A^2B^2C^2$ (D) None of these

16. Water flows at the rate of 10 metres per minute from a cylindrical pipe 5 mm. in diameter. The time taken to fill up a conical vessel, whose diameter at the base is 40 cm and depth 24 cm, is:
(A) 55 minute
(B) 52 minute 1 sec
(C) 51 minutes 12 sec
(D) 48 minutes 15 sec

ARCHIVE CORNER

17. The radius of a sphere is r and radius of base of a cylinder is r and height is $2r$. The ratio of their volumes will be.

(A) 2 : 1 (B) 3 : 2
(C) 3 : 1 (D) 2 : 3

18. A metallic spherical shell of internal and external diameters 4 cm. and 8 cm. respectively is melted and recast into the form of a cone of base diameter 8 cm. The height of the cone is

(A) 12 cm. (B) 14 cm.
(C) 15 cm. (D) 18 cm.

19. An empty pool being filled with water at a constant rate takes 8 hours to fill $\frac{3}{5}^{th}$ of its capacity. How much more time will it take to finish filling the pool?

(A) 5 hours 30 minutes
(B) 5 hours 20 minutes
(C) 4 hours 48 minutes
(D) 4 hours 50 minutes

20. If the volume of two cubes is in the ratio 27 : 64, then the ratio of their total surface area is:

(A) 27 : 64 (B) 3 : 4
(C) 9 : 16 (D) 3 : 8

21. The volume and whole surface area of a cylindrical solid of radius r units are v and s respectively. If the height of cylinder is 1 unit then v/s is equal to:

(A) $\frac{1}{2}\left(1-\frac{1}{r+1}\right)$ (B) $\frac{1}{2}\left(1+\frac{1}{r+1}\right)$

(C) $\frac{1}{2}\left(1-\frac{1}{r+1}\right)$ (D) $\frac{1}{2}\left(1+\frac{1}{r}\right)$

22. If the height of right circular cylinder is increased by 10% while the radius of base is decreased by 10% then the curved surface area of cylinder:

(A) Remains same
(B) Decreases by 1%
(C) Increases by 1%
(D) Increases by 0.1%

23. The volume of a cube is 2744 cm^3, its surface area is:

(A) 196 cm^2 (B) 1176 cm^2
(C) 784 cm^2 (D) 588 cm^2

24. If r is the radius of the base of a cylinder and h is the height of cylinder, then the total surface area will be:

(A) $2\pi rh$
(B) $2\pi rh + 2\pi r^2$
(C) $\pi r^2 h$
(D) None of these

25. The length of the longest pole that can be kept in a room of size 12 m × 9 m × 8 m is:

(A) 29 m (B) 17 m
(C) 21 m (D) 19 m

26. The height of a cylinder is 14 cm and its curved surface area is 264 cm^2, the volume of the cylinder is:

(A) 308 cm^3 (B) 396 cm^3
(C) 1232 cm^3 (D) 1848 cm^3

27. A right circular cone is 8.4 cm high and the radius of its base is 2.1 cm. The cone is melted and recast into a sphere. Find the radius of the sphere.

(A) 2.1 cm (B) 4.2 cm
(C) 5.3 cm (D) 6.4 cm

28. The internal and external diameters of a hollow hemispherical vessel are 24 cm and 25 cm respectively. If the cost for painting 1 cm^2 of the surface area is ₹0.05 then the total cost of painting the vessel all over is:

(A) ₹90.05 (B) ₹96.28
(C) ₹95.20 (D) ₹96.29

29. If each edge of a cube is increased by 50% then the percentage increase in its surface area is:

(A) 50% (B) 125%
(C) 130% (D) 140%

30. Maximum length of the pole which can be put in the room whose length, breadth and height are 10 m, 10 m and 5 m respectively.

(A) 25 m (B) 20 m
(C) 15 m (D) 10 m

31. A right-angled triangle with sides 3 cm, 4 cm and 5 cm is rotated about the side of 3 cm as the axis to form a cone. The volume of the cone that is formed by the triangle will be:

(A) 12π cm^3 (B) 15π cm^3
(C) 16π cm^3 (D) 20π cm^3

32. The capacity of two pots are 240 litres and 112 litres respectively. Find the capacity of a container which can exactly measure the contents of the two pots.

(A) 9000 cc (B) 12000 cc
(C) 16000 cc (D) 8000 cc

33. The curved surface area of a right circular cylinder of base radius r is obtained by multiplying its volume by:

(A) $\frac{2}{r^2}$ (B) $2r^2$

(C) $\frac{2}{r}$ (D) $2r$

34. If the side of each cube is 3 cm, then the volume of the given figure is:

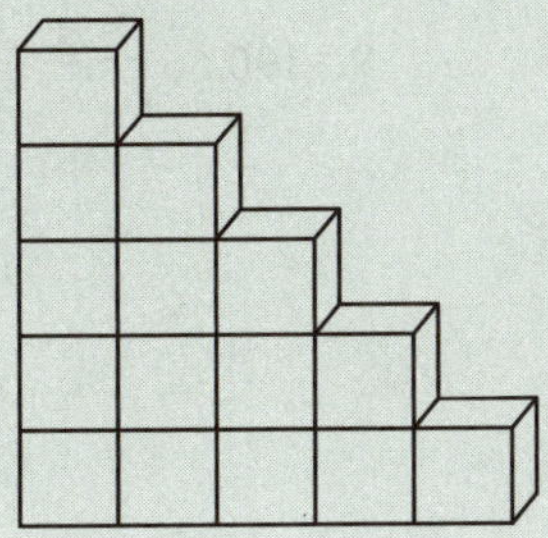

(A) 3 cm^3 (B) 27 cm^3

(C) 15 cm^3 (D) 405 cm^3

35. The radii of a right circular cone and a right circular cylinder are in the ratio 4 : 3 and their heights are in the ratio 2 : 3. The ratio of their volumes is:

(A) 32 : 27 (B) 32 : 9

(C) 32 : 81 (D) 27 : 32

ANSWER KEY

CHECK POINTS

Check Point 1

1. 616 m^3 2. 968 m^2 3. 140 cm 4. 37.71 m^3 5. 17248 cm^3

Check Point 2

6. 154 cm^2, 179.66 cm^3 7. 179.66 cm^3 8. 16761.90 litre 9. 190.66 cm^3 10. ₹24640

Check Point 3

11. Volume = 160000 cm^3, Total surface area = 18400 cm^2
12. (i) Volume = 64000 cm^3, Total surface area = 9600 cm^2
    (ii) Volume = 1728000 cm^3, Total surface area = 86400 cm^2
    (iii) Volume = 3375 cm^3, Total surface area = 1350 cm^2
13. 6 meters 14. 1.5 days
15. (i) 191250 cm^3 (ii) 42750 cm^3 (iii) 3 kg 420 g

Assessment Corner

FIXED RESPONSE TYPE

Fill in the Blanks

1. Volume 2. $100 \times 50 \times 50 = 250000$ cm^3 3. Total 4. Spherical
5. Curved Surface area = $\frac{22}{7} \times 7 \times 10 = 220$ sq.cm 6. Curved

True/False

1. True 2. True 3. True 4. True 5. False

Single Correct Type Questions

1. D 2. B 3. A 4. B 5. C 6. B 7. D 8. B 9. C
10. B 11. B 12. C 13. B 14. C 15. A 16. C 17. C 18. D
19. B 20. D 21. C 22. A 23. C 24. B 25. C

Multiple Correct Type Questions

1. ABC 2. AC 3. ABD 4. BD 5. AB 6. ABD 7. C 8. A 9. C
10. B

Match Type Questions

1. (A) → (R); (B) → (S); (C) → (P); (D) → (Q)
2. (A) → (R); (B) → (P); (C) → (Q); (D) → (S)
3. (A) → (S); (B) → (R); (C) → (Q); (D) → (P)
4. (A) → (Q); (B) → (R); (C) → (P); (D) → (S)

Assertion and Reason Type Questions

1. C 2. C 3. C

Comprehension Type Questions

1. C 2. C 3. D

Numerical Type Questions

1. 392 sq.cm 2. 395366.4 grams or 395.37kg 3. ₹27.970 4. ₹6400 5. 16 cm 6. 6080
7. $\sqrt{130}$ 8. 40 cm 9. 1408 sq.cm 10. ₹96.29 11. 523.9 m^3 12. 127527400 sq.km
13. 56.83 cubic cm 14. 672 15. ₹132

Higher Order Thinking Skills (HOTS)

1. A 2. A 3. D 4. A 5. A 6. C 7. C 8. A 9. A
10. B 11. A 12. B 13. C 14. D 15. D

Free Response Type

Very Short Answer Type Questions

1. $\frac{32}{3}\pi r^3$ 2. 64 cm^3 3. $\pi r(l + r/4)$ 4. 15 m 5. 6 cm 6. $\frac{6}{\pi}$ 7. 2.1 cm 8. $\frac{20}{27}$

Short Answer Type Questions

1. 1 : 4 2. $\frac{1}{12}\pi r^3$ 3. 38.81 cm^3 4. 471.43 m^2 5. $\frac{16}{9}$ 6. 30.48 cm^3
7. 50.29 cm^3 8. 33.1% 9. 488.16 cm^3 10. 188.57 cm^2

Long Answer Type Questions

1. 191.08 cm 2. 8800 cm^3 3. 622.37 cm^3 4. 668.67 m^3 5. 40
6. 241.74 m

Archive Corner

1. A 2. A 3. C 4. D 5. C 6. B 7. A 8. B 9. A
10. A 11. D 12. B 13. A 14. C 15. B 16. C 17. D 18. B
19. B 20. C 21. A 22. B 23. B 24. B 25. B 26. B 27. A
28. D 29. B 30. C 31. C 32. C 33. C 34. D 35. C

ANSWER KEY

CHAPTER 12

Statistics

Learning Outcomes

After reading this chapter, you would be able to understand:

- tabular representation of statistical data.
- graphical represantion of data.
- measures of central tendancy.

Geekspeak

- Data
- Frequency
- Cumulative frequency
- Mean
- Median
- Mode
- Histograph
- Bar graph
- Frequency polygon
- Distribution table
- Variate
- Discrete variate
- Continuous variate
- Range
- Class frequency
- Class interval
- Class limits
- Class mark

Introduction

Statistics deals with collection of numerical facts i.e., data, their classification and tabulation and their interpretation.

Statistical Data

Statistical data refers to the collection, analysis, and interpretation of numerical information to draw conclusions or make decisions. It is often used to analyze and summarize large amounts of information across various fields.

Collection of Data

On the basis of methods of collection, data can be divided into two categories:

(i) **Primary data:** Data which are collected for the first time by the statistical investigator or with help of his workers is called primary data.

(ii) **Secondary data:** These are the data already collected by a person or a society and these may be in published or unpublished form. These are generally obtained from the following two sources:

1. **Published sources** 2. **Unpublished sources**

Classification of Data

When the data is compiled in the same form and order in which it is collected, it is known as **Raw Data** and it is also called **Crude Data.** For example, the marks obtained by 20 students of class IX in English out of 10 marks are as follows:

7	4	9	5	8	9	6	7	9	2
0	3	7	6	2	1	9	8	3	8

(i) **Variate:** A number whose value varies objectively is called a random variable, and in general a random variable is represented by x.

1. **Discrete variate:** Its magnitude is fixed. For example, the number of faculties in different branches of an institute are 20, 25, 30 etc.
2. **Continuous variate:** Its magnitude is not fixed. It is expressed in groups like 10–20, 20–30, etc.

(ii) **Range:** The difference between the maximum and minimum values of variable x is called range.

(iii) **Class frequency:** Within each class, the frequency with which the data repeats is known as the class frequency.

(iv) **Class interval** $= \dfrac{\text{Range}}{\text{Number of classes}}$

It is generally denoted by h or i.

(v) **Class limits:** The lowest and the highest value of the class are known as lower and upper limits respectively of that class.

(vi) **Class mark:** The average of the lower and upper class limits is called the class mean or class mark. It is generally denoted by x. If x be the mid value and h be the class interval, then the class limits are $\left(x-\frac{h}{2}, x+\frac{h}{2}\right)$.

Frequency Distribution

The marks scored by 30 students of IX class, of a school in the first test of Mathematics out of 50 marks are as follows:

6	32	10	17	22	28	0	48	6	22
32	6	36	26	48	10	32	48	28	22
22	22	28	26	17	36	10	22	28	0

The number of times a mark is repeated is called its **frequency**. It is denoted by *f*.

Marks obtained	Tally mark	Frequency	Marks obtained	Tally mark	Frequency
0	||	2	26	|||	2
6	|||	3	28	||||	4
10	|||	3	32	|||	3
17	||	2	36	||	2
22	~~||||~~ |	6	48	|||	3

The above types of frequency distributions are called unclustered frequency distributions. Although this data plot is shorter than the raw data plot, it is considerably larger from a comparison and analysis point of view. To make the frequency distribution smaller, it can be grouped into the following ways and is called a clustered frequency distribution.

Class	Frequency
1–10	8
11–20	2
21–30	12
31–40	5
41–50	3

Kinds of Frequency Distribution

Statistical methods like comparison, decision taken etc., depend on frequency distribution. Frequency distributions are of three types:

I. **Individual frequency distribution:** Here each item or original price of unit is written separately. In this category, frequency of each variable is one. For example, the total marks obtained by 10 students in a class are given as follows:

S. No.	1	2	3	4	5	6	7	8	9	10
Marks obtained	46	18	79	12	97	80	5	27	67	54

II. **Discrete frequency distribution:** When number of terms is large and variable are discrete, i.e., variate can accept some particular values only under finite limits and is repeated then it is called **discrete frequency distribution**. For example, the wages of employees and their numbers is shown in the following table.

Monthly wages	No. of employees
4000	10
6000	8
8000	5
11000	7
20000	2
25000	1

The above table shows ungrouped frequency distribution the same facts can be written in grouped frequency as follows:

Monthly wages	No. of employees
0–10,000	23
11,000–20,000	9
21,000–30,000	1

Keystone

If a variable is repeated in individual distribution then it can be converted into a discrete frequency distribution.

III. Continuous frequency distribution: When the number of terms is large and variate is continuous. i.e., variate can accept all values under finite limits and they are repeated then it is called **continuous frequency distribution**. For example age of students in a school is shown in the following table:

Age (in year)	Class	No. of students
Less than 5 year	0–5	72
From 5 and less than 10 year	5–10	103
From 10 and less than 15 year	10–15	50
From 15 and less than 20 year	15–20	25

Competition Corner

Series in Frequency Distribution

I. **Inclusive series:** In this method values of upper and lower limits are both contained in the same class. In this method, the upper limit of the class and lower limit of the other class are not the same. Sometimes the value is not a whole number, it is a fraction or in decimals and lies in between the two intervals then in such situation the class interval can be constructed as follows:

A	
Class	Frequency
1–10	4
11–20	7
21–30	6
31–40	3
41–50	3

II. **Exclusive series:** In this method upper limit of the previous class and lower limit of the next class is same. In this method the term of upper limit in a class is not considered in the same class, it is considered in the next class. Conversion of above inclusive frequency distribution into exclusive frequency distribution is as follows:

A	
Class	Frequency
0.5–10.5	4
10.5–20.5	7
20.5–30.5	6
30.5–40.5	3
40.5–50.5	3

IV Cumulative Frequency: Cumulative frequency is a statistical concept used to describe the total number of observations that fall below or above a particular value in a dataset.

(i) Discrete frequency distribution: Here we add all previous frequencies and get the cumulative frequency. It will be more clear from the following table:

Class	Frequency (f)	Cumulative frequency (cf)	Explanation
4000	10	10	10
6000	8	18	$10+8=18$
8000	5	23	$18+5=23$
11000	7	30	$23+7=30$
20000	2	32	$30+2=32$
25000	1	33	$32+1=33$

(ii) Continuous frequency distribution: A continuous frequency distribution is a way of organizing and representing data where the data values are grouped into continuous intervals, or classes, instead of individual values.

Monthly income variate (x)	No. of employee frequency (f)
0–5	72
5–10	103
10–15	50
15–20	25

Class	Cumulative frequency	Explanation
Less than 5	72	$72=72$
Less than 10	175	$72+103=175$
Less than 15	225	$175+50=225$
Less than 20	250	$225+25=250$

From this table the number of students of age less than the upper limit of a class, i.e., the number of students whose age are less than 5, 10, 15, 20 years can be determined by merely seeing the table but if we need the number students whose age are more than zero, more than 5, more than 10 or more than 15, then table should be constructed as follows:

Illustration 12.1

The mid values of distribution are 54, 64, 74, 84 and 94. Find the class interval and class limits.

Solution: The class interval is the difference between the two consecutive class marks, therefore class interval $(h) = 64 - 54 = 10$.

Here, the mid values are given and the class interval is 10.

So class limits are:

For 1st class $54 - \frac{10}{2}$ to $54 + \frac{10}{2}$ or 49 to 59

For 2nd class $64 - \frac{10}{2}$ to $64 + \frac{10}{2}$ or 49 to 59

For 3rd class $74 - \frac{10}{2}$ to $74 + \frac{10}{2}$ or 69 to 79

For 4th class $84 - \frac{10}{2}$ to $84 + \frac{10}{2}$ or 79 to 89

For 5th class $94 - \frac{10}{2}$

Therefore, class limits are 49–59, 59–69, 69–79, 79–89, and 89–99.

Illustration 12.2

The blood groups of 30 students of class IX are recorded as follows: *A, B, O, O, AB, O, A, O, B, A, O, B, A, O, O, A, AB, O, A, A, O, O, AB, B, A, O, B, A, B, O.* Represent this data in the form of a frequency distribution table. Find out which is the most common and which is the rarest blood group among these students.

Solution: Frequency distribution table:

Blood group	Frequency
A	9
B	6
O	12
AB	3

From the frequency table it is clear that the most common blood group is *O* and *AB* is the rarest blood group among the students.

Illustration 12.3

For the following data of daily wages (in rupees) received by 30 labourers in a certain factory, construct a grouped frequency distribution table by dividing the range into class intervals of equal width, each corresponding to 2 rupees, in such a way that the mid-value of the first class interval corresponds to 12 rupees: 14, 16, 16, 14, 22, 13, 15, 24, 12, 23, 14, 20, 17, 21, 22, 18, 18, 19, 20, 17, 16, 15, 11, 12, 21, 20, 17, 18, 19, 23.

Solution: Minimum daily wage = ₹11

Maximum daily wage = ₹24

∴ Range = ₹24 − ₹11 = ₹13

Size of class intervals = ₹2 [Given]

∴ Number of class intervals = 7 $\left[\because \dfrac{\text{Range}}{\text{Class size}} = \dfrac{13}{2} = 6.5\right]$

Since, the mid-value of the first class interval is 12 and the size of the class interval is ₹2

∴ $$\text{Lower limit of first class interval} = 12 - \frac{2}{2} = 11$$

$$\text{Upper limit of first class interval} = 12 + \frac{2}{2} = 13.$$

∴ First class intervals are 11–13.

Thus, the class intervals are:

11–13, 13–15, 15–17, 17–19, 19–21, 21–23, 23–25.

The frequency distribution table is as given under.

Daily wages (in ₹)	Frequency
11–13	3
13–15	4
15–17	5
17–19	6
19–21	5
21–23	4
23–25	3
Total	**30**

Illustration 12.4

Thirty children were asked about the number of hours they watched T.V. programs in the previous week. The results were found as follows:

1,	6,	2,	3,	5,	12,	5,	8,	4,	8
10,	3,	4,	12,	2,	8,	15,	1,	17,	6
3,	2,	8,	5,	9,	6,	8,	7,	14,	12

(i) Make a grouped frequency distribution table for this data, taking class width 5 and one of the class intervals as 5–10.

(ii) How many children watched television for 15 or more hours a week?

Solution:

(i) Frequency distribution table is as follows:

Class intervals	Frequency
0–5	10
5–10	13
10–15	5
15–20	2

(ii) Numbers of children that watched 15 or more hours a week = 2 children.

Illustration 12.5

The weights in grams of 50 apples picked at random from a consignment are as follows: 131, 113, 82, 75, 204, 81, 84, 118, 104, 110, 80, 107, 111,141,136, 123, 90, 78, 90, 115, 110, 98, 106, 99,107, 84, 76, 186, 82, 100,109,128,115, 107,115,119, 93, 187,139,129,130, 68,195,123, 125, 111, 92, 86, 70, 126. Form the grouped frequency table by dividing the variable range into intervals of equal width of 20 g, such that the mid-value of the first class interval is 70 g.

Solution: Size of each class = 20.

Let the lower limit of the first class interval be a.

Then, its upper limit = $(a + 20)$.

Mid-value of the first class interval = 70.

$$\therefore \quad \frac{a+(a+20)}{2} = 70$$

$$\Rightarrow \quad 2a = 120 \Rightarrow a = 60.$$

$\therefore$ The first class interval is 60–80.

Frequency distribution table is as follows:

Weight (in grams)	Frequency
60–80	5
80–100	13
100–120	17
120–140	10
140–160	1
160–180	0
180–200	3
200–220	1
Total	**50**

Check Point 1

1. Find the mid value of the class interval $(a - b)$.
2. Consider the class intervals 1–10, 11–20, 21–30, etc., Here what is the class boundary of class interval 11–20?
3. The following are data on the number of rooms occupied each day in a resort hotel during the month of June: 55 49 37 57 46 40 64 35 73 62 61 43 72 48 54 69 45 78 46 59 40 58 56 52 49 42 62 53 46 81. Organize the data by grouping them into class intervals of size 5. Construct a frequency table.
4. Given the following series: 3, 3, 4, 3, 4, 3, 1, 3, 4, 3, 3, 3, 2, 1, 3, 3, 3, 2, 3, 2, 2, 3, 3, 3, 2, 2, 2, 2, 2, 3, 2, 1, 1, 1, 2, 2, 4, 1. Construct a frequency distribution table for the data and draw the corresponding histogram. Draw also the frequency polygon.
5. Construct a cumulative frequency table of both types for the table given below:

Class interval	Frequency
110–120	6
120–130	10
130–140	8
140–150	10
150–160	6
Total frequency	**40**

Graphical Representation of Data

Graphical representation is essential for visualizing data in a way that makes patterns and insights easy to identify. Different types of charts and graphs are used depending on the type of data and the information we want to highlight.

Bar Graph

A bar graph is a pictorial representation of the numerical data by a number of bars (rectangles) of uniform width erected horizontally or vertically with equal spacing between them.

While constructing bar graphs the following points should be kept in mind:

(i) The width of the bars should be uniform throughout.

(ii) The gap between one bar and another should be uniform throughout.

(iii) Bars may be either horizontal or vertical.

Histogram

Histogram is a rectangular representation of grouped and continuous frequency distribution in which class intervals are taken as base and height of rectangles are proportional to corresponding frequencies. To draw the histogram class intervals are marked along the x-axis on a suitable scale. Frequencies are marked along the y-axis on a suitable scale, such that the areas of drawn rectangles are proportional to corresponding frequencies.

Construction of histograms is related to four different kinds of frequency distributions.

(i) When frequency distribution is grouped and continuous and class intervals are also equal.

(ii) When frequency distribution is grouped and continuous but class intervals are not equal.

(iii) When frequency distribution is grouped but not continuous.

(iv) When frequency distribution is ungrouped and middle points of the distribution are given.

Difference Between Bar Graph and Histogram

(i) In the histogram there is no gap in between consecutive rectangles as in the bar graph.

(ii) The width of the bar is significant in histogram. In bar graph, width is not important at all.

(iii) In histogram the areas of rectangles are proportional to the frequency, however if the class size of the frequencies is equal then the height of the rectangle is proportional to the frequencies.

Frequency Polygon

A frequency polygon is also a form of graphical representation of frequency distribution. Frequency polygon can be constructed in two ways:

(i) With the help of histogram

(ii) Without the help of histogram

Case I: Following procedure is useful to draw a frequency polygon with the help of histogram.
Construct the histogram for the given frequency distribution.
Find the middle point of each upper horizontal line of the rectangle.
Join these middle points of the successive rectangle with straight lines.
Join the middle point of the initial rectangle with the middle point of the previous expected class interval on the x-axis.

Case II: Following procedure is useful to draw a frequency polygon without the help of histogram.
Choose the class interval and mark the values on the horizontal axes
Mark the mid value of each interval on the horizontal axes.
Mark the frequency of the class on the vertical axes.
Corresponding to the frequency of each class interval, mark a point at the height in the middle of the class interval.
Connect these points using line segment.

Illustration 12.6

A family with monthly income of ₹20,000 had planned the following expenditure per month under various heads. Draw a bar graph for the data given below.

Heads	Expenditure (in ₹1000)
Grocery	4
Rent	5
Education of children	5
Medicine	2
Fuel	2
Entertainment	1
Miscellaneous	1

Solution: Take the heads along the x-axis and expenditure (in thousand rupees) along the y-axis. All bars should be of the same width and the same space should be left between the consecutive bars.

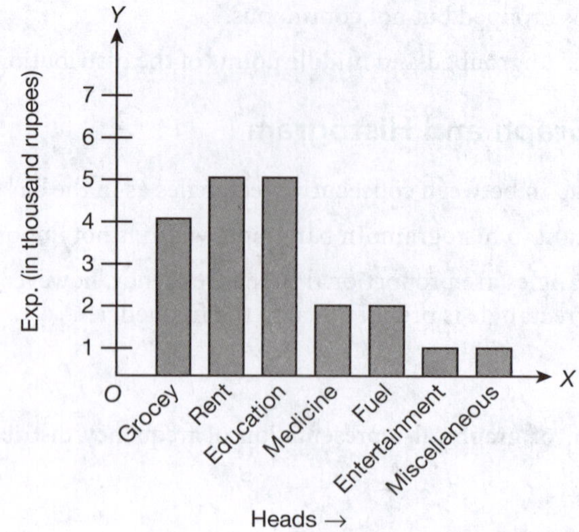

Illustration 12.7

Given below is a table which shows the year-wise strength of a school. Represent this data with a bar graph.

Year	2001–02	2002–03	2003–04	2004–05	2005–06
No. of students	800	975	1100	1400	1625

Solution: Take the year along the x -axis and number of students along the y–axis.

All bars should be of the same width and same the space should be left between the consecutive bars. Number of Students:

$$\frac{500}{1000}\times 6=13$$

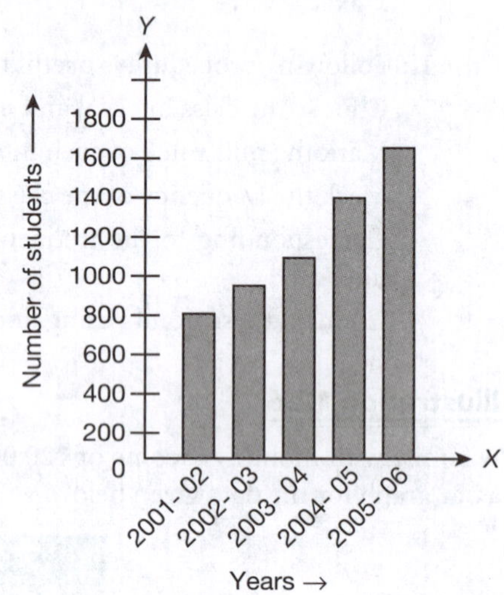

Illustration 12.8

Draw a histogram of the following frequency distribution.

Class (Age in years)	0–5	5–10	10–15	15–20
No. of students	72	103	50	25

Solution: Here frequency distribution is grouped and continuous and class intervals are also equal. So mark the class intervals on the x-axis i.e., age in year (scale 1 cm = 5 years). Mark frequency i.e., number of students (scale 1 cm = 25 students) on the y-axis.

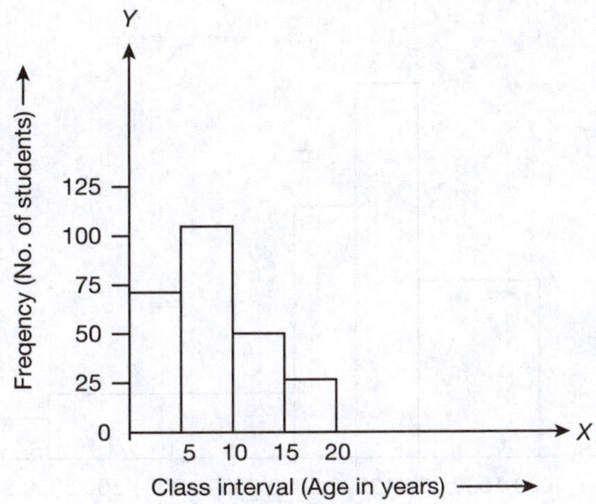

Illustration 12.9

The weekly wages of workers of a factory are given in the following table. Draw a histogram for it.

Weekly wages	1000–2000	2000–2500	2500–3000	3000–5000	5000–5500
No. of workers	26	30	20	16	3

Solution: Here frequency distribution is grouped and continuous but class intervals are not the same. Under such circumstances the following method is used to find heights of the rectangle so that heights are proportional to frequencies.

(i) Write interval (h) of the least interval, here $h = 500$.

(ii) Redefine the frequencies of classes by using the following formula.

$$\text{Adjusted frequency of class} = \frac{h}{\text{class interval}} \times \text{frequency of class interval.}$$

So here the redefined frequency table is obtained as follows:

Weekly wages (in ₹)	No. of workers	Adjust Frequency
1000–2000	26	$\frac{500}{1000} \times 26 = 13$
2000–2500	30	$\frac{500}{500} \times 30 = 30$
2500–3000	20	$\frac{500}{500} \times 20 = 20$
3000–5000	16	$\frac{500}{2000} \times 16 = 4$
5000–5500	3	$\frac{500}{500} \times 3 = 3$

Now mark class interval on the x-axis (scale 1 cm = 500) and no. of workers on the y-axis (scale 1 cm = 5).

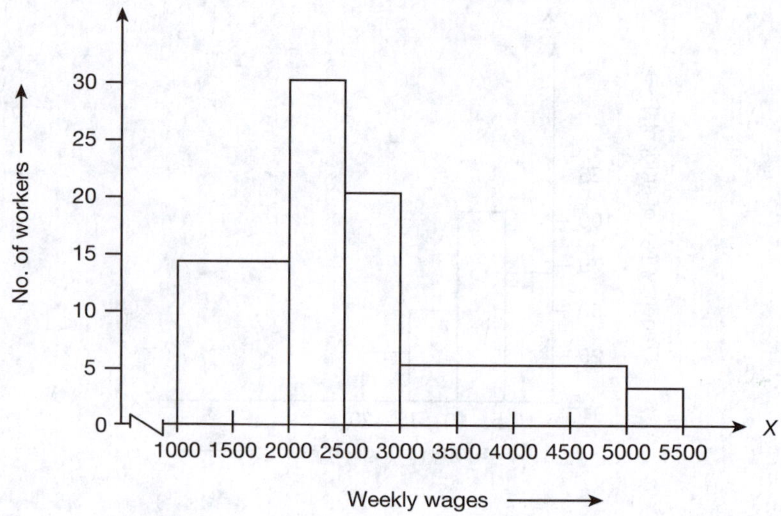

This is the required histogram of the given frequency distribution.

Illustration 12.10

The following table shows the number of illiterate persons in the age–group (10–58) years in a town:

Age group (in years)	10–16	17–23	24–30	31–37	38–44	45–51	52–58
Number of Illiterate persons	175	325	100	150	250	400	525

Solution: The given frequency distribution is not continuous. So, first convert it into a continuous frequency distribution. The difference between the lower limit of a class and the upper limit of the preceding class is 1 i.e., $h = 1$. To convert the given frequency distribution into a continuous frequency distribution subtract $\frac{h}{2} = \frac{1}{2} = 0.5$ from each lower limit and add $\frac{h}{2} = \frac{1}{2} = 0.5 = 0.5$ to each upper limit. The distribution so obtained is as given below:

Age group (in years)	9.5–16.5	16.5–23.5	23.5–30.5	30.5–37.5	37.5–44.5	44.5–51.5	51.5–58.5
Number of illiterate persons	175	325	100	150	250	400	525

Now mark age group on X-axis (Scale 1 cm = 7yrs) and Number of persons on Y-axis (Scale 1 cm = 100)

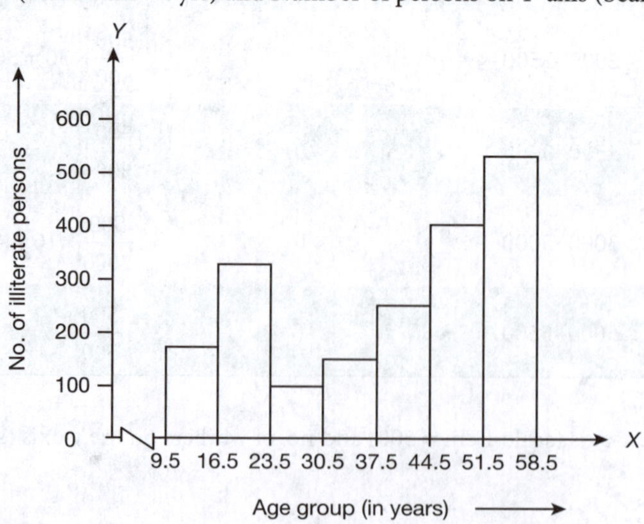

Illustration 12.11

Construct a histogram from the following distribution of total marks obtained by 65 students of IX class in the final examination:

Marks (mid-points)	150	160	170	180	190	200
No. of students	8	10	25	12	7	3

Solution: Since, the difference between the second and first mid-point is 160–150 = 10.

$$\therefore \quad h = 10$$

$$\Rightarrow \quad \frac{h}{2} = 5$$

So, the lower and upper limits of the first class are 150–5 and 150 + 5 i.e., 145 and 155 respectively.

∴ First class interval is 145–155.

Using the same procedure, we get the classes of other mid-points as under:

Marks	145–155	155–165	165–175	175–185	185–195	195–205
No. of students	8	10	25	12	7	3

The histogram of the above frequency distribution is as follows:

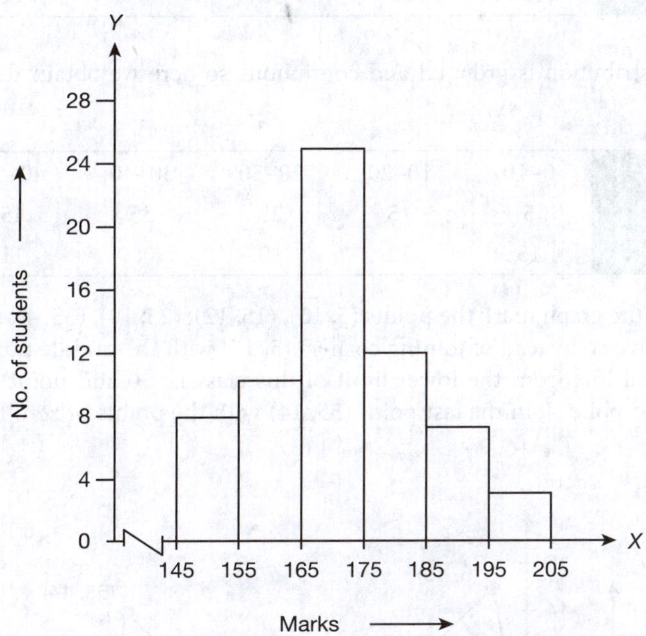

Illustration 12.12

For the following frequency distribution, draw a histogram and construct a frequency polygon with it.

Class	20–30	30–40	40–50	50–60	60–70
Frequency	8	12	17	9	4

Solution: The given frequency distribution is grouped and continuous, so we construct a histogram by the method given earlier. Join the middle points *P*, *Q*, *R*, *S*, *T* of the upper horizontal line of each rectangle *A*, *B*, *C*, *D*, *E* by straight lines.

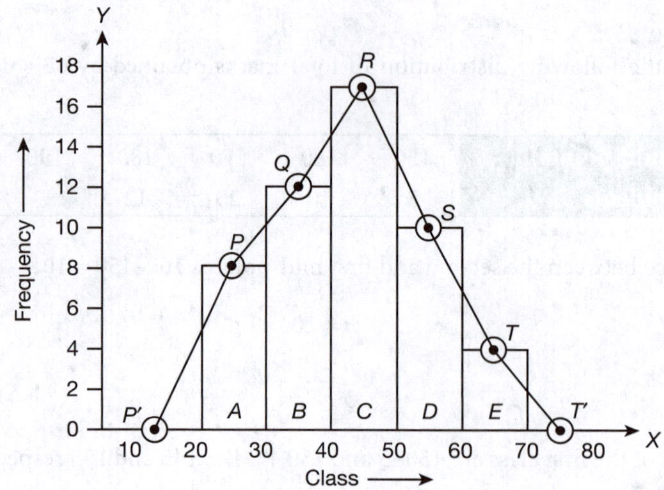

Illustration 12.13

Draw a frequency polygon of the following frequency distribution.

Age (in years)	0–10	10–20	20–30	30–40	40–50	50–60
Frequency	15	12	10	4	11	14

Solution: Here frequency distribution is grouped and continuous so here we obtain the following table on the basis of class.

Age (in years)	0–10	10–20	20–30	30–40	40–50	50–60
Class mark	5	15	25	35	45	55
Frequency	15	12	10	4	11	14

Now taking a suitable scale on the graph mark the points (5, 15), (15, 12), (25, 10), (35, 4), (45, 11), (55, 14).

Since age cannot be negative so instead of joining corners (5, 15) with the middle point of zero frequency of earlier assumed class, we draw vertical line from the lower limit of this class i.e., 0 and point of half frequency on this line i.e., (0, 7.5) is joined by the end point. Join the last point (55, 14) with the points of zero frequency of the next assumed class i.e., with (65, 0).

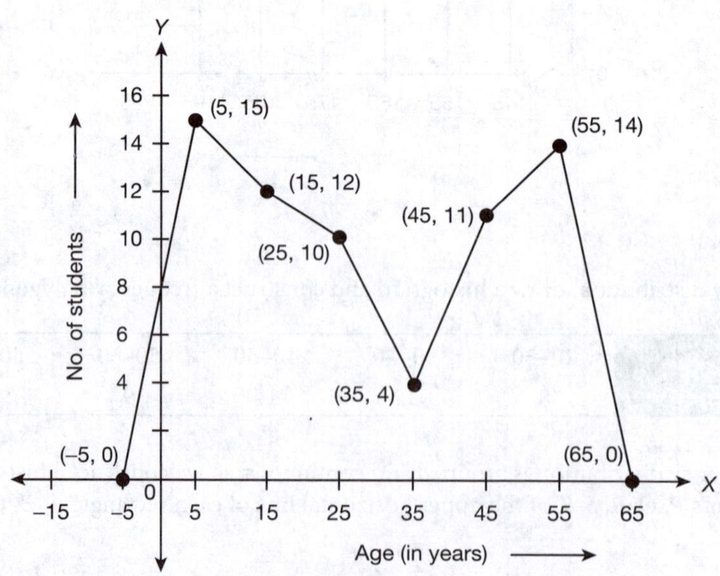

Check Point 2

6. The following table gives the population of a village in 1000*s* in different years:

Year	2008	2009	2010	2011	2012	2013
Population	10	15	16	20	23	25

Draw a bar graph.

7. The following table gives the number of runs scored by a team in the course of a cricket match.

Overs	1–5	5–10	10–15	15–20	20–25	25–30
No. of runs	20	32	45	25	30	15

Represent the data as a histogram.

8. Weights of 65 adults are given by the following table:

Weights	50–60	60–70	70–80	80–90	90–100	100–110	110–120
F_1	8	10	16	14	10	5	2

Construct the histogram.

9. Draw the histogram for the data given below.

Age (in yrs.)	1–5	5–15	15–30	30–40	40–45	45–50
No. of persons	10	14	36	22	12	10

Represent the data as a histogram.

10. Draw a frequency polygon for the following distribution.
    (i) Using histogram
    (ii) Without using histogram

Class interval	Frequency
10–20	3
20–30	6
30–40	8
40–50	12
50–60	9
60–70	5

Measures of Central Tendency

The commonly used measures of central tendency are

(a) Mean **(b)** Median **(c)** Mode

Mean

The mean of a number of observations is the sum of the values of all the observations divided by the total number of observations. It is denoted by the symbol $\overline{x}$, read as ***x* bar**.

Mean of raw data: If $x_1, x_2, x_3 \dots xn$ are the n values (or observations) then, **A.M.** (Arithmetic mean) is

$$\overline{x} = \frac{x_1 + x_1 + \dots + x_n}{n} = \frac{\sum_{i=1}^{n} x_1}{n}$$

$$n\overline{x} = \text{sum of observations} = \sum_{i=1}^{n} x_1$$

i.e., product of mean and number of items gives sum of observations.

Method for Mean of Ungrouped Data

x_i	f_i	$f_i x_i$
x_1	f_1	$f_1 x_1$
x_2	f_2	$f_2 x_2$
x_3	f_3	$f_3 x_3$
.	.	.
.	.	.
.	.	.
.	.	.
	$\Sigma f_i =$	$\Sigma f_i x_i =$

If $x_1, x_2, x_3 \dots x_n$ are the n values (or observations) and $f_1, f_2, f_3 \dots f_n$ are corresponding frequencies, then A.M. (Arithmetic mean) is:

$$\overline{x} = \frac{f_1x_1 + f_2x_2 + \dots + f_nx_n}{f_1 + f_2 + f_3} = \frac{\sum_{i=1}^{n} f_i x_i}{\sum_{i=1}^{n} f_i}$$

Uses of Arithmetic Mean

It is used for calculating average marks obtained by a student.
It is extensively used in practical statistics.
It is used to obtain estimates.

It is used by businessman to find out profit per unit article, output per machine, average monthly income and expenditure etc.

Median

Median of a distribution is the value of the variable which divides the distribution into two equal parts.

Median of Ungrouped Data

Arrange the data in ascending order.

Count the no. of observations (Let there be 'n' observations)

If n is odd then median = value of $\left(\frac{n+1}{2}\right)^{\text{th}}$ observation.

If n is even then median = value of mean of $\left(\frac{n}{2}\right)^{\text{th}}$ observation and $\left(\frac{n}{2}+1\right)^{\text{th}}$ observation or

$$\text{Median} = \frac{\left(\frac{n}{2}\right)^{\text{th}} \text{observation} + \left(\frac{n}{2}+1\right)^{\text{th}} \text{observation}}{2}$$

Uses of Median

Median is the only average to be used while dealing with qualitative data which cannot be measured quantitatively but can be arranged in ascending or descending order of magnitude.

It is used for determining the typical value in problems concerning wages, distribution of wealth, etc.

Mode

(i) **Mode of ungrouped data (By inspection only):** Arrange the data in an array and then count the frequencies of each variate. The variate having maximum frequency is the mode.

(ii) **Uses of Mode:** Mode is the average to be used to find the ideal size, e.g., in business forecasting, in the manufacture of readymade garments, shoes, etc.

Illustration 12.14

Find the mean of the factors of 10.

Solution: Factors of 10 are 1, 2, 5 and 10.

$$\bar{x} = \frac{1+2+5+10}{4} = \frac{18}{4} = 4.5$$

Illustration 12.15

If the mean of 6, 4, 7, P and 10 is 8 find P.

Solution:

$$8 = \frac{6+4+7+P+10}{5} \Rightarrow P = 13.$$

Illustration 12.16

If the mean of five observations x, $x+2$, $x+4$, $x+6$, $x+8$ is 11, find the mean of first three observations.

Solution:

$$11 = \frac{x+(x+2)+(x+4)+(x+6)+(x+8)}{5}$$

$$55 = 5x + 20$$

$$5x = 35$$

$$x = 7.$$

$$\text{Mean of first three observations} = \frac{x+(x+2)+(x+4)}{3} = \frac{3x+6}{3}$$

$$= x + 2 = 7 + 2 = 9.$$

Illustration 12.17

The mean of marks scored by 100 students was found to be 40. Later on, it was discovered that a score of 53 was misread as 83. Find the correct mean.

Solution: $n = 100$, $\bar{x} = 40$

$$\bar{x} = \frac{1}{n}(\Sigma x_1) \Rightarrow 40 = \frac{1}{100}(\Sigma x_1)$$

∴ Incorrect value of $\Sigma x_i = 4000$.

Now, Correct value of $\Sigma x_i = 4000 - 83 + 53 = 3970$

∴ $$\text{Correct mean} = \frac{\text{correct value of } \Sigma x_1}{n} = \frac{3970}{100} = 39.7$$

So, the correct mean is 39.7

Illustration 12.18

The mean monthly salary of 10 members of a group is ₹1445, one more member whose monthly salary is ₹1500 has joined the group. Find the mean monthly salary of 11 members of the group.

Solution: $n = 10, \bar{x} = 1445$

So, total monthly wages of 10 persons = 10 × 1445 = 14450.

Monthly salary of one more person who joined the group is ₹1500

∴ Total monthly wages of 11 persons = ₹14450 + ₹1500 = ₹15950

So, the average monthly salary of 11 persons $= \frac{15950}{11} =$ ₹1450

Illustration 12.19

Find the missing value of P for the following distribution whose mean is 12.58.

x	5	8	10	12	P	20	25
y	2	5	8	22	7	4	2

Solution:

Given $\bar{x} = 12.58$

Calculation of Mean:

x_i	f_i	$f_i x_i$
5	2	10
8	5	40
10	8	80
12	22	264
P	7	$7P$
20	4	80
25	2	50
	$\Sigma f_i = 50$	$\Sigma f_i x_i = 524 + 7P$

$$\bar{x} = \frac{\Sigma f_i x_i}{\Sigma f_i}$$

$$\Rightarrow \quad 12.58 = \frac{524 + 7P}{50}$$

$$\Rightarrow \quad 629 = 524 + 7P$$

$$7P = 105, P = 15.$$

Illustration 12.20

Find the mean for the following distribution:

Marks	10–20	20–30	30–40	40–50	50–60	60–70	70–80
Frequency	6	8	13	7	3	2	1

Solution:

Marks	Mid values x_i	No. of students f_i	$f_i x_i$
10–20	15	6	90
20–30	25	8	200
30–40	35	13	455
40–50	45	7	315
50–60	55	3	165
60–70	65	2	130
70–80	75	1	75
		$\Sigma f_i = 40$	$\Sigma f_i x_i = 1430$

$$\bar{x} = \frac{\Sigma f_i x_i}{\Sigma f_i} = \frac{1430}{40} = \frac{143}{4} = 35.75$$

Illustration 12.21

Find the median of the following values: 37, 31, 42, 43, 46, 25, 39, 45, 32

Solution: Arranging the data in ascending order, we have

25, 31, 32, 37, 39, 42, 43, 45, 46

Here, the number of observations $n = 9$ (odd)

$$\therefore \quad \text{Median} = \text{Value of} \left(\frac{9+1}{2}\right)^{\text{th}} \text{observation} = \text{Value of } 5^{\text{th}} \text{ observation} = 39.$$

Illustration 12.22

Following are the lives in hours of 15 pieces of the components of the aircraft engine. Find the median:

715, 724, 725, 710, 729, 745, 649, 699, 696, 712, 734, 728, 716, 705, 719, 737.

Solution: Arranging the data in ascending order

649, 696, 699, 705, 710, 712, 715, 716, 719, 724, 725, 728, 729, 734, 737, 745

$$N = 16 \text{ (Even)}$$

So,

$$\text{Median} = \frac{\left(\frac{16}{2}\right)^{\text{th}} \text{obdervation} + \left(\frac{16}{2}+1\right)^{\text{th}} \text{observation}}{2}$$

$$= \frac{8^{\text{th}} \text{ Obs.} + 9^{\text{th}} \text{ Obs.}}{2} = \frac{716+719}{2} = 717.5$$

Illustration 12.23

The median of the observation 11, 12, 14, 18, $x + 2$, $x + 4$, 30, 32, 35, 41 arranged in ascending order is 24. Find the value of x.

Solution: Here, the number of observations $n = 10$. Since n is even, therefore

$$\text{Median} = \frac{\left(\frac{n}{2}\right)^{\text{th}} \text{obdervation} + \left(\frac{n}{2}+1\right)^{\text{th}} \text{observation}}{2}$$

$$\Rightarrow \quad 24 = \frac{5^{\text{th}} \text{ obdervation} + 6^{\text{th}} \text{ observation}}{2}$$

$$\Rightarrow \quad 24 = \frac{(x+2)+(x+4)}{2} \Rightarrow 24 = \frac{2x+6}{2}$$

$$\Rightarrow \quad 24 = x+3 \Rightarrow x = 21.$$

Hence, $x = 21$.

Illustration 12.24

Find the mode of the following array of an individual series of scores 7, 7, 10, 12, 12, 12, 11, 13, 13, 17.

Solution: Arranging the data in the form of a frequency table:

Numbers	7	10	11	12	13	17
Frequency	2	1	1	3	2	1

From the above table, it is clear that 12 is occurring the most number of times.
$\therefore$ Mode is 12.

Check Point 3

11. The mean of the data 16, 20, 26, 40, 50, 60, 70, 30.

12. Calculate the mean of the data:

x_i	61	64	67	70	73
f_i	5	18	42	27	8

13. The mean of $x_1, x_2 \ldots x_{50}$ is M, if every x_i $(i = 1, 2 \ldots 50)$ is replaced by $\frac{x_i}{50}$, then find new mean.

14. While driving past stores, Tarun counted the number of cars in the parking lots. He counted: 19, 9, 1, 15, 19, 3 and 5. Determine the median and mode of the cars he counted.

15. Mode of some observation is 4 and the median is 3. Then find mean.

Competition Corner

Properties of Mean:

(a) If a constant real number 'a' is added to each of the observations then the new mean will be $\bar{x} + a$.
(b) If a constant real number 'a' is subtracted from each of the observations then the new mean will be $\bar{x} - a$.
(c) If a constant real number 'a' is multiplied with each of the observations then the new mean will be $a\bar{x}$.
(d) If each of the observations is divided by a constant number 'a' then the new mean will be $\frac{\bar{x}}{a}$.

Empirical Relation between Modes, Median and Mean:

Mode = 3 Median – 2 Mean.

STRUCTURAL OUTLINE

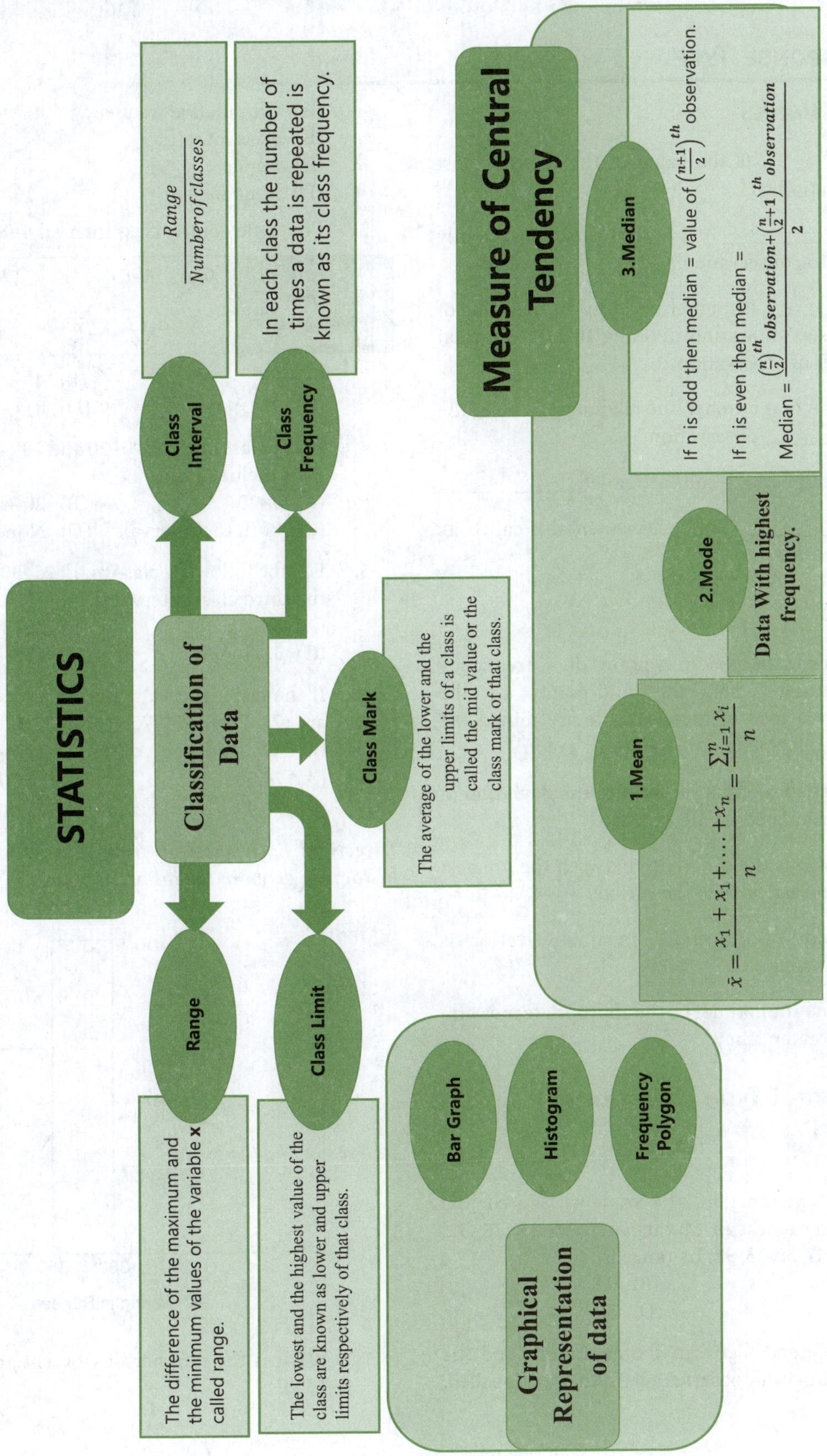

ASSESSMENT CORNER

Fixed Response Type

Fill in the Blanks

1. __________ is the value of the middle most observation (s).
2. The __________ is the most frequently occurring observation.
3. __________ is found by adding all the value of the observations and dividing this by the total number of observations.
4. If n is an odd number, the median = value of the __________ observation.
5. Total number of results are called __________.
6. The __________ of a class interval is called its class mark.

True/False

1. After drawing the histogram of a frequency distribution when the mid-points of the respective tops of the rectangle are joined the figure so formed is known as bar 'graph'.
2. In a statistical data, the sum of the deviation of items from mean is always zero.
3. The range is the difference between the greatest and the least value of the variate.
4. The value of the middle-most observation is called median.
5. Mean may or may not be the appropriate measure of central tendency.

Single Correct Type Questions

Level 1

1. In an examination, 10 students scored the following marks in Mathematics 35, 19, 28, 32, 63, 02, 47, 31, 13, 98. Its range is:
   (A) 96 (B) 02
   (C) 98 (D) 50
2. The difference between the maximum and the minimum value observations in the data is called:
   (A) Cumulative frequency
   (B) class interval
   (C) Range
   (D) frequency
3. Frequency of the class interval 4–8 is:

Class	0–4	4–8	8–12	12–16	16–20
Cumulative Frequency (f)	6	15	23	27	30

   (A) 15 (B) 4
   (C) 9 (D) 8
4. In the class intervals 0–20 and 20–40, the number 20 is included in:
   (A) 0–20 (B) 20–40
   (C) Both the intervals (D) None of these
5. For the following class mark 25, 30, 35, 40, 45, 50 the third class interval is:
   (A) 30–35 (B) 25–30
   (C) 32.5–37.5 (D) 27.5–32.5
6. If the class intervals in a frequency distribution are (72–73.9), (74–75.9), (76–77.9), (78–79.9) etc., then the mid-point of the class (74–75.9) is:
   (A) 74.50 (B) 74.70
   (C) 74.95 (D) 75.00

Direction: Each question from 7 to 10 is based on the histogram given in the adjacent figure.

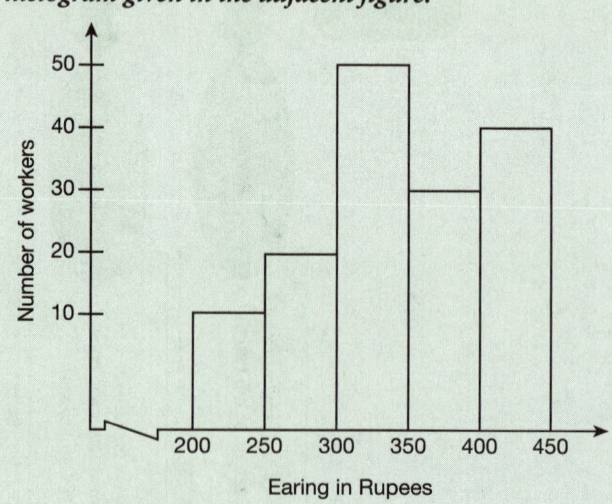

7. What is the number of worker earning ₹300 to ₹350?

(A) 50 (B) 40
(C) 45 (D) 130

8. In which class interval of wages there is the least number of workers?
(A) 400–450 (B) 350–400
(C) 250–300 (D) 200–250

9. What is the upper limit of the class interval 200–250?
(A) 200 (B) 250
(C) 225 (D) None of these

10. The median of the following series 520, 20, 340, 190, 35, 800, 1210, 50, 80:
(A) 1210 (B) 520
(C) 190 (D) 35

Level 2

11. If the arithmetic mean of 5, 7, 9, x is 9 then the value of x is:
(A) 11 (B) 15
(C) 18 (D) 16

12. The mode of the distribution 3, 5, 7, 4, 2, 1, 4, 3, 4 is:
(A) 7 (B) 4
(C) 3 (D) 1

13. If the mean and median of a set of numbers are 8.9 and 9 respectively, then the mode will be:
(A) 7.2 (B) 8.2
(C) 9.2 (D) 10.2

14. A student got marks in 5 subjects in a monthly test is given below: 2, 3, 4, 5, 6, in these obtained marks, 4 is the:
(A) Mean and median
(B) Median but no mean
(C) Mean but no median
(D) Mode

15. What is the mode from the following table?

Marks obtained	3	1	23	33	43
Frequency (f)	7	11	15	8	3

(A) 13 (B) 43
(C) 33 (D) 23

16. If the first five elements of a set replaced by $(x_i + 5)$, where $i = 1, 2, 3 \ldots 5$ and the next five elements are replaced by $(x_j - 5)$,
where $j = 6, 7 \ldots 10$ then the mean will change by:
(A) 25 (B) 10
(C) 5 (D) 0

17. The following numbers are given 61, 62, 63, 61, 63, 64, 64, 60, 65, 63, 64, 65, 66, 64. The difference between their mean and median is (approximately):
(A) 0.4 (B) 0.3
(C) 0.2 (D) 0.1

18. The average of 15 numbers is 18. The average of first 8 is 19 and the last 8 is 17, then the 8th number is:
(A) 15 (B) 16
(C) 18 (D) 20

19. The average age of group of eight members is the same as it was 3 years ago, when a young member is substituted for an old member. The incoming member is younger to the outgoing member by:
(A) 11 years (B) 24 years
(C) 28 years (D) 16 years

20. The average of n numbers $x_1, x_2, x_3 \ldots x_n$, is A. If x_1 is replaced by $(x + a)\, x_1$, x_2 is replaced by $(x + a)\, x_2 \ldots x_n$ is replaced by $(x + a)\, x_n$; then the new average is:

(A) $\dfrac{(n+1)A + x_n}{n}$

(B) $\dfrac{(n-1)A + nx_n}{n}$

(C) $\dfrac{nA + 1(n+1)x_n}{n}$

(D) $(x + a)\, A$

Multiple Correct Type Questions

1. Which of the following is/are measure of central tendency?
(A) Mean (B) median
(C) Variance (D) mode

2. Given below are the seats won by different political parties in the polling outcome of a state assembly election:

Seats won	75	55	37	29
Political party	*A*	*B*	*C*	*D*

The graphical representation will be:
(A) A histogram
(B) A vertical bar graph
(C) A horizontal bar graph
(D) A frequency polygon curve

3. A frequency polygon can be:
   (A) Drawn using histogram
   (B) drawn using bar graph
   (C) Drawn independently
   (D) drawn using tally marks

4. Measure of central tendency represents:
   (A) Averages
   (B) central value
   (C) Mean, median, mode
   (D) None of these

5. For drawing a frequency polygon of a continuous frequency distribution, we plot the points whose ordinates are the frequencies of the respective classes and abscissa are respectively, the:
   (A) Upper limits of the classes
   (B) Lower limits of the classes
   (C) Class marks of the classes
   (D) Upper limits of preceding classes

6. The runs scored by 11 members of a cricket team are: 0, 91, 104, 13, 15, 25, 08, 0, 02, 10, 05. The median score is:
   (A) 27 (B) 11.5
   (C) 13 (D) 10

7. The median of the numbers 9, 5, 7, 17, 13, 18, 13, 9, 5, 17, 13, 12, 17
   (A) 7 (B) 9
   (C) 13 (D) 15

8. The median of the numbers 45, 34, 65, 48, 93, 54, 22, 86, 45, 87
   (A) 51 (B) 49.5
   (C) 54 (D) 56

9. Mode of the data 51, 14, 71, 15, 91, 2, 51, 19, 41, 51, 18, 15, 51
   (A) 51 (B) 15
   (C) 16 (D) 17

Match Type Questions

1.

Column-I	Column-II
(A) Mean of first 10 odd prime numbers is	(p) 27.5
(B) Mean of first 10 multiples of 5 is	(q) 11
(C) Mean of first 9 doublets of natural number is	(r) 15.8
(D) Mean of first 10 even numbers is	(s) 14

2.

Column-I	Column-II
(A) Data which is collected for the first time by The statistical investor or with the help of his Workers is called	(p) Secondary data
(B) These are the data already collected by a person or a society and these may be in published from. These data should be carefully used.	(q) Variable
(C) When the data is compiled in the same form and order in which it is collected, it is known as	(r) Primary Data
(D) A quantity which can vary from one individual to another is called	(s) Raw Data

3. Use the table to match column I and II.

Class interval	Frequency
30–34	7
35–39	10
40–44	12
45–49	13
50–54	8
55–59	4

Column-I	Column-II
(A) The actual class size of the fourth class	(p) 45–49
(B) The class boundaries of the sixth class	(q) 5
(C) The class mark of the third class	(r) 55 and 59
(D) The mode of the given data lies in the class interval	(s) 42

Assertion and Reason Type Questions

Direction: In the following questions as Assertion (A) is given followed by a Reason (R). Mark your responses from the following options.

(A) Both Assertion and Reason are true and Reason is the correct explanation of 'Assertion'

ASSESSMENT CORNER

(B) Both Assertion and Reason are true and Reason is not the correct explanation of 'Assertion'.
(C) Assertion is true but Reason is false
(D) Assertion is false but Reason is true

1. **Assertion**: Mode of the given data 110, 120, 130, 120, 110, 140, 130, 120, 140, 120, is 120.
Reason: The observation that occurs most frequently, i.e., the observation with maximum frequency is called mode.

2. **Assertion**: The difference between the maximum and minimum values of a variable is called its range.
Reason: The number of times a variate (observation) occurs in a given data is called range.

3. **Assertion**: The following is the data of wages per day: 8, 4, 7, 5, 8, 8, 5, 7, 9, 5, 7, 9, 10, 8 then the mode of the data is 8.
Reason: Mode = Highest observation – lowest observation.

Comprehension Type Questions

Comprehension-1: The ages of ten students of a group are given below. The ages have been recorded in years and months.
8 Year 6 Months, 9 Years 0 Months, 8 Years 4 Months, 9 Years 3 Months, 7 Years 8 Months, 8 Years 11 Months, 8 Years 7 Months , 9 Years 2 Months, 7 Years 10 Months, 8 Years 8 Months

1. What is the lowest age?
(A) 7 years, 8 months (B) 9 years, 3 months
(C) 8 years, 11 months (D) 1 year, 7 months

2. What is the highest age?
(A) 7 years, 8 months (B) 9 years, 3 months
(C) 8 years, 11 months (D) 1 year, 7 months

3. Determine the range.
(A) 7 years, 8 months
(B) 9 years, 3 months
(C) 8 years, 11 months
(D) 1 year, 7 months

Comprehension-2:

A, B, C are three sets of values of x:

A: 2, 3, 7, 1, 3, 2, 3

B: 7, 5, 9, 12, 5, 3, 8

C: 4, 4, 11, 7, 2, 3, 4

4. Find the mean of A, B, and C respectively.
(A) 7, 5, 3 (B) 7, 3, 5
(C) 3, 7, 5 (D) 5, 3, 7

5. Find the difference between A's and B's mean.
(A) 3 (B) 4
(C) 5 (D) 2

6. The difference between median and mode of C is:
(A) 1 (B) 2
(C) 3 (D) 0

Numerical Type Questions

1. Find the mode of the following data 2, 2, 6, 5, 4, 3, 4, 5, 7, 9, 4, 5, 3, 1, 10, 4.

2. Find the value of p, if the median of the following observations is 48. 14, 17, 33, 35, $p-5$, $p+7$, 57, 63, 69, 80. The above observations are in ascending order.

3. The mean of 16 items was found to be 30. On rechecking, it was found that the two items were wrongly taken as 22 and 18 instead of 32 and 28 respectively. Find the correct mean.

4. If the mean of the following data is 18.75, find the value of p.

x	10	15	P	25	30
f	5	10	7	8	2

5. Find the mean of the following frequency distribution:

Variable (x_1)	10	30	50	70	89
Frequency	7	8	10	15	10

6. The weights (in kg) of 16 students are: 31, 35, 27, 29, 32, 43, 37, 41, 34, 28, 36, 44, 45, 42, 30, 48. Find the median. If the weight 44 kg is replaced by 46 kg and 27 kg by 25 kg, find the new median.

7. The mean age of a one group of persons is 40. Another group has mean age of 48. If the ratio of number of persons in two groups is 5 : 3, then find the mean age of all the persons.

8. Find the mean of the following data 13, 17, 16, 14, 11, 13, 10, 16, 11, 18, .12, 17.

9. Find the median of the following data 38, 70, 48, 34, 42, 55, 63, 46, 54, 44.

10. The class marks of a distribution are: 47, 52, 57, 62, 67, 72, 77, 82, 87, 92, 97, 102. Determine the class size.

ASSESSMENT CORNER

Higher Order Thinking Skills (HOTS)

1. Let L be the lower class boundary of a class in a frequency distribution and m be the midpoint of the class. Which one of the following is the upper class boundary of the class?

(A) $m+\frac{m+L}{2}$ (B) $L+\frac{m+L}{2}$

(C) $2m-L$ (D) $m-2L$

2. The arithmetic mean of the set of observations 1, 2, 3 … n is:

(A) $\frac{n+1}{2}$ (B) $\left(\frac{n}{2}+1\right)$

(C) $\frac{n}{2}$ (D) $\frac{1}{2}(n-1)$

3. Mean of a certain number of observations is m. If each observation is divided by x $(x \neq 0)$ and increased by y, then the mean of new observation is:

(A) $mx+y$ (B) $\frac{mx+y}{x}$

(C) $\frac{m+xy}{x}$ (D) $m+xy$

4. The mean of a variable x having 50 observations is 45. If a new variable is defined as $U=x+45$, the mean of the new variable is:

(A) 45 (B) 0

(C) 95 (D) 90

5. The mean of a set of observations is a. If each observation is multiplied by b and each product is decreased by c, then the mean of the new set of observations is:

(A) $\frac{a}{b}+c$ (B) $ab-c$

(C) $\frac{a}{b}-c$ (D) $ab+c$

6. The arithmetic mean of 5 numbers is 27. If one of the numbers be excluded, their mean is 25. The excluded number is:

(A) 28 (B) 26

(C) 25 (D) 35

7. The combined mean of three groups is 12 and the combined mean of the first two groups is 3. If the first, second and third groups have 2, 3 and 5 times respectively, then the mean of the third group is:

(A) 10 (B) 21

(C) 12 (D) 13

8. Out of 100 numbers, 20 were 5*s*, 30 were 6*s* and the remaining were 7*s*. The arithmetic mean of the numbers is:

(A) 6.3 (B) 5.4

(C) 6.1 (D) 6.5

9. The arithmetic mean of 12 observations is 15. If two observations 20 and 25 are removed, then the arithmetic mean of the remaining observations is:

(A) 14.5 (B) 13.5

(C) 12.5 (D) 13

10. The median of 21 observations is 18. If two observations 15 and 24 are included in the observation, then the median of new series is:

(A) 15 (B) 18

(C) 24 (D) 16

FREE RESPONSE TYPE

Very Short Answer Type Questions

1. Find the class mark of the class 130–150.

2. Find the range of the data: 25, 18, 20, 22, 16, 6, 17, 15, 12, 30, 32, 10, 19, 8, 11, 20.

3. In a frequency distribution, the mid value of a class is 10 and the width of the class is 6. Then find the lower limit of the class.

4. Let m be the mid-point and l be the upper class limit of a class in a continuous frequency distribution. Then find the lower class limit of the class.

5. In the class intervals 10–20, 20–30, then find the interval in which number 20 is included in.

6. A grouped frequency table with class intervals of equal sizes using 250–270 (270 not included in this interval) as one of the class intervals is constructed for the following data: 268, 220, 368, 258, 242, 310, 272, 342, 310, 290, 300, 320, 319, 304, 402, 318, 406, 292, 354, 278, 210, 240, 330, 316, 406, 215, 258, 236. Then find the frequency of class 310-330.

7. If $\bar{x}$ represents the mean of n observations $x_1, x_2 \ldots x_n$, then find the value of $\sum_{i=1}^{n}(x_i-\bar{x})$.

8. Find the median of the data 78, 56, 22, 34, 45, 54, 39, 68, 54, 84 is:

Short Answer Type Questions

1. Draw a histogram to represent the following frequency distribution:

Class interval	5–10	10–15	15–25	25–45	45–75
Frequency	6	12	10	8	15

2. The mean of five numbers is 30. If one number is excluded, their mean becomes 28. Then find the excluded number.

3. If the mean of the observations: x, $x + 3$, $x + 5$, $x + 7$, $x + 10$ is 9, the mean of the last three observations is:

(A) $10\frac{1}{3}$ (B) $10\frac{2}{3}$

(C) $11\frac{1}{3}$ (D) $11\frac{2}{3}$

4. The mean of 100 observations is 50. If one of the observations which was 50 is replaced by 150, then find the resulting mean.

5. There are 50 numbers. Each number is subtracted from 53 and the mean of the numbers so obtained is found to be – 3.5. Then find the mean of the given numbers.

6. The following observations are arranged in ascending order: 26, 29, 42, 53, x, $x+2$, 70, 75, 82, 93 If the median is 65, find the value of x.

7. Prepare a continuous grouped frequency distribution from the following data:

Mid-point	Frequency
5	4
15	8
25	13
35	12
45	6

8. If the mean of the following data is 20.2, find the value of p:

x	10	15	20	25	30
f	6	8	P	10	6

9. If x is the mean of $x_1, x_2 \dots x_n$, then for $a \neq 0$, the mean of $ax_1, ax_2, \dots ax_n, \frac{x_1}{a}, \frac{x_2}{a}, \dots, \frac{x_n}{a}$

(A) $\left(a+\frac{1}{a}\right)\bar{x}$ (B) $\left(a+\frac{1}{a}\right)\frac{\bar{x}}{2}$

(C) $\left(a+\frac{1}{a}\right)\frac{\bar{x}}{n}$ (D) $\frac{\left(a+\frac{1}{a}\right)\bar{x}}{2n}$

10. Mean of 50 observations was found to be 80.4. But later on, it was discovered that 96 was misread as 69 at one place. Find the correct mean.

Long Answer Type Questions

1. The points scored by a basketball team in a series of matches are as follows: 17, 2, 7, 27, 25, 5, 14, 18, 10, 24, 48, 10, 8, 7, 10, 28. Find the median and mode for the data.

2. The lengths of 62 leaves of a plant are measured in millimetres and the data is represented in the following table:

Length (in mm)	Number of leaves
118–126	8
127–135	10
136–144	12
145–153	17
154–162	7
163–171	5
172–180	3

3. Following table shows a frequency distribution for the speed of cars passing through at a particular spot on a highway.

Class interval (km/h)	Frequency
30–40	3
40–50	6
50–60	25
60–70	65
70–80	50
80–90	28
90–100	14

Draw a histogram and frequency polygon representing the data above.

4. The marks obtained (out of 100) by a class of 80 students are given below:

Marks	Number of students
10–20	6
20–30	17
30–50	15
50–70	16
70–100	26

Construct a histogram to represent the data above.

5. Following table gives the distribution of students of sections *A* and *B* of a class according to the marks obtained by them.

Section *A*		Section *B*	
Marks	Frequency	Marks	Frequency
0–15	5	0–15	3
15–30	12	15–30	16
30–45	28	30–45	25
45–60	30	45–60	27
60–75	35	60–75	40
75–90	13	75–90	10

Represent the marks of the students of both sections on the same graph by two frequency polygons. What do you observe?

6. The mean of the following distribution is 50.

x	f
10	18
30	$5a + 3$
50	32
70	$7a - 11$
90	19

Find the value of a and hence the frequencies of 30 an 40.

ARCHIVE CORNER

1. From the following table, mode–mean is:

x	2	5	7	8
f	2	4	6	3

(A) 0 (B) 1
(C) 6 (D) 7

2. If the arithmetic means of the marks 3, 4, 8, 5, x, 3, 2, 1 is 4, then the value of x is:
(A) 4 (B) 5
(C) 6 (D) 8

3. If the median of distribution 2, x, 7, 5, 0, 1 is 3, then the value of x is:
(A) 2 (B) 4
(C) 5 (D) 6

4. Mean temperature of last week of September was 24°C. If the mean temperature on Monday, Tuesday, Wednesday and Thursday was 22°C and that of Thursday, Friday, Saturday and Sunday was 25° then the temperature on Thursday is:
(A) 24°C (B) 23°C
(C) 22°C (D) 20°C

5. Which of these numbers is the average of the remaining three?
(A) 26 (B) 39
(C) 30 (D) 61

6. If the arithmetic mean of the distribution x, $2x$, $2x + 1$, 2 is 7, then the value of x is:
(A) 5 (B) $\frac{27}{5}$
(C) $\frac{26}{5}$ (D) $\frac{265}{6}$

7. The median of the following distribution 2, 3, 2, 6, 5, 4, 5, 5 is:
(A) 3 (B) 4
(C) 4.5 (D) 6.5

8. If the median of $\frac{x}{7}, \frac{x}{5}, \frac{x}{6}, x, \frac{x}{4}, \frac{x}{3}, \frac{x}{2}$ is 8, then the value of x is ___________.
(A) 8 (B) 24
(C) 32 (D) 48

9. The Arithmetic mean of a set of scores is $\bar{X}$. If each score is first divided by α, $\alpha \neq 0$, and then increased by 10, the mean of the new score is:
(A) $\frac{\bar{X}-10}{\alpha}$ (B) $\frac{\bar{X}+10}{\alpha}$
(C) $\frac{\bar{X}+10\alpha}{\alpha}$ (D) $\frac{\alpha\bar{X}+10}{\alpha}$

10. The median and mode of a frequency distribution are 525 and 500 then the mean of the same frequency distribution is:
(A) 75 (B) 107.5
(C) 527.5 (D) 537.5

11. If the mean of x and $\frac{1}{x}$ is M, then the mean of x^2 and $\frac{1}{x^2}$ is:
(A) M^2 (B) $\frac{M^2}{4}$
(C) $2M^2 - 1$ (D) $2M^2 + 1$

12. Positional mean is:
(A) Arithmetic mean (B) Geometric mean
(C) Median (D) Harmonic mean

13. Four times the arithmetic mean of x and 10 is 70, then what is the value of x?
(A) 65 (B) 25
(C) 50 (D) 35

14. The mean of n numbers $x_1, x_2 \ldots x_n$ is M. If x_1 is replaced by 'a', the new mean is:
(A) $\frac{nM - x_1 + a}{n}$ (B) $\frac{M - x_1 + a}{n}$
(C) $\frac{nM - a + x_1}{n}$ (D) None of these

15. Which of the following is correct for the given data 55, 38, 69, 24, 89?
(A) Median = mode (B) mean = mode
(C) Mean = median (D) None of these

16. The mean of n numbers is M. If 1 is added to the first number, 2 is added to the second number … n is added to the nth number then the new mean is:
(A) $M + \frac{n+1}{2}$ (B) $M + \frac{n}{2}$
(C) $M + n$ (D) None of these

17. The median of first 12 prime numbers is:
(A) 13 (B) 14
(C) 15 (D) 17

ARCHIVE CORNER

18. Median of 4, 5, 10, 6, 7, 14, 9 and 15 will be:
(A) 6 (B) 7
(C) 8 (D) 9

19. If the numbers 13, 15, 17, 18 and n are arranged is ascending order and their arithmetic mean and median are equal then value of n will be:
(A) 27 (B) 22
(C) 28 (D) none of these

20. The average marks scored by Ajay in certain number of tests is 84. He scored 100 marks in his last test. His average score of all these tests is 86, then the total number of tests he appeared is:
(A) 8 (B) 7
(C) 9 (D) 10

21. If the arithmetic mean of 9 observations is 100 and that of 6 observations is 80, then the combined mean of all the 15 observations will be:
(A) 100 (B) 80
(C) 90 (D) 92

22. On 13 consecutive days the number of persons booked for violating speed limit of 40 km/hr. were as follows: 59, 52, 58, 61, 68, 57, 62, 50, 55, 62 53 54, 51. The median number of speed violations per day is:
(A) 61 (B) 52
(C) 55 (D) 57

23. Which of the following is correct for the given data .1, 0, 1, 2, 3, 5, 5, 6, 8, 10, 11?
(A) Mean = mode = median
(B) mean = 5
(C) Mean = mode
(D) mode = median

24. If $\bar{x}$ is the mean of the terms $x_1, x_2, x_3 \ldots x_n$ and $\sum_{i=1}^{n} x_1 = x_1 + x_2 + x_3 + \ldots + x_n$ then value of $\sum_{i=1}^{n} x_1 - n\bar{x}$ is
(A) 0 (B) 1
(C) n (D) x

25. If the mean of 5, 10, 15, P, 20, 35, 40 is 21. Then the value of P will be:
(A) 18 (B) 22
(C) 25 (D) 30

26. The median of first 10 prime numbers will be:
(A) 5 (B) 11
(C) 12 (D) 13

27. If mode of any series is 9 and median is 7 then mean of that series will be:
(A) −6 (B) 6
(C) −5/3 (D) 5/3

28. The mean of the first ten even natural numbers is:
(A) 10 (B) 11
(C) 12 (D) 13

29. The median of a series is 10. Two additional observations 7 and 20 are added to the series. The new median will be:
(A) 9 (B) 20
(C) 7 (D) 10

30. The mean income of 50 persons was calculated as ₹169. Later it was found that one figure was wrongly taken as 134 instead of the correct value of 143. The correct mean should be:
(A) ₹168
(B) ₹169.18
(C) ₹168.92
(D) ₹168.18

31. An additional value of 15 is included in a series of 11 values and the mean remains unchanged. The mean of the series was:
(A) 12 (B) 15
(C) 20 (D) None of these

32. The relation between mean, mode and median is:
(A) Mode = 3x Mean − 2x Median
(B) Mode = 3x Median − 2x Mean
(C) Mean = 3x Median − 2x Mode
(D) Median = 3x Mean − 2x Mode

33. The marks of 10 students in certain subjects in a class are 20, 19, 50, 48, 50, 36, 35, 50, 40, 40. The mean and mode are respectively as:
(A) 38.8, 50 (B) 50, 40
(C) 40, 35 (D) 35, 40

34. The average weight (in kg) of all the students in a class equals the number of students in the class. The increase in the average weight when a teacher to 21 kg is included equals the decrease in average weight when a student of 19 kg is included. The strength of the class is:
(A) 15 (B) 10
(C) 20 (D) 17

35. In a frequency distribution median is $\frac{11}{10}$ times the mean, and mode is 5.2. Find the median.

(A) 4.4 (B) 4.3
(C) 4.1 (D) 4.0

36. If numbers 6, 8, $2x$, -5, $2x-1$, 15, 17, 20 and 22 are in ascending order and its median is 14 then the value of x will be:
(A) 14 (B) 7
(C) 15 (D) 20

37. The mean of 25 observations is 36. If the mean of the first 13 observations is 32 and that of the last 13 observations is 39 then the 13th observation is:
(A) 32 (B) 30
(C) 28 (D) 23

38. The average weight of pupils of a class is 46 kg. The average weights of boys and girls are respectively 50 kg and 40 kg. The ratio of the number of boys to the number of girls is:
(A) 2 : 3 (B) 3 : 2
(C) 2 : 5 (D) 5 : 2

39. The mean of the first seventeen whole numbers is:
(A) 8 (B) 7.5
(C) 8.5 (D) 18

40. If the mode of the 64, 60, 48, x, 43, 48, 43, 34 is 43. Then the value of x is:
(A) 60 (B) 40
(C) 43 (D) 48

41. The width of the class 55.5–60.5 is ________.
(A) 10 (B) 5
(C) 2.5 (D) 7

42. If the number of observations n is even, then the median is:

(A) $\left(\frac{n+1}{2}\right)^{\text{th}}$ term

(B) $\left(\frac{n}{2}\right)^{\text{th}}$

(C) Mean of $\left(\frac{n}{2}\right)^{\text{th}}$ and $\left(\frac{n+1}{2}\right)^{\text{th}}$ term

(D) None of these

43. Mean of the first n natural numbers is:
(A) $\frac{n(n+1)}{2}$ (B) $\frac{n+1}{2}$
(C) $\frac{n}{2}$ (D) $\frac{n(n-1)}{2}$

44. Mean of 35 observation is 75. The mean of first 18 observations is 70 and the mean of last 18 observations is 80. Find the 18th observation.
(A) 80 (B) 70
(C) 68 (D) 75

45. Find the mean of $x+1$, $x+3$, $x+4$, $x+8$ is:
(A) $(x+1)$ (B) $(x+3)$
(C) $(x+4)$ (D) $(x+8)$

ANSWER KEY

CHECK POINTS

Check Point 1

1. $\frac{a+b}{2}$ 2. Upper limit 20, lower limit 11 3. 4. 5.

Check Point 2

6. 7. 8. 9. 10.

Check Point 3

11. 39 12. 67.45 13. $\frac{M}{50}$ 14. Median= 9, Mode =19 15. 2.5

Assessment Corner

FIXED RESPONSE TYPE

Fill in the Blanks

1. Median 2. Mode 3. Mean 4. $\frac{(n+1)}{2}$th value 5. Frequency 6. Mid Value

True/False

1. False 2. True 3. True 4. True 5. False

Single Correct Type Questions

1. A 2. C 3. A 4. B 5. C 6. A 7. A 8. D 9. B
10. C 11. B 12. B 13. C 14. A 15. D 16. D 17. B 18. C
19. B 20. D

Multiple Correct Type Questions

1. ABD 2. ABCD 3. ABD 4. ABC 5. C 6. D 7. C 8. A 9. A

Match Type Questions

1. (A) → (R); (B) → (P); (C) → (S); (D) → (Q)
2. (A) → (S); (B) → (R); (C) → (P); (D) → (Q)
3. (A) → (P); (B) → (R); (C) → (S); (D) → (P)

Assertion and Reason Type Questions

1. A 2. C 3. C

Comprehension Type Questions

1. A 2. B 3. D 4. C 5. B 6. D

Numerical Type Questions

1. 4 2. 47 3. 31.25 4. 20 5. 55 6. 36.375 and 35.5 7. 43 8. 14
9. 47 10. 5

Higher Order Thinking Skills (HOTS)

1. C 2. A 3. C 4. D 5. B 6. D 7. B 8. A 9. B
10. B

FREE RESPONSE TYPE

Very Short Answer Type Questions

1. 140 2. 19 3. 7 4. $m=\frac{l+x}{2}$ then $x=2m-l$ 5. 20–30 6. 6 7. 0
8. 54

Short Answer Type Questions

2. 38 3. D 4. 49 5. 56.5 6. 64 8. 20 9. B 10. 80.94

Long Answer Type Questions

1. Median = 12 and Mode = 10 6. $a=6$

Archive Corner

1. B 2. C 3. B 4. D 5. B 6. A 7. C 8. A 9. C
10. D 11. C 12. C 13. B 14. A 15. C 16. A 17. C 18. C
19. B 20. B 21. D 22. D 23. D 24. A 25. B 26. C 27. B
28. B 29. D 30. B 31. B 32. B 33. A 34. B 35. A 36. B
37. D 38. B 39. A 40. C 41. B 42. D 43. B 44. D 45. C

Hints and Explanations

CHAPTER 1 NUMBER SYSTEM

Check Point 1

1. Represent $\frac{3}{5}$ on the number line

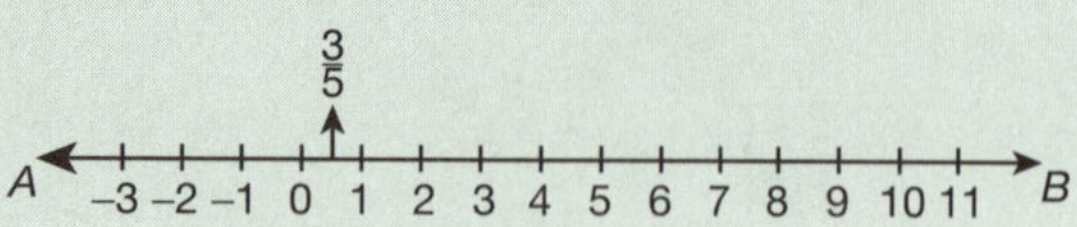

2. $\frac{3}{8}$ and $\frac{2}{5}$ then $\frac{30}{80}$ and $\frac{32}{80}$ then fraction between them will be $\frac{31}{80}$.

3. $\frac{18}{6}$ and $\frac{24}{6}$ then $\frac{19}{6}, \frac{20}{6}, \frac{21}{6}, \frac{22}{6}, \frac{23}{6}$

4. $\frac{5}{3}, \frac{9}{14}, \frac{5}{7}, \frac{6}{11}$

5. $1.129129129\ldots = \frac{1129-1}{999} = \frac{1128}{999}$

Check Point 2

6. 0.05005000500005.; 5.51551555151

7. $\sqrt{5.1}, \sqrt{5.2}$

8. The irrational numbers are non-terminating decimals and this can be proved in the case of root 3 as well. Divide 3 using the long division algorithm.
   - Write 3 as 3 00 00 00. Consider the number in pairs from the right. So 3 stands alone.
   - Now divide 3 with a number such that the number × number gives 3 or a number lesser than that. We determine $1 \times 1 = 1$.
   - Subtract this product from 3 and get the remainder as 2. Obtain 1 as the quotient. Bring down the first pair of zeros. 200 becomes the new dividend.
   - Double the quotient obtained. It is 2 and now let us have our new divisor, $2n$ which when multiplied by n should get the product less than or equal to 200.
   - We determine $27 \times 7 =$ **189**. Subtract this from 200 and get the remainder as 11. Bring down the next pair of zeros. 1100 becomes the new dividend.
   - Double the quotient obtained. It is 34 and now let us have our new divisor, $34n$. Find a digit 'n' such that $34n \times n$ gives the product less than or equal to 1100.
   - We determine $343 \times 3 =$ **1029**. Subtract this from 1100 and get the remainder as 71. Bring down the next pair of zeros. 7100 becomes the new dividend.
   - Repeat the same division process until we get the quotient approximated to 3 decimal places. Thus, we have evaluated $\sqrt{3} = 1.732$
   - This is a never-ending process. We get non-terminating and non-repeating digits after the decimal point. $\sqrt{3} = 1.7320508075688772$ and it goes on.

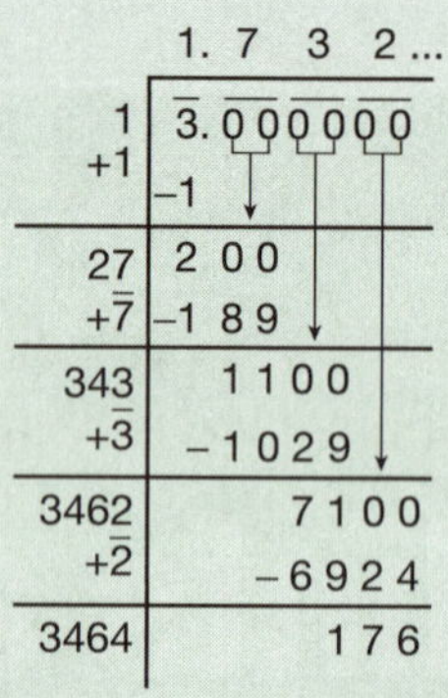

9. Same as above.

10.

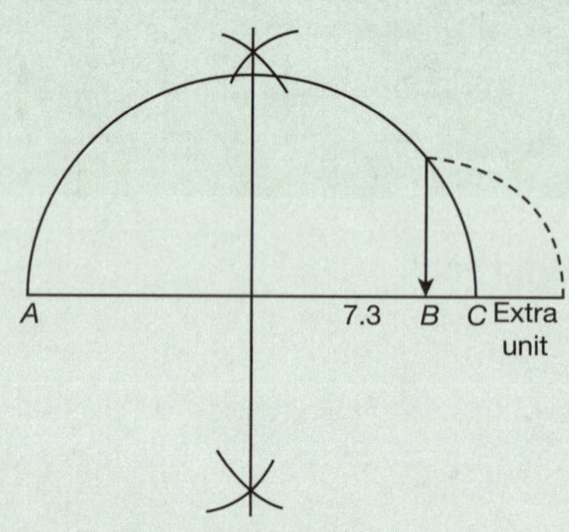

Check Point 3

11. $10\sqrt{2} - 5\sqrt{2} = 5\sqrt{2}$

12. $\frac{5\times\left(\sqrt{10}-\sqrt{5}\right)}{\left(\sqrt{10}+\sqrt{5}\right)\left(\sqrt{10}-\sqrt{5}\right)} = \sqrt{10}-\sqrt{5}.$

13. If $x = \sqrt{2}-1$ and $\frac{1}{x} = \sqrt{2}+1$

    then $x - \frac{1}{x} = \sqrt{2}-1-\sqrt{2}-1 = -2$

14. $(\sqrt{5}+1)^2 + (\sqrt{5}-1)^2 = 5+1+2\sqrt{5}+5+1-2\sqrt{5} = 12$

15. $x=\dfrac{(\sqrt{5}-2)\times(\sqrt{5}-2)}{(\sqrt{5}+2)\times(\sqrt{5}-2)}=5+4-4\sqrt{5}=9-4\sqrt{5}$

and $\dfrac{1}{x}=9+4\sqrt{5}$ then $x+\dfrac{1}{x}=18$

CHECK POINT 4

16. (i) $81^{1/4}=(3^4)^{\frac{1}{4}}=3$ (ii) $64^{1/3}=(4^3)^{\frac{1}{3}}=4$

(iii) $32^{3/5}=(2^5)^{\frac{3}{5}}=8$ (iv) $27^{2/3}=(3^3)^{\frac{2}{3}}=9$

17. (i) $3^{1/3}\cdot 3^{2/5}=3^{\frac{1}{3}+\frac{2}{5}}=3^{\frac{11}{15}}$

(ii) $\left(\dfrac{4}{9}\right)^{1/2}\left(\left(\dfrac{2}{3}\right)^2\right)^{\frac{1}{2}}=\dfrac{2}{3}$

(iii) $2^{2/3}.3^{2/3}(2\times 3)^{\frac{2}{3}}=(6)^{\frac{2}{3}}$

(iv) $(2^{1/3})^3=2$

18. $2^n\times 4^n\times 8^{1-n}$ $2^n\times(2^2)^n\times(2^3)^{1-n}$

$=2^n\times 2^{2n}\times 2^{3-3n}$

$=2^{n+2n+3-3n}=2^3=8$

19. $8^x=16$ then

$(2^3)^x=2^4$ then $2^{3x}=2^4$ then $3x=4$ then $x=\dfrac{4}{3}$

20. $3^3\times 5^3\times 3^2\times 4^2\times(2^4)^4=3^5\times 5^3\times 2^{20}$

then $x=20$, $y=5$ and $z=3$

FIXED RESPONSE TYPE

Fill in the Blanks

1. $x=2+\sqrt{3}$ then $\dfrac{1}{x}=2-\sqrt{3}$, then

$x^3+\dfrac{1}{x^3}=\left(x+\dfrac{1}{x}\right)^3-3\left(x+\dfrac{1}{x}\right)=4^3-3\times 4=52$

2. $5^{x-2}\times 3^{2x-3}=3^3\times 5$ then $x-2=1$ then $x=3$.

3. Evaluate: $\dfrac{3^{-3}\times 6^2\times\sqrt{98}}{5^2\times\sqrt{1/25}\times(15)^{-4/3}\times 3^{1/3}}$.

$=\dfrac{3^{-3}\times 3^2\times 2^2\times 7\times\sqrt{2}}{5^2\times\frac{1}{5}\times 3^{-\frac{4}{3}}\times 5^{-\frac{4}{3}}\times 3^{\frac{1}{3}}}=2^{\frac{5}{2}}\times 7\times 5^{1/3}$

4. $\dfrac{1}{1+x^{b-a}+x^{c-a}}+\dfrac{1}{1+x^{a-b}+x^{c-b}}+\dfrac{1}{1+x^{a-c}+x^{b-c}}$

$=\dfrac{1}{1+\frac{x^b}{x^a}+\frac{x^c}{x^a}}+\dfrac{1}{1+\frac{x^a}{x^b}+\frac{x^c}{x^b}}+\dfrac{1}{1+\frac{x^a}{x^c}+\frac{x^b}{x^c}}$

$=\dfrac{x^a}{x^a+x^b+x^c}+\dfrac{x^b}{x^a+x^b+x^c}+\dfrac{x^c}{x^a+x^b+x^c}$

$=\dfrac{x^c+x^b+x^a}{x^a+x^b+x^c}=1$

5. If $\dfrac{9^n\times 3^2\left[3^{-n/2}\right]^{-2}-(27)^n}{3^{3m}\times 2^3}=\dfrac{1}{27}$

then $\dfrac{3^{3n}(9-1)}{3^{3m}\times 8}=3^{-3}$ then $n-m=-1$

6. $\dfrac{3^{5x}\times(81)^2\times 6561}{3^{2x}}=3^7$, then

$3^{3x+8+8}=3^7$ then $3x=-9$ then $x=-3$

True/False

1. False
2. False
3. False
4. False
5. False, it can be irrational.

Single Correct Type Questions

1. (C) $x=2+\sqrt{3}$, $\dfrac{1}{x}=2-\sqrt{3}$ then $\left(x+\dfrac{1}{x}\right)=4$

2. (C) $\sqrt{\sqrt{2}\sqrt{3}}=\sqrt{\sqrt{6}}=6^{\frac{1}{4}}$ is:

3. (B) $\sqrt{50}=5\sqrt{2}$ is $\sqrt{2}$:

4. (B) If $x=3+\sqrt{8}$ and $y=3-\sqrt{8}$ where $xy=1$

then $x^2+y^2=(3+\sqrt{8})^2+(3-\sqrt{8})^2=34$

5. (D) $\dfrac{(3+\sqrt{7})(2+\sqrt{7})}{(2-\sqrt{7})(2+\sqrt{7})}=\dfrac{6+3\sqrt{7}+2\sqrt{7}+7}{-3}$

$=\dfrac{13+5\sqrt{7}}{-3}=a+b\sqrt{7}$ then (a, b)

$=(-13/3, -5/3)$

6. **(C)** $2^{\frac{1}{2}}$ $3^{\frac{1}{3}}$ $4^{\frac{1}{3}}$ $2^{\frac{1}{3}}$

$8^{\frac{1}{6}}$ $9^{\frac{1}{6}}$ $16^{\frac{1}{6}}$ $4^{\frac{1}{6}}$

7. **(A)** The value of

$\sqrt[5]{(32)^{-3}} = \sqrt[5]{\left(2^5\right)^{-3}} = \sqrt[5]{2^{-15}} = 2^{-3} = \frac{1}{8}$

8. **(A)** $x = \frac{\left(\sqrt{3}-\sqrt{2}\right)(\sqrt{3}-\sqrt{2})}{(\sqrt{3}+\sqrt{2})\times(\sqrt{3}-\sqrt{2})} = 5-2\sqrt{6}$ and

$y = \frac{\sqrt{3}+\sqrt{2}}{\sqrt{3}-\sqrt{2}} = 5+2\sqrt{6}$ then $x+y=10$

and $xy = 1$

$x^2+xy+y^2 = (x+y)^2 - xy = 100-1 = 99$

9. **(B)** $\frac{2}{\sqrt{5}+\sqrt{3}} + \frac{1}{\sqrt{3}+\sqrt{2}} - \frac{3}{\sqrt{5}+\sqrt{2}}$

$= \sqrt{5}-\sqrt{3}+\sqrt{3}-\sqrt{2}-\sqrt{5}+\sqrt{2} = 0.$

10. **(B)** $5^{\frac{1}{4}}$ $4^{\frac{1}{5}}$ $4^{\frac{1}{2}}$ $3^{\frac{1}{2}}$

$5^{\frac{5}{20}}$ $4^{\frac{4}{20}}$ $4^{\frac{10}{20}}$ $3^{\frac{10}{20}}$

$3125^{\frac{1}{20}}$ $256^{\frac{1}{20}}$ $4^{\frac{10}{20}}$ $3^{\frac{10}{20}}$

11. **(B)** $3^{\frac{1}{2}} \times 5^{\frac{1}{3}} = 27^{\frac{1}{6}} \times 25^{\frac{1}{6}} = 675^{\frac{1}{6}}$

12. **(C)** Prime No. {2, 3, 5, 7}

13. **(B)** $\sqrt[3]{\frac{54}{250}} = \sqrt[3]{\frac{2\times3^3}{2\times5^3}} = \frac{3}{5}$

14. **(D)** $5^{x-3}\,3^{2x-8} = 3^2\times5^2$ Then $x-3=2$ then $x=5$

15. **(A)** Terminating

16. **(C)** Non-terminating and repeating

17. **(D)** Composite number < 15 = {4, 6, 8, 9, 10, 12, 14}

18. **(A)** Except 1 every natural number is either prime or composite.

19. **(C)** $\sqrt{5}+3$

20. **(C)**

21. $x = 0.1\overline{2}$

$10x = 1.\overline{2}$ (1)

$100x = 12.\overline{2}$ (2)

(2) – (1)

$90x = 11$

$X = \frac{11}{90}$

$P = 11, q = 90$

22. **(C)** (i) Rational + Irrational = Irrational

(ii) (Rational) (Rational) = rational

(iii) (Irrational) (Irrational) = rational / Irrational

(iv) Rational + Rational = Rational

(v) Irrational + Irrational = Rational / Irrational

23. **(B)** A real number

24. **(C)** 1.6

25. **(B)** $\frac{1}{\sqrt{3}-\sqrt{2}} = \sqrt{3}+\sqrt{2} = 3.146$

Multiple Correct Type Questions

1. **(A,C,D)**

2. **(A,C,D)** $\left[\sqrt{7+4\sqrt{3}}-\sqrt{3} = 2+\sqrt{3}-\sqrt{3} = 2\right]$

3. **(A,B,C)** Obvious

4. **(B,C,D)** $\left(\frac{a^x}{a^y}\right)^{x+y} \cdot \left(\frac{a^y}{a^z}\right)^{y+z} \cdot \left(\frac{a^z}{a^x}\right)^{z+x}$

$= \left(a^{x-y}\right)^{x+y} \times \left(a^{y-z}\right)^{z+y} \times \left(a^{z-x}\right)^{x+z}$

$= a^{x^2-y^2} a^{y^2-z^2} a^{z^2-x^2} = a^0 = 1$

5. **(A,B,D)** $\frac{39\sqrt{2}-5}{3-\sqrt{2}} \times \frac{3+\sqrt{2}}{3+\sqrt{2}} = 9+b\sqrt{2}$

$\Rightarrow \frac{112\sqrt{2}+63}{7} = a+b\sqrt{2}$

$16\sqrt{2}+9 = a+b\sqrt{2}$

$\Rightarrow A = 9, b = 16$

6. **(B,D)** $1+\frac{6}{5+\frac{4}{3-\frac{1}{2}}} = 1+\frac{6}{5+\frac{8}{5}}$

$= 1+\frac{30}{33} = \frac{63}{33} = \frac{21}{11}$

7. **(B,D)**

8. **(A,B,C,D)** (A) $\sqrt{x} = Q, \Rightarrow x = Q_1^2$

Also rational number

(B) $x^2 = Q_1 \Rightarrow x^6 = Q_1^3$

$x^7 = Q_2$

$\frac{x^7}{x^6} = \frac{Q_2}{Q_1^3}$ (rational number) similar (D)

HINTS AND EXPLANATIONS

(C) $x^3 = Q_1 \Rightarrow x^6 = Q_1^2$ (rational number)

$$x^7 = Q_2 \frac{x^7}{x^6} = \frac{Q_1}{Q_1^2}$$

$$x^7 = \frac{Q_1}{Q_1^2} \text{ (rational number)}$$

9. **(A)**

10. **(B)**

11. **(D)**

12. **(A,B,C)**

13. **(C)**

14. **(C)** $4.\overline{26} + 4.2\overline{6}$

$= 4.26262626\ldots\ldots + 4.266666666\ldots$

$= 8.529292929\ldots$

15. **(A,C,D)** $\dfrac{\left(a^{x+y}\right)^3\left(a^{y+z}\right)^3\left(a^{z+x}\right)^3}{\left(a^x a^y a^z\right)^6}$ is

$$= \frac{\left(a^{3x+3y}\right)^1\left(a^{3y+3z}\right)^1\left(a^{3z+3x}\right)^1}{\left(a^{6x}a^{6y}a^{6z}\right)^1} = 1$$

16. **(A,B)** $\left(\dfrac{\sqrt{6}+\sqrt{3}}{\sqrt{8}-\sqrt{3}}\right)\left(\dfrac{\sqrt{6}-\sqrt{3}}{\sqrt{8}+\sqrt{3}}\right) = \dfrac{6-3}{8-3} = \dfrac{3}{5}$

17. **(B,D)** $\dfrac{2\left(\sqrt{2}+\sqrt{6}\right)}{3\sqrt{\left(2+\sqrt{3}\right)}} = \dfrac{2\times 2\left(1+\sqrt{3}\right)}{3\left(1+\sqrt{3}\right)} = \dfrac{4}{3}$

18. **(B)** 2^{250} 3^{200} 4^{150} 5^{100}

32^{50} 81^{50} 64^{50} 25^{50}

19. **(D)**

20. **(A,D)**

21. **(B)** $48^{\frac{1}{4}} = 2\times 3^{\frac{1}{4}}$ then $3^{\frac{3}{4}} = \sqrt[4]{27}$

22. **(D)** $\sqrt[3]{2}\times\sqrt[4]{3} = 2^{\frac{1}{3}}\times 3^{\frac{1}{4}} = 2^{\frac{4}{12}}\times 3^{\frac{3}{12}}$

$$= (16\times 27)^{\frac{1}{12}} = (432)^{\frac{1}{12}}$$

23. **(B)** $x+y=4$ and $x-y=\dfrac{1}{4}$ then $2x = 4+\dfrac{1}{4} = \dfrac{17}{4}$

then $x = \dfrac{17}{8}$ and $y = \dfrac{15}{8}$

24. **(A,C)**

25. **(A,B,D)**

Match Type Questions

1.

Column-I	Column-II
(i) $\sqrt{7+4\sqrt{3}}$	(R) $2+\sqrt{3}$
(ii) $\sqrt[6]{216}$	(P) $\sqrt{6}$
(iii) $\left(\dfrac{2ab^3}{5c^3b}\right)^0$	(S) 1
(iv) $\sqrt[3]{3}\times\sqrt[2]{2}$	(Q) $\sqrt[6]{72}$

2.

Column-I	Column-II
(i) x^{1-y}	(S) 16
(ii) $(x-y)^{x-y}$	(P) 1
(iii) $(x+y)^{y-x}$	(R) $-\dfrac{1}{5}$
(iv) y^{-x}	(Q) 9

3.

Column-I	Column-II
(i) $\dfrac{4+\sqrt{5}}{4-\sqrt{5}}+\dfrac{4-\sqrt{5}}{4+\sqrt{5}}$	(P) 42/11
(ii) $\left(\sqrt{8}-\sqrt{2}\right)\left(\sqrt{8}+\sqrt{2}\right)$	(S) 6
(iii) $\dfrac{\sqrt[4]{243\times 16}}{\sqrt[4]{3}}$	(R) 6
(iv) 6^{-2}	(Q) Rational

4.

Column-I	Column-II
(i) $\left(\sqrt{3}+\sqrt{5}\right)^2$	(R) $8+2\sqrt{15}$
(ii) $0.\overline{54}$	(Q) Non-terminating and recurring
(iii) $\sqrt[3]{\dfrac{216}{1331}}$	(S) $\dfrac{6}{11}$
(iv) $\sqrt[3]{\dfrac{216}{1331}}$	(R) Irrational

Assertion and Reason Type Questions

1. **(A)**

2. **(A)**

Comprehension Type Questions

1. **(B)** $x = 7 - 4\sqrt{3}$ then

$$\frac{1}{x} = \frac{1}{7-4\sqrt{3}} = 7 + 4\sqrt{3} \text{ then } x + \frac{1}{x} = 14$$

2. **(D)** $x^3 + \frac{1}{x^3} = \left(x + \frac{1}{x}\right)^3 - 3 \times x \times \frac{1}{x}\left(x + \frac{1}{x}\right)$

$$= 14^3 - 3 \times 14 = 2702$$

3. **(A)** $x^2 - \frac{1}{x^2} = \left(x + \frac{1}{x}\right)\left(x - \frac{1}{x}\right)$

$$= -14 \times 8\sqrt{3} = -112\sqrt{3}$$

4. **(D)** $x^2 = \left(7 - 4\sqrt{3}\right)^2 = 97 - 56\sqrt{3}$

$$\Rightarrow x^2 - 1 = 96 - 56\sqrt{3} \text{ and } x^2 + 1 = 98 - 56\sqrt{3}$$

Numerical Type Questions

1. $\frac{6}{7}$ = 0.857142857142857142 ……… 100th digit will be 1

2. Let the given prime numbers be a, b, c, d. Then, abc = 385 and bcd = 1001.

$$\therefore \frac{abc}{bcd} = \frac{385}{1001} \Rightarrow \frac{a}{d} = \frac{5}{13} \text{ So, } a = 5, d = 13.$$

3. **16**

$$0.45454545\ldots = \frac{45}{99} = \frac{5}{11}$$

4. $\sqrt{9-(n-2)^2}$ then $9-(n-2)^2 \geq 0$

then $(n-2)^2 - 3^2 \leq 0$

then $(n-5)(n+1) \leq 0$ then $-1 \leq n \leq 5$

$\Rightarrow n = -1, 0, 1, 2, 3, 4, 5$

5. $\sqrt{1+2+3+4+x} = \sqrt{10+x}$

then $x = 6, 15, 26, 30, 54, 71, 90$

6. $$\frac{\sqrt{954+\sqrt{\sqrt{484}+\sqrt{704+\sqrt{25}}}}}{0.00155}$$

$$= \frac{\sqrt{954+\sqrt{22+27}}}{0.00155} = \frac{\sqrt{954+7}}{0.00155}$$

$$= \frac{3100000}{155} = \frac{100000}{5} = 2000$$

$$= \frac{40000}{81.x} \text{ then } x = \frac{20}{81}.$$

7. 913913913913…….. then 100th digit will be 9

8. Let $\left(\frac{1}{2} + \frac{1}{3} \ldots\ldots + \frac{1}{2007}\right) = x$

$$\left(x + \frac{1}{2008}\right)(1+x) - \left(1 + x + \frac{1}{2008}\right)(x)$$

$$= x + x^2 + \frac{1}{2008} + \frac{x}{2008} - x - x^2 - \frac{x}{2008} = \frac{1}{2008}$$

9. $100 \leq 3x < 999$ & $1000 \leq 4x < 9999 \Rightarrow 250 \leq x < 333$

$\Rightarrow$ 84 such integral

10. $N = \frac{1}{2-1}(2^{64} - 1) + 1 = 2^{64}$

11. $$x = \frac{(\sqrt{3}-\sqrt{2})(\sqrt{3}-\sqrt{2})}{(\sqrt{3}+\sqrt{2}) \times (\sqrt{3}-\sqrt{2})} = 5 - 2\sqrt{6} \text{ and}$$

$$y = \frac{\sqrt{3}+\sqrt{2}}{\sqrt{3}-\sqrt{2}} = 5 + 2\sqrt{6} \text{ then } x + y = 10 \text{ and } xy = 1$$

$$x^2 + xy + y^2 = (x+y)^2 - xy = 100 - 1 = 99$$

12. $$\sqrt{\frac{1}{\sqrt{2}+1} + \frac{1}{\sqrt{3}+\sqrt{2}} + \frac{1}{\sqrt{4}+\sqrt{3}+}\ldots\ldots}$$

$$= \sqrt{\sqrt{2} - 1 + \sqrt{3} - \sqrt{2} + \sqrt{3} - \sqrt{2} + \ldots\sqrt{100} - \sqrt{99}}$$

$$\sqrt{10-1} = 3$$

13. If $2^{2008} - 2^{2007} - 2^{2006} + 2^{2005} = 2^{2005}\left(2^3 - 2^2 - 2 + 1\right)$

$= 2^{2005}(8 - 4 - 2 + 1) = 3 \times 2^{2005} = k \cdot 2^{2005}$ then $k = 3$.

14. Let $2^x = 3^y = 6^{-z} = k$ then

$$2 = k^{\frac{1}{x}} \text{ and } 3 = k^{\frac{1}{y}} \text{ and } 6 = k^{\frac{-1}{z}}$$

$$\Rightarrow 2 \times 3 = 6 \text{ then } k^{\frac{1}{x}+\frac{1}{y}} = k^{\frac{-1}{z}}$$

$$\text{then } \left(\frac{1}{x} + \frac{1}{y} = -\frac{1}{z}\right) \Rightarrow \left(\frac{1}{x} + \frac{1}{y} + \frac{1}{z}\right) = 0$$

15. If $$a = \frac{\left(3+2\sqrt{2}\right)}{\left(3-2\sqrt{2}\right)\left(3+2\sqrt{2}\right)} = \left(3+2\sqrt{2}\right),$$

$$b = \frac{\left(3-2\sqrt{2}\right)}{\left(3+2\sqrt{2}\right)\left(3-2\sqrt{2}\right)} = \left(3-2\sqrt{2}\right) \text{ then}$$

$a + b = 6$ and $ab = 1$

$$a^2 + b^2 = (a+b)^2 - 2ab = 36 - 2 = 34$$

Higher Order Thinking Skills (HOTS)

1. (D) $(m + n)(m - n) = 7 \times 1 = (-7) \times (-1)$
$m + n = 7$ or $m + n = 1$
$m - n = 1$ or $m - n = 7 \Rightarrow m = 4, n = 3$ $m = 4, n = +3$
$m + n = -7$ or $m + n = -1$
$m - n = -1$ or $m - n = -7 \Rightarrow m = -4, n = -3$ $m = -4, n = +3$

2. (A) $x+\frac{1}{x}=3\left(x-\frac{1}{x}\right)=2x=\frac{4}{x}$ then $x^2=2$
then $x=\pm\sqrt{2}$

3. (D) $\frac{2^{x-3}}{8^{-x}}=\frac{32}{4^{\left(\frac{1}{2}\right)x}}\Rightarrow\frac{2^{x-3}}{2^{-3x}}=\frac{2^5}{2^x}$
$\Rightarrow 2^{x-3}\times 2^x\times 2^{3x}=2^5$
$\Rightarrow 2^{5x-3}=2^5\Rightarrow 5x-3=5$ then $x=\frac{8}{5}=1\frac{3}{5}$

4. (A) $2.\overline{6}-0.\overline{82}$
$=2.6666....-0.82828282....=1.83838383...$
$=\frac{183-1}{99}=\frac{182}{99}$

5. (?) $\frac{6^{r+s}\times 12^{r-s}}{8^r\times 9^{r+2s}}=\frac{\left(2^{r+s}\times 3^{r+s}\right)\left(2^{2r-2s}\times 3^{r-s}\right)}{2^{3r}3^{2r+4s}}$
$=2^{r+s+2r-2s-3r}.3^{r+s+s-r-2r-4s}$
$=2^{-s}.3^{-3s}$

6. (C) $4^x-\frac{4^x}{4}=24$ then $4^x\left(1-\frac{1}{4}\right)=4^x\times\frac{3}{4}=24$
then $4^x=32=2^5$ then $2x=5$
$(2x)^x=5^{\frac{5}{2}}=25\sqrt{5}$

7. (C) $2^{73} - 2^{72} - 2^{71} = 2^{71}$

8. (B) $n_1 = 3$, $n_2 = 8$

9. (A) $(n + m)(n - m) = 7.2$ or $(-7) \times (-2)$
$= 14.1$ or $(-14) \times (-1)$
On solving
We do not get any integer value of n & m.

10. (D) $x=7+4\sqrt{3}$, $\sqrt{x}=2+\sqrt{3}$ then
$\frac{1}{\sqrt{x}}=2-\sqrt{3}$ then $\sqrt{x}+\frac{1}{\sqrt{x}}=4$

11. (A) $\frac{\left(\sqrt{3}-1\right)\left(\sqrt{3}-1\right)}{\left(\sqrt{3}-1\right)\left(\sqrt{3}-1\right)}=\frac{4-2\sqrt{3}}{2}$
$=2-\sqrt{3}=a+b\sqrt{3}$

12. (C) $\frac{\left(\sqrt{3}+\sqrt{2}+1\right)}{\left(\sqrt{3}+\sqrt{2}-1\right)\left(\sqrt{3}+\sqrt{2}+1\right)}=\frac{\left(\sqrt{3}+\sqrt{2}+1\right)}{\left(\sqrt{3}+\sqrt{2}\right)^2-1}$
$=\frac{\left(\sqrt{3}+\sqrt{2}-1\right)\left(4-2\sqrt{6}\right)}{\left(4+2\sqrt{6}\right)\left(4-2\sqrt{6}\right)}$
$=\frac{-4+4\sqrt{3}-6\sqrt{2}+4\sqrt{2}-4\sqrt{3}-4+2\sqrt{6}}{16-24}$
$=\frac{4+2\sqrt{2}-2\sqrt{6}}{8}=\frac{2+\sqrt{2}-\sqrt{6}}{4}$
$=\frac{0.9647}{4}=0.466$

13. (C) $a=3+2\sqrt{2}$ and $b=3-2\sqrt{2}$
then $ab=1 a+b=6$
$a^3+b^3=\left(a+b\right)^3-3ab\left(a+b\right)$
$=6^3-18=216-18=198$

14. (B) $x=\left(7+4\sqrt{3}\right)$ and $\frac{1}{x}=7-4\sqrt{3}$ then
$x+\frac{1}{x}=14$ then $x^2+\frac{1}{x^2}=196-2=194$

15. (B) $\left(1-\frac{1}{3}\right)\left(1-\frac{1}{4}\right)\left(1-\frac{1}{5}\right)......\left(1-\frac{1}{n}\right)$
$=\frac{2}{3}\times\frac{3}{4}\times\frac{4}{5}\times\frac{5}{6}...........\frac{n-1}{n}=\frac{2}{n}$

16. (C) $\frac{\left(x^{a+b}\right)^2(x^{b+c})^2(x^{c+a})^2}{(x^a.x^b.x^c)^4}$
$=\frac{x^{2a+2b}x^{2b+2c}x^{2a+2c}}{x^{4a}x^{4b}x^{4c}}=\frac{x^{4a+4b+4c}}{x^{4a+4b+4c}}=1$

17. (A) $x^3 + y^3 + z^3 - 3xyz = \frac{1}{2}(x + y + z)\ [(x - y)^2 + (y - z)^2 + (z - x)^2] \geq 0$ then $x^3 + y^3 + z^3 \geq 3xyz$

18. (C) The value of $\sqrt[\ell+m]{\frac{x^{\ell^2}}{x^{m^2}}}.\sqrt[m+n]{\frac{x^{m^2}}{x^{n^2}}}.\sqrt[n+\ell]{\frac{x^{n^2}}{x^{\ell^2}}}=x^0=1$

19. (C) Given: $2^x = 4^y = 8^z \Rightarrow 2^x = 2^{2y} = 2^{3z}$
$\Rightarrow x = 2y = 3z = k$ (i)
$\frac{1}{2x}+\frac{1}{4y}+\frac{1}{6z}=\frac{24}{7}$
Substitute (i) in (ii)
$\frac{1}{2k}+\frac{1}{2k}+\frac{1}{2k}\frac{24}{7}\Rightarrow\frac{3}{2k}=\frac{24}{7}$ then $k=\frac{7}{16}$
$\therefore 3z = k \Rightarrow z = k/3 = 7/48$

20. (B) $a^x=b, b^y=c$ and $c^z=a$ then $b=\left(c^z\right)^x$
$=c^{xz}=\left(b^y\right)^{xz}=b^{xyz}$ then $xyz=1$

FREE RESPONSE TYPE

Very Short Answer Type Questions

1. $123 \times 42y$
must be divisible by 3 and
must be divisible by 2
$y = 0, 2, 4, 6, 8$ smallest
$x = 0$
$y = 2 \Rightarrow$ The correct number is 1230432

2. 1.6.

3. $x = 1.9$

$$x = \frac{18}{9} \Rightarrow x = \frac{2}{1}$$

4. $$\frac{(\sqrt{7}+2)}{(\sqrt{7}-2)(\sqrt{7}+2)} = \frac{\sqrt{7}+2}{3}.$$

5. $x = 3.1\overline{45}$

$10x = 31.\overline{45}$ (1)

$1000x = 31.45.\overline{45}$ (2)

on subtraction (1) & (2)

$990x = 3114$

$$x = \frac{173}{55}$$

6. $$\frac{\sqrt{32}+\sqrt{48}}{\sqrt{8}+\sqrt{12}} = \frac{4\sqrt{2}+4\sqrt{3}}{2\sqrt{2}+2\sqrt{3}} = \frac{4}{2} = 2.$$

7. $$\sqrt[4]{\sqrt[3]{2^2}} = \left((2^2)^{\frac{1}{3}}\right)^{\frac{1}{4}} = 2^{\frac{2}{12}} = \sqrt[6]{2}.$$

8. Because LCM is not divisible by H.C.F.

9. $$\sqrt{\frac{(\sqrt{2}-1)(\sqrt{2}-1)}{(\sqrt{2}-1)(\sqrt{2}+1)}} = \sqrt{2}-1 = 0.4142.$$

10. $$(256)^{0.16} \times (256)^{0.09} .= 256^{0.16+0.09} = \left(4^4\right)^{0.25} = 4$$

Short Answer Type Questions

1. $$\sqrt[3]{2}.\sqrt[4]{2}.\sqrt[12]{32} = 2^{\frac{1}{3}+\frac{1}{4}+\frac{5}{12}} = 2^{\frac{4+3+5}{12}} = 2.$$

2. Equality can hold only when
$x + y = 2x - y \Rightarrow x - 2y = 0$ ...(1) and $x - 2y = x - y - 1 = 0$ ...(ii)
(i) – (ii) we get $-y + 1 = 0 \Rightarrow y = 1$ and $x = 2$.

3. 1. Draw a line segment of length $13 + 1 = 14$ cm

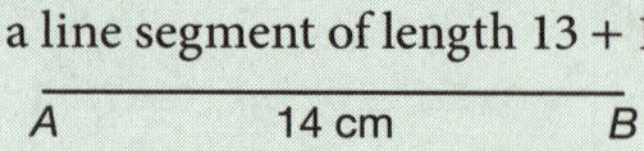

2. Mark $AC = 13$ cm and $AD = (13 + 1)/2 = 7$ cm

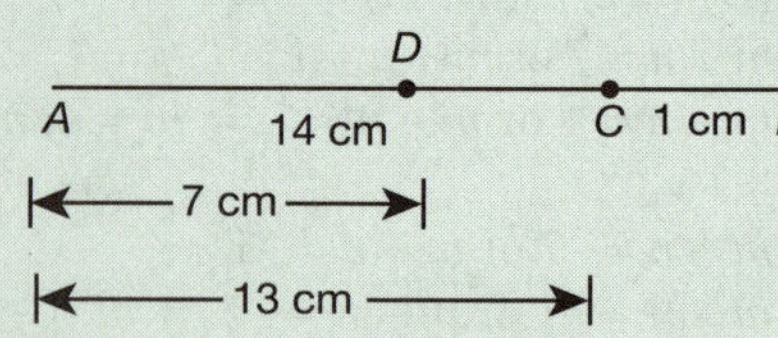

3. With D as centre and AD as radius, draw a semi circle as shown in the figure

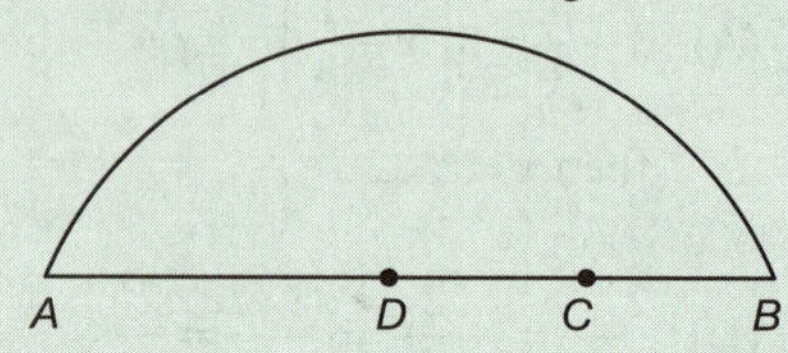

4. Draw perpendicular at C to reach the semi circle at E.

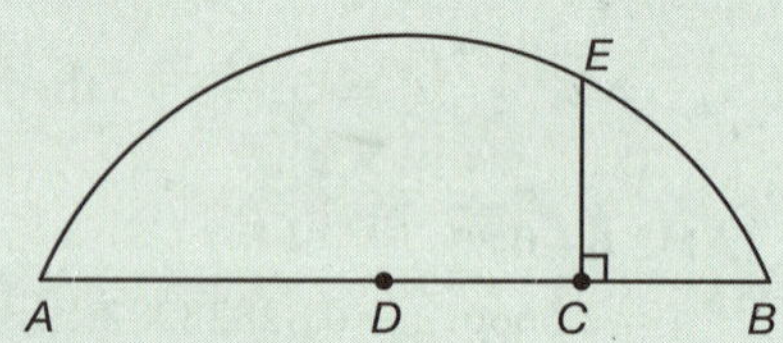

5. Measure EC using a compass and mark the same on a horizontal line.

4. Let $x = 0.123333333...$ (i)
multiply this by 100
$100x = 12.3333333...$ (ii)
multiply this by 10
$1000x = 123.3333333...$ (iii)
Subtract (ii) from (iii)

$$900x = 123 - 12 = 111 \text{ then } x = \frac{111}{900} = \frac{37}{300}$$

5. $$\frac{6(3\sqrt{2}+2\sqrt{3})}{(3\sqrt{2}-2\sqrt{3})(3\sqrt{2}+2\sqrt{3})} = \frac{6(3\sqrt{2}+2\sqrt{3})}{6}$$

$$= (3\sqrt{2}+2\sqrt{3}) = 3\sqrt{2} - a\sqrt{3} \text{ then } a = -2.$$

6. $$B = \frac{12}{3+\sqrt{5}+\sqrt{8}} = \frac{12(3+\sqrt{5}-\sqrt{8})}{6+6\sqrt{5}}$$

$$= \frac{2(3+\sqrt{5}-\sqrt{8})}{(\sqrt{5}+1)}$$

$$= \frac{6+2\sqrt{5}}{\sqrt{5}+1} - \frac{4\sqrt{2}(\sqrt{5}-1)}{4} = \frac{(\sqrt{5}+1)^2}{(\sqrt{5}+1)} - \sqrt{10} + \sqrt{2}$$

$$= 1 + \sqrt{5} + \sqrt{2} - \sqrt{10}$$

Hence A = B

7. 7 =

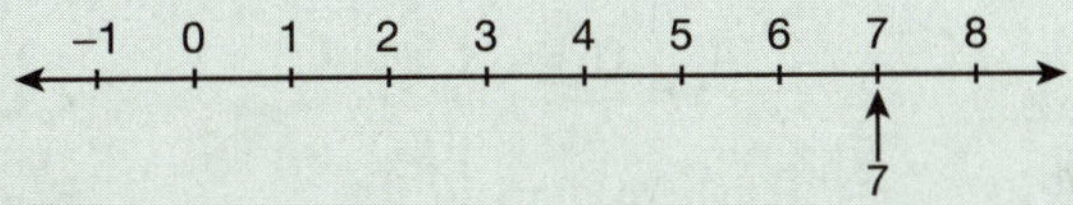

7.2 =

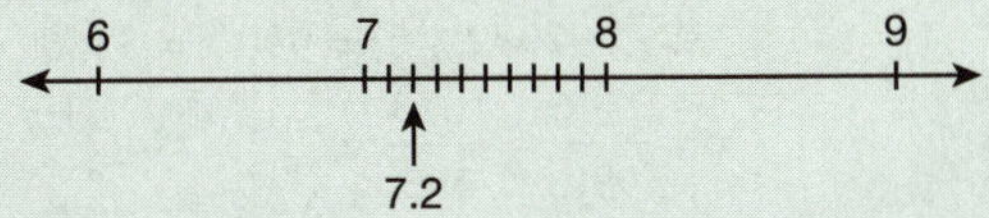

–3/2 =

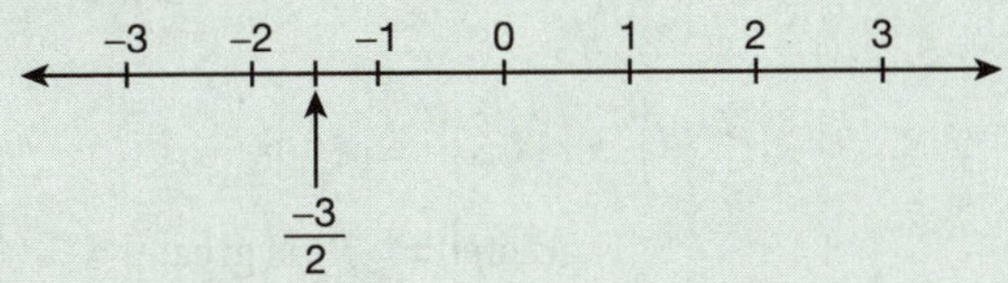

–12/5 =

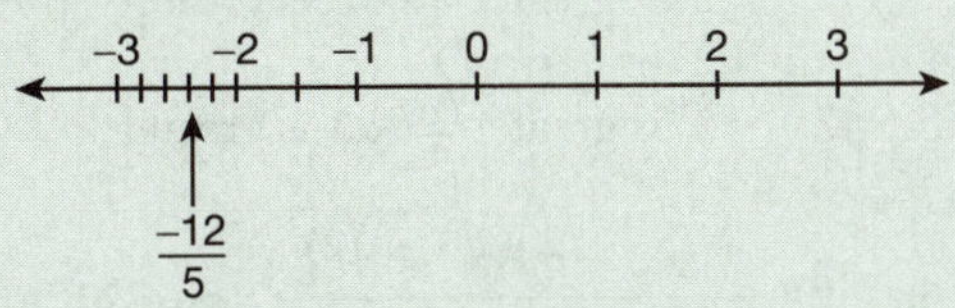

8. $p^2 - q^2 = r$

$(p - q)(p + q) = r$

As r is prime $\therefore$ $p - q$ must be 1

$p = 3 : q = 2$ (p, q are also prime) $\therefore$ $r = 5$

9. Insert a rational number and an irrational number between the following:

(i) $\sqrt{5}$

(ii) 0.41414243444546474849…….

(iii) 0.42123165698……

(iv) $\sqrt{2.5}$

(v) 0.0001010203040506070809

10. Presentation of $\sqrt{5}$ on number line:

We write 5 as the sum of the square of two natural numbers:

$5 = 1 + 4 = 1^2 + 2^2$ On the number line, take $OA = 2$ units.

Draw $BA = 1$ unit, perpendicular to OA. Join OB.

By Pythagoras theorem, $OB = \sqrt{5}$

Using a compass with centre O and radius OB, draw an arc which intersects the number line at the point C. Then, C corresponds to $\sqrt{5}$.

Presentation of $\sqrt{10}$ on the number line:

We write 10 as the sun of the square of two natural numbers:

$10 = 1 + 9 = 1^2 + 3^2$

On the number line, taken $OA = 3$ units.

Draw $BA = 1$ unit, perpendicular to OA, Join OB.

By Pythagoras theorem, $OB = \sqrt{10}$

Using a compass with centre O and radius OB, draw an arc which intersects the number line at the point C. Then, C corresponds to $\sqrt{10}$

Presentation of $\sqrt{17}$ on the number line:

We write 17 as the sum of the square of two natural numbers.

$17 = 1 + 16 = 1^2 + 4^2$

On the number line, take $OA = 4$ units.

Draw $BA = 1$ units, perpendicular to OA. Join OB.

By Pythagoras theorem, $OB = \sqrt{17}$

Using a compass with centre O and radius OB, draw an arc which intersects the number line at the point C. Then, C corresponds to $\sqrt{17}$.

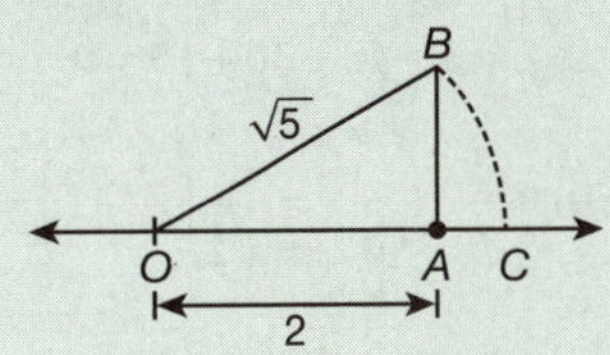

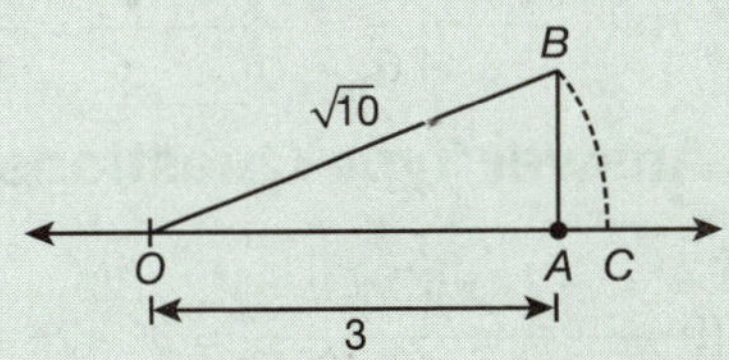

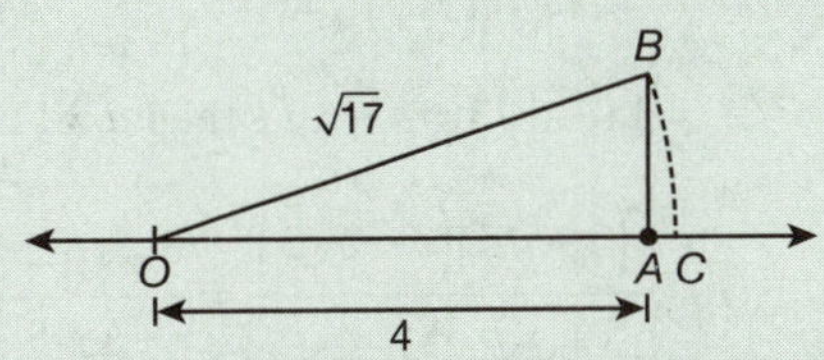

11.

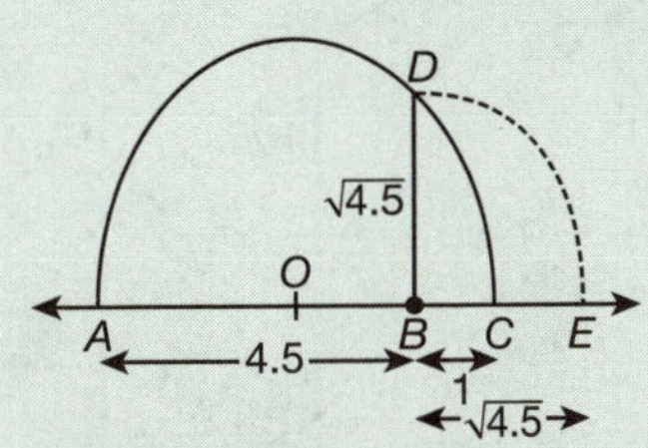

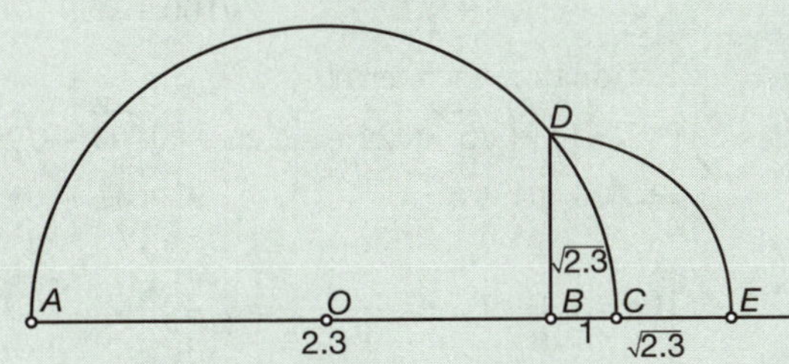

12. (i) $\sqrt{45} - 3\sqrt{20} + 4\sqrt{5}$

$= 3\sqrt{5} - 6\sqrt{5} + 4\sqrt{5} = \sqrt{5}$

(ii) $\dfrac{\sqrt{24}}{8} + \dfrac{\sqrt{54}}{9} = \dfrac{2\sqrt{6}}{8} + \dfrac{3\sqrt{6}}{9}$

$= \dfrac{\sqrt{6}}{4} + \dfrac{\sqrt{6}}{3} = \dfrac{7\sqrt{6}}{12}$

(iii) $\sqrt[4]{12}\times\sqrt[7]{6}=3^{\frac{1}{4}+\frac{1}{7}}\times 2^{\frac{1}{2}+\frac{1}{7}}=3^{\frac{11}{28}}\times 2^{\frac{18}{28}}$

(iv) $4\sqrt{28}\div 3\sqrt{7}=\dfrac{8\sqrt{7}}{3\sqrt{7}}=\dfrac{8}{3}$

(v) $3\sqrt{3}+2\sqrt{27}+\dfrac{7}{\sqrt{3}}$

$=3\sqrt{3}+6\sqrt{3}+\dfrac{7\sqrt{3}}{3}=\dfrac{34\sqrt{3}}{3}$

(vi) $(\sqrt{3}-\sqrt{2})^2=3+2-2\sqrt{6}=5-2\sqrt{6}$

(vii) $\sqrt[4]{81}-8\sqrt[3]{216}+15\sqrt[5]{32}+\sqrt{225}$

$=3-48+30+15=0$

(viii) $\dfrac{3}{\sqrt{8}}+\dfrac{1}{\sqrt{2}}=\dfrac{1}{\sqrt{2}}\left(\dfrac{3}{2}+1\right)=\dfrac{5}{2\sqrt{2}}$

(ix) $\dfrac{2\sqrt{3}}{3}-\dfrac{\sqrt{3}}{6}=\dfrac{4\sqrt{3}}{6}-\dfrac{\sqrt{3}}{6}=\dfrac{3\sqrt{3}}{6}=\dfrac{\sqrt{3}}{2}$

Long Answer Type Questions

1. (i) $\dfrac{\left(5+2\sqrt{3}\right)\left(7-4\sqrt{3}\right)}{\left(7+4\sqrt{3}\right)\left(7-4\sqrt{3}\right)}=35-24-20\sqrt{3}+14\sqrt{3}$

$=11-6\sqrt{3}=a-6\sqrt{3}$ then $a=11$.

(ii) $\dfrac{\left(3-\sqrt{5}\right)\left(3-2\sqrt{5}\right)}{\left(3+2\sqrt{5}\right)\left(3-2\sqrt{5}\right)}=\dfrac{9+10-6\sqrt{5}-3\sqrt{5}}{9-20}$

$=\dfrac{19-9\sqrt{5}}{-11}=-\dfrac{19}{11}+\dfrac{9\sqrt{5}}{11}$

$=a\sqrt{5}-\dfrac{19}{11}$ then $a=\dfrac{9}{11}$

2. $\dfrac{1}{\sqrt{2}+1}+\dfrac{1}{\sqrt{3}+\sqrt{2}}+\ldots\ldots+\dfrac{1}{\sqrt{100}+\sqrt{99}}$

Rationalize each term

$\left(\sqrt{2}-1\right)+\left(\sqrt{3}-\sqrt{2}\right)+\ldots\ldots\ldots+\left(\sqrt{100}-\sqrt{99}\right)$

$\Rightarrow 10-1=9$

3. If $a=2+\sqrt{3},\ \dfrac{1}{a}=\dfrac{1}{2+\sqrt{3}}=2-\sqrt{3}$

then $a-\dfrac{1}{a}=2+\sqrt{3}-2+\sqrt{3}=2\sqrt{3}$

4. (i) $2.35=\dfrac{235}{100}=\dfrac{47}{20}$

(ii) let $x=1.1444\ldots\ldots\Rightarrow 10x=11.444\ldots\ldots$

$\Rightarrow 100x=114.444\ldots\ldots$

taking difference we get $\Rightarrow 90x=103$

$\Rightarrow x=\dfrac{103}{90}$

(iii) Let $x=3.3\overline{79}$

then $10x=33.797979\ldots\ldots$ and $1000x=3379.797979\ldots\ldots\Rightarrow 990x=3346$

$x=\dfrac{3346}{990}=\dfrac{1673}{495}$

(iv) $\sqrt{12}$ is an irrational number. $\sqrt{12}$

5. (i) $\sqrt[3]{3}$ or $\sqrt[4]{5}$

$\left(\sqrt[3]{3}\right)^{12}$ or $\left(\sqrt[4]{5}\right)^{12}\Rightarrow 3^4$ or 5^3

$\therefore 5^3$ is greater $\Rightarrow \sqrt[4]{5}$ is greater

(ii) 12 or 6^2

6^2 is greater $\Rightarrow \sqrt[4]{6}$ is greater

(iii) 2^3 or 3^2

3^2 is greater $\Rightarrow \sqrt[3]{3}$ is greater

6. $y=\dfrac{\left(\sqrt{3}-\sqrt{2}\right)\left(\sqrt{3}-\sqrt{2}\right)}{(\sqrt{3}+\sqrt{2})\times(\sqrt{3}-\sqrt{2})}=5-2\sqrt{6}$ and

$x=\dfrac{\sqrt{3}+\sqrt{2}}{\sqrt{3}-\sqrt{2}}=5+2\sqrt{6}$ then $x+y=10$ and $xy=1$

$x^2+y^2=\left(x+y\right)^2-2xy=100-2=98$

7. $\dfrac{6}{10}+\dfrac{7}{9}+\dfrac{47-4}{90}=\dfrac{54}{90}+\dfrac{70}{90}+\dfrac{43}{90}=\dfrac{167}{90}$

8. $\dfrac{7\sqrt{3}}{\sqrt{10}+\sqrt{3}}-\dfrac{2\sqrt{5}}{\sqrt{6}+\sqrt{5}}-\dfrac{3\sqrt{2}}{\sqrt{15}+3\sqrt{2}}$

$=\dfrac{7\sqrt{3}\times\left(\sqrt{10}-\sqrt{3}\right)}{\left(\sqrt{10}+\sqrt{3}\right)\times\left(\sqrt{10}-\sqrt{3}\right)}$

$-\dfrac{2\sqrt{5}\times(\sqrt{6}-\sqrt{5})}{(\sqrt{6}+\sqrt{5})\times(\sqrt{6}-\sqrt{5})}$

$-\dfrac{3\sqrt{2}\times\left(\sqrt{15}-3\sqrt{2}\right)}{\left(\sqrt{15}+3\sqrt{2}\right)\times\left(\sqrt{15}-3\sqrt{2}\right)}$

$=\dfrac{7\sqrt{3}\times\left(\sqrt{10}-\sqrt{3}\right)}{7}-\dfrac{2\sqrt{5}\times(\sqrt{6}-\sqrt{5})}{1}$

$-\dfrac{3\sqrt{2}\times\left(\sqrt{15}-3\sqrt{2}\right)}{-3}$

$=\sqrt{3}\times\left(\sqrt{10}-\sqrt{3}\right)-(2\sqrt{5}\times\left(\sqrt{6}-\sqrt{5}\right))$

$+\sqrt{2}\times\left(\sqrt{15}-3\sqrt{2}\right)$

$=\left(\sqrt{30}-3\right)-\left(2\sqrt{30}-10\right)+\sqrt{30}-6=1$

Archive Corner

1. (C) $9+2\sqrt{14}=\left(\sqrt{2}+\sqrt{7}\right)^2=\sqrt{2}+\sqrt{7}$

2. (B) $\sqrt[3]{1-\frac{127}{343}}=\sqrt[3]{\frac{343-127}{343}}=\sqrt[3]{\frac{216}{343}}=\frac{6}{7}=1-\frac{1}{7}$

3. (A) $2.\bar{6}-1.\bar{9}=2.\bar{6}-2=\bar{6}$

4. (A) $\frac{5\left(7-4\sqrt{5}\right)}{\left(7+4\sqrt{5}\right)\times\left(7-4\sqrt{5}\right)}=\frac{\left(35-20\sqrt{5}\right)}{49-80}$

$=\frac{\left(35-20\sqrt{5}\right)}{-31}$

5. (A)

6. (C) $2(a^2-2ab+b^2)-ab=2\left(a-b\right)^2-1$

$=2\times4\times5-1=39$

7. (B) $\sqrt{m^4n^4}\times\sqrt[6]{m^2n^2}\times\sqrt[3]{m^2n^2}=\left(mn\right)^{2+\frac{1}{3}+\frac{2}{3}}$

$=\left(mn\right)^3=\left(mn\right)^k$ then $k=3$.

8. (D)

9. (D)

10. (C) $2\times3\times5\times7=210$

11. (B)

12. (D) HCF $\times$ LCM = product of numbers

then 8 LCM = 384 then LCM = 48

13. (A) A terminating decimal

14. (C) $a+a+1+a+2+a+3+a+4=170$

then $5a=160$ then $a=32$ and $a+4=36$

$32\times36=1152$

15. (D) HCF $\times$ LCM = product of numbers

then $15\times225=75\times X$ then $X=45$

16. (A) $2^{x-1}+2^{x+1}=2^{x-1}\left(1+4\right)=2^{x-1}\times5=2560$

then $2^{x-1}=2^9$ then $x=10$

17. (A) $6-\{9-[18-(15-12-9)]\}$

$=6-\{9-[18-(-6)]\}$

$=6-\{9-24\}=6+15=21$

18. (A) 2 number

Let the numbers are $36a$ and $36b$ then $12960=36a\times36b$ then $ab=10$ so $a=1$ and $b=10$ $a=2$ and $b=5$

19. (D) $\frac{5}{9}\times\frac{60}{100}\times x=2790$ then $x=8370$

20. (D) Number r is termed as Rational number if it can be expressed as p/q, where p and q are integers and, $q\neq0$

21. (D) $2n\times\left(2n+2\right)\times\left(2n+4\right)$

$=8n\left(n+1\right)\left(n+2\right)$ then 4, 16, 12

22. (C) If $x=\frac{1}{3-2\sqrt{2}}=3+2\sqrt{2}$ and

$y=\frac{1}{3+2\sqrt{2}}=3-2\sqrt{2}$ then $x+y$

$=3+2\sqrt{2}+3-2\sqrt{2}=6$

23. (C)

24. (C) $0.\bar{6}+0.\bar{7}=\frac{6}{9}+\frac{7}{9}=\frac{13}{9}=1.\bar{4}$

25. (D) Let 5^x be t then $5t+\frac{25}{t}=126$

then $5t^2-126t+25=0$

then $5t^2-125t-t+25=0$

$5t\left(t-25\right)-1\left(t-25\right)=\left(t-25\right)\left(5t-1\right)=0$

then $t=25$ and $\frac{1}{5}$ so $5^x=5^2$ and 5^{-1}

then $x=2$ and -1

CHAPTER 2 POLYNOMIALS

Check Point 1

1. (a) binomial (b) trinomial
(c) binomial (d) monomial
(e) trinomial (f) monomial
(g) binomial (h) trinomial

2. (a) quadratic (b) cubic
(c) linear (d) quadratic
(e) cubic (f) cubic
(g) linear

3. (a) $7x - 14 = 0$ Then $x = 2$

(b) $8x + 1 = 0$ then $x = -\frac{1}{8}$

(c) $x^2 - 5x - 6x^2 - 6x + x - 6 = 0$
then $x(x-6)+1(x-6)=0$
then $(x-6)(x+1)=0$
$x = -1$ and 6

(d) $2x^2 + 3x + 1 = 0$ then $2x^2 + 2x + x + 1 = 0$
then $2x(x+1)+1(x+1)=0$
then $(x+1)(2x+1)=0$ then $x=-1$ and $-\frac{1}{2}$

4. $6x^2+13x+16 = 6x^2+9x+4x+6+10$
$= 3x(2x+3)+2(2x+3)+10$
$= (2x+3)(3x+2)+10$

5. Remainder will be $P(2) = 5\times 4 + 7\times 2 + 3 = 37$

Check Point 2

6. $(2x+3y-2z)^2$
$= 4x^2+9y^2+4z^2+12xy-8xz-12yz$

7. $a^3+b^3=(a+b)^3-3ab(a+b)$
$= 7^3-3\times 12\times 7 = 343-252 = 91$

8. $\left(a+\frac{1}{a}\right)^2 = a^2+\frac{1}{a^2}+2 \Rightarrow 23 = a^2+\frac{1}{a^2}$

9. $a^3+\frac{1}{a^3} = \left(a+\frac{1}{a}\right)^3 - 3\left(a+\frac{1}{a}\right) = 64-12 = 52$

10. $p-q=9$ then cube for both sides.
$(p-q)^3 = 729$ then $p^3-q^3-3pq(p-q)=729$
$p^3-q^3-27pq=729$

Check Point 3

11. $x^2(xy+5) - 2y^2(xy+5) = (xy+5)(x^2-2y^2)$

12. $3x^2+8x+4 = 3x^2+6x+2x+4$
$= 3x(x+2)+2(x+2) = (x+2)(3x+2)$

13. $2a+4b-ac-2bc$
$= 2(a+2b)-c(a+2b) = (2-c)(a+2b)$

14. $27a^3 - b^3 + c^3 + 9abc$
$= (3a - b + c)(9a^2 + b^2 + c^2 + 3ab + bc - 3ac)$

15. $32x^3 - 4d^3 = 4(2x - d)(4x^2 + 2xd + d^2)$

Fixed Response Type

Fill in the Blanks

1. 0

2. $P\left(\frac{b}{a}\right)$

3. $(3x^2 - 5)(4 + 4x^2) = 12x^2+12x^4-20-20x^2$
$= 12x^4-8x^2-20$ then -8

4. $P(-a) = a^3-2a^3+b^3 = 0$ then $b^3 = a^3$ then $a = b$

5. If $a^3 - 3a^2b + 3ab^2 - b^3 = (a - b)^3$ then remainder is 0.

6. $P(1) = 1 + 1 + 1 + 1 + \ldots 1(2007 \text{ times}) = 2007$

True/False

1. **True**
If $\frac{p}{q}+\frac{q}{p} = 2$ then $p^2+q^2 = 2pq$
$\Rightarrow (p-q)^2 = 0 \Rightarrow p = q$ then $\frac{p}{q} = 1$ the value of $\left(\frac{p}{q}\right)^{23} + \left(\frac{q}{p}\right)^7$ is 2

2. **False**
If $p(2) = 16 - 12 + 10 - 4 = 10$.

HINTS AND EXPLANATIONS

3. **False**
The co-efficient of x^2y^2 in the expansion of $(x+y)^4$ $= x^4+4x^3y+6x^2y^2+4xy^3+y^4$ is 6

4. **True**
If $x^2-3x+1=0 \Rightarrow x^2+1=3x \Rightarrow x+\frac{1}{x}=3$, then

$x^2+\frac{1}{x^2}=7$ and $x^3+\frac{1}{x^3}+3\left(x+\frac{1}{x}\right)=27$

Then $x^3+\frac{1}{x^3}=27-9=18$

now $\left(x^2+\frac{1}{x^2}\right)\left(x^3+\frac{1}{x^3}\right)$

$=x^5+1/x+x+1/x^5=126$

the value of $x^5+\frac{1}{x^5}=126-3=123$

5. **False**
If $(x+2)$, is a factor of $P(-2)=-16+10+k=0$ then the value of k is 6

Single Correct Type Questions

1. **(D)** $P(-1)=50$

2. **(A)** Let $2x-3y=a$ then $a^2-10a+3a-30$
$=a(a-10)+3(a-10)$
$=(a+3)(a-10)=(2x-3y+3)(2x-3y-10)$

3. **(D)** $x+\frac{1}{x}=3$ then $x^2+\frac{1}{x^2}=7$ now $x^6+\frac{1}{x^6}$
$=\left(x^2+\frac{1}{x^2}\right)^3-3\left(x^2+\frac{1}{x^2}\right)=343-21=322$

4. **(D)** As sum of perfect square is 0 then $a=5$ and $b=c=d=3$ then $11\times 9=99$

5. **(A)** $(x+y+z)^2=x^2+y^2+z^2+2xy+2yz+2xz$
$-3(x^2+y^2+z^2)=-3+6xy+6yz+6xz$ (i)
$x^3+y^3+z^3-3xyz$
$=(x+y+z)(x^2+y^2+z^2-xy-yz-xz)$
$=(x^2+y^2+z^2-xy-yz-xz)$
$2x^3+2y^3+2z^3$
$=6xyz+(2x^2+2y^2+2z^2-2xy-2yz-2xz)$ (ii)
$1-3(x^2+y^2+z^2)+2x^3+2y^3+2z^3$
$=1-3+6xy+6yz+6xz+6xyz$
$+(2x^2+2y^2+2z^2-2xy-2yz-2xz)=6xyz$

6. **(D)** $x+\frac{1}{x}=4$ then $x^2+\frac{1}{x^2}=14$ now $x^6+\frac{1}{x^6}$
$=\left(x^2+\frac{1}{x^2}\right)^3-3\left(x^2+\frac{1}{x^2}\right)$
$=2744-3\times 14=2702$

7. **(B)** $a^2-ap+q=0$ and $a^2-am+n=0$
then $a(m-p)=n-q$ then $a=\frac{n-q}{m-p}$

8. **(C)** $(a-b)^3+(b-c)^3+(c-a)^3=3(a-b)(b-c)(c-a)$ $\{\because (a-b)+(b-c)+(c-a)=0\}$

9. **(C)** $P(-p)=p^2-p^2+3-p=0$ then $p=3$

10. **(A)** x^3+3x^2-4x+3

11. **(A)** $x^2+(a+b)x+ab$

12. **(C)**

13. **(C)** $x^2+y^2+z^2+2xy-2yz-2zx$

14. **(D)** $(x+2y+2z)^2+(x-2y-2z)^2$
$=x^2+4y^2+4z^2+4xy+4xz+8yz$
$+x^2+4y^2+4z^2-4xy-4xz+8yz$
$=2x^2+8y^2+8z^2+16yz$

15. **(C)** $25x^2+16y^2+40xy=(5x+4y)^2$
$=[5(1)]+4(-1)]=1$

16. **(D)** $a^3+3a^2b+3ab^2+b^3+a^3-3a^2b$
$+3ab^2-b^3+6a^3-6ab^2=8a^3$

17. **(A)** Let $p(x)=x^3+3x^2+4x+12$ be the given polynomial. By factor theorem, $(x-a)$ is a factor of a polynomial $p(x)$ iff $p(a)=0$. Therefore, in order to prove that $x+3$ is a factor of $p(x)$, it is sufficient to show that $p(-3)=0$. Now,
$p(x)=x^3+3x^2+4x+12$
$\Rightarrow p(-3)=-27+27-12+12=0$
Hence, $(x+3)$ is a factor of $p(x)=x^3+3x^2+4x+12$.

18. **(B)** $x^3+y^3+z^3-3xyz$
$=(x+y+z)\left((x+y+z)^2-3(xy+yz+xz)\right)$
$x^3+y^3+z^3-(-3)=(1)\left((1)^2-3(-1)\right)=4$
$x^3+y^3+z^3=4-3=1$

19. **(B)** $P(1)=1-3+2+1=1$

20. $x^2+y^3+1^3-3(x)(y)(1)=0$
$\Rightarrow (x+y+1)(x^2+y^2-x-y+1-xy)=0$
$x+y+1=0$

HINTS AND EXPLANATIONS

21. **(C)** $-\left[x^2+x-42\right]$
$=-\left[x^2+7x-6x-42\right]=-\left[(x+7)(x-6)\right]$
$=(x+7)(6-x)$

22. **(B)** $\left(x^2+\frac{x}{6}-\frac{1}{6}\right)$
$=\frac{1}{6}\left(6x^2+x-1\right)=\frac{1}{6}(2x+1)(3x-1)$

23. **(A)** The sum of three non-negative numbers is zero only when they are all zero
but $x-1$, $x-2$ & $x-3$ cannot be equal to zero simultaneously.

24. **(A)** $(2a+5b)^3+(2a-5b)^3$
$=(2a+5b+2a-5b)$
$\left((2a+5b)^2+(2a-5b)^2-(2a+5b)(2a-5b)\right)$
$=(4a)\left(4a^2+75b^2\right)$

25. **(C)** $x=a$ satisfies the given expression
$\therefore a^3-a^3+a+2=0 \Rightarrow a=-2.$

Multiple Correct Type Questions

1. **(B,D)** The value of $\left(2x-\frac{y}{3}\right)^3$
$=$ (B) $\left(2x-\frac{y}{3}\right)\left(4x^2+\frac{y^2}{9}-\frac{4xy}{3}\right)$
$=$ (D) $8x^3-\frac{y^3}{27}-2xy\left(2x-\frac{y}{3}\right)$

2. **(B,C)** $p=x^{\frac{1}{3}}+\frac{1}{x^{\frac{1}{3}}}\Rightarrow p^3=x+\frac{1}{x}+3p$

3. **(B,D)** $\frac{x^2}{yz}+\frac{y^2}{xz}+\frac{z^2}{xy}=\frac{x^3+y^3+z^3}{xyz}=\frac{3xyz}{xyz}=3$

4. **(A,C)** As $x=\pm1$ are the roots of $p(x)$
then $a+b+c+d+e=0$
and $a-b+c-d+e=0$

5. **(C)** If $p+q+r=0$ then $p^3+q^3+r^3=3pqr$

6. **(A,C)** $x^4+x^2+1=\left(x^2+x+1\right)\left(x^2-x+1\right)$
$x^4-2x^2+1=\left(x^2-1\right)\left(x^2-1\right)$

7. **(A,B,C,D)** $P(a)=P(b)=P(c)=P(d)=3$
$\Rightarrow P(x)=3$ has a, b, c, d as it roots
$\Rightarrow P(x)-3=(x-a)(x-b)(x-c)(x-d)Q(x)$
[$Q(x)$ has integral coefficient]
Given $P(e)=5$, then
$(e-a)(e-b)(e-c)(e-d)Q(e)=2$
This is possible only when at least three of the five integers $(e-a)$, $(e-b)$, $(e-c)$, $(e-d)$, $Q(e)$ are equal to 1 or -1. Hence two of them will be equal, which is not possible. Since a, b, c, d are distinct integers, therefore $P(e)=5$ is not possible.

8. **(D)** let $(a-b)=x,(b-c)=y$ and $(c-a)=z$ then
$\frac{x^2}{yz}+\frac{y^2}{xz}+\frac{z^2}{xy}=\frac{x^3+y^3+z^3}{xyz}=\frac{3xyz}{xyz}=3$

9. **(A,C)** $x^{100}=Q(x)\,.\,(x-1)(x-2)+(ax+b)$
Solve to get a and b.

10. **(B,A)** $x^2+\frac{1}{x^2}-2=\left(x-\frac{1}{x}\right)^2=36$
then $x-\frac{1}{x}=6$ or -6

11. **(A)** $(2x+3)^3-(2x-3)^3=(2x+3-2x+3)$
$\left((2x+3)^2+(2x-3)^2+(2x+3)(2x-3)\right)$
$6\left(8x^2+18+4x^2-9\right)=72x^2+54$

12. **(A)** $p(x)=\sqrt{3}x^2+11x+6\sqrt{3}=\sqrt{3}x^2+9x+2x+6\sqrt{3}=$
$\sqrt{3}x\left(x+3\sqrt{3}\right)+2\left(x+3\sqrt{3}\right)$
$=\left(\sqrt{3}x+2\right)\left(x+3\sqrt{3}\right)$

13. **(C)** LCM of $8x\left(x^2-x+1\right)$
and $28(x+1)\left(x^2-x+1\right)=56x\left(x^3+1\right)$

14. **(C)**

15. **(C)** $(a+b)^3-(a-b)^3=(a+b-a+b)$
$\left[(a+b)^2+(a-b)^2+(a-b)(a+b)\right]$
$=(2b)\left[b^2+a^2+2ab+a^2+b^2-2ab+a^2-b^2\right]$
$=2b\left(3a^2+b^2\right)$

16. **(A)** Cube both side $(x+y)^3=-64$
then $x^3+y^3+3xy(x+y)=-64$
$x^3+y^3-12xy=-64$
$\Rightarrow x^3+y^3-12xy+64=0$

17. **(D)** $\left[\frac{a^2-5ab}{a^2-6ab+5b^2}\times\frac{a^2-b^2}{a^2+ab}\right]$
$=\frac{a(a-5b)}{(a-5b)(a-b)}\times\frac{(a-b)(a+b)}{a(a+b)}=1$

18. **(C)** $x=\sqrt{2}-1$ then $x+1=\sqrt{2}$ square both side

$x^2+2x+1=2$ then $x^2+2x+3=4$

19. **(B)** $x^3-5x^2+x+\frac{1}{x^3}-\frac{5}{x^2}+\frac{1}{x}$

$=x^3+\frac{1}{x^3}-5\left(x^2+\frac{1}{x^2}\right)+x+\frac{1}{x}$

$=\left(x+\frac{1}{x}\right)^3-3\left(x+\frac{1}{x}\right)-5\left(\left(x+\frac{1}{x}\right)^2\right)+10+5$

$=125-15-125+10+5=0$

20. **(B)** $x^3+y^3+3xy(x+y)=1$

then $x^3+y^3+3xy=1$

21. **(B)** $(x+y)^2=(x-y)^2+4xy$

$=25+96=121$ then $x+y=11.$

$x^3+y^3=(x+y)^3-3xy(x+y)$

$=11^3-3\times24\times11=539$

22. **(B)** $x+\frac{1}{x}+2=4$ then $\left(\sqrt{x}+\frac{1}{\sqrt{x}}\right)^2=2^2$

23. **(B)** $x^2+y^2=(x+y)^2-2xy=64-30=34$

24. **(B)** p^3-q^3

$=(p-q)^3+3pq(p-q)=-512+288=-224$

25. **(A)**

Match Type Questions

1. (i) → (B,C)

$x^2-x-2=x^2-2x+x-2=(x-2)(x+1)$

(ii) → (C)

$5x-4x^2+6$

$\Rightarrow 4x^2-5x-6=4x^2-8x+3x-6$

$=(4x+3)(x-2)$

(iii) → (A)

$3x^4-4x^3-3x+4$

$=x^3(3x-4)-(3x-4)=(3x-4)(x^3-1)$

$=(x-1)(x^2+x+1)(3x-4)$

(iv) → (B)

$x^3+1=(x+1)(x^2-x+1)$

2. (i) → (A,B,C)

$x^3+6x^2+11x+6$

$=x^3+x^2+5x^2+5x+6x+6$

$=(x+2)(x+1)(x+3)$

(ii) → (A,B)

$x^3+13x^2+32x+20$

$=x^3+x^2+12x^2+12x+20x+20$

$=(x+1)(x^2+10)(x+2)$

(iii) → (A,D)

$2x^3-x^2-2x+1$

$=x^2(2x-1)-1(2x-1)=(2x-1)(x-1)(x+1)$

(iv) → (A,C)

$x^3-10x^2-53x-42$

$=x^3-14x^2+4x^2-56x+3x-42$

$=(x-14)(x^2+4x+3)=(x-14)(x+1)(x+3)$

3. (i) → (B,D)

$(x+1)^2-(x-1)^2=4x$

(ii) → (B,C)

$x(x+5)=-x(3-x)+7\Rightarrow 8x-7=0$

(iii) → (A,C)

$x(x+y-z)-xy\Rightarrow x^2-xz=0$

(iv) → (A)

$\left(\sqrt{2x^2}-1\right)^2-3\sqrt{2x^2}\Rightarrow 2x^2-5\sqrt{2}x+1=0$

4. (i) → (D)

$a^3-\frac{1}{a^3}+4$

(ii) → (A)

$a^3+\frac{1}{a^3}-2$

(iii) → (C)

a^4+a^2+1

(iv) → (B)

a^4+5a^2+9

$=a^4+6a^2+9-a^2=(a^2+3)^2-a^2$

$=(a^2-a+3)(a^2+a+3)$

5. (i) → (C)

$p(-2)=32+48+8+2+2$

(ii) → (A)

$p(2)=16-12+4=8$

(iii) → (B)

$f(2/3)=8/3-4/3+2/3-5=-3$

(iv) → (D)

$f(-4)=-64+64+12+10=22$

Assertion and Reason Type Questions

1. (A)
2. (B)
3. (A)

Comprehension Type Questions

1. (B) $p(1)=q(1)\Rightarrow 1+a+3+2=2+3-4-7$
$\Rightarrow a+6=-6\Rightarrow a=-12$
2. (D) $p(1)=1-12+3+2=-6$
3. (C) let $g(x)=3x^3-9x^2-x-5$ now the remainder $g(1)=3-9-1-5=-12$

Numerical Type Questions

1. $P(3)=3^4+3^3-3^2+2\times 3+3=81+27=108$
2. $P(3)=27+27+9+p=0$ then $p=-63$
3. According to question $c=6$
$P(-1)=a-b+6=6$ then $a=b$
$P(-2)=4a-2a+6=8$ then $a=1=b$ and $c=6$
4. $x^3-8x^2+20x-13=(x-1)(x^2-7x+13)$ is prime
so, either $x-1=1\Rightarrow x=2$
or $x^2-7x+13=1\Rightarrow x=3, 4$
$\therefore$ number of positive integers $x=3$ i.e. {2, 3, 4}.
5. $P(-2)=-8a+36-8-1=-6$
then $-8a+27=6$ then $8a=33\Rightarrow a=\frac{33}{8}$
6. $(x+y+2)^2=x^2+y^2+2(xy+yz+zx)$
$100=60+2(xy+yz+zx)$
$Xy+yz+zx=20$
7. $x^2+\frac{1}{x^2}=62$ then $x^4+\frac{1}{x^4}+2=3844$
then $x^4+\frac{1}{x^4}=3842.$
8. $P(4)=64k+48-3$
$=64k+45$
$Q(4)=128-20+k$
$=108+k$
$\because P(4)=Q(4)$
$64k+45=108+k$
$63k=63\Rightarrow k=1$
9. $x^2+y^2-2xy=0$
$\Rightarrow (x-y)^2=0$
$\Rightarrow x=y$ then $\lambda^2=4$
$\Rightarrow \lambda=\pm 2$
$\lambda>0, \lambda=2$
10. $x^3-x^2-2x-2002=0$ then $x=13$
11. $P(4)=Q(4)$
$64a+48-3=128-20+a$
then $63a=108-45=63$ then $a=1$
12. $P(1)=P(-1)=0$
$1+p+q-1-1-3=0$ and $1-p+q-1+1-3=0$
add both equation $2+2q-2-6=0$ then $q=3$
and $p=1$ so required value $=10$
13. 0
14. $(x-4)^2=x^2-8x+16$ then coefficient of x is -8.
15. $P(3)=9a+15+12=0$ then $a=-3$

Higher Order Thinking Skills (HOTS)

1. (A) $\frac{1}{(x-y)^2}+\frac{1}{(y-z)^2}+\frac{1}{(z-x)^2}$
$=\frac{1}{(x-y)^2}+\frac{1}{(1-y)^2}+\frac{1}{(z-x)^2}$
$+\left(\frac{1}{(x-y)(y-z)}+\frac{1}{(y-z)(z-x)}+\frac{1}{(z-x)(x-y)}\right)$
$+\lambda$
$\Rightarrow \lambda=0$
2. (C) $P(2)=8-16+2a+b=0$ then $2a+b=8$ (i)
$Q(2)=8-4a+2b+8=0$ then $-2a+b=-8$
then $b=0$ and $a=4$
3. (A) Let $2008^{1004}=a$ then $x=a+\frac{1}{a}$ and $y=a-\frac{1}{a}$
then $x^2-y^2=(x+y)(x-y)=2a\times\frac{2}{a}=4$
4. (A) $(a^2+b^2)^3=(a^3+b^3)^2$ then
$a^6+b^6+3b^2a^2(a^2+b^2)=a^6+b^6+2b^3a^3$
$=3b^2a^2(a^2+b^2)=2b^3a^3$ then $\frac{a}{b}+\frac{b}{a}=\frac{2}{3}$
5. (D) $\frac{(\sqrt{a}-\sqrt{b})^2+4\sqrt{ab}}{a-b}=\frac{5}{3}$
$=\frac{(\sqrt{a}+\sqrt{b})^2}{(\sqrt{a}+\sqrt{b})(\sqrt{a}-\sqrt{b})}$
$=\frac{\sqrt{a}+\sqrt{b}}{\sqrt{a}-\sqrt{b}}$ then $a:b=16:1$

6. (A) $2x^4 + x^3 - 5x^2 - x + 1 = (x^2 - x) . g(x) + ax + b$

Put $x = 1$ then $2+1-5-1+1 = a+b$

then $a+b = -2$ and put $x = 0$ then $b = 1$

$a+b = -2$

7. (A) $\frac{x^3+x^2+x+1}{x^3-x^2+x-1} = \frac{x^2+x+1}{x^2-x+1}$

$\Rightarrow \frac{x^3+x}{x^2+1} = \frac{x^2+1}{x}$ (By C & D)

$\Rightarrow x^2(x^2 + 1) = (x^2 + 1)^2$

$\Rightarrow x^2 = x^2 + 1$, which is not possible.

8. (A) $2x^3 - 5x^2 + x + 2 = ax^3 - (2a + b)x^2 + (2b - 1)$
$x + 2$

$\therefore a = 2$

$2a + b = 5$ and $2b - 1 = 1$

9. (B) $f(x) = (x - 1)\, g(x) + 5$; $f(x) = (x + 1)\, h(x) + 3$

$f(x) = (x + 2)\, \phi(x) + 2$;

$f(x) = (x^3 + 2x^2 - x - 2)\, p(x) + ax^2 + bx + c$ (1)

$f(1) = 0 + a + b + c$; $f(-1) = 0 + a - b + c$

$f(-2) = 4a - 2b + c \Rightarrow a + b + c = 5,\ a - b + c = 3,$
$4a - 2b + c = 2$

$\Rightarrow a = 0, b = 1, c = 4$ from equation (1) remainder is $x + 4$

10. (D) $x^2 = 2+\sqrt{2}$ and $\frac{2}{x^2} = 2-\sqrt{2}$

then $\left(x^2+\frac{2}{x^2}\right)^2 = x^4+\frac{4}{x^4}+4$

then $x^4+\frac{4}{x^4} = 12$

11. (B) $x^2 + xy - 2xz - 2yz = x(x+y) - 2z(x+y)$
$= (x+y)(x-2z)$

12. (B) $\frac{1}{x} = 3-\sqrt{8}$ and $\frac{1}{y} = 3+\sqrt{8}$ then $\frac{1}{x^2}+\frac{1}{y^2}$

$= \left(3+\sqrt{8}\right)^2 + \left(3-\sqrt{8}\right)^2 = 9+8+9+8 = 34$

13. (C) $7x^2 + 17xy - 14y^2$

14. (A) $P(3) = 162-27-63+3a+b = 0$

and $P(-1) = 2+1-7-a+b = 0$

then $b-a = 4$ and $b+3a = -72$ then $4a = -76$ and $a = -19$ and $b = -15$ then $a+b = -34$

15. (C) $\frac{x}{y}+\frac{y}{x} = -1 \Rightarrow x^2+y^2 = -xy$

$\Rightarrow x^2 + y^2 + xy = 0.$

$\therefore (x^3 - y^3) = (x - y)\,(x^2 + y^2 + xy)$

$= (x - y) \times 0 = 0.$

16. (B) Let $P(x) = ax^3 + 3x^2 - 13$

and $P_2(x) = 2x^3 - 5x + a$

according to question $P_1(4) + P_2(4) = 0$

$64a + 48 - 3 + 128 - 20 + a = 0$

then $65a + 153 = 0$ then $a = -\frac{153}{65}$

17. (B) $\left(\frac{a+b}{a-b}\right)^2$

18. (A) The correct answer is 0.

It is given that $3s = a + b + c$

$\Rightarrow (s - a) + (s - b) + (s - c) = 0$

Therefore, we have:

$(s - a)^3 + (s - b)^3 + (s - c)^3 - 3(s - a)\,(s - b)\,(s - c) = 0$

$\left[\begin{array}{l} a^3+b^3+c^3-3abc = 0 \\ \text{if } a+b+c = 0 \end{array}\right]$

19. (B) We know that $x^3 + y^3 + z^3 - 3xyz = (x + y + z)(x^2 + y^2 + z^2 - xy - yz - zx)$.

Hence, $a^3 + b^3 + c^3 - 3abc$

$= (a + b + c)\,(a^2 + b^2 + c^2 - ab - bc - ca)$

$= 9(a^2 + b^2 + c^2 - 26).$

Now, we know that

$(x + y + z)^2 = x^2 + y^2 + z^2 + 2xy + 2yz + 2zx.$

Hence,

$a^2 + b^2 + c^2 = (a + b + c)^2 - 2(ab + bc + ca)$

$= (9)^2 - 2(26)$

$= 81 - 52$

$= 29.$

Hence, $a^3 + b^3 + c^3 - 3abc = 9(a^2 + b^2 + c^2 - 26)$

$= 9(29 - 26)$

$= 9(3)$

$= 27.$

20. (B) $(3x - 5)$

HINTS AND EXPLANATIONS

Free Response Type

Very Short Answer Type Questions

1. 0

2. $\frac{x}{x-y}-\frac{y}{x+y}-\frac{2xy}{x^2-y^2}$

$=\frac{x(x+y)-y(x-y)}{x^2-y^2}-\frac{2xy}{x^2-y^2}$

$=\frac{x^2+xy-xy+y^2}{x^2-y^2}-\frac{2xy}{x^2-y^2}$

$=\frac{x^2+y^2}{x^2-y^2}-\frac{2xy}{x^2-y^2}$

$=\frac{x^2+y^2-2xy}{x^2-y^2}$

$=\frac{(x-y)^2}{x^2-y^2}$

$=\frac{(x-y)(x-y)}{(x-y)(x+y)}$

$=\frac{x-y}{x+y}$

3. $P(2\sqrt{2})=(2\sqrt{2})^2-2\sqrt{2}\times 2\sqrt{2}+1=1$

4. $x^2+kx+6=(x+2)(x+3)$
$=x^2+5x+6$ then $k=5$

5. $x^2+\frac{1}{x^2}=\left(x+\frac{1}{x}\right)^2-2=4-2=2$

6. $a+\frac{1}{a}=\pm\sqrt{3}$

$a^3+\frac{1}{a^3}=\left(a+\frac{1}{a}\right)^3-3\left(a+\frac{1}{a}\right)=3\sqrt{3}\pm 3\sqrt{3}=0.$

7. $49x^2-b=\left(7x+\frac{1}{2}\right)\left(7x-\frac{1}{2}\right)$

$=\left(49x^2-\frac{1}{4}\right)$ then $b=\frac{1}{4}$

8. $3abc$

9. $P(-1)=-a+1+2+4a-9=0\Rightarrow 3a-6=0$ then $a=2$

10. (i) $x^2+9x+18=(x+6)(x+3)$

(ii) $6x^2+7x-3$

$=6x^2+9x-2x-3=3x(2x+3)-1(2x+3)$

$=(3x-1)(2x+3)$

(iii) $2x^2-7x-15$

$=2x^2+3x-10x-15=x(2x+3)-5(2x+3)$

$=(x-5)(2x+3)$

(iv) $84-2r-2r^2$

$=-2(r^2+7r-6r-42)$

$=-2(r(r+7)-6(r+7))$

$=-2(r+7)(r-6)$

Short Answer Type Questions

1. Remainder $=P(1)=2$ and quotient $=x^3+x^2+x+1$

2. (i) $P(-3)=69-33-9-27=0$

(ii) $P(3/2)=\frac{3}{2}+2\times\frac{27}{8}-9\times\frac{9}{4}+12$

$=\frac{3}{2}+\frac{27}{4}-\frac{81}{4}+12=\frac{3}{2}-\frac{27}{2}+12=0.$

3. $x=\sqrt{3}+\sqrt{2}$

$\frac{1}{x}=\frac{1}{\sqrt{3}+\sqrt{2}}=\sqrt{3}-\sqrt{2}$

Now solve.

$x+\frac{1}{x}=2\sqrt{3}$

$\Rightarrow\left(x+\frac{1}{x}\right)^2=12$

$\Rightarrow x^2+\frac{1}{x^2}+2=12$

$\Rightarrow x^2+\frac{1}{x^2}=10$

$x^3+\frac{1}{x^3}=\left(x+\frac{1}{x}\right)\left(x^2+\frac{1}{x^2}-1\right)=2\sqrt{3}(9)=18\sqrt{3}$

$\Rightarrow\left(x^2+\frac{1}{x^2}\right)^2=100$

$x^4+\frac{1}{x^4}+2=100$

$\Rightarrow x^4+\frac{1}{x^4}+2=98$

4. (i) $p(2/3)=\frac{8}{27}-\frac{2}{3}+1$

$=\frac{8-18+27}{27}\neq 0$ so not a factor

(ii) $p(3/4)=8\times\frac{27}{64}-6\times\frac{9}{16}-4\times\frac{3}{4}+3=0$ yes

$g(x)$ is factor of $f(x)$.

5. $P(a)=3a-1=0$ then $a=\frac{1}{3}$

6. (i) $48^3 - 30^3 - 18^3 = 3\times 48\times 30\times 18 = 7760$
(ii) $(x - y)^3 + (y - z)^3 + (z - x)^3 = 3(x - y)(y - z)(z - x)$

7. (i) 6 (ii) 1/5 (iii) –1 (iv) 1/5

8. (i) $2x$ (ii) $x^{20}+20x$ (iii) $x^2 + 5x + 12$

9. $(a + b + c)^2 = a^2 + b^2 + c^2 + 2(ab + bc + ca)$

$(a + b + c)^2 = a^2 + b^2 + c^2 + 2abc\left(\frac{1}{a}+\frac{1}{b}+\frac{1}{c}\right)$

$\therefore 4 = 1 + 6\left(\frac{1}{a}+\frac{1}{b}+\frac{1}{c}\right)\ \therefore \left(\frac{1}{a}+\frac{1}{b}+\frac{1}{c}\right)=\frac{1}{2}$

10. $10^3 + (-8)^3 + (-2)^3 = 3\times 10\times(-8)\times(-2) = 480$

11. $P(3)=9a+15+12=0$ then $a=-3$

12. $P(3)=27-27+12-12=0$, Yes

Long Answer Type Questions

1. (i) $a^3 - 8b^3 - 64c^3 - 24abc$

$=a^3+(-2b)^3+(-4c)^3-3\times a\times(-2b)\times(-4c)$

$=(a-2b-4c)$

$(a^2+4b^2+16c^2+2ab+4ac-8bc)$

(ii) $2\sqrt{2}a^3 + 8b^3 - 27c^3 + 18\sqrt{2}abc$

$=(\sqrt{2}a)^3+(2b)^3+(-3c)^3$

$-3\times\sqrt{2}a\times(2b)\times(-3c)$

$=(\sqrt{2}a+2b-3c)$

$(2a^2+4b^2+9c^2-2\sqrt{2}ab+3\sqrt{2}ac+6bc)$

2. (i) Cube both side $(x+y)^3=-64$

then $x^3+y^3+3xy(x+y)+64=0$

$x^3+y^3-12xy+64=0$

(ii) Cube both side $(x-2y)^3=216$

then $x^3-8y^3-6xy(x-2y)=216$

$x^3-8y^3-36xy-216=0$

3. $x^3+y^3=(x+y)^3-3xy(x+y)$

$=12^3-3\times 27\times 12=1728-324\times 3$

$=1728-972=756$

4. Let $P(z)=az^3+4z^2+3z-4$

and $Q(z)=z^3-4z+a$

Then $P(3)=27a+36+9-4=27-12+a$

then $26a+41=15$ then $26a=-26$ then $a=-1$

5. $(x^2 + 4y^2 + z^2 + 2xy + xz - 2yz)(-z + x - 2y)$

$=(x^3-z^3-8y^3-6xzy$

6. $(a+b+c)^2=a^2+b^2+c^2+2(ab+bc+ac)$

then $(5)^2=a^2+b^2+c^2+2(10)$

then $a^2+b^2+c^2=5$

$a^3+b^3+c^3-3abc=(a+b+c)[(a^2+b^2+c^2)$

$-(ab+bc+ac)]=5\times(5-10)=-25$

7. $(2x - 5y)^3 - (2x + 5y)^3 = (2x-5y-2x-5y)$

$\left((2x-5y)^2+(2x+5y)^2+(2x-5y)(2x+5y)\right)$

$=(-10y)(4x^2+25y^2+20xy+4x^2$

$+25y^2-20xy+4x^2-25y^2)$

$=(-10y)(12x^2+25y^2)$

8. As $x^2 - 3x + 2$

$=(x-1)(x-2)$ then $x=1$ and $x=2$

are roots of polynomials.

$P(1)=2-5+2-1+2=0$

$P(2)=32-40+8-2+2=0$ hence proved.

Archive Corner

1. (C) Put $x=y=1$ then $A_0-A_1+A_2-A_3+A_4-A_5+A_6=1$

2. (A) $-x+2$

3. (C) $(a + b + c)^2 + (a + b - c)^2 + (a - b + c)^2 + (b + c - a)^2$

$=a^2+b^2+c^2+2ab+2bc+2ac$

$+a^2+b^2+c^2+2ab-2bc-2ac$

$+a^2+b^2+c^2-2ab-2bc+2ac$

$+a^2+b^2+c^2-2ab+2bc-2ac$

$=4(a^2+b^2+c^2)$

HINTS AND EXPLANATIONS

4. **(D)** $a^2 + b^2 + 2(ab + bc + ca)$
$= (a+b)^2 + 2c(a+b) = 0$

5. **(C)** Given: $2^x = 4^y = 8^z \Rightarrow 2^x = 2^{2y} = 2^{3z}$
$\Rightarrow x = 2y = 3z = k$ (i)
$\frac{1}{2x} + \frac{1}{4y} + \frac{1}{6z} = \frac{24}{7}$
Substitute (i) in (ii)
$\frac{1}{2k} + \frac{1}{2k} + \frac{1}{2k} = \frac{3}{2k} = \frac{24}{7}$ then $k = \frac{7}{16}$
$\therefore 3z = k \Rightarrow z = k/3 = 7/48$

6. **(B)** Now, we have relations from the problem are
$a + b + x = 2$ (iii)
Put $x = 3$ to the equation (iii) to get two equation in 'a' and 'b'. so, we get equation (iii) as
$a + b + 3 = 2$
$a - b = 3$ (iv)
$a + b = -1$ (v)
Now, add equation (iv) and (v)
$a - b + a + b = 3 - 1$
$2a = 2$
$a = 1$ (vi)
Put $a = 1$ in the equation (iv) to get value of 'b'. so, we get
$1 - b = 3$
$b = -2$ (vii)
Now, put the values of a, b from the equations (vi) and (vii) to the equation (i) and put $x = 3$ as well.
So, we get
$f(x) = f(3) = 3[3^3 - 2 \times 1 \times 3^2 + 1^2 \times 3 - (1 - 2)(-2)^2]$
$= 3\,[27 - 18 + 3 - (-4)]$
$= 3(34 - 18)$
$= 3 \times 16$
$= 48$

7. **(C)** If $x = 2\sqrt{2} + \sqrt{7}$ and $\frac{1}{x} = 2\sqrt{2} - \sqrt{7}$
then $x + \frac{1}{x} = 4\sqrt{2}$

8. **(B)** $x^2 + \frac{x}{6} - \frac{1}{6}$
$= \frac{1}{6}(6x^2 + x - 1) = \frac{1}{6}(6x^2 + 3x - 2x - 1)$
$= \frac{(2x+1)(3x-1)}{6}$

9. **(C)** $x^4 + 4x^3 + 4x^2 - 13$
$= x^2(x^2 + 2x) + 2x(x^2 + 2x) - 13$
$= (x^2 + 2x)^2 - 13$
$= 45^2 - 13 = 2025 - 13 = 2012$

10. **(A)** $4z^2 - 16z\pi + z\pi - 4\pi^2$
$= 4z(z - 4\pi) + \pi(z - 4\pi)$
$= (4z + \pi)(z - 4\pi)$
then $z = 4\pi$ and $-\frac{\pi}{4}$

11. **(C)** Remainder
$= P(1) = 1 + 1 + 1 + 1\ldots\ldots(2013 \text{ times}) = 2013$

12. **(D)** $p + q = -p$ then $q = -2p$ and $pq = q$
then either $q = p = 0$ and $p = 1$ and $q = -2$

13. **(B)**

14. **(D)** Remainder $= p\left(-\frac{2}{3}\right)$
$= 2 \times -\frac{8}{27} - 9 \times \frac{4}{9} - \frac{2}{3} + 12$
$= 8 - \frac{16+18}{27} = \frac{182}{27}$

15. **(A)**

16. **(D)** $p(-1) = 1 - p + 3 - 3p + 5 - 2p + 9 + 6 = 0$
then $24 - 6p = 0$ then $p = 4$

17. **(A)** Let $a - 2b = x$ then $8x^2 - 2x - 1$
$= 8x^2 - 4x + 2x - 1 = 4x(2x - 1) + 1(2x - 1)$
$= (4x + 1)(2x - 1) = (4a - 8b + 1)(2a - 4b - 1)$

18. **(C)** $p = \frac{1+x^2}{x}$ then $\frac{1}{p} = \frac{x}{1+x^2}$
then $p - \frac{1}{p} = \frac{(1+x^2)^2 - x^2}{x(1+x^2)} = \frac{x^4 + x^2 + 1}{x^3 + x}$

19. **(C)** $\frac{1}{3}c^2 - 3c + c - 9 = \frac{1}{3}c(c - 9) + 1(c - 9)$
$= (c - 9)\left(\frac{1}{3}c + 1\right)$

20. **(B)** Remainder $= 1 - 4 + 1 + 2 + 1 = 1$

21. **(A)** $x^2 + 4y^2 + 9z^2 - 4xy - 12yz + 6xz = 0$, then
$(x - 2y + 3z)^2 = 0$ then $x = 2y - 3z$

22. **(B)** $P(x) = (x+2)(2x^2 - 3x + 1) + 5$

$= 2x^3 - 3x^2 + x + 4x^2 - 6x + 2 + 5$

$= 2x^3 + x^2 - 5x + 7$

23. **(C)** We know, $(a + b)^2 = a^2 + b^2 + 2ab$

So, $(a + b)^2 = 234 + 2 \times 108 = 234 + 216$ **(given)**

$(a + b) = \sqrt{450}$ (1)

$(a - b)^2 = a^2 + b^2 - 2ab = 234 - 216$

$(a - b) = \sqrt{18}$ (2)

From (1) and (2),

$(a + b)/(a - b) = \sqrt{(450/18)} = \sqrt{25} = 5$

24. **(A)** $p(x) = 2x + 1 = 0$ then $x = -1/2$

25. **(B)** For verification, $(x^3 - 3x^2 + 3x - 5)$

$= (-x + 2)(-x^2 + x - 1) - 3$

CHAPTER 3 COORDINATE GEOMETRY

Check Point 1

1. (a) IV quadrant (b) II quadrant
   (c) III quadrant (d) on positive x axis
   (e) on Negative x axis (f) on Positive y axis
   (g) I quadrant
2. (i) 3 (ii) 8
3. 7
4. 20
5. Rectangle

Fixed Response Type

Fill in the Blanks

1. Second
2. –ve and +ve
3. 0
4. Third
5. Y axis

True/False

1. True
2. True
3. True
4. False

Single Correct Type Questions

1. **(B)** Y-axis
2. **(D)** 1st and 4th Quadrant
3. **(C)** Third quadrant
4. **(B)** on Y-axis
5. **(C)** 5
6. **(B)** OX′
7. **(C)** The point (1, -1), (2, -2) and (4, -5) lies in the fourth quadrant, where (-3, -4) lies in the third quadrant.
8. **(C)** II and IV quadrants respectively
9. **(A)** (–4, 0)
10. **(A)** III and IV quadrant
11. **(D)** Y-axis
12. **(D)** negative x-axis
13. **(C)** Find the perpendicular distance of that point with the y-axis.
14. **(B)** Move 'a' units in the negative direction of x-axis then b units vertically downward in the negative direction of y-axis parallel to the y-axis.
15. **(C)** The signs of abscissa (x-value) and ordinate(y-value) in the second quadrant are – and + respectively.

Multiple Correct Type Questions

1. **(D)** II and IV quadrants
2. **(D)** Any point in the first quadrant can be written in the form (x, y), where $x > 0, y > 0$.
3. **(A)** P and R only
   (C) P, R and T
4. **(B)** $\sqrt{2}C$
5. **(D)** y co-ordinate = 5 or –5.
6. **(A)** I quadrant
   (C) III quadrant
7. **(A)** The coordinate axes are mutually perpendicular to each other.
   (B) The y-axis is also called as ordinate.
   (C) The point of intersection of x-axis and y-axis is called as origin.
   (D) The x-axis is also called as abscissa.
8. **(A)** x-coordinate
   (D) abscissa
9. **(C)** ordinate
   (D) y-coordinate

Match Type Questions

1. (i) → Q; (ii) → P; (iii) → S; (iv) → R
2. (i) → S; (ii) → P; (iii) → Q; (iv) → R
3. (i) → QR; (ii) → P; (iii) → R; (iv) → PS

Assertion and Reason Type Questions

1. A
2. D

Comprehension Type Questions

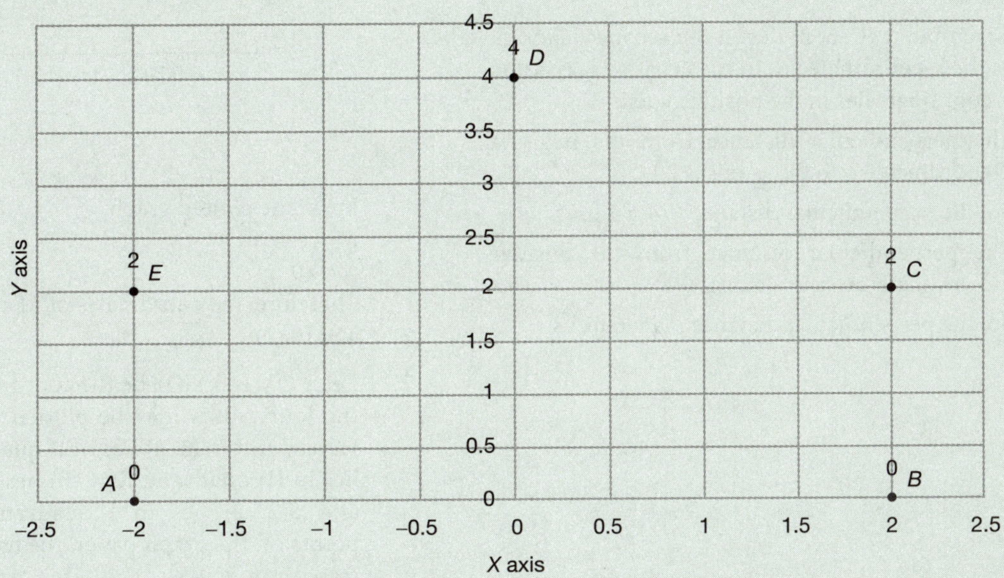

1. (D) pentagon
2. (A) 12 sq. units
3. (D) 2 units

Numerical Type Questions

1. $-2-(-3)=1$
2. 3
3. $\frac{1}{2}\times 1\times 1=\frac{1}{2}$
4. $\sqrt{\left(\frac{2}{5}-\left(-\frac{8}{5}\right)\right)^2}=\sqrt{2^2}=2$
5. $1+1+\sqrt{2}=2+\sqrt{2}$
6. 3 units
7. The coordinates of any point on the x-axis is (x, 0), where x can take any value.
8. 5 units

Higher Order Thinking Skills (HOTS)

1. **(D)** The point (1, -1), (2, -2) and (4, -5) lies in the fourth quadrant, where (-3, -4) lies in the third quadrant.
2. **(D)**
3. **(D)** Quadrant

FREE RESPONSE TYPE

Very Short Answer Type Questions

1. II
2. –ve and +ve
3. Abscissa is distance of a point from y - axis
4. III
5. On X axis.
6. P (II), Q (IV), R(IV), S(III) and T (II)
7. The distance of a point from the y-axis is the abscissa of the point. So, 4 units.
8. II or IV
9. (0, 4)
10. 3

Short Answer Type Questions

1. Given, the point $P(-6, 2)$

From the point P draw PM and PN as perpendicular to x-axis and y-axis.

We have to find the coordinates of the points M and N.

Given point $P(-6, 2)$ lies in the second quadrant as the x-coordinate lies in the negative x-axis and y-coordinate lies in the positive y-axis.

The perpendicular distance from the negative x-coordinate -6 to the x-axis is 2.

So, the perpendicular distance $PM = 2$ units

The perpendicular distance from the positive y-coordinate 2 to the y-axis is 6.

So, the perpendicular distance $PN = 6$ units

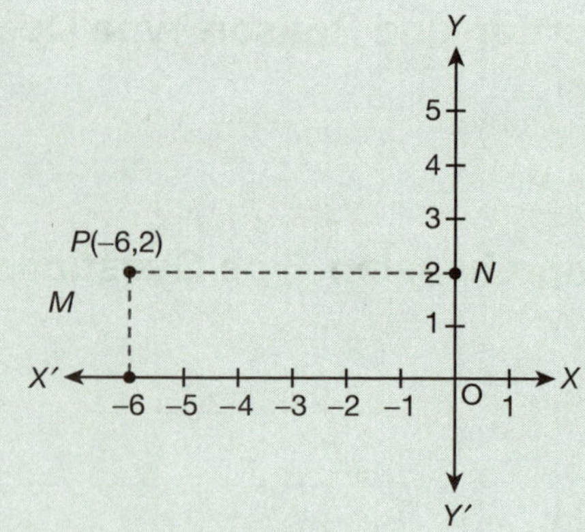

From the plotted graph,

$M = (-6, 0)$

$N = (0, 2)$

Therefore, the coordinates of M and N are $(-6, 0)$ and $(0, 2)$

2. Let $X'OX$ and $Y'OY$ be the coordinate axes. Then, the four points may be plotted as given below: Here, point $P(-3, 2)$ lies in II quadrant, $Q(-7, -3)$ lies in III quadrant, $R(6, -3)$ lies in IV quadrant and $S(2, 2)$ lies in I quadrant. Plotting the points on the graph paper, the figure obtained is trapezium $PQRS$.

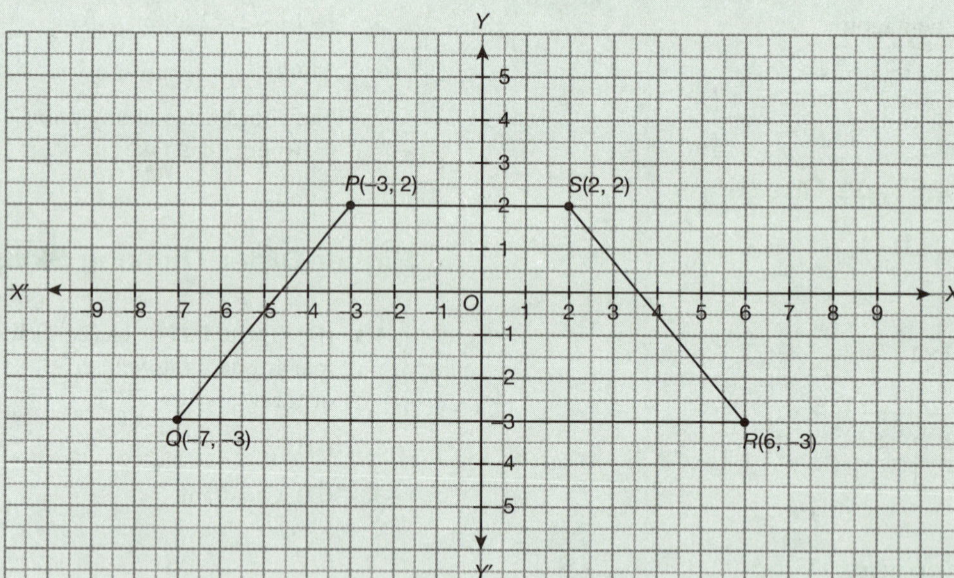

3.

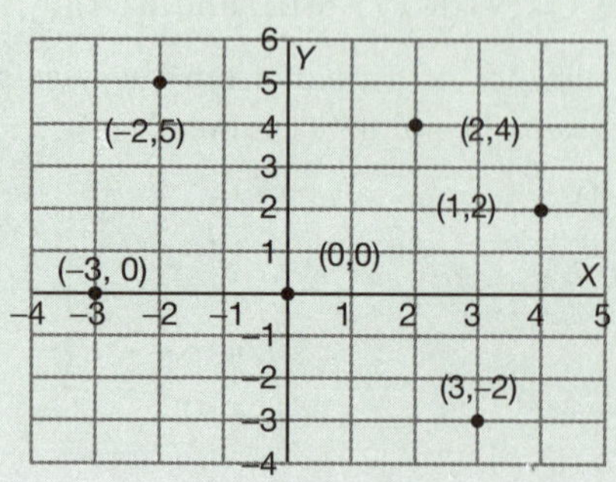

4. (i) From the graph, we find that all the three points lie on the same straight line. Hence, the given points are collinear.

(ii) From the graph, we find that all the three points do not lie on the same straight line. Hence, the given points are not collinear.

(iii) From the graph, we find that all the three points lie on the same straight line. Hence, the given points are collinear.

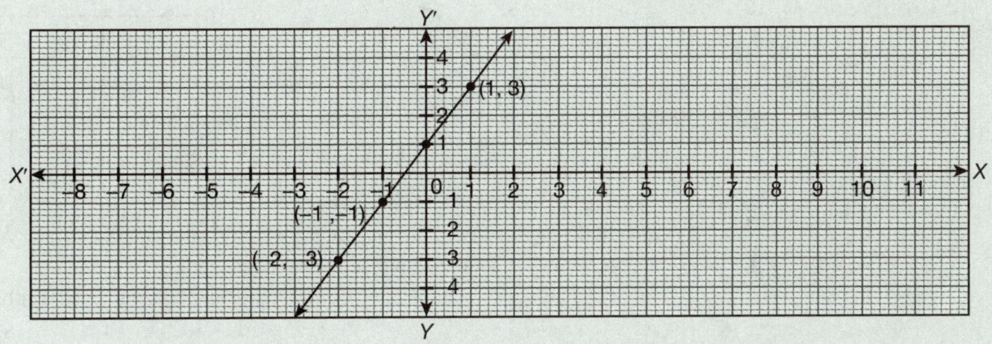

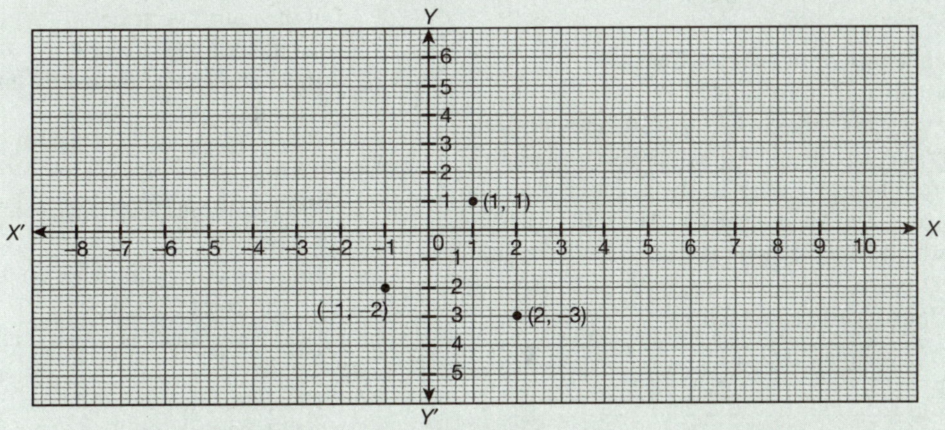

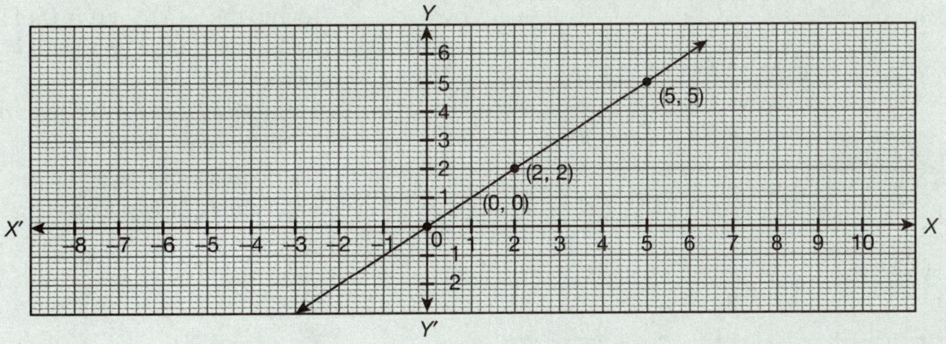

5.

Let A(–2, 0), B(0, 1), C(2, 0) and D(0, –1)

AB = $\sqrt{5}$ = CD = BC = AD

AC = 4, BD = 2 so rhombus

As the sides are equal but diagonal are unequal.

6. C (0, 1), D (0, 0), E (0, –1), G (0, 5).

7. We know that if a point is of the form, $(x, 0)$, i.e., its y-coordinate is zero, then it will lie on x-axis otherwise not.

8. Abscissa of point P = –2

Abscissa of point Q = –3

We have to find (abscissa of P) – (abscissa of Q)

Substituting the values

(abscissa of P) – (abscissa of Q) = –2 – (–4)

= –2 + 4

= 2

9. Here, in point $A(1, 3)$ both x and y-coordinates are positive, so its lies in I quadrant. In point $B(-3, -1)$, both x and y-coordinates are negative, so it lies in III quadrant. In point $C(1, -4)$ x-coordinate is negative and y-coordinative is positive, so it lies in II quadrant. In point $E(0, 8)$ x-coordinate is zero, so it lies on y-axis and in point $F(1, 0)$ y-coordinate is zero, so it lies on x-axis. On plotting the given points, we can get the graph

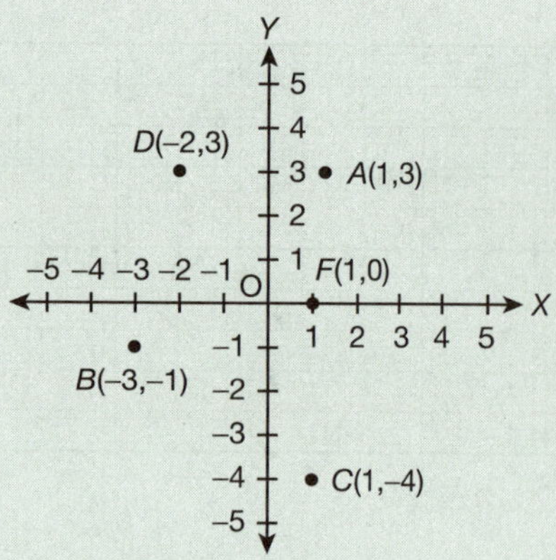

10. Given length of rectangle = 5 units
Given breadth of rectangle = 3
One vertex is at origin i.e..., $D(0, 0)$ and one of the other vertices lies in III quadrant. So the length of the rectangle is 5 units in the negative direction of x-axis and then vertex is $A(-5, 0)$. Also the breadth of the rectangle is 3 units is the negative direction of Y-axis and them vertex is $C(0, -3)$. The fourth vertex B is $(-5, -3)$

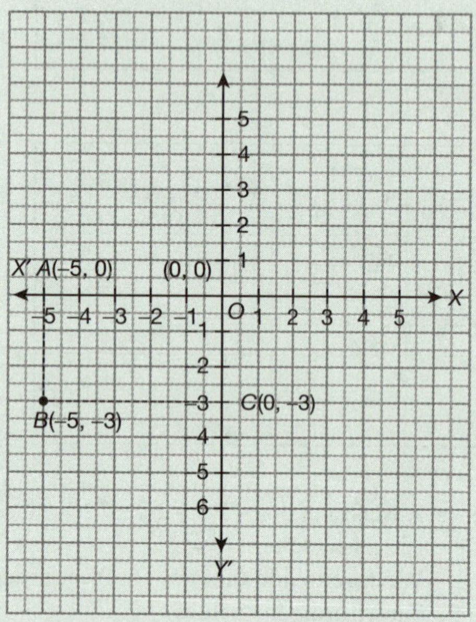

11. We plot the given points $P(1, 0)$, $Q(4, 0)$, $S(1, 3)$.
From S we draw a line parallel to X-axis and from Q we draw a line parallel to Y-axis.
Both the lines will meet at R.
From the graph find co-ordinates of R are (4, 3)

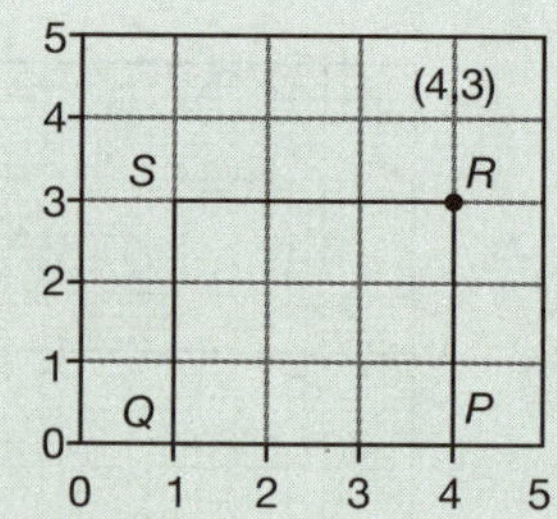

12. Given, three vertices of a rectangle are (3, 2), (−4, 2) and (−4, 5)
We have to plot the points and find the coordinates of the fourth vertex.
Let the point (3, 2) be A
The x-coordinate is positive and the y-coordinate is positive
Therefore, the point A lies on the first quadrant
Let the point (−4, 2) be B
The x-coordinate is negative and the y-coordinate is positive
Therefore, the point B lies on the second quadrant
Let the point (−4, 5) be C
The x-coordinate is negative and the y-coordinate is positive
Therefore, the point C lies on the second quadrant
On plotting the points A, B and C
To find the fourth vertex D of the rectangle $ABCD$
We know that the opposite sides of a rectangle are equal.
So the abscissa of A is equal to abscissa of D
So, abscissa of $D = 3$
The ordinate of C is equal to ordinate of D
So, ordinate of $D = 5$

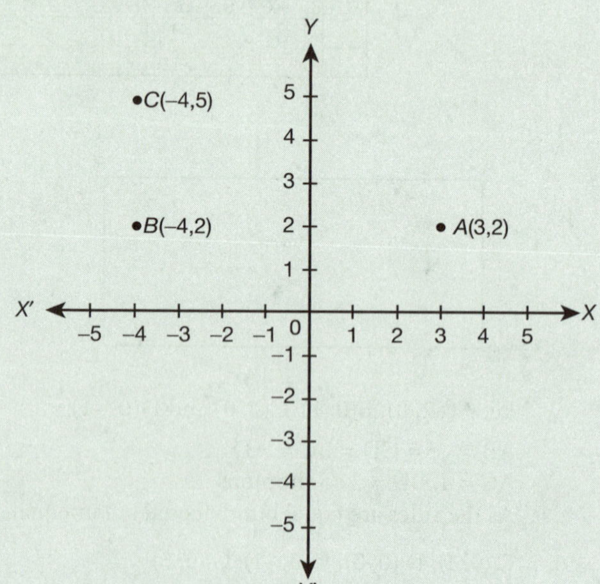

Long Answer Type Questions

1.

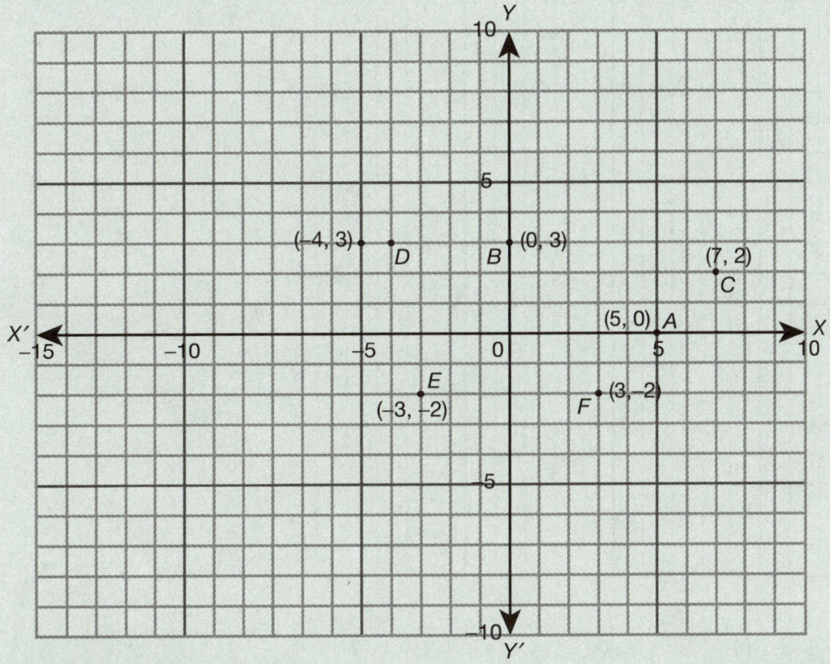

Point	(5, 3)	(0, 3)	(7, 2)	(–4, 3)	(–3, –2)	(3, –2)
Location	I quadrant	Y axis	I Quadrant	II Quadrant	III Quadrant	IV Quadrant

2.

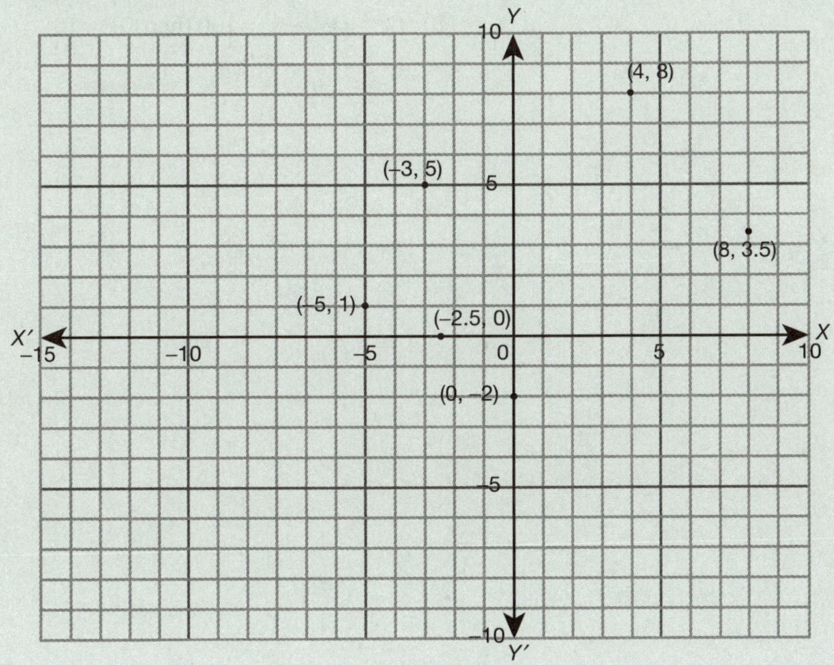

3.

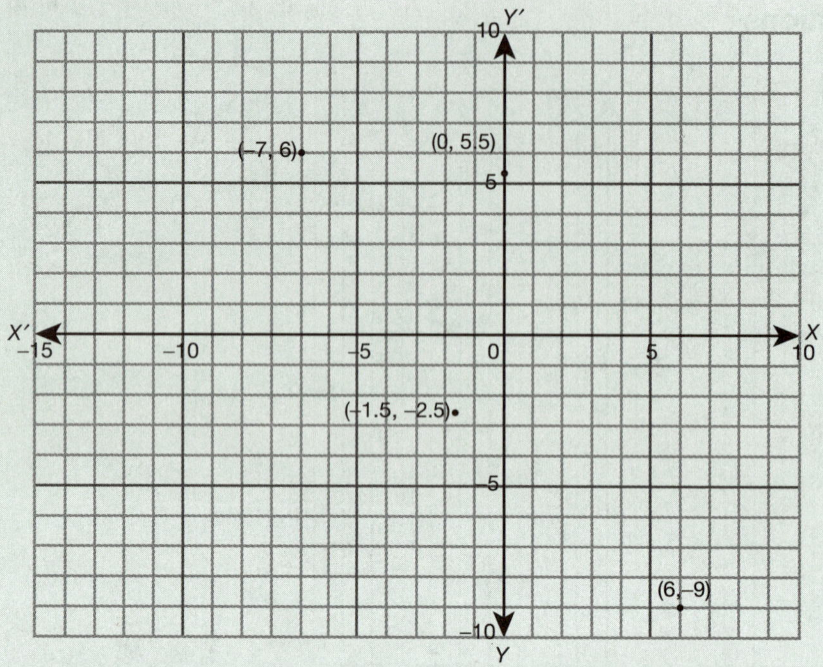

4. (i) $-a$ (ii) $-b$ (iii) $(-a, -b)$

5. (a) (0, 6) (b) (–3, 0)

Archive Corner

1. **(B)** (0, 2)

2. **(D)** ∞

3. **(B)** $OP^2 = 6^2 + 8^2 = 100$ then $OP = 10$

CHAPTER 4 LINEAR EQUATIONS

Check Point 1

1. (b), (d), (e)

2. (a) $5x - 7y - 1 = 0; a = 5, b = -7, c = -1$
   (b) $-3x + 8y - 1 = 0; a = -3, b = 8, c = -1$
   (c) $3x - 5y = 0; a = 3, b = -5, c = 0$
   (d) $9x - 4 = 0; a = 9, b = 0, c = -4$
   (e) $7y + 4 = 0; a = 0, b = 7, c = 4$

3. (a) $y = \frac{-6}{7}x + \frac{3}{7}; m = \frac{-6}{7}, c = \frac{3}{7}$
   (b) $y = \frac{3}{4}x + \frac{1}{2}; m = \frac{3}{4}, c = \frac{1}{2}$
   (c) $y = \frac{-7}{6}x + \frac{1}{3}; m = \frac{-7}{6}, c = \frac{1}{3}$
   (d) $y = \frac{3}{5}x - \frac{2}{5}; m = \frac{2}{5}, c = \frac{-2}{5}$

4. (a) $4x - 7y + 2 = 0$
   If $x = 0$ then $-7y + 2 = 0$ then $y = \frac{2}{7}\left(0, \frac{2}{7}\right)$
   If $y = 0$ then $4x + 2 = 0$ then $x = \frac{-1}{2}\left(\frac{-1}{2}, 0\right)$
   If $y = 2$ then $4x - 14 + 2 = 0$
   then $4x = 12$ then $x = 3(3, 2)$
   (b) $2x - y = 6$
   If $x = 0$ then $-y = 6$ then $y = -6(0, -6)$
   If $x = 1$ then $2 - y = 6$ then $y = -4(1, -4)$
   If $x = 2$ then $4 - y = 6$ then $y = -2(2, -2)$
   (c) $x + 3y - 6 = 0$
   If $x = 0$ then $3y = 6$ then $y = 2(0, 2)$
   If $x = 3$ then $3y = 3$ then $y = 1(3, 1)$
   If $x = 6$ then $y = 0$ then $y = 0(6, 0)$
   (d) $10x - 9y + 5 = 0$
   If $x = 0$ then $-9y + 5 = 0$ then $y = \frac{5}{9}\left(0, \frac{5}{9}\right)$
   If $x = 1$ then $-9y + 15 = 0$
   then $y = \frac{-5}{3}\left(1, \frac{-5}{3}\right)$
   If $x = 2$ then $-9y + 25 = 0$
   then $y = \frac{-25}{9}\left(2, \frac{-25}{9}\right)$

5. $150x + 225y = 900$

Check Point 2

6. **Yes** $2 \times -3 - 5 \times 5 + 31 = 0$

7. **Yes** $7 \times 0 + 3 \times 0 = 0$

8. (a) parallel to y-axis (b) parallel to x-axis
   (c) parallel to y-axis (d) parallel to y-axis

9. (a)

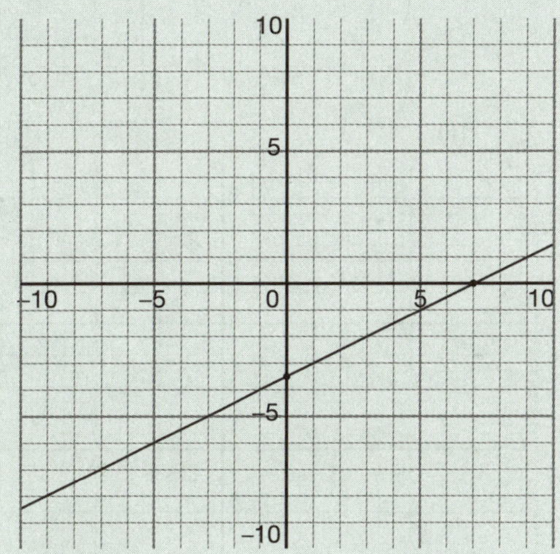

(b)

x	0	1	–1	2
y	0	3	–3	6
(x,y)	(0,0)	(3,0)	(–1,–3)	(2,6)

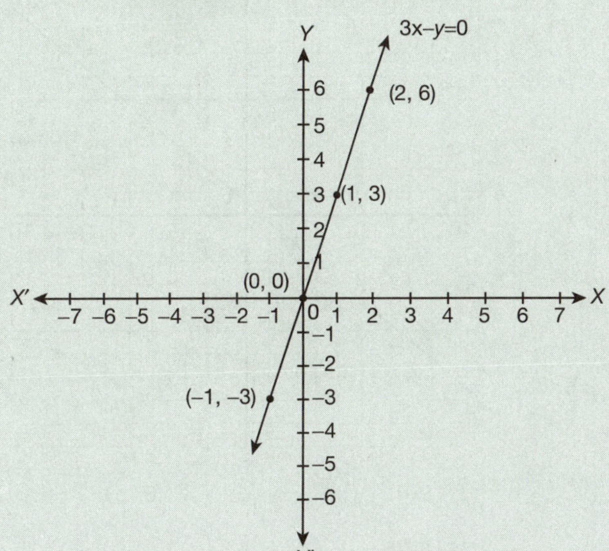

(c) Same as *e*
(d) Same as *f*

(e)

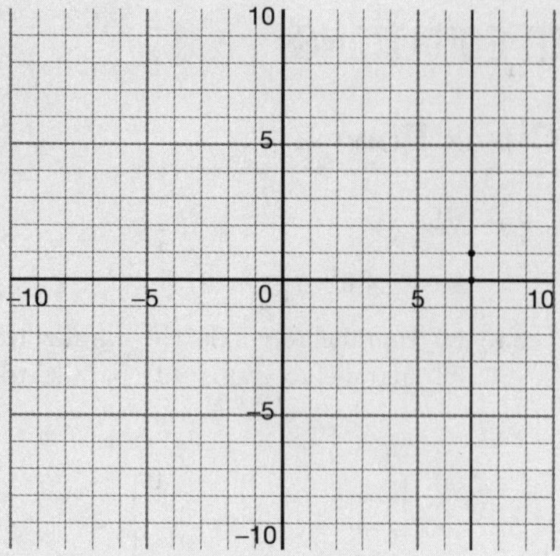
10
5
−10
−5
0
5
10
−5
−10

(f)

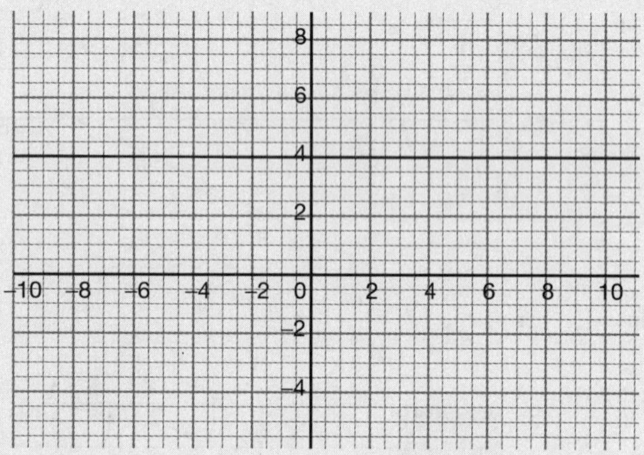
8
6
4
2
−10
−8
−6
−4
−2
0
2
4
6
8
10
−2
−4

10.

(a)

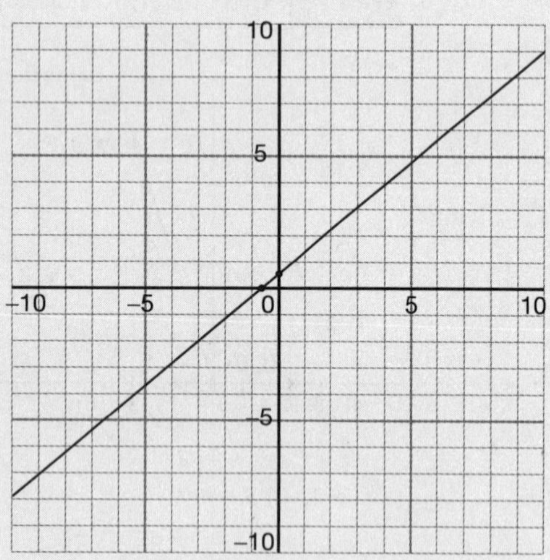
10
5
−10
−5
0
5
10
−5
−10

(b)

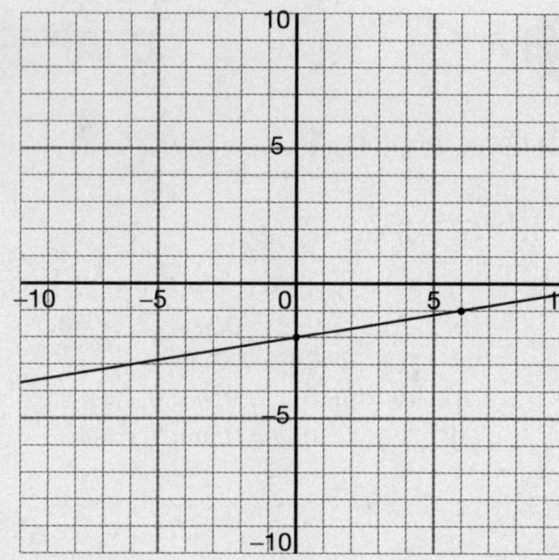
10
5
−10
−5
0
5
10
−5
−10

(c)

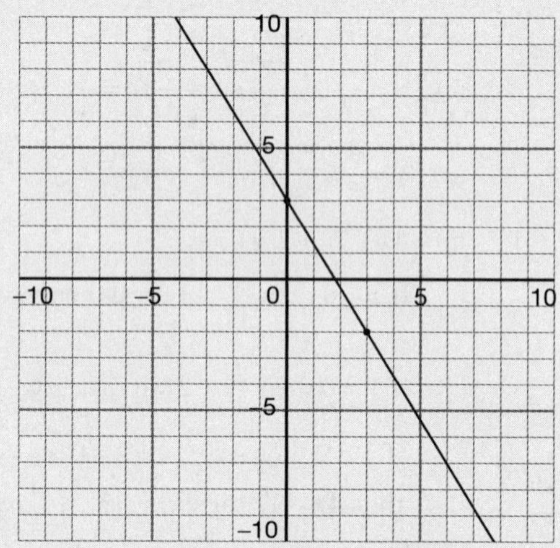
10
5
−10
−5
0
5
10
−5
−10

(d)

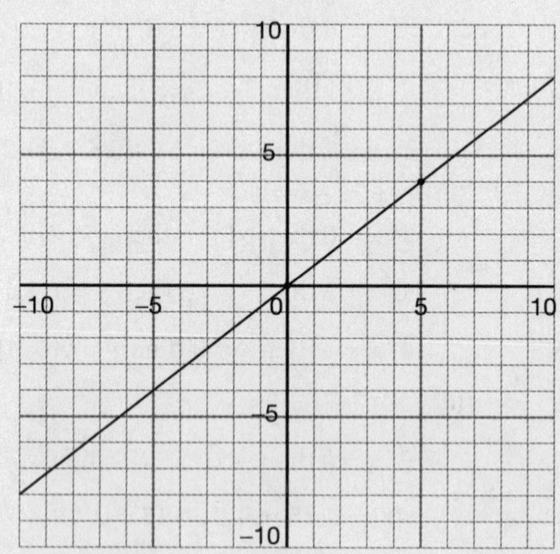
10
5
−10
−5
0
5
10
−5
−10

Fixed Response Type

Fill in the Blanks

1. 29/2 cm or 14.5 cm
2. a straight line
3. 1
4. $k = 10 + 4 = 14$
5. infinite
6. $\frac{2x}{5} + 1 = \frac{x}{3} + 3$

   $\frac{2x}{5} - \frac{x}{3} = 2$ then $\frac{x}{15} = 2$ then $x = 30$

True/False

1. True
   $5 - 8 = -3$
2. True
3. True
4. True
5. True

Single Correct Type Questions

1. **(C)** $x^2 + 3 = 5x - 3$
2. **(D)** $x = \frac{2\sqrt{3}+6}{\sqrt{3}} = 2\left(1+\sqrt{3}\right)$
3. **(B)** $(6x+5)(2x+6) = (3x+5)(4x+7)$

   $12x^2 + 46x + 30 = 12x^2 + 41x + 35$

   then $5x = 5$ then $x = 1$
4. **(B)** Given that the graph of the linear equation $2x + 3y = 6$ cuts the y-axis at the point. Let the point be "P". Hence, the x -coordinate of point P is 0.
   Now, substitute $x= 0$ in the given equation,
   $2(0) + 3y = 6$
   $3y = 6$
   $y = 2$
   Hence, the coordinate point is (0, 2).
5. **(C)** infinite solution
6. **(B)** $1 \times x + 0 \times y = 7$
7. **(C)** $3x - 11y = 10$
   $y = (3x - 10)/11$
   Now for infinite values of x, y will also have infinite solutions.
8. **(A)** $\left(0, \frac{4}{3}\right)$
9. **(D)** The linear equation $2x$-$5y$ has infinitely many solution. Because, the equation $2x$-$5y = 7$ is a single equation, that involves two variables. Hence, for different values of x, we will get different values of y and vice-versa.
10. **(C)** x+$2y = 2$
    $y = (2\text{-}x)/2$
    If x=0, then;
    y=(2-0)/2 = 2/2 = 1
    Hence, x+$2y$=2 cuts the y-axis at (0,1).
11. **(D)** $y = \frac{2}{3}x - \frac{11}{3}$
12. **(D)** Both (A) and (B) are correct
13. **(B)** $3x - 4y = 1$; $8y - 6x = 4$
14. **(D)** All of these

Multiple Correct Type Questions

1. **(ABC)** (1, 1)
   As $2x + 3y = 6$
   $2\,(A) + 3\,(A) \neq 6$
   $5 \neq 6$
2. **(A)** (0, –2)
   (B) (–2, –5)
   (D) (2, 1)
3. **(A, B, C)**
4. **(A, B C)**
5. **(B)** $\left(\sqrt{2}, 4\sqrt{2}\right)$
   (C) (1, 1)
   (D) (2, 0)
6. **(B)** Given that the graph of the linear equation $2x + 3y = 6$ cuts the y-axis at the point. Let the point be "P". Hence, the x -coordinate of point P is 0.
   Now, substitute $x= 0$ in the given equation,
   $2(0) + 3y = 6$
   $3y = 6$
   $y = 2$
   Hence, the coordinate point is (0, 2).
7. **(ABD)**

Match Type Questions

1. (A) (i) → R, (ii) → S, (iii) → P, (iv) → Q
2. (C) (i) → R, S (ii) → Q, (iii) → Q, R (iv) → P
3. (A) (i) → Q, (ii) → S, (iii) → R, (iv) → P
4. (C) (i) → R, (ii) → Q, (iii) → S, (iv) → P
5. (D) (i) → R, (ii) → S, (iii) → Q, (iv) → P
6. (B) (i) → Q, S (ii) → P (iii) → T, U (iv) → R

Assertion and Reason Type Questions

1. (A)
2. (D)
3. (B)
4. (A)
5. (C)

Comprehension Type Questions

Let the salary of Ram and Shyam are $9x$ and $7x$ respectively. And their expenditures are $4y$ and $3y$ respectively.

$9x-4y=7x-3y=200 \Rightarrow y=2x$

then $9x-8x=200$ then $x=200$

and $y=400$

Their Salary is 1800 and 1400 and their expenditures are 1600 and 1200

1. (B) ₹1400
2. (A) $=\frac{400}{1200}\times 100=33.33\%$
3. (D) $\frac{1200}{1400}\times 100=85\frac{5}{7}\%$

Numerical Type Questions

1. $(2x+7)(2x-7)=(4x+3)(x+2)$

   then $4x^2-49=4x^2+11x+6$

   then $11x=-55$ then $x=-5$

2. $2x+cx=8$ then $c=\frac{8-2x}{x}$
3. $4a=-15+11=-4$ then $a=-1$
4. Making denominator equal:

   $9x+18-(11x-8)+8x=18x-x-7$

   $6x+26=17x-7$ then $11x=33$ then $x=3$

5. $9a+12a=63$ then $a=3$
6. $3y = kx + 7$

   Here, $x = 3$ and $y = 4$

   Hence,

   $(3\times4) = (k \times 3) + 7$

   $12 = 3k + 7$

   $3k = 12 - 7$

   $3k = 5$

7. $4x - 3y + 4 = 0$ (i)

   $4x + 3y - 20 = 0$ (ii)

   In (i) $4x + 4 = 3y$

   $y=\frac{4x+4}{3}=$

x	2	−1	−4
y	4	0	−4

   In (ii) $3y = 20 - 4x$

   $y=\frac{20-4x}{3}=$

x	2	5	8
y	4	0	−4

   Drawing the equations, we get: Since two lines are meeting at (2, 4) their solution is $x = 2, y = 4$

   Area $\Delta=\frac{1}{2}\times6\times4=12$ unit^2

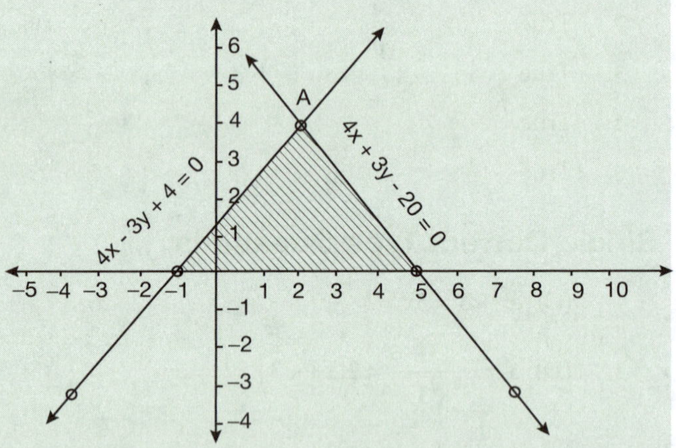

Higher Order Thinking Skills (HOTS)

1. (A) First quadrant
2. (D) $-3=-5a+7$ then $a=2$ and $-5=-b+7$ then $b=12$ then $a+b=14$
3. (C) let the x boys inside the class. outside the class will be $36-x$

   Boys outside $=\frac{x}{4}$.

   According to question $\frac{3x}{4}=36-x+\frac{x}{4}$

   then $\frac{3x}{2}=36$ then $x=24$.

4. (A) Let A have x then B have $x+30$

   then c had $x+50$

   $3x+80=380$ then $x=100$

5. **(D)** Infinite solution.

6. **(B)** $\frac{1}{2}\times 6\times 6=18$ sq. unit

7. **(A)** $\frac{1}{2}\times 1\times 1=\frac{1}{2}$

8. **(A, B)**

Free Response Type

Very Short Answer Type Questions

1. $2\times 2+3\times 0=k$ then $k=4$

2. For y axis $x = 0$ then $3y = 6$ then $y = 2$ Point is (0, 2)

3. $x = a$ and $y = b$ will intersect at (a, b).

4. (a, a)

5. $y=0$

6. For x axis y Coordinate will be 0 then $2x=6$ then $x=3$ then point is (3, 0)

7. $5-2\times 4=-3$ Yes

8. $K=5\times 3-2\times 4=7$

9. $Y=3$

Short Answer Type Questions

1. We have to find the point at which the equation meets a line parallel to the y-axis at a distance of 2 units from the origin and in the positive direction of the x-axis.

   The coordinates of the point lying on the line parallel to the y-axis, at a distance x units from the origin and in the positive direction of the x-axis is given by (x, a)

   Now, the distance $x = 2$ units

   So, the coordinates of the point = $(2, a)$

   Now put $x = 2$ and $y = a$ in the given equation,

   $2 + a = 5$

   $a = 5 - 2$

   $a = 3$

   Therefore, the point is (2, 3).

3. Given, a straight line is parallel to the x-axis 4 units above it.

   We have to draw the graph of the equation.

   The equation of a straight line parallel to x-axis is given by $y = a$

   Where a is the distance of the line from x-axis

   Given, distance of the line from the x-axis is 4 units

   Therefore, the equation of the line is $y = 4$

   To plot the graph, the points are (1, 4) (2, 4) (3, 4)

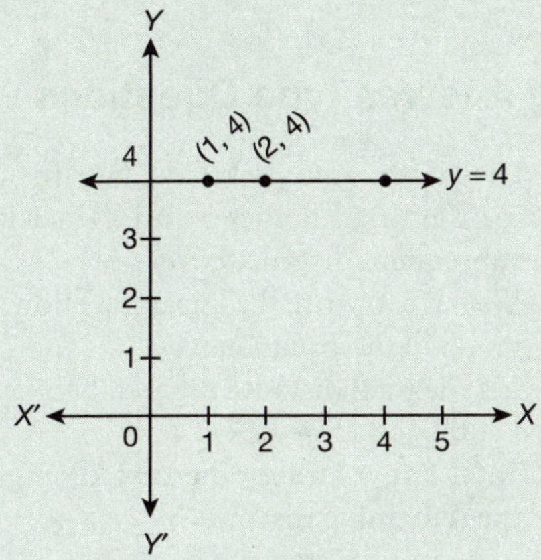

4. Let the abscissa is x then y-coordinate will be $\frac{3}{2}x$ then $2\times x+5\times\frac{3x}{2}=19$ then $19x=19\times 2$

   then $x=2$ and $y=1.5$ point is $(2, 1.5)$

5. (i) 1 (ii) Infinite

6. (i) x-axis: $y=0$ then $x=8$ point is (8, 0)
   (ii) y-axis: $x=0$ then $2y=8$ then point is (0, 4)

7. $3x+2y=20$

   $3(a+b)+2(a-b)=20$

   $=5a+b=20$ (i)

   $4(a+b)-5(a-b)=42$

   $-a+9b=42$ (ii)

   After solving (i) and (ii)

   $a=3$ and $b=5$

8. $\frac{9x+3}{9x+13}=\frac{6}{5}$ then $45x+15=54x+78$

   then $9x=63$ then $x=-7$.

9. Suppose my age is x years and my son's age is y years. Then,

   $x=3y$ (i)

   Five years later, my age will be $(x + 5)$ years and my son›s age will be $(y+5)$ years.

   $\therefore\ x+5=(2+1/2)(y+5)$ [Given]

   $\Rightarrow\ 2x-5y-15=0$ (ii)

   Putting $x=3y$ in equation (ii), we get

   $6y-5y-15=0\Rightarrow y=15$

   Putting $y=15$ in equation (i), we get

   $x=45$

   Hence, my present age is 45 years and my son's present age is 15 years.

10. (i) $F = \frac{9}{5} \times 30 + 32 = 54 + 32 = 86$

(ii) $95 = \frac{9}{5} \times C + 32 \Rightarrow C = 35$

(iii) $F = \frac{9}{5} \times F + 32 \Rightarrow F = -40$

Long Answer Type Questions

1. Given, an auto rickshaw fare in a city is ₹10 for the first kilometer and ₹4 per kilometer for subsequent distance covered.
We have to write the linear equation and draw the graph of the equation.
Let the total distance covered be x km
Let the total fare be ₹y
Total fare = fare for the first kilometer + fare for the remaining distance
Remaining distance = $x - 1$
Fare for the remaining distance = $4(x - 1)$
So, total fare = $10 + 4(x - 1)$
$= 10 + 4x - 4$
Total fare = $6 + 4x$
$y = 6 + 4x$
Therefore, the linear equation is $y = 6 + 4x$
When $x = 0$, $y = 6 + 4(0) = 6$
When $x = -1$, $y = 6 + 4(-1) = 6 - 4 = 2$
When $x = -2$, $y = 6 + 4(-2) = 6 - 8 = -2$
The points are (0, 6), (–1, 2) and (–2, –2)
On plotting the points and joining them,

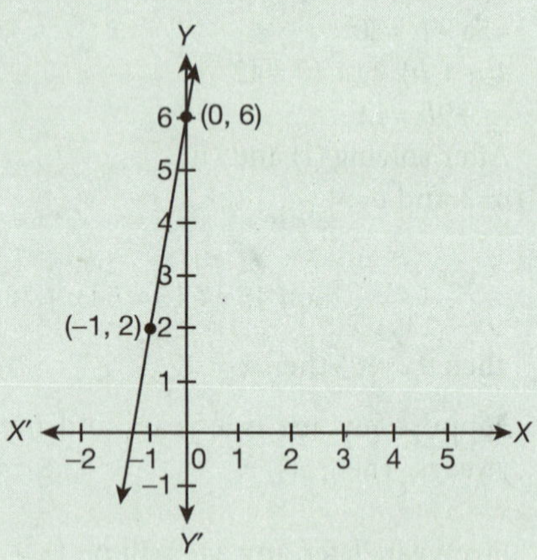

2. According to the given details
The equation is
$3x + 4y = 6$.
We require at least 2 points on the graph to draw the graph of this equation,
Thus, the points the graph cuts
(i) x-axis
Since, the point is on x axis, we have, $y = 0$.
On substituting $y = 0$ in the equation, $3x + 4y = 6$,
We obtain,
$3x + 4 \times 0 = 6$
$\Rightarrow 3x = 6$
$\Rightarrow x = 2$
Hence, the point at which the graph cuts x-axis = (2, 0).
(ii) y-axis
Since, the point is on y axis, we have, $x = 0$.
On substituting $x = 0$ in the equation, $3x + 4y = 6$,
We obtain,
$3 \times 0 + 4y = 6$
$\Rightarrow 4y = 6$
$\Rightarrow y = 6/4$
$\Rightarrow y = 3/2$
$\Rightarrow y = 1.5$
Hence, the point at which the graph cuts the x-axis = (0, 1.5).
On plotting the points (0, 1.5) and (2, 0) on the graph

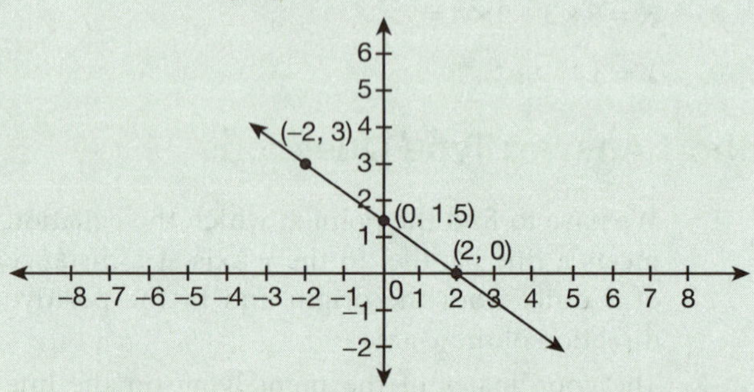

3. We have to write a linear equation and draw the graph of the equation by taking the constant mass equal to 6 kg.
We have to read from the graph the force required when the acceleration produced is 5 m/sec^2
Given, $F \propto a$
So, $F = ma$
Where m is the arbitrary constant i.e.,constant mass
Given, $m = 6$ kg
Now, $F = 6a$
(i) The force required when acceleration is 5 m/sec^2 is
$F = 6(5)$
$F = 30$ N
Therefore, the force is 30 N
(ii) The force required when acceleration is 6 m/sec^2 is
$F = 6(6)$
$F = 36$ N
Therefore, the force is 36 N
The points are (5, 30) and (6, 36)
On plotting the points on the graph and joining them

HINTS AND EXPLANATIONS

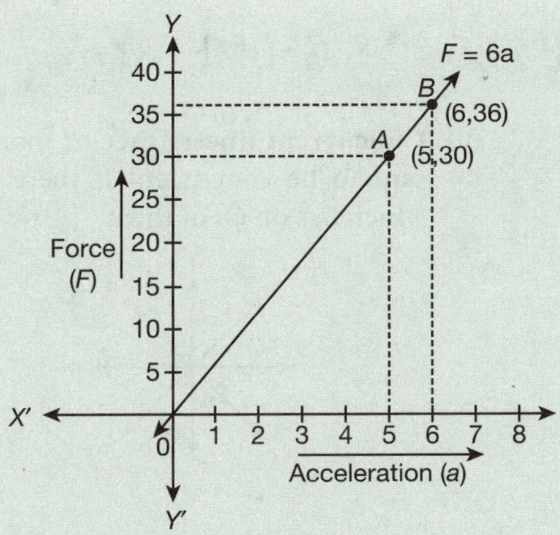

4. (i) Putting $F = 86°$, we get
$C = (5(86) - 160)/9$
$= (430 - 160)/9 = 270/9 = 30$
Hence, the temperature in Celsius in 30°C.

(ii) Putting $C = 35°$, we get $35° = \dfrac{5(F)-160}{9}$
$\Rightarrow 315° = 5F - 160$
$\Rightarrow 5F = 315 + 160 = 475$
$\therefore F = \dfrac{475}{5} = 95°$
Hence, the temperature in Fahrenheit is 95°F.

(iii) Putting $C = 0°$, we get
$0 = (5F - 160)/9 \Rightarrow 0 = 5F - 160$
$\Rightarrow 5F = 160$
$\therefore F = 160/5 = 32°$
Now, putting $F = 0°$, we get
$C = (5F - 160)/9$
$\Rightarrow C = (5(0) - 160)/9 = (-160/9)°$
If the temperature is 0°C, the temperature in Fahrenheit is 32° and if the temperature is 0°F, then the temperature in Celsius is (–160/9)°C.

(iv) Putting $C = F$, in the given relation, we get
$F = (5F - 160)/9 \Rightarrow 9F = 5F - 160$
$\Rightarrow 4F = -160$
$\therefore F = -160/4 = -40°$
Hence, the numerical value of the temperature which is same in both the sacales is –40.

5. The correct option is (D) 104
Given relation is
$y = 9(x - 273)/5 + 32$ (i)
Given, $x = 313$ K
By subtituting value of x in (i), we get
$y = 9(313 - 273)/5 + 32$
$= 9 \times 40/5 + 32$
$= 72 + 32 = 104°F$
$\therefore$ The temperature of the liquid of 313 K in fahrenheit is 104°.

6. (i) $y = 10 + 7(x-1) = 7x + 3$
(ii) $y = 16 \times 7 + 3 = 115.$

7. $2x + 3y = 6$
Since, the line intersects at y-axis.
Put $x = 0$ in the given equation
$\Rightarrow y = 2$
Hence, the line intersects y-axis at (0, 2)
Since, the line intersects at x-axis.
Put $y = 0$ in the given equation
$\Rightarrow x = 3$
Hence, the line intersects y-axis at (3, 0)

8. $y = 2x + \frac{7}{2}(-1, -1)$ is not solution

Archive Corner

1. **(A)** $\frac{15}{x} + \frac{2}{y} = 17 \Rightarrow \frac{15}{3} + \frac{2}{y} = 17 \Rightarrow y = \frac{1}{6}$

2. **(A)** Ramesh = x Mahesh = $x - 5$ Suresh = $x + 3$

3. **(B)** $\frac{x}{2} + \frac{x}{4} + \frac{x}{5} + 7 = x$ then $x - \frac{x}{2} - \frac{x}{4} - \frac{x}{5} = 7$
then $\dfrac{20x - 10x - 5x - 4x}{20} = 7$ then $x = 140$.

4. **(B)** Let the second number is $6x$ then first number is $3x$ and third number is $2x$
$44 = \dfrac{6x + 3x + 2x}{3}$
$\Rightarrow x = 12$ then largest number is 72.

5. **(B)** $x = 15$

6. **(D)** 1st, 2nd, 4th

7. **(C)** Let the age of father is F and age of son is S then
$F - 3 + S - 3 = 40 \Rightarrow F + S = 46$
$F + S + 4 = 50$

8. **(B)** Let the age of son is S and age of father is F then $F = 7S$
$F - 2 = 13(S - 2)$
$F = 13S - 24$
$6S = 24$
$S = 4$ and $F = 28$

CHAPTER 5 INTRODUCTION TO EUCLID'S GEOMETRY

Check Point 1

1. (i) **Axiom:** The basic facts which are taken for granted, without proof, are called axioms.
   Ex. Halves of equal are equal.

   (ii) **Theorem:** A statement that requires a proof, is called a theorem. Establishing the truth of a theorem is known as proving the theorem.
   Ex. The sum of all angles around a point is 360°

2. (i) **Collinear point:** Three or more points are said to be collinear if there is a line which contains all of them.

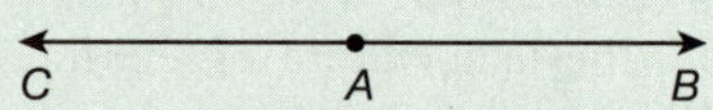

   (ii) **Concurrent lines:** Three or more lines are said to be concurrent if there is a point which lies on all of them.

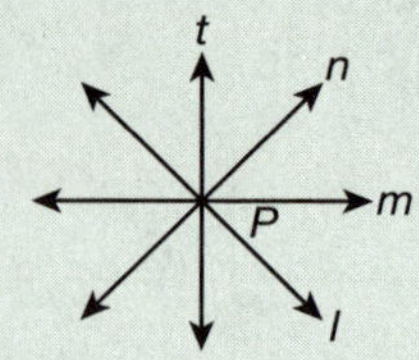

3. ONE
4. 

   $CA = BD$ Add AB both side
   $CA + AB = AB + BD$
   $CB = AD$
5. Points are collinear

Fixed Response Type

Fill in the Blanks

1. Point
2. 3
3. Equal
4. Postulate
5. Axioms

True/False

1. True
2. False
3. True
4. False
5. False
6. False

Single Correct Type Questions

1. (C) Theorem
2. (A) 1
3. (C) Meeting place of two walls
4. (C) 6 lines
5. (C) straight line
6. (B) a definition
7. (A) Only one line can pass through a single point
8. (C) 2
9. (B) Three
10. (C) $MC + CN = MN$
11. (D) equal
12. (B) a postulate
13. (C) Things which are equal to the same things are equal to one another
14. (A) A circle can be drawn with any centre and any radius
15. (C) an axiom
16. (C) Postulate
17. (A) $PQ + QR = PR$

Multiple Correct Type Questions

1. (A,B,C,D)
2. (A,B,C,D)
3. (A,B,C)

4. (A,C)
5. (C)
6. (D)
7. (D)
8. (C)
9. (A,D)
10. (D)
11. (C)

Free Response Type

Very Short Answer Type Questions

1. 1
2. Triangle or Rectangle
3. If equal are added to equals, the wholes are equal.
4. (i) False (ii) False (iii) False (iv) True (v) True (vi) True (vii) True
5. (i) Infinite (ii) One
6. 1.
7. AB, AC, BC then $BC = BA + AC$
8. (i) 0 (ii) 1
9. (a) A Part of a line.
   (b) Distance between circumference and centre of a circle
10. (a) A quadrilateral in which all sides and angles are equal.
    (b) Angle between two lines is 90°

Short Answer Type Questions

1. $AC + BC = AB$
   $2AC = AB$
   $AC = \frac{1}{2}AB.$

2. Every line segment consist of infinte points.
4. $3x + 5 = 17$ then $3x + 5 - 5 = 17 - 5$
   then $3x = 12$ then $x = 4$
   If equal are subtracted from equals, the remainders are equal.
5. (i) 1 (ii) Infinite
6. AB and CD are parallel.
8. $AB = CD$ then add BC in both
   $AB + BC = BC + CD$
   $AC = BD$
9. If equal are added to equals, the remainders are equal.
   $a - 15 = 25$ add 15 both side
   $a - 15 + 15 = 25 + 15$ then $a = 40$.
10. $AC = CB$ and $XD = DY$
    $AC = XD$
    $2AC = 2XD$
    $AB = XY$
11. As from above
12. $\angle 1 + \angle 2 = \angle 3 + \angle 4$ then $\angle A = \angle C$

Long Answer Type Questions

1. (i) $AB = BC \Rightarrow \frac{AB}{2} = \frac{BC}{2} \Rightarrow AM = CN$
   (ii) $BM = BN \Rightarrow 2BM = 2BN \Rightarrow AB = BC$
3. Yes for that they should be parallel.
4. (i) False
   (ii) Yes.
5. Read the following axioms:
   (i) Yes
   (ii) Yes
   (iii) Yes

CHAPTER 6 LINES AND ANGLES

Check Point 1

1. $180 - 100° 48' = 79° 12'$
2. $x = 180 - x$ then $x = 180$
3. $x = 90 - x$ then $x = 45$
4. $5y + 5y + 2y = 180$ then $12y = 180$ then $y = 15$

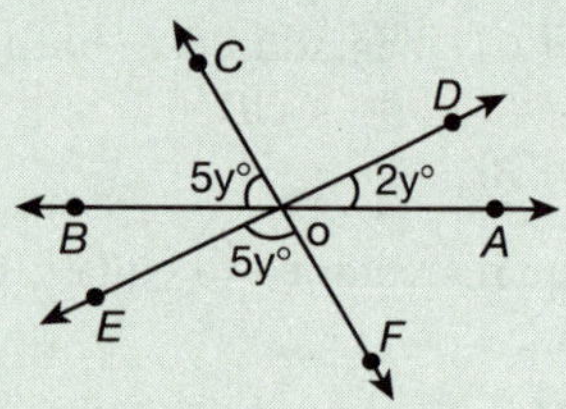

5. $7x + 5x = 180$ then $12x = 180$ then $x = 15$
   then angles are 105 and 75

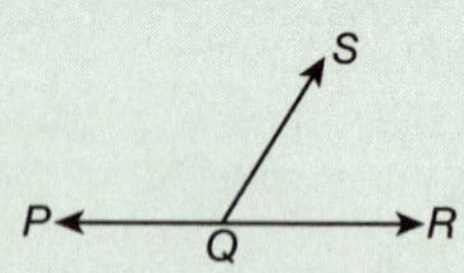

Check Point 2

6. (i) None
   (ii) (1, 6) and (2, 5)

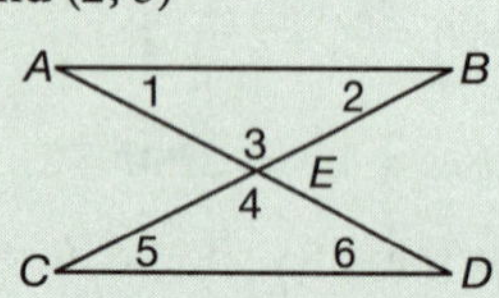

7. $4x = 2.5x + 24$ then $1.5x = 24$ then $x = 16$

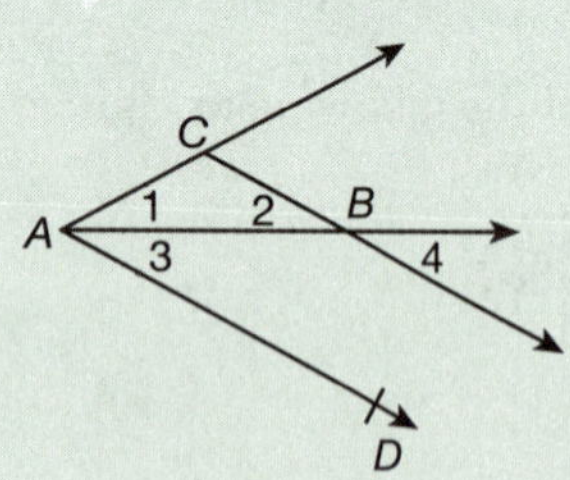

8. $2x + 105 = 180$ then $2x = 75$ then $x = 37.5$

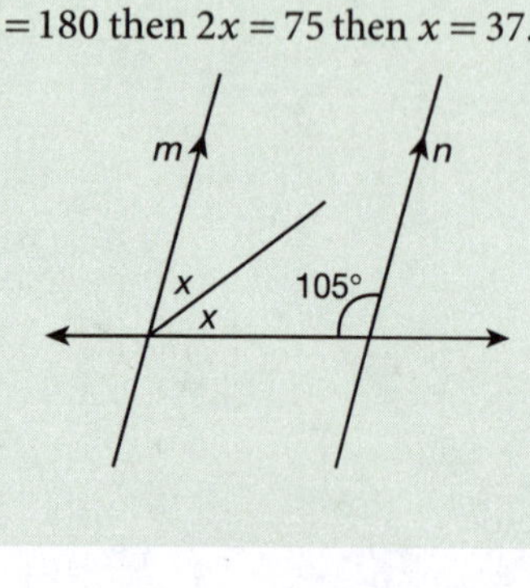

9. $y = 75$ and $x + 75 = 180$ then $x = 105$

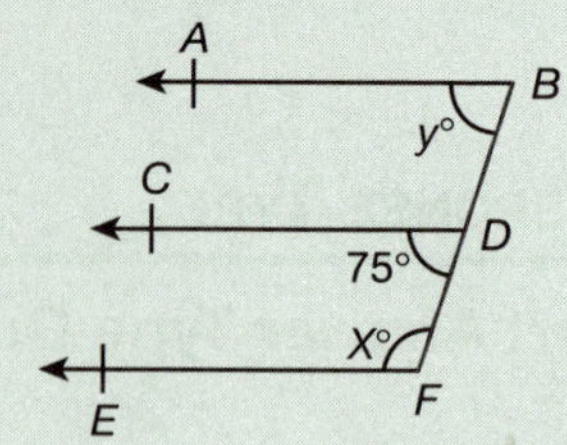

10. $\angle FEX = 180 - 110 - 30 = 40°$ and $\angle XFE = 60°$
    then $\angle FXE = 100°$

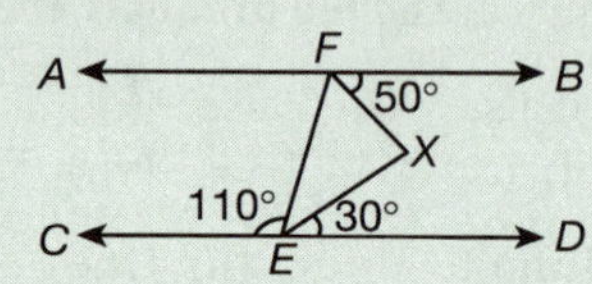

Check Point 3

11. Let the angles are a, b, c then $a + b + c = 180$
    then $70 + c = 180$ then $c = 110$
    $a + b = 70$ and $a - b = 10$ then $a = 40$ and $b = 30$
12. Let the angles are
    a, b and c then $a = b + c$
    then $a + b + c = 180$ then $2a = 180°$
    then $a = 90$ so triangle is right angled triangle
13. As $A + B + C = 180$ then $2A + 2B + 2C = 360°$
    then $3B + 2B + 5B = 10B = 360°$
    then $B = 36°$ and $2A = 108°$
    then $A = 54°$ and $C = 90°$
14. Let the angles are
    a, b and c then $a = \frac{b+c}{2}$ then $b + c = 2a$
    then $a + 2a = 180°$
    then $3a = 180°$ then $a = 60°$ and $b + c = 120°$ as $b = c$
    then $b = c = 60$ so triangle is equilateral triangle
15. $AB = AC$ then $\angle B = \angle C$ then $\angle B + \angle C = 140°$
    then $2\angle B = 140°$ then $\angle B = 70°$
    In triangle HBC $\angle B + 2\angle HCK = 180°$
    then $\angle HCK = 55°$

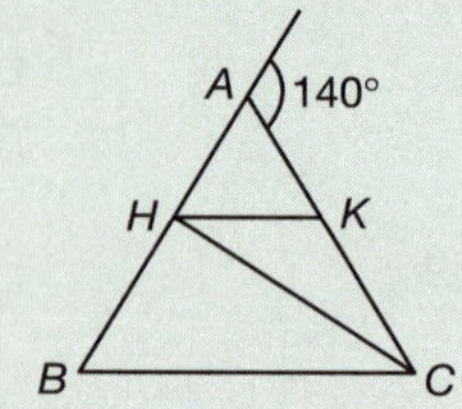

FIXED RESPONSE TYPE

Fill in the Blanks

1. $a+b=90$ and $b+c=180$ and $a+c=170$ then $2(a+b+c)=440$ then $a+b+c=220$
2. $180-x+90-y=\frac{x+y}{2}$ then $540=3(x+y)$ then $x+y=180$ and $x-y=10$ then $2x=190$ $x=95$ and $y=85$
3. $x-(180-x)=100$ then $2x=180$ then $x=140$ and $180-x=40$ then ratio $=\frac{140}{40}=\frac{7}{2}$
4. $180-3b=2(90-b-15)\Rightarrow 180-3b=180-2b-30$ then $b=30$ and $a=45$
5. let the angle is x. Then $\frac{90-x}{180-x}=\frac{1}{2}$ then $180-2x=180-x$ then $x=0$.
6. Then $AB:AC=1:1$ triangle is isosceles.

True/False

1. True
2. False
3. False
4. True
5. True

Single Correct Type Questions

1. (C)
2. (B) $x+x-14=90$ then $2x=104$ then $x=52$
3. (B)
4. (A) $\angle BAC=\angle BAX+\angle XAC$ then $\angle XAC=70-42=28°$
5. (D) $180-x=3(90-x)$ then $180-x=270-3x$ then $2x=90$ so $x=45$.
6. (B) $a+b=180$ then $3a+3b=540$ and $2a-3b=60$ then $5a=600$ then $a=120$ and $b=60$ $\frac{a}{b}=\frac{120}{60}=2$ then $\frac{4a}{5b}=\frac{8}{5}$
7. (B)
8. (D)
9. (A) $45+110+\angle FDC=180°$ then $\angle FDC=25°$

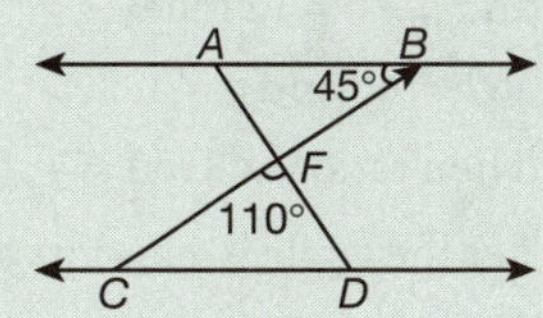

10. (D) $x+20=70$ then $x=50$

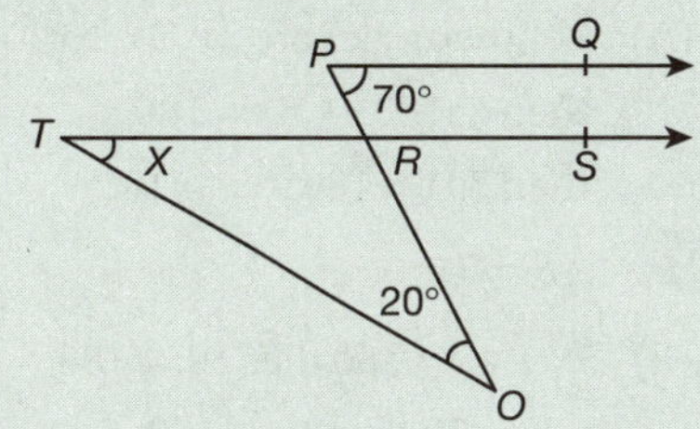

11. (C) Let the angles are a, b and c then $a=b+c$ then $a+b+c=180$ then $2a=180$ then $a=90$ so triangle is right angled triangle
12. (B) $\angle ADC=\angle ACD=x$ and $\angle DBA=\angle DAB=y$ then $y+y=x$ then $y=\frac{x}{2}$ $x+\frac{x}{2}=75$ then $\frac{3x}{2}=75$ then $x=50$

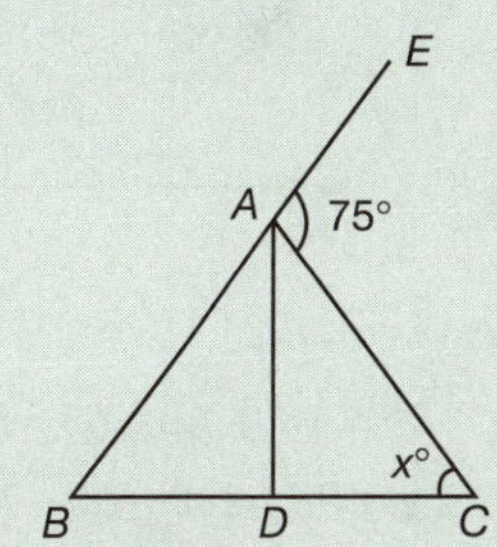

13. (C) $\angle PQR+75=105°$ then $\angle PQR=30°$

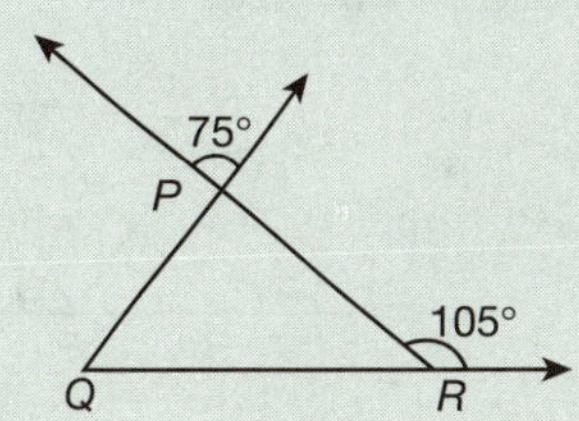

14. (D)
15. (A)

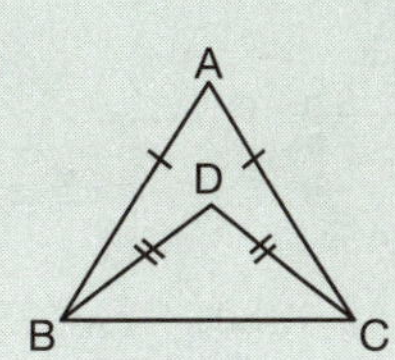

16. **(A)** Let the angles are a and b
then $a+b+72=180$ then $a+b=108$
and $a-b=12$ then $2a=120$
so $a=60$ and $b=48$.
Then ratio is $48:60=4:5$.

17. **(A)** Let the angle is x and its complementary is $90-x$
then $90-x-x=18$ then $2x=72$ then $x=36$.

18. **(A)** Let the angles are $2x, 3x, 5x$
then $2x+3x+5x=180$
then $10x=180$ so $x=18$
$\angle B=54$.

19. **(B)** $5x+4x=180$ then $9x=180$
so $x=20$ then $5x=100$

20. **(A)**

21. **(C)** Let the angles are a, b and c
then $a+b+c=180$
and $a=b+c$ then $2a=180$
then $a=90$.

22. **(A)** $\angle BOD=\angle AOC$ and $\angle BOE=100-60=40°$
and $\angle COE=180-100=80°$
Reflex $\angle COE=280°$.

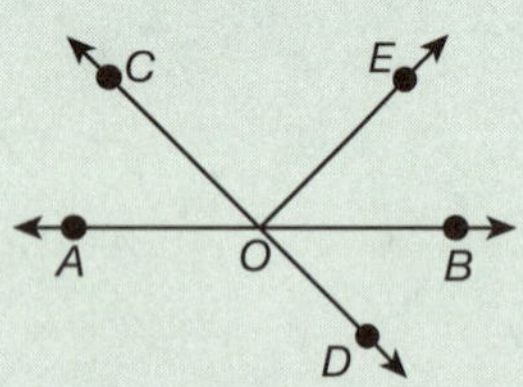

23. **(B)** $\angle YBP=180-60-65=55°$
and $\angle YPB=180-60-75=45°$
then $\angle BYP=180-45-55=80°$.
$\angle CYX=80°$ then $\angle CXY=100-80-60=40°$.

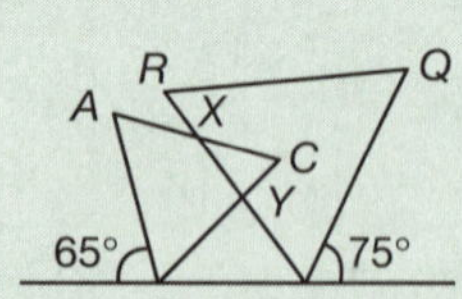

24. **(B)**

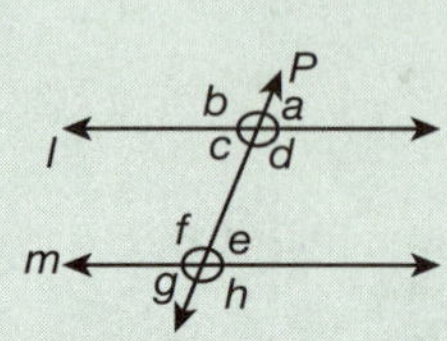

$c=a=e=g=45°$
and $b=d=f=h=180-45=135°$

25. **(C)**

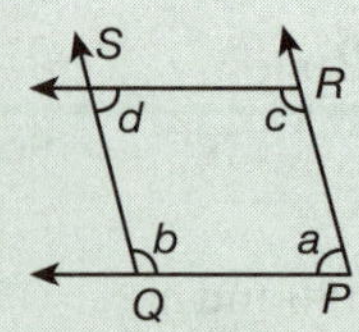

$a+c=180°$ then $a=60°$

Multiple Correct Type Questions

1. **(A,B,C)**

2. **(C)** $x=45$ and $y=90$ then $\frac{x}{y}=\frac{1}{2}$

3. **(A,C)**

4. **(B)**

5. **(A,B)**

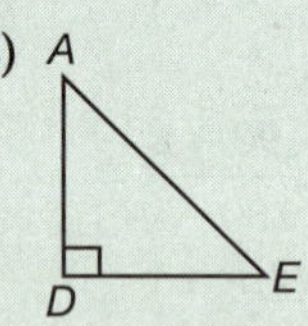

6. **(A)** Correct option is (A)
Exterior angles = Sum of internally opposite angles in a triangle
$\therefore z=w+n,\ n=b+a,\ m=y+x,\ c=w+m$
$x+y+n=x+y+b+a=m+b+a$
$(\because m=y+x)$
$\therefore x+y+n=a+b+m$

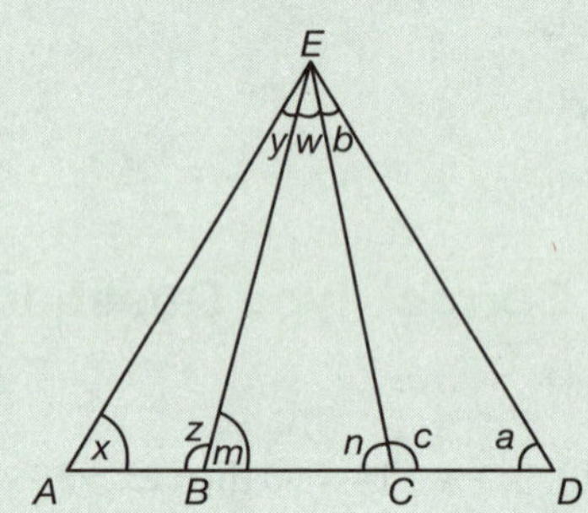

7. **(A)**

8. **(A,C)**

9. **(A,C,D)** $\angle FAB=65-25=40°$
$=\angle BFA$ and $\angle FBG=80°$

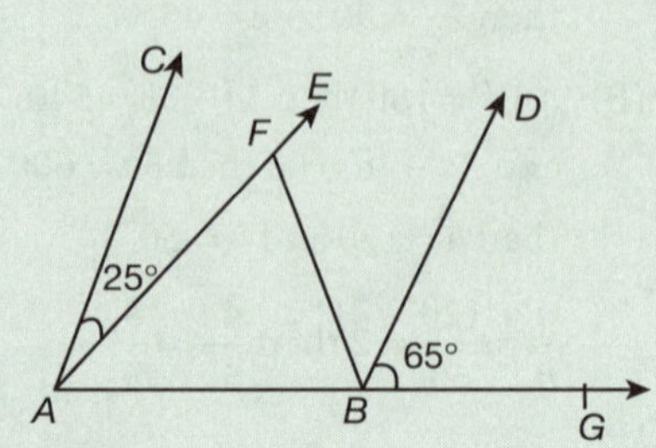

10. **(A,B,D)** $\angle 1 = \angle 3 = 75°$ and $\angle 2 = 105°$

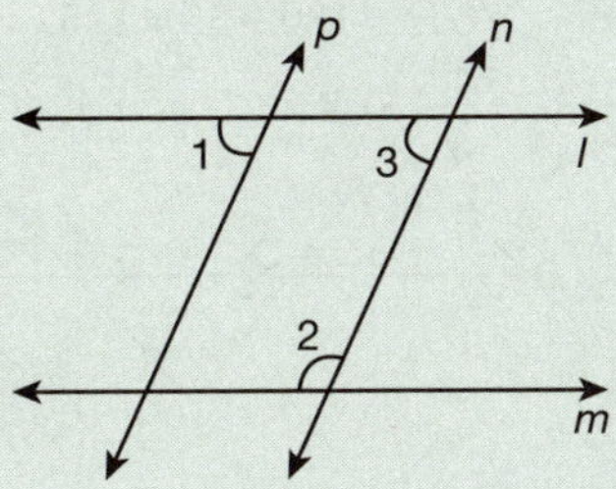

11. **(D)**

12. **(A)**

13. **(B)** $(x-40)° + (x-20)° + \left(\frac{1}{2}x - 10\right)° = 180°$

then $\frac{5x}{2} = 250$ then $x = 100$ then angles are 60, 80 and 40.

Match Type Questions

1. (i) $90 - 13 = 77$ (R)

(ii) $Y + 50 = 127$ then $y = 77$ (R)

(iii) $y + 167 = 180$ then $y = 13$ (P)

(iv) $180 - 13 = 167$ (S)

2. (i) $X + 50 + 20 = 180$ then $x = 110$ (Q)

(ii) $x + 45 + 60 = 180$ then $x = 75$ (P)

(iii) $x = 360 - 55 - 25 = 280$ (S)

(iv) $x + 30 = 75$ then $x = 45$ (R)

3. (i) $\frac{(3-2)180}{3} = 60$ (S)

(ii) $\frac{(4-2)180}{4} = 90$ (R)

(iii) $\frac{(5-2)180}{5} = 108$ (P)

(iv) $\frac{(6-2)180}{6} = 120$ (Q)

Assertion and Reason Type Questions

1. **(A)**

2. **(A)**

Comprehension Type Questions

Passage-1

ΔABC is an isosceles triangle in which $\angle B = \angle C$ and $LM \parallel BC$. If $\angle A = 50°$.

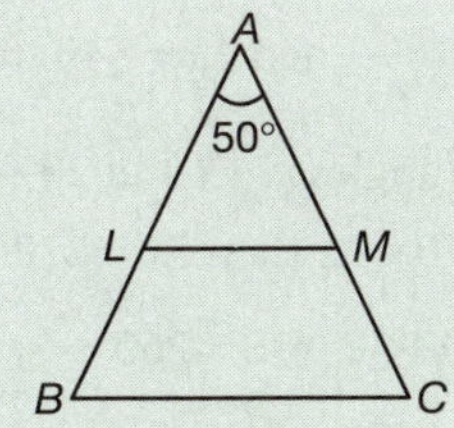

1. **(A)**

2. **(B)** $\angle LMC = \angle LAM + \angle ALM = 50 + 65 = 115°$ is:

3. **(C)** $\angle ALM = \angle LBC = 65°$

Passage-2

4. **(A)** $\angle CBO = \frac{180 - y}{2}$ is:

5. **(A)**

6. **(A,B,D,C)**

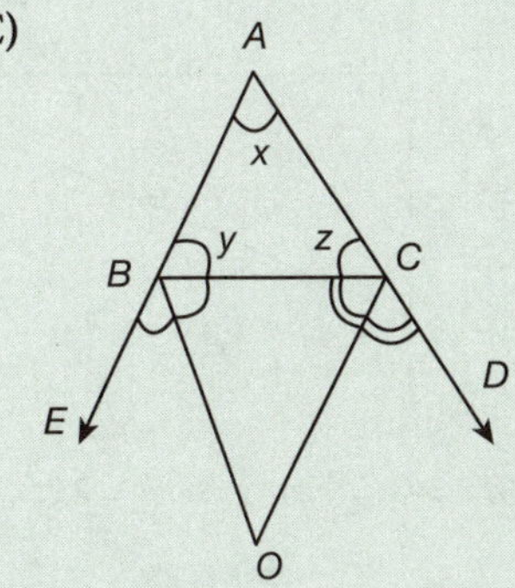

Numerical Type Questions

1.

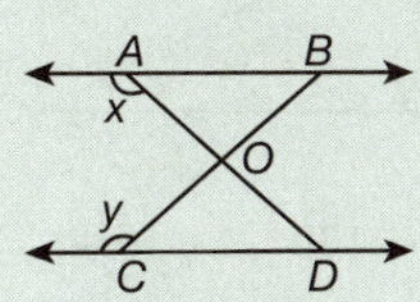

$\angle OAB = 180 - 125 = 55°$

and $\angle OBA = \angle OCD = 180 - 135 = 45°$

then $\angle AOB = 180 - 45 - 55 = 80°$.

2. $\frac{AB}{BC} = \frac{2}{1} = \frac{DE}{EF} = \frac{5}{EF}$ then $EF = \frac{5}{2} = 2.5$

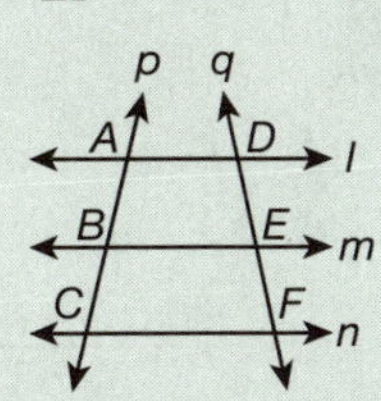

3. $\angle COD + \angle AOC + \angle BOD = 180°$

then $\angle COD = 180 - 100 = 80°$.

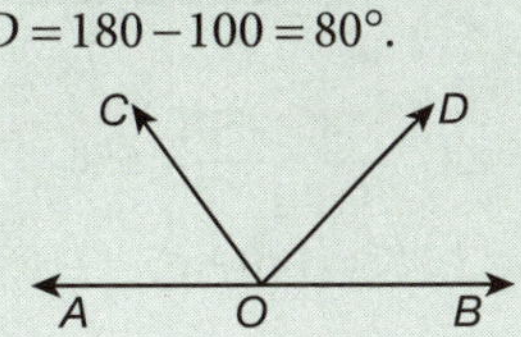

4. $180 - x = \frac{x}{3}$ then $4x = 540$ then $x = 135$

5. Let the angles are x and $90 - x$

$2x = 270 - 3x$ then $5x = 270$ then $x = 54$.

6. $x = 360 - 30 - 70 = 260$

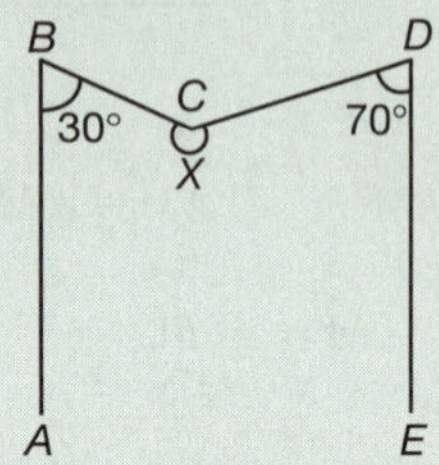

7. From the figure $x = y$ and $y + 55 = 180$

then $y = 125$ and $z + 55 = 90$ then $z = 35$

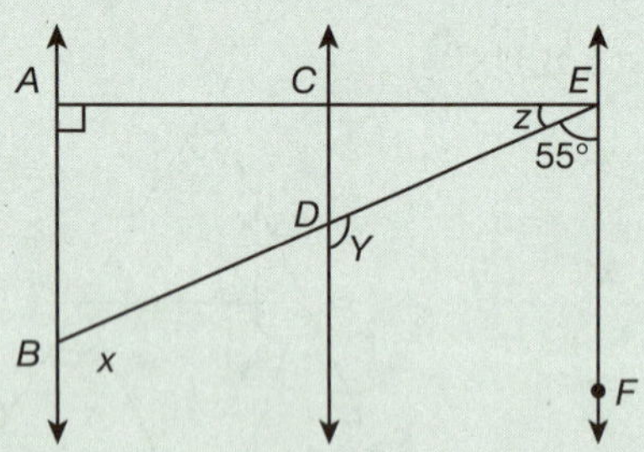

8. As $BD = DC$ then $\angle BDA = 2x = 60°$ then $x = 30$.

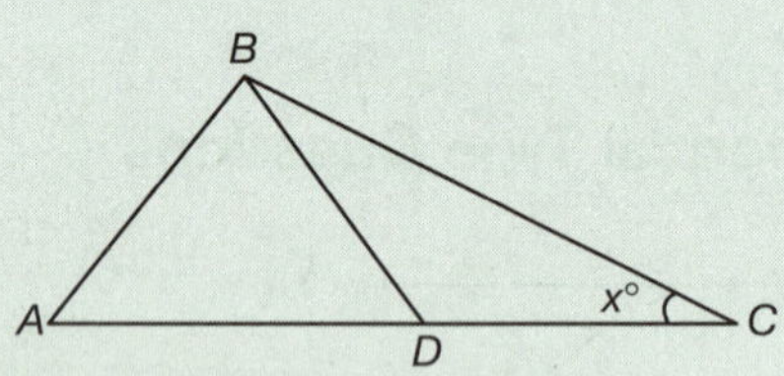

9. $y : z = 3 : 7$ then $3a + 7a = 180$

then $a = 18$. then $x = z = 126$.

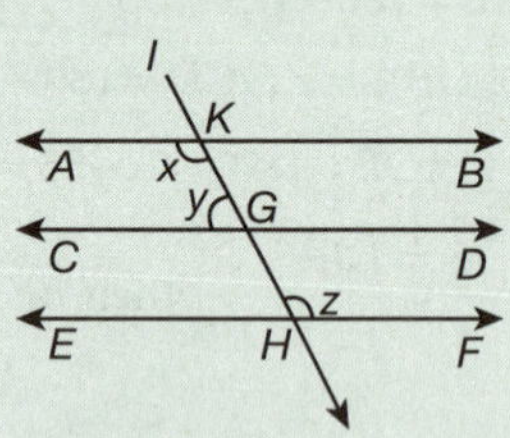

10. $\angle GEF = 126 - 90 = 36°$ and $\angle FGE = 90 - 36 = 54°$.

$\angle AGE = \angle GED = 126°$.

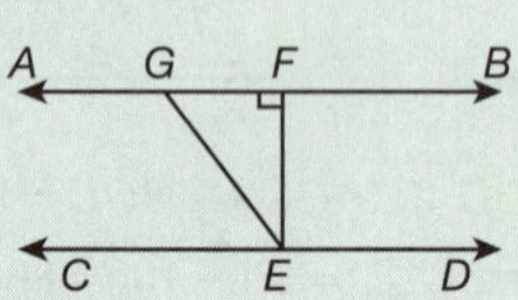

11. $\angle B = \angle C = \frac{180 - 50}{2} = 65°$.

then $\angle LMC = 180 - 65 = 115°$

12. $\angle FGE = \angle ECD = \angle ACB = 55°$

then $\angle FGH = 180 - 55 = 125°$

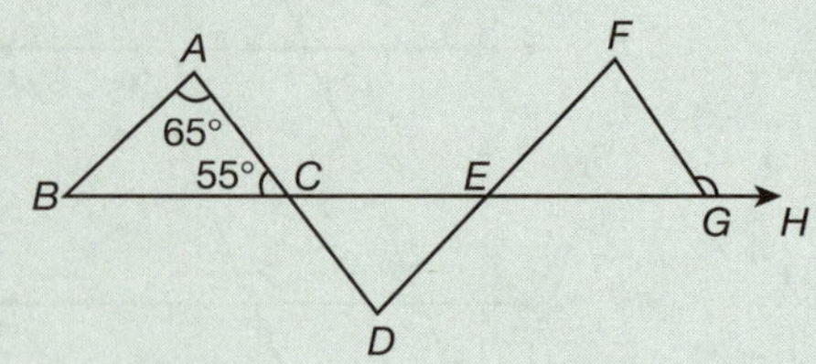

13. $x + 28 = 65$ and $x = 37$ then $y = 90 - 37 = 53$.

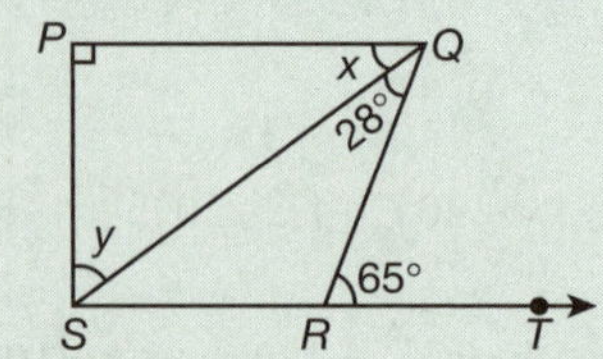

14. $\angle MAB + \angle BAP + \angle PAC + \angle CAN = 180°$

$2x + x + 2y + y = 180$ then $x + y = 60$

then $\angle MAB + \angle PAC = 2(x + y) = 120°$.

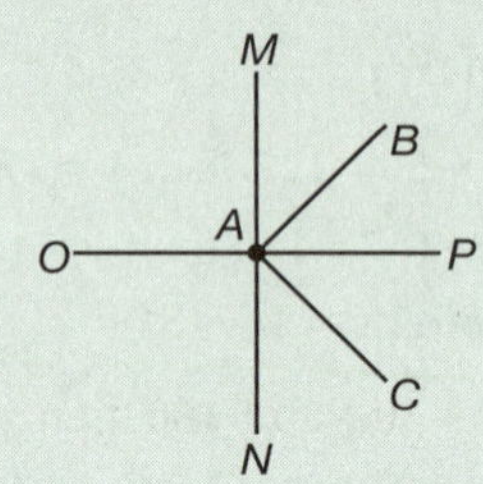

15.

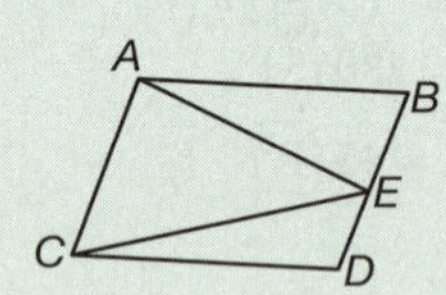

$\angle AEC = 25 + 30 = 55°$.

Higher Order Thinking Skills (HOTS)

1. **(B)** $\angle GFE = 180 - 50 = 130°$

then $\angle FGE = 180 - 40 - 130 = 10°$

then $\angle BHJ = 20°$.

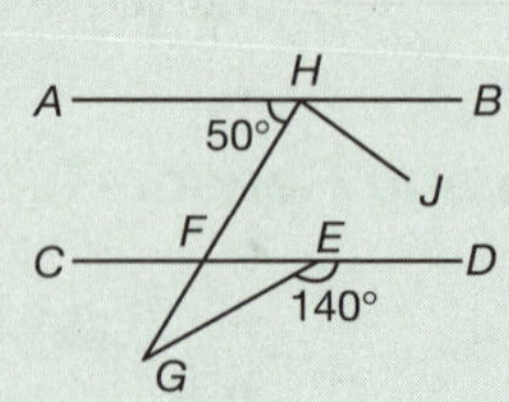

2. **(D)** Required Angle $= 360 - 100 - 40 = 220$

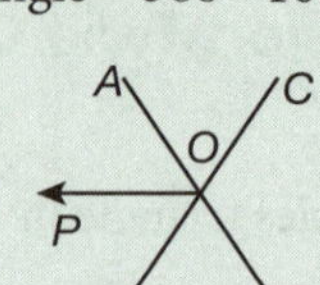

3. **(B)** Then ratio of sides are 5 : 4 : 3 then triangle is right angled triangle.

4. **(B)** $\angle P + \angle Q + \angle R + \angle S + \angle T + \angle U$
$= 540 - 180 = 360°$.

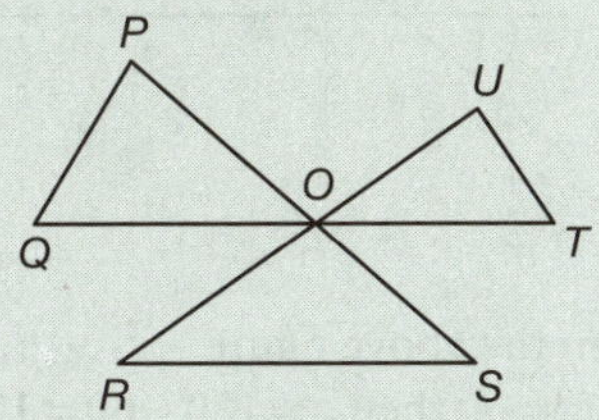

5. **(C)** In ΔABC
$AB = AC$
$\angle B = \angle C$ (isosceles triangle property) (1)
$\angle ADC = \angle B + 30$ (Exterior angle property) (2)
Also, $\angle AED = \angle EDC + \angle C$
(Exterior angle property)
$\angle AED = \angle EDC + \angle B$ **(From 1)**
Now, given, $AD = AE$
hence, $\angle ADE = \angle AED$
(Isosceles triangle property)
Thus, $\angle ADE = \angle EDC + \angle B$
$\angle ADE + \angle EDC = 2\angle EDC + \angle B$
$\angle ADC = 2\angle + \angle B$
$\angle B + 30 = 2\angle EDC + \angle B$ (From 2)
$\angle EDC = 15°$

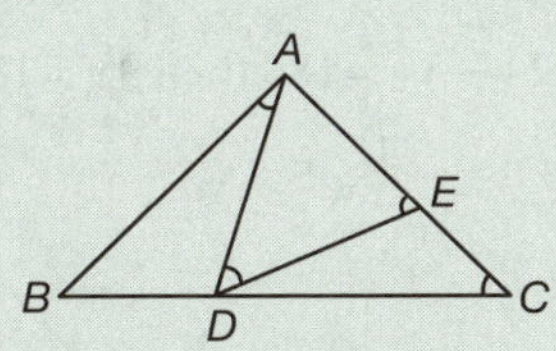

6. **(B)** In $\angle PQR$,
$p + q + \angle R = 180°$
$\Rightarrow \angle R = 180° - (p - q)$
RS is the bisector of $\angle R$.
So, $\angle SRP = \{180° - (p + q)\}/2$
$= 90° - (p + q)/2$
Given $n = 90°$
From ΔRTO, $m + \angle SRT = 90°$
$\Rightarrow \angle m + 90° - (p + q)/2 = 90°$
$\Rightarrow \angle m = (\angle p + \angle q)/2$

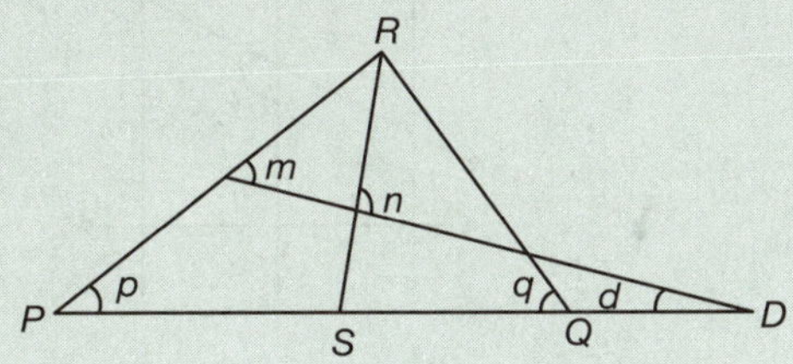

7. **(A)**

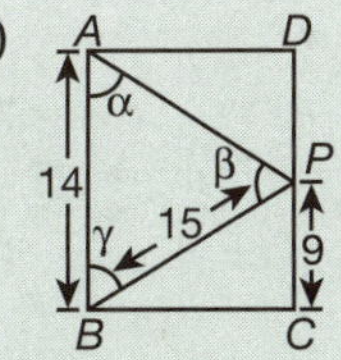

8. **(D)** Let $\angle EAD = \alpha$, then, $\angle AFG = \alpha$ and also $\angle ACB = \alpha$.
Hence $\angle CBD = 2\alpha$ (exterior angle to ΔABC)
Since $CB = CD$, hence $\angle CDB = 2\alpha$
$\angle FGC = 2\alpha$ (exterior angle to ΔAFG).
Since $GF = EF$, $\angle FEG = 2\alpha$
Now, $\angle DCE = \angle DEC = \beta$ (say)
Then, $\angle DEF = \beta - 2\alpha$
Since, $\angle DCB = 180° - (\alpha + \beta)$
Therefore, on ΔDCB,
$180° - (\alpha + \beta) + 2\alpha + 2\alpha = 180°$ or $\beta = 3\alpha$
Further $\angle EFD = \angle EDF = \gamma$ (say)
Then, $\angle EDC = \gamma - 2\alpha$
If CD and EF meet at P,
then $\angle FPD = 180° - 5\alpha$ [$\because \beta = 3\alpha$]
Now in ΔPED, $180° - 5\alpha + \gamma + 2\alpha = 180°$ or $\gamma = 3\alpha$
Therefore, in ΔEFD,
$\alpha + 2\gamma = 180°$ or $\alpha + 6\alpha = 180°$ or $\alpha = 26°$ or approximately 25°

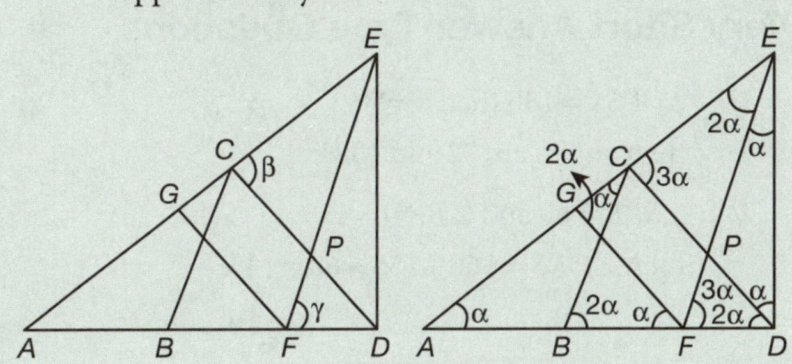

9. **(A)** $\angle BFA = 90 + \dfrac{100}{2} = 140°$

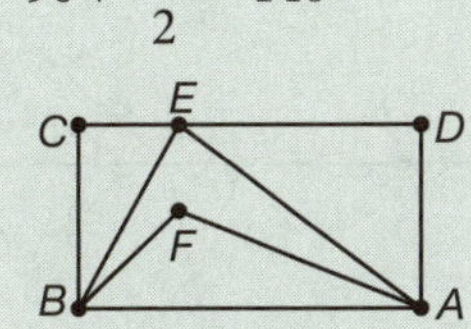

10. **(D)** $y + z = 120$ then $3y = 120$ so $y = 40$ and $z = 80$
Now $x + y + z + 180 = 360$ then $x = 60$
Then $\dfrac{x + z}{y} = \dfrac{140}{40} = \dfrac{7}{2}$

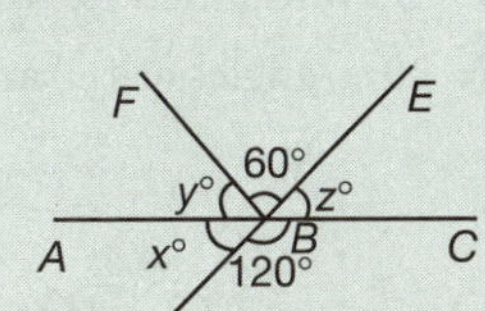

11. **(B)**

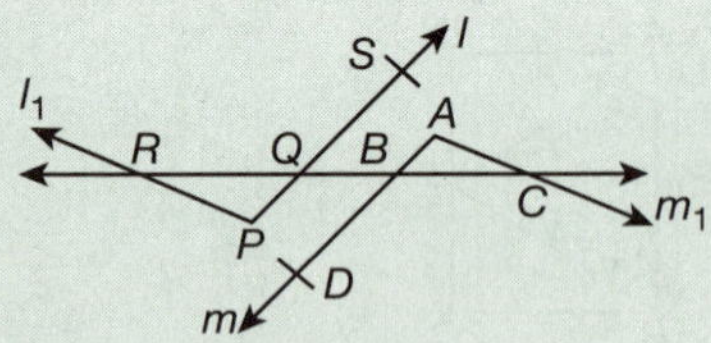

$\angle DBC = \angle PQB = 110$ then $\angle PQR = 70$

and $\angle RPQ = 40$ then $\angle QPR = 180 - 70 - 40 = 70$

12. **(C)**

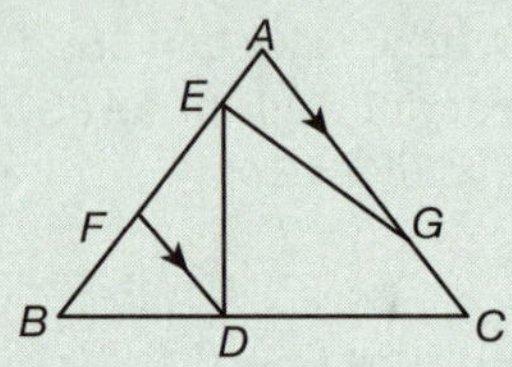

In ΔABC $\angle FDB + \angle FDE = 180$

then $\angle FDB = 115$ then $\angle EGA = 115$

13. **(D)**

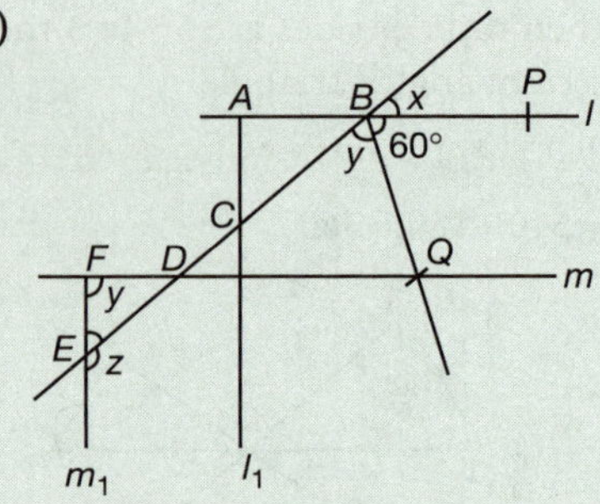

From the above figure

$x = y = 60$ then $z = 180 - 60 = 120$

14. **(D)**

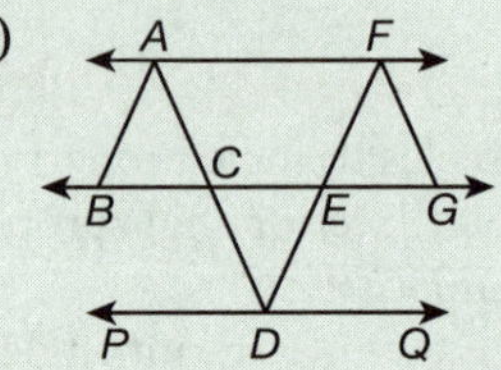

$\angle ABC = \angle FEG = 30$

and $\angle FGE = \angle ACB = 70$ then $\angle CDE = 80$.

15. **(C)**

Free Response Type

Very Short Answer Type Questions

1. $2x + 3x = 180$ then $x = 36$

   then angles are 72 and 108.

2. $\angle SRB = 60$ and $\angle BRQ = 155$

   then $\angle QRS = 360 - 155 - 60 = 145$

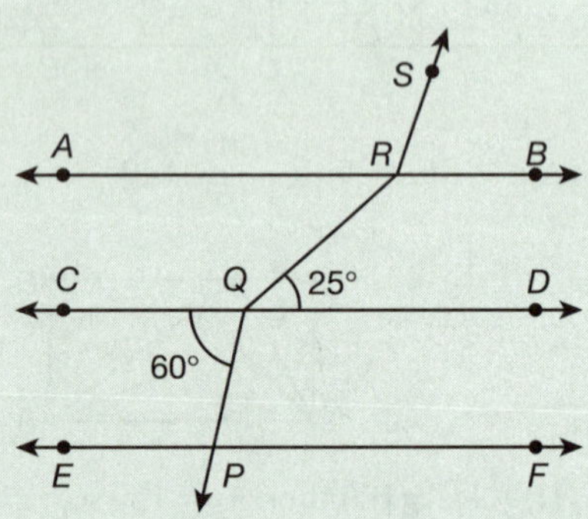

3. $x + x = 105$ then $x = \dfrac{105}{2} = 52.5$

4. $40 + 4x + 3x = 180$ then $7x = 140$

   then $x = 20$ so angles are 60 and 80

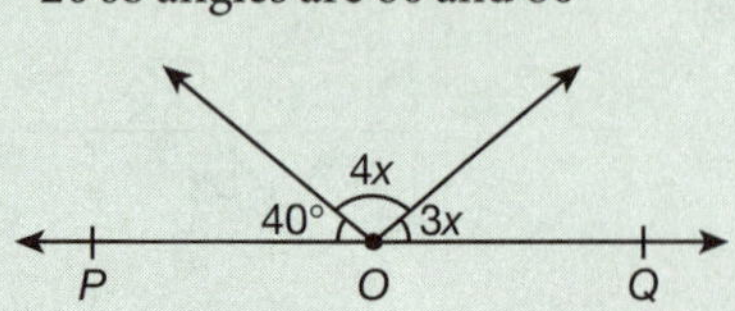

5. $2x + 3x + 4x = 180$ then $9x = 180$ then $x = 20$.

   So angles are 40, 60 and 80

6. $2y + 2y + 5y = 180$ then $9y = 180$ then $y = 20$.

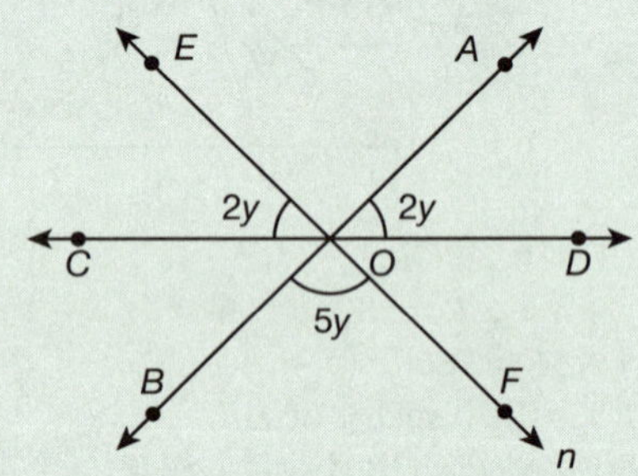

7. Corresponding angles are equal so lines are parallel.

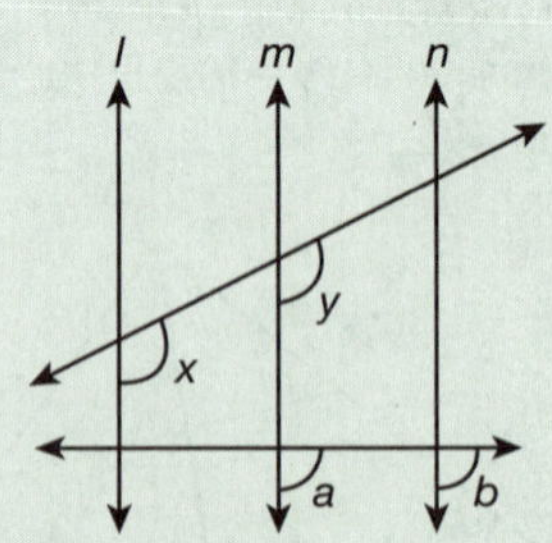

8. Let $\angle DOC = x$ then $\angle COE = 90 - x$

   then $\angle DOC = \angle DOA = x$

   and $\angle COE = \angle EOB = 90 - x$

$\angle AOD + \angle DOC + \angle COE + \angle EOB = 180.$

Then A, O, B are collinear.

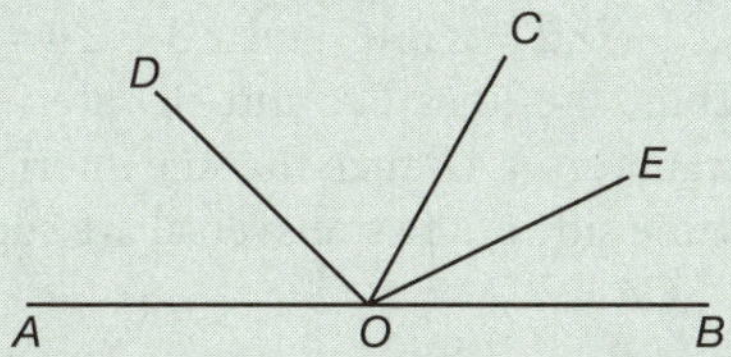

Short Answer Type Questions

1. We know that if a transversal intersects two parallel lines, then alternate interior angles are equal.

From the figure,

The alternate interior angles are $\angle EAB$ and $\angle ABH$

So, $\angle EAB = \angle ABH$ (1)

Dividing (1) by 1/2 on both sides,

$\angle EAB/2 = \angle ABH/2$ (2)

Since AP is the bisector of $\angle EAB$

$\angle EAP = \angle PAB$

$\angle EAB = \angle EAP + \angle PAB$

$\angle EAB = \angle PAB + \angle PAB$

$\angle EAB = 2\angle PAB$

$\angle PAB = \angle EAB/2$ (3)

Since BQ is the bisector of $\angle ABH$

$\angle ABQ = \angle HBQ$

$\angle ABH = \angle ABQ + \angle HBQ$

$\angle ABH = \angle ABQ + \angle ABQ$

$\angle ABH = 2\angle ABQ$

$\angle ABQ = \angle ABH/2$ (4)

Using (3) and (4) in (2) we get,

$\angle PAB = \angle ABQ$

$\angle PAB$ and $\angle ABQ$ are the alternate interior angles of the lines AP and BQ with transversal AB

Therefore, the lines AB and BQ are parallel.

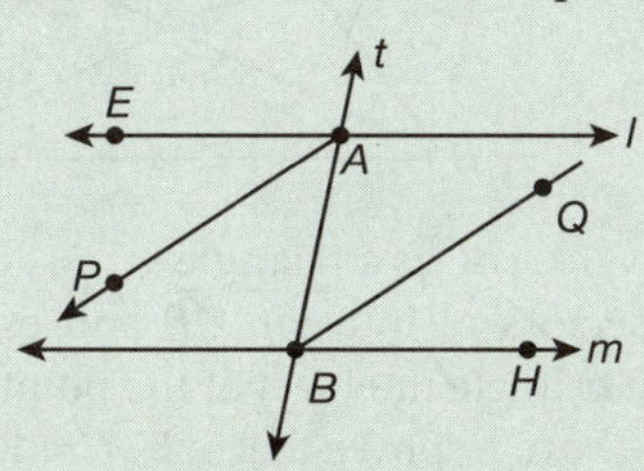

2. It is given that, $BA \parallel ED$ and $BC \parallel EF$.

Construction: Extend ED such that it intersects BC at G. Now, $BA \parallel GE$ and BC is a transversal.

$\therefore \angle ABC = \angle EGC$ (1)

(Pair of corresponding angles)

Also, $BC \parallel EF$ and EG is a transversal.

$\therefore \angle EGC + \angle GEF = 180°$ (2)

(Interior angles on the same side of the transversal are supplementary)

From (1) and (2), we have

$\angle ABC + \angle GEF = 180°$

Or $\angle ABC + \angle DEF = 180°$

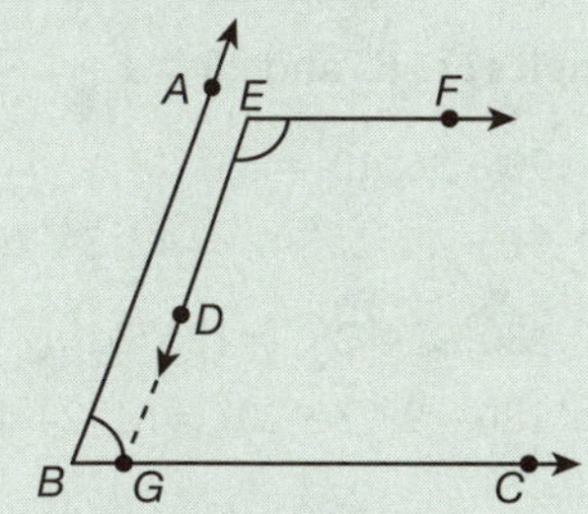

3. $\angle EAP = \angle PAB = x$ and $\angle RBP = \angle PBA = y$

$\angle EAB + \angle RBA = 180 = 2x + 2y = 2(x + y)$

then $x + y = 90$

$\angle APB = 180 - 90 = 90°.$

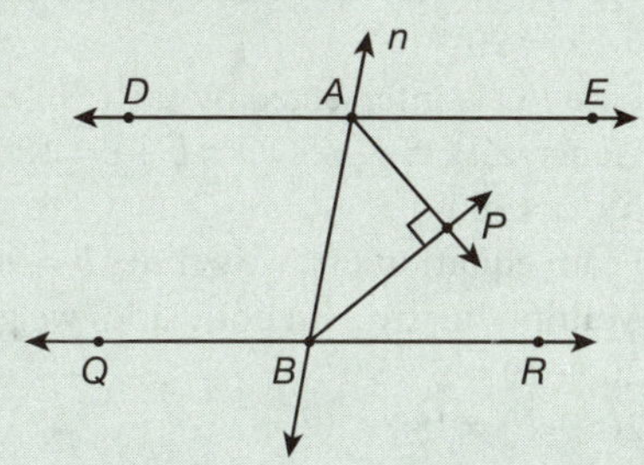

4. $2x + 3x + 4x = 180$ then $9x = 180$ then $x = 20.$

So angles are 40, 60 and 80

5. $x + y + w + z = 360$ then $2(x + y) = 360$

then $x + y = 180.$

Adjacent angles which are supplimentary then AOB is straight line.

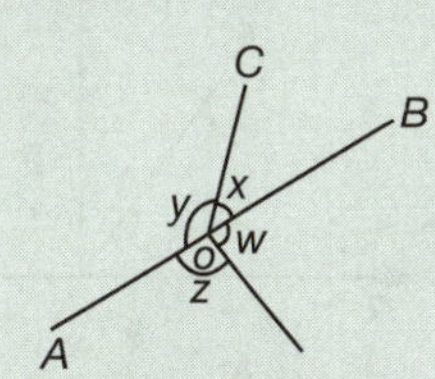

6. $x + y + z = 180$ then $5a + 4a + 6a = 180$

then $15a = 180$ then $a = 12$

$x = 60$ and $y = 48$ and $z = 72$

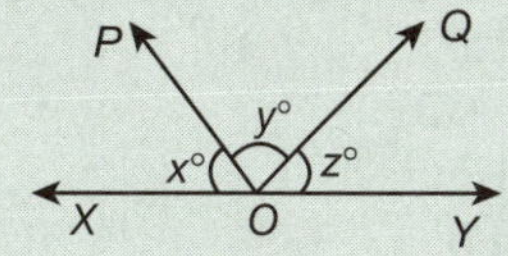

7. $\angle POA = \angle ROB$ then $2\angle POA = 180 - 112 = 68°$

then $\angle POA = 34°$

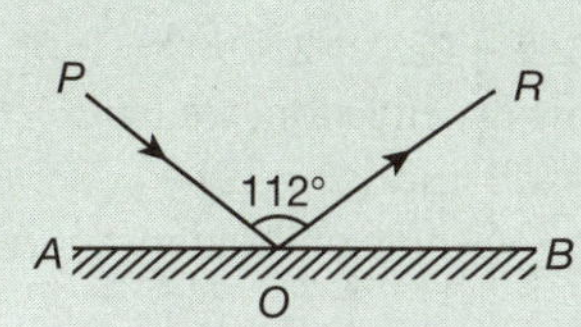

8. $13x + 5x = 90$ then $18x = 90$ then $x = 5$

so angles are 65 and 25.

9. (i) $90 - 36°40' = 53°20'$

(ii) $90 - 42°25'36'' = 47°34'24''$

10. (i) $180 - 54°28'' = 125°32''$

(ii) $180 - 98°35'20'' = 81°24'40''$

Long Answer Type Questions

1. Let $\angle ROS = a$, $\angle POS = b$ and $\angle SOQ = c$.
To prove that: $a = 1/2(c - b)$.
Since $\angle ROQ = \angle ROP = 90°$,
We can say, $\angle POS + \angle SOR = \angle POR$
$b + a = 90°$ (1)
Line PQ is intersected by ray OS.
Hence $\angle POS + \angle SOQ = b + c = 180°$
$b + c = 180°$ (2)
From equation (1), we get $a + b = 90°$
Multiplying by 2 on both sides we get,
$2(a + b) = 2 \times 90°$
$2(a + b) = 180°$ (3)
Comparing equations (3) and (2),
$2(a + b) = b + c$
$2a + 2b = b + c$
$2a = b + c - 2b$
$2a = c - b$
$a = \frac{1}{2}(c - b)$
$\therefore \angle ROS = 1/2\ (\angle QOS - \angle POS)$

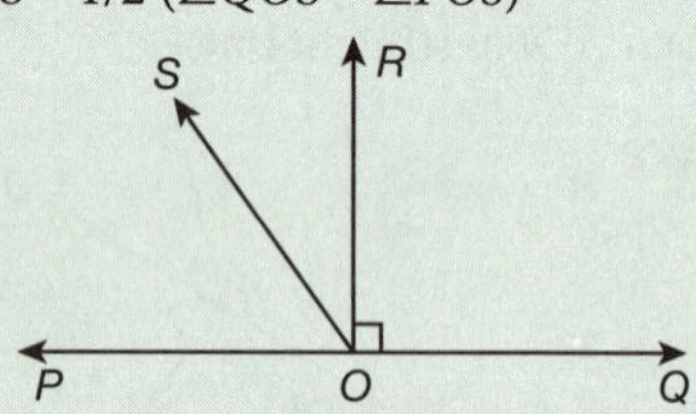

2. AP is normal to the plane mirror OA and BP is normal to the plane mirror OB.
It is given that the two plane mirrors are perpendicular to each other.
Therefore, $BP \parallel OA$ and $AP \parallel OB$.
So, $BP \perp AP$
$(OA \perp OB)$
$\Rightarrow \angle APB = 90°$ (1)
In ΔAPB,
$\angle 2 + \angle 3 + \angle APB = 180°$ (Angle sum property)
$\therefore \angle 2 + \angle 3 + 90° = 180°$ [Using (1)]
$\Rightarrow \angle 2 + \angle 3 = 180° - 90° = 90°$
$\Rightarrow 2\angle 2 + 2\angle 3 = 2 \times 90° = 180°$ (2)
By law of reflection, we have
$\angle 1 = \angle 2$ and $\angle 3 = \angle 4$ (3)
(Angle of incidence = Angle of reflection)

From (2) and (3), we have
$\angle 1 + \angle 2 + \angle 3 + \angle 4 = 180°$
$\Rightarrow \angle BAC + \angle ABD = 180°$
$(\angle 1 + \angle 2 = \angle BAC$ and $\angle 3 + \angle 4 = \angle ABD)$
Thus, the lines CA and BD are intersected by a transversal AB such that the interior angles on the same side of the transversal are supplementary.
$\therefore CA \parallel BD$

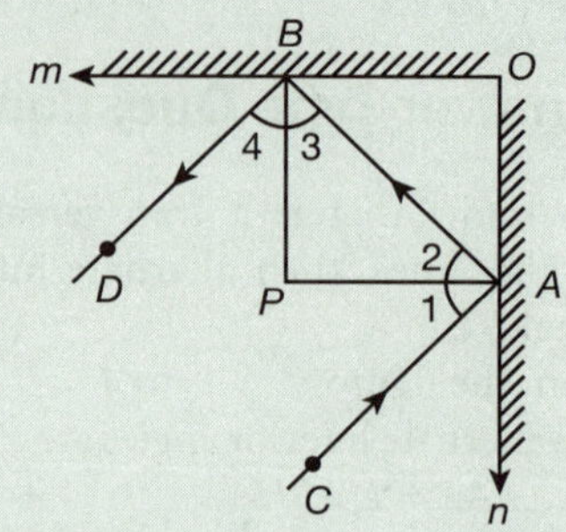

3. **Given:** A ΔABC such that the bisectors of $\angle ABC$ and $\angle ACB$ meet at a point O.
To prove: $\angle BOC = 90° + \angle A/2$
Proof:
In ΔBOC, we have
$\angle 1 + \angle 2 + \angle BOC = 180°$ (1)
In ΔABC, we have,
$\angle A + \angle B + \angle C = 180°$
$\angle A + 2(\angle 1) + 2(\angle 2) = 180°$
$\angle A/2 + \angle 1 + \angle 2 = 90°$
$\angle 1 + \angle 2 = 90° - \angle A/2$
Therefore, in equation 1,
$90° - \angle A/2 + \angle BOC = 180$
$\angle BOC = 90° + \angle A/2$

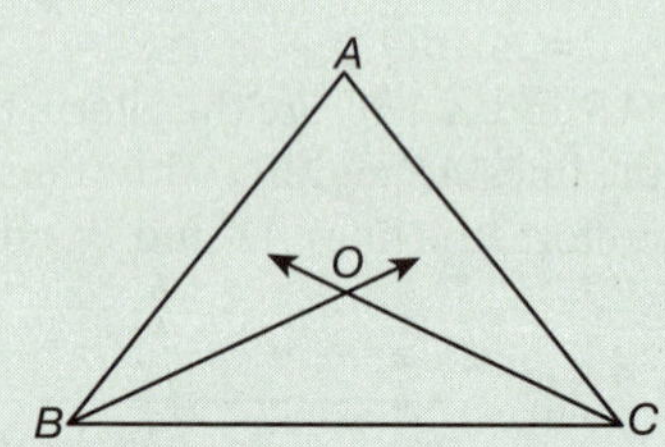

4. Given, ABC is a triangle
Bisectors of interior $\angle B$ and exterior $\angle ACD$ of the triangle intersect at the point T.
We have to prove that $\angle BTC = 1/2\ \angle BAC$.
Extend BC to D.
Bisectors of $\angle ABC$ and $\angle ACD$ meet at T.
Considering triangle ABC,
$\angle C$ is the exterior angle
We know that the exterior angle is equal to the sum of the two opposite interior angles.
$\angle ACD = \angle ABC + \angle CAB$
Dividing by 2 on both sides,
$1/2\ \angle ACD = 1/2\ \angle ABC + 1/2\ \angle CAB$
Given, CT is the bisector of $\angle ACD$

$\angle ACD = \angle ACT + \angle TCD$
$\angle ACT = \angle TCD$
So, $\angle ACD = \angle TCD + \angle TCD$
$\angle ACD = 2\,\angle TCD$
$\angle TCD = 1/2\,\angle ACD$
Now, $\angle TCD = 1/2\,\angle ABC + 1/2\,\angle CAB$ (1)
Considering triangle BTC,
$\angle TCD = \angle BTC + \angle TBC$
Given, BT is the bisector of $\angle ABC$
$\angle ABC = \angle ATB + \angle BTC$
$\angle ATB = \angle BTC$
$\angle ABC = \angle BTC + \angle BTC$
$\angle ABC = 2\angle BTC$
$\angle BTC = 1/2\,\angle ABC$
Now, $\angle TCD = \angle BTC + 1/2\,\angle ABC$ (2)
From (1) and (2),
$1/2\,\angle ABC + 1/2\,\angle CAB = \angle BTC + 1/2\,\angle ABC$
Cancelling common term,
$1/2\,\angle CAB = \angle BTC$
Therefore, $\angle BTC = 1/2\,\angle BAC$

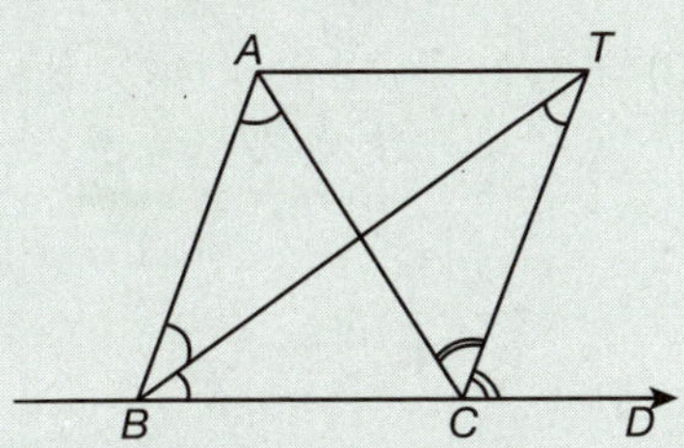

5. Same as Question number 6.

6. Since $AB \parallel CD$
$\angle AGH = \angle DHG$ (Alternate interior angles)
Dividing both side by 2, we have
$\Rightarrow \angle AGH/2 = \angle DHG/2 \Rightarrow \angle 1 = \angle 2$
(GM and HL are bisectors of $\angle AGH$ and $\angle DHG$ respectively)
$\Rightarrow GM \parallel HL$ ($\angle 1$ and $\angle 2$ from a pair of alternate interior angles are equal)
Similarly, $GL \parallel MH$
So, $GMHL$ is a parallelogram.
Since $AB \parallel CD$
We have $\angle BGH + \angle DHG = 180°$
as the sum of interior angles on the same side of the transversal is equal to 180°
Dividing both sides by 2, we have
$\Rightarrow \angle BGH/2 + \angle DHG/2 = 90° \Rightarrow \angle 3 + \angle 2 = 90°$ (1)
In ΔGLH
As the sum of the angles is equal to 180°, we have
$\Rightarrow \angle 2 + \angle 3 + \angle L = 180° \Rightarrow 90° + \angle L = 180°$ (Using (1))
$\Rightarrow \angle L = 180° - 90°$
$\therefore \angle L = 90°$
Thus, in a parallelogram $GMHL$, $\angle L = 90°$
We know that if one of the angles is the right angle in the parallelogram then it is also a rectangle.
Hence, proved that $GHML$ is a rectangle.
Thus, if two parallel lines are intersected by a transversal, then bisectors of the interior angles form a rectangle.

Note: The sum of interior angles on the same side of the transversal is equal to 180°. When two lines are crossed by another line which is called as the transversal the alternate interior angles are equal..

Archive Corner

1. **(D)**

2. **(C)** $x = 180 - 50 - 70 = 60$

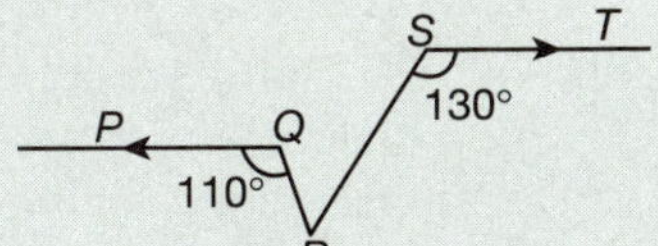

3. **(D)** $\angle PRQ = 180 - 90 - 40 = 50$
then $y = 30 + 50 = 80$.

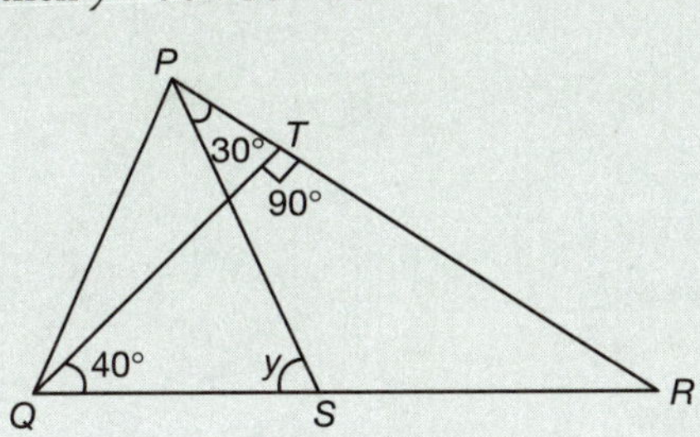

4. **(B)** $x = 180 - 60 - 70 = 50$

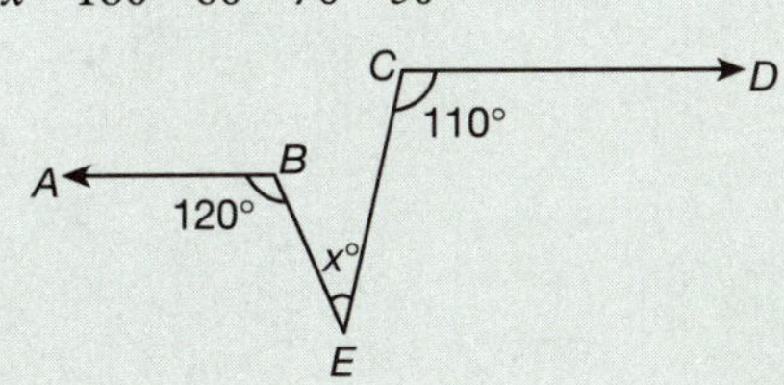

5. **(A)**

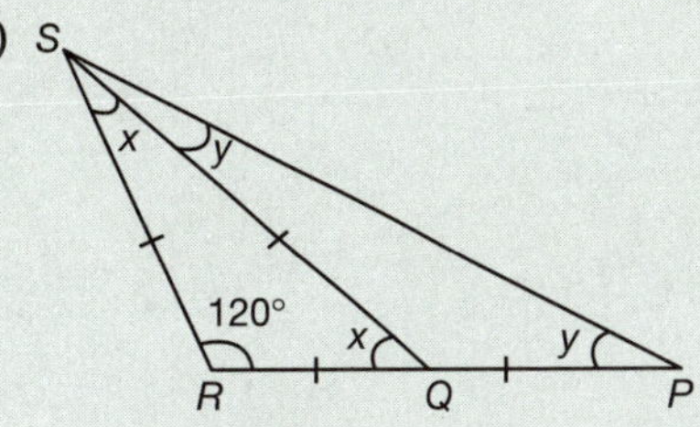

$2x + 120 = 180$ then $x = 30$.
$x + y + y + 120 = 180$
then $2y = 30$ then $y = 15$

6. **(D)** $\angle CEB = \frac{180-150}{2} = 15$ then $x = 60 - 15 = 4$

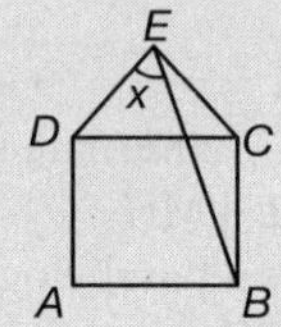

7. **(B)**

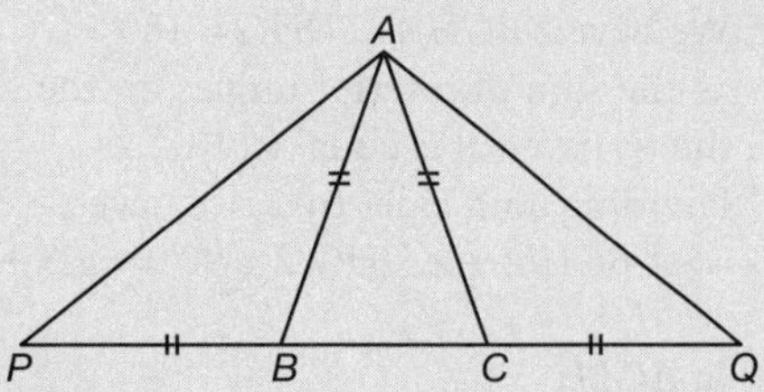

In ΔABC, $AB = AC$

$\Rightarrow \angle ABC = \angle ACB = x$ (say) (i)

[Angles opposite to equal sides are themselves equal]

Similarly, in ΔABP and ΔACQ, $AB = PB$ and $AC = CQ$

$\Rightarrow \angle APB = \angle BAP = y$ (say)

and $\angle AQC = \angle QAC = z$ (say) (ii)

Now, in ΔABC,

$\angle ABC + \angle ACB + \angle BAC = 180°$

$\Rightarrow \angle BAC = 180° - 2x$ (iii)

In ΔABP,

$\angle ABP + \angle APB + \angle BAP = 180°$

$\Rightarrow \angle ABP = 180° - 2y$

From (ii)

Also, $\angle ABP = 180° - x$

[$\because \angle ABC + \angle ABP = 180°$] (iv)

$\Rightarrow 180 - 2y = 180° - x$

$\Rightarrow y = x/2$

$\Rightarrow \angle APB = \angle BAP = x/2 = \angle AQC = \angle QAC$

From (ii)

Now, $\angle PAQ = \angle PAB + \angle BAC + \angle CAQ$

$= x/2 + 180° - 2x + x/2$

$= 180° - x = \angle ABP$

From (iv)

Hence, $\angle PAQ = \angle ABP$

8. **(C)** $1 : \sqrt{2}$

HINTS AND EXPLANATIONS

CHAPTER 7 TRIANGLES

Check Point 1

1. (i) SAS (ii) ASA (iii) RHS

2. In ΔABC and ΔADC
   $AD = BC$ (i)
   $AB = CD$ (ii)
   $AC = AC$ (iii)
   By SSS criteria $\Delta ABC \cong \Delta ADC$.

3. In ΔABD and ΔACD
   $AB = AC$ (Given) (i)
   $DB = CD$ (AD bisects BC) (ii)
   $AD = AD$ (Common side) (iii)
   By SSS criteria $\Delta ABD \cong \Delta ACD$.

4. In ΔAEF and ΔCDB
   $AB = FC$ (given) (i)
   Add BF both sides
   $AF = BC$ (ii)
   $EF = BD$ (given) (iii)
   $\angle AFE = \angle DBC$
   By *SAS* criteria $\Delta AFE \cong \Delta CBD$.

5. $\angle P = \angle R$ (given)
   $PQ = RQ$ (given)
   $\angle PQR = \angle RQP$ (Common angle)
   Then by ASA $\Delta PQT \cong \Delta RQS$

Check Point 2

6. $\angle BCD = \angle BAC + \angle ABC$ then $\angle BCD > \angle BAC$.
   (Exterior angle of a triangle is greater than either of the two interior opposite angles)

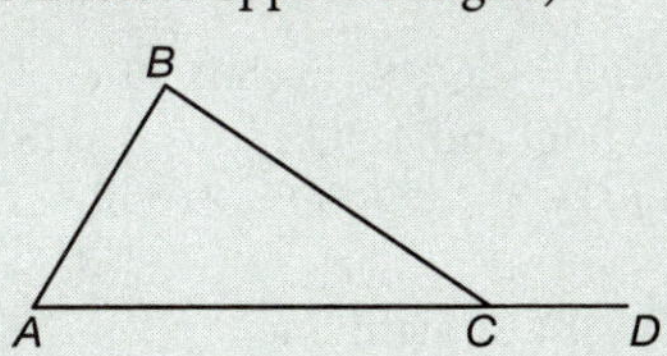

7. $\angle FED = \angle DCE + \angle CDE$
   then $\angle FED > \angle CDE = \angle CBA$.

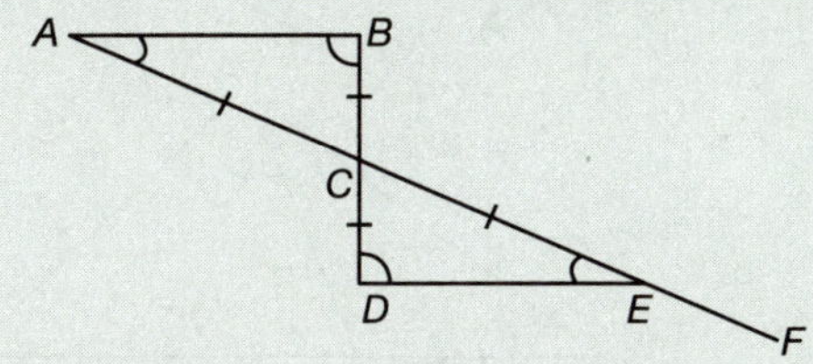

8. As $\angle A > \angle B$
   $AB > AC$

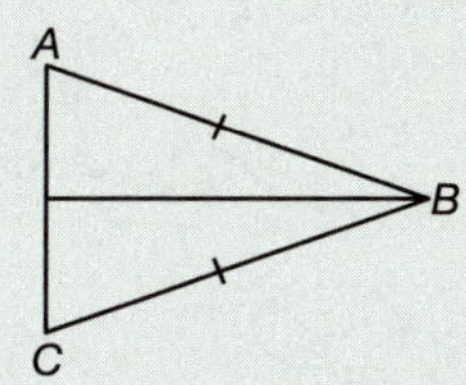

9. $CA < BC < AB$

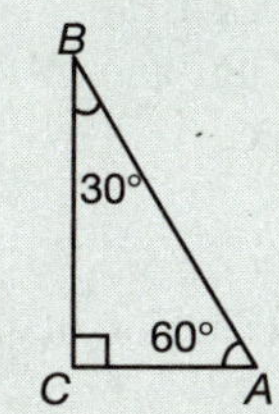

10. $\angle B < \angle A < \angle C$

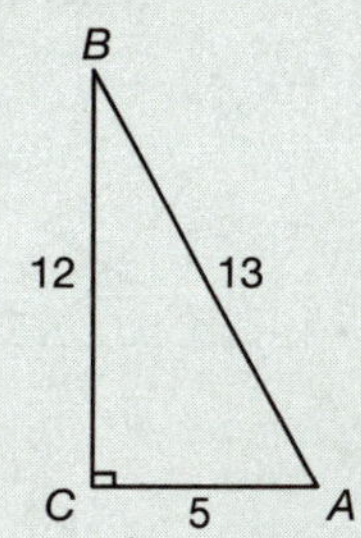

Fixed Response Type

Fill in the Blanks

1. $\Delta AFE \cong \Delta CBD$

2. $\Delta ABD \cong \Delta CED$

3. $\angle ABC = \angle ACB$ and $\angle ADC = \angle ACD$
   then $\angle ADC + \angle DCA + \angle ACB + \angle ABC = 180$
   then $\angle DCA + \angle ACB = 90$

4. Isosceles

5. $AB = AC$
   $\Rightarrow \angle ABC = \angle ACB$ (i)
   [$\because$ Angle opp. to equal sides are equal]
   In ΔABD, we have
   Ext $\angle ABC > \angle ADB$
   $\Rightarrow \angle ABC > \angle ADB$ (ii)

From (i) and (ii), we get

$\angle ACB > \angle ADB \Rightarrow \angle ACD > \angle ADC$

$[\because \angle ACB = \angle ACD, \angle ADB = \angle ADC]$

$\Rightarrow AD > AC$

[$\because$ Side opp. to greater angle is larger]

$\Rightarrow AD > AB$ $[\because AB = AC]$

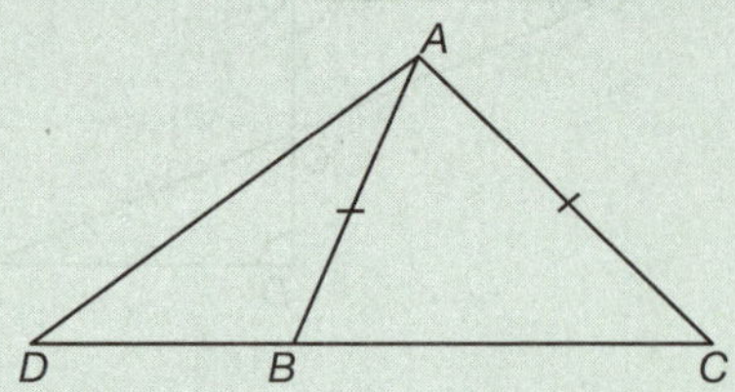

6. In ΔPQR, S is any point on the side QR. Show that $PQ + QR + RP > 2PS$.

True/False

1. **True**

We have,

$\angle DCA = \angle ECB$

$\Rightarrow \angle DCA + \angle ECD = \angle ECB + \angle ECD$

$\Rightarrow \angle ECA = \angle DCB$ (i)

Now, in Δs DBC and EAC, we have

$\angle DCB = \angle ECA$ [From (i)]

$BC = AC$ [Given]

and $\angle DBC = \angle EAC$ [Given]

So, by ASA criterion of congruence

$\Delta DBC \cong \Delta EAC$

$\Rightarrow DC = EC$ [Corresponding parts of congruent triangles are equal]

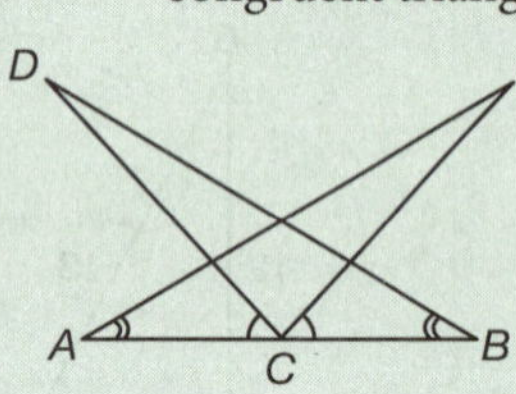

2. **False**

Proof: In ΔABD and ACE, we have

$\angle ADB = \angle AEC = 90°$

$\angle BAD = \angle CAE$ [Common angle]

and, $BD = CE$ [Given]

So, by AAS criterion of congruence, we have

$\Delta ABD \cong \Delta ACE$

$\Rightarrow AB = AC$ [Corresponding parts of congruent triangle are equal]

Hence, ΔABC is isosceles.

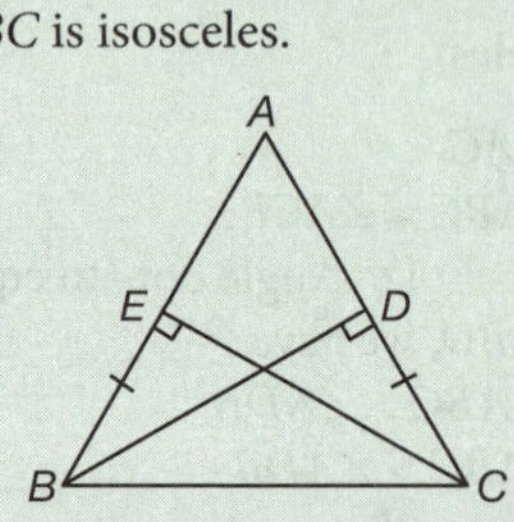

3. **True**

4. **True**

(i) In ΔABD and ΔACD,

$AB = AC$ (Equal sides of isosceles ΔABC)

$BD = CD$ (Equal sides of isosceles ΔDBC)

$AD = AD$ (Common)

$\Delta ABD \cong \Delta ACD$ (By SSS congruence rule)

By CPCT, we get

$\angle BAD = \angle CAD$

$\angle BAP = \angle CAP$ (1)

$\angle ADB = \angle ADC$ (2)

5. **True**

We know that the sum of two sides of a triangle is greater than twice the median bisecting the third side,

Hence in triangle ABD, AD is a median

$\Rightarrow AB + AC > 2(AD)$

Similarly, we get

$\Rightarrow BC + AC > 2(CF)$

$\Rightarrow BC + AB > 2(BE)$

On adding the above inequations, we get

$(AB + AC) + (BC + AC) + (BC + AB) > 2AD + 2CF + 2BE$

$2(AB + BC + AC) > 2(AD + BE + CF)$

$AB + BC + AC > AD + BE + CF$

Then perimeter of a triangle is greater than sum of its three medians.

Single Correct Type Questions

1. **(A)** $ABCD$ is a square

$BC = CD$.

Given $QC = RD$

$\therefore BC - QC = CD - RD$

$\Rightarrow BQ = CR$ (ii)

In ΔPBQ and QCR)

$PB = QC$ [given]

$BQ = CR$ [Proved in (a)]

$\angle PBQ = \angle QCR$ [Each is 90°]

$\therefore \Delta PBQ$ and ΔQCR [SAS Congruency]

$\Rightarrow PQ = QR, \angle BPQ = \angle CQR, \angle BQP = \angle CRQ$ **[C.P.C.T.]**

BQC is a straight line

$\therefore \angle BQP + \angle PQR + \angle CQR = 180°$

$\Rightarrow \angle BQP + \angle PQR + \angle BPQ = 180°$

$\Rightarrow (\angle BQP + \angle BPQ) + \angle PQR = 180°$

$\Rightarrow 180° - \angle PBQ + \angle PQR = 180°$

[Angle sum property for ΔPBQ]

$\Rightarrow 180° - 90° + \angle PQR = 180°$

$\Rightarrow \angle PQR = 90°$ (iii)

ΔPQR is an isosceles right angled triangle, as $PQ = QR$ and $\angle PQR = 90°$.

$\Rightarrow \angle PQR + \angle QRP + \angle QPR = 180°$

$\Rightarrow 90° + 2\angle QPR = 180°$ $\therefore \angle QPR = 45°$

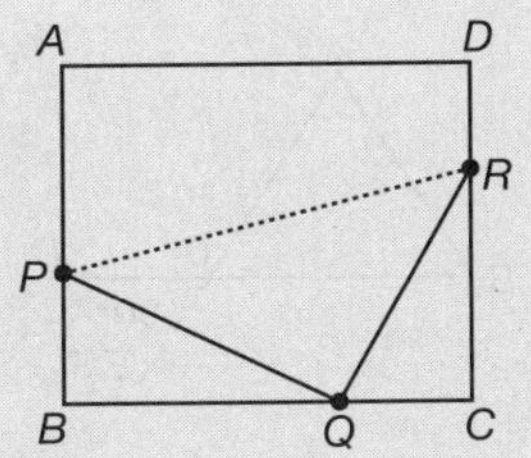

2. **(D)**

3. **(A)** SAS

4. **(B)**

5. **(A)**

6. **(B)** $\angle ABD = \angle ACD = 40$ then $\angle BAC = 100$ then $\angle BAD = 50$.

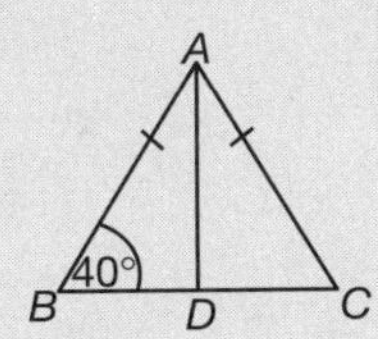

7. **(B)** $QP = 5$ cm, $\angle R = 60^\circ$

8. **(B)**

9. **(B)** According to question,
$\angle QPR = 180^\circ - (70^\circ + 30^\circ) = 80^\circ$
So, $\angle QPS = \angle SPR = 40^\circ$
$\angle PSQ = 180^\circ - (40^\circ + 70^\circ) = 70^\circ$
As, $\angle PRQ < \angle PQR$
So, $PQ < PR$ (1)
Similarly,
$\angle QPS < \angle PQS$
So, $QS < PR$
And, $\angle QPS < \angle PSQ$
So, $QS < PQ$ (3)
Therefore, from eq. (1), (2), (3)
$QS < PQ < PR$.

10. **(A)** $AB + BC + CA > 2AD$

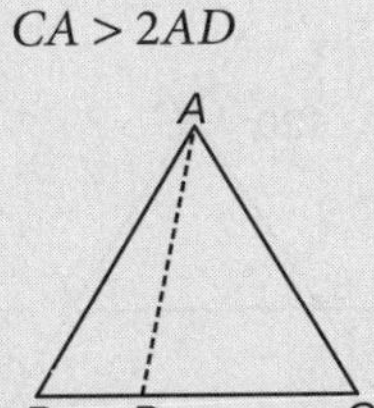

In ΔABD, $AB + BD > AD$ (i)
(Sum of two sides of a triangle is greater than the third side)
In ΔACD, $AC + DC > AD$ (ii)
(Sum of two sides of a triangle is greater than the third side)
On adding (i) and (ii)
$AB + BD + AC + DC > AD + AD$
$AB + (BD + DC) + AC > 2AD$
$AB + BC + AC > 2AD$

11. **(A)**

12. **(B)**

13. **(B)** It is given that
In ΔABC, AP is the angular bisector
AP meets BC at the point P
We know that AP is the bisector of $\angle BAC$
$\angle BAP = \angle CAP$.
In ΔACP, external angle is $\angle APC$
As the external angle of a triangle is greater than each internal opposite angle of the same triangle
$\angle APB = \angle PAC + \angle PCA$
Here $\angle PAC = \angle BAP$
$\angle APB = \angle BAP + \angle PCA$
i.e. $\angle APC > \angle BAP$
$BA > BP$
Therefore, if P is a point on the side BC of a ΔABC such that AP bisects $\angle BAC$ then $BA > BP$.

14. **(C)**

15. **(D)**
(i) In ΔABC,
It is given that M is the mid-point of AB and $MD \parallel BC$.
$\therefore$ D is the mid-point of AC.
[Converse of mid-point theorem]
(ii) As $DM \parallel CB$ and AC is a transversal,
$\angle MDC + \angle DCB = 180^\circ$
[Co-interior angles]
$\angle MDC + 90^\circ = 180^\circ$
$\angle MDC = 90^\circ$
$\therefore MD \perp AC$
(iii) Join MC
In ΔAMD and ΔCMD,
$AD = CD$ (D is the mid-point of side AC)
$\angle ADM = \angle CDM$ (Each 90°)
$DM = DM$ (Common)
$\therefore \Delta AMD \cong \Delta CMD$
(By SAS congruence rule)
Therefore, $AM = CM$ (By CPCT)
However, we also know that $AM = 1/2\ AB$
(M is the mid-point of AB)
$\therefore CM = AM = 1/2\ AB$

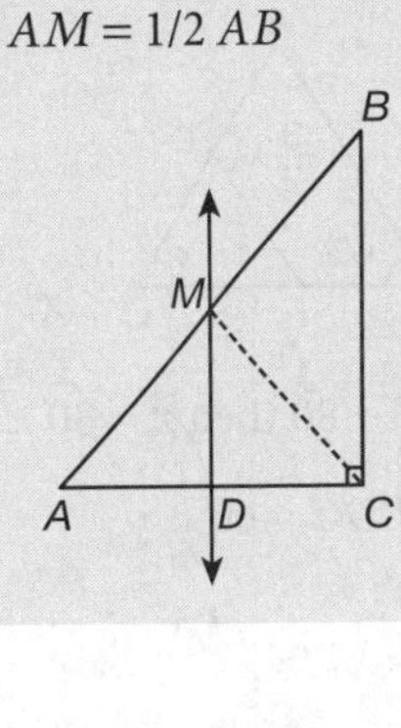

16. **(D)**

17. **(C)**

18. **(A)**

19. **(B)** $\angle CAD = 65 - 30 = 35$ and $\angle BAC = 50$.
Then $\angle BAD = 85$ and $\angle ABD = 65$ then $AD > BD$
In Triangle ACD $\angle A > \angle D$ then $AC > CD$.

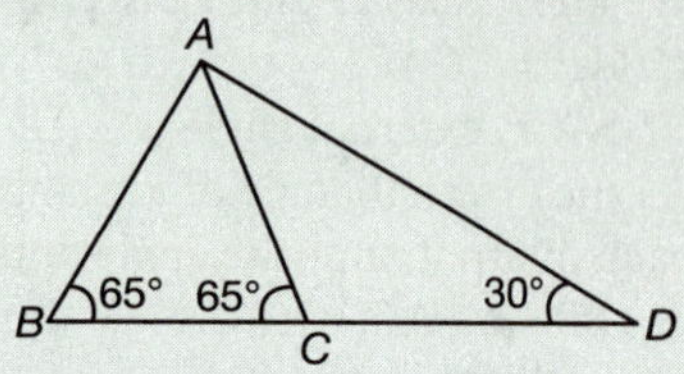

20. **(A) Given:** $\angle Q = 70°$, $\angle R = 30°$
$\angle QPR = 180° - (70° + 30°) = 80°$
{angle sum property of a triangle}
$\therefore \angle QPS = \angle SPR = 40°$
$\angle PRQ < \angle PQR$
$\therefore PQ < PR$ (i)
{Side opposite to the larger angle is larger}
$\angle QPS < PQS$
$\therefore QS < PR$ (ii)
{Side opposite to the larger angle is larger}
In ΔPQS,
$\angle PSQ = 180° - (70° + 40°) = 70°$
{angle sum property of a triangle}
$\angle QPS < \angle PSQ$
$\therefore QS < PQ$ (iii)
{Side opposite to the larger angle is larger}
From (i), (ii) and (iii)
$QS < PQ < PR$.

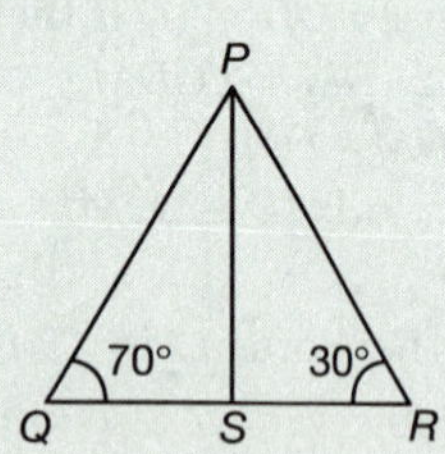

21. **(B)**

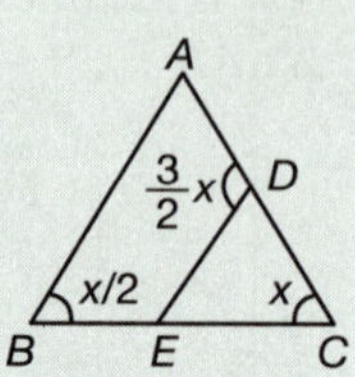

$\frac{3}{2}x = \frac{x}{2} + 80$ then $x = 80$ $\angle BAC = 60$
and $\angle EDC = 60$

22. **(D)**

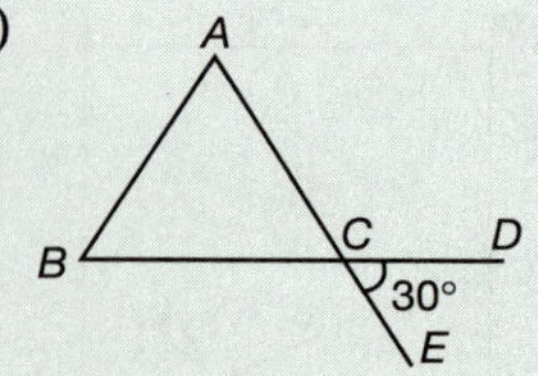

$\angle BAC = 180 - 30 - 30 = 120$

23. **(B)**

24. **(A)** $ACBD$ is parallelogram then $AD = BC$.

25. **(D)**

Multiple Correct Type Questions

1. **(B,C,D)**
2. **(A,B,C)**
3. **(B,C)**
4. **(A,B,D)**
5. **(A,C,D)**
6. **(B,D,C)**
7. **(B,C)**
8. **(A,B,C,D)**
9. **(D)**

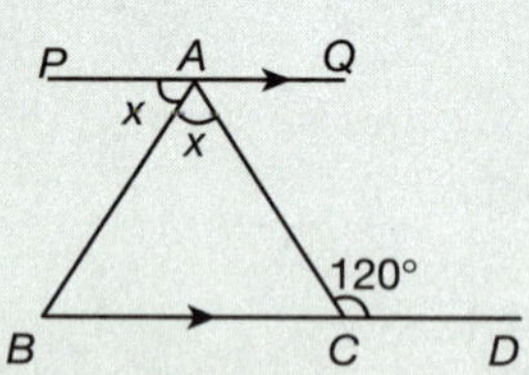

$2x = 120$ then $x = 60$.

10. **(C)**

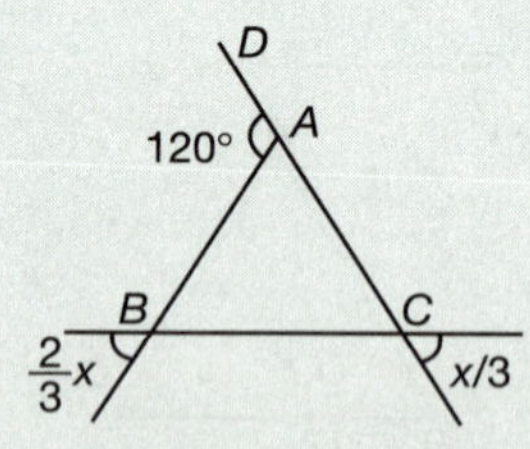

$60 + \frac{2}{3}x + \frac{1}{3}x = 180$ then $x = 120$
then angle of triangle are 40, 60, 80

11. **(A,B,C,D)**

12. **(D)**

13. **(B)**

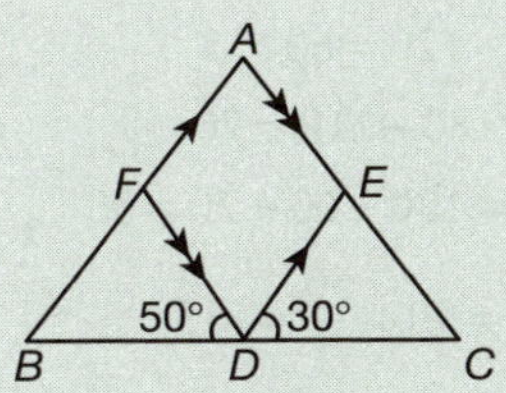

14. **(D)**

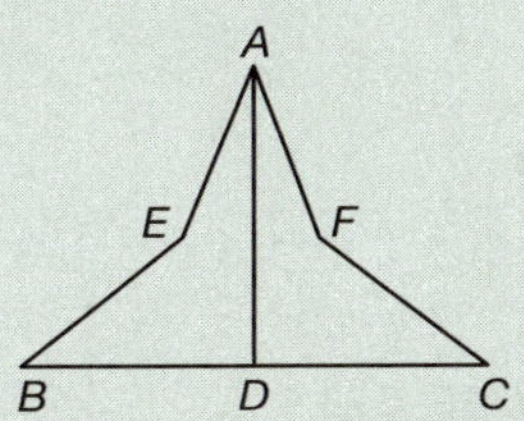

$3\times180-250-60-20-10=540-340=200$

then Angle $AEB=160°$.

15. **(D)**

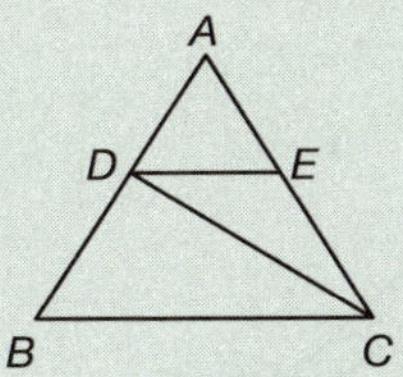

$6\angle BCD=4\angle DBC=3\angle BDC.$

Then $\angle BCD+\angle DBC+\angle BDC=180°$

$12\angle BCD+12\angle DBC+12\angle BDC=12\times180$

$27\angle BDC=12\times180$ then $\angle BDC=80°$

and $\angle DBC=60$ and $\angle BCD=40°$

and $\angle DCE=20°$

Then $\angle BAC=180-60-20-40=60°$

Match Type Questions

1. (A) → (Q); (B) → (P); (C) → (S); (D) → (S)
2. (A) → (PR)
   $\angle PSR>\angle PSQ>\angle PRQ$ then $PR>SR$
   (B) → (PR)
   (C) → (S)
   In triangle PQS. $\angle PSQ>\angle PQS$
   (D) → (Q)
   Hypotenuse is largest.
3. (A) → (R)
   By SAS $\Delta AOD\cong\Delta BOC$ then $AD=BC$.
   (B) → (P)
   (C) → (Q)
   (D) → (PS)
   $\Delta BEC\cong\Delta CDB$ then $AB=AC$

Assertion and Reason Type Questions

1. **(A)**
2. **(A)**
3. **(A)**

Comprehension Type Questions

1. **(C)**
2. **(B)**
3. **(C)**

Numerical Type Questions

1.

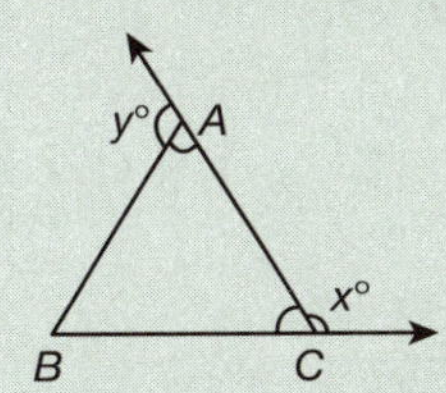

$x=180-50=130°$ and $y=180-30=150°$

then $x+y=130+150=280°$.

2.

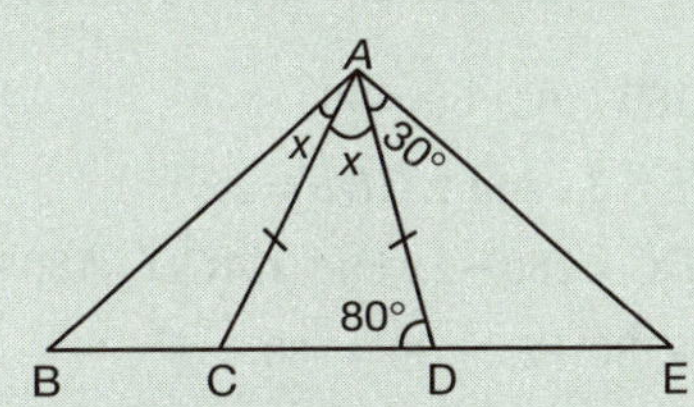

$x=180-80-80=20°=\angle CBA$

3.

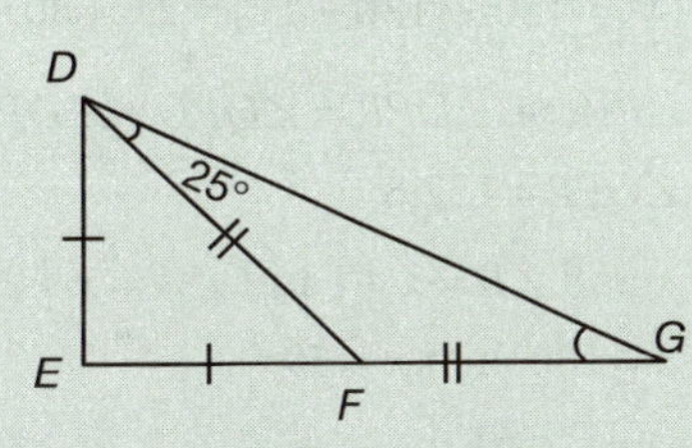

$\angle DFE=25+25=50=\angle EDF.$

Then $\angle EDG=50+25=75°.$

4.

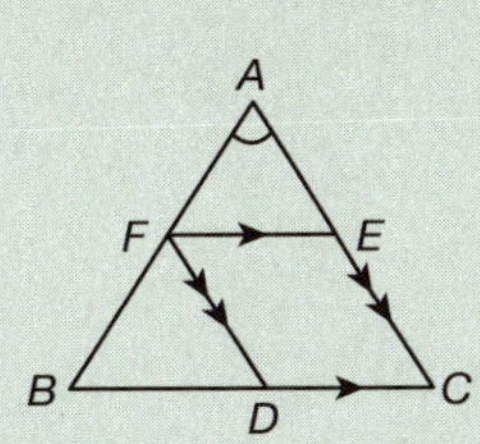

$\angle EFD = \angle FDB = \frac{1}{3}\angle BAC = \frac{1}{3}\angle BFD.$

$\angle FBD + \angle BFD + \angle FDB = 180$

then $4\angle FDB = 140$ then $\angle FDB = 35.$

$\angle BFD = \angle BAC = 105$

then $\angle FEA = 180 - 105 - 40 = 35.$

5. 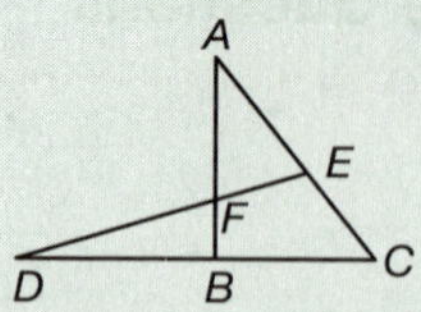

$\angle EFB = 40 + 100 = 140.$

$\angle FBD = 140 - 30 = 110 = \angle BAC + \angle ACB$

then $\angle ACB = 110 - 40 = 70$

6. 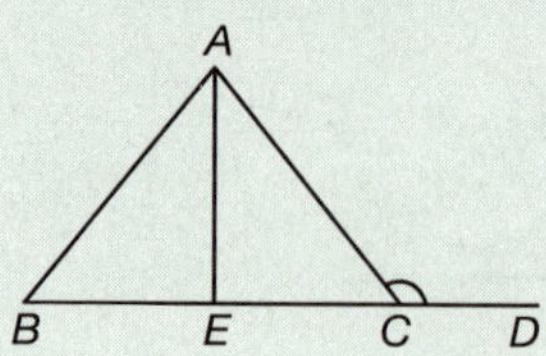

Let $\angle BAE = \angle CAE = x$ then $\angle BEA = x + 30.$

According to question: $x = \frac{1}{2}(x+30)$ then $x = 30$

$\angle ABE = 180 - 30 - 60 = 90.$

7. Let $\angle DCE = 3x$ and $\angle CDF = 2x$

then $\angle ADC = 180 - 2x$ and $\angle ACD = 180 - 3x.$

$180 - 2x + 180 - 3x + 20 = 180$

then $5x = 200$ so $x = 40.$

Then $\angle BDA = 180 - (180 - 2x) = 2x = 80.$

8. $\angle PDQ = \angle PRD + \angle DPR = \angle QPD + \angle DPR$

$= \angle QPR = 122.5$

9. Let $\angle C = x$ and $\angle B = x + 1$ and $\angle A = x + 2$

then $3x + 3 = 180$ then $x = 59$

and $\angle A = x + 2 = 61.$

10. 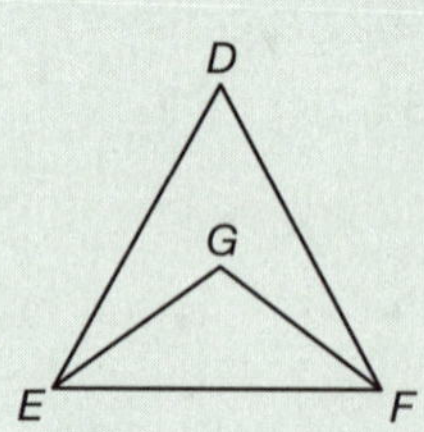

$\angle EGF = 90 + \frac{63.5}{2} = 121.75$

11. 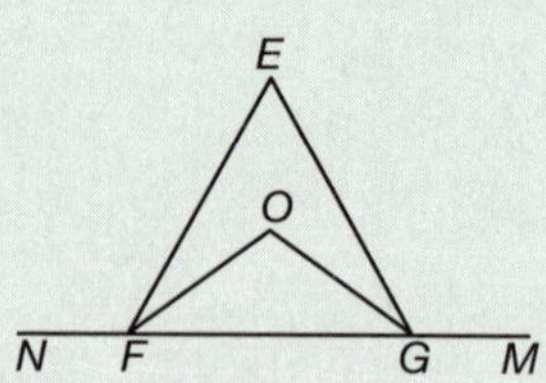

$\angle EGF = 180 - 120 = 60$

and $\angle EFG = 180 - 110 = 70$

Then $\angle FEG = 180 - 60 - 70 = 50$

Then $\angle FOG = 90 + \frac{50}{2} = 115°$

12. 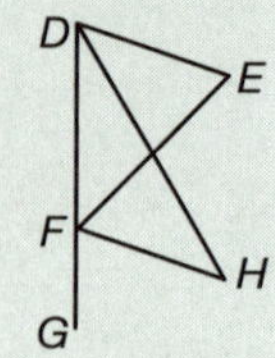

$\angle DHF = \frac{\angle DEF}{2} = \frac{23.5}{2} = 11.75$

13. $\angle QPR = 180 - 65 - 23.5 = 88.5.$ $\angle OPR = 44.25$

Then $\angle POD = 44.25 + 23.5 = 67.75$

$\angle DPO = 90 - 67.75 = 22.25$

14. 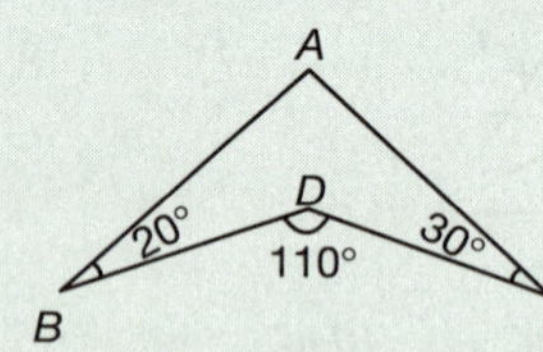

$\angle BAC = 360 - 20 - 30 - 250 = 60$

15. 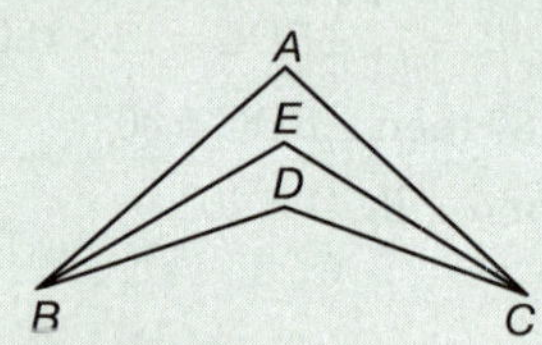

$\angle ABE = \angle ECD = x$ and $\angle EBD = \angle ACE = y.$

Then $80 + x + y + x + y +$ Reflex $\angle BDC = 360$

Reflex $\angle BDC = 280 - 2x - 2y$ (i)

$100 + x + y +$ Reflex $\angle BDC = 360$

then Reflex $\angle BDC = 260 - x - y$ (ii)

$280 - 2x - 2y = 260 - x - y$ then $x + y = 20$

then $\angle BDC = 360 - 240 = 120.$

Higher Order Thinking Skills (HOTS)

1. **(D)** We have the fact that sum of lengths of 2 sides of a triangle is always greater than the 3rd side.

Let us take the minimum and maximum values of the third side as 'x' and 'y'

Minimum value is $\geq 6 - 4$ i.e ≥ 2

Maximum value is $\leq 6 + 4$ i.e ≤ 10

So, $|x - y| \leq |10 - 2|$ i.e ≤ 8

The smallest positive number that is not the possible value of $|x - y|$ is 8

2. **(D)** According to problem sides are $4x$, $6x$ and $11x$ then sum of two sides is less than the third side.

   So triangle is not possible.

3. **(C)** Only possible case is 4, 6, 8.

4. **(A)** In isosceles triangle median on base is also angle bisector.

5. **(A)**

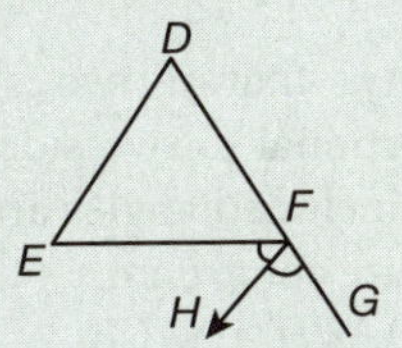

$\angle D + \angle E = \angle EFG = \angle EFH + \angle HFG = x + y.$

6. **(D)** $\angle DAC = \angle DAB = 20°$ then $\angle BAC = 40°$.

   and $\angle ABC = \angle ACB = 70°$.

   Then $\angle BCE = 70 + 40 = 110°$.

7. **(A)**

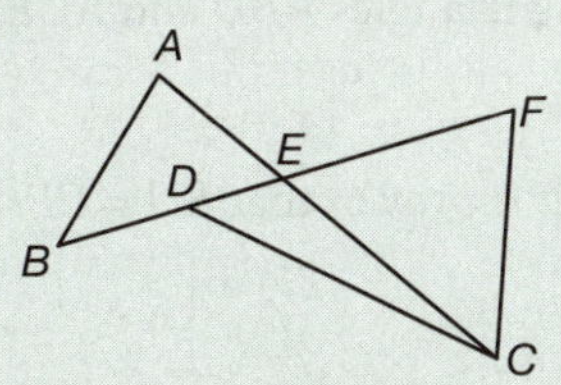

$\angle AEB = 180 - 80 - 20 = 80 = \angle FEC$

and $\angle BFC = 100°$.

$\angle EDC = 60°$ then $\angle DCE = 180 - 100 - 60 = 20°$.

$\angle EFC = 100 - 30 = 70°$.

8. **(C)** Triangle is Right Angled Triangle then $QR = 10$.

9. **(B)**

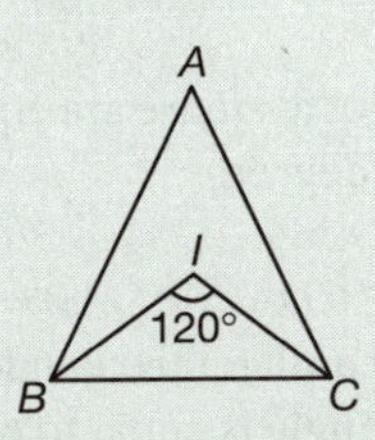

$120 = 90 + \frac{A}{2}$ then $A = 60°$

10. **(C)** $\angle BIC = 90 + \frac{70}{2} = 90 + 35 = 125°$

11. **(C)** $\frac{1}{2} \times 5 \times 12 = \frac{1}{2} \times 13 \times H$ then $H = \frac{60}{13}$

12. **(C)**

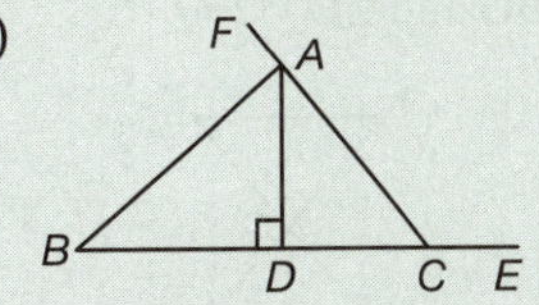

$\angle ACE = 15x$ and $\angle DAC = 6x$ and $\angle BAF = 10x$.

According to diagram $15x = 90 + 6x$ then $x = 10$.

$\angle BAD = 20$ then $\angle ABC = 180 - 90 - 20 = 70°$.

13. **(A)**

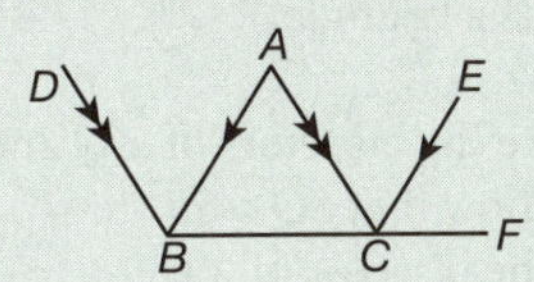

$\angle DBA = \angle BAC = 40°$.

Then $\angle ABC + \angle ACB = 140°$.

14. **(C)** In isosceles triangle median, altitude and angle bisector on base are same.

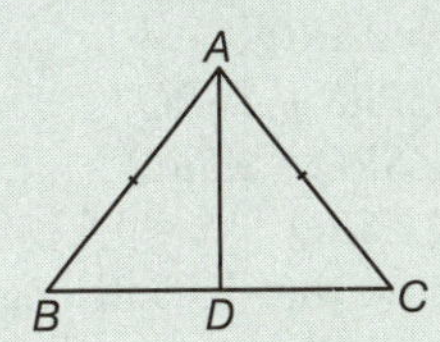

15. **(A)**

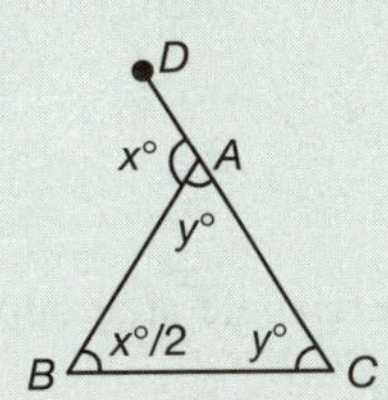

$x = y + \frac{x}{2}$ then $x = 2y$.

Now All angle of triangles are equal.

Free Response Type

Very Short Answer Type Questions

1. ΔABC is isoceles triangle in which angle B and angle C are equal then $\angle C = 50$.

2. ΔPQR is isoceles triangle in which angle R and angle P are equal then $RQ = PQ = 4$ cm.

3. $\Delta ABC \cong \Delta FDE$ then $AB = FD = 5$ cm.

4. $\angle R > \angle Q$ then $PQ > PR$.

5. $AC = DE$

6. $PQ = PR$ (i)

   $\angle Q = \angle R$ (ii)

   $\angle P = \angle P$ (iii)

   Common angle. Then by ASA criteria

   $\Delta PQS \cong \Delta PRT$.

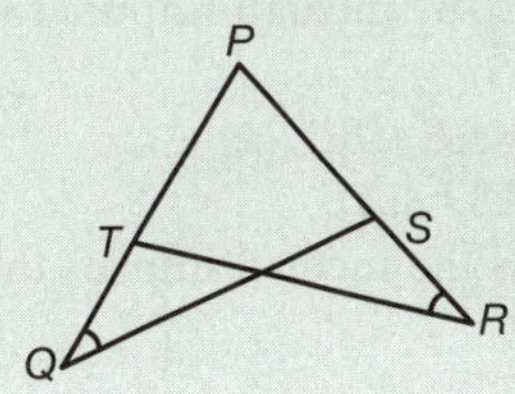

7. 2 angles already equal then ASA or AAS criteria will be applied.
Then $PQ = AB$ or $PR = AC$ or $QR = BC$.

8. As $BC = DA$ and $\angle O = \angle O$ and $\angle CBO = \angle DAO$ then $\Delta CBO \cong \Delta DAO$.
Then $AO = BO$ and $CO = DO$.

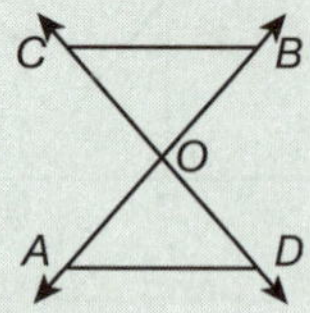

Short Answer Type Questions

1. Given, PQR is a triangle.
$PQ > PR$
QS and RS are the bisectors of $\angle Q$ and $\angle R$
We have to show that $SQ > SR$
Since QS is the bisector of $\angle Q$
$\angle PQS = \angle SQR$
$\angle Q = \angle PQS + \angle SQR$
$\angle Q = \angle SQR + \angle SQR$
$\angle Q = 2\angle SQR$ (1)
Since RS is the bisector of $\angle R$
$\angle PRS = \angle SRQ$
$\angle R = \angle PRS + \angle SRQ$
$\angle R = \angle SRQ + \angle SRQ$
$\angle R = 2\angle SRQ$ (2)
We know that in a triangle angle opposite the longer side is greater.
So, $\angle R > \angle Q$
From (1) and (2),
$2\angle SRQ > 2\angle SQR$
$\angle SRQ > \angle SQR$ (3)
We know that in a triangle side opposite to the greater angle is longer.
From (3),
$SQ > SR$
Therefore, it is proven that SQ is greater than SR.

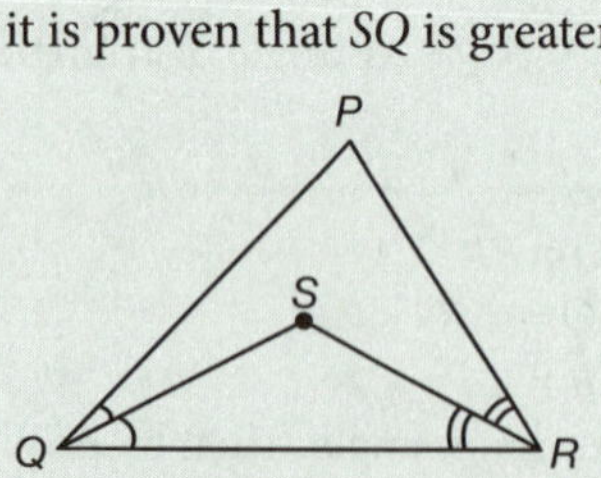

2. CE is the median implies that E is the midpoint of AB
$AB = AE + BE$
So, $AB = 2AE$ (1)
BD is the median implies that D is the midpoint of AC
$AC = AD + CD$
So, $AC = 2AD$ (2)
Consider triangles ABD and ACE,
$AB = AC$ (given)
$\angle A$ = common angle
$AB = AC$
From (1) and (2),
$2AE = 2AD$
$AE = AD$
SAS criterion states that if two sides of one triangle are proportional to two sides of another triangle and their included angles are congruent, then the triangles are congruent.
By SAS criterion, $\Delta ABD \cong \Delta ACE$
The Corresponding Parts of Congruent Triangles are Congruent (CPCTC) theorem states that when two triangles are congruent, then their corresponding sides and angles are also congruent or equal in measurements.
Considering triangles ABD and ACE,
By CPCT,
$BD = CE$
Therefore, it is proven that $BD = CE$

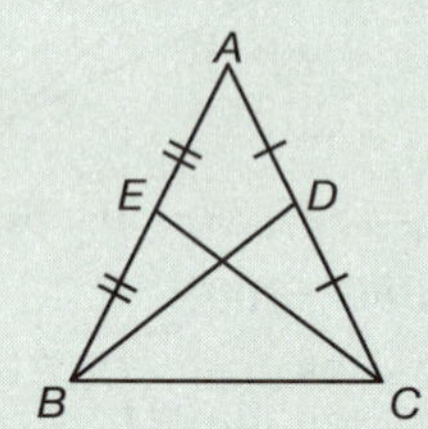

3. Given, CDE is an equilateral triangle formed on the side CD of a square $ABCD$.
We have to show that the triangles ADE and BCE are congruent.
We know that sides of a square are equal and each angle is equal to 90 degrees.
$AB = BC = CD = AD$
$\angle ABC = \angle BCD = \angle CDA = \angle DAB = 90°$
We know that in an equilateral triangle all the sides are equal and each angle is equal to 60 degrees.
$CD = CE = DE$
$\angle CDE = \angle DCE = \angle DEC = 60°$
Considering triangles ADE and BCE,
Sides of a square, $AD = BC$
Sides of equilateral triangle, $DE = CE$
$\angle ADE = \angle ADC + \angle CDE$
$\angle ADE = 90° + 60°$
$\angle ADE = 150°$
$\angle BCE = \angle BCD + \angle DCE$
$\angle BCE = 90° + 60°$
$\angle BCE = 150°$
$\angle ADE = \angle BCE$
By SAS criterion, $\Delta ADE \cong \Delta BCE$

Therefore, the triangles ADE and BCE are congruent.

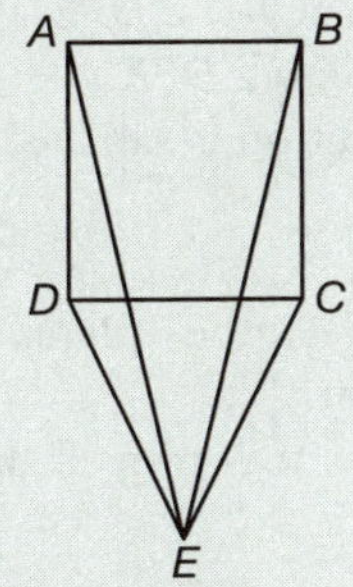

4. We know that the angles opposite to the equal sides are equal.
$\angle ABC = \angle ACB$ (1)
Considering triangles ABC and DBC,
$\angle B =$ common angle
Since $\angle DBC$ is a internal angle of $\angle B$
So, $\angle ABC > \angle DBC$
From (1), $\angle ACB > \angle DBC$
We know that in a triangle a side opposite to a greater angle is longer.
$BD > CD$
Therefore, $CD < BD$

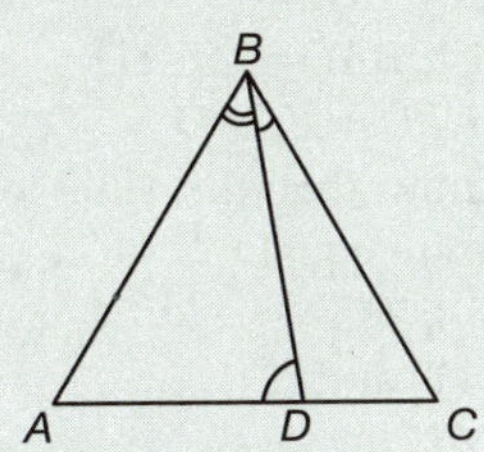

5. As $AM = BM$ and $\angle M = \angle M$
and $\angle MCA = \angle MDB$ then $\Delta CAM \cong \Delta DBM$.
Then $CM = DM$.

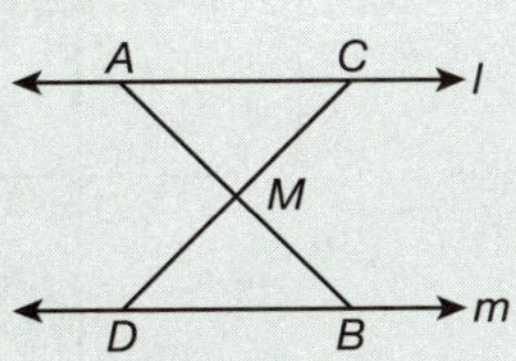

6. Given, ABC is a triangle
AD is the bisector of $\angle BAC$
We have to prove that $AB > BD$
Since AD is the bisector of $\angle BAC$
$\angle BAD = \angle CAD$ (1)
We know that the exterior angle of a triangle is greater than each of the opposite interior angles.
$\angle ADB > \angle CAD$
From (1),
$\angle ADB > \angle BAD$
We know that in a triangle a side opposite to a greater angle is longer.
The side AB is greater than BD.
Therefore, $AB > BD$

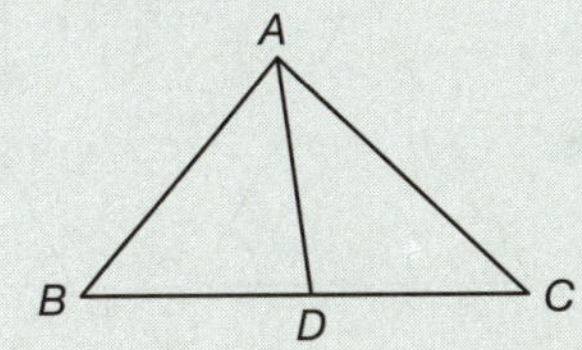

7. Extend CB to a point D such that $BC = BD$
Let $\angle BAC = x$
So, $\angle BCA = 2x$
Considering triangles ABC and ABD,
$BC = BD$ (1)
$AB =$ common side
$\angle ABC = \angle ABD = 90$
SAS criterion states that if two sides of one triangle are proportional to two sides of another triangle and their included angles are congruent, then the triangles are congruent.
By SAS criterion, the triangles ABC and ABD are congruent.
Considering triangles ABC and ABD,
$AD = AC$ (2)
The Corresponding Parts of Congruent Triangles are Congruent (CPCT) theorem states that when two triangles are congruent, then their corresponding sides and angles are also congruent or equal in measurements.
By CPCT, $\angle DAB = \angle BAC$
$\angle DAB = x$
From the figure,
$\angle DAC = \angle DAB + \angle BAC$
$\angle DAC = x + x$
$\angle DAC = 2x$
So, $\angle DAC = \angle ACD$
We know that the sides opposite to equal angles are equal.
$DC = AD$
From (2), $AC = DC$
From (1), $AC = BC + BC$
Therefore, $AC = 2BC$

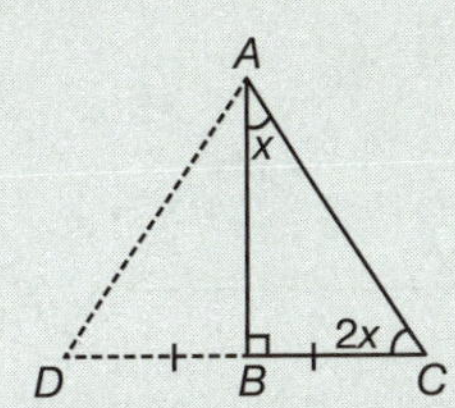

8. Consider two triangles ABC and DEF
$\angle B = \angle E$ and $\angle C = \angle F$
$BC = EF$
We have to prove that the triangles ABC and DEF are congruent.

Case 1: Let $AB = DE$

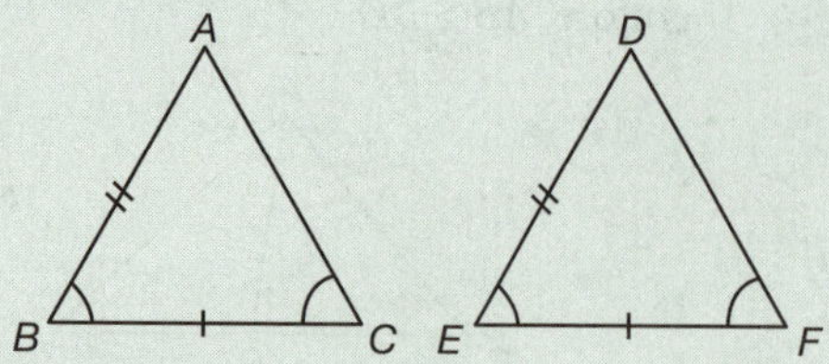

In triangles ABC and DEF,
$AB = DE$
$\angle B = \angle E$
Given, $BC = EF$
By SAS criterion, the triangles ABC and DEF are congruent.
Case 2: $AB > DE$
Take a point P on AB such that $PB = DE$

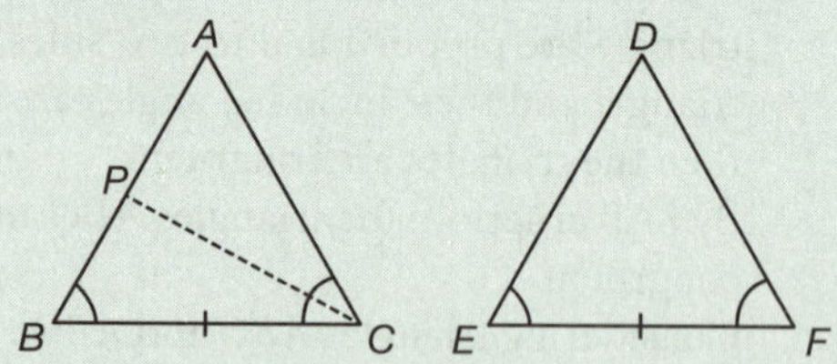

In triangles PBC and DEF,
$PB = DE$
Given, $\angle B = \angle E$
Given, $BE = EF$
By SAS criterion, the triangles PBC and DEF are congruent.
By CPCTC,
$\angle PCB = \angle DFE$
Given, $\angle ACB = \angle DFE$
So, $\angle PCB = \angle ACB$
The condition is satisfied only when P coincides with A.
$AB = DE$
By case 1, the triangles ABC and DEF are congruent.
Case 3: If $AB < DE$
Take a point M on DE such that $AB = ME$

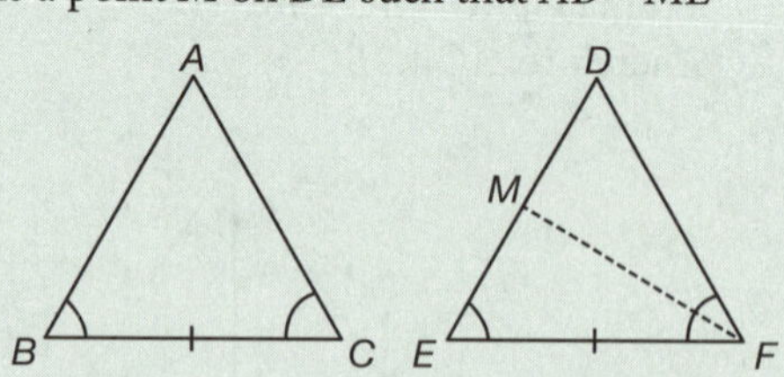

In triangles ABC and MEF,
$AB = ME$
Given, $\angle B = \angle E$
Given, $BE = EF$
By SAS criterion, the triangles ABC and MEF are congruent.
By CPCTC,
$\angle ACB = \angle MFE$
Given, $\angle ACB = \angle DFE$
So, $\angle MFE = \angle DFE$
The condition is satisfied only when M coincides with D.
$AB = DE$
By case 1, the triangles ABC and DEF are congruent.
Therefore, it is proved that the two triangles are congruent.

9. Extend AD to meet E such that $AD = DE$ and join CE.
Considering triangles ABD and ECD,
Given, $BD = CD$
Given, $AD = DE$
We know that the vertically opposite angles are equal.
$\angle ADB = \angle EDC$
By SAS criterion, the triangles ABD and ECD are congruent.
In triangles ABD and ECD,
$AB = EC$ (1)
$\angle BAD = \angle CED$
Given, $\angle BAD = \angle CAD$
So, $\angle CED = \angle CAD$
We know that the sides opposite to the equal angles are equal.
So, $AC = EC$ (2)
From (1) and (2),
$AB = AC$
Therefore, the triangle ABC is isosceles.

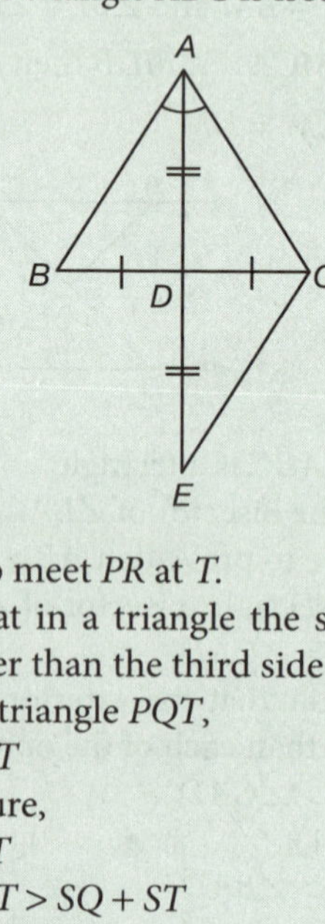

10. Extend QS to meet PR at T.
We know that in a triangle the sum of any two sides is greater than the third side
Considering triangle PQT,
$PQ + PT > QT$
From the figure,
$QT = SQ + ST$
Now, $PQ + PT > SQ + ST$ (1)
Considering triangle TSR,
$ST + TR > SR$ (2)

Adding (1) and (2),

$PQ + PT + ST + TR > SQ + ST + SR$

Cancelling common term,

$PQ + PT + TR > SQ + SR$

From the figure,

$PR = PT + TR$

So, $PQ + PR > SQ + SR$

Therefore, $SQ + SR < PQ + PR$.

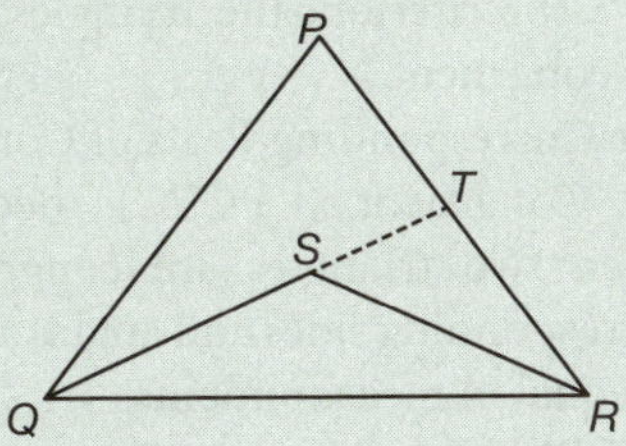

Long Answer Type Questions

1. **Join *OC* and *OD*.**

Given, *AOB* is an equilateral triangle

$\angle OAB = \angle OBA = 60°$ (1)

We know that each angle of a square is equal to 90 degrees.

$\angle DAB = \angle CBA = 90°$ (2)

Subtracting (1) and (2),

$\angle DAB - \angle OAB = \angle CBA - \angle OBA$

From the figure,

$\angle DAB - \angle OAB = \angle DAO$

$\angle CBA - \angle OBA = \angle CBO$

So, $\angle DAO = \angle CBO = 90° - 60° = 30°$

Considering triangles *AOD* and *BOC*,

Sides of equilateral triangle, $AO = BO$

$\angle DAO = \angle CBO$

Sides of a square, $AD = BC$

SAS criterion states that if two sides of one triangle are proportional to two sides of another triangle and their included angles are congruent, then the triangles are congruent.

By SAS criterion, the triangles *AOD* and *BOC* are congruent

Considering triangle *COD*,

By CPCT,

$OC = OD$

Therefore, *OCD* is an isosceles triangle.

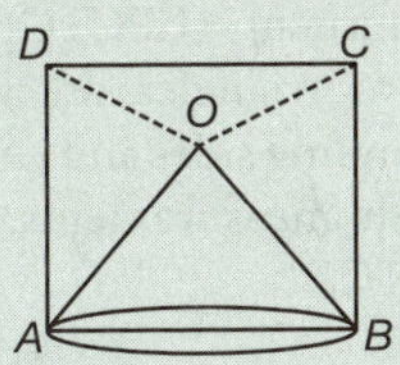

2. Let *P* be the mid point of the hypotenuse of the right ΔABC right angled at *B*

Draw a line parallel to *BC* from *P* meeting *AB* at *D*

Join *PB*

In ΔPAD and ΔPBD

$\angle PDA = \angle PDB = 90°$ each due to conv of mid point theorem

$PD = PD$ (common)

$AD = DB$ (As *D* is mid point of *AB*)

So ΔPAD and *PBD* are congruent by SAS rule

$PA = PB$ (C.P.C.T)

As $PA = PC$ (Given as *P* is mid-point)

$\therefore PA = PC = PB$

3. Considering triangles *ABC* and *ADC*,

Common side = *AC*

Given, $AB = AD$

$BC = BD$

SSS Criterion (Side-Side-Side) states that if all the three sides of one triangle are equal to the three corresponding sides of another triangle, the two triangles are said to be congruent.

By SSS criterion, the triangles *ABC* and *ADC* are congruent

The Corresponding Parts of Congruent Triangles are Congruent (CPCTC) theorem states that when two triangles are congruent, then their corresponding sides and angles are also congruent or equal in measurements.

By CPCTC,

$\angle 1 = \angle 2$

Considering triangles *AOB* and *AOD*,

Common side = *AO*

Given, $AB = AD$

$\angle 1 = \angle 2$

By SSS criterion, the triangles *AOB* and *AOD* are congruent

By CPCTC,

$BO = DO$

$\angle 3 = \angle 4$

We know that the linear pair of angles is always supplementary.

So, $\angle 3 + \angle 4 = 180°$

$\angle 3 + \angle 3 = 180°$

$2\angle 3 = 180°$

$\angle 3 = 180°/2$

$\angle 3 = 90°$

This implies that *AC* is perpendicular to *BD*

Therefore, *AC* is the perpendicular bisector of *BD*.

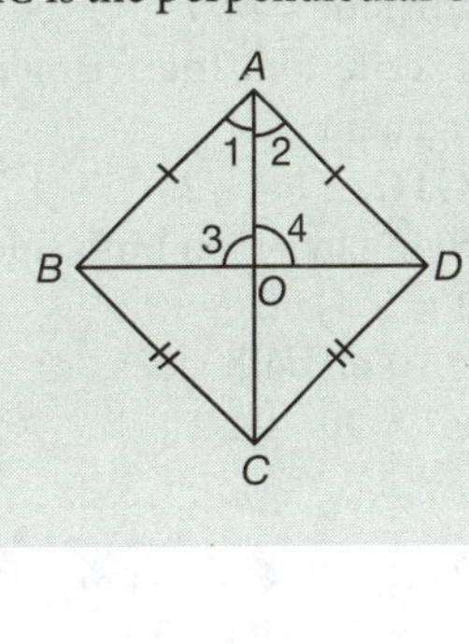

4. Join the diagonals AC and BD of the quadrilateral.
Consider the triangle OAB,
We know that the sum of two sides of a triangle is greater than the third side.
$OA + OB > AB$ (1)
Consider the triangle OBC,
We know that the sum of two sides of a triangle is greater than the third side.
$OB + OC > BC$ (2)
Consider the triangle OCD,
$OC + OD > CD$ (3)
In triangle ODA,
$OD + OA > DA$ (4)
Adding (1), (2), (3) and (4), we get
$OA + OB + OB + OC + OC + OD + OD + OA > AB + BC + CD + DA$
$2(OA + OB + OC + OD) > AB + BC + CD + DA$
From the figure,
$AC = OA + OC$
$BD = OB + OD$
$2[(OA + OC) + (OB + OD)] > AB + BC + CD + DA$
$2(AC + BD) > AB + BC + CD + DA$
The above expression can be rewritten as
$AB + BC + CD + DA < 2(AC + BD)$
Therefore, it is proven that
$AB + BC + CD + DA < 2(BD + AC)$

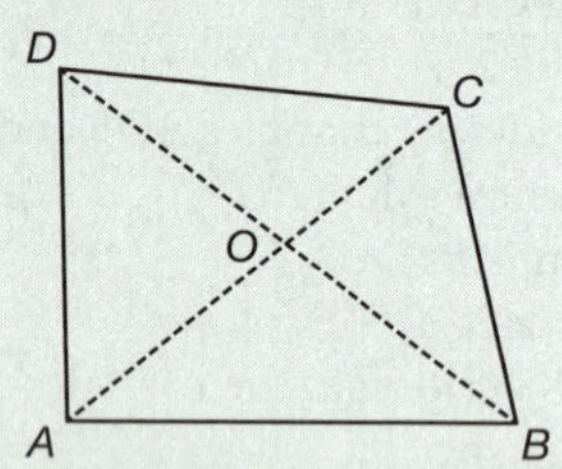

5. Given, $ABCD$ is a trapezium
M and N are the midpoints of parallel sides AB and DC of the trapezium.
The line segment joining M and N is perpendicular to both the sides AB and DC.
We have to prove that $AD = BC$
Since M is the midpoint of AB
$AM = MB$
Considering triangles AMN and BMN,
$AM = MB$
$\angle 3 = \angle 4 = 90$
Common side $= MN$
By SAS criterion, the triangles AMN and BMN are congruent
By CPCTC, $\angle 1 = \angle 2$
Multiplying by –1 on both sides,
$(-1)\angle 1 = (-1)\angle 2$
Adding 90 on both sides,
$90° - \angle 1 = 90° - \angle 2$
From the figure,
$\angle AND = \angle BNC$
Considering triangle ADN and BCN,
Since triangles AMN and BMN are congruent,
$AN = BN$
$\angle AND = \angle BNC$
Since N is the midpoint of CD
$CN = DN$
By SAS criterion, the triangles AMN and BMN are congruent.
The Corresponding Parts of Congruent Triangles are Congruent (CPCTC) theorem states that when two triangles are congruent, then their corresponding sides and angles are also congruent or equal in measurements.
By CPCTC,
$AD = BC$
Therefore, it is proved that $AD = BC$

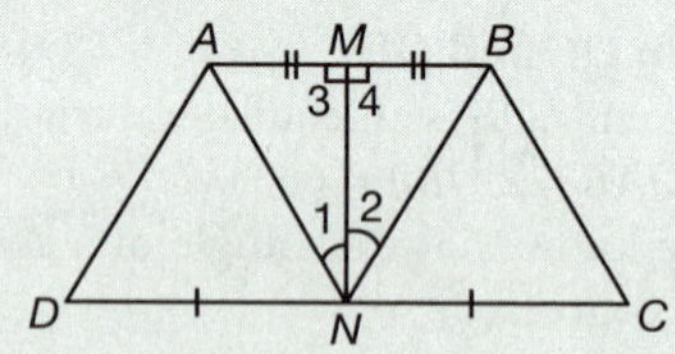

6. In right triangle ABC,
$AB = AC$
BC is the hypotenuse
$\angle A = 90°$
Draw DE perpendicular to BC
$\angle E = 90°$
$\angle 3 = \angle 4 = 90°$
Considering triangles DAC and DEC,
$\angle A = \angle 3 = 90°$
CD is the bisector of angle C.
So, $\angle 1 = \angle 2$
Common side $= CD$
AAS criterion (Angle-angle-side) states that when two angles and a non-included side of a triangle are equal to the corresponding angles and sides of another triangle, then the triangles are said to be congruent.
By AAS criterion, the triangles DAC and DEC are congruent.
The Corresponding Parts of Congruent Triangles are Congruent (CPCTC) theorem states that when two triangles are congruent, then their corresponding sides and angles are also congruent or equal in measurements.
By CPCTC,
$DA = DE$ (1)
$AC = EC$ (2)
In triangle ABC,
$AB = AC$

We know that the angles opposite to equal sides are equal.

So, $\angle C = \angle B$ (3)

By angle sum property,

$\angle A + \angle B + \angle C = 180°$

From (3), $\angle A + \angle B + \angle B = 180°$

$\angle A + 2\angle B = 180°$

$90° + 2\angle B = 180°$

$2\angle B = 180° - 90°$

$\angle B = 90°/2$

$\angle B = 45°$

In triangle BED,

$\angle B + \angle E + \angle D = 180°$

$\angle B + \angle 4 + \angle 5 = 180°$

$90° + \angle 5 = 180° - \angle B$

$\angle 5 = 180° - 45° - 90°$

$\angle 5 = 45°$

So, $\angle B = \angle 5$

We know that the sides opposite to equal angles are equal.

$DE = BE$ (4)

From (1) and (4),

$DA = DE = BE$ (5)

From the figure,

$BC = BE + CE$

From (2) and (5),

$BC = CA + DA$

Therefore, $BC = AC + AD$

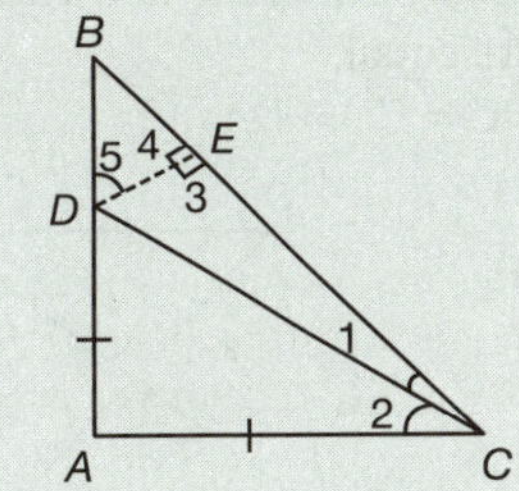

Archive Corner

1. **(C)** As area of both triangle are equal and base and height exchanged so opposite angle are complementary angle.

2. **(C)** We know that the sum of any two sides of a triangle is greater than the third side. (1)
Here the perimeter of the triangle is 14 units.
Let divide 14 into 3 parts, so that $a + b + c = 14$, when a, b and c are integers.
To comply with (1), the sum of any two of a, b or c should be greater than $14/2 = 7$.
Such possible combinations are
(i) $2 + 6 + 6$
(ii) $3 + 5 + 6$
(iii) $4 + 5 + 5$
(iv) $4 + 6 + 4$
No other combination is possible.
So, number of distinct triangles are 4.

3. **(C)** In triangle ABC,
$AB + BC > AC$ (1)
In triangle ADC,
$AD + CD > AC$ (2)
In triangle ADB,
$AD + AB > DB$ (3)
In triangle DCB,
$DC + CB > DB$ (4)
Adding equation (1), (2), (3) and (4) we get,
$AB + BC + AD + CD + AD + AB + DC + CB > AC + AC + DB + DB$
$AB + AB + BC + BC + CD + CD + AD + AD > 2AC + 2DB$
$2AB + 2BC + 2CD + 2AD > 2AC + 2DB$
$AB + BC + CD + AD > AC + DB$
Hence, $AB + BC + CD + DA > AC + BD$ is true

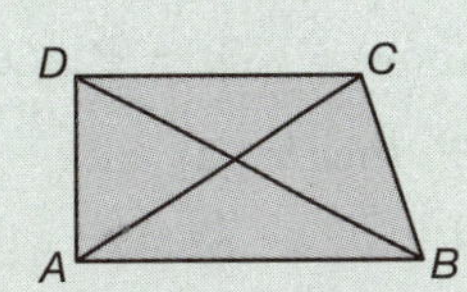

4. **(A)** $\frac{1}{2} \times BC \times AD = \frac{1}{2} \times AC \times BE$
then $AC = 16 \times \frac{6}{8} = 12.$

CHAPTER 8 QUADRILATERALS

CHECK POINT 1

1. **Given:** A rhombus $ABCD$ whose diagonals AC and BD intersect at O.
To prove: $\angle BOC = \angle DOC = \angle AOD = \angle AOB = 90°$.
Proof: Parallelogram is a rhombus, if all of its sides are equal.
$AB = BC = CD = DA$ (i)

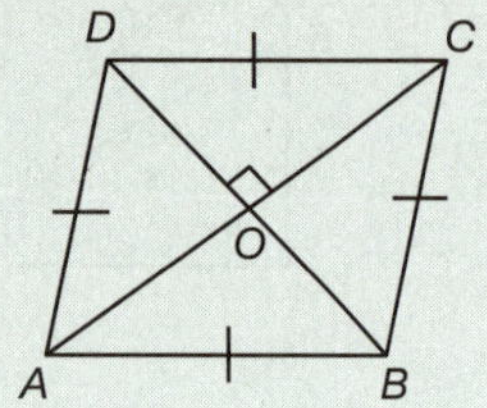

Since the diagonals of a parallelogram bisect each other.
$\therefore$ $OB = OD$ and $OA = OC$ (ii)
In ΔBOC and ΔDOC
$BO = OD$ [From (ii)]
$BC = DC$ [From (i)]
$OC = OC$
So, by SSS criterion of congruence
$\Delta BOC \cong \Delta DOC$
$\angle BOC = \angle DOC$ [By CPCT]
But, $\angle BOC + \angle DOC = 180°$ [Linear pair]
$\angle BOC = \angle DOC = 90°$
Similarly, $\angle AOD = \angle AOB = 90°$
Hence, $\angle BOC = \angle DOC = \angle AOD = \angle AOB = 90°$.

2. From Above $\angle$ $AOD = \angle$ $AOB = 90°$

3. $AD = BC$ then $x + 2y = 2x + 3$ then $x = 2y - 3$
and $AB = CD$ $x + 7 = 3y + 2$ then $x = 3y - 5$
then $x = 2y - 3 = 3y - 5$ then $y = 2$
and $x = 1$ then $AB = 3y + 2 = 8$
and $BC = 2x + 3 = 5$

4. In ΔDEO and ΔBFO
then $DO = BO$ (Diagonal bisect each other)
$\angle OED = \angle OFB = 90°$ (Given)
$\angle DOE = \angle FOB$ (Vertically Opposite angle)
$\Delta DEO \cong \Delta BFO$ then $DE = FB$.

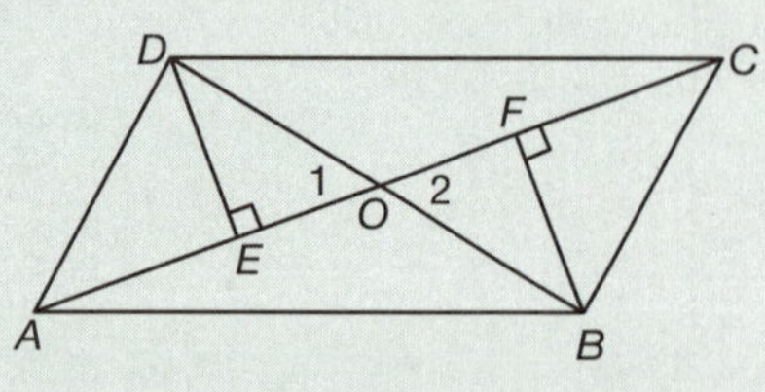

5. $AD \parallel BC$ and $AD \parallel EF$ and $GH \parallel CB$
then $EF \parallel GH$ and $EG \parallel FH$
then $EFGH$ is parallelogram.

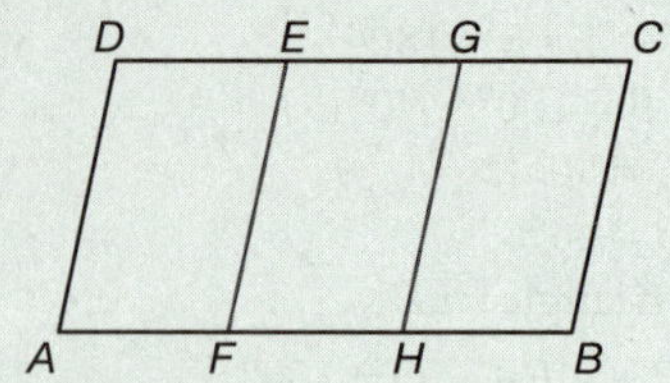

CHECK POINT 2

6. **Proof:** $DE \perp BC$ (by construction) and D is the mid-point of hypotenuse AC.
$\therefore BE = EC$ (by converse of mid-point theorem)
Now, Δ's DBE and DEC
$BE = EC$
$DE = DE$ (common side)
$\angle DEB = \angle DEC = 90°$ (by construction)
$\therefore$ $\Delta DBE \cong \Delta DEC$ (by SAS congruency)
$\Rightarrow DC = DB$ (i)
Again, D is mid-point of AC $2DC = AC$ (ii)
From (i) and (ii), we get $\Rightarrow 2DB = AC$
$\Rightarrow BD = \dfrac{AC}{2}$

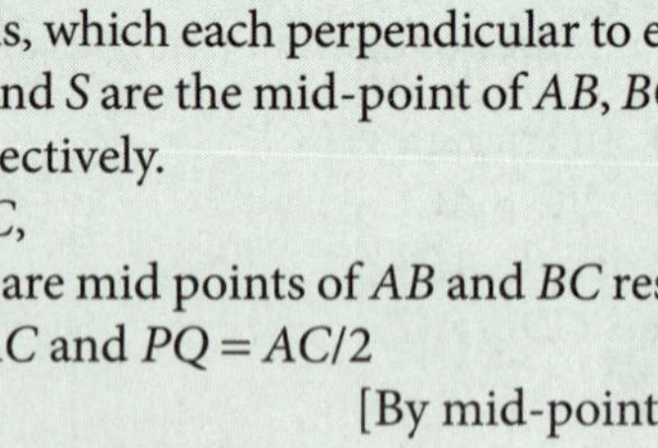

7. Here, $ABCD$ is a quadrilateral. AC and BD are diagonals, which each perpendicular to each other. P, Q, R and S are the mid-point of AB, BC, CD and AD respectively.
In ΔABC,
P and Q are mid points of AB and BC respectively.
$\therefore$ $PQ \| AC$ and $PQ = AC/2$ (1)
[By mid-point theorem]
Similarly, in ΔACD,
R and S are mid-points of sides CD and AD respectively.
$\therefore$ $SR \| AC$ and $SR = AC/2$ (2)
[By mid-point theorem]
From (1) and (2), we get
$PQ \| SR$ and $PQ = SR$
$\therefore$ $PQRS$ is a parallelogram.
Now, $RS \| AC$ and $QR \| BD$.
$\Rightarrow$ Also, $AC \perp BD$ [Given]

$\therefore RS \perp QR$

$\therefore PQRS$ is a rectangle.

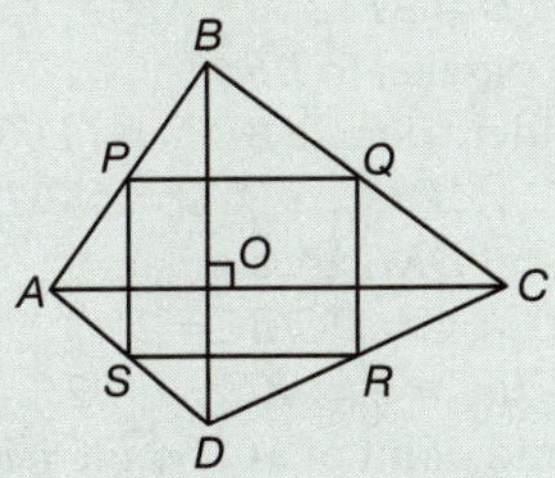

8. By midpoint Theorem
$DF \parallel EG$ and $DE \parallel FG$ then $DEGF$ is parallelogram then $DE = FG$.

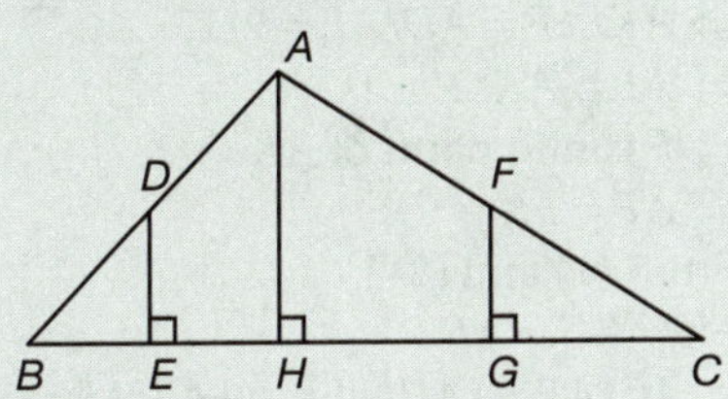

9. $AXBC$ is a ||gm||gm
$AYCB$ is also a ||gm
$AX \| CB$
$AY \| BC$
$A + B + C = 180°$
$AX = CB$ and $AY = BC$
So, $AX = AY$
A is the midpoint of XY
Hence proved.

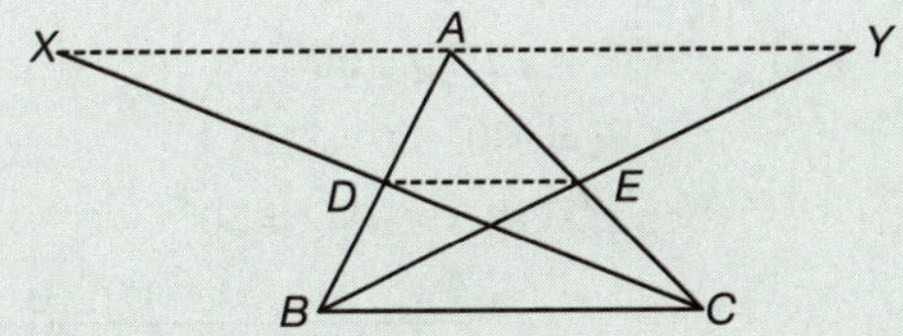

10. As, D and E and F are the mid points of sides AB, and BC of ΔABC
$\therefore DE \| AC$ (By mid point theorem)
Similarly , $DF \parallel BC$ and $EF \parallel AB$
Therefore, $ADEF$, $BDFE$ and $DFCE$ are all parallelograms.
Now, DE is the diagonal of the parallelogram $BDFE$.
$\therefore \Delta BDE \cong \Delta FED$
Similarly DF is the diagonal of the parallelogram $ADEF$.
$\therefore \Delta DAF \cong \Delta FED$
And, EF is the diagonal of the parallelogram $DFCE$.
$\therefore \Delta \cong \Delta FED$
So, all the four triangles are congruent.

Check Point 3

11. $\frac{360}{n-1} - \frac{360}{n+2} = 6$ then $360 \times 3 = 6 \times (n-1)(n+2)$
then $(n-1)(n+2) = 180$ then $n = 13$

12. Number of diagonal $= \frac{10 \times 7}{2} = 35$

Fixed Response Type

Fill in the Blanks

1. Parallelogram
2. Equal
3. Rhombus
4. Square
5. Equilateral triangle
6. Equal

True/False

1. True
2. True
3. False
4. False
5. False

Single Correct Type Questions

1. **(B)** $\angle D = \angle B = 105$ and $\angle A = 180 - 105 = 75$
2. **(D)**
3. **(C)**
4. **(A)** $\angle 2 + \angle 3 + \angle P = 180$ and $2(\angle 2 + \angle 3 + \angle P)$
$= 360° = 2(\angle 2 + \angle 3) + \angle C + \angle D$
then $2\angle P = \angle C + \angle D$

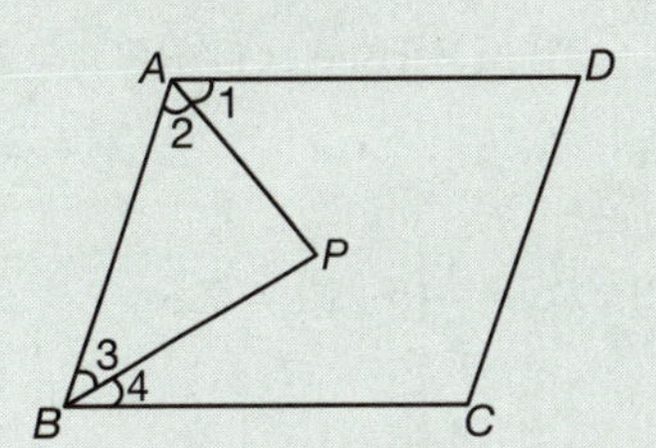

5. **(D)** $x + 2x + 3x + 4x = 360°$ then $10x = 360°$
then $x = 36$ Then all angles are 36, 72, 108 and 144

6. **(A)** $\angle SQR = \angle PSQ = 50°$.
$\angle PQR = 180 - 70 = 110°$
then $\angle SQP = \angle RSQ = 60°$.

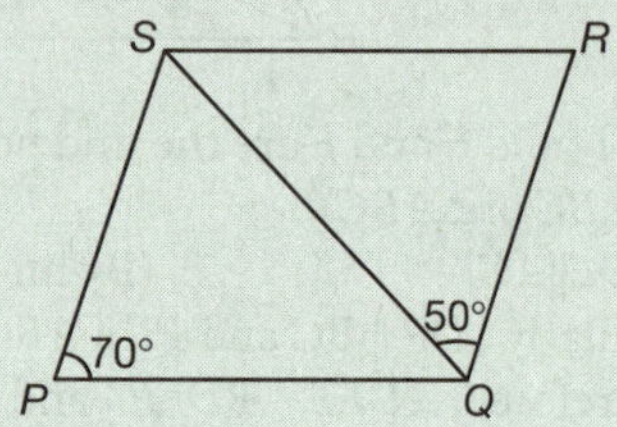

7. **(C)** Same as Q.No. 4

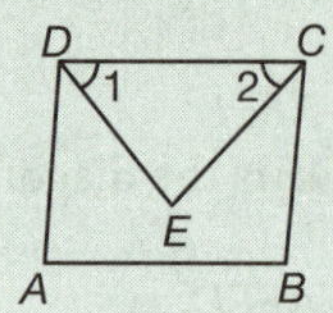

8. **(D)**

9. **(A)**

10. **(B)** In triangle DRB. $PQ = \frac{1}{2}RB = \frac{1}{2}CD$

$ABCD$ is a trapezium and P, Q are the mid-points of the diagonal's AC and BD. Then PQ is equal to

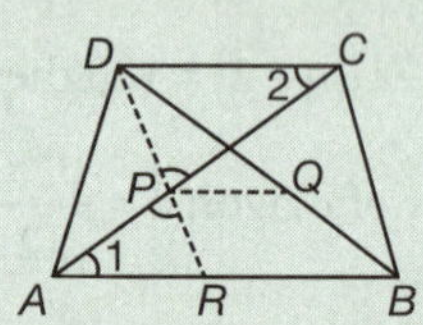

11. **(C)** In isosceles trapezium base angles are equal.

12. **(C)** Area (ΔPXS) + Area (ΔRXQ) = Area (ΔSRX) + Area (ΔPXQ)

13. **(B)** CQ By congruency of triangle ADP and triangle CQB.

14. **(A)**

15. **(C)** Perimeter $(ARPQ) = AR + RP + PQ + AQ$.
Where $AR = BR = PQ = 12$
and $AQ = QC = RP = 8$.
Then Perimeter $(ARPQ) = 2(AR + RP)$
$= 2(12 + 8) = 40$ cm

16. **(C)** $PQ = \frac{1}{2}(5 + 10) = 7.5$

17. **(B)** ar $(ADE) = \frac{1}{2} \times AD \times DE = \frac{1}{2} \times 4.5 \times 6$
$= 13.5$ sq.cm

18. **(B)** Given $BD = DC = \frac{BC}{2}$
$AE = ED = AD/2$
DK is parallel to BF.
Consider triangle BFC and DKC
$\angle BFC = \angle DKC$, $\angle FCD = \angle KCD$
BFC and DKC are similar. (AAA similarity)
and $KC/FC = DC/BC = 2$
$\Rightarrow KC/FC = 2 \Rightarrow KC = FC/2$
K is mid point of FC. So $FK = KC$ (1)
Consider triangles AEF and AKD
$\angle EAF = \angle DAK$
$\angle BFA = \angle DKA$ (size $BF \| DK$)
$\therefore \Delta AFE$ and ΔAKD are similar (AAA similirity)
$\Rightarrow AK/AF = AD/AE = 2/1$
$\Rightarrow AF = AK/2$
$\Rightarrow F$ is mid point of AK
$\Rightarrow AF = FK$ (2)
From (1) and (2)
$FK = KC = AF$
$\therefore AC/AF = (AF + FK + KC)/AF = 3AP/AF = 3/1$
$\Rightarrow AF = AC/3$

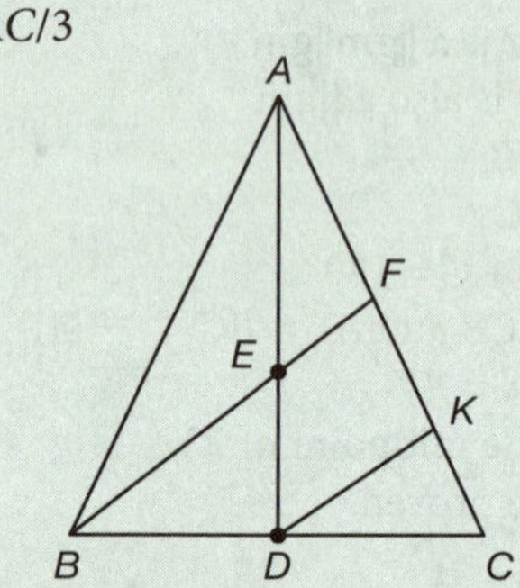

19. **(B)** $\angle PSR = \angle PQR = \angle SPQ = \angle SRQ = 90°$.
Then its a rectangle.

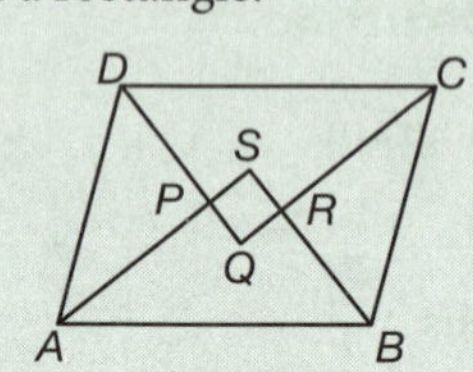

20. **(A)** Let the sides are n and $2n$ then

$\frac{(n-2)180}{n} : \frac{(2n-2)180}{2n} = 3:4$. Then $\frac{n-2}{n-1} = \frac{3}{4}$
then $4n - 8 = 3n - 3$ then $n = 5$.

21. **(C)** Given $ABCD$ is a square and $DQ = AP$.
In ΔADQ and ΔBAP,
$AD = BA$ (sides of square $ABCD$)
$DQ = AP$ (given)
$\angle ABP = \angle DAQ = 90°$
$\Delta ADQ \cong \Delta BAP$ (By RHS rule of congruency)

Therefore $\angle ADQ = \angle BAP$ (1)

Now $\angle BAD = \angle DAP + \angle BAP$

$\Rightarrow \angle BAD = \angle DAP + \angle ADQ$ {from 1}

Since $\angle BAD = 90°$ so $\angle DAP + \angle ADQ = 90°$

$\Rightarrow \angle DAR + \angle ADR = 90°$

In ΔARD, $\angle ARD + \angle ADR + \angle DAR = 180°$

$\Rightarrow \angle ARD + 90° = 180°$

$\Rightarrow \angle ARD = 90°$

Hence proved that $AP \perp DQ$.

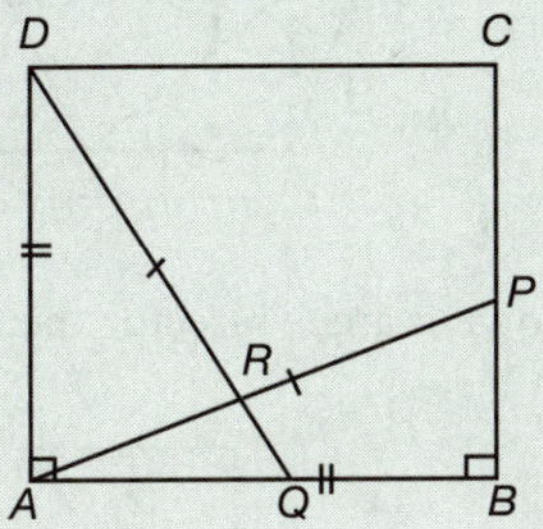

22. **(C)**

23. **(A)** $10x = 60$ then $x = 6$ and $4y = 28$ then $y = 7$.

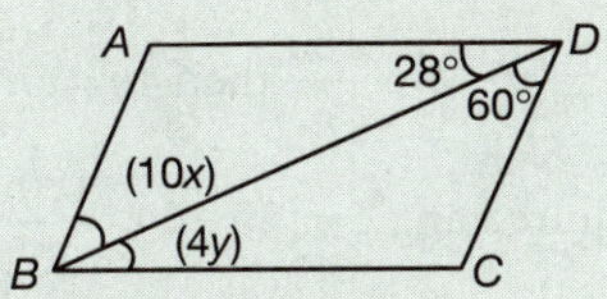

24. **(C)** Let the angles are $2x$ and $3x$

then $2x + 3x = 180$

then $2x + 3x = 180$

then $5x = 180$ so $x = 36$

then angles are 72 and 108.

25. **(C)**

Multiple Correct Type Questions

1. **(A,B,C)**
2. **(A,B,D)**
3. **(A,B,C,D)**
4. **(A,C,D)**
5. **(B,C)**
6. **(A,B,D)**
7. **(B,C,D)** $PQRS$ is a rectangle. Then $QS = PR$ (Diagonal are equal)

   $\Delta APS \cong \Delta CQR$ and $\angle PSR = \angle PQR = 90°$
8. **(B,D)** By midpoint Theorem

   $MN = \frac{1}{2}XZ = \frac{1}{2}XY = XM = MY$
9. **(C,D)**
10. **(A,B)**
11. **(A,B,C)**
12. **(A,B,C)**

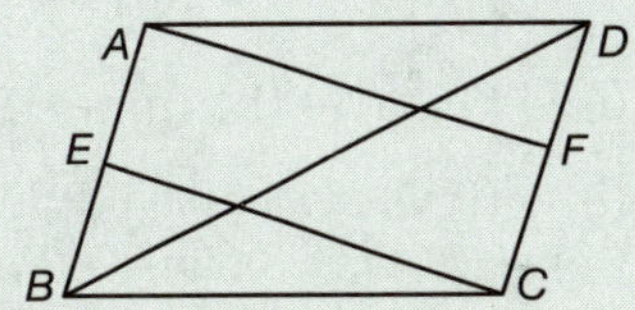

13. **(A,B,C,D)**

$\Delta BMR \cong \Delta DNR$ as $BR = DR$

and $\angle M = \angle N = 90$

and $\angle BRM = \angle DRN$...BY AAS.

In Similar way (B) $\Delta BRC \cong \Delta DRA$ and (D) $\Delta BMC \cong \Delta DNA$

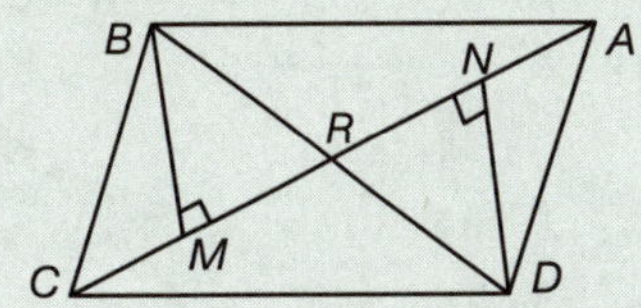

14. **(A,C)**

(A) $\angle C = 50° = \angle E$ (Corresponding angles)

(C) $\angle D = \angle B$ (Corresponding angles)

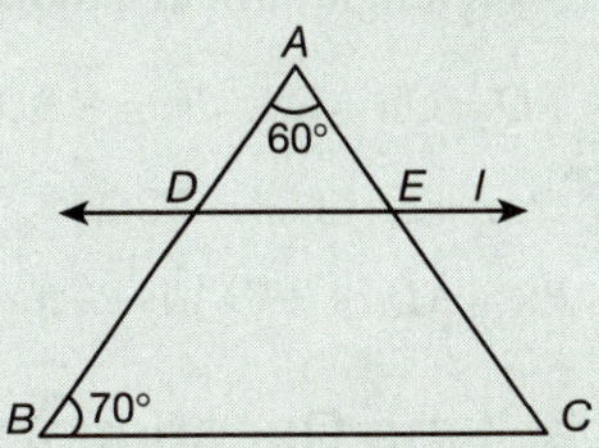

15. **(A,C,D)**

(A) $\angle OBC + \angle OCB = 65°$

(Sum of opposite interior angle equal to exterior angle)

(C) $\angle ODC = 80° = \angle OBA = 180 - 35 - 65 = 80$.

(D) $\angle CBD = 25° = \angle ADO = 65 - 40 = 25$.

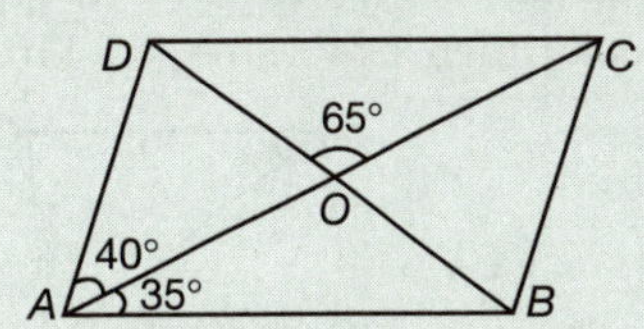

16. **(A,B)**

(A) $\angle CAP = \angle MNP$ (Corresponding angles)

(B) $\angle ABP = \angle NLP$ (Corresponding angles)

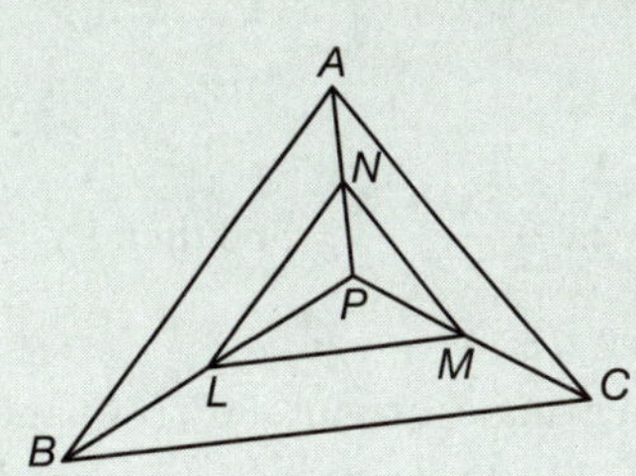

Match Type Questions

1. **(A)** (i) → (S), (ii) → (R), (iii) → (P), (iv) → (Q)
2. **(C)** (i) → (P, Q, R, S), (ii) → (P, Q, S, R), (iii) → (P, Q, R, S), (iv) → (P, Q, R, S)

Assertion and Reason Type Questions

1. **(D)**
2. **(B)**
3. **(C)**
4. **(A)**
5. **(D)**
6. **(A)**
7. **(A)**
8. **(A)**

Comprehension Type Questions

1. **(C)** Quadrilateral Formed by joining midpoint of rectangle formed a rhombus.
2. **(B)** $PQ = QR = RS = PS = \frac{1}{2}BD$

   then sum of all $= 2BD$.
3. **(A)** $PR = AD$ as $PRDA$ is Rectangle.

Numerical Type Questions

1. $x + x - 10 + x + 30 + 2x = 360$ then $5x = 340$

   then $x = \frac{340}{5} = 68$.

   Then smallest angle will be $x - 10 = 58°$.
2. $ABCD$ is rhombus then diagonal are angle bisector then $2x = 180 - 70 = 110$ so $x = 55°$.

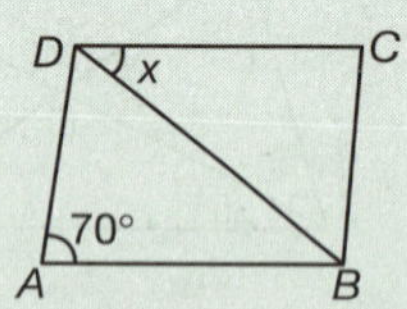

3. In square diagonal intersect at 90°.

   Then $\angle POQ = 90°$.
4. **(A)**
5. $x + 2x + \frac{5x}{2} + \frac{7x}{2} = 360$ then $9x = 360°$

   then $x = 40$.

   Then angles are 40°, 80°, 100° and 140°.

   Then required difference $= 140 - 40 = 100°$.
6. $\angle DCE = \angle ECB = \angle CEB = x°$.

   Then $EB = BC = AE = AD$

   and now $\angle DAE = 2x°$

   Then $\angle AED = 90 - x = \angle EDC = 90 - x$.

   Then $\angle DEC = 180 - 90 + x - x = 90°$.

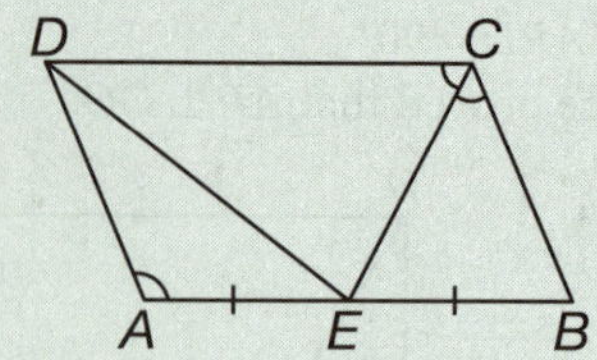

7. Diagonal is angle bisector then $\angle SRP = \frac{90}{2} = 45°$.

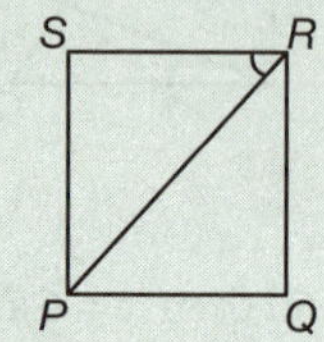

8. $144 = (n-2) \times \frac{180}{n}$ then $4n = 5n - 10$ then $n = 10$.

   Required angle $= (20-2) \times \frac{180}{20} = 18 \times 9 = 162°$.
9. $x + 2x + 3x + 4x + 140 = (5-2) \times 180 = 540$

   Now $10x = 400$ then $x = 40$.

   Largest angle $= 4x = 160$
10. $3x - 2 = 50 - x$ then $4x = 52$ then $x = 13$.
11. $\angle ABC = 56°$ then $\angle BCD = 180 - 56 = 124°$.

    Then $\angle ACD = \frac{124}{2} = 62°$.
12. As Isosceles trapezium is cyclic then $A + C = 180$ then $C = 135°$.
13. $2\angle AOD = 105 + 70 = 175°$.

    Then $\angle AOD = \frac{175}{2} = 87.5°$
14. In triangle OAD

    $\angle OAD = \angle ODA$. Then $\angle AOD = 44°$.

    Then $\angle OAD = \frac{180 - 44}{2} = 90 - 22 = 68°$.
15. $\angle BEC = 180 - 60 - 60 = 60 = \angle EBA$

    Then $\angle ABC = 120°$ and

    $\angle DAB = 180 - 120 = 60°$

    Then $\angle FAB = 60 - 30 = 30°$

    Then $x = 180 - 30 - 60 = 90°$.

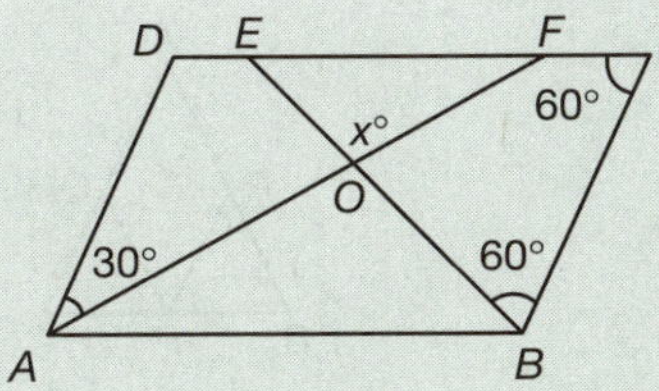

Higher Order Thinking Skills (HOTS)

1. **(A)** Intrior angle $= \dfrac{(8-2)180}{8} = 135°$ and

   Exterior angle $= \dfrac{360}{8} = 45°$

   Then ratio $= \dfrac{135}{45} = \dfrac{3}{1}$

2. **(B)** Let interior angle is $3x$ then exterior angle will be x then $x + 3x = 180$ then $x = 45$.

   $\dfrac{360}{n} = 45$ then $n = 8$.

3. **(D)** $\angle AED = 108$ (angle of regular polygon)

   Now in triangle AED, $AE = ED$

   Let $\angle ADE = x$ then

   $x + x + 108 = 180$ then $x = 36$.

   Then $\angle ADC = 108 - 36 = 72°$ then $= \dfrac{36}{72} = \dfrac{1}{2}$

4. **(A)** Let interior angle is $7x$ then exterior angle will be $2x$ then $2x + 7x = 180$ then $x = 20$.

   $\dfrac{360}{n} = 40°$ then $n = 9$.

5. **(D)** Sum of angles on a straight line = 180°

   $\Rightarrow \angle PAE = 180° - \angle 1$

   Similarly, $\angle PEA = 180° - \angle 5$

   InΔPAE

   $\angle PAE + \angle PEA + \angle APE = 180°$

   $\Rightarrow 180 - \angle 1 + 180 - \angle 5 + \angle APE = 180°$

   $\Rightarrow \angle APE = \angle 1 + \angle 5 - 180° = \angle P$

   Similarly, $\angle BSC = \angle 2 + \angle 3 - 180° = \angle S$

   $\angle DRC = \angle 3 + \angle 4 - 180° = \angle R$

   $\angle DQE = \angle 4 + \angle 5 - 180° = \angle Q$

   $\angle ATS = \angle 1 + \angle 2 - 180° = \angle T$

   $\Rightarrow \angle P + \angle Q + \angle R + \angle S + \angle T$

   $= \angle 1 + \angle 2 + \angle 3 + \angle 4 + \angle 2 + \angle 3 + \angle 4 + \angle 5 + \angle 1 + \angle 5 - (180 \times 5)$

   $= 2(\angle 1 + \angle 2 + \angle 3 + \angle 4 + \angle 5) - 900$ – (1)

   From pentagon $ABCDE$,

   Sum of angles of pentagon $= ((2 \times 5) - 4) \times 90°$

   ($\because$ Sum of angles $= (2n - 4) \times 90°$)

   $= 6 \times 90 = 540°$

   $\Rightarrow \angle P + \angle Q + \angle R + \angle S + \angle T = 2(540°) - 900°$

   $= 1080° - 900° = 180°$

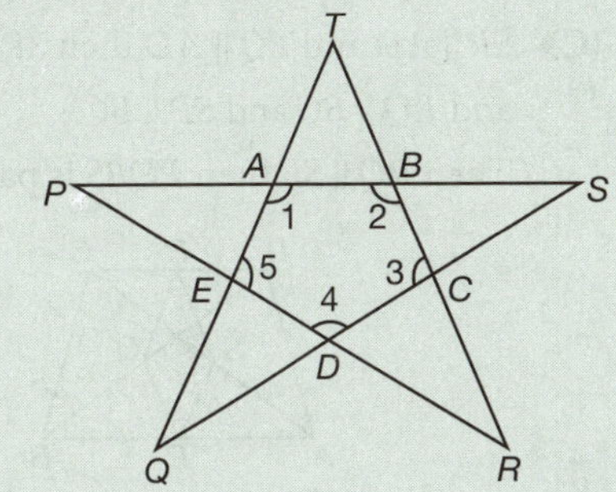

6. **(C)** In Regular pentagon angle bisector will be also perpendicular. Then $\angle AMC = 90°$.

7. **(C)** As diagonal bisect each other then triangle so formed is right angle triangle.

   Then area of rhombus

   $= \dfrac{1}{2} \times 8 \times 6 = 24$ sq.units

8. **(B)** By using Applonious theorem $2(AB^2 + BC^2) = AC^2 + BD^2$ then

   $2(14^2 + 18^2) = 16^2 + DB^2$

   $2(196 + 324) = 256 + DB^2$

   Then $DB^2 = 1040 - 256 = 784$

   then $DB = 28$ cm.

9. **(B)** $EF = \dfrac{1}{2}AD$ and $FG = \dfrac{1}{2}DC$

   and $GH = \dfrac{1}{2}BC$ and $HE = \dfrac{1}{2}AB$.

   Then $\dfrac{EF + FG + GH + HE}{AD + DC + CB + BA} = \dfrac{1}{2}$

10. **(C)** $\text{ar}(ARB) = \dfrac{1}{2}\text{ar}(ABPQ)$

    $= \dfrac{1}{2} \times \dfrac{1}{2} \times \text{ar}(ABCD)$

    $= \dfrac{1}{4} \times \text{ar}(ABCD)$.

11. **(C)** $5 = \dfrac{1}{2}(60 - AB)$ then $60 - AB = 10$ So $AB = 50$.

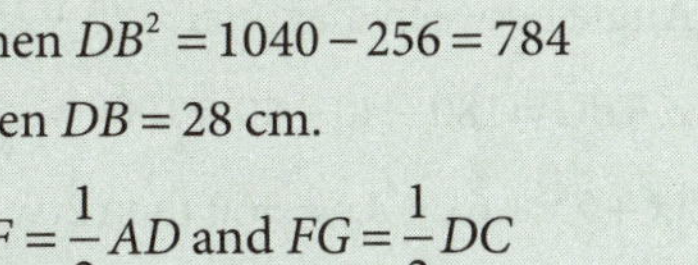

12. **(C)** $3 = \frac{1}{2}(97 - x)$ then $97 - x = 6$ then $x = 91$.

13. **(C)** $SR \parallel AD$ and $PQ \parallel AD$ then $SR \parallel PQ$
and $RQ \parallel BC$ and $SP \parallel BC$
Then $RQ \parallel SP$ then $PQRS$ is parallelogram.

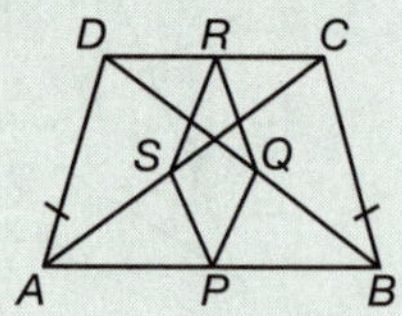

14. **(C)** By using mid-point theorem. $AR = RB = PQ$
and $AQ = QC = RP$ and $BP = PC$
$AR + RP + PQ + AQ = 2AR + 2AQ$
$= 30 + 21 = 51$ cm.

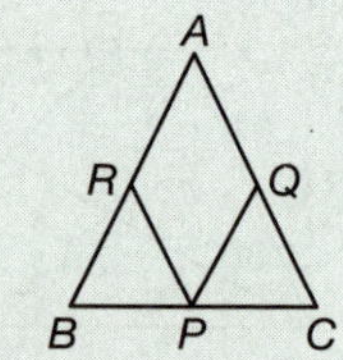

15. **(B)** Using Pythagoras Theorem
$AC^2 + BD^2$
$= (AL^2 + LC^2) + (BM^2 + MD^2)$
$= (AM + ML)^2 + LC^2 + (BL + LM)^2 + MD^2$
$= (AM^2 + MD^2) + (BL^2 + LC^2) + 2ML^2 + 2AM.$
$ML + 2BL.ML$
$= AD^2 + BC^2 + 2ML.$ $\quad (ML + AM + BL)$
$= AD^2 + BC^2 + 2CD.AB$ $\quad \{ML = CD\}$

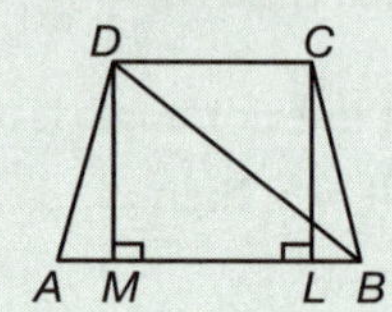

Free Response Type

Very Short Answer Type Questions

1. $\angle OCD = \angle OAB = 90 - 50 = 40°$.
2. Fourth angle $= 360 - (75 + 90 + 75) = 120°$.
3. Angle between diagonal $= 25 + 25 = 50°$.
4. $\angle ABC = 180 - 40 - 40 = 100° = \angle ADB$
5. $3x + 7x + 6x + 4x = 360$ then $20x = 360°$
then $x = 18$. Then angles are 54, 126, 108 and 72
Not specific quadrilateral.
6. Quadrilateral formed by the bisectors of the angles APQ, BPQ, CQP and PQD is rectangle.
7. $AC = 2.\,OA = 2 \times 3 = 6$ unit.
Then $BD = 2.\,OD = 2 \times 2 = 4$ unit
8. $x + x + x + 108 = 360$ then $3x = 360 - 108 = 252$
then $x = \frac{252}{3} = 84$.

Short Answer Type Questions

1. $\angle ADC$ and $\angle ABC$ are the two obtuse angles of the parallelogram
DQ and DP are the two altitudes of the parallelogram
$DP \perp AB$
$DQ \perp BC$.
$\angle PDQ = 60°$
In quadrilateral $DPBQ$,
We know that according to the quadrilateral angle sum property, the sum of all the four interior angles is 360 degrees.
Sum of all interior angles of a quadrilateral is = 360°
We have,
$\angle PDQ + \angle Q + \angle P + \angle B = 360°$
$60 + 90 + 90 + \angle B = 360°$
$240 + \angle B = 360°$
$\angle B = 360° - 240°$
$\angle B = 120°$
Since, opposite angles in parallelogram are equal,
$\angle B = \angle D = 120°$
Since, opposite sides are parallel in parallelogram,
$AB \| CD$
Also, since sum of adjacent interior angles is 180 degrees
$\angle B + \angle C = 180°$
$120 + \angle C = 180°$
$\angle C = 180° - 120°$
$\angle C = 60°$
Since, opposite angles in parallelogram are equal,
$\angle C = \angle A = 60°$
Therefore, areas of the parallelogram are 60°, 120°, 60° and 120°

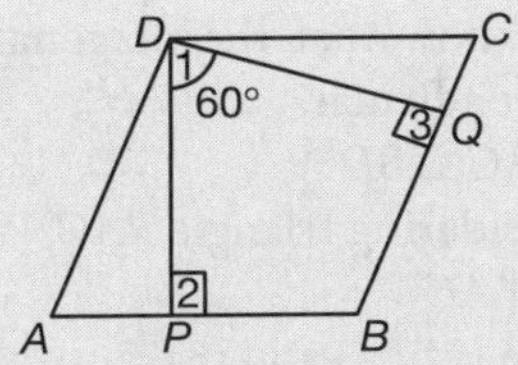

2. Considering triangles ALD and BLD,
As DL is the perpendicular bisector of AB
$\angle DLA = \angle DLB = 90°$
Also, $AL = BL = x/2$
Common side $= DL$
SAS criterion states that if two sides of one triangle are proportional to two sides of another triangle and their included angles are congruent, then the triangles are congruent.
By SAS criteria, the triangles ALD and BLD are congruent.
The Corresponding Parts of Congruent Triangles are Congruent (CPCTC) theorem states that when two triangles are congruent, then their corresponding sides and angles are also congruent or equal in measurements.
By CPCTC,
$AD = BD$
Now, in triangle ADB $AD = AB = DB = x$
Therefore, ADB is an equilateral triangle
We know that the angles of an equilateral triangle is always equal to 60 degrees
So, $\angle A = \angle ADB = \angle ABD = 60°$ (1)
Considering triangle DBC,
$DB = BC = CD = x$
Therefore, DBC is an equilateral triangle
So, $\angle C = \angle CBD = \angle DBC = 60°$ (2)
From (1) and (2), $\angle A = \angle C$
By angle sum property,
$\angle C + \angle B + \angle D = 180°$
$60 + \angle B + \angle D = 180°$
We know, $\angle B = \angle D$
$\angle B = \angle D = 180 - 60°$
$\angle B = \angle D = 120°$
Therefore, the angles of the rhombus are
$\angle A = \angle C = 60°$ and $\angle B = \angle D = 120°$

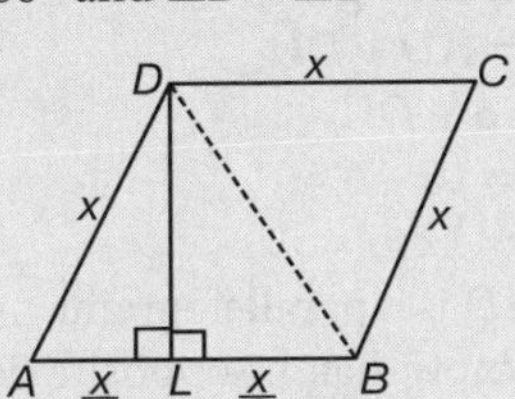

3. Join the other diagonal BD of the parallelogram.
The diagonal BD meets AC at O
We know that diagonals of a parallelogram bisect each other.
From the figure,
$OA = OC$
$OD = OB$
Given, $AE = CF$
From the figure,
$OA - AE = OE$
$OC - CF = OF$
So, $OE = OF$
Therefore, $BDEF$ is a parallelogram as the diagonals EF and BD bisect each other at O

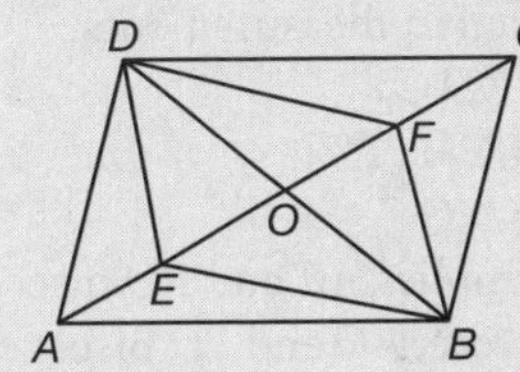

4. Considering triangle ABC,
E and F are the midpoints of AC and AB
The midpoint theorem states that "The line segment in a triangle joining the midpoint of two sides of the triangle is said to be parallel to its third side and is also half of the length of the third side."
By Midpoint theorem,
$EF \parallel BC$
$EF = 1/2\ BC$ (1)
$DF \parallel AC$
$DF = 1/2\ AC$ (2)
$DE \parallel AB$
$DE = 1/2\ AB$ (3)
Since ABC is an equilateral triangle
The sides $AB = BC = AC$
Dividing by 2,
$1/2\ AB = 1/2\ BC = 1/2\ AC$
From (1), (2) and (3)
$DE = EF = DF$
This implies the sides of triangle DEF are equal.
Therefore, DEF is an equilateral triangle.

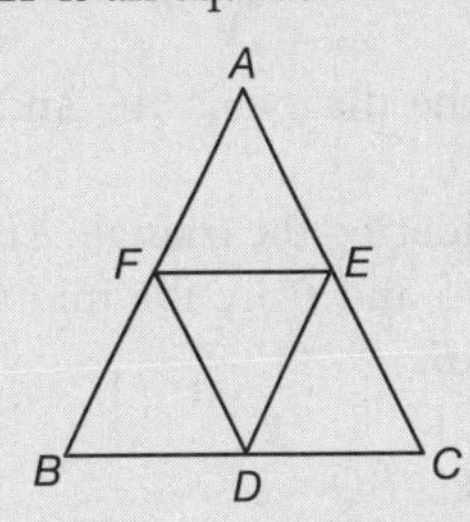

5. Considering triangles AMP and CMQ,
We know that alternate interior angles are equal.
So, $\angle PAM = \angle QCM$
Given, $AP = CQ$
Also, the alternate interior angles $\angle MPA$ and $\angle MQC$ are equal.
So, $\angle MPA = \angle MQC$

SAS criterion states that if two sides of one triangle are proportional to two sides of another triangle and their included angles are congruent, then the triangles are congruent.
By SAS criteria, the triangles *AMP* and *CMQ* are congruent.
The Corresponding Parts of Congruent Triangles are Congruent (CPCTC) theorem states that when two triangles are congruent, then their corresponding sides and angles are also congruent or equal in measurements.
By CPCTC,
$AM = CM$
$PM = MQ$
This implies *AC* and *BQ* bisect each other at *M*.
Therefore, *AC* and *PQ* bisect each other.

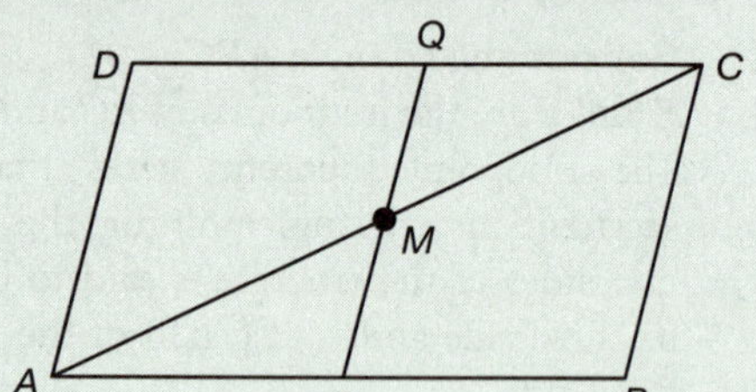

6. Given, $\angle 1 = \angle 2$
Since *AB* is parallel to *CD* and *AC* is the transversal, the alternate interior angles are equal.
So, $\angle 1 = \angle 4$ (1)
Similarly, $\angle 2 = \angle 3$ (2)
From (1) and (2),
$\angle 3 = \angle 4$
Therefore, the diagonal bisects the other angle.

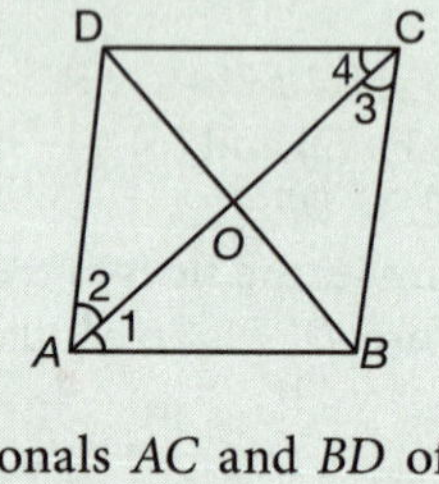

7. Join the diagonals *AC* and *BD* of the rhombus *ABCD*.
Considering the triangle *ABD*,
Since *S* and *P* are the midpoints of the sides *AD* and *AB*.
$SP \parallel BD$ (1)
$SP = 1/2\ BD$ (2)
Similarly, $RQ \parallel BD$
$RQ = 1/2\ BD$ (3)
From (2) and (3),
$SP = RQ$
Also, $SP \parallel RQ$
Therefore, *PQRS* is a parallelogram
We know that the diagonals of a rhombus are perpendicular.
So, $AC \perp BD$ (4)
Considering triangle *BAC*,
$PQ \parallel AC$ (5)
From (1), (4) and (5),
$SP \perp PQ$
i.e., $\angle SPQ = 90°$
We know that a rectangle is a quadrilateral with four right angles. The opposite sides are parallel and equal to each other.
Therefore, *PQRS* is a rectangle.

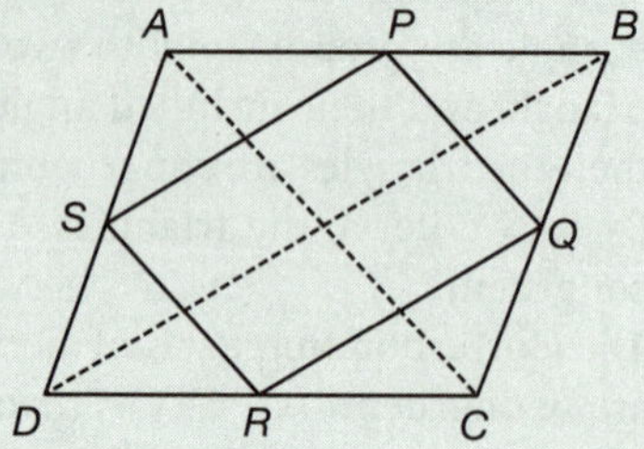

8. The bisector of $\angle A$ meets *DC* in *E*.
AE and *BC* are produced to meet at *F*.
We have to find the length of *CF*.
Now extend *AD* to *H* and join *HF*.
So, *ABFH* is a parallelogram
We know that the opposite sides of a parallelogram are parallel and congruent.
$AB \parallel HF$ and $HF = AB$
We know that the alternate interior angles are equal.
$\angle AFH = \angle FAB$ (1)
Since *AF* is the bisector of $\angle A$
$\angle HAF = \angle FAB$ (2)
From (1) and (2),
$\angle AFH = \angle HAF$
We know that the sides opposite to equal angles are equal.
$HF = AH$
Since, $HF = AB$
$HF = 10$ cm
Since $HF = AH$, $AH = 10$ cm
From the figure,
$AH = AD + DH$
$10 = 6 + DH$
$DH = 10 - 6$
$DH = 4$ cm
CFHD is a parallelogram
We know that the opposite sides of a parallelogram are parallel and congruent.
So, $DH = CF$
Therefore, $CF = 4$ cm

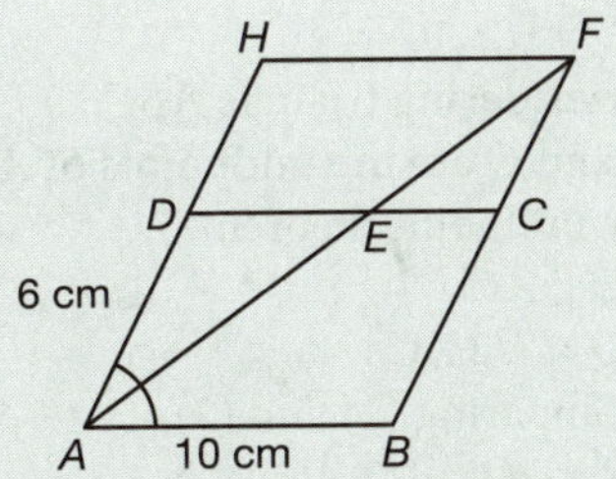

9. The midpoint theorem states that "The line segment in a triangle joining the midpoint of two sides of the triangle is said to be parallel to its third side and is also half of the length of the third side." Considering triangle ADC, S and R are the midpoints of AD and DC By midpoint theorem,

$SR \parallel AC$ and $SR = 1/2\ AC$ (1)

Considering triangle ABC, P and Q are the midpoints of AB and BC

By midpoint theorem,

$PQ \parallel AC$ and $PQ = 1/2\ AC$ (2)

Comparing (1) and (2),

$SR = PQ = 1/2\ AC$ (3)

Considering triangle BCD, By midpoint theorem,

$RQ \parallel BD$ and $RQ = 1/2\ BD$ (4)

Considering triangle BAD, $SP \parallel BD$

By midpoint theorem,

$SP = 1/2\ BD$ (5)

Comparing (4) and (5),

$SP = RQ = 1/2\ BD$ (6)

Given, $AC = BD$

Dividing by 2 on both sides,

$1/2\ AC = 1/2\ BD$

From (3) and (6),

$SR = PQ = SP = RQ$

This implies all the sides of the quadrilateral are equal.

Therefore, $PQRS$ is a rhombus.

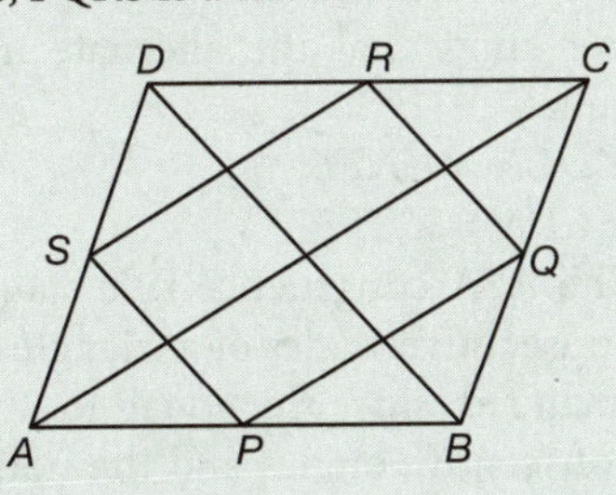

10. Extend AB to E and join CE such that $AD \parallel CE$

So, $AECD$ is a parallelogram.

We know that the opposite sides of a parallelogram are parallel and congruent.

$AD = EC$

Given, $AD = BC$

So, $BC = EC$

We know that the angles opposite to equal sides are equal.

$\angle CBE = \angle CEB$ (1)

We know that the linear pair of angles is always supplementary.

$\angle B + \angle CBE = 180°$ (2)

Since $AD \parallel EC$ and cut by transversal AE,

We know that two parallel lines are cut by a transversal, the sum of interior angles lying on the same side of the transversal is always supplementary.

$\angle A + \angle CEB = 180°$ (3)

From (1),

$\angle A + \angle CEB = 180°$ (4)

Comparing (2) and (4),

$\angle A = \angle B$

We know that the sum of supplementary angles of a parallelogram is always equal to 180 degrees.

$\angle A + \angle D = 180°$

$\angle B + \angle C = 180°$

On comparing,

$\angle A + \angle D = \angle B + \angle C$

since, $\angle A = \angle B$

$\angle A + \angle D = \angle A + \angle C$

$\angle C = \angle D$

Therefore, it is proven that $\angle A = \angle B$ and $\angle C = \angle D$

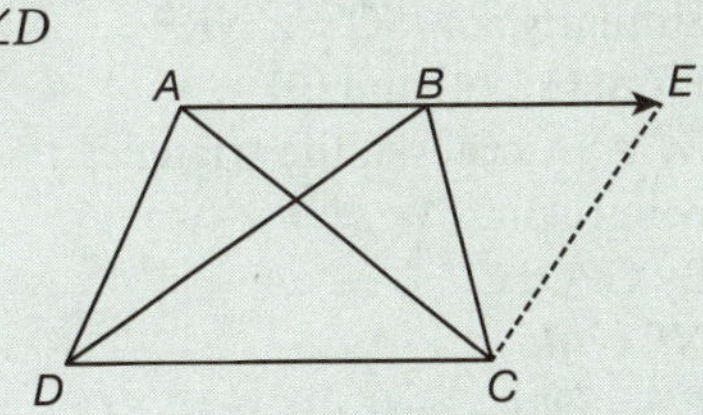

Long Answer Type Questions

1. Draw DP parallel to EF

Considering triangle ADP,

E is the midpoint of AD

$EF \parallel DP$

By converse of midpoint theorem,

F is the midpoint of AP.

Considering triangle FBC,

D is the midpoint of BC

$DP \parallel BF$

By converse of midpoint theorem,

P is the midpoint of FC

So, $AF = FP = PC$

Therefore, $AF = \frac{1}{3}\ AC$

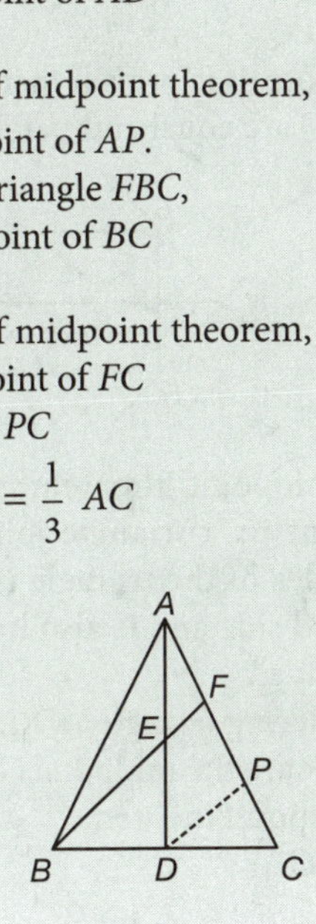

2. Given, PQ and RS are two equal and parallel line-segments
Any point M not lying on PQ or RS is joined to Q and S.
The lines through P and R parallel to QM and SM meet at N.
We have to prove that the line segments MN and PQ are equal and parallel to each other.
We know that the opposite sides of a parallelogram are parallel and congruent.
$PQ = RS$ and $PQ \parallel RS$ (1)
$PQRS$ is a parallelogram.
We know that the sum of interior angles lying on the same side of the transversal is always supplementary.
$\angle RPQ + \angle PQS = 180°$
Now,
$\angle RPQ + \angle PQM + \angle MQS = 180°$ (2)
Also, $PN \parallel QM$
So, $\angle NPQ + \angle PQM = 180°$
Now,
$\angle NPR + \angle RPQ + \angle PQM = 180°$ (3)
Comparing (2) and (3),
$\angle MQS = \angle NPR$ (4)
Similarly, $\angle MSQ = \angle NRP$ (5)
From (1), (4) and (5)
By ASA criteria, the triangles PNR and QMS are congruent.
By CPCTC,
$NR = MS$
$PN = QM$
So, $PN \parallel QM$
Therefore, $PQMN$ is a parallelogram
We know that the opposite sides of a parallelogram are parallel and congruent.
$MN = PQ$
$NM \parallel PQ$
Therefore, it is proven that the line segments MN and PQ are equal and parallel to each other.

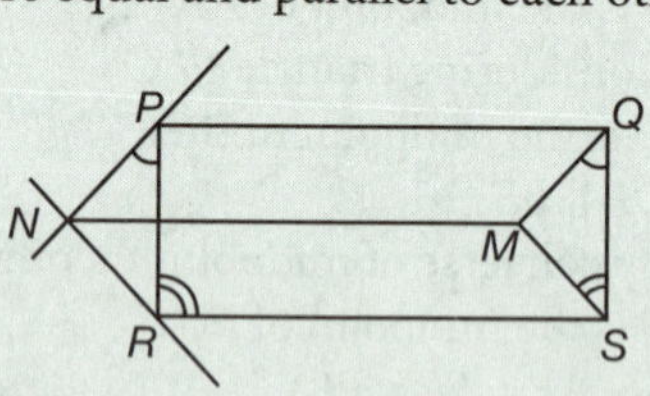

3. The midpoint theorem states that "The line segment in a triangle joining the midpoint of two sides of the triangle is said to be parallel to its third side and is also half of the length of the third side."
Considering triangle ADC,
S and R are the midpoints of AD and DC
By midpoint theorem,
$SR \parallel AC$
$SR = 1/2\ AC$ (1)
Considering triangle ABC,
P and Q are the midpoints of AB and BC
By midpoint theorem,
$PQ \parallel AC$
$PQ = 1/2\ AC$ (2)
Comparing (1) and (2),
$SR = PQ = 1/2\ AC$ (3)
Considering triangle BAD,
$SP \parallel BD$
By midpoint theorem,
$SP = 1/2\ BD$ (5)
Comparing (4) and (5),
$SP = RQ = 1/2\ BD$ (6)
and Given, $AC = BD$
Dividing by 2 on both sides, $1/2\ AC = 1/2\ BD$
From (3) and (6), $SR = PQ = SP = RQ$
This implies all the sides of the quadrilateral are equal. Considering quadrilateral $OERF$,
$OE \parallel FR$ and $OF \parallel ER$
$\angle EOF = \angle ERF = 90°$
Sinc $AC \perp BD$ and $\angle DOC = \angle EOF = 90°$
$\angle QRS = 90°$ and $\angle RQS = 90°$
Therefore, $PQRS$ is a square.

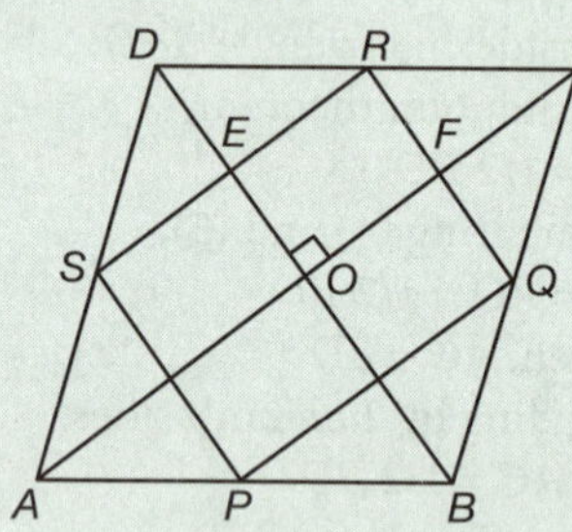

4. Join CN and extend it to meet AB at E.
Considering triangles CDN and EBN,
Since N is the midpoint of BD
$DN = BN$
We know that the alternate interior angles are equal.
$\angle DCN = \angle NEB$
$\angle CDN = \angle NBE$
The ASA congruence rule states that if any two consecutive angles of a triangle along with a non-included side are equal to the corresponding consecutive angles and the non-included side of another triangle, the two triangles are said to be congruent.
By ASA criterion, the triangles CDN and EBN are congruent.
By CPCTC,
$DC = EB$
$CN = NE$
Considering triangle CAE,
M and N are the midpoints of AC and CE

$MN \parallel AE$

By midpoint theorem,

$MN \parallel AB \parallel CD$

Therefore, it is proved that the line joining the mid-points of the diagonals of a trapezium is parallel to the parallel sides of the trapezium.

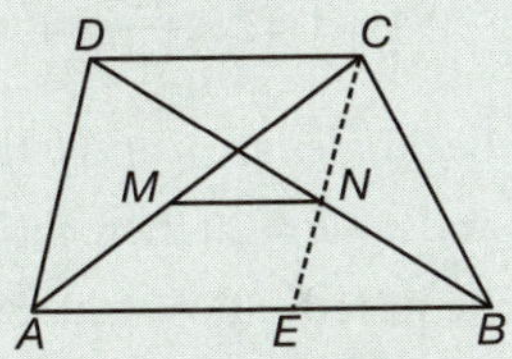

5. We know that the opposite sides of a parallelogram are parallel and congruent.

$BC \parallel AD$ and $BC = AD$

$AB \parallel CD$ and $AB = CD$

Since P is the midpoint of DC.

$DP = PC = 1/2\ CD$ (1)

Given, $QC \parallel AP$

$PC \parallel AQ$

Therefore, $APCQ$ is a parallelogram

So, $AQ = PC$

From (1),

$AQ = PC = 1/2\ CD$

Since $AB = CD$

$PC = 1/2\ AB = BQ$

Considering triangles AQR and BQC,

$AQ = BQ$

We know that the vertically opposite angles are equal

$\angle AQR = \angle BQC$

We know that the alternate interior angles are equal

$\angle ARQ = \angle BCQ$

By ASA criterion, the triangles AQR and BQC

The Corresponding Parts of Congruent Triangles are Congruent (CPCTC) theorem states that when two triangles are congruent, then their corresponding sides and angles are also congruent or equal in measurements.

By CPCTC,

$AR = BC$

Given, $BC = AD$

So, $AR = AD$

By CPCTC,

$CQ = QR$

Therefore, it is proved that $AR = AD$ and $CQ = QR$.

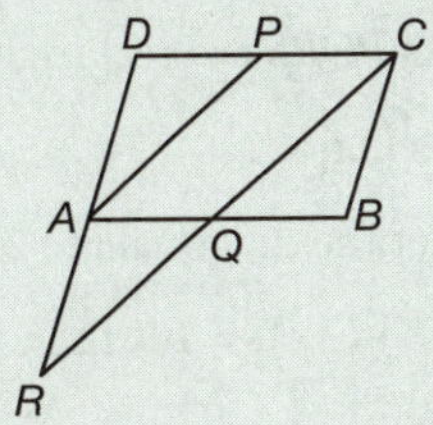

6. **In ΔAXD and ΔCYB**

$\angle ADX = \angle CBY$

(alternate interior angles for $BC \parallel AD$)

$AD = CB$

(opposite sides of parallelogram $ABCD$)

$DX = BY$ (given)

$\Rightarrow$ $\Delta AXD \cong \Delta CYB$ by SAS congruency rule.

$\Rightarrow$ $AX = CY$ by C.P.C.T

Now, in ΔAYB and ΔCXD,

$\angle ABY = \angle CDX$

(alternate interior angles for $AB \parallel CD$)

$AB = CD$

(opposite sides of parallelogram $ABCD$)

$DX = BY$ (Given)

$\Rightarrow \Delta AYB \cong \Delta CXD$ by SAS congruency rule.

$\Rightarrow AY = CX$ by C.P.C.T

From the result we obtained $AX = CY$ and $AY = CX$

Since opposite sides of quadrilateral $AXCY$ are equal to each other.

$\therefore$ $XACY$ is a parallelogram.

Hence proved

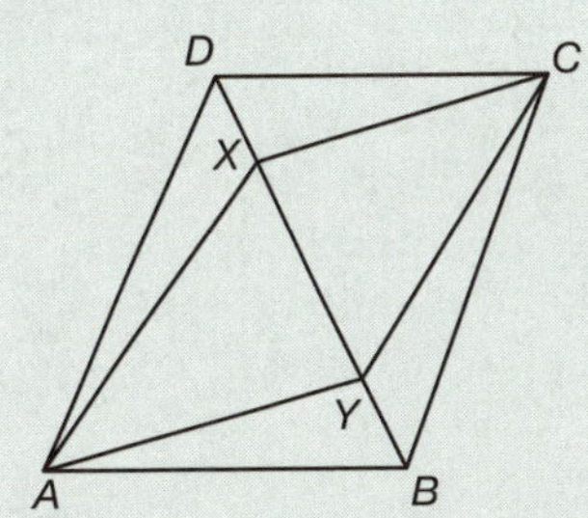

Archive Corner

1. **(C)** $\angle AXB = \frac{1}{2}(\angle C + \angle D) = \frac{1}{2} \times 180 = 90°$.

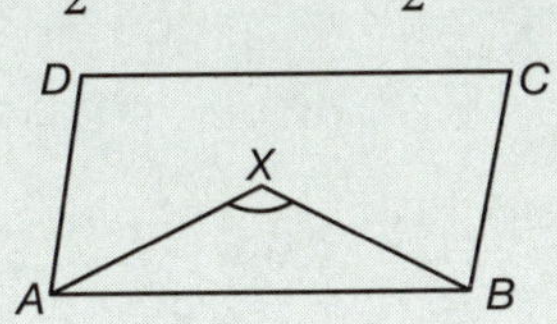

2. **(D)** 2 equilateral triangle formed so one of the angle will be 60. Larger angle will be 120°.

3. **(A)**

4. **(D)**

5. **(A,B)** Let the acute angle be x and obtuse angle be y then $x+y=180°$
and $y=2x+30$ then $x+2x+30=180°$
then $3x=150$ so $x=50$ and $y=130$.

6. **(B)** As $PQRS$ is a rectangle then $\angle RSP=90°$.

7. **(A)** As Q.no. 1

8. **(A)** Let the diagonal are $2x$ and $6x$ then
$x^2+(3x)^2=10^2$ then $10x^2=100$. So $x^2=10$.
Then $x=\sqrt{10}$.
Then larger diagonal $=6\sqrt{10}$ cm

9. **(C)** $\angle CDA+b=180$ and $a+\angle CBA=180$
and $x+y+\angle CDA+\angle CBA=360$.
then $x+y=a+b$.

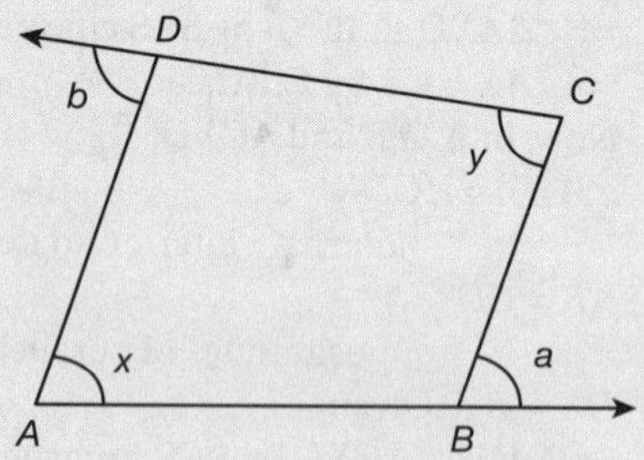

10. **(C)** (6, 8, 10) Pythagorean triplet

11. **(A)**

12. **(D)** Let the diagonal be $2x$.
Then $x^2+6^2=10^2$ then $x=8$.

13. **(D)** $\frac{1}{2}\times4\times d=2\times\frac{\sqrt{3}}{4}\times4^2$ then $d=4\sqrt{3}$ cm.

14. **(A)** Let angles are a and b then $a+b=180$
and $a-b=20$ then $a=100$ and $b=80$.
Required ratio $=100:80=5:4$

15. **(A)**

16. **(C)** In triangle ABC. $AB+BC>AC$
In triangle ADC. $AD+DC>AC$
In triangle DBC. $DC+BC>BD$
In triangle ABD. $AB+AD>BD$
After adding all four equation we will get
$AB+BC+CD+DA>AC+BD$

17. **(D)** Angle sum $=(7-2)\times180=900$

HINTS AND EXPLANATIONS

CHAPTER 9 CIRCLES

Check Point 1

1. 3
2. Suppose you are given a circle. Give a construction to find its centre.

Solution:

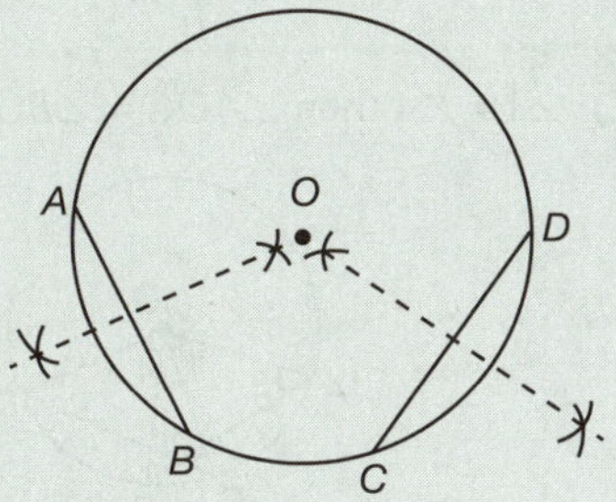

The construction steps to find the center of the circle are:

Step I: Draw a circle first.

Step II: Draw 2 chords AB and CD in the circle.

Step III: Draw the perpendicular bisectors of AB and CD.

Step IV: Connect the two perpendicular bisectors at a point. This intersection point of the two perpendicular bisectors is the centre of the circle.

3. Let the two circles with centre P and Q intersect at points A and B.
Join AB. AB is the common chord.
Join PQ. AB and PQ bisect each other at M.
Let M be the midpoint of AB.
Hence, $PM \perp AB$
[Since, the line drawn through the centre of a circle to bisect a chord is perpendicular to the chord]
$\Rightarrow \angle PMA = 90°$
Now, since M is the midpoint of AB
Hence, $QM \perp AB$
$\Rightarrow \angle QMA = 90°$
Thus, $\angle PMQ = \angle PMA + \angle QMA$
$= 90° + 90° = 180°$
Hence PMQ is a straight line and $PMQ \perp AB$
Therefore, PMQ is the perpendicular bisector of the common chord AB and passes through the two centers P and Q.
So, the centres lie on the perpendicular bisector of the common chords.

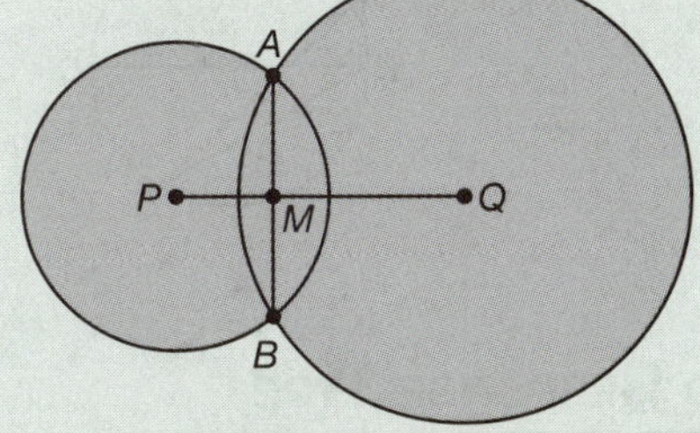

4. $x^2 = 20^2 - 16^2 = 12^2$ then $x = 12$
length of chord $= 24$
5. $AP = PB = 10$. Then $AQ = BQ = 17$. and $PQ = 21$.
Let $PM = x$ and $MQ = 21 - x$
then In triangle $APM : AP^2 = AM^2 + PM^2$
then $10^2 = AM^2 + x^2$. In triangle AMQ
$AQ^2 = AM^2 + QM^2$
then $17^2 = AM^2 + (21 - x)^2$
$= AM^2 + x^2 + 441 - 42x = 100 + 441 - 42x$
then $x = 6$
$AM^2 = 100 - 36 = 64$ then $AM = 8$. Then $AB = 16$.

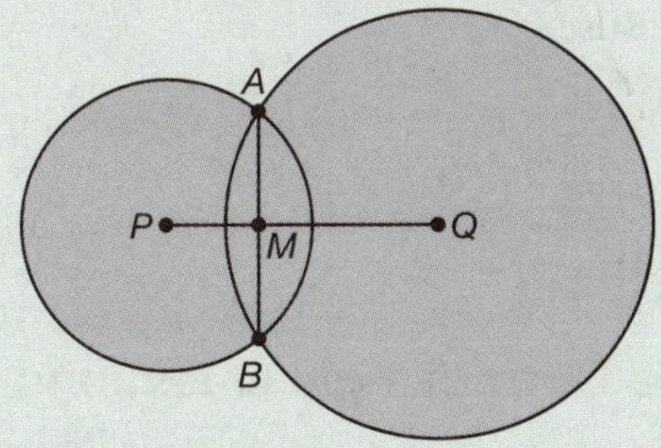

Check Point 2

6. $2x + 10 = x + 45$ then $x = 35$
7. $x + 2x = 180$ then $x = 60$.
8. Reflex $\angle POR = 360 - 114 = 246°$
then $\angle PQR = \frac{246}{2} = 123°$

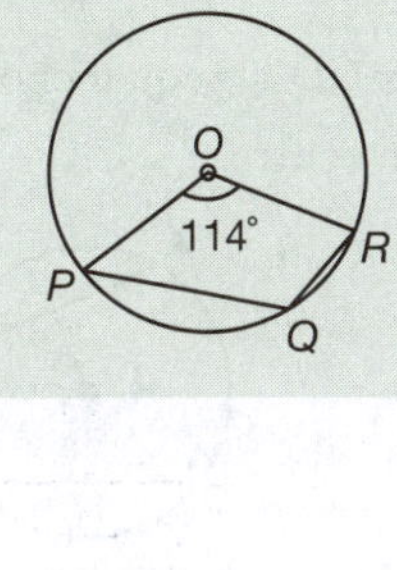

9. $\angle AOB = 2 \times 20 = 40$ then $\angle AOD = 180 - 40 = 140°$

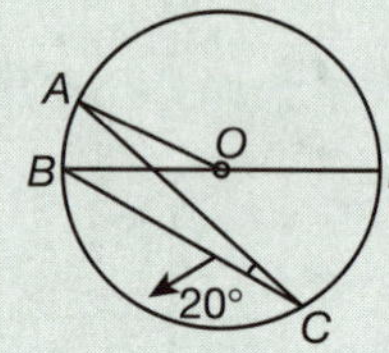

10. $\angle Q = \angle R$ and $\angle R + \angle S = 90°$

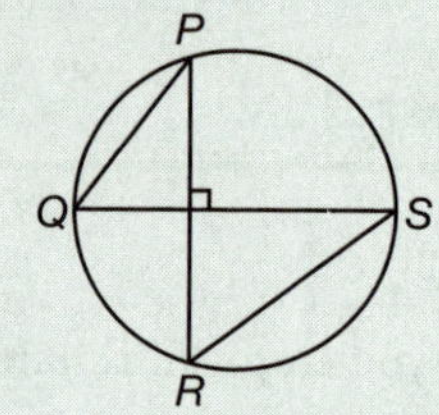

Fixed Response Type

Fill in the Blanks

1. Equal
2. Equidistant
3. Congruent
4. Isoceles trapezium
5. 180
6 Diameter

True/False

1. False
2. False
3. False
4. True
5. True

Single Correct Type Questions

1. (D) $x^2 = 10^2 - 6^2 = 64$ then $x = 8$
then length of chord $= 2x = 16$.

2. (A) Reflex $\angle AOC = 310$ then $\angle ABC = 155°$
then $\angle CBD = 180 - 155 = 25°$

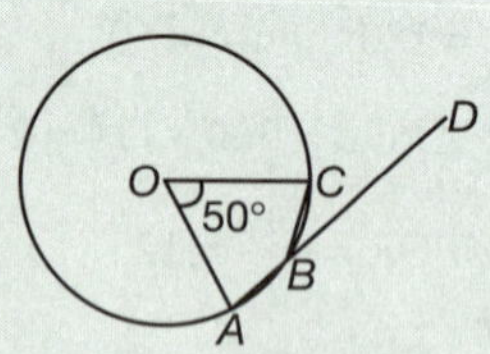

3. (A) $AB = CD = 9$ equal chord equidistant from centre.

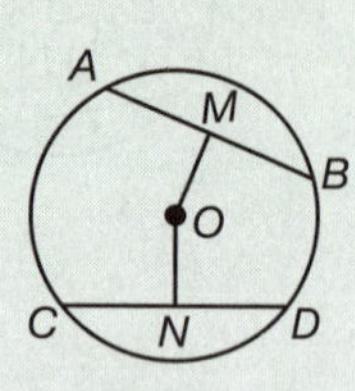

4. (C) $\angle 1 = \angle 4$ then $\angle AOC = \angle BOD$ then $\angle 2 = \angle 3$

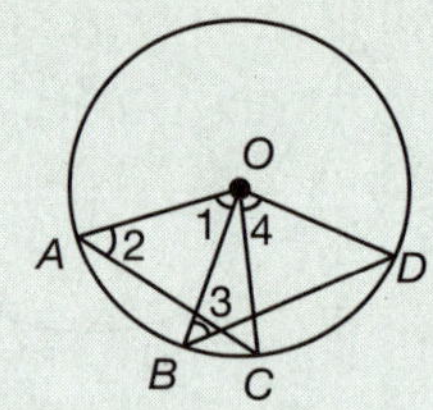

5. (A) $\angle BDC = \angle CAB$ then $\angle ACB = 90 - 42 = 48°$

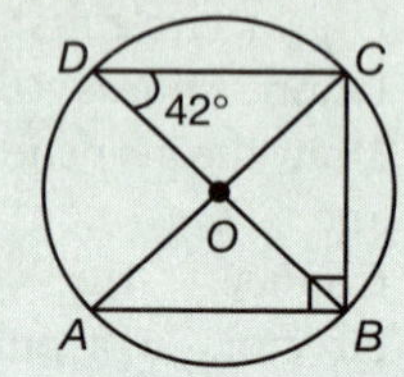

6. (C) $\angle ACB = 180 - 80 - 40 = 60° = \angle ADB$.
Then $\angle DAB + \angle ABD = 120°$

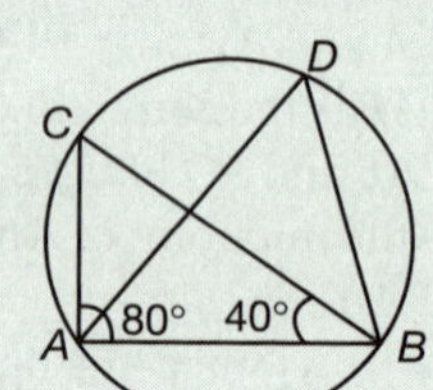

7. (C) $\angle QPC = 25°$ and $\angle RPC = 15°$
then $\angle QPR = 40°$ then $\angle QCR = 80°$

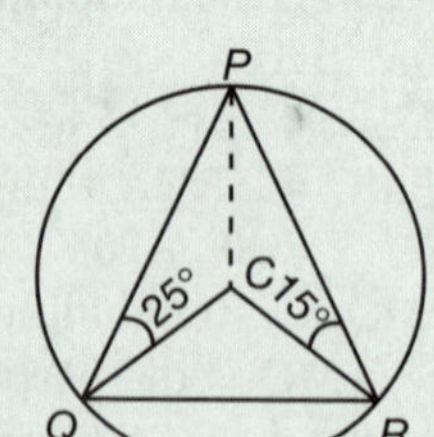

8. (C) 30°

9. (B) $\angle ACB = \angle ADB = 40°$
then $y = 180 - 120 - 40 = 20°$.

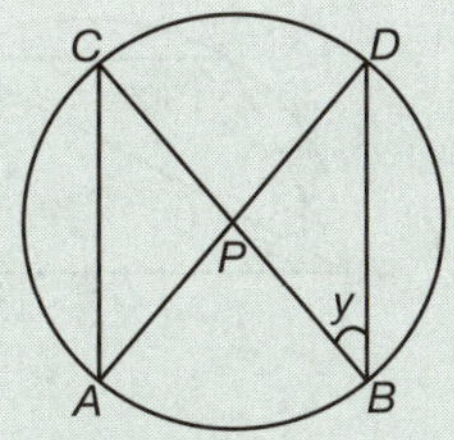

10. **(C)** $\angle A + \angle C = 180°$ and $\angle A - \angle C = 70°$

then $2\angle A = 250°$

Then $\angle A = 125°$ and $\angle C = 55°$

11. **(A)** chord = radius then triangle is equilateral

then angle at circumference $= \frac{60}{2} = 30°$

12. **(D)** $\angle BAC = \angle BDC = \angle CBD$

$= \angle CAD = \angle BDA = 25°$.

Then $\angle AED = 180 - (180 - 25 - 25 - 25) = 75°$

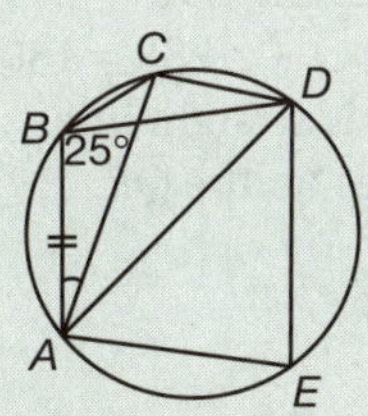

13. **(B)** $t + 2y = 180$ then $t + z = 360$

then $t + 2x = 360$

then $2x - 2y = 180$

then $x - y = 90$.

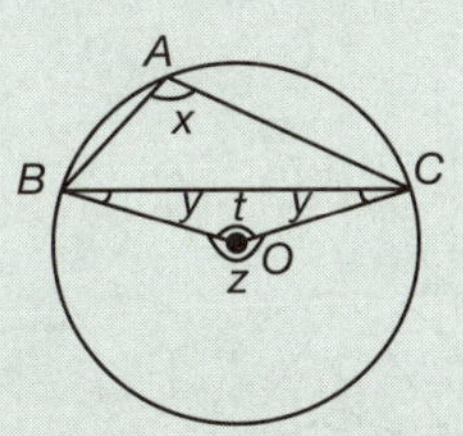

14. **(B)** $\angle BOC = 2x$ then $2x + 2y = 180°$

then $x + y = 90°$

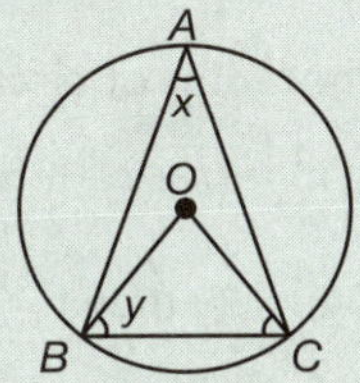

15. **(A)** Let $\angle ACB = x$ then $\angle ABC = 2x$

then $x + 2x + 60 = 180°$ then $3x = 120°$

then $x = 40°$

Now $\angle ABC = 80°$ Required angle $= 80°$.

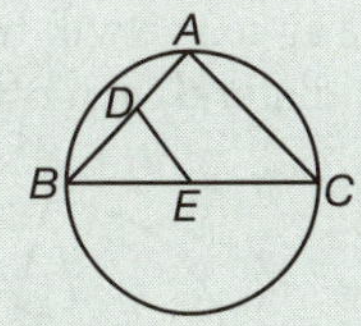

16. **(D)**

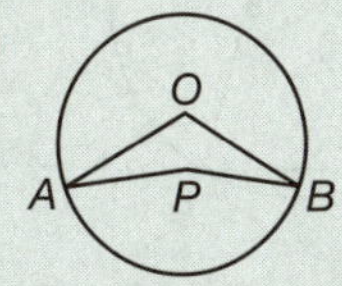

$\angle AOP = \angle OAP = 20°$.

Then $\angle POB = \angle OPB = 60°$.

Then $\angle APB = 360 - 60 - 140 = 160°$.

17. **(D)**

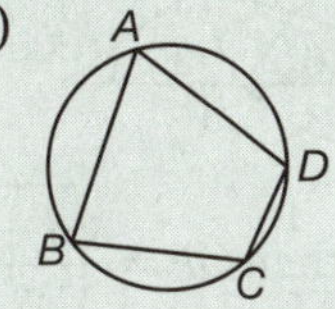

Let $\angle BAD = x$ then $x + 2x = 180°$ then $x = 60°$

then required angle $= 120°$.

18. **(D)**

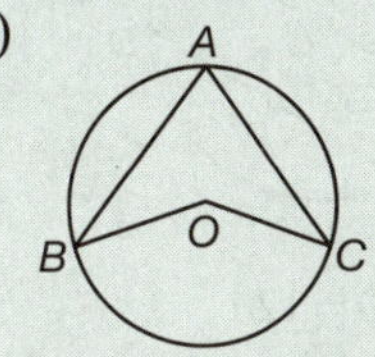

$\angle BOC = 100°$ then $\angle AOC = AOB = 130°$

then $\angle ACO = \frac{180 - 130}{2} = 25°$

19. **(C)**

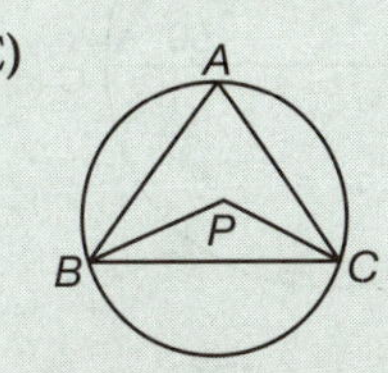

$\angle ABC = \angle ACB = \frac{180 - 40}{2} = 70°$

Now $\angle PBC = \angle PCB = \frac{70}{2} = 35°$

then $\angle BPC = 180 - 35 - 35 = 110°$

20. **(A)**

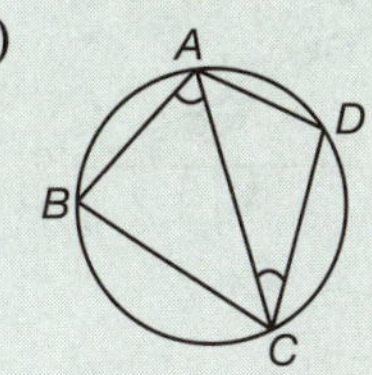

$\angle ACB = \angle BAC = 40°$

then $\angle CAD = 180 - 70 - 40 - 40 = 30°$

21. **(C)** Angle at centre will be 60 then triangle will be equilateral then $r = 5$ diameter will be 10.

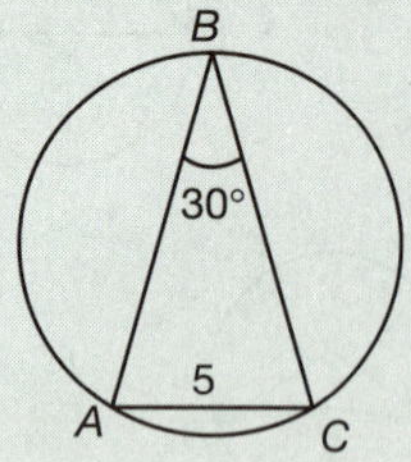

22. **(D)** $y + 18 + 18 + 35 = 180$ then $y = 180 - 71 = 109$

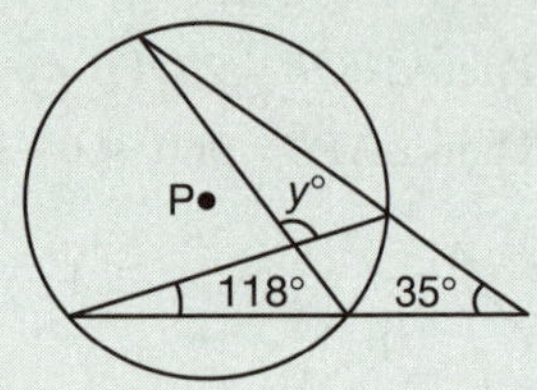

23. **(D)** $OD^2 = PD^2 + OP^2$ then $OP = \frac{\sqrt{d^2 - l^2}}{2}$

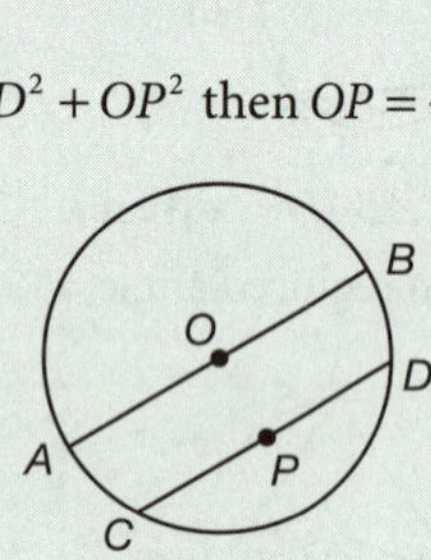

24. **(B)** $\angle DAB = 180 - 60 = 120$

Now $\angle ADB = 180 - 120 - 35 = 25$.

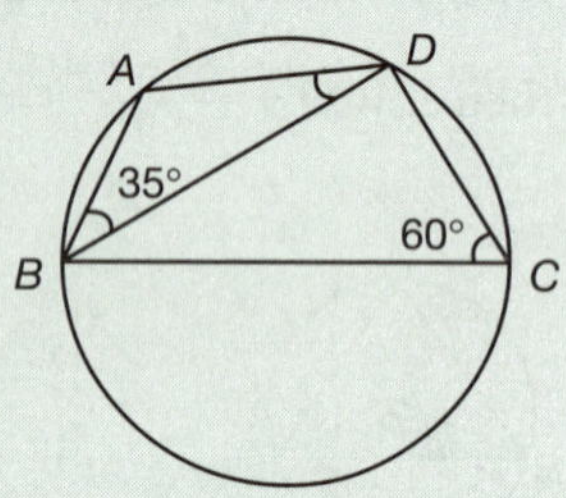

25. **(C)** $\angle CBE = a + 30$ and $\angle ADC$

$= 180 - a - 30 = 150 - a = b + 30$

then $120 = a + b = 3a$ then $a = 40$ and $b = 80$

so $a + b = 120$.

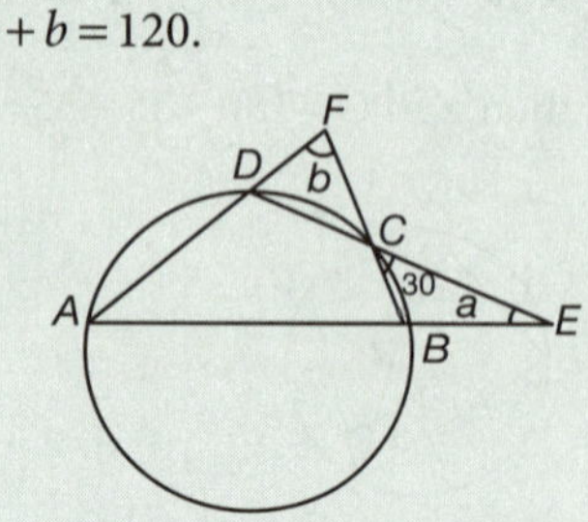

26. **(B)** $b = 90$ and $\angle CBA = 180 - 130 = 50$

then $a = 180 - 90 - 50 = 40$

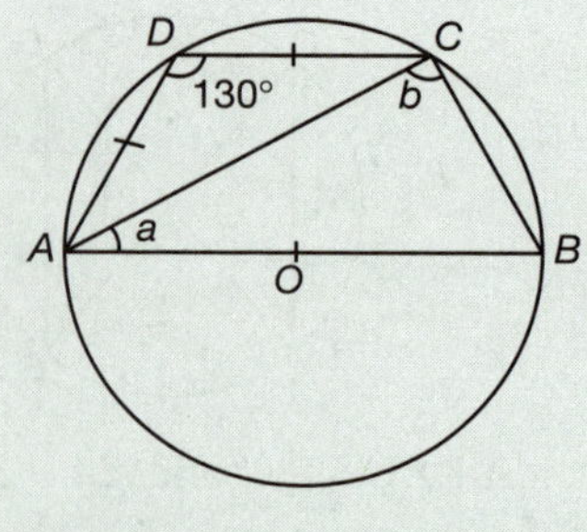

Multiple Correct Type Questions

1. **(A,C,D)** Two circles are drawn on the sides PQ and PR of the triangle PQR as diameters. The circles intersected at S.

Construction: PS is joined.

To prove: S lies on QR. We have to prove that QSR is a straight line.

Proof:

$\angle PSQ = \angle PSR = 90°$ Angle in the semi circle

Now, $\angle PSQ + \angle PSR = 180°$

$\Rightarrow \angle QSR$ is straight line.

Thus, S lies on the QR.

2. **(A,C,D)**

3. **(A,B,C)**

4. **(C)**

5. **(B,C)**

6. **(B,D)**

7. **(D)**

8. **(A,C)**

9. **(A,C)**

10. **(B)**

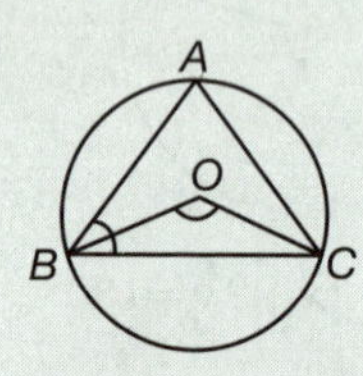

$\angle BOC = 2(180 - 80 - 80) = 40°$

11. **(B)** Let the radius of circle be r and $OB = r - 2$.

Then $r^2 = (r-2)^2 + 5^2$

then $4r = 29$ then $r = \frac{29}{4}$.

$OB = \frac{29}{4} - 2 = \frac{29-8}{4} = \frac{21}{4}$ cm $= 5.25$ cm.

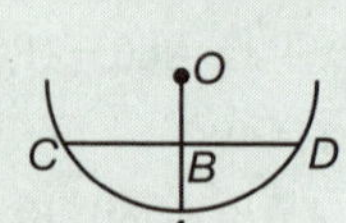

12. **(A,B)** In triangle OCQ. $OC^2 = CQ^2 + OQ^2$

Then $25 = 16 + OQ^2$ So $OQ = 3$.

In triangle OCQ. $OA^2 = AP^2 + OP^2$

Then $25 = 9 + OP^2$ So $OP = 4$.

Then $PQ = 4 - 3 = 1$cm (if chord on same side)

or $PQ = 4 + 3 = 7$ cm (If chord on either side)

13. **(B,D)** Same as 12.

14. **(C)**

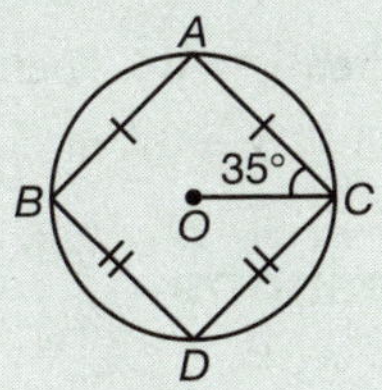

$\angle OCA = \angle OAC = 35°$

then $\angle AOC = \angle AOB = 110°$

and $\angle COD = \angle BOD = 70°$.

$\angle OBD = \angle ODB = \dfrac{110}{2} = 55$

then $\angle ABD = \angle ABO + \angle OBD$

$= 35 + 55 = 90°$.

15. **(B)** $\angle ABC = 180 - 80 = 100°$

then $\angle ABC = \angle OBA + \angle OBC$

then $\angle OBC = 50°$.

So $\angle AOB = 180 - 100 = 80°$.

Match Type Questions

1. (A) → (R)

$a = \sqrt{8^2 - 6^2} = \sqrt{28} = 2\sqrt{7} = 5.291$

(B) → (P)

$a = \sqrt{17^2 - 8^2} = \sqrt{225} = 15$

and $b = \sqrt{17^2 - 15^2} = \sqrt{64} = 8$

then distance between chords $= 15 + 8 = 23$ cm

(C) → (S)

$x^2 = 6^2 - 4^2 = 20$ then $2x = 4\sqrt{5} = 8.94$ cm

(D) → (Q)

$9^2 = \left(\dfrac{9}{2}\right)^2 + (3r)^2$ then $r^2 = 9 - \dfrac{9}{4} = \dfrac{27}{4}$

then $r = \dfrac{3\sqrt{3}}{2} = 1.5 \times 1.732 = 5.196$ cm

2. (A) → (Q)

$\angle ACB = x = \angle AOB$ and

reflex $\angle AOB = 360 - x$. Then $2x = 360 - x$

then $3x = 360$ so $x = \dfrac{360}{3} = 120$.

(B) → (R)

$\angle CBE = \angle CAE = 55$. and $\angle AEC = 90$

then $\angle ACE = 90 - 55 = 35 = \angle DEC$

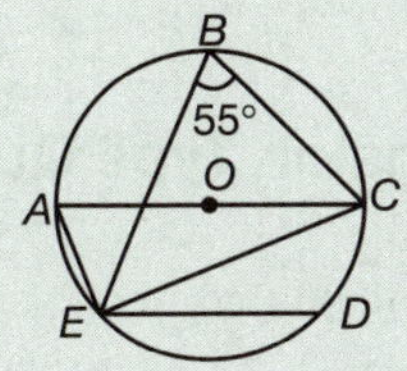

(C) → (S)

$\angle AOB = 2\angle ACB = 120$. and $\angle OAB = 30$.

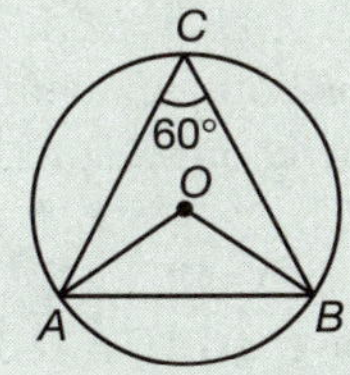

(D) → (P)

$\angle ACB = \dfrac{40}{2} = 20$.

Then $\angle OBC = 180 - 100 - 20 = 60$.

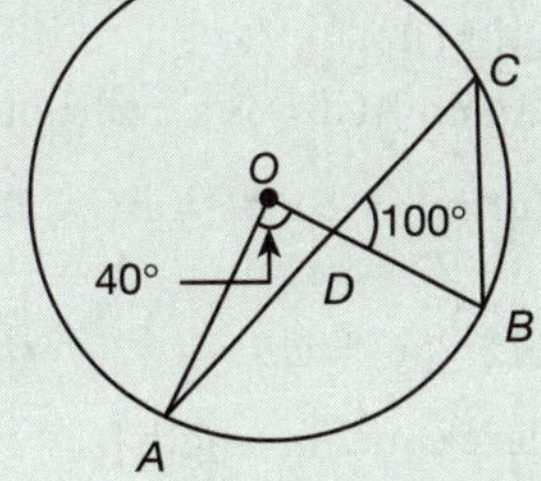

3.

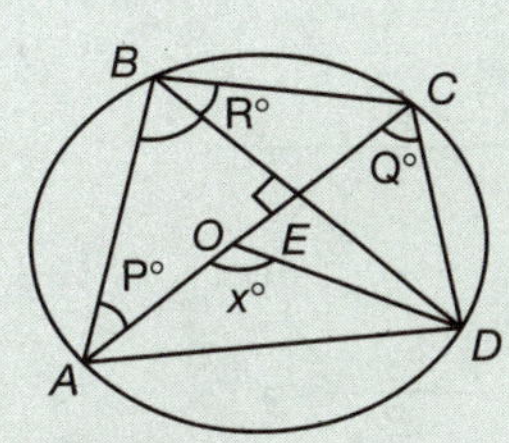

(A) → (S)

$P = 90 - Q = 90 - \dfrac{x}{2}$

(B) → (P)

$Q = \dfrac{x}{2}$

(C) → (Q)

$R = \dfrac{(180 - x)}{2} = 90 - \dfrac{x}{2}$

(D) → (R)

$\angle B = 90°$

Assertion and Reason Type Questions

1. **(B)**
2. **(A)**
3. **(C)**
4. **(B)**

Comprehension Type Questions

1. **(B)** $\angle DBC = 90 + 25 = 115°$ sum of exterior angles
2. **(A)** $\angle DCB = 35°$.
3. **(C)** Again $\angle ABD = \angle ACD = 55°$
[since both of them have been subtended by the chord AD to the circumference at B and C].
Now in ΔACE,
we have $\angle CAD = 180° - (\angle ACB + \angle BEA) = 180° - (90° + 25°) = 65°$.
$\therefore \angle BAC = \angle CAD - \angle BAD$
$= 65° - 35° = 30°$.
$\therefore \angle BDC = \angle BAC = 30°$ (ii)
[since both of them have been subtended by the chord BC to the circumference at A and D].
Again $ACBD$ is a cyclic quadrilateral.

Common solution (4-6): $BP = BQ = 27$ cm.
$CQ = CR = 38 - 27 = 11$ cm
Then $DR = SD = SO = OR$
(Sides of square equal in length)
$= 25 - 11 = 14$ cm.

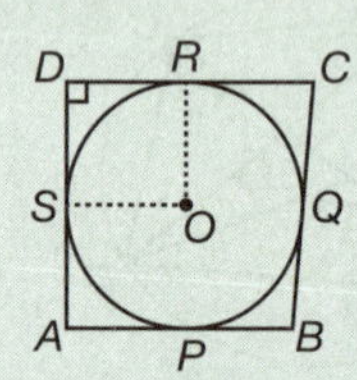

4. **(B)**
5. **(C)**
6. **(B)** Area of $DROS = 14 \times 14 = 196$ cm^2

Comprehension-3:

7. **(B)** $d^2 = 13^2 - 169 - 25 = 144$. Then $d = 12$.
8. **(C)** $r^2 = x^2 + (5)^2$
Also, $r^2 = (17 - x)^2 + (12)^2$
So, $x^2 + (5)^2 = (17 - x)^2 + (12)^2$
$x^2 + 25 = (17 - x)^2 + 144$
$\Rightarrow x = 12$
$\therefore r^2 = 144 + 25 = 169$
$\Rightarrow r = 13$ cm

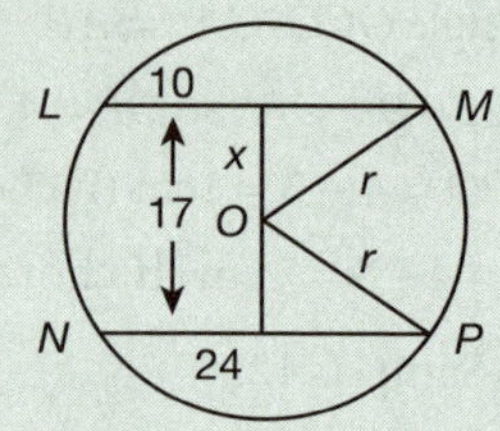

9. **(D)** $x^2 = 10^2 - 6^2$. Then $x^2 = 64$. Then $x = 8$.
Length of chord $= 2x = 16$ cm.

Numerical Type Questions

1.

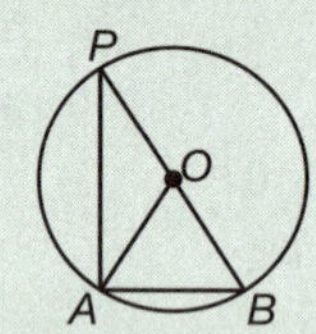

$\angle POA = 180 - 40 - 40 = 100°$.
and $\angle AOB = 80$ then $\angle OBA = 50°$.

2.

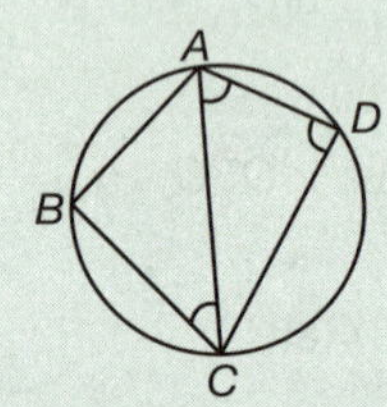

$\angle BAC = 180 - 100 = 80°$.
$\angle ACD = 180 - 100 - 40 = 40°$.
Then $\angle BCD = 20 + 40 = 60°$
$\angle BAD = 180 - 60 = 120° = \angle BAC + 40$
then $\angle BAC = 80°$.

3.

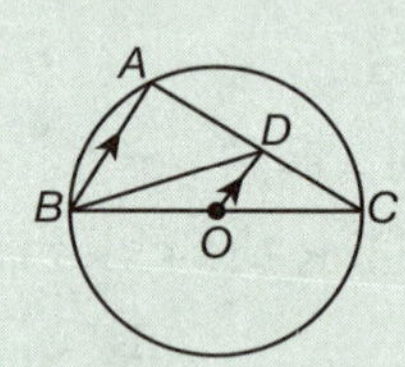

$\angle BAC = \angle ODC = 90$ then $\angle ACB = 90 - 40 = 50°$.

4. 45

5.

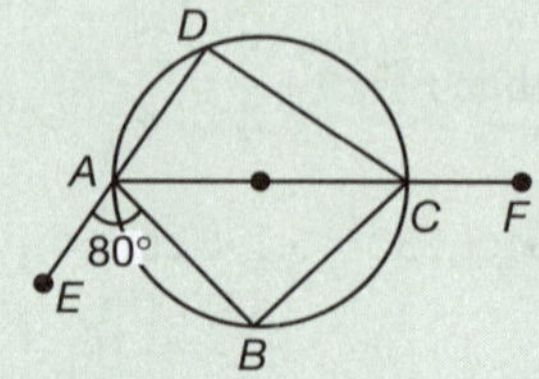

$\angle DCA = 180 - 110 = 70°$ and $\angle ACB = 80 - 70 = 10°$

Then $\angle AOB = 2 \times 10 = 20°$.

6.

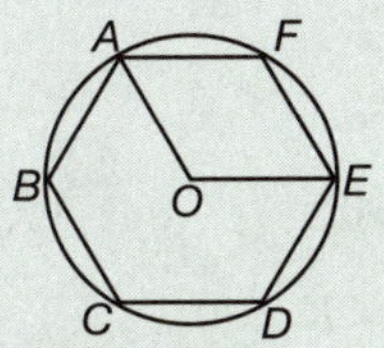

$$\angle AFE = \frac{(6-2)180}{6} = 120°$$

then $\angle AOE = (360 - 240) = 120°$.

7.

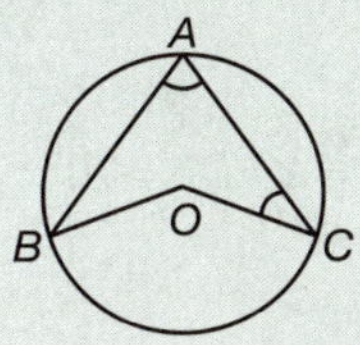

$\angle ABO = \angle ACO = 40°$.

8.

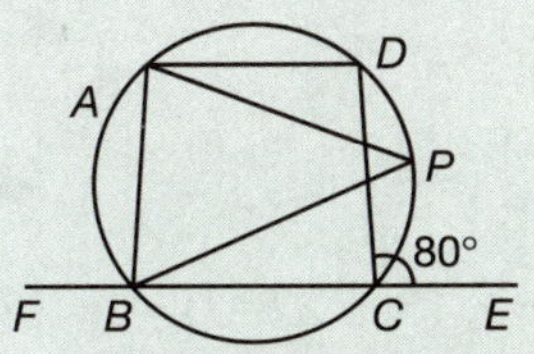

$\angle BAD = \angle DCE = 80°$ then

$\angle PAB = \angle PBA = 80 - 30 = 50°$

Then $\angle APB = 180 - 50 - 50 = 80°$.

9.

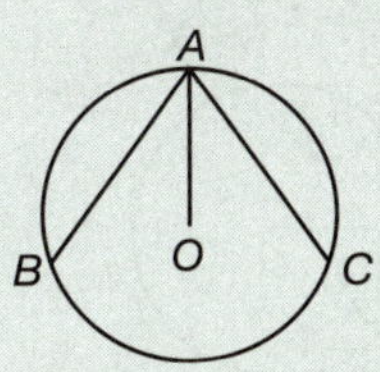

$\angle BOA = \angle COA = 180 - 25 - 25 = 130°$.

Then $\angle BOC = 360 - 130 - 130 = 100°$.

10.

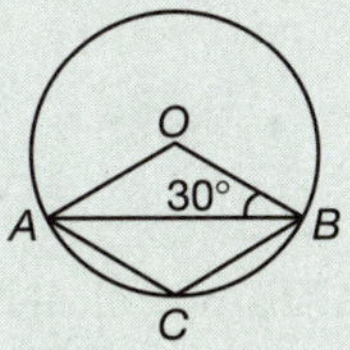

$$\angle AOB = 120 \text{ then } \angle ACB = \frac{360 - 120}{2} = 120°.$$

11. $\angle BOC = 180 - 30 - 30 = 120°$.

$\angle COD = 180 - 50 - 50 = 80°$.

$\angle AOB = 180 - 40 - 40 = 100°$

$\angle AOD = 360 - 120 - 100 - 80 = 60° = \angle OAD$.

12. $r^2 = 3^2 + 4^2 = 9 + 16 = 25$ then $r = 5$.

13.

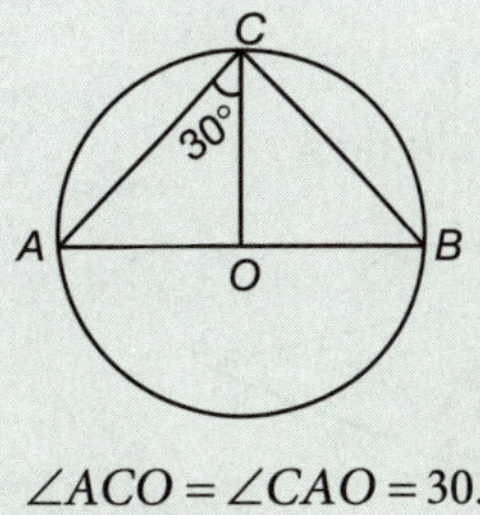

$\angle ACO = \angle CAO = 30$. Then $\angle BOC = 60°$.

14.

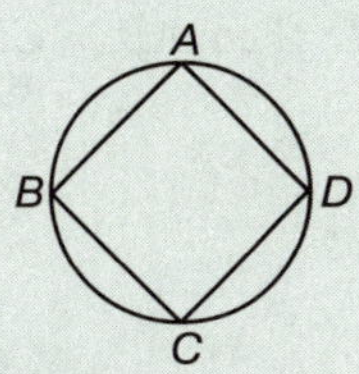

All sides are equal then it's a square so angle is 90^0

15.

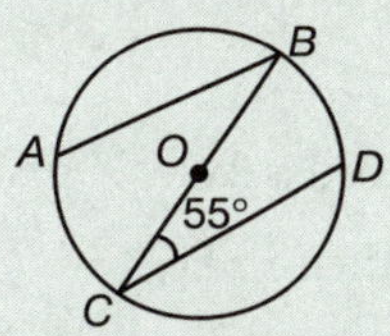

$\angle BCD = \angle ABC = 55°$. $\angle AOC = 2 \times 55 = 110°$.

then $\angle AOB = 70$.

Higher Order Thinking Skills (HOTS)

1. **(C)** $\angle ABC = \angle ADC = \dfrac{95}{2} = 47.5°$.

$\angle BEA + \angle BXD + \angle EBX + \angle EDX = 360°$

Then $\angle BXD = 360 - 360 + 95 - 25 = 70°$.

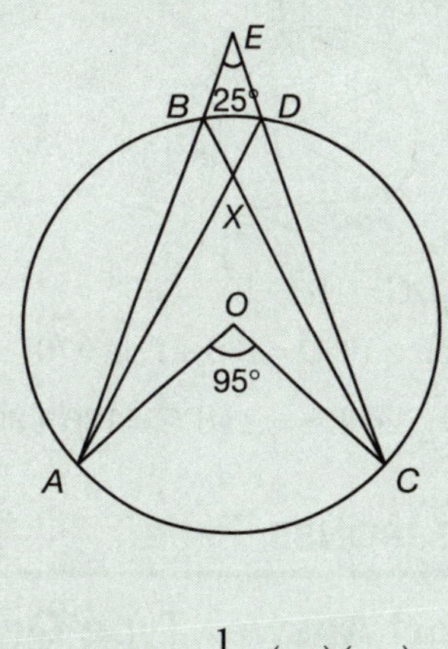

2. **(A)**

3. **(A)** $5x = 6$ then area $= \dfrac{1}{2} \times (3x)(4x)$

$$= 6x^2 = \frac{216}{25} = 8.64$$

4. **(B)** Area inside the circle but outside the triangle = the area inside the triangle but outside the circle

Add Common area to Both sides

Ar (Circle) = ar (Triangle)

$$\pi r^2 = \frac{1}{2}\times 8\sqrt{\pi}\times 9\times\sqrt{\pi} \text{ then } r = 6$$

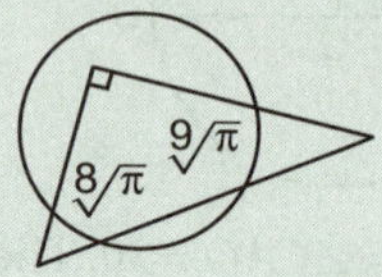

5. **(D)** $AE + EB = CE + ED$ then $AB = CD$ then $DQ = AP$ and $OP = OQ$.

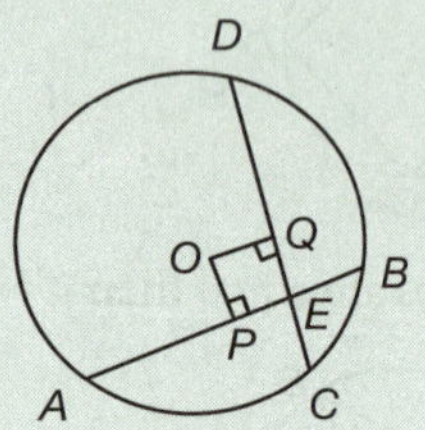

6. **(C)** Let the length of chord is $2x$.

Then $x^2 = 10^2 - 5^2 = 75$ then $x = 5\sqrt{3}$

Then $2x = 10\sqrt{3}$.

7. **(A)**

8. **(A)** As EG is diameter then $\angle EFG = 90°$.

By using Pythagoras theorem.

$EG^2 = 7^2 + 7^2 = 98$

$EG = 7\sqrt{2}$.

9. **(B)**

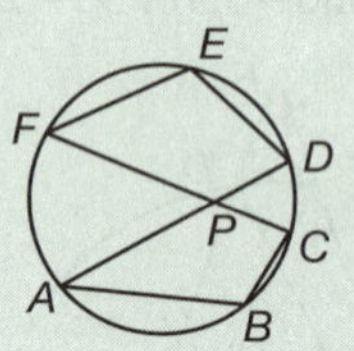

$\angle ADC = 180 - 100 = 80°$.

Then $\angle FCD = 180 - 110 = 70°$

Then $\angle FPA = \angle DPC = 180 - 80 - 70 = 30°$

10. **(D)** $\theta + 2\theta + 3\theta + 4\theta = 360$ then $10\theta = 360°$

then $\theta = 36$. Then $\angle BCO = \dfrac{180-72}{2} = 54°$.

$\angle DCO = \dfrac{180-108}{2} = 36°$.

then $\angle BCD = 36 + 54 = 90°$.

11. **(C)** By Similarity $CM = CK = 20$
Then $CL = 20 - 12 = 8$ cm

12. **(B)**

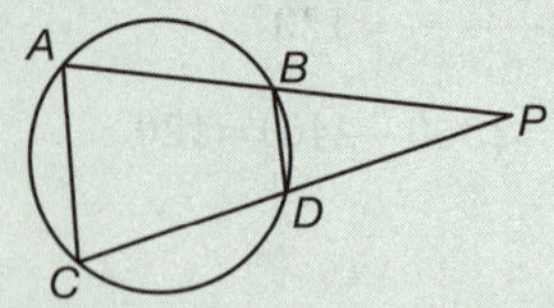

$\angle BAC = \angle ACD = \angle PBD = \angle PDB = 70°$

Then $\angle BPD = 180 - 70 - 70 = 40°$.

13. **(D)**

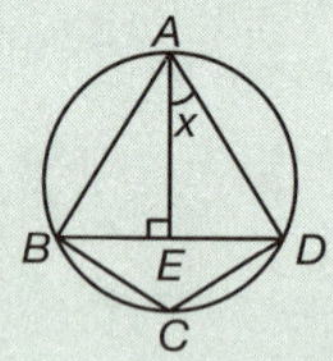

$\angle DAE = \angle BAE = x$. Then $\angle BAD = 2x$

So $\angle BCD = 180 - 2x$.

14. **(C)**

15. **(D)** $CD = 2\sqrt{17^2 - 15^2} = 2\times\sqrt{64} = 16$ units.

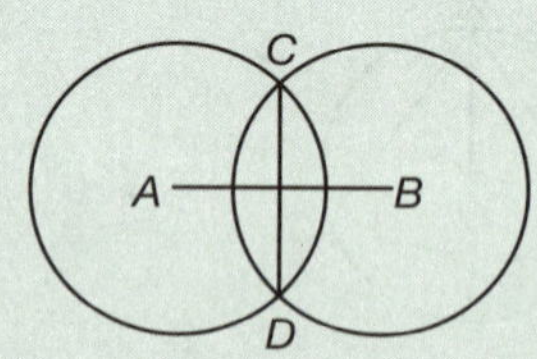

Free Response Type

Very Short Answer Type Questions

1. Let us use the area of arc formula
Area of arc = $1/2 r^2\theta$

In case I
Area of $AXB = 1/2\ r^2\ (75°)$

In case II
Area of $A'YB' = 1/2\ r^2\ (25°)$
So the ratio will be

Required ratio = Area of AXB/Area of $A'YB'$
Substituting the values
$= 1/2\ r^2\ (75°)/1/2\ r^2\ (25°) = 75/25 = 3$
Therefore, the ratio of arcs $A\ X\ B$ and $A'YB'$ is 3 : 1.

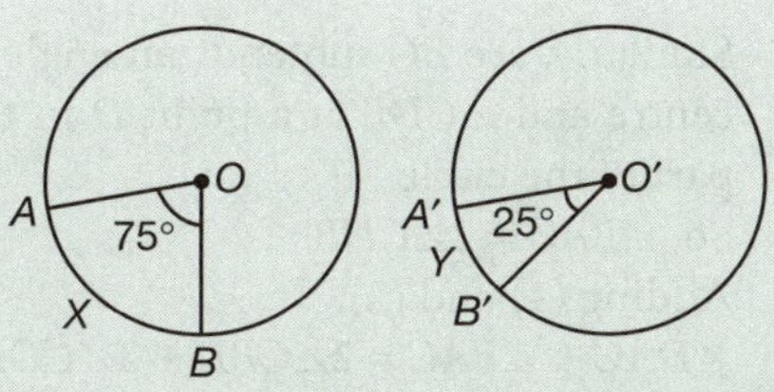

2. Equal chords are situated at equal distance
$OP = OQ$
If two chords are equal, its angles are equal in a triangle
$\angle P = \angle Q = x$
From the angle sum property in triangle OPQ
$150 + x + x = 180°$
$150 + 2x = 180°$
$2x = 180 - 150 = 30°$
Dividing both sides by 2. $x = 15°$
Here $\angle APO = x + \angle APQ = 90°$
So we get $\angle APQ = 90 - 15 = 75°$
Therefore, $\angle APQ$ is equal to 75°.

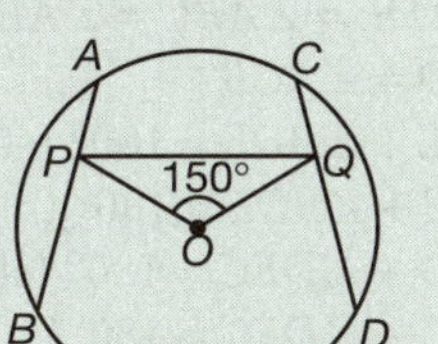

3. $OA^2 = AC^2 + OC^2$ then $OC^2 = 5^2 - 4^2 = 25 - 16 = 9$ then $OC = 3$. Then $CD = 5 - 3 = 2$.

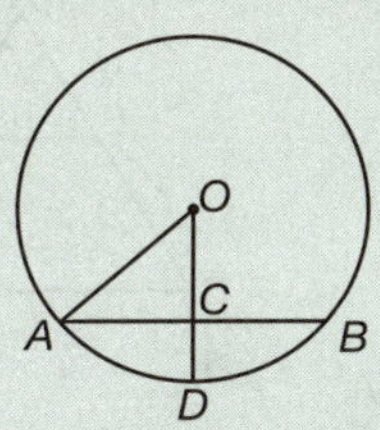

4. In the circle, BC is perpendicular to AB which means that AC is the diameter
In triangle ABC,
Using the Pythagoras theorem
$AC^2 = AB^2 + BC^2$
Substituting the values
$AC^2 = 12^2 + 16^2$
By further calculation $AC^2 = 144 + 256$ $AC^2 = 400$
So $AC = 20$ cm
We know that
Radius of circle $= 1/2\ AC = 1/2 \times 20 = 10$ cm

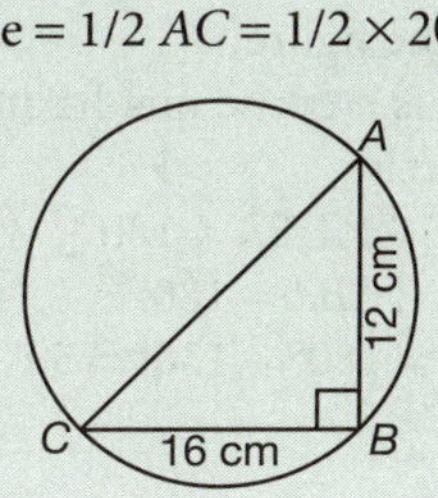

5. $\angle AOC = 2\angle ABC = 40$.

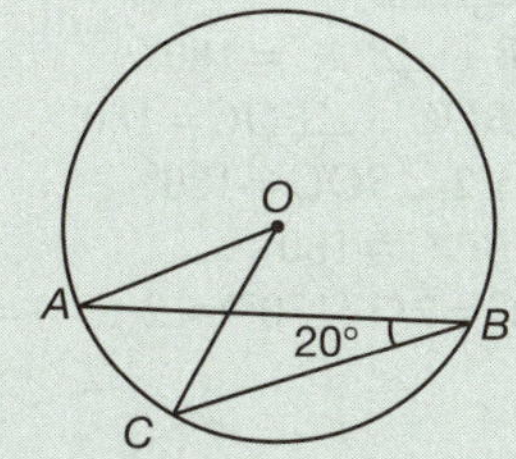

6. $\angle CAB = (180 - 90)\frac{1}{2} = 45$.

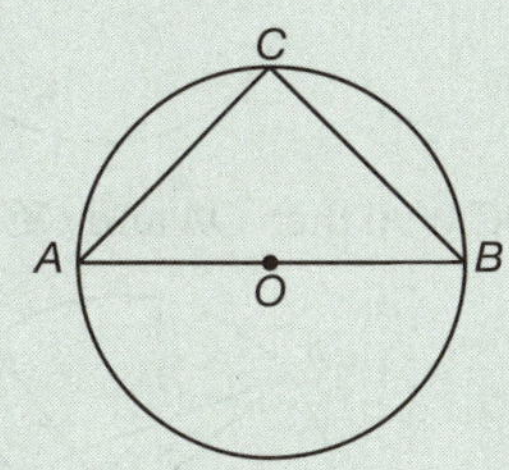

7. $\angle ACB = \angle\frac{AOB}{2} = \frac{100}{2} = 50$.

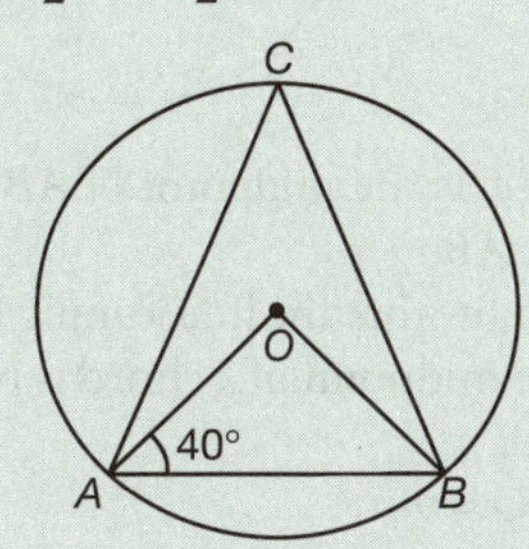

8. $\angle ACB = \angle ADB = 180 - 60 - 50 = 70$.

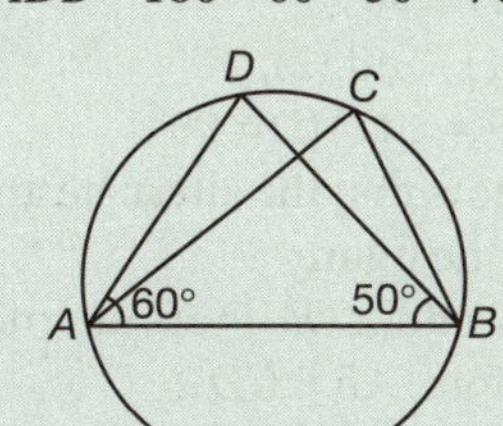

Short Answer Type Questions

1. $\angle ADC = \angle ABC = \angle BAO = 60$.

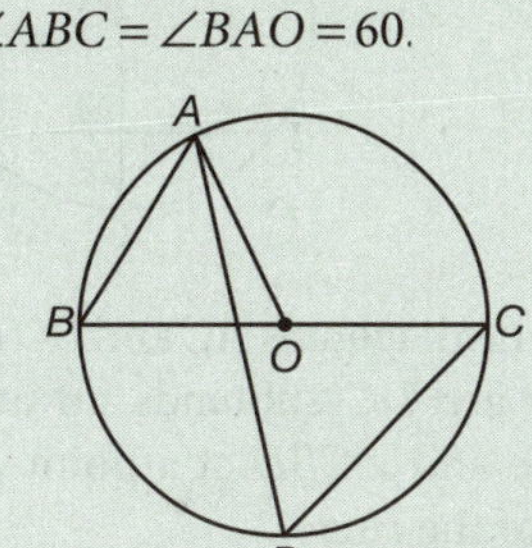

2. Given, AOC is the diameter of the circle
arc $AXB = 1/2$ arc BYC
Given, arc $AXB = 1/2$ arc BYC
So, $\angle AOB = 1/2\ \angle BOC$

HINTS AND EXPLANATIONS

We know that the linear pair of angles is equal to 180 degrees.
$\angle AOB + \angle BOC = 180°$
$1/2\ \angle BOC + \angle BOC = 180°$
$(1 + 2)/2\ \angle BOC = 180°$
$3/2\ \angle BOC = 180°$
$\angle BOC = 2/3\ (180°) = 2(60°) = 120$

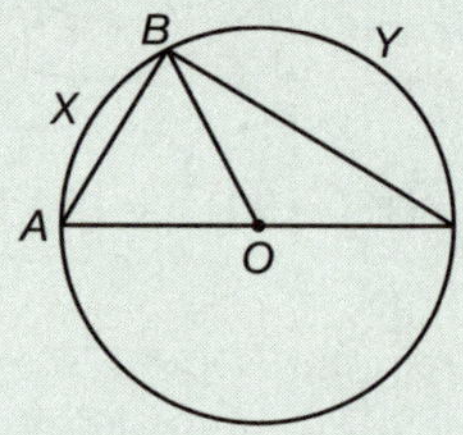

3. $\angle AOC = 90$ then OA and OC are perpendicular.

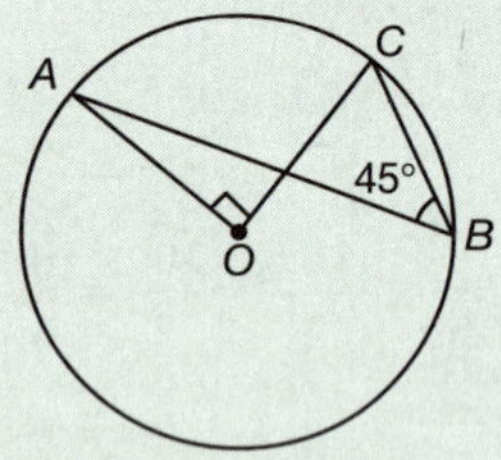

4. Since L is the midpoint of AB
$OL \perp AB$
We know that the line joining the centre of a circle to the midpoint of a chord is perpendicular to the chord.
$\angle ALO = 90°$ (1)
Similarly, $OM \perp CD$
$\angle OMD = 90°$ (2)
From (1) and (2),
$\angle ALO = \angle OMD = 90°$
We know that the alternate angles are equal.
From the figure,
$\angle ALO$ and $\angle OMD$ are alternate angles.
Therefore, $AB \parallel CD$

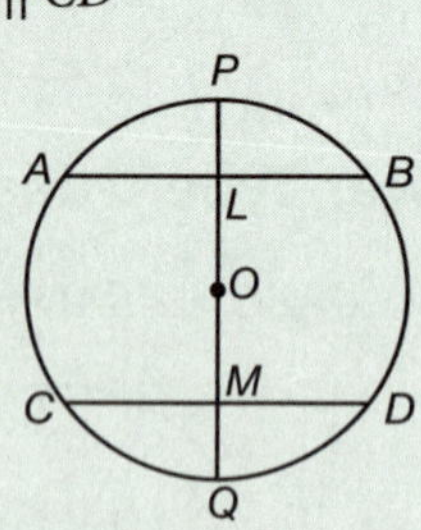

5. Join the diagonals AC and BD of the quadrilateral
Now, arc DC subtends an angle $\angle DAC$ at the centre and $\angle CBD$ at a point B in the remaining part of the circle.
We know that in a circle the angle subtended by an arc at the centre is twice the angle subtended by it at the remaining part of the circle.
So, $\angle DAC = 2\angle CBD$ (1)
Similarly, arc BC subtends an angle $\angle BAC$ at the centre and $\angle CDB$ at a point D in the remaining part of the circle.
So, $\angle BAC = 2\angle CDB$ (2)
Adding (1) and (2),
$\angle DAC + \angle BAC = 2\angle CBD + 2\angle CDB$
From the figure,
$\angle DAC + \angle BAC = \angle DAB$
So, $\angle DAB = 2(\angle CBD + \angle CDB)$
Therefore, $\angle CBD + \angle CDB = 1/2\ \angle DAB$

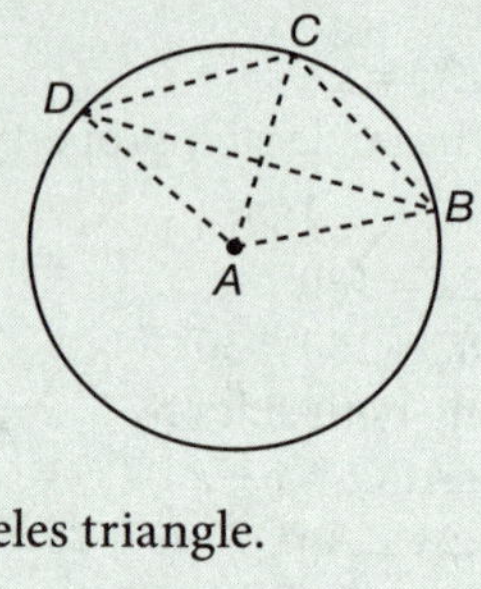

6. ABC is isosceles triangle.
$DE \parallel BC$
$\therefore\ \angle ADE = \angle ABC = \angle AED$ (1)
$\angle AED = \angle ACB$ (2)
$\angle ADE + \angle BDE = 180°$ (straight line)
$\angle ACB + \angle BDE = 180°$ ($\because\ \angle AED = \angle ACB$) (3)
$\angle AED + \angle DEC = 180°$ (straight line)
$\angle ABC + \angle DEC = 180°$($\because\ \angle ABC = \angle AED$) (4)
from (3) and (4),
Sum of opposite angles are 180°, which is the property of cyclic quadrilateral.

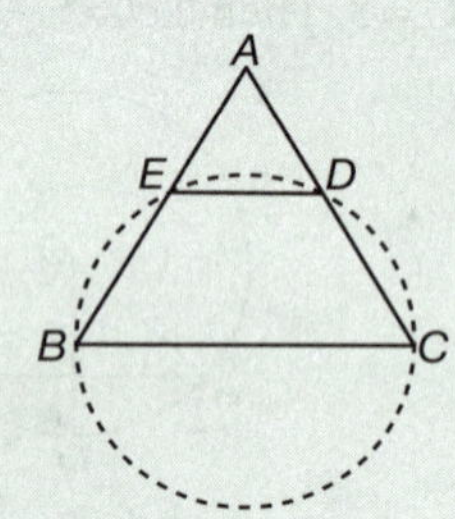

7. Given, $\angle ADC = 130°$
Chord BC = chord BE
In triangle BCO and BEO,
Given, $BC = BE$
So, $\angle BCO = \angle BEO$
Common side = BO
By SAS criterion, the triangles BCO and BEO are similar.
By CPCTC,
$\angle CBO = \angle OBE$ (1)
From the figure,
$ABCD$ is a cyclic quadrilateral since its points lie on a circle.
$\angle ADC + \angle CBA = 180°$
$130° + \angle CBA = 180°$
$\angle CBA = 180° - 130° = 50°$

From the figure,
$\angle CBA = \angle CBO = 50°$
From (1),
$\angle OBE = 50°$
Then $\angle CBE = \angle CBO + \angle CBO = 50° + 50° = 100°$

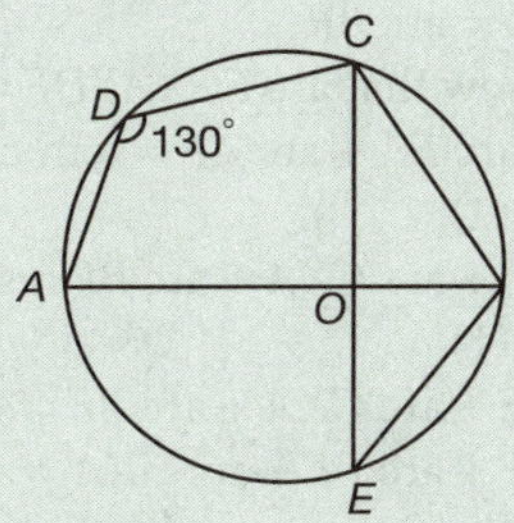

8. Join OO', OP, $O'Q$, OM and $O'N$
In triangle OPB,
Since OM is the perpendicular bisector of PB
$BM = PM$ (1)
Considering triangle $O'BQ$,
Since $O'N$ is the perpendicular bisector of BQ
$BN = NQ$ (2)
Adding (1) and (2),
$BM + BN = PM + NQ$
Adding $BM + BN$ on both sides,
$BM + BN + BM + BN = PM + NQ + BM + BN$
$2(BM + BN) = (BM + PM) + (BN + NQ)$
We know, $OO' = MN = BM + BN$
So, $2OO' = BP + BQ$
Also, $PQ = BP + BQ$
$2OO' = PQ$

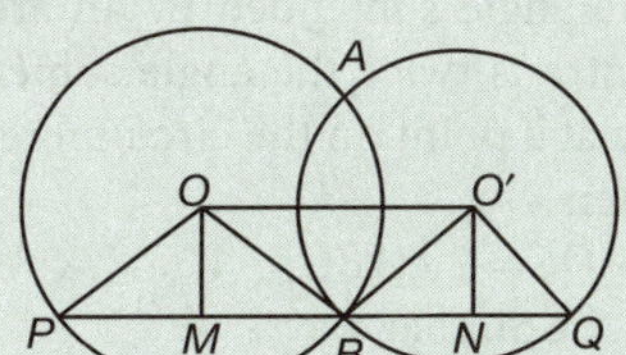

9. Join AE
Since the points A, C, D and E lie on the circle
$ACDE$ is a cyclic quadrilateral
$\angle ACD + \angle AED = 180°$ (1)
AB is the diameter of the circle
So, $\angle AEB = 90°$ (2)
Adding (1) and (2),
$\angle ACD + \angle AED + \angle AEB = 180° + 90°$
From the figure,
$\angle BED = \angle AED + \angle AEB$
Therefore, $\angle ACD + \angle BED = 270°$

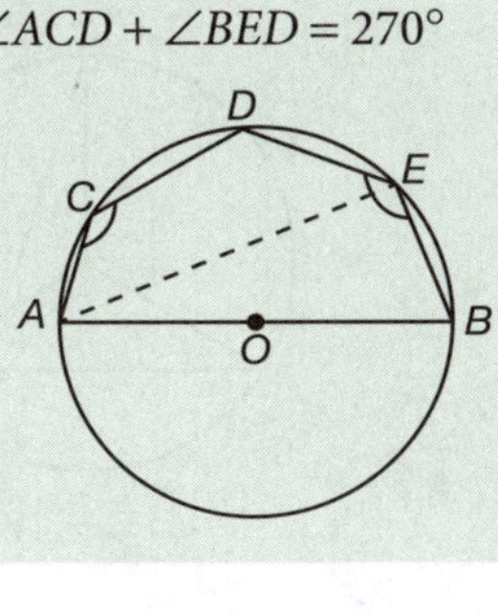

10. Considering triangle AOB,
$OA = OB$ = radius of the circle
We know that the angles opposite to the equal sides are equal.
$\angle OBA = \angle BAO = 30°$
In triangle AOB,
$\angle AOB + \angle OBA + \angle OAB = 180°$
$\angle AOB + 30° + 30° = 180°$
$\angle AOB = 180° - 60° = 120°$ (1)
Considering triangle OCB,
$\angle OBC = \angle OCB = 57°$
$\angle COB + \angle OBC + \angle OCB = 180°$
$\angle COB + 57° + 57° = 180°$
$\angle COB = 180° - 114° = 66°$ (2)
From the figure,
$\angle AOB = \angle AOC + \angle COB$
From (1) and (2),
$120° = \angle AOC + 66°$
$\angle AOC = 120° - 66° = 54°$

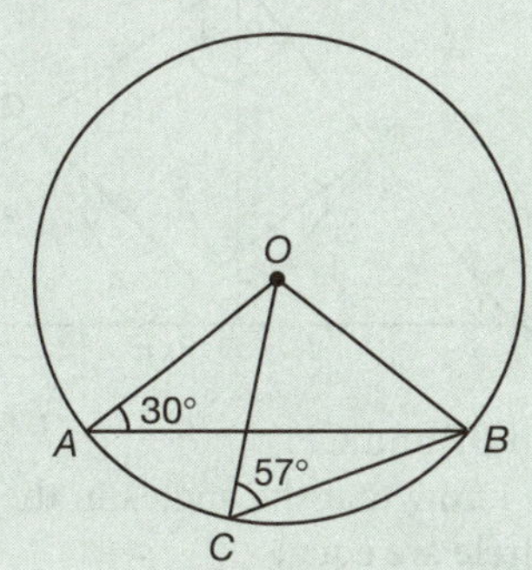

Long Answer Type Questions

1. Join OM perpendicular to CD.
In right angled triangle OMR,
OR is the longest side
$OR > OM$
OR = Distance of the chord PQ from centre O
OM = Distance of the chord CD from centre O
We know that the chord nearer to the centre is larger than the chord which is farther to the centre.
Therefore, chord PQ is the smallest.

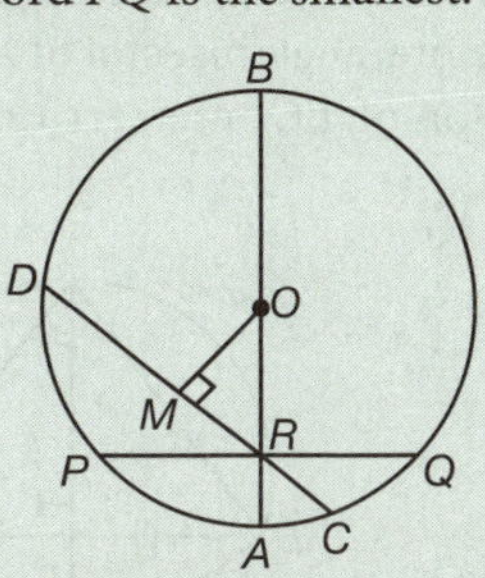

2. Now Join RD, QD, PR and PQ. RP joins the mid-point of AB, R, and the mid-point of BC, that is P.
From the midpoint theorem
$RP \parallel AC$ Likewise $PQ \parallel AB$

HINTS AND EXPLANATIONS

Hence $ARPQ$ is a parallelogram.
So, $\angle RAQ = \angle RPQ$
[Opposite angles of a parallelogram] (1)
ABD is a right-angled triangle and DR is a median, $RA = DR$ since DR divides the base into equal parts.
and $\angle 1 = \angle 2$ (2)
since $\angle ARD = 90°$ and the sum of the angles of a triangle is 180°.
Similarly $\angle 3 = \angle 4$ (3)
On adding equations (2) and (3),
$\angle 1 + \angle 3 = \angle 2 + \angle 4$
$\Rightarrow \angle RDQ = \angle RAQ$
Since $\angle D$ and $\angle P$ are subtended by RQ on the same side of it, we get the points R, D, P and Q concyclic.
Hence, R, D, P and Q are concyclic.

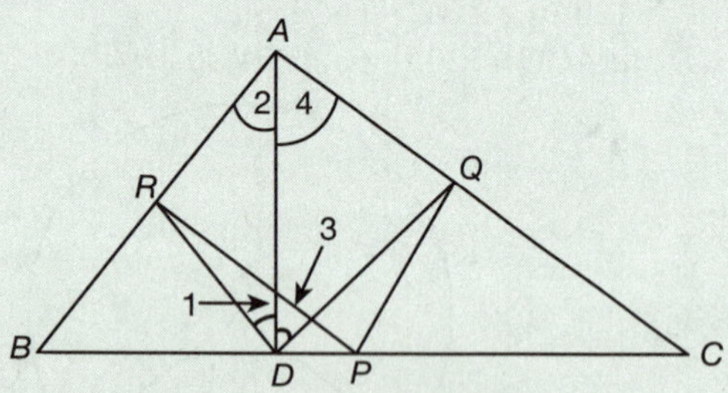

3. Join BP and CP.
We know that the angles in the same segment of a circle are equal
So, $\angle BAP = \angle BCP$
Since, AP is bisector of $\angle A$.
$\angle BAP = \angle BCP$
$\angle A = \angle BAP + \angle BCP$
So, $\angle BAP = \angle BCP = 1/2\ \angle A$ (1)
Similarly, $\angle PAC = \angle PBC = 1/2\ \angle A$ (2)
From (1) and (2),
$\angle BCP = \angle PBC$
We know that, if the angles subtended by two Chords of a circle at the centre are equal, then the chords are equal.
So, $BP = CP$
P lies on the perpendicular bisector of BC.
Therefore, angle bisector of $\angle A$ and perpendicular bisector of BC intersect on the circumcircle of ΔABC.

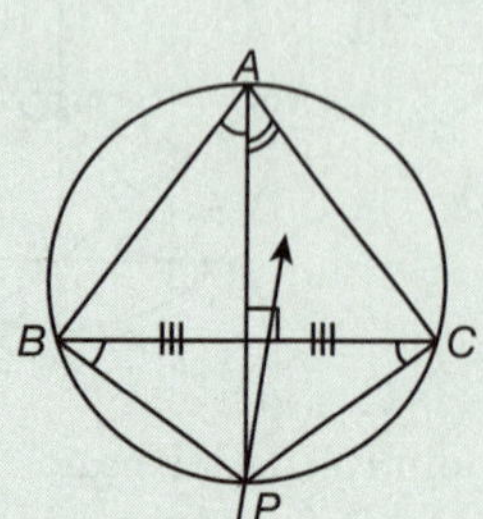

4. Draw a diameter EF parallel to the CD having centre M.
Since, $CD \parallel EF$
arc EC = arc DF (1)
arc $ECXA$ = arc EWB
arc AF = arc BF (2)
We know that arc $ECXAYDF$ = semicircle
Now, arc EA + arc AF = semicircle
From (2),
arc EC + arc CXA + arc BF = semicircle
From (1),
arc DF + arc CXA + arc BF = semicircle
arc DF + arc BF + arc CXA = semicircle
From the figure,
arc DF + arc BF = arc DZB
So, arc DZB + arc CXA = semicircle
We know that the circle divides itself into two semicircles, the remaining portion of the circle is also equal to the semicircle.
Therefore, arc AYD + arc BWC = semicircle.

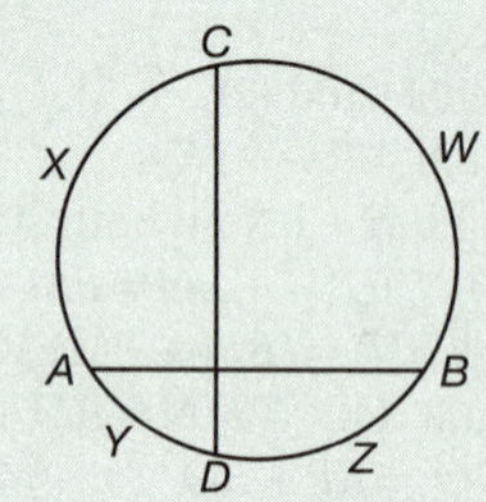

5. Join line AC and BC
The angle subtended by an arc of a circle at its centre is twice the angle subtended by the same arc at a point on the circumference.
Then
$\angle AOC = 2\angle ABC$ (1)
In the Similar way
$\angle BOD = 2\angle BCD$ (2)
From equation (i) and (ii)
$\angle AOC + \angle BOD = 2(\angle ABC + \angle BCD)$
$= 2(\angle EBC + \angle BCE)$
$\angle AOC + \angle BOD = 2(180o - \angle CEB)$
Then $\angle AOC + \angle BOD = 2(180° - (180° - \angle AEC))$
$= 2\angle AEC$
So $\angle AEC = 1/2(\angle AOC + \angle BOD)$
$\angle AEC = 1/2$
(angle subtended by arc CXA at the centre + angle subtended by arc DYB at the centre)

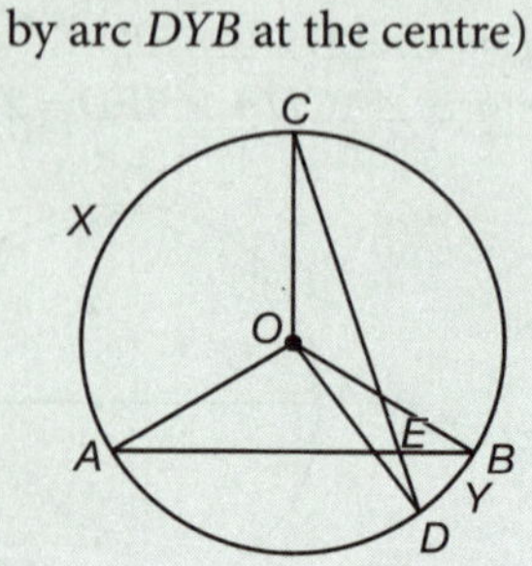

6. 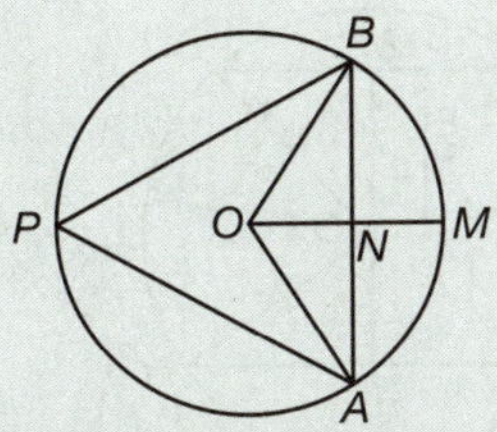

Let circle with centre O. Let $AB = 2$ cm is a chord of a circle

A chord AB is divided by the line OM into two equal segments. Now, $AN = NB = 1$ cm

$OB = \sqrt{2}$ cm. In triangle ONB, By Pythagoras theorem,

$OB^2 = ON^2 + NB^2$

$(\sqrt{2})^2 = ON^2 + (1)^2$

$ON^2 = 2 - 1$

$ON = 1$ cm

So, $\angle NOB = \angle NBO = 45°$

Then, $\angle AON = 45°$

Now, $\angle AOB = \angle AON + \angle NOB = 45° + 45° = 90°$

We know that the chord subtends an angle to the circle equal to half the angle subtended by it to the centre.

$\angle APB = 1/2\ \angle AOB = 1/2\ (90°) = 45°$

Therefore, $\angle APB = 45°$

Archive Corner

1. **(A)** $x = \dfrac{120}{2} = 60.$

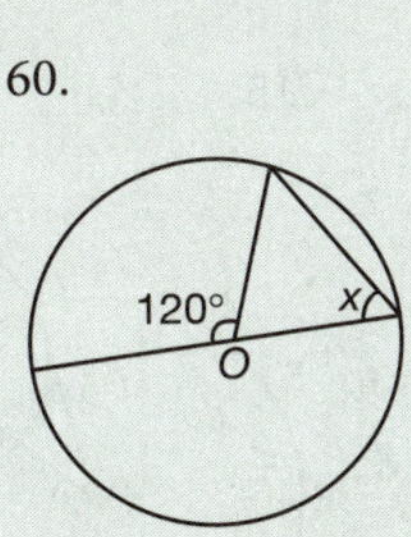

2. **(C)** $AC = OB$ (Rectangle's diagonal are equal.) then $AC = OB = 5$ cm.

3. **(D)** $r^2 = 6^2 + 8^2 = 100$ then $r = 10$.
Then $d^2 = 10^2 - 6^2 = 64$ then $d = 8$ cm.

4. **(C)** $x = 90 - 50 - 45 = 85$

5. **(C)** Diameter.

6. **(A)** $\angle BAC = \angle BDC = 125 - 30 = 95.$

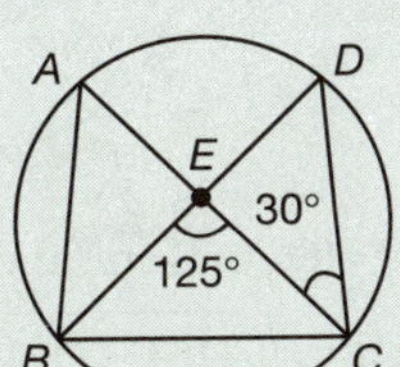

7. **(C)** $r^2 = x^2 + (5)^2$
Also, $r^2 = (17 - x)^2 + (12)^2$
So, $x^2 + (5)^2 = (17 - x)^2 + (12)^2$
$x^2 + 25 = (17 - x)^2 + 144$
$\Rightarrow x = 12$
$\therefore r^2 = 144 + 25 = 169$
$\Rightarrow r = 13$ cm

8. **(B)** Let them intersect at D and E.
Now AC, AD, AE, CD, CA, CE all are radii of those two circles so their lengths must be r

By symmetry F is the midpoint of AC.
So AF, AC must be $r/2$
Also DE and AC must intersect at right angles.
So by Pythagoras theorem:
$AF^2 + DF^2 = AD^2$
$DF^2 = AD^2 - AF^2$
$DF^2 = r^2 - (r/2)^2$
$DF = \sqrt{3}r/2$
$DE = \sqrt{3}r$

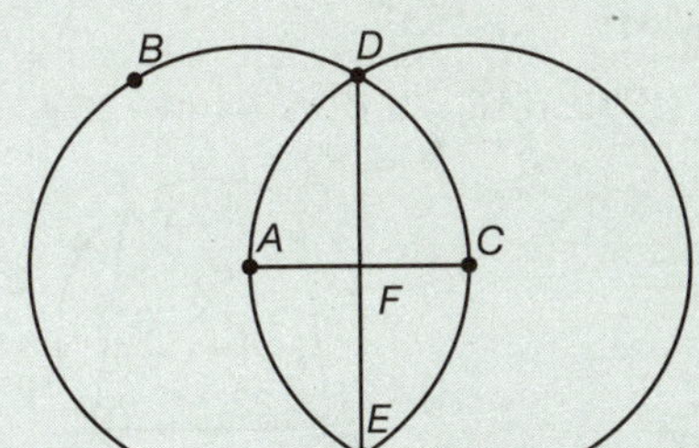

9. **(A)** $\angle BOC = 2n$. Then $2n + 2m = 180$ then $m + n = 90$.

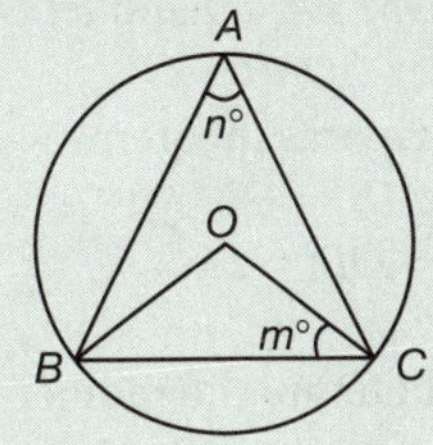

10. **(C)** **Given:** AB and CD are two equal chord of the circle.
Prove: Center O lies on the bisector of the $\angle BAC$.
Construction: Join BC. Let the bisector on $\angle BAC$ intersect BC in P.
Proof: In ΔAPB and ΔAPC
$AB = AC$ (Given)
$\angle BAP = \angle CAP$ (Given)

$AP = AP$ (common)

$\therefore \Delta APB \cong \Delta APC$ SAS test

$\Rightarrow BP = CP$ and $\angle APB = \angle APC$ CPCT

$\angle APB + \angle APC = 180°$ (Linear pair)

$\therefore 2\angle APB = 180°$ $(\angle APB = \angle APC)$

$\Rightarrow \angle APB = 90°$

$\therefore AP$ is perpendicular bisector of chord BC.

Hence, AP passes through the center of the circle.

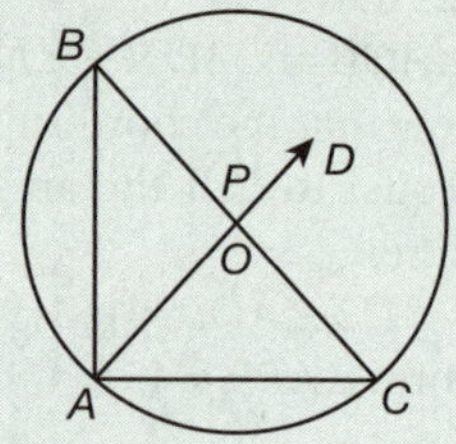

11. **(B)** $\angle POR = 360 - 120 - 80 = 160$

then $\angle PQR = \dfrac{160}{2} = 80.$

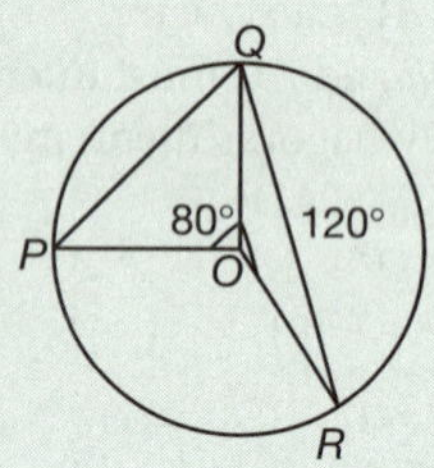

12. **(A)**

13. **(B)** $\angle BAC = \angle BDC = 180 - 22 - 78 = 80.$

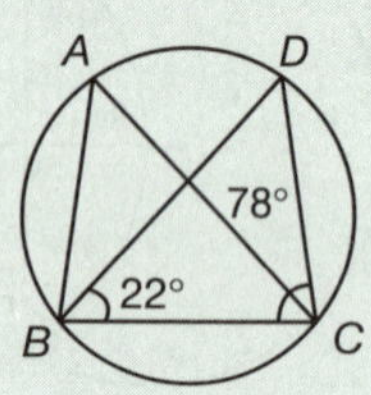

14. **(C)** $AB = 6$ cm $CD = 8$ cm $MB = 3$ cm $ND = 4$ cm

Given $OM = 4$ cm and let $ON = x$ cm

Consider ΔOMB

By Pythagoras theorem,

$OM^2 + MB^2 = OB^2$

$4^2 + 3^2 = OB^2 = 25$

$OB = 5$ cm

OB and OD are the radii of the circle.

Therefore $OD = OB = 5$ cm.

Consider ΔOND

By Pythagoras theorem,

$ON^2 + ND^2 = OD^2$

$x^2 + 4^2 = 5^2$

$x^2 = 25 - 16 = 9$

$x = 3$

The distance of the chord CD from the center is 3 cm.

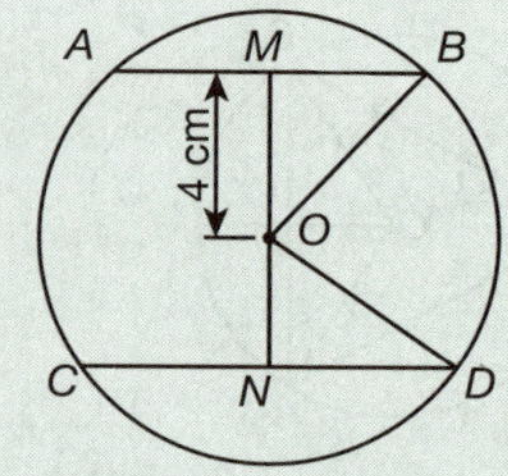

15. **(A)** Let the radius of smaller circle be AP in this diagram $AOBP$ is kite then area of AOP

$= \sqrt{\left(\frac{5}{2}\right)\left(\frac{1}{2}\right)\left(\frac{1}{2}\right)\left(\frac{5}{2} - 1\right)}$

$= \sqrt{\left(\frac{5}{2}\right)\left(\frac{1}{2}\right)\left(\frac{1}{2}\right)\left(\frac{3}{2}\right)}$

$= \dfrac{\sqrt{15}}{4} = \dfrac{1}{2} \times AB \times OP$

then $AB = \dfrac{\sqrt{15}}{2}$

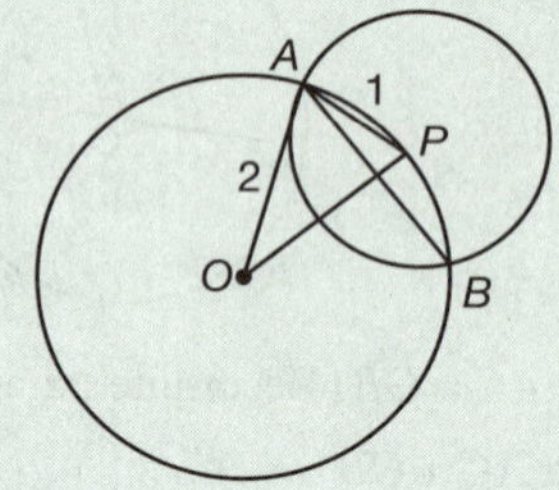

16. **(B)** Reflex $\angle POR = 280$ then $\angle PQR = 140.$

Then $\angle SQR = 180 - 140 = 40.$

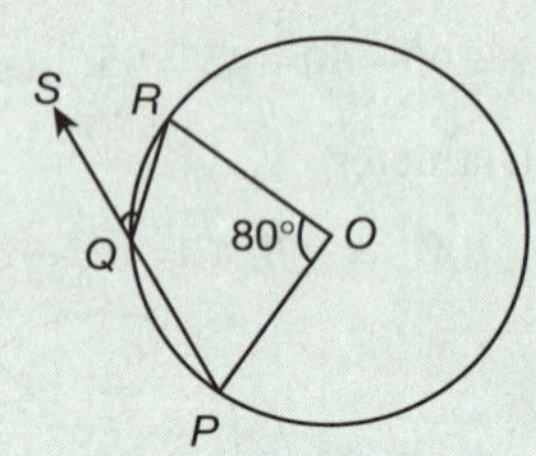

17. **(D)** $AO = OD = 3$ cm. and $BC = 2$ cm.

$\text{ar}(BOC) = \sqrt{(4)(4-3)(4-3)(4-2)}$

$= 2\sqrt{2} = \dfrac{1}{2} \times BC \times (\text{height})$ then height $= 2\sqrt{2}$

$\text{ar (trapezium)} = \dfrac{1}{2} \times (6+2) \times 2\sqrt{2} = 8\sqrt{2}$

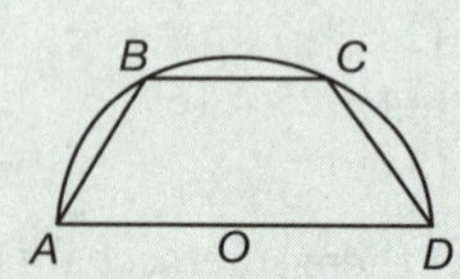

18. **(C)** $r^2 = 12^2 + 5^2 = 144 + 25 = 169$ Then $r = 13.$

Then $2r = 26.$

CHAPTER 10 HERON'S FORMULA

Check Point 1

1. Area $=\frac{1}{2}\times 25\times 60=750\text{ m}^2$

2. Third side $=324-154-85=85$ then area

$=\sqrt{(162)(162-85)(162-85)(162-154)}$

$=\sqrt{(81\times 2)(77)(77)(8)}=77\times 4\times 9=2772\text{ m}^2$

3. $s=\dfrac{50+78+112}{2}=120$ then

area $=\sqrt{(120)(120-50)(120-78)(120-112)}$
$=\sqrt{(120)(70)(42)(8)}=1680\text{ m}^2$

$\frac{1}{2}\times 112\times h=1680$ then $h=30$ m.

4. Let $AB=25$, $BC=15$, $CD=11$ and $AD=13$ From C a parallel line CE to AD draw E is a point on AB. Then triangle in BCE $BC=15$, $CE=13$ and $EB=14$ then $\text{ar}(EBC)=\sqrt{(21)(7)(6)(8)}=84=\frac{1}{2}\times 14h$ then $h=12$

Now $\text{ar}(ABCD)=\frac{1}{2}\times(11+25)\times 12=216\text{ cm}^2$.

5. Required area $=\frac{1}{2}\times 32\times(12+20)=512\text{ m}^2$

Fixed Response Type

Fill in the Blanks

1. Area $=\frac{1}{2}\times 3\times 4=6\text{ cm}^2$

2. $\frac{1}{2}\times 10h=\sqrt{(18)(5)(5)(8)}=5h$ then $h=12\times\frac{5}{5}=12$

3. Area $=\frac{\sqrt{3}}{4}\times 4\times 4=4\sqrt{3}\text{ cm}^2$

4. Base $\times$ altitude $=2\times$ Altitude$^2=392$
then Altitude $=14$ and base $=28$.

5. $900=1.25\times 30\times b$ then $b=30\times\frac{4}{5}=24$ m

6. Let $AB=52$, $BC=12$, $CD=39$ and $AD=5$ From C a parallel line CE to AD draw E is a point on AB. Then triangle in BCE $BC=12$, $CE=5$ and $EB=13$ then $\text{ar}(EBC)=\frac{1}{2}\times 5\times 12=\frac{1}{2}\times 13h$ then $h=\frac{60}{13}$.

Now $\text{ar}(ABCD)=\frac{1}{2}\times(39+52)\times\frac{60}{13}=210\text{ cm}^2$.

True/False

1. False.
area $=\sqrt{(75)(40)(21)(14)}=\sqrt{882000}=210\sqrt{10}$
$=\frac{1}{2}\times 61\times h$ then $h=21.77$

2. True.
$\text{ar}=\frac{1}{2}\times 8\times 15=60$ then weight $60\times 1.6=96$ gm.

3. True
(Pythagoras)

4. True.

5. False.
$3x+5x+7x=300$ then $15x=300$ so $x=20$.
Then area $=\sqrt{(150)(90)(50)(10)}\neq 1500$

Single Correct Type Questions

1. **(B)** $\text{ar}(\text{parallelogram})=2\sqrt{(48)(14)(28)(6)}$
$=672$ sq.units

2. **(A)** $A=\sqrt{(9)(2)(3)(4)}+\sqrt{(9)(2)(3)(4)}=12\sqrt{6}$

3. **(D)**

4. **(C)** Sides of rhombus $=8$ cm then cost
$=2\sqrt{(13)(13-8)(13-8)(13-10)}\times 10$
$=100\times\sqrt{39}=100\times 6.25=625$ Rs

5. **(C)** Let $AB=25$, $BC=13$, $CD=10$ and $AD=14$ From C a parallel line CE to AD draw E is a point on AB. Then triangle in BCE $BE=15$, $CE=14$ and $CB=13$ then
$\text{ar}(EBC)=\sqrt{(21)(7)(6)(8)}=84=\frac{1}{2}\times 15h$
then $h=84\times\frac{2}{15}=11.2$ cm.

6. **(D)** By using pytagoras $AB=13$.
$\text{ar}(\text{shaded})=\sqrt{(21)(21-14)(21-15)(21-13)}$
$-\frac{1}{2}\times 5\times 12=84-30=54$ sq. units.

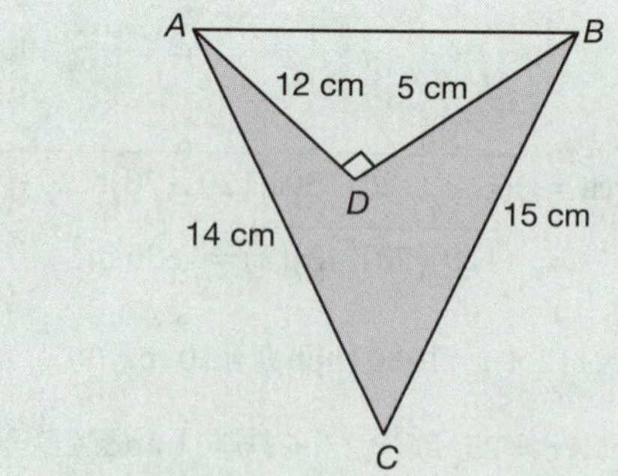

7. **(C)** Sides of triangle are 9, 9 and 6 then

$$\text{ar}(\text{Triangle}) = \sqrt{(12)(12-9)(12-9)(12-6)}$$
$$= 18\sqrt{2} \text{ sq.cm}$$

8. **(B)** Then triangle in BCA $BC = 15$, $CA = 13$ and $AB = 14$ then

$$\text{ar}(ABC) = \sqrt{(21)(7)(6)(8)} = 84 = 15h$$

then $h = 5.6$ cm.

9. **(B)**

10. **(B)** Total Cost $= 4 \times 100 \times$

$$\sqrt{(125)(125-120)(125-110)(125-20)}$$
$$= 400 \times \sqrt{(125)(5)(105)(15)}$$
$$= 400 \times 25 \times 15\sqrt{7}$$
$$= 150000 \times 2.65 = \text{Rs.}397500$$

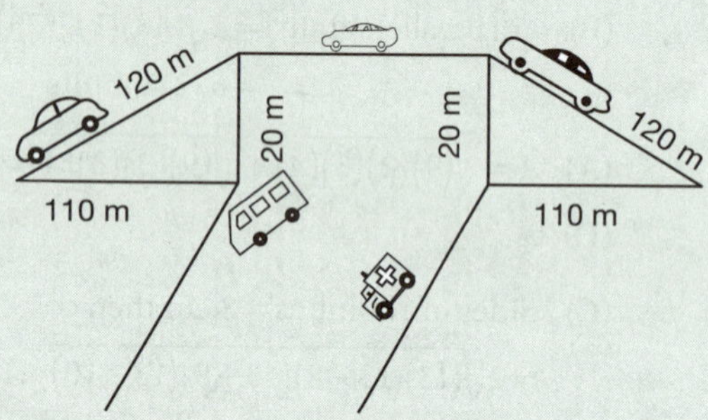

11. **(C)** $\text{Cost} = 60 \times (60 \times 5 - 5 \times 5 + 5 \times 40)$

$$= 60 \times (300 - 25 + 200)$$
$$= 60 \times 475 = \text{Rs.}285$$

12. **(A)** Total area = 2ar(Parllelogram) + ar(triangle) + ar(Square) + ar(Semicircle)

ar(parallelogram) $= 6 \times 2 = 12$ sq.units

$$\text{ar}(\text{triangle}) = \sqrt{(8)(8-5)(8-5)(8-6)} = 12.$$

ar(square) $= 6 \times 6 = 36$

$$\text{ar}(\text{circle}) = \frac{1}{2} \times 3.14 \times 9 = 14.13$$

Total Area

$= 24 + 12 + 36 + 14.13 = 86.13$ sq.cm.

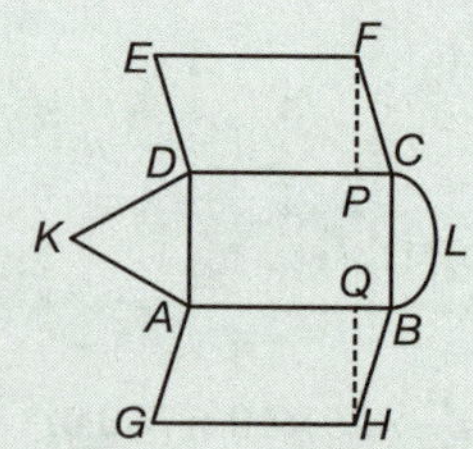

13. **(A)** $\frac{1}{2} \times 4d = 28$ then $d = 14$.

Then Side $= \sqrt{7^2 + 2^2} = \sqrt{53}$

Then Perimeter $= 4\sqrt{53}$

14. **(A)** $\frac{1}{2} \times (20 + a) \times 30 = 960$ then $20 + a = \frac{960}{15} = 64$ then $a = 44$ m.

Multiple Correct Type Questions

1. **(A,C)** Let the base be x.

$$\text{Then } \sqrt{\left(5 + \frac{x}{2}\right)\left(\frac{x}{2}\right)\left(\frac{x}{2}\right)\left(5 - \frac{x}{2}\right)}$$
$$= 12 \text{ then } \left(25 - \frac{x^2}{4}\right)(x^2) = 576$$

$(100 - x^2)(x^2) = 2304$ then $x = 6$ cm and 8 cm

2. **(A,D)** $\frac{1}{2} \times a \times h = \frac{\sqrt{3}}{4} \times a^2 = 4\sqrt{3}$ then $a = 4$ cm then $h = 2\sqrt{3}$

3. **(C)**

4. **(B,C)**

5. **(A,C)**

(A) $\frac{1}{2} \times 5 \times 12$ (B) 5×12

(C) $\sqrt{(15 \times 10 \times 2 \times 3)}$ (D) None of these

Match Type Questions

1. (A) → (S)

ar(Quad) $= 24 \times 10 = 240$ sq.cm

(B) → (P)

$$\text{ar}(\text{quad}) = \sqrt{(42)(42-41)(42-15)(42-28)} + \frac{1}{2} \times 40 \times 9 = 306 \text{ sq.cm}$$

(C) → (Q)

$$\text{ar}(\text{quad}) = \sqrt{(48)(48-42)(48-20)(48-34)} + \frac{1}{2} \times 20 \times 21 = 546 \text{ sq.cm}$$

(D) → (R)

$BC = 8$

Then $\text{ar}(\text{Quadrilateral}) = \frac{1}{2} \times 8 \times 15 + \frac{1}{2} \times 9 \times 12$

$= 60 + 54 = 114$ sq.cm

2. (P) → (A)

$\text{Area} = 9 \times 4 = 36 \text{ cm}^2$

(R) → (B)

$\text{Area} = \frac{\sqrt{3}}{4} \times 36 = 9\sqrt{3}$

(P) → (C)

Area of square = 36

(Q) → (D)

$\frac{1}{2} \times 3\sqrt{3} \times h = \frac{\sqrt{3}}{4} \times 27$ then $h = 4.5$

Assertion and Reason Type Questions

1. (C)
2. (D)

Comprehension Type Questions

Common solution(1-3):

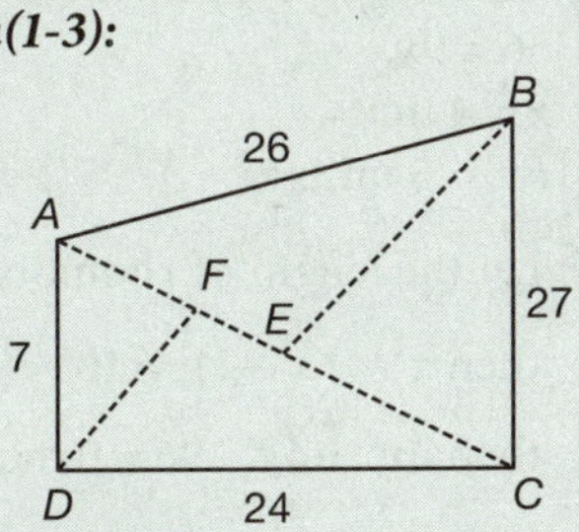

$AC = 25$ by using pythagoras.

$DF = 7 \times \frac{24}{25} = \frac{168}{25}$ cm

and $EB = \frac{2\sqrt{(39)(13)(12)(14)}}{25} = \frac{156\sqrt{14}}{25}$

$DF + EB = \frac{168 + 156\sqrt{14}}{25} = \frac{12}{25} \times \left(14 + 13\sqrt{14}\right)$

Required area $= \frac{1}{2} \times 7 \times 24 + 78\sqrt{14} = 84 + 78\sqrt{14}$

1. (B)
2. (A)
3. (B)

Numerical Type Questions

1. $\text{ar}(\text{Triangle}) = \frac{1}{2} \times 18h = 9h$

$= \sqrt{(36)(36-18)(36-24)(36-30)}$

$= 6 \times 36$ then $h = 24$ cm.

2. $\text{ar} = \frac{1}{2} \times 10 \times 24$

$= 120$ sq.units and longest altitude = 24 cm

3. $\text{ar} = \frac{1}{2} \times 40 \times 9 + \sqrt{(42)(42-41)(42-28)(42-15)}$

$= 180 + 126 = 306$ sq.cm

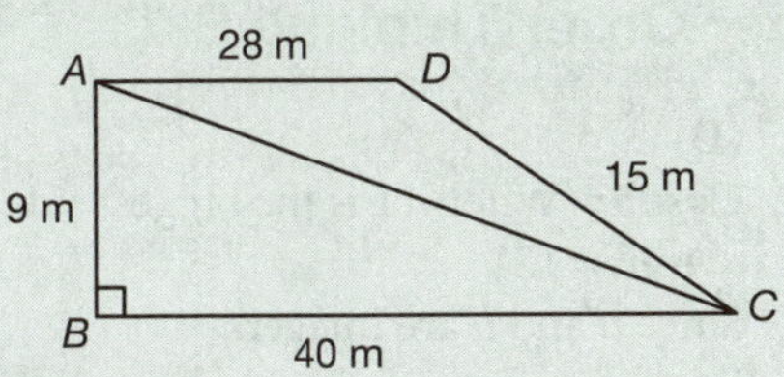

4. Using Pythagoras theorem $BC = 8$ then

$\text{area}(\text{Quadrilatral}) = \frac{1}{2} \times 8 \times 15 + \frac{1}{2} \times 9 \times 12$

$= 60 + 54 = 114$ sq.cm

5. Third side $= 324 - 154 - 85 = 85$.

Then area $= \sqrt{(162)(162-154)(162-85)(162-85)}$

$= 2772$ sq.cm

6. $\text{ar}(\text{triangle})$

$= \sqrt{(231)(231-143)(231-165)(231-154)}$

$= \sqrt{(231)(88)(66)(77)} = 10164$ sq.cm.

Then total cost $= 10164 \times 1219.68$ rs.

7. Let the side of triangle is a. Then $\frac{1}{2} \times 3a = \frac{\sqrt{3}}{4} \times a^2$.

a then $2\sqrt{3} = a$ then area(triangle)

$= \frac{1}{2} \times 3 \times 2\sqrt{3} = 3\sqrt{3}$ sq.cm.

8. $a + b + 17 = 40$. Then $a + b = 23$.

Now $a^2 + b^2 + 2ab = 529$.

Then $2ab = 529 - 289 = 240$

then $\frac{1}{2} \times ab = \frac{240}{4} = 60$ sq.cm

9. Let the sides are $3x$, $3x$ and $2x$ then $8x = 32$

then $x = 4$ then sides are 12, 12 and 8 cm

Area $= \sqrt{(16)(16-12)(16-12)(16-8)}$

$= 4 \times 4 \times 2\sqrt{2} = 32\sqrt{2}$ sq.cm.

10. Total cost $= 20 \times (50+80+120-3)$

$= 20 \times 247 = 4940$ Rs.

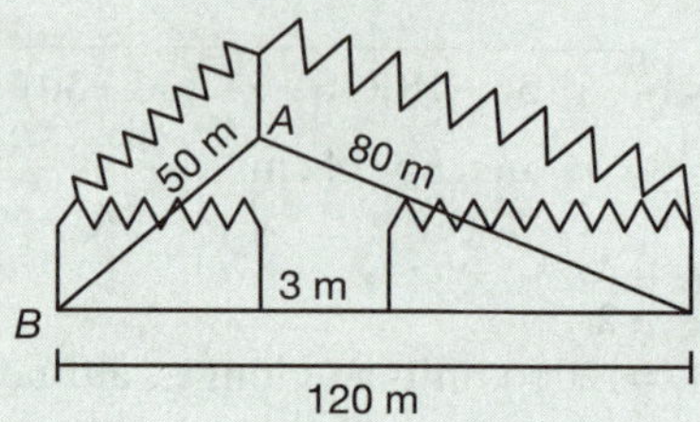

11. 1644 m^2. For solution, refer to fill in the blank Q. No. 6

Higher Order Thinking Skills (HOTS)

1. **(D)**

Case 1: (When 11 is the biggest side)

$a^2 + b^2 = 121$

Since a and b are integers

Possible values of a^2 and b^2 are: 1, 4, 9, 16, 25, 36, 49, 64, 81, 100

but none of them sum up to be 121

Hence the case is VOID

Case 2: (Let us assume a is hypotenuse)

$b^2 + 11^2 = a^2$

$a^2 - b^2 = 121$

$(a - b)(a + b) = 121$

Now $(a - b)$ and $(a + b)$ are integers as well

Only 2 combinations are possible

11×11 and 121×1

(11×11) is not possible

Hence

$a + b = 121$

$a = (121 - b)$

$a^2 - b^2 = 121$

$121^2 + b^2 - 242b - b^2 = 121$ then $b = 60$ and $a = 61$.

So area >300.

2. **(B)** $PQ + QR + PR = PQ + QX + XR + PR$

$= PQ + QM + RN + PR$

$= PM + PN = 10 + 17 = 27.$

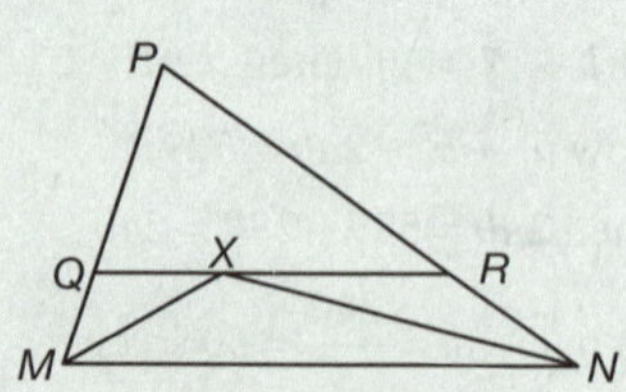

3. **(B)** $\frac{\sqrt{3}}{4} \times 36 = 9y$ then $y = \sqrt{3}$ cm.

4. **(C)** Sides of triangle will be 50, 50 and $50\sqrt{2}$

then cost $= 50\left(2+\sqrt{2}\right) \times 3 = 150 \times 3.4 > 510$

5. **(D)** Sides are 5, 5 and 4 then area $= \sqrt{(7)(2)(2)(3)}$

$= 2\sqrt{21}$ sq.cm

6. **(B)** Area of the rectangle $ABCD = 12 \times 7 = 84$ sq cm.

Let $AP = x$ cm. So, $PB = (12 - x)$ cm.

Area of shaded region $= 0.4 \times 84 = 33.6$ sq cm.

Area of triangle $EAP = 0.5 \times 5 \times x = 2.5x$ sq cm

Area of triangle $CPB = 0.5 \times 7 \times (12 - x) = 42 - 3.5x$ sq cm

Sum of the area of triangles EAP and CPB = area of shaded region

$2.5x + 42 - 3.5x = 33.6$

$42 - x = 33.6$ or $x = 8.4$ cm

Point P should at 8.4 cm from vertex A.

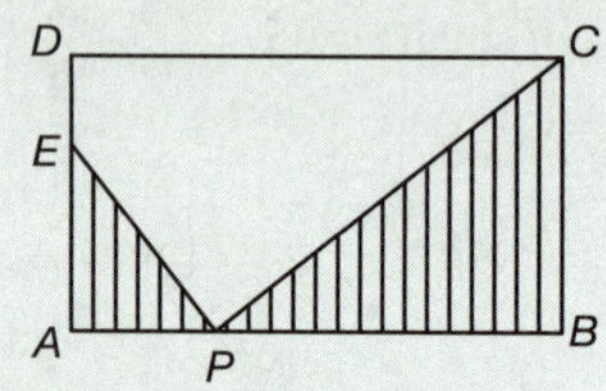

7. **(B)** The trapezium can be divided in 3 parts, a rectangle of 6 units, 2 equal triangles.

Let the height be x,

Area of trapezium = Area of rectangle + 2(Area of triangle)

$36 = 6 \times x + 2(1/2 \times 3 \times x)$, base = 3 units, the sides are equally divided.

$36 = 9x$,

$x = 4$ units,

$BC = 5$ units (Pythagoras theorem)

8. **(B)** Let the length of rhombus are $2x$ and $2x + 4$

then $x^2 + (x+2)^2 = 10^2$

then $2x^2 + 4x - 96 = 0$ then $x = 6$

then area $= \frac{1}{2} \times 12 \times 16 = 96$ sq. units.

9. **(D)** $DE = \sqrt[4]{3}$ and $DC + FE = \sqrt[4]{3}$

Area of $AEF = \frac{1}{2}xb$

and Area of $ABDE = b.\sqrt[4]{3}$

From triangle AEF,

$x^2 + b^2 = \left(\sqrt[4]{3}\right)^2 = \sqrt{3}$

then $b^2 = \sqrt{3} - \frac{\sqrt{3}}{4} = \frac{3\sqrt{3}}{4}$

then $b = \frac{\sqrt[4]{3^3}}{2}$

Area of trapezium $= \frac{1}{2}(a+b)h = \frac{9}{4}$

So, $m + n = 13$.

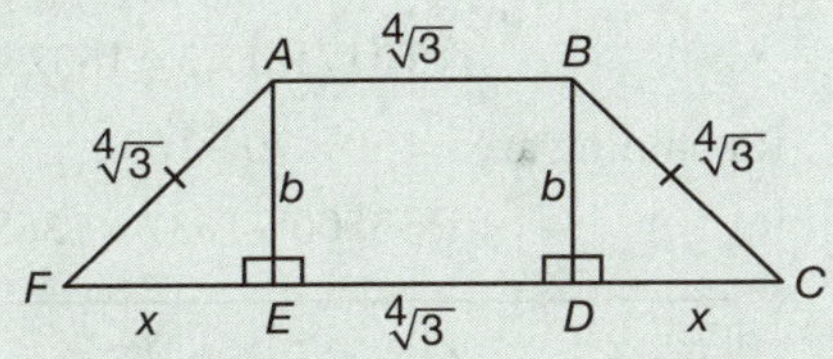

10. **(C)** Let the square $ABCD$ is divided into 4 triangles.
$\therefore$ sum of the area of these triangles = area of square $ABCD$

$\therefore 200 =$ area of square $ABCD$

$\therefore 200 = (AB)^2$

$\therefore AB = 10\sqrt{2}$ cm

$\therefore$ Diagonal $AC = BD = AB \times \sqrt{2} = 20$ cm

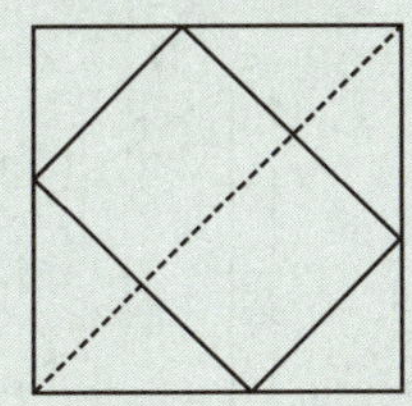

Free Response Type

Very Short Answer Type Questions

1. If base is 8 cm then height will be 6 cm.

then area $= \frac{1}{2} \times 6 \times 8 = 24$ sq.units.

2. Let the base and height are a then

$\frac{1}{2}a^2 = 8$ then $a^2 = 16$. So $a = 4$ unit

and Hypotenuse $= 4\sqrt{2}$

3. Side of triangle = 20 m Then area $= \frac{\sqrt{3}}{4} \times 400$

$= 100\sqrt{3}$ sq.m.

4. Area $= \sqrt{(84)(84-56)(84-60)(84-52)}$

$= \sqrt{(84)(28)(24)(32)} = 1344$ sq.cm.

5. Ar $= \frac{\sqrt{3}}{4} \times \left(2\sqrt{3}\right)^2 = 3\sqrt{3}$ sq.cm.

6. $\frac{\sqrt{3}}{4}a^2 = 9\sqrt{3}$ then $a^2 = 36$ then $a = 6$ cm.

7. Area $= \sqrt{(5)(5-2)(5-4)(5-4)} = \sqrt{15}$ sq.cm.

8. Area $= \sqrt{(75)(75-35)(75-54)(75-61)}$

$= \sqrt{(75)(40)(21)(14)} = 420\sqrt{5}$ sq.cm.

Short Answer Type Questions

1. Area $= \frac{1}{2} \times 9 \times 40 = 180$ sq.meter then number of

rose $= \frac{1800000}{900} = 2000$.

2. Let the sides are $3x$, $3x$ and $2x$ then $8x = 32$

then $x = 4$ then sides are 12, 12 and 8 cm

Area $= \sqrt{(16)(16-12)(16-12)(16-8)}$

$= 4 \times 4 \times 2\sqrt{2} = 32\sqrt{2}$ sq.cm.

3. Ar(parallelogram)

$= 2 \times \sqrt{(90)(90-60)(90-40)(90-80)}$

$= 200 \times \sqrt{9 \times 3 \times 5} = 600\sqrt{15}$ sq.cm

4. Ar(shaded part) $= \frac{1}{2} \times 22 \times 120$

$- \sqrt{(36)(36-22)(36-24)(36-26)}$

$= 1320 - 6 \times \sqrt{(14)(12)(10)}$

$= 1320 - 24\sqrt{105}$ sq. units.

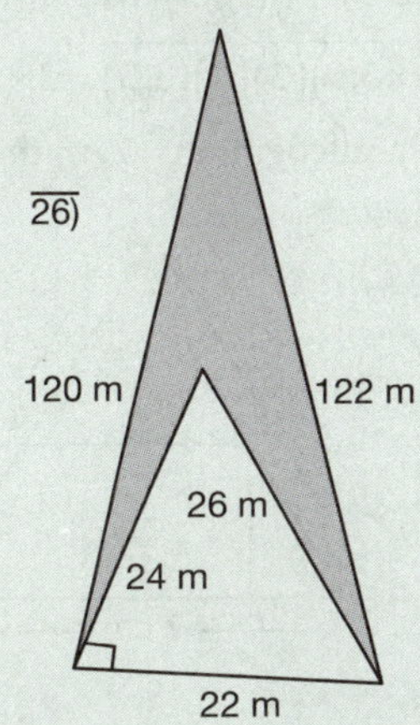

5. Let the sides are $6x$, $7x$ and $8x$ then $21x = 420$

then $x = 20$.

area(triangle)

$= \sqrt{(210)(210-120)(210-140)(210-160)}$

$= \sqrt{(210)(90)(70)(50)} = 100 \times 3 \times 7\sqrt{15}$

$= 2100\sqrt{15}$ sq. units

6. Let the second diagonal $= 2x$ then $x^2 + 6^2 = 10^2$

then $x = 8$.

Now area of rhombus $= \frac{1}{2} \times 12 \times 16 = 96$ sq.cm

Total cost $= 2 \times 5 \times 96 = 960$ Rs.

7. Using pythagoras theorem $PQ = 12$ then $\text{ar}(\text{trapezium}) = \frac{1}{2}\times(7+12)\times 12 = 114$ sq. units.

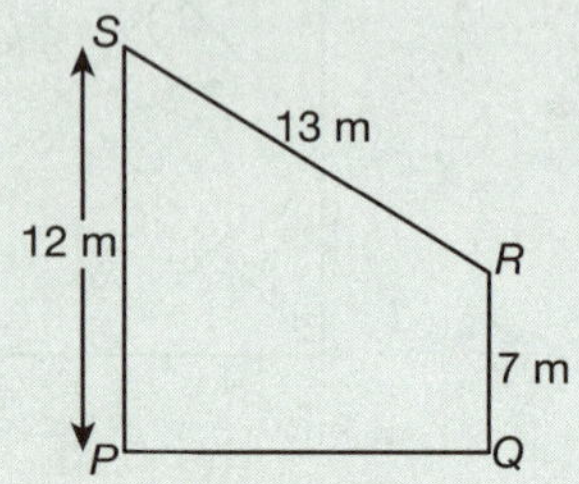

8. Let the smaller side be x. Then second side $= x+4$ and third side $y = 2x-6$

$x + x + 4 + 2x - 6 = 50$ then $4x = 52$ then $x = 13$ then sides of triangle are 13, 17, 20.

$\text{area}(\text{triangle}) = \sqrt{(25)(25-13)(25-20)(25-17)}$
$= 5\times 2\times 2\sqrt{30}.$ sq. units.

9. $475 = \frac{1}{2}\times(x+x+4)\times 19$ then $2x+4 = 50$ then $2x = 46$ then $x = 23$ cm and $x+4 = 27$ cm.

10. $\text{Ar}(ABC) = \sqrt{(10.5)(10.5-7.5)(10.5-6.5)(10.5-7)}$
$= \sqrt{(3\times 3.5)(3)(4)(3.5)} = 3\times 2\times 3.5 = 21$ sq. units.
$= \text{ar}(\text{Paralleogram}) = 7\times h$ then $h = 3$ units.

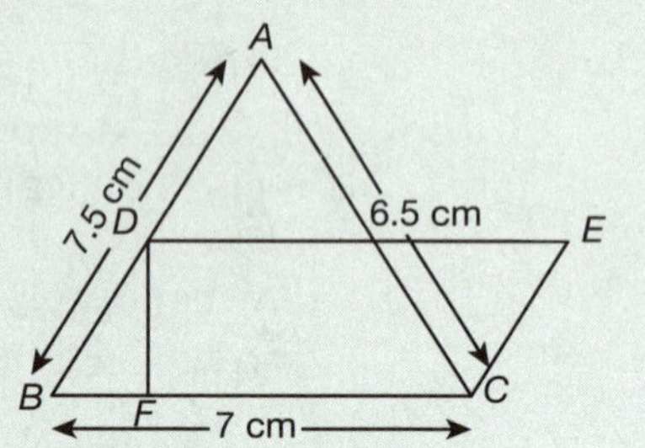

Long Answer Type Questions

1. $\text{Ar}(\text{trapezium}) = \frac{1}{2}\times(9x+8x)\times 25$
$= \frac{5}{6}\times 51\times 25$ then $17x$
$= \frac{5}{3}\times 51.\ x = 5$

So. $QC = 9x = 45$ and $PD = 8x = 40$ cm.

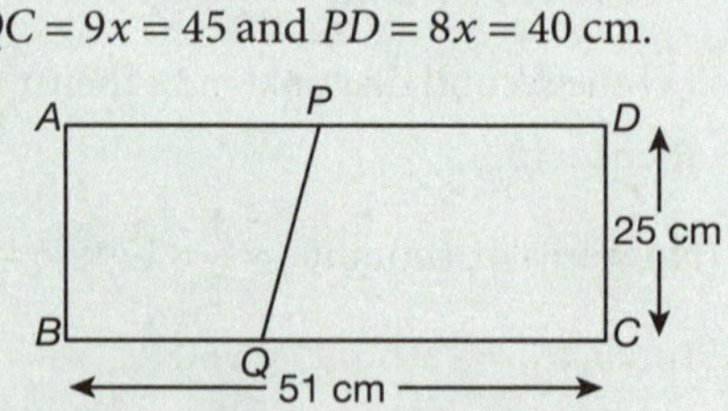

2. $\text{Area}(\text{Design}) = 8\times\sqrt{(34)(17)(9)(8)}$
$= 8\times 17\times 4\times 3 = 1632$ sq.units.

Remaining area $= 50\times 70 - 1632$
$= 3500 - 1632 = 1868$ sq.units.

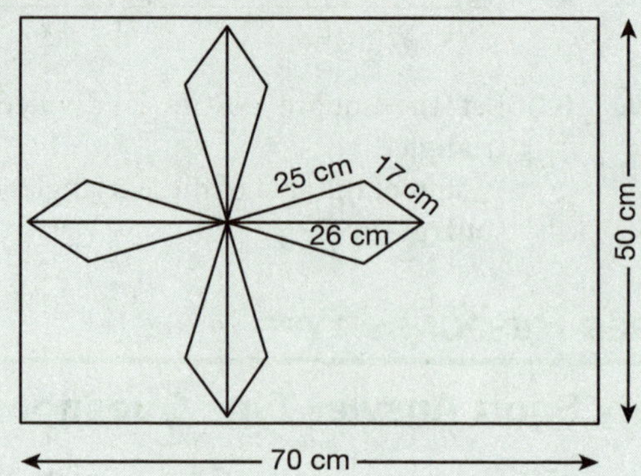

3. $\frac{\sqrt{3}}{4}\times a^2 = \frac{1}{2}\times a\times(14+10+6)$

then $a = 60\sqrt{3}.$

Then $\text{area}(\text{triangle}) = \frac{1}{2}\times(60\sqrt{3})\times(30)$
$= 900\sqrt{3}$ sq.units.

4. 4 : 1

5. fourth side let x then $x^2 = 100^2 - 60^2$ then $x = 80.$

$\text{area}(\text{trapezium}) = \frac{1}{2}\times(90+30)\times 80 = 120\times 40$
$= 4800$ sq.m. Then cost $= 4800\times 4 = 19200$ Rs.

6. $\text{area}(\text{wheat}) = \sqrt{(400)(160)(40)(200)}$
$= 20\times 100\times 8\sqrt{2} = 16000\sqrt{2}$ sq.units.

area(potatos)
$= \frac{\sqrt{(480)(480-400)(480-240)(480-320)}}{2}$

$= \frac{38400}{2} = 19200$ sq.units

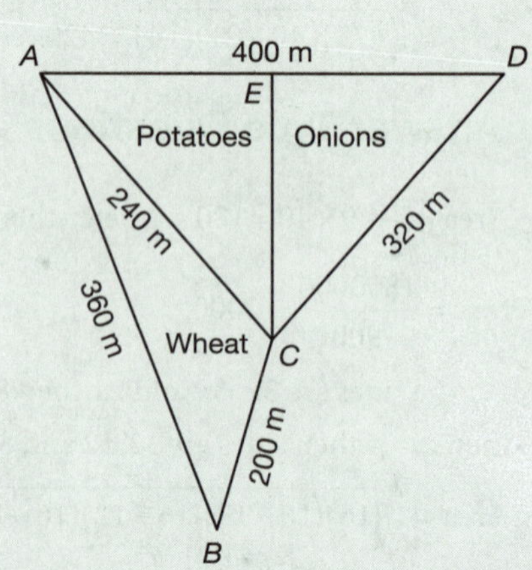

ARCHIVE CORNER

1. **(B)** Sides of triangle are 2, 3 and 3 then area $=\sqrt{(4)(4-2)(4-3)(4-3)}=2\sqrt{2}$

2. **(B)** Area $=\frac{1}{2}\times24\times32=384$ sq.m.

3. **(B)** Area of regular polygon $\frac{na^2}{4\tan\frac{\pi}{n}}$ then for Square $=a^2$ then for hexagon $=\frac{\sqrt{3}}{2}b^2$ then ratio of their ratio $=\frac{2a^2}{\sqrt{3b^2}}$. Now $6b=4a$ then $\frac{a^2}{b^2}=\frac{9}{4}$. So final ratio $=\frac{2}{\sqrt{3}}\times\frac{9}{4}$.

4. **(D)** Required area $=\frac{\sqrt{3}}{4}\left(6^2-3\times4\right)=6\sqrt{3}$ sq.cm

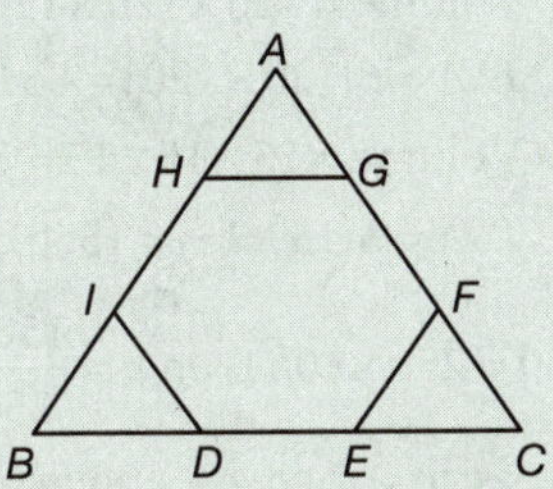

5. **(C)**

6. **(C)** $ar(\text{II})=\frac{3}{4}\times2=\frac{3}{2}$ then $ar(\text{III})=\frac{3}{4}\times\frac{3}{2}=\frac{9}{8}$.
$ar(\text{IV})=\frac{3}{4}\times\frac{9}{8}=\frac{27}{32}$.

7. **(B)** Required Ratio $=\dfrac{\frac{\sqrt{3}}{4}\times9a^2-2\times\frac{\sqrt{3}}{4}\times a^2}{\frac{\sqrt{3}}{4}\times9a^2}=\frac{7}{9}$

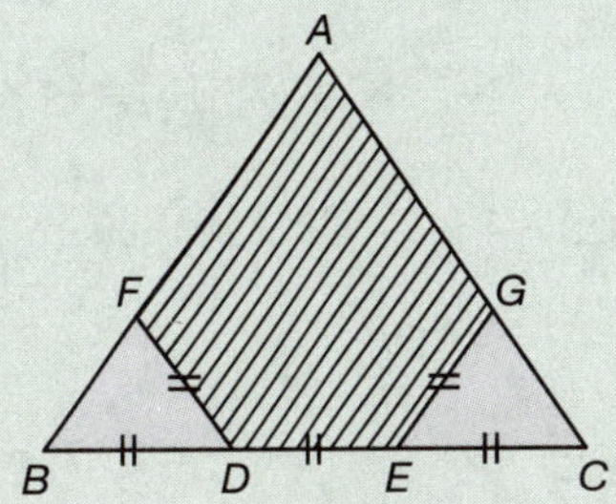

8. **(C)** $\frac{\sqrt{3}}{4}\times a^2=\frac{1}{2}\times a\times\sqrt{6}$ then $a=2\sqrt{2}$.
Then area $=\frac{\sqrt{3}}{4}\times8=2\sqrt{3}$ sq.cm.

9. **(B)**

10. **(C)** $ar(\text{parallelogram})$
$=2\times\sqrt{(9)(9-6)(9-4)(9-5)}$
$=2\times3\times2\sqrt{15}=12\sqrt{15}$ sq.cm.

11. **(A)** Side of triangle $=8$.
Then area $=\frac{\sqrt{3}}{4}\times64=16\sqrt{3}$ sq.cm

CHAPTER 11 SURFACE AREAS AND VOLUMES

Check Point 1

1. Volume $=\frac{1}{3}\times\frac{22}{7}\times 7\times 7\times 12=22\times 28=616\text{ m}^3$

2. $TSA=2\times\frac{22}{7}\times 7\times(7+15)=44\times 22=968\text{ cm}^2$

3. $4928=\frac{1}{3}\times\frac{22}{7}\times r^2\times 24$ then $r^2=196$
then $r=14$ cm

4. $\frac{1}{3}\times\frac{22}{7}\times 9\times 4=12\times\frac{22}{7}=37.71\text{ m}^3$

5. $\frac{22}{7}(21^2-7^2)\times 14=44\times 28\times 14=17248\text{ cm}^3$

Check Point 2

6. Surface Area $=4\times\frac{22}{7}\times\frac{7}{2}\times\frac{7}{2}=154\text{ cm}^2$
then Volume $=\frac{4}{3}\times\frac{22}{7}\times\frac{7}{2}\times\frac{7}{2}\times\frac{7}{2}=179.66\text{ cm}^3$

7. $154=4\times\frac{22}{7}\times r^2$ then $r=\frac{7}{2}$
then Volume $=\frac{4}{3}\times\frac{22}{7}\times\frac{7}{2}\times\frac{7}{2}\times\frac{7}{2}=179.66\text{ cm}^3$

8. Volume $=\frac{2}{3}\times\frac{22}{7}\times 8=16.761\text{ m}^3=16761.90$ litre

9. Volume $=\frac{2}{3}\times\frac{22}{7}\times(R^3-r^3)=\frac{44}{21}(6^3-5^3)$
$=\frac{44}{21}\times 91=190.66\text{ cm}^3$

10. Circumference of the base of dome (r) = 17.6 m
∴ Radius $= c/2\pi = 17.6\times 7/(2\times 22) = 2.8$ m
∴ Surface area $= 2\pi r^2 = 2\times 22/7\times(2.8)^2\text{ m}^2$
$= 44/7\times 2.8\times 2.8\text{ m}^2 = 49.28\text{ m}^2$
Rate of painting the surface
= ₹5 per 100 cm²
∴ Total cost $= 49.28\times 5\times 10000/100 =$ ₹24640

Check Point 3

11. Volume $=80\times 50\times 40=160000\text{ cm}^3$
$TSA=2(80\times 50+50\times 40+80\times 40)=18400\text{ cm}^2$

12. (i) Volume $=40\times 40\times 40=64000\text{ cm}^3$
$TSA=6(40\times 40)=9600\text{ cm}^2$
(ii) Volume $=120\times 120\times 120=1728000\text{ cm}^3$
$TSA=6(120\times 120)=86400\text{ cm}^2$
(iii) Volume $=15\times 15\times 15=3375\text{ cm}^3$
$TSA=6(15\times 15)=1350\text{ cm}^2$

13. $15000=250\times 10h$ then $h=\frac{15000}{2500}=6$ m

14. $8000\times 150\times 1000=n\times 2000\times 1500\times 600$
then $n=1.5$ days

15. (i) Capacity $=75\times 60\times 42.5=191250\text{ cm}^3$
(ii) Volume of wood
$=80\times 65\times 45-75\times 60\times 42.5=42750\text{ cm}^3$
(iii) Cost $=42750\times\frac{8}{100}=$ Rs.3420

Fixed Response Type

Fill in the Blanks

1. Volume
2. $100\times 50\times 50=250000\text{ cm}^3$
3. Total
4. Spherical
5. Curved Surface area $=\frac{22}{7}\times 7\times 10=220$ sq.cm
6. Curved

True/False

1. True.
$\frac{4}{3}\pi\times 27=36\pi$ cubic cm.
2. True.
3. True.
4. True.
$\frac{4}{3}\pi r^3:\pi r^2(2r)$ then $2:3$
5. False.
Volume $=100\times 50\times 48=240000$ cubic cm

Single Correct Type Questions

1. (D) $\left(\frac{9}{4}-1\right)\times 100 = 125$

2. (B) New volume $= 1.01\times 0.97\times 1.02 = 0.999$ then decreased.

3. (A) $a^3 = 216$ Then $a = 6$. now diagonal $= 6\sqrt{3}$ cm

4. (B) Let dimension of cuboid are $5x$, $4x$ and $3x$ then $2(20+12+15)x^2 = 846$ then $x^2 = 9$ then $x = 3$. Then sides are 15, 12 and 9

5. (C) $R^2 = 13^2 - 5^2 = 144$ then $R = 12$. $CSA = \pi\times 12\times 13 = 156\pi$ sq cm.

6. (B) $2\times\frac{22}{7}\times R = 22$ then $R = \frac{7}{2}$ and $2\times\frac{22}{7}\times r = 12$ then $r = \frac{21}{11}$

   Then $\frac{22}{7}\times\left(\frac{49}{4}\times 12 - \frac{441}{121}\times 22\right)$

   $= 462 - 252 = 210$ c.c.

7. (D) $\frac{\pi(1.2R)^2(1.2H) - R^2H}{\pi R^2 H}\times 100 = 72.8\%$

8. (B) Volume $= \pi l\left((r+t)^2 - r^2\right) = \pi l(2r+t)(t)$

9. (C) $5h = \frac{22}{7}\times 7\times 25$ then $h = 110$ m

10. (B) $TSA = \frac{\pi r}{2}\left(2l + \frac{r}{2}\right) = \pi r$

11. (B) Volume $= \frac{1}{3}\pi\times 36\times 10 = 120\pi\ \text{cm}^3$

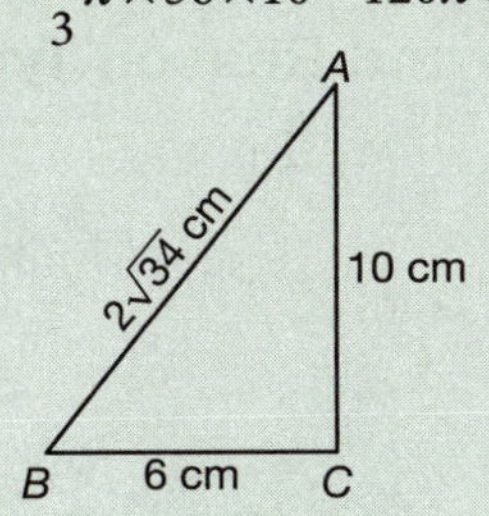

12. (C) $\pi 4^2 H = \frac{4}{3}\pi 3^3$ then $H = \frac{9}{4} = 2.25$ cm.

13. (B) $1:4^3 = 1:64$

14. (C) $4\times\frac{22}{7}\times r^2 = 154 = 22\times 7$ then $r = \frac{7}{2}$.

    Volume $= \frac{4}{3}\times\frac{22}{7}\times\frac{343}{8} = 11\times\frac{49}{3} = \frac{539}{3}\ \text{cm}^3$

15. (A) Volume $= \frac{2}{3}\times\frac{22}{7}\times 5.6\times 5.6\times 5.6$

    $= 3670.96$ ml.

16. (C) $\frac{2}{3}\times\pi R^3 : \pi R^2\times R$ Then Ratio $= 2:3$.

17. (C) $2\pi rh = \pi rl$ then $l = 2h$. then $l = 6$

18. (D) $\frac{4\pi R^3}{3} = 27\times\frac{4\pi r^3}{3}$ then $\frac{R}{r} = 3$.

    Now surface area $= \frac{4\pi R^2}{4\pi r^2} = 9$.

19. (B) Ratio of volume $= \pi(2r)^2 5h : \pi(3r)^2 3h$

    $= 20:27$

20. (D) $2\pi R - 2\pi r = 396 - 352$ then $\frac{44}{7}(R - r) = 44$

    Then $R - r = 7$ m

21. (C) Required area $= \pi(52^2 - 50^2) = 204\pi$.

22. (A) $\frac{22}{7}(21+24.5)(24.5-21.5)(4)$

    $= 22\times 45.5\times 0.5\times 4$

    $= 2002$ Rs

23. (C) $2\pi r = \pi r^2$ then $r = 2$. Then $2r = 4$

24. (B) As $OA = OB = OC = AB = r$ (triangle OAB is equilateral)

    Then ar(Rhombus) $= 2\times\frac{\sqrt{3}}{4}\times r^2 = 32\sqrt{3}$

    then $r = 8$ m.

25. (C) Required area

    $= 196 - \frac{22}{7}\times 49 = 196 - 154 = 42$ sq cm

Multiple Correct Type Questions

1. (A,B,C) Volume $= 12\times 4\times 2.5\times 1.5\ \text{cm}^3$

2. (A,C) Let the dimension of cube be a then dimension of cuboid will be a, a and $a/2$.

   $6a^2 : 2\left(a\times\frac{a}{2} + a\times\frac{a}{2} + a^2\right) = 6:4 = 3:2$

3. (A,B,D) $\frac{22}{7}\times(1.2^2 - 1^2)\times 350\times 11$

   $= 22\times 50\times 11\times 0.44$

   $= 5324$ gm $= 5.324$ Kg

4. (B,D)

5. **(A,B)** Ratio of radius are 4 : 3 then radius are $4x$ and $3x$ then $7x = 7$ then $x = 1$.

$$4\times\frac{22}{7}\times\left(4^2-3^2\right)=88\text{ cm}^2$$

6. **(A,B,D)**

7. **(C)** $n\times\frac{4}{3}\times\pi\times3^3=\pi\times2^2\times45$ then $n=5$.

8. **(A)** $\frac{4}{3}\pi r^3=\frac{1}{3}\pi R^2 r$ then $R^2=4r^2$ then $R=2r$

9. **(C)** $\frac{4}{3}\times\frac{22}{7}\times3\times3\times3=\frac{22}{7}\times\frac{1}{10}\times\frac{1}{10}\times H$
Then $H = 3600$ cm $= 36$ m.

10. **(B)** Compare volume

Match Type Questions

1. (A) → (R); (B) → (S); (C) → (P); (D) → (Q)

2. (A) → (R)
Let height and radius of the cylinder be h and r respectively. Let R be the radius of sphere.
In ΔOAB $(OA)^2 = (OB)^2 + (AB)^2$

$$\Rightarrow R^2=\left(\frac{h}{2}\right)^2+r^2\Rightarrow R^2-r^2=\frac{h^2}{4}$$

$$\Rightarrow h=2\sqrt{R^2-r^2}=8\text{ cm}$$

Volume of cylinder $= \pi\times3\times3\times8 = 72\,\pi$ cm^3

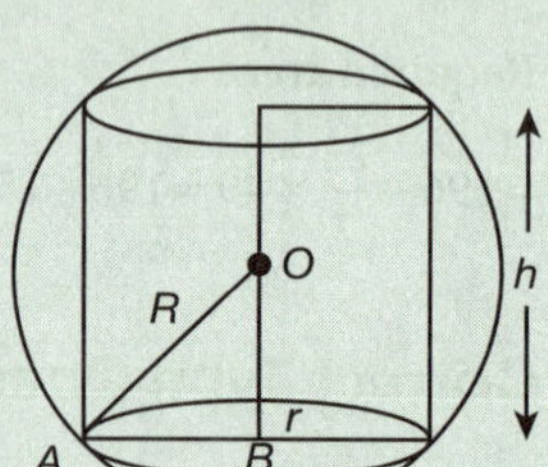

(B) → (P)
Radius of conical pit (r) = 3.5/2 cm Depth of conical pit (h) = 12 cm.
Volume of conical pit = $1/3\,\pi\, r^2 h$

$$=\frac{1}{3}\times\frac{22}{7}\times\frac{3.5}{2}\times\frac{3.5}{2}\times12=38.5\text{ sq.cm.}$$

(C) → (Q)
Let the side of cube $= a$.
Then $a\sqrt{3}=8\sqrt{3}$ then $a = 8$.
Then Volume $= 8^3 = 512$ cubic cm.

(D) → (S)
Volume $=\frac{1}{3}\pi\times5^2\times12=100\pi$ cubic cm.

3. (A) → (S)
$\frac{2}{3}\pi\times r^3=\frac{1}{3}\pi r^2 h$ then $h = 2r$.
(B) → (R)
$\frac{1}{3}\pi 4R^2H:\pi R^2 H$ then $4:3$
(C) → (Q)
$4\pi R^2 : 2\pi R\times2R = 1:1$
(D) → (P)
$27\times\frac{4}{3}\pi\times R^3=\frac{4}{3}\times\pi\times r^3$ then $r = 3R$.
Then Ratio of Curved Surface Area
$=4\pi(3R)^2:4\pi(R)^2=9:1$

4. **(A)** → (Q)
$\frac{1}{3}\pi r^2\times2r:\frac{4}{3}\pi r^3=1:2$
(B) → (R).
$\frac{1}{3}\pi(2r)^2\times H=\frac{1}{3}\pi r^2\times h$ Then $\frac{H}{h}=\frac{1}{4}$
(C) → (P)
$\frac{1}{3}\pi(3r)^2\times h:\frac{1}{3}\pi(4r)^2\times2h=9:32$
(D) → (S)
$2\pi r(h+r):\pi r(l+r)=2(17):(13+5)=17:9$

Assertion and Reason Type Questions

1. (C)
2. (C)
3. (C)

Comprehension Type Questions

1. **(C)** Required ratio $=\frac{4}{3}\pi3^3:4\pi3^2=1:1$

2. **(C)** Total surface area $=3\times\pi3^2=27\pi$ sq.cm

3. **(D)** Sum $=27\pi+27\pi=54\,\pi$cm^2

Numerical Type Questions

1. Total surface area $= 2(12\times8+8\times5+12\times5)$

$= 2\times(96+100) = 2\times196$

$= 392$ sq.cm.

2. Volume of the pillar = Volume of the cylindrical part + Volume of conical part

Volume of a Cylinder of Radius "R" and height "h" $= \pi R^2h$

Volume of a cone

$= \frac{\pi}{3}r^2h$ where r is the radius of the base of the cone and h is the height.

Hence, Volume of the pillar

$= \left(\frac{22}{7}\times8\times8\times240\right)+\left(\frac{1}{3}\times\frac{22}{7}\times8^2\times36\right)$

$= 50688\ \text{cm}^3$

If one cu cm weighs 7.8 grams, then 50688 cm^3 weighs $50688\times7.8 = 395366.4$ grams or 395.37 kg

3. Length of open wood box (L) = 1. 48 m = 148 cm

Breadth (B) = 1.16 m = 116 cm

and height (H) = 8.3 dm = 83 cm

Thickness of wood = 3 cm

$\therefore$ Inner length (l) $= 148 - 2\times3 = 148 - 6 = 142$ cm

Breadth (b) $= 116 - 2\times3 = 116 - 6 = 110$ cm

And height (h) $= 83 - 3 = 80$ cm

$\therefore$ Surface area of inner of box $= 2h(l + b) + l\times b$

$= 2\times80[142 + 110] + 142\times110\ \text{cm}^2$

$=160[252] + 142\times110\ \text{cm}^2$

$=160\times252 + 142\times110\ \text{cm}^2$

$= 40320 + 15620\ \text{cm}^2$

$= 55940\ \text{cm}^2 = 5.594\ \text{m}^2$

Rate of painting = ₹5 per m^2

$\therefore$ Total cost = ₹5 × 5.594 = ₹27.970

4. Area of walls to be papered

= Area of 4 walls – Area of 2 windows – Area of door

Dimensions of 2 walls will be 8 × 3 other two will be 6 × 3

So Area of walls to be papered

$= 2(8\times3)+2(6\times3)-2\left(\frac{3}{2}\times1\right)-\left(2\times\frac{1}{2}\right)$

$= 84-3-1 = 80\ \text{m}^2$

Length of paper required

$= \frac{80}{50}\times100 = 160$

Cost $= 160\times40 =$ Rs.6400

5. Que. rectangular box 2 : 3 : 4

Length $= 2x$, breadth $= 3x$, height $= 4x$

Surface Area $= 2(2x.3x + 3x.4x + 4x.2x)$

$= 2(6x^2 + 12x^2 + 8x^2)$

$= 52x^2$

$\Rightarrow 9.5\times52x^2 - 8\times52x^2 = 1248$

$\therefore\ 1.5\times52x^2 = 1248$

$\therefore\ x^2 = 16$ Then $x = 4$

$\Rightarrow l = 2x = 8$ cm, $b = 3x = 12$ cm, $h = 4x = 16$ cm.

6. $n\times25\times12.5\times7.5 = \frac{19}{20}\times600\times500\times50$

then $n = 6080$.

7. $2\times\frac{22}{7}\times r = 44$ then $r = 7$ m

Then $l^2 = 9^2+7^2 = 81+49 = 130$ then $l = \sqrt{130}$.

8. $2\pi rh = 4400$ then $110h = 4400$ then $h = 40$ cm.

9. $2\times\frac{22}{7}\times7\times\frac{1}{2}\times50+2\times\frac{22}{7}\times7\times7$

$= 22\times50+44\times7 = 1100+308 = 1408$ sq.cm

10. Internal diameter of spherical vessel=24 cm

External diameter of hemispherical vessel = 25 cm

Internal radius $= r = 12$ cm

and External radius $= R = 12.5$ cm

Total surface area to be painted

= External curved surface

+ Internal curved surface

+ Area of ring

$= 2\pi R^2 + 2\pi r^2 + \pi\left(R^2 - r^2\right)$

$= \pi\left(2R^2 + 2r^2 + R^2 - r^2\right)$

$= \pi\left(3R^2 + r^2\right)$

$= \frac{22}{7}(3\times12.5^2+12^2)$

$= \frac{22}{7}(468.75+144)$

$= \frac{22}{7}\times612.75$

$= 1925.78$ sq.cm

Rate of painting = 5paise per sq.cm

Thus, cost of painting = Area × Rate

$= 1925.78\times\frac{5}{100}=$ ₹ 96.29

11. Surface area of a hemisphere = $2\pi r^2$
Volume of a hemisphere = $2/3\pi r^3$
   (i) Inside surface area of the dome = Total cost for whitewashing the dome inside/Rate of whitewashing
   $\Rightarrow 498.960/2 = 249.48\ m^2$
   (ii) Let 'r' be the radius of a hemispherical dome.
   Inner surface area of the hemispherical dome = $2\pi r^2$
   $2\pi r^2 = 249.48\ m^2$
   $\Rightarrow r^2 = 249.48/2\pi\ m^2$
   $= 249.48 \div (2\times 22/7) = 39.69$
   $\Rightarrow r = \sqrt{39.69} = 6.3$ m
   The volume of the air inside the dome will be the same as the volume of the hemisphere.
   Now the volume of the air inside the dome $= 2/3\pi r^3 = 2/3\times22/7\times6.3\ m\times6.3\ m\times6.3\ m$
   $= 523.9\ m^3$ (approx.)

12. $\frac{1}{4}\times4\times\frac{22}{7}\times6370\times6370=127527400$ sq.km

13. $\frac{2}{3}\times\frac{22}{7}\times(4.5^3-4^3)=\frac{44}{21}\times(91.125-64)$
$= 56.83$ cubic cm.

14. $\frac{4}{3}\times\frac{22}{7}\times14\times14\times14=n\times\frac{1}{3}\times\frac{22}{7}\times\frac{7}{3}\times\frac{7}{3}\times3$
then $n=672$

15. Surface area $=\frac{2}{3}\times\frac{22}{7}\times6^2+\frac{22}{7}\times6^2+2\times\frac{22}{7}\times6\times9$
$=\frac{22}{7}\times(24+36+108)=\frac{22}{7}\times168$
$= 528$ sq.cm

Total Cost $= 2.5\times\frac{528}{10}=$ Rs.132

Higher Order Thinking Skills (HOTS)

1. (A) Circumference of cylinder, $2\pi r$ = length of sheet
$\Rightarrow 2\pi r=12\Rightarrow r=\frac{6}{\pi}$
Volume of cylinder $=\pi r^2h$
$=\pi\times\frac{6}{\pi}\times\frac{6}{\pi}\times5$
$=\frac{180}{\pi}\ cm^2$

2. (A) Let the radius of the cylinder is r and height is h
∴ Volume of the cylinder $=\pi r^2h$
According to the question new radius is half of the initial radius
∴ New radius $= r/2$
Height is h.
∴ New volume of the cylinder
$=\pi\left(\frac{r}{2}\right)^2h=\frac{\pi r^2h}{4}$
∴ The ratio of the new volume of the cylinder and initial volume of the original cylinder = 1/4
∴ Ratio = 1 : 4.

3. (D) Wire is in the shape of a cylinder.
Let the radius of the original cylinder $= r$ cm and height $= h$ cm
Original volume $=\pi r^2h$
New Radius after decrease $=\frac{r}{3}$
Let the new height be H.
Given, $\pi r^2h=\pi(3r)^2H$
$H=9h$
Hence, the height becomes 9 times.

4. (A) $\frac{4}{3}\pi(5^3+4^3+3^3)=\frac{4}{3}\pi r^3$ then $r=6$ cm.

5. (A) $\frac{4}{3}\times\frac{22}{7}\times10^3=8\times\frac{4}{3}\times\frac{22}{7}\times r^3$ then $r=5$.
Surface area $=4\times\pi\times5^2=100\pi$

6. (C) $\frac{4}{3}\pi r^3=\pi\times3^2\times32$
then $r^3=9\times32\times\frac{3}{4}=9\times24=216$.
Then $r=6$ cm.

7. **(C)** As half of the water in the spherical cup is transferred to the conical cup, half of the volume of water in the spherical cup is equal to the volume of water in the conical cup up to 2 cm.

Volume of a cone $= \dfrac{\pi r^2 h}{3}$.

where r is the radius of the base of the cone and h is the height.

Volume of a sphere of radius 'r' $= \dfrac{4}{3}\pi r^3$

Hence, $\dfrac{(\text{Volume of sphere})}{2}$

= Volume of the cone

$\therefore \dfrac{1}{2} \times \dfrac{4}{3} \times \pi \times 4^3 = \dfrac{1}{3}\pi r^2 \times 2$

$\therefore r^2 = 64$

$\therefore r = 8$ cm

8. **(A)** Change in area $= 4rh = 4 \times 7 \times 14 = 392$ sq.cm

9. **(A)**

10. **(B)** $v = x^3 - 2x^2 - 24x = x(x^2 - 2x - 24)$

$= x(x-6)(x+4)$

11. **(A)** $\dfrac{1}{3}\pi r^2 \times r : \dfrac{2}{3}\pi r^3 : \pi r^2 \times r$ then $1:2:3$

12. **(B)** Since the length breadth and height of a room are in the ratio 3: 2: 1.
Let us consider that, length (l), breadth (b), and height (h) are $3x$, $2x$ and x respectively.
The area of the walls is computed as,
$A1 = 2(l + b) \times h \Rightarrow = 2(3x + 2x)x \Rightarrow = 10x^2$
When the breadth and height are halved while the length is doubled, then the total area of the four walls is computed as,

$A_2 = 2(6x + x)x/2 \Rightarrow = 7x^2$

The percent decrease in area is computed as,
Decrease = 30%
Thus, the total area is decreased by 30 %.
Hence, the option (B) is correct.

13. **(C)** Total surface area of a cube of edge $a = 6a^2$

Let side of cube A be A and side of cube B be B.

Given $6A^2 = \dfrac{64}{100} \times 6B^2 \Rightarrow A = \dfrac{8}{10}B = \dfrac{4}{5}B$

Volume of a cube = side^3

Given, $\dfrac{512}{1000}B^3 = k\% \times B^3 \Rightarrow k\% = \dfrac{512}{1000}$

$\Rightarrow k = \dfrac{512}{1000} \times 100 = 51.2$

14. **(D)** Let the radius of the original cylinder $= r$ cm and height $= h$ cm

Original volume $= \pi r^2 h$

New Radius after increase $= \dfrac{150}{100}r = \dfrac{3}{2}r$

New height after decrease $= \dfrac{80}{100}h = \dfrac{4}{5}h$

Now, new volume of the cylinder

$= \pi \times \left(\dfrac{3}{2}r\right)^2 \times \dfrac{4}{5}h = \dfrac{9}{5}\pi r^2 h$

% increase $= \dfrac{(\text{Change in volume})}{\text{Original volume}}$

$= \dfrac{4}{5} \times 100 = 80\%$

15. **(D)** Area of the rectangles on either side of the wedge

$= 2 \times \text{radius} \times \text{height} = 2 \times 18 = 36$ sqcm.

Area of the sector (top and bottom)

$= 2 \times \dfrac{4}{360} \times \pi \times 6^2 = 9\pi$ sq cm

Curved area of the cylinder

$= \dfrac{(2\pi \times 6 \times 3)}{8} = \dfrac{9}{2}\pi$ sq cm.

Total area of each wedge $= \dfrac{9}{2}\pi + 9\pi + 36$

$= 36 + \dfrac{27}{2}\pi$

$= \dfrac{9}{2}(3\pi + 8)$ sqcm

Free Response Type

Very Short Answer Type Questions

1. Volume of sphere = $32/3\pi r^3$

2. Let 'a' be the edge of cube.
Surface area of cube is $6(a)^2$
Given is the surface area of cube is 96 cm^2
$96 = 6a^2$
$a^2 = 16$ then $a = 4$ cm. Volume of cube = a^3 = 64 cm^3

3. Given, the radius of the cone is $r/2$ and Slant height is $2l$
We have to find the total surface area of the cone.
Total surface area of the cone = $\pi r\,(l + r)$
Where, r is the radius of the cone and l is the slant height
Given, $r = r/2$ and $l = 2l$
Total surface area = $\pi(r/2)(2l + r/2)$
$= \pi[(r/2)(2l) + (r/2)(r/2)] = \pi[rl + r^2/4]$
$= \pi r(l + r/4)$
Therefore, the total surface area is $\pi r\,(l + r/4)$.

4. Given, dimensions of a room is
10 m × 10 m × 5 m
We have to find the length of the longest pole that can be put in the room.
Given, length of the room, l = 10 m and Breadth of the room, b = 10 m
Height of the room, h = 5 m
We know that the longest pole that can be placed in the room will be equal to the length of the diagonal of the room and Length of longest pole = diagonal of room
Diagonal of room = $\sqrt{l^2 + b^2 + h^2}$
$= \sqrt{(10)^2 + (10)^2 + (5)^2} = \sqrt{100 + 100 + 25}$
$= \sqrt{225} = 15$ m
Therefore, the length of the longest pole is 15 m.

5. Given, the length of the diagonal of a cube is $6\sqrt{3}$ cm
The length of the edge of the cube is 3 cm.
Diagonal of the cube = $a\sqrt{3}$
Where, a is the length of the edge of the cube.
Given, $a\sqrt{3} = 6\sqrt{3}$. So, $a = 6$ cm

6. The ratio of the volume of the cube to the volume of the sphere will be $6 : \pi$
Volume of cube = a^3, Where a is the edge of the cube
Given, sphere is inscribed in a cube. Radius of sphere = $a/2$
Volume of the sphere = $4/3\pi r^3$. Where, r is the radius of the sphere
$= 4/3\pi\,(a/2)^3 = 4/3\pi\,(a^3/8) = 1/6\pi a^3$
Ratio of the volumes = volume of cube/volume of sphere
$= a^3/1/6\;\pi a^3 = 6/\pi$

7. Given, the height of the cone is 8.4 cm. Base radius is 2.1 cm
The cone is melted and recast into a sphere. We have to find the radius of the sphere.
Volume of the cone = $1/3\pi r^2 h$. Where, r is the radius of the cone
h is the height of the cone. Here, r = 2.1 cm and h = 8.4 cm
Now, volume of cone = $1/3\pi\,(2.1)^2(8.4)$
$= 1/3\pi\,(4.41)(8.4)$
$= \pi\,(1.47)(8.4)$ cm^3
Volume of sphere = $4/3\pi r^3$. Where, r is the radius of the sphere
Let the radius of the sphere be R.
Volume of sphere = $4/3\pi R^3$
Given, volume of cone = volume of sphere
So, $4/3\pi R^3 = \pi\,(1.47)(8.4)$
$4/3\;R^3 = 1.47 \times 8.4$
$1/3\;R^3 = 1.47 \times 2.1$
$R^3 = 1.47 \times 2.1 \times 3 = 9.261$. Taking cube root,
R = 2.1 cm

8. Given, the radii of two cylinder are in the ratio 2 : 3. and The heights are in the ratio 5 : 3
We have to find the ratio of their volumes. Let the radii of two cylinders be $2r$ and $3r$
Let the heights of the two cylinders be $5h$ and $3h$.
Volume of the cylinder = $\pi r^2 h$. Where, r is the radius of the cylinder
h is the height of the cylinder
Volume of cylinder with radius $2r$ and height $5h = \pi\,(2r)^2(5h) = \pi\,(4r^2)(5h) = 20\pi r^2 h$
Volume of cylinder with radius $3r$ and height $3h$
$= \pi\,(3r)^2(3h)$
$= \pi\,(9r^2)(3h) = 27\pi r^2 h$
Ratio of the volume = $20\pi r^2 h/27\pi r^2 h$
= 20/27

Short Answer Type Questions

1. Total surface area of a Hemisphere = $2\pi r^2 + \pi r^2$
$= 3\pi r^2$
$r = 6$, Surface area = $3\pi\,(6)^2$
$r = 12$, Surface area = $3\pi\,(12)^2$
Ratio = 36 : 144 = 1 : 4

2. Given, an edge of a cube measures r cm
If the largest possible right circular cone is cut out of this cube, then the volume of the cone is $1/6\pi r^3$ cm^3

We have to determine if the given statement is true or false

Volume of the cone = $1/3\pi r^2h$

Where, r is the radius of the cone

h is the height of the cone

Diameter of cone = r

Radius of cone, $r = r/2$

Height of cone, $h = r$

So, volume = $1/3\pi(r/2)^2r = 1/3\pi(r^2/4)r = 1/12\pi r^3$

3. Given, diameter of spherical ball = 4.2 cm

We have to find the amount of water displaced by a spherical ball when it is completely immersed in water. By Archimedes principle,

A body at rest in a fluid is acted upon by a force pushing upward called the buoyant force, which is equal to the weight of the fluid that the body displaces. If the body is completely submerged, the volume of fluid displaced is equal to the volume of the body.

Amount of water displaced = volume of solid spherical ball

Volume of sphere = $4/3\ \pi r^3$.

Given, $r = 4.2/2 = 2.1$ cm

Volume = $4/3\ (22/7)(2.1)^3$

$= (4 \times 22 \times 2.1 \times 2.1 \times 2.1)/(3 \times 7)$

$= (88 \times 2.1 \times 2.1 \times 0.3)/3$

$= 88 \times 2.1 \times 0.7 \times 0.3$

$= 38.81\ cm^3$

4. Given, height of conical tent, $h = 3.5$ m

The radius of the base, $r = 12$ m

We have to find the canvas area of the conical tent

Canvas area = curved surface area

We know, $l^2 = r^2 + h^2 = (12)^2 + (3.5)^2$

$= 144 + 12.25 = 156.25$

Taking square root, $l = 12.5$ m

Curved surface area of cone = πrl

$= (22/7)(12)(12.5) = 3300/7 = 471.43\ m^2$

5. Consider $r1$ and $r2$ as the radius of two spheres

The ratio of volumes of two spheres is 64 : 27

$$\frac{V_1}{V_2} = \frac{64}{27}$$

$4/3\pi r_1^3/4/3\pi r_2^3 = 64/27$.

By further simplification

$(r_1/r_2)^3 = (4/3)^3$.

Taking cube root on both sides

$r_1/r_2 = 4/3$

Consider S_1 and S_2 as the surface areas of the two spheres

$S_1/S_2 = 4\pi r_1^2/4\pi r_2^2 = (r_1/r_2)^2$

Here $S_1 : S_2 = (4/3)^2 = 16/9$

6. Given, side of cube = 4 cm

Volume of gap in between

= volume of cube – volume of sphere

Volume of cube = $(\text{side})^3 = (4)^3 = 64\ cm^3$

Since the sphere is inside the cube, the diameter of the sphere = 4 cm

Volume of sphere = $4/3\pi r^3$

$= 4/3\ (22/7)(2)^3 = 4(22)(8)/21$

$= 32(22)/21 = 704/21 = 33.52\ cm^3$

Volume of gap in between = 64 – 33.52

$= 30.48\ cm^3$

7. Given, the radius of cone = 4 cm

The radius of sphere = 5 cm

The surface area of the sphere is five times the curved surface area of the cone.

Surface area of the sphere = $4\pi r^2$

Where, r is the radius of the sphere

Given, $r = 5$ cm

Surface area of sphere = $4\pi(5)^2$

$= 4(25)\pi = 100\pi\ cm^2$

Curved surface area of cone = πrl

Given, $r = 4$ cm

Curved surface area = $\pi(4)l = 4\pi l\ cm^2$

Given, surface area of sphere = 5 (curved surface area of cone)

$100\pi = 5(4\pi l)$

$100 = 5(4l)$

$20l = 100$

$l = 100/20 = 5$ cm

We know, $l^2 = r^2 + h^2$

$(5)^2 = (4)^2 + h^2$

$25 = 16 + h^2$

$h^2 = 25 - 16 = 9$

Taking square root,

$h = 3$ cm

Volume of the cone = $1/3\pi r^2h$

$= 1/3\ (22/7)(4)^2(3) = (22/7)(16)$

$= 352/7 = 50.29\ cm^3$

8. Given, radius of sphere is increased by 10%

We have to prove that the volume will increase by 33.1%.

Volume of sphere = $4/3\pi r^3$

Where, r is the radius of the sphere

Given, $r = r + 10\%\ r = r + 10/100\ r = 110/100\ r$

Increased radius = $11/10\ r$

Increased volume = $4/3\pi(11/10\ r)^3$

$= 4/3\pi(1331/1000)r^3 = 4/3\pi(1.331)r^3$

$= 1.331(4/3\pi r^3)$

Increase in volume

= increased volume – old volume

$= 1.331(4/3\pi r^3) - (4/3\pi r^3)$

$= (1.331 - 1)(4/3\pi r^3) = 0.331(4/3\pi r^3)$

Percentage increase in volume

= (increase in volume/old volume) × 100

$= [0.331(4/3\pi r^3)/(4/3\pi r^3)] \times 100$

$= 0.331 \times 100 = 33.1\%$

9. Given, radius of metal sphere = 2 cm
Internal dimensions of rectangular box = 16 cm × 8 cm × 8 cm
Metal spheres are packed into rectangular box
16 spheres area filled with preservative liquid
Volume of rectangular box
= length × breadth × height
Given, Length = 16 cm and Breadth = 8 cm and Height = 8 cm
Volume = 16 × 8 × 8 = 1024 cm^3
Volume of sphere = $4/3\pi r^3$
Given, r = 2 cm
Volume = $4/3\ (3.14)(2)^3 = 4/3\ (3.14)(8)$
$= 100.48/3 = 33.49\ cm^3$
Volume of 16 spheres = 16(33.49) = 535.84 cm^3
Volume of preservative liquid
= volume of box – volume of 16 spheres
= 1024 – 535.84 = 488.16 cm^3

10. Given, a right triangle with sides 6 cm, 8 cm and 10 cm
The right triangle is revolved about the same side 8 cm
When the right triangle is revoked about the side 8 cm, the solid so formed is a cone with height 8 cm, radius of base 6 cm and slant height 10 cm.
Volume of cone = $1/3\pi r^2 h$
Given, r = 6 cm and h = 8 cm
So, volume = $1/3\pi(6)^2(8) = (22/7)(12)(8)$
$= 22(96)/7 = 2112/7 = 301.71\ cm^3$
Curved surface area = πrl
Given, r = 6 cm and l = 10 cm
Curved surface area = $(22/7)(6)(10) = 220(6)/7$
$= 1320/7 = 188.57\ cm^2$

Long Answer Type Questions

1. Given, rainwater falls on a flat rectangular surface of length 6 m and breadth 4 m
Rainwater is transferred into a cylindrical vessel of internal radius 20 cm
We have to find the height of the water in the cylindrical vessel if the rainfall is 1 cm.
Volume of rainwater = volume of water in the rectangular surface with 1 cm rainfall
Volume of rainwater = 600 × 400 × 1 = 240000 cm^3
Volume of cylinder = $\pi r^2 h$
$240000 = \pi(20)^2 h = \pi(400)h$
$\pi h = 240000/400 = 2400/4 = 600$
$h = 600/\pi = 600/3.14 = 191.08$ cm

2. Given, a cylindrical tube is open at both ends
The tube is made of iron sheet 2 cm thick
The outer diameter of tube is 16 cm and length is 100 cm
Volume of cylindrical tube = $\pi r^2 h$
Volume of cylindrical tube
= outer volume – inner volume
Given, outer radius $r = 16/2 = 8$ cm and $h = 100$ cm
Outer volume = $\pi(8)^2(100) = \pi(64)(100)$
$= 6400\pi\ cm^3$
To find inner volume, Inner radius r = outer radius – 2 – 2 = 8 – 2 = 6 cm and h = 100 cm
Inner volume = $\pi(6)^2(100) = \pi(36)(100)$
$= 3600\pi\ cm^3$
Volume of cylindrical tube = $6400\pi - 3600\pi$
$= (6400 - 3600)\pi = 2800\pi = 2800(22/7)$
$= 400(22) = 8800\ cm^3$

3. Circumference of base of cone = circumference of semicircle
Let the radius of cup be R.
Circumference of base of cone = $2\pi R$
Diameter of semicircle = 28 cm
So, radius = 28/2 = 14 cm
Circumference of semicircle = $\pi r = \pi(14) = 14\pi$
Now, $2\pi R = 14\pi$
$2R = 14 = 14/2 = 7$ cm
Volume of cone = $1/3\pi r^2 h$
We know, $l^2 = r^2 + h^2$
$(14)^2 = (7)^2 + h^2$
$196 = 49 + h^2$
$h^2 = 196 - 49 = 147.$
Taking square root,
$h = 7\sqrt{3}$ cm
Volume of cup = $1/3\ (22/7)(7)^2(7\sqrt{3})$
$= 22(49)(\sqrt{3})/3 = 1867.096/3 = 622.37\ cm^3$

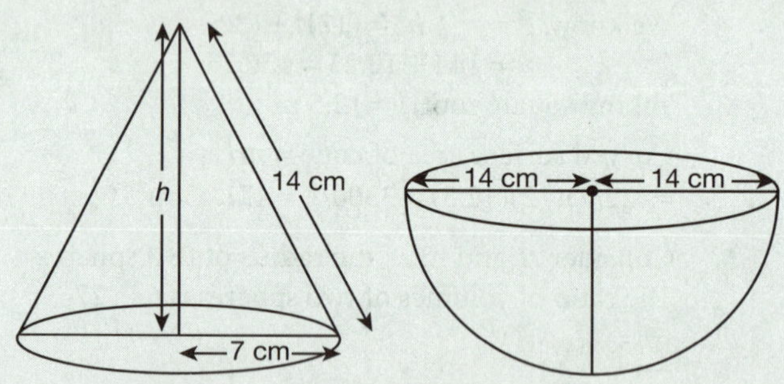

4. Internal radius, $r = 14/2 = 7$ m
Quantity of water in the tank = 50 Kilo litres
= 50(1000) = 50000 litres
We know, 1 m^3 = 1000 litres
Volume of water in the tank = 50000/1000 = 50 m^3
Volume of hemisphere = $2/3\ \pi r^3 = 2/3\ (22/7)(7)^3$
$= 2/3\ (22)(49) = 44(49)/3$
$= 2156/3 = 718.67\ m^3$
Volume of water pumped into the tank = volume of water in the hemispherical tank – volume of water in the tank

$= 718.67 - 50 = 668.67 \text{ m}^3$

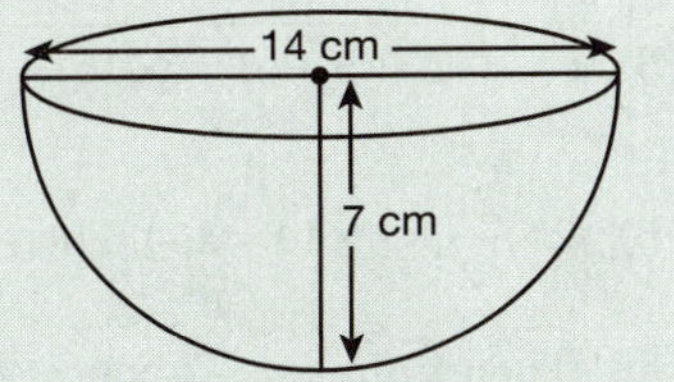

5. Given, small village has population of 5000
The village requires 75 litres of water per head per day
The overhead tank has dimension 40 m × 25 m × 15 m
We have to find the number of days for which the water in the tank will be sufficient.
Quantity of water required per day = (75 × 5000) = 375000 litres.
Volume of water = 375000/1000 = 375 m^3
Volume of overhead tank
= length × breadth × depth
Given, length = 40 m, breadth = 25 m and depth = 15 m
Volume of tank = 40(25)(15) = 1000(15)
= 15000 m^3
Number of days = total capacity of overhead tank/volume of water needed per day
= 15000/375 = 40

6. Given, area of cloth is 165 m^2
Area of cloth = curved surface area of tent
Curved surface area of cone = πrl
$\pi(5)l = 165$
$(22/7)l = 165/5$
$(22/7)l = 33$
$l = 33(7)/22 = 3(7)/2 = 21/2 = 10.5$ m
We know, $l^2 = r^2 + h^2$
$(10.5)^2 = (5)^2 + h^2$
$110.25 = 25 + h^2$
$h^2 = 110.25 - 25 = 85.25.$
Taking square root,
$h = 9.23$ m
Volume of the cone = 1/3 $\pi r^2 h$
$\frac{1}{3}\left(\frac{22}{7}\right)(5)^2(9.23) = 22(25)(9.23)/21$
$= 5076.5/21 = 241.74$ m

ARCHIVE CORNER

1. **(A)** Numbers of cube $= \frac{18\times12\times9}{3\times3\times3} = 72$

2. **(A)** Required ratio $= \frac{3^2\times1}{1^2\times3} = 3$

3. **(C)** Sides of cuboid are 3, 4 and 5 cm then volume = 60 cm^3

4. **(D)**

5. **(C)**

6. **(B)** $\frac{4}{3}\pi R^3 = 4\pi R^2$ then $R = 3$.

7. **(A)**

8. **(B)** ⇒ Length of box (l) = 35 – (5 + 5) = 25 cm
⇒ Breadth of box (b) = 25 – (5 + 5) = 15 cm
⇒ Height of box (h) = 5 cm
⇒ Volume of box = $l \times b \times h$
∴ Volume of box = 15 × 25 × 5 = 1875 cm^3.

9. **(A)** Volume of water in the pool

$$= 40\times15\times\frac{(1.2+2.42)}{2} = 1080 \text{ cubic metre}$$

10. **(A)** Here $r = \frac{12.6}{2} = 6.3$ cm

Volume of the sphere $= \frac{4}{3}\pi r^3$

$$= \frac{4}{3}\times\frac{22}{7}\times6.3\times6.3\times6.3$$

Volume of a cone $= \frac{1}{3}\pi r^2 h = \frac{1}{3}\times\frac{22}{7}\times25.2\times r^2$

we can understand that Volume of the sphere = Volume of cone

$$\Rightarrow \frac{4}{3}\times\frac{22}{7}\times6.3\times6.3\times6.3 = \frac{1}{3}\times\frac{22}{7}\times25.2\times r^2$$

$$\Rightarrow r^2 = 6.3\times6.3$$

11. **(D)** Because C is right.

12. **(B)** Let initial $r = 100$ And initial $h = 100$
∴ initial volume = $\pi(100)^2 \times 100$.
later volume = $\pi(90)^2 \times h$.
According to condition. $\pi(90)\ 2 \times h$
$= \pi(100)^2 \times 100$
$h = 123.45679$. Then
∴ % increment in height = 123.45 – 100
= 23.45

13. **(A)** $2\pi rh = 628$
$rh = 100$ (1)

$h - r = 15$ (2)

By (1) and (2) $h = 20$ and $r = 5$.

Volume $\equiv \pi(20)(25) \equiv 500\,\pi$ cu.m

14. **(C)**

15. **(B)** Let the sides of cuboid are x, y and z then $xy = A$ and $yz = B$ and $xz = C$ then $xyz = \sqrt{ABC}$

16. **(C)** Let the radius of cylindrical pipe be r. Suppose the radius and height of the conical vessel be R and H respectively.

$\therefore r = 14$ cm

$2R = 40$ cm

$\therefore R = 20$ cm

and $H = 24$ cm

Volume of conical vessel $= 1/3\pi R^2 H$

$= 1/3 \times \pi \times 20^2 \times 24\ \text{cm}^3$

Rate of water flow $= 10$ m/min

$= 1000$ cm/min

$\therefore$ Volume of water flowing out of the pipe in one minute $= \pi r^2 \times 1000$ cm

$= \pi \times (1/4)^2 \times 1000\ \text{cm}^3$

Let the time taken to fill the conical vessel be t minutes.

$\therefore$ Volume of water flowing out of the pipe in t minutes $= \pi \times (1/4)^2 \times 1000\ \text{cm}^3$

Volume of water flowing out of the pipe in t minutes = Volume of conical vessel

$\pi/16 \times 1000\,t = (\pi/3)\,400 \times 24$

$t = 51.2$

17. **(D)** $\frac{4}{3}\times\frac{22}{7}\times r^3 : \frac{22}{7}\times r\times r\times 2r = 2:3$

18. **(B)** $\frac{4}{3}\times\frac{22}{7}\times\left(4^3-2^3\right)=\frac{1}{3}\times\frac{22}{7}\times 16H$

Then $H = 14$ cm.

19. **(B)**

20. **(C)**

21. **(A)** Put Values

22. **(B)** There will be a 1% decrease in the curved surface area.

23. **(B)** $a^3 = 2744$ then $a = 14$

Then Surface area $= 6\times 14^2$

$= 6\times 196 = 1176\ \text{cm}^2$

24. **(B)**

25. **(B)** $l = \sqrt{12^2+9^2+8^2} = \sqrt{15^2+8^2} = 17$ m

26. **(B)** $2\times\frac{22}{7}\times r\times 14 = 264$. Then $r = \frac{264}{88} = 3$.

Then Volume $= \frac{22}{7}\times 9\times 14 = 396\ \text{cm}^3$

27. **(A)** $\frac{1}{3}\times\frac{22}{7}\times 2.1\times 2.1\times 8.4 = \frac{4}{3}\times\frac{22}{7}\times r^3$

then $r = 2.1$ cm

28. **(D)** Internal diameter of spherical vessel

$= 24$ cm

External diameter of hemispherical vessel

$= 25$ cm

Internal radius $= r = 12$ cm

and External radius $= R = 12.5$ cm

Total surface area to be painted

= External curved surface

+ Internal curved surface

+ Area of ring

$= 2\pi R^2 + 2\pi r^2 + \pi\left(R^2 - r^2\right)$

$= \pi\left(2R^2 + 2r^2 + R^2 - r^2\right)$

$= \pi\left(3R^2 + r^2\right)$

$= \frac{22}{7}\left(3\times 12.5^2 + 12^2\right)$

$= \frac{22}{7}(468.75 + 144)$

$= \frac{22}{7}\times 612.75$

$= 1925.78$ sq.cm

Rate of painting = 5 paise per sq.cm

Thus, cost of painting = Area × Rate

$= 1925.78\times\frac{5}{100} =$ ₹96.29

HINTS AND EXPLANATIONS

29. **(B)** % change $= \dfrac{\frac{9}{4}-1}{1} \times 100 = \dfrac{5}{4} \times 100 = 125\%$

30. **(C)** $l = \sqrt{10^2 + 10^2 + 5^2} = \sqrt{100 + 100 + 25} = 15$ m

31. **(C)** Volume $= \dfrac{1}{3} \times \pi \times 16 \times 3 = 16\pi$ cubic cm.

32. **(C)** HCF (240, 112) = 16000 cc

33. **(C)**

34. **(D)** Volume $= 15 \times 27 = 405$ cubic cm

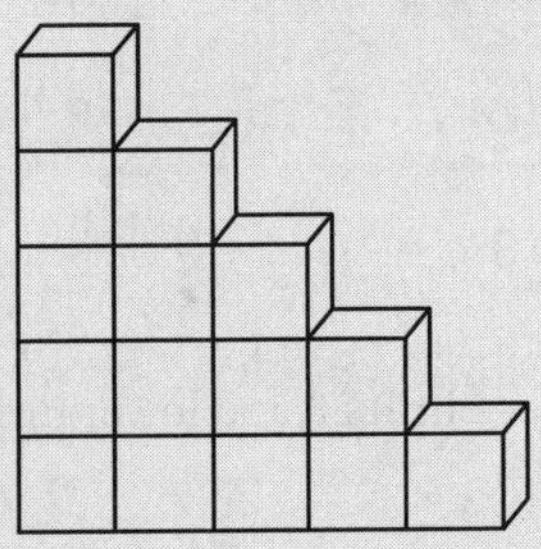

35. **(C)** $\dfrac{1}{3}\pi \times 16 \times 2 : \pi \times 9 \times 3 = 32 : 81$

CHAPTER 12 STATISTICS

Check Point 1

1. $\frac{a+b}{2}$
2. Upper Limit 20 and lower limit 11

Check Point 3

11. 39
12. 67.45
13. $\frac{M}{50}$
14. Median = 9, Mode = 19
15. 2.5

Fixed Response Type

Fill in the Blanks

1. Median
2. Mode
3. Mean
4. $\left(\frac{n+1}{2}\right)$th
5. Frequency
6. Mid Value

True/False

1. False
2. True
3. True
4. True
5. False

Single Correct Type Questions

1. **(A)**
2. **(C)**
3. **(C)**
4. **(B)**
5. **(C)**
6. **(A)**
7. **(A)**
8. **(D)**
9. **(B)**
10. **(C)**
11. **(B)**
12. **(B)**
13. **(C)**
14. **(A)**
15. **(D)**
16. **(D)**
17. **(B)**
18. **(C)**
19. **(B)**
20. **(D)**

Multiple Correct Type Questions

1. **(A,B,D)**
2. **(A,B,C,D)**
3. **(A,B,D)**
4. **(A,B,C)**
5. **(C)**
6. **(D)**
7. **(C)**
8. **(A)**
9. **(A)**

Match Type Questions

1. (A) → (R); (B) → (P); (C) → (S); (D) → (Q)
2. (A) → (S); (B) → (R); (C) → (P); (D) → (Q)
3. (A) → (P); (B) → (R); (C) → (S); (D) → (P)

Assertion and Reason Type Questions

1. **(A)**
2. **(C)**
3. **(C)**

Comprehension Type Questions

1. **(A)**
2. **(B)**
3. **(D)**
4. **(C)**
5. **(B)**
6. **(D)**

Numerical Type Questions

1. 4
2. 47
3. 31.25
4. 20
5. 55
6. 36.375 and 35.5
7. 43
8. 14
9. 47
10. 5

Higher Order Thinking Skills (HOTS)

1. **(C)**
2. **(A)**
3. **(C)**
4. **(D)**
5. **(B)**
6. **(D)**
7. **(B)**
8. **(A)**
9. **(B)**
10. **(B)**

FREE RESPONSE TYPE

Very Short Answer Type Questions

1. 140
2. 19
3. 7
4. $m = \frac{l+x}{2}$ then $x = 2m - l$
5. 20–30
6. 6
7. 0
8. 54

Short Answer Type Questions

2. 38
3. **(D)**
4. 49
5. 56.5
6. 64
8. 20
9. **(B)**
10. 80.94

Long Answer Type Questions

1. Median = 12 and Mode = 10.
6. $a = 6$.

Archive Corner

1. (B)
2. (C)
3. (B)
4. (D)
5. (B)
6. (A)
7. (C)
8. (A)
9. (C)
10. (D)
11. (C)
12. (C)
13. (B)
14. (A)
15. (C)
16. (A)
17. (C)
18. (C)
19. (B)
20. (B)
21. (D)
22. (D)
23. (D)
24. (A)
25. (B)
26. (C)
27. (B)
28. (B)
29. (D)
30. (B)
31. (B)
32. (B)
33. (A)
34. (B)
35. (A)
36. (B)
37. (D)
38. (B)
39. (A)
40. (C)
41. (B)
42. (D)
43. (B)
44. (D)
45. (C)